The
ENCYCLOPEDIA
of
ELECTRONICS

Edited by

CHARLES SUSSKIND

Associate Professor of Electrical Engineering

University of California, Berkeley, California

REINHOLD BOOK CORPORATION
New York   Amsterdam   London

Printed in the United States of America

To my wife

and to Pamela, Peter, and Amanda

for their loss of my leisure hours

CONTRIBUTING AUTHORS

A

M. R. AARON
Bell Telephone Laboratories

NORMAN ABRAMSON
Stanford University

SUMNER ACKERMAN
Instrument Development Laboratories

N. M. ALBERT
Pacific Gas and Electric Co.

REXFORD G. ALEXANDER
Burroughs Laboratories

JAMES S. ALLEN
University of Illinois

WILLIAM S. AMENT
U. S. Naval Research Laboratory

JAMES P. ANDERSON
Burroughs Laboratories

KINSEY A. ANDERSON
University of California, Berkeley

DONALD H. ANDREWS
Johns Hopkins University

DIOGENES J. ANGELAKOS
University of California, Berkeley

J. ARNAUD
Compagnie Générale de T.S.F.

JOHN A. ASELTINE
Aerospace Corp.

PAUL T. ASTHOLZ
Federal Aviation Agency

SAARA K. ASUNMAA
Owens-Illinois

MICHAEL ATHANASSIADES
University of California, Berkeley

B

DEAN F. BABCOCK
Stanford Research Institute

NORMAN BALABANIAN
Syracuse University

FRANK M. BALLOU
Ballou, Inc.

EDWARD W. BARANKIN
University of California, Berkeley

RALPH R. BATCHER
Consultant

RICHARD C. BECKER
Amphenol-Borg Electronics Corp.

F. S. BECKMAN
International Business Machines, New York, N.Y.

R. A. VON BEHREN
Minnesota Mining and Manufacturing Co.

ROBERT M. BESANCON
U. S. Air Force Aeronautical Systems Div.

VLADISLAV BEVC
University of California, Berkeley

BEHRAM H. BHARUCHA
University of California, Berkeley

F. E. BIRBECK
S.E.R.L., Baldock (England)

CHARLES K. BIRDSALL
University of California, Berkeley

ERIC E. BITTMANN
Burroughs Laboratories

A. C. BLACKMAN
American Society of Safety Engineers

JOHN D. BLADES
Burroughs Laboratories

M. HILDRED BLEWETT
Brookhaven National Laboratory

JOHN J. BOHRER
International Resistance Co.

HENRY C. BOURNE, JR.
University of California, Berkeley

J. J. BOWE
Sperry Semiconductor Div.

SHERMAN H. BOYD
Ryan Aeronautical Co.

RONALD N. BRACEWELL
Stanford University

RICHARD J. BRADY
Burroughs Corp. Electronic Components Div.

JULIUS J. BRANDSTATTER
Stanford Research Institute

JEROME BREWER
Air Products, Inc.

HENRY E. BRIDGERS
Bell Telephone Laboratories
WILLIAM B. BRIDGES
Hughes Research Laboratories
GEORGE J. BROWN
Bourns, Inc.
LAWRENCE E. BROWN
Varian Associates
RICHARD H. BUBE
RCA Laboratories
OSCAR BUNEMAN
Stanford University

C

ROBERT CALVERT
Patent Attorney, The Borden Co.
D. B. CAMERON
Union Carbide Consumer Products Co.
ROBERT N. CARLILE
University of California, Berkeley
JOHN W. CARR III
University of North Carolina
ANTHONY CASABONA
ITT Federal Laboratories
STUART CASPER
NARDA Microwave Corp.
FRANCIS M. CHARBONNIER
Linfield Research Institute
C. K. CHOW
Burroughs Laboratories
GEORGE L. CLARK
University of Illinois
MELVILLE CLARK, JR.
Massachusetts Institute of Technology
MARTIN L. COHEN
Arthur D. Little, Inc.
RICHARD L. COHEN
California Institute of Technology
ROBERT P. COLEMAN
Burroughs Laboratories
STIRLING A. COLGATE
U. C. Lawrence Rad. Lab., Livermore
RONALD T. H. COLLIS
Stanford Research Institute
JOHN L. CORL
Beckman Instruments
CULLEN M. CRAIN
RAND Corp.

HEWITT D. CRANE
Stanford Research Institute
JOSÉ B. CRUZ, JR.
University of Illinois
ROBERT L. CUMMEROW
Union Carbide Corp.
RAY C. CUMMING
Stanford University

D

RICHARD H. DALITZ
University of Chicago
CHARLES F. DALZIEL
University of California, Berkeley
RICHARD W. DAMON
Microwave Associates, Inc.
FRANCES R. DARNE
U. S. Navy Bureau of Ships
EDWARD E. DAVID, JR.
Bell Telephone Laboratories
KENNETH DAVIES
National Bureau of Standards, Boulder, Colo.
DALE S. DAVIS
University of Alabama
JAMES K. DAVIS
Corning Glass Works
SUMNER P. DAVIS
University of California, Berkeley
JACK E. DAY
Tektronix, Inc.
LOUIS D. DeLALIO
Filtors, Inc.
VICTOR E. DeLUCIA
Resitron Laboratories
FRANK DEMPSEY
Arnold Engineering Co.
CHARLES A. DESOER
University of California, Berkeley
WARREN DeSORBO
General Electric Research Laboratory
R. T. DOLLOFF
Union Carbide Corp.
GEORGE E. DOMBROWSKI
Raytheon Co., Burlington, Mass.
DANIEL G. DOW
Varian Associates
WILLIAM G. DOW
University of Michigan

WALTER G. DRISCOLL
Baird-Atomic, Inc.

E

DAVID EDELSON
Bell Telephone Laboratories
HAROLD E. EDGERTON
Edgerton, Germeshausen & Grier
WILLIAM A. EDSON
Electromagnetic Technology Corp.
STANTON L. EILENBERG
Hughes Research Laboratories
CARL G. EILERS
Zenith Radio Corp.
W. ELENBAAS
Philips Co., Eindhoven (Netherlands)
DONALD S. ELKORT
Decitron Electronics Corp.
R. T. ELLICKSON
University of Oregon
ROBERT S. ELLIOTT
University of California, Los Angeles
BERNARD ELSPAS
Stanford Research Institute
GEORGE W. ENGERT
MEPCO, Inc.
CHARLES A. ESCOFFERY
International Rectifier Corp.
VON R. ESHLEMAN
Stanford University
ROY F. ESTOPPEY
Daystrom, Inc.
THOMAS E. EVERHART
University of California, Berkeley

F

CARL E. FAFLICK
Sylvania Electronic Systems
LAURENCE E. FERREIRA
Coors Porcelain Co.
ROBERT B. FISCHER
Indiana University
FRANK J. FISHMAN
Avco-Everett Research Laboratory
MILAN D. FISKE
General Electric Research Laboratory
TAYLOR C. FLETCHER
Beckman Instruments

ARTHUR FONG
Hewlett-Packard Co.
DONALD C. FORSTER
Hughes Research Laboratories
L. C. FOSTER
Zenith Radio Research Corp.
GENE F. FRANKLIN
Stanford University
W. J. FREDERICKS
Stanford Research Institute
BERNARD FRIEDMAN
University of California, Berkeley
HAROLD P. FURTH
U. C. Lawrence Rad. Lab., Livermore
NORMAN F. FYLER
Litton Industries

G

ROBERT G. GALLAGER
Massachusetts Institute of Technology
G. F. J. GARLICK
University of Hull (England)
KENNETH J. GERMESHAUSEN
Edgerton, Germeshausen & Grier
HORACE D. GILBERT
Miniature Precision Bearings
NORMAN E. GILBERT
Rollins College
A. E. GLASSGOLD
University of California, Berkeley
W. E. GLENN
General Electric Research Laboratory
EARL G. GODDARD
Varian Associates
JACK GOLDBERG
Stanford Research Institute
SEYMOUR GOLDBERG
Edgerton, Germeshausen & Grier
ELI M. GOLDFARB
Radiation at Stanford
JOHN GONCZ
Edgerton, Germeshausen & Grier
HARRY H. GOODE*
University of Michigan
DANIEL I. GORDON
U. S. Naval Ordance Lab., White Oak, Md.

* Deceased

Eiichi Goto
University of Tokyo

Georg Goubeau
U. S. Army Signal Corps (SRDL)

Lawrence Gould
Microwave Associates

F. S. Goulding
Atomic Energy of Canada Ltd.

E. S. Graham
Gould-National Batteries

George W. Gray
RCA Laboratories

R. A. Green
Burroughs Corp. Electronic Components Div.

Victor H. Grinich
Fairchild Semiconductor

H. E. Gruen
Delta-f, Inc.

William H. Guier
Johns Hopkins University

H

Cecil E. Hall
Massachusetts Institute of Technology

B. P. Hand
Hewlett-Packard Co.

Robert C. Hansen
Aerospace Corp.

Aubrey Harris
Ampex Electronics Ltd. (England)

Donald B. Harris
Stanford Research Institute

Shirley W. Harrison
General Telephone & Electronics Laboratories, Bayside, N. Y.

E. O. Hartig
Goodyear Aircraft Corp.

Hermann A. Haus
Massachusetts Institute of Technology

Ernst A. Hauser*
Massachusetts Institute of Technology

Joseph K. Hawkins
Aeronutronic

F. E. Haworth
Bell Telephone Laboratories

* Deceased

Harry G. Heard
Radiation at Stanford

Oskar Heil
Eitel-McCullough

Gerald S. Heller
MIT Lincoln Laboratory

Robert A. Helliwell
Stanford University

George Hetland, Jr.
Space Technology Laboratories

Jack Hilibrand
RCA Semiconductor and Materials Div.

Charles J. Hirsch
RCA, Princeton, N. J.

Louis R. Hirschel
U. S. Naval Ordnance Lab., White Oak, Md.

Paul R. Hoffman
Burroughs Laboratories

Ragnar Holm
Stackpole Carbon Co.

Richard C. Honey
Stanford Research Institute

George W. Hoover
Consultant

William G. Hoover
Stanford University

Charles O. Hopkins
Hughes Aircraft Co.

Edward L. Hubbard
U. C. Lawrence Rad. Lab., Berkeley

Lawrence P. Huelsman
University of Arizona

David A. Huffman
Massachusetts Institute of Technology

Charles d'A. Hunt
Temescal Metallurgical Corp.

Harry D. Huskey
University of California, Berkeley

Edwin C. Hutter
RCA Astro-Electronic Products Div.

Rudolf G. E. Hutter
Sylvania Electric Products (Division of General Telephone & Electronics Corp.), Mountain View, Calif.

Earl K. Hyde
U. C. Lawrence Rad. Lab., Berkeley

I

JOHN M. IDE
SACLANT ASW Research Center, NATO

R. A. ISBERG
University of California Extension, Berkeley

HENRY F. IVEY
Westinghouse Electric Corp., Bloomfield, N. J.

J

PAUL E. JACOBSON
American-Marietta Co.

BERNARD JAFFE
Brush Laboratories Co.

HANS JAFFE
Clevite Corp.

THOMAS JASKI
Consultant

F. W. JENKINSON
Systron-Donner Corp.

ROBERT L. JEPSEN
Varian Associates

DAVID L. JOHNSON
University of Washington

FRANCO P. JONA
International Business Machines, Yorktown Heights, N. Y.

R. NORMAN JONES
National Research Council

DAVID L. JUDD
U. C. Lawrence Rad. Lab., Berkeley

ELIAHU I. JURY
University of California, Berkeley

K

HERMAN KAHN
Hudson Institute

H. F. KAISER
U. S. Naval Research Laboratory

JOSEPH KAYE*
Massachusetts Institute of Technology

B. KAZAN
Hughes Research Laboratories

* Deceased

KENNETH S. KELLEHER
Aero Geo Astro Corp.

ROBERT W. KENNEY
U. C. Lawrence Rad. Lab., Berkeley

R. K. KILBON
RCA Laboratories

E. M. KINDERMAN
Stanford Research Institute

GILBERT W. KING
International Business Machines, Yorktown Heights, N. Y.

GORDON S. KINO
Stanford University

ROY H. KIRKLAND, JR.
RCA Electron Tube Div.

A. J. KIRSCHBAUM
U. C. Lawrence Rad. Lab., Livermore

R. E. KITSON
E. I. duPont de Nemours and Co.

MYRON W. KLEIN
U. S. Army Engineer Research and Development Laboratories

O. KLEMPERER
Imperial College, University of London

CURT W. KLOSTERMAN
Amphenol-Borg Electronics Corp.

HAROLD K. KNUDSEN
University of California, Berkeley

WINSTON E. KOCK
Bendix Corp.

W. A. KOEHLER
West Virginia University

WALTER H. KOHL
Consultant

JAMES S. KOUVEL
General Electric Research Laboratory

ERNEST S. KUH
University of California, Berkeley

ROBERT KUNIN
Rohm and Haas Co.

L

PETER D. LACY
Wiltron Co.

I. LADANY
U. S. Naval Research Laboratory

J. M. LAFFERTY
General Electric Research Laboratory

T. K. LAKSHMANAN
  Daystrom, Inc.
LLOYD M. LAMBERT, JR.
  Aeronutronic
LEE V. LANGAN
  Varian Associates
W. J. LAWLESS, JR.
  International Business Machines, New York, N. Y.
CARLTON G. LEHR
  Raytheon Co., Waltham, Mass.
SAMUEL C. LIND
  Union Carbide Nuclear Co., Oak Ridge, Tenn.
B. R. LINDEN
  CBS Laboratories
D. A. LINDEN
  Philco Corp., Palo Alto, Calif.
WILLIAM K. LINVILL
  Stanford University
EDWARD J. LOFGREN
  U. C. Lawrence Rad. Lab., Berkeley
WILLIAM H. LOUISELL
  Bell Telephone Laboratories
LEE B. LUSTED
  University of Rochester
JOHN T. LYNCH
  Burroughs Laboratories
DAVID K. LYNN
  University of California, Berkeley
HAROLD LYONS
  Electro-Optical Systems, Inc.

M

C. S. McCAMY
  National Bureau of Standards
S. E. McCARTHY
  Hewlett-Packard Co.
J. W. McCLURE
  Union Carbide Corp.
K. R. McCONNELL
  Westrex Corp.
DAVID E. McELROY
  International Resistance Co.
P. K. McELROY
  General Radio Co.
ROBERT E. MACHOL
  Purdue University and Conductron Corp.

JOSEPH E. MACHUREK
  U. S. Atomic Energy Commission
ALBERT MACOVSKI
  Stanford Research Institute
T. H. MAIMAN
  Quantatron, Inc.
T. C. MANLEY
  Welsbach Corp.
JERRE V. MANNING
  Micro Switch
LAWRENCE A. MANNING
  Stanford University
DONALD E. MARSHALL
  Westinghouse Electronic Tube Div.
GEORGE L. MATTHAEI
  Stanford Research Institute
HOWARD C. MEL
  University of California, Berkeley
RUDOLF X. MEYER
  Aerospace Corp.
HERBERT B. MICHAELSON
  IBM Journal of Research and Development
JOSEPH E. MITCH
  Arnold Engineering Co.
ALTON B MOODY
  U. S. Navy Hydrographic Office
GORDON E. MOORE
  Fairchild Semiconductor
R. K. MOORE
  University of New Mexico
MERLE L. MORGAN
  Electro Scientific Industries, Inc.
TETSU MORITA
  Stanford Research Institute
ALBERT J. MORRIS
  Radiation at Stanford
FRED MOSKOWITZ
  Laboratory for Electronics
HANS MOTZ
  Oxford University (England)
CLIFF MOULTON
  Tektronix, Inc.
STEPHEN W. MOULTON
  Philco Corp.
WILLIAM W. MUMFORD
  Bell Telephone Laboratories
W. R. MYERS
  University of Southampton (England)

N

ERVIN J. NALOS
  General Electric Research Laboratory
RAJ NANAVATI
  Syracuse University
JOSEPH J. NARESKY
  USAF Rome Air Development Center
RICHARD B. NEAL
  Stanford University
RICHARD B. NELSON
  Varian Associates
ROBERT W. NEWCOMB
  Stanford University
WILLIAM A. NICHOLS
  Goddard Space Flight Center

O

STEFAN A. OCHS
  RCA Laboratories
JAMES D. O'CONNELL
  General Telephone & Electronics Laboratories, Palo Alto, Calif.
ROBERT J. O'CONNELL
  Burroughs Laboratories
J. A. OGLE
  Burroughs Laboratories
GEORGE D. O'NEILL
  General Telephone & Electronics Laboratories, Bayside, N. Y.

P

RICHARD H. PANTELL
  Stanford University
A. T. PARKER
  Solar Electronics Company
EMANUEL PARZEN
  Stanford University
SIDNEY PASSMAN
  RAND Corp.
JOHN D. PATTERSON
  University of California, Berkeley
MARTIN PETER
  Bell Telephone Laboratories
JOHN PILLSBURY
  Wells Fargo Bank American Trust Co.

LOUIS A. PIPES
  University of California, Los Angeles
JOHN E. PIPPIN
  Sperry Microwave Electronics Co.
P. R. PONDY
  Wellington Electronics
ALAN M. PORTIS
  University of California, Berkeley
EDGAR A. POST
  Stanford Research Institute
R. K. POTTER
  Consultant
HOWARD C. POULTER
  Hewlett-Packard Co.

R

ROBERT C. RAMSEY
  Electro-Voice, Inc.
WALTER RANDOLPH
  MEPCO, Inc.
HAROLD J. READ
  Pennsylvania State University
HOWARD REISS
  Atomics International
DONALD K. REYNOLDS
  University of Washington
PHILIP RICE
  Stanford Research Institute
STEPHEN O. RICE
  Bell Telephone Laboratories
E. RAYMOND RIEGEL
  Consultant
WILLIAM W. RIGROD
  Bell Telephone Laboratories
GEORGE A. ROBINSON
  RCA Electron Tube Div.
DENIS M. ROBINSON
  High Voltage Engineering Corp.
G. P. RODRIGUE
  Sperry Microwave Electronics Co.
LOUIS H. RORDEN
  Stanford Research Institute
STANLEY N. ROSCOE
  Hughes Aircraft Co.
SYLVAN RUBIN
  Stanford Research Institute
JOHN E. RUEDY
  RCA Laboratories

S

MEYER SAPOFF
  Victory Engineering Corp.
ROBERT M. SCARLETT
  Shockley Transistor Unit of Clevite Transistor
H. M. SCHLICKE
  Allen-Bradley Co.
STANLEY SCHNEIDER
  Burroughs Laboratories
GEORGE W. SCHROEDER
  General Electric Co., Louisville, Ky.
M. R. SCHROEDER
  Bell Telephone Laboratories
PETER M. SCHULTHEISS
  Yale University
HERBERT J. SCOTT
  University of California, Berkeley
LARRY SCOTT
  U. C. Lawrence Rad. Lab., Berkeley
ALBERT SEGEN
  National Aviation Facilities Experimental Center
SUNDARAM SESHU
  Syracuse University
HAROLD SHNITKIN
  Avien, Inc.
B. M. SIFFORD
  Stanford Research Institute
CHARLES A. SIMMONS
  Burroughs Laboratories
CLAUDE C. SIMS
  U. S. Navy Underwater Sound Reference Laboratory
JEROME R. SINGER
  University of California, Berkeley
JOHN G. SKALNIK
  Yale University
A. M. SKELLETT
  Tung-Sol Electric
JOHN M. SLATER
  Autonetics
DAVID H. SLOAN
  University of California, Berkeley
JAMES M. SLOSS
  University of California, Santa Barbara
JOHN C. SMACK*
  Curtiss-Wright Corp.

* Deceased

GILBERT SMILEY
  General Radio Co.
BOB H. SMITH
  U. C. Lawrence Rad. Lab., Berkeley
GEORGE E. SMITH
  Bell Telephone Laboratories
GEORGE F. SMITH
  Hughes Research Laboratories
HUGH R. SMITH, JR.
  Temescal Metallurgical Corp.
JARED S. SMITH
  General Electric Co., Lynchburg, Va.
OTTO J. M. SMITH
  University of California, Berkeley
PHILLIP H. SMITH
  Bell Telephone Laboratories
CHARLES P. SMYTH
  Princeton University
ROBERT A. SODERMAN
  General Radio Co.
H. S. SOMMERS, JR.
  RCA Laboratories
WALTER W. SOROKA
  University of California, Berkeley
ROY SPENCER
  Martin Co.
W. E. SPICER
  RCA Laboratories
WILLIAM S. SPRING
  Magnetics, Inc.
IRVING F. STACY
  RCA Electron Tube Div.
A. L. STANFORD
  Sperry Microwave Electronics Co.
FLOYD GEORGE STEELE
  Consultant
JACK E. STEELE
  USAF Aerospace Medical Laboratory
K. H. STEIGERWALD
  Carl Zeiss
SEYMOUR STEIN
  Sylvania Electric Products (Division of General Telephone & Electronics Corp.), Waltham, Mass.
SIDNEY J. STEIN
  International Resistance Co.
ELLIS P. STEINBERG
  Argonne National Laboratory

THOMAS E. STERN
  Columbia University
ERNEST J. STERNGLASS
  Westinghouse Research Laboratories
JOHN L. STEWART
  University of Arizona
GERALD STOLAR
  Daystrom, Inc.
PETER A. STURROCK
  Stanford University
E. V. SUNDT
  Littelfuse, Inc.
CHARLES SUSSKIND
  University of California, Berkeley
JOSEPH P. SWANSON
  Radiation at Stanford
WILLARD SWEETMAN, JR.
  Cragmont Metals
ROBERT C. SWENGEL
  AMP, Inc.
ROBERT L. SWIGGETT
  Photocircuits Corp.
R. SYSKI
  University of Maryland

T

JOHN E. TABER
  Space Technology Laboratories
WILSON P. TANNER, JR.
  University of Michigan
PAUL B. TAYLOR
  University of Dayton
JAMES B. THOMAS
  Raytheon Co., Burlington, Mass.
MICHAEL TINKHAM
  University of California, Berkeley
E. ROBERT TRIBKEN
  Sperry Phoenix Co.
ALVIN W. TRIVELPIECE
  University of California, Berkeley
GEORGE L. TURIN
  University of California, Berkeley
FRANKLIN M. TURNER
  Stanford University

U

FRANZ UCKO
  Motorola Semiconductor Div.
ARTHUR UHLIR, JR.
  Microwave Associates

V

J. VAN DEN HANDEL
  University of Leiden (Netherlands)
DAVID D. VANORMER
  RCA Electron Tube Div.
M. E. VAN VALKENBURG
  University of Illinois
K. M. VAN VLIET
  University of Minnesota
JOSEPH H. VOGELMAN
  Capehart Corp.

W

RALPH L. WAGNER
  Zenith Radio Corp.
CHARLES B. WAKEMAN
  Magnetics, Inc.
ROGER W. WALLACE
  U. C. Lawrence Rad. Lab., Berkeley
J. T. WALLMARK
  RCA Laboratories
ARNOLD WALTER
  University of Toronto
SHYH WANG
  University of California, Berkeley
STANLEY H. WARD
  University of California, Berkeley
ALAN T. WATERMAN, JR.
  Stanford University
WILLIAM E. WATERS
  Microwave Electronics Corp.
DEAN A. WATKINS
  Watkins Johnson Co.
WILLIAM H. WATKINS
  Federal Communications Commission
WILLARD H. WATTENBURG
  University of California, Berkeley
JOHN F. WAYMOUTH
  *Sylvania Electric Products (Division of
    General Telephone & Electronics Corp.),
    Salem, Mass.*
GLENN WEATHERSPOON
  Hughes Aircraft Co.
ELBERT C. WEAVER
  Phillips Academy
MAX T. WEISS
  Aerospace Corp.

ROBERT H. WEITBRECHT
Stanford Research Institute

WILLIAM J. WELCH
University of California, Berkeley

GERSHON J. WHEELER
Sylvania Electric Products (Division of General Telephone & Electronics Corp.), Mountain View, Calif.

JOHN R. WHINNERY
University of California, Berkeley

ROMAYNE F. WHITMER
General Telephone & Electronics Corp. Laboratories, Palo Alto, Calif.

F. C. WILLIAMS
University of Manchester (England)

HOWARD G. WILSON
Hughes Aircraft Co.

A. N. WINCHELL*
Consultant

HORACE WINCHELL
Yale University

ALVIN WINGER
Rohm and Haas Co.

MARTIN WOLF
Heliotek Corp.

ROGER W. WOLFE
Burroughs Corp. Electronic Components Div.

JOHN R. WOODYARD
University of California, Berkeley

Y

LEO YOUNG
Stanford Research Institute

* Deceased

PREFACE

Users of the Encyclopedia will appreciate the difficulties inherent in dividing all of electronics into some 500 topics and securing an authoritative article on each, the whole to fit into a single volume directed primarily at professional readers. Various groupings suggested themselves. The scheme finally adopted, of single entries alphabetically arranged (which had been so successfully employed in the Clark-Hawley *Encyclopedia of Chemistry* published by Reinhold previously), proved to be the most suitable. The bulk of the material is arranged in this manner, but there are a few entries (e.g., Antennas, Magnetism, Navigation and Navigational Systems, Network Theory, Propagation) in which it was manifestly preferable to group articles written by several contributors under a single heading. Other hints to readers appear further below.

Editorial space was a severe limitation: massive textbooks have been written on many a subject covered here in two pages (in not a few instances, by the same authors). The motto for the entire enterprise was inadvertently supplied by a literate electronics engineer—a type, the editor was relieved to find as contributions began to pour in, far more prevalent than his years of reading college examinations would have given him any right to expect; this contributor protested the space limitations imposed on his entry but ended by accepting the challenge of compressing his material with good grace, citing Goethe to the effect that *"in der Beschränkung zeigt sich erst der Meister"* ("under restraint the Master first shows plain"). Goethe's sonnet, intended above all as an epigrammatic appeal to the artist to keep himself in check, surely has much broader implications, extending even to the exacting task of the technical encyclopedist.

The editor wishes to acknowledge the conscientious (and eminently successful) efforts of the contributors to work within these limitations. Authors were drawn from several countries and represent universities, industrial and government laboratories, and private concerns. Several organizations supplied a number of contributors, sometimes with one of them acting as a volunteer coordinator. The campuses of the editor's own university and of nearby Stanford University provided the largest contingents, but particular thanks are also due to D. B. Harris of the Stanford Research Institute and H. P. McCartney of the Burroughs Laboratories (now with IBM) for coordinating the contributions of the sizable groups of authors at their respective institutions. Finally, the editor gratefully acknowledges the help of G. G. Hawley, Executive Editor of the Reinhold Book Division, who conceived the idea of publishing a series of technical encyclopedias; if the present volume is a worthy addition to the series, some of the credit should go to him for his encouragement, his unfailing courtesy, and his wise counsel and guidance at every point of the publication process.

Berkeley, California, 1962

CHARLES SUSSKIND

PLAN OF THE BOOK

Entries are arranged alphabetically. Further cross-headings have been added to aid in the location of the appropriate articles, but not simple inversions: it is assumed that a reader who cannot find an entry on, say, Linear Systems will be willing to look also for Systems (Linear). (In particular, the adjective *electronic* invariably appears second in main headings.) Each entry is followed by a list of other articles in the book that bear on allied topics. Additional in-text references to other articles are frequently made by a parenthetic *q. v.* (*quod vide*, "which see"). As a final aid, a list of all the entries, arranged according to an approximate subject grouping, is as follows:

1. **ANTENNAS, PROPAGATION, and RADI- ATION**
Antennas
  General Considerations
  Antenna Arrays
  End-Fire Antennas
  Frequency-Independent Antennas
  Horn Antennas
  Lenses
  Reflector Antennas
  Electronically Scanned Antennas
  Slotted-Guide Antennas
  Special Types
Extraterrestrial Radio Sources
Propagation
  General Considerations
  Ionospheric Propagation
  Tropospheric Propagation
  Ground-Wave Propagation
  Propagation Through Conducting Media
  VLF Propagation
  Radio Effects of Aurorae
Radar Astronomy
Radiation (Terrestrial)
  Whistlers
Radiometeorology
Radomes
Satellite Communications

2. **BIOELECTRONICS**
Bionics
Electric Shock
Hearing Aids
Human Engineering
Larynx (Electronic)
Medical Electronics
Neuristor
Neuron
Radiation Hazards (Nonionizing Radiation)

3. **CIRCUITS and NETWORKS**
Amplifiers
  AC Amplifiers
  DC Amplifiers
Feedback Amplifiers
Pulse Amplifiers
Counter and Scaler Circuits
Coupled Circuits
Equivalent Circuits
Filters
Network Synthesis
  Approximation
  Realization
Network Theory
  Generalized Equations and Topological Analysis
  Mesh-Node Analysis
  Time-Domain Analysis
  Two-Port Networks
  Linearity
  Reciprocity
Nonlinear Circuits
Oscillators
  Harmonic Oscillators
  Relaxation Oscillators
Sequential Circuits
Switching Circuits

4. **COMMUNICATION THEORY and MATH- EMATICAL TECHNIQUES** (*see also* Control, Modulation, Transmission)
Boolean Algebra and Symbolic Logic
Channel Capacity
Complex Notation
Congestion and Waiting Systems
Decision and Game Theory
Distribution Functions
Fourier Analysis
Fourier Integrals and Their Applications
Information Theory
Laplace and Fourier Transforms
Linear Programming
Markov Processes
Matrix Algebra
Minimal-Time Problems
Monte Carlo Method
Phase-Space Representation

A

ABBREVIATIONS

Abbreviations used in electronics are listed below in two parts: (1) electronic terms and (2) units. Unit systems (*q.v.*) are described separately.

Electronic Terms

ac	Alternating current
ACA	Adjacent-channel attenuation
ACC	Automatic chrominance control; automatic contrast control
ACSR	Aluminum conductor, steel-reinforced
ADF	Automatic direction finder
af	Audio frequency
AFC	Automatic frequency control
AGC	Automatic gain control
AGS	Automatic gain stabilization
alt	Altitude
AM	Amplitude modulation
AMT	Amplitude-modulated transmitter
ANL	Automatic noise limiter
APC	Automatic phase control
ASC	Automatic sensitivity control
ATR	Anti-transmit-receive
av	Average
AVC	Automatic volume control
AVE	Automatic volume expansion
BFO	Beat frequency oscillator
BWO	Backward-wave oscillator
CPA	Color phase alternation
CPD	Contact-potential difference
CRO	Cathode-ray oscilloscope
CRT	Cathode-ray tube
CT	Center tap
CW	Continuous wave
DBB	Detector balanced bias
dc	Direct current
DDM	Difference in depth of modulation
DET	Detector
DF	Direction finder
DSB	Double sideband
ECM	Electronic countermeasures
ECO	Electron-coupled oscillator

emf	Electromotive force
ENSI	Euqivalent noise-sideband input
EPR	Electron paramagnetic resonance
ESR	Effective signal radiated
FM	Frequency modulation
FSK	Frequency-shift keying
FSM	Field strength meter
FTC	Fast time constant
GAW	Gram-atomic weight
HA	Hour angle; high altitude
hf	High frequency (3–30 Mc)
HPF	Highest probable frequency
IAGC	Instantaneous automatic gain control
IC	Internal connection
ICW	Interrupted continuous wave
IF	Intermediate frequency
IR	Infrared
IS	Internal shield
LET	Linear energy transfer
lf	Low frequency (30–300 kc)
MCW	Modulated continuous wave
MDI	Magnetic direction indicator
mf	Medium frequency (300–3000 kc)
MHD	Magnetohydrodynamics
mmf	Magnetomotive force
MPD	Maximum permissible dose
MPE	Maximum permissible exposure
MTI	Moving target indicator
MUF	Maximum usable frequency
NC	Normally closed, in reference to relay or other contacts; no connection, on electron-tube sockets
NMR	Nuclear magnetic resonance
NO	Normally open, used with reference to relay or other contacts
OFHC	Oxygen-free, high-conductivity (copper)
PAM	Pulse-amplitude modulation
PCM	Pulse-code modulation; pulse-count modulation
PD	Potential difference
PDM	Pulse-duration modulation
PEM	Photoelectromagnetic effect

PEP	Peak envelope power
PF	Power factor
PFM	Pulse frequency modulation
PM	Phase modulation; permanent magnet
PP	Peak-to-peak
PPI	Plan position indicator
PPM	Pulse-position modulation
PPPI	Precision plan position indicator
pps	Pulse per second
PRF	Pulse repetition frequency
PTM	Pulse-time modulation
PWM	Pulse-width modulation
Q	Quality factor
RBE	Relative biological effectiveness
rf	Radio frequency
RFC	Radio-frequency choke
RFI	Radio-frequency interference
RMI	Radio magnetic indicator
SHM	Simple harmonic motion
SNR	Signal-to-noise ratio
SSB	Single sideband
STC	Sensitivity time control
STP	Standard temperature and pressure
SWR	Standing-wave ratio
TE	Transverse electric
TEM	Transverse electromagnetic
TM	Transverse magnetic
TPTG	Tuned plate—tuned grid
TR	Transmit-receive
TWT	Traveling-wave tube
uhf	Ultrahigh frequency (300–3000 Mc)
uv	Ultraviolet
vhf	Very high frequency (30–300 Mc)
VFO	Variable frequency oscillator
vlf	Very low frequency (10–30 kc)
VSB	Vestigial sideband
VSWR	Voltage standing-wave ratio
VTVM	Vacuum-tube voltmeter

Units*

Units of measure are abbreviated when they appear after numerals. The same ab-

* This material is adapted from C. Susskind, *Dictionary of Style for Typewritten Technical Reports and Manuscripts for Publication*, San Francisco Press, 1960, by permission.

breviations are used for plural and singular, and are written without a period, with the exception of at. (for "atomic") and in. (for "inch" or "inches"). Note that certain units are not abbreviated (except sometimes in compound forms): dyne, erg, farad, gauss, henry, joule, liter, mho, mile, ohm, weber.

Å	Ångstrom (10^{-10} m)
abamp	absolute ampere
amp	ampere
atm	atmosphere
at. wt.	atomic weight
AWG	American wire gage
Bev	billion electron volt (10^9 ev)
Btu	British thermal unit
C	Curie
°C	degree centigrade, Celsius
cal	calorie
cc	cubic centimeter (liquid)
cir mil	circular mil
cp	candlepower, centipoise
cgs	centimeter-gram-second
cm	centimeter (10^{-2} m)
coul	coulomb
cps	cycles per second
db	decibel
dbm	db referred to 1 mw
dbv	db referred to 1 v
deg	degree
dg	dekagram (10 g)
diam	diameter
dm	decimeter (10^{-1} m)
emu	electromagnetic units
esu	electrostatic units
ev	electron volt
°F	degree Fahrenheit
f	fermi (10^{-15} m)
ft	foot
ft-c	foot-candle
ft-L	foot-lambert
g	gram
gal	gallon
Gc	gigacycle (10^9 cps; also kMc)
gpm	gallons per minute
gr	grain
hl	hectoliter
hp	horsepower
hr	hour
ID	inside diameter

in.	inch
°K	degree Kelvin (absolute centigrade)
kc	kilocycle (10^3 cps)
kcal	kilocalorie
kev	kilo electron volt
kg	kilogram (10^3 g)
kMc	kilomegacycle (10^9 cps; also Gc)
km	kilometer (10^3 m)
kohm	kilohm (10^3 ohms)
kv	kilovolt
kw	kilowatt
L	lambert
lat	latitude
lb	pound
lu	lumen
M	mole, molar
m	meter
ma	milliampere
Mc	megacycle (10^6 cps)
mc	millicurie
meg	megohm (10^6 ohms)
Mev	million electron volt
mg	milligram (10^{-3} g)
mh	millihenry
mi	mile
mil	thousandth of an inch
min	minute
mks	meter-kilogram-second
ml	milliliter
mM	millimole
mm	millimeter (10^{-3} m)
mph	miles per hour
msec	millisecond
mv	millivolt
Mw	megawatt
mw	milliwatt
mμ	millimicron (10^{-9} m)
mμsec	millimicrosecond (also ns)
OD	outside diameter
oz	ounce
ppm	part per million
pps	pulses per second
psi	pounds per square inch
°R	degree Rankin (absolute Fahrenheit)
r	roentgen
rad	radian
rms	root-mean-square
rpm	revolutions per minute
rps	revolutions per second
ry	Rydberg
sec	second
tpi	turns per inch
v	volt
vu	volume unit
w	watt
yd	yard
μ	micron (10^{-6} m)
μa	microampere
μf	microfarad
μg	microgram (10^{-6} g)
$\mu\mu$f	micromicrofarad
μh	microhenry
μsec	microsecond
$\mu\mu$	micromicrom, bicrom (10^{-12} m)

CHARLES SUSSKIND

Cross-references: *Chemical Elements, Color Codes (RETMA), Symbols, Unit Systems*

ACCELERATORS

Among the basic tools of science is the particle accelerator. Electron accelerators are used to make x-rays which are used directly in industrial and commercial applications, in the field of food preservation, in medicine as a diagnostic and therapeutic agent, as well as in the nuclear sciences. Ion accelerators have been used for basic nuclear and cosmic ray research, and the preparation of artificial isotopes; ion accelerator techniques have been used for isotope separation.

All accelerators involve some mechanism for the creation of charged particles, accelerating them electrically through a vacuum chamber and into a target, either external of the machine, or internal, depending on the design. For electrons, a simple incandescent filament produces enough electrons for any purpose. For an increase in filament life, low-work-function coatings are used in some applications. Positive ions are produced by allowing a stream of electrons to pass through the gas to be ionized, and electrical extraction is used to remove the ions from the ion source.

Some systems maintain a static electric field for the acceleration of the particles. Typically, the total energy of particles from such machines is small compared to other schemes, since the total voltage necessary for the acceleration must be maintained continuously within the electrical system. The Cockroft-Walton cascade rectifier is being used successfully to produce ions of 500 kilovolts energy. The Van de Graaff accelerator (static electricity generator using a charged belt for the accumulation of charge) has been used up to 4 million volts; a machine is planned giving 12-million volt ions. Condenser storage systems and pulse transformers will give energies up to about 1 million volts of electrons or ions.

Circular machines deliver high-energy particles using moderate acceleration voltages. The particles move in a circular path as a result of their interaction with a magnetic field; during each circuit they are given an acceleration. (For example, the bevatron accelerates protons to 6,000 Mev in about 2 sec, with a total effective path length of about 200,000 miles.)

Circular machines are of two general types, those having a constant magnetic field (cyclotrons) and those having time-varying magnetic fields (synchrotrons and betatrons). Cyclotrons are of two types: constant-frequency acceleration systems, which produce medium energy ions at high currents (typically 20-Mev deuterons at 300 ma); and frequency-modulated acceleration systems, which produce high-energy ions. High-energy ions are produced by designing the acceleration system to change the ion acceleration frequency to accommodate the relativistic increase in mass of the particles due to their high velocity. The necessity of changing frequency causes a severe reduction in beam current, since frequency is proper over only a small part of the operating time.

Synchrotrons and betatrons are circular machines which use a time-varying magnetic field to keep the particles at a constant radius. The particles are injected into the machine with small energy at a time when the magnetic field is low. The particles are accelerated to higher energies in the machine as the magnetic field is increased. The highest-energy ion accelerators are proton synchrotrons using a very large radius of curvature for the beam. Synchrotrons have also been used successfully for the acceleration of electrons (325 Mev at a 1 m radius and 1000 Mev at 12.5 ft radius). In the case of high-energy electron accelerators, the electrons travel at approximately the velocity of light, and as a consequence all of the accelerating voltages can be applied on a constant-frequency basis.

Betatrons are circular machines which are unique in that no rf energy is fed to the beam for acceleration. The betatron accelerates electrons from low energy ($\sim$100 kev) to moderate energies (conventionally in the range of 10 to 100 Mev) using the changing magnetic field across the beam tube to focus and guide the beam, and using a changing magnetic field at the center of the machine for the acceleration in exactly the same fashion that electrons are accelerated in a wire in the secondary of a transformer. These machines are useful for industrial x-ray production, and are commercially available for such purposes. Betatron injection into electron synchrotrons has been used successfully.

Linear accelerators are of two kinds: the standing-wave ion accelerators, and the traveling-wave electron accelerators. In the standing-wave accelerators, the ions are accelerated between drift tubes in a cavity which has a rf electric field impressed along its axis. The spacing of the drift tubes is such that the ion will be between drift tubes when the electric field is oriented for acceleration of the particle, and within the drift tubes when the electric field is improper for acceleration. Injection energy for the linear accelerator must be high enough to give reasonable drift-tube lengths. The beam energy from such machines is generally low (10- to 30-Mev protons); however, the space and energy collimation is extremely good.

This arrangement is used for injecting protons into the betatron.

The traveling-wave machine is used for the acceleration of electrons. Since the rest mass of the electron is low (~511 kev), a small energy will give the electron an appreciable velocity (1-Mev electrons travel at 93 per cent of the velocity of light), and as a consequence the acceleration of electrons can be made in a constant-velocity-of-propagation apparatus (traveling-wave accelerator). A beam of low-energy electrons is accelerated along a tube by means of a traveling electric field. Successful acceleration of ions has not been made, the requirement of a variable velocity of propagation of the accelerating field offering a severe technical obstacle. Development of two linear accelerators for the production of low-energy (~10 Mev per nucleon) ions of the mass ranges of C_{12}, N_{14}, O_{16}, N_{20}, etc. for high mass isotope preparation is under way.

New accelerators are being built, where practical, using a new concept—strong focusing—wherein the beam particles are passed through volumes of electric or magnetic fields oriented normal to the trajectory and alternately at right angles. Special advantage has been found in the linear accelerator and synchrotron type machine; many of these machines are being retrofitted to accommodate this advance. This technique leads to more efficient design therefore higher energy for the same capital outlay.

LAWRENCE E. BROWN

Cross-references: *Alternating-Gradient Focusing, Betatron and Cyclotron, Cockcroft-Walton Accelerator, Cosmotron, Linear Accelerators, Microtron, Synchrotron and Bevatron, Van de Graaff Accelerator*

ACCELEROMETERS: see TRANSDUCERS

ACOUSTICS

Physical acoustics deals with the properties and behavior of longitudinal waves of "infinitesimal" amplitude in solid, liquid, or gaseous media. The waves are propagated, reflected, refracted, diffracted, and absorbed. They are accompanied by pressure- and particle-velocity fluctuations usually detectable by ear or by instruments capable of measuring the frequency and mean intensity of the fluctuations. Geometrical acoustics is a special case of physical acoustics in which diffraction is neglected.

Electroacoustics deals with the manner and means of energy transfer between electromechanical devices and the medium propagating sound waves.

Architectural acoustics deals with the problems of distribution of beneficial sounds within buildings, and with the exclusion or reduction of undesirable sounds.

Psychological acoustics deals with the emotional and mental reactions of persons and animals to various sounds.

Physiological acoustics deals with hearing and its impairment, the voice mechanism, and physical effects in general of sounds on living bodies.

The frequency range of sound is divided into three somewhat overlapping regions, namely, an *audio-frequency* band ranging from approximately 20 to 20,000 cps flanked by an *infrasonic* region below 30 cps and an *ultrasonic* region above 15,000 cps. Human ears do not respond in general to frequencies outside the audio band, although small animals such as cats and bats do hear in the lower ultrasonic region.

The strength of a sound field is measured by its mean square pressure expressed as *sound pressure level* (L_p) in decibels *re* 0.0002 microbar (dynes/cm², rms); i.e., $L_p = 20 \log_{10} (p/0.0002)$ db, where $p =$ rms sound field pressure in microbars and 0.0002 microbar is the international standard reference rms sound pressure. Other reference pressures can be used and it is essential to specify them when quoting values of L_p.

The strength of a sound field is also judged by ear at audio frequencies. Loudness judgments by groups of observers have established a *loudness level* scale. The loudness level (L_N) in *phons* is arbitrarily equal to L_p in db *at the reference frequency* of 1000 cps in the range from the faintest sound detectable by good young adult ears (4 db, 4 phons—the *threshold of hearing**) to the loudest sound heard without discomfort (120 db, 120 phons—the *threshold of feeling*, or of *discomfort*). Jury judgments of equality in loudness between test tones at different frequencies (f) and 1000-cps reference tones of known L_p have established equal loudness contours (constant L_N) in the $L_p - f$ plane.

These contours show in general a marked decrease in ear sensitivity to sounds at frequencies below about 200 cps, and that this decrease is much more pronounced in the lower loudness levels. For example, at 50 cps the 4-phon contour has an L_p of about 43 db, the 80-phon contour about 93 db. At higher frequencies the ear shows some 8 db *increase* in sensitivity in the region around 3500 cps, then a loss in sensitivity beyond about 6000 cps. These characteristics of hearing are significant in the design of lecture and music halls, noise-control devices, and high-fidelity audio equipment.

Also based on jury judgments a scale of *loudness* (in sones) has been established for sounds. On this scale a given percentage change in sone-value denotes an equal percentage change in the loudness of a sound. The scale provides single numbers for judging the relative loudnesses of different acoustical environments, for evaluating the percentage reduction in noise due to various noise control measures, and for setting limits on permissible noise in factories, from motor vehicles, etc.

Loudness N is related to loudness level L_N above 40 phons by the equation $N = \log_{10}^{-1} (0.03 L_N - 1.2)$. A loudness of 1 sone corresponds to a loudness level of 40 phons and is typical of the low-level background noise in a quiet home.

Various methods are available for estimating loudnesses of complex sounds from their pressure levels in octave, half-octave, or third-octave bands. For traffic noise, readings on a standard sound level meter using

* 0 db, 0 phons at 1000 cps is defined as the threshold of hearing in older work.

the A-scale (which incorporates a frequency-weighting network approximating the variation of ear sensitivity to tones of 40 db sound pressure level) correlate well with jury judgments of vehicle loudness.

The acoustic power output of various sources is given either in *watts* (W), or as a *sound power level* (L_w) in decibels (*dbp*) *re* one *picowatt* (micromicrowatt). $L_w = 10 \log_{10} (W/10^{-12})$ dbp. (It should be noted that 0.1 picowatt is sometimes used as reference for sound power level.) Conversational speech power averages about 10 μw and loudest shouting about 1 mw. A heavy orchestra in its loudest passages may develop a peak power of 70 w, but its long-time average is about 0.1 w. Typical acoustic power outputs for induction motors are approximately 3 w for a 4000-hp motor, 1 w for a 600-hp motor, and 30 mw for a ¾-hp motor. Jet engines with an efflux velocity of 2000 ft/sec produce about 100 w of acoustical power *per square inch of nozzle exit area* (about 30,000 w for a 20-in. diameter jet). Rocket-engine acoustic output is about 10 to 100 times greater. Sound-pressure levels produced by such large acoustic outputs affect the reliability of electronic and electrical components in the aircraft or rocket and induce fatigue failures in structural elements. Personnel exposed to nearby jet and rocket engine noise may suffer hearing impairment and unpleasant vibration in body cavities unless suitably protected. At more distant points severe interference with speech, music, and rest may occur.

Acoustics of Enclosures. Among other things enclosures are presumed to produce desirable acoustical environments for communication, entertainment, and repose. A first criterion for all such enclosures is keeping the intruding background noise level below predetermined limits. Additional criteria for enclosures in which communication and entertainment are important include reverberation time, sound diffusion, and freedom from echoes. The upper limit of background noise is expressed in terms of an *SC* (*speech communication*) criterion, which shows the permissible sound pressure levels in octave bands for various types of enclosures. The *SC*-criteria range from 15–20 for broadcast studios, 20–25 for concert halls, 25 for sleeping areas and conference rooms, 30 for motion picture theaters, churches, and courtrooms, 40 for small private offices, 45 for restaurants, 55 for secretarial offices, up to 65 for factories. The numbers are averages of L_p in the three octave bands between 600 and 4800 cps; they are also termed *speech interference levels* (*SIL*).

Walls, doors and windows must be heavy enough and sufficiently sealed against sound leaks to reduce intruding noise to the desired limits. Also, ventilating systems and room equipment must be sufficiently quiet to prevent interior noise from exceeding the *SC* criteria.

Measured reverberation times T for rooms rated as acousticaly excellent by performers and auditors provide design criteria for new construction. By definition, T is the time required for the sound level in a room to drop 60 db after the source is stopped; it is given by the formula

$$T = 0.05V/[-2.3S \log_{10}(1 - \bar{\alpha})],$$

or, when $\bar{\alpha} < 0.2$, by the formula $T = 0.05V/(S\alpha) = 0.05V/a$. V = room volume (ft³), S = total room surface (ft²), $\bar{\alpha}$ = average sound absorption coefficient given by a/S, where a = the total number of absorption units in the room. The absorption a is obtained from

$$a = \sum^i \alpha_i S_i + \sum^j n_j a_j$$

where S_i is the portion of the room surface having the absorption coefficient α_i and n_j is the number of objects in the room (e.g., chairs, persons, or tables, etc.) each equivalent to a_j units of absorption. The absorption coefficient α for a surface is the ratio of absorbed to incident energy in a random sound field. It is frequency dependent and is obtained by reverberation time measurements in a reverberant test room. Values of α for various types of materials and values of a

for various objects and persons have been tabulated for a series of frequencies.

Optimum values of reverberation time (T_{opt}) are given for 500 cps and depend on the use of a room. For organ music or Roman Catholic churches $T_{opt} \approx 0.47 \log_{10}V - 0.5$, for concert halls and Protestant churches $T_{opt} \approx 0.54 \log_{10}V - 1.26$, for school auditoriums, opera houses and broadcast studios for music $T_{opt} \approx 0.5 \log_{10}V - 1.2$, for class rooms, conference rooms, and motion picture theaters $T_{opt} \approx 0.32 \log_{10}V - 0.62$. Although T_{opt} at 500 cps is the more important criterion for reverberation time and often the only one used, further improvement in hearing conditions may be attained by adjusting reverberation times at other frequencies according to criteria depending on room use. For speech alone the reverberation time should be the same at all frequencies. For music the reverberation time should gradually rise as the frequency decreases below 500 cps, attaining at 60 cps a value double that at 500 cps. Above 500 cps the reverberation time should remain substantially constant for all frequencies.

REFERENCES

Leo L. Beranek, *Acoustics*, New York, McGraw-Hill, 1954.
Cyril M. Harris, *Handbook of Noise Control*, New York, McGraw-Hill, 1957.

W. W. Soroka

Cross-references: *Electroacoustics*

ADAPTIVE SYSTEMS: see SYSTEMS (NON-LINEAR)

AIR-TRAFFIC CONTROL

Government aviation responsibilities for writing safety rules and regulations, allocating and regulating airspace, managing air traffic and related research and development were placed under the Federal Aviation Agency (FAA) by the Federal Aviation Act of 1958. The traffic-management functions are the major responsibility of the Agency and are based on three major factors: accurate navigation of the individual aircraft, communications between aircraft and ground-based control facilities, and coordination of aircraft movements.

Air Navigation. The majority of the air traffic flows on an airway structure which is aligned with ground-based, very high-frequency omni-directional radio ranges and distance-measuring systems, commonly known as VORTAC and consisting of the VOR and TACAN equipments. These primary navigation facilities operate in 100- and 1,000-mc bands and are superseding those provided by the low-medium-frequency four-course ranges. The VORTAC system supplies pilots of equipped aircraft with information on the bearing to or from the ground station and distance to the station. Other navigation systems, both self-contained and ground based, are also employed for enroute and instrument-approach purposes. The navigation function is normally performed in the aircraft by the pilot or navigator. While this is not technically a function of traffic control, it is vital to the efficiency of any system for handling air traffic.

Air-Ground Communication. Flight advisory, weather, flight-plan revisions, and control information is handled by vhf and uhf voice communication channels between the aircraft and air-route traffic-control centers, airport towers, and air-traffic communication stations. The channels are in the 100- to 130-Mc band for civil aircraft and 200- to 400-Mc band for military aircraft. Interference and communication delays owing to channel loading and human factors are system problems. Development is under way to provide automatic digital data links to handle the routine type of messages, including position reporting to the ground.

Ground Data Acquisition. Two systems are in use to provide the ground control facilities information on the position and movement of the air traffic under surveillance. In the first, the pilot, using airborne-derived navigational data, reports his position to the ground via voice communica-

tion channels. Normally, these position reports are required when the aircraft are over predesignated geographic points used to post information on ground displays. The second system uses data from ground radars located in the vicinity of busy terminals to maintain a minimum interval between successive landings and departures. Radar information is also used in extended areas around airports where severe problems associated with the climb and descent of aircraft are encountered, and in enroute areas for traffic advisory and separation services to aircraft. Both long-range L- and S-band radars are employed enroute with coverage up to 200 miles in range and 60,000 ft in altitude. S-band radars are used in terminal areas around the airport, X-band radars for precision approach control, and K-band radars for airport surface surveillance. Since the accuracy and rate of data acquisition are major factors in determining the separation criteria, improvements in equipments and data links are a continuing requirement.

Control Concept. Control of air traffic is performed under two general procedures, Visual Flight Rules (VFR) and Instrument Flight Rules (IFR). Separation of air traffic is largely performed by the pilot by a "seen-and-be-seen" concept under the first procedure. A ground agency assumes the responsibility for separation between controlled aircraft under the latter. Two route structures aligned with the navigation facilities are provided, one structure below 24,000 ft and the other above. In general, traffic below 14,500 ft can fly under VFR or IFR, depending upon the weather and area, and traffic above 14,500 ft must be operated under positive control of a ground station. Where a ground responsibility, traffic is primarily separated by altitude, time, or distance, the actual separation criteria depending upon the data-acquisition system employed. The control of air traffic is performed at two types of ground facilities, airport control towers and enroute air-traffic control centers. Some additional and special facilities are required for military aviation purposes.

Communication and coordination functions are a major concern in the system. All major airports are connected through an extensive telephone and teletype network. The ground network in turn connects to ground-air-ground radio transmitters/receivers and communication stations. Flights are initiated in the IFR system with the filing of a flight plan, which is used to probe for potential conflicts on a manual tabular display. Each aircraft in the system, except when radar procedures are being used, is cleared between successive predesignated geographic points, and areas containing a number of these "fixes" are under the cognizance of a specific controller. The flight is handled from one controller's cognizance to the next through each regime of flight, in accordance with an active flight plan updated to correct for changes in winds, cruising speed, and other factors.

Data Processing and Display. The majority of the data processing, display, decision, coordination, and communication functions are performed manually. Automation is being introduced that will relieve the traffic controller of all routine functions except communicating with the pilot. Information is inserted into the system through keyboards and teletype, with the controller making decisions. Some systems using digital computers of the IBM-650 RAMAC and UNIVAC File types are being used to perform some of the calculations and printing and distributing of flight progress strips (paper strips arranged on a tabular display). Plans are being developed to expand the system to update the tabular display, provide conflict prediction, and to transfer data automatically.

The major problem encountered in air-traffic control systems is the relationship of the human controller to equipment. Two types of displays are required; the first consists of a tabular display to provide basic flight-plan information with rigid safety requirements in case of system failure, and the other, a pictorial display of identified present-position information for conflict resolution, aircraft vectoring, and over-all monitoring purposes. The use of a fail-safe automatic type of tabular display to replace the operationally complex paper strip is required. At present, manual tracking is performed on a large, bright, horizontal radar scope using radar-to-television scan-conversion techniques. Automatic tracking with associated identification, altitude, and other required information will be employed in the future.

Continued development of the Air-Traffic Control system, using present and advanced electronic techniques, to provide capacity, efficiency, and growth capability consistent with the demands of aviation is required.

PAUL T. ASTHOLZ

Cross-references: *Automatic Pilot, Navigation, Radar, Radar Displays*

ALPHA PARTICLES

Alpha particles, sometimes called rays, are spontaneously ejected from the nuclei of many radioactive elements as doubly charged helium nuclei with extremely high velocity $\frac{1}{15}$ to $\frac{1}{20}$ that of light. Until recently the radioactive alpha particle represented the highest concentration of kinetic energy known to science. But with the advent of the cyclotron of Lawrence, helium (and other light nuclei) could be raised to much higher energies limited only by the cyclotron voltage, thus generating so-called artificial alpha particles, which are used to bombard nuclei to produce other isotopes and to study their effects in radiation chemistry.

All alpha particles have the same mass as the helium atom (4) and the same charge of 2 units representing the loss of two orbital electrons giving the stripped nucleus He^{+2}.

An alpha particle travels in straight line through the electronic field of a large number of atoms or molecules (150–200 thousand in air) and only rarely suffers a large deflection by close collision with a nucleus. The kinetic energy is spent in collision by producing ionization (removal of one or more electrons), by excitation, and in other minor ways. In the five noble gases when highly pure, Jesse has found that the proportion of total energy expended by the alpha particle to the energy used in producing ionization is constant, having the value 1.73, or that 36.6 per cent is spent in ionization and 63.4 per cent in excitation, etc. The proportion of energy spent by alpha particles in exciting gas molecules (principally organic molecules in contrast to atomic gases) is somewhat higher and variable (67 per cent for butane, 73 per cent for oxygen).

When an alpha particle impinges on certain solid materials, especially phosphorescent zinc sulfide, a scintillation is produced which can be observed under suitable magnification. By counting the number of scintillations per unit time from a known quantity of radioactive material much valuable information is obtained about the properties of alpha particles and their interaction with matter. Historically this was of the highest importance. Later other types of counting by electrical discharge (Geiger counters) were introduced. More recently scintillation counting, especially for gamma rays (*q.v.*), has again been successfully adapted by the use of photomultipliers. Luminous paints, such as are used on watch and clock dials, are made by mixing radium (or mesathorium) sulfate with phosphorescent zinc sulfide. The large number of scintillations gives a continuous luminescence visible to the rested eye.

If alpha particles pass through a chamber containing a gas saturated with water vapor they produce ionization along their paths. If the gas is suddenly expanded so as to produce supersaturation, condensation of water droplets occurs on the ions before they can diffuse. With suitable illumination the Wilson cloud tracks can be observed or photographed. Path length and form, including pictures of nuclear collisions and energy distribution among the fragments, are thus disclosed.

Owing to their high energy and ease of absorption by gases, alpha particles have been used as activating agent for many chemical reactions. Radon mixed with the gas or mixture of gases is a suitable system for chemical kinetic studies.

S. C. LIND

Cross-references: *Electrons, Protons, Radiation, Scintillation Counters*

ALTERNATING-GRADIENT FOCUSING

Alternating-gradient or "strong" focusing is a method of producing bounded oscillatory transverse motion of a beam of charged particles, in which the restoring forces are proportional to the transverse displacements from the desired path but also vary periodically with respect to distance along the beam. The mathematical description of such systems has long been understood and is known as the theory of the Mathieu-Hill equation or, more generally, of linear differential equations with periodic coefficients. Nonlinear effects may also be present and require careful analysis since they can destroy stability through resonances, which are complicated and will not be discussed here. (See, for example, P. A. Sturrock, "Static and Dynamic Electron Optics; and Account of Focusing in Lens, Deflector, and Accelerator," Cambridge University Press, Cambridge, England, 1954.)

The terms "alternating-gradient focusing" and "strong focusing" (which are used interchangeably in connection with particle accelerators), and the extensive application of this method in recent years, arose from a discovery in 1949 by Christofilos and independently in 1952 by Courant, Livingston, and Snyder (*Phys. Rev.* **88:** 1190, 1952 and **91:** 202, 1953. This discovery was that a beam of charged particles could be held together if passed through regions of transverse magnetic (or electric) fields having large gradients, arranged to produce rapid convergence and divergence, successively, in a periodic pattern along the beam path. The resulting net focusing action can be made much stronger than that formerly obtained in circular particle accelerators through use of a weak gradient held constant along the path. (These simpler accelerators are now called "weak-focusing" machines.) The two particle accelerators with highest energy now operating, the Brookhaven National Laboratory's alternating-gradient synchrotron on Long Island, New York, and the proton synchrotron at the international laboratory of CERN at Geneva, Switzerland, employ strong focusing, as do a number of other existing and projected circular accelerators. The method is also used to focus particle beams in standing-wave linear accelerators, and to transmit and focus beams before injecting them into or after extracting them from an accelerator. (For a detailed account of proton synchrotrons and linear accelerators using this focusing, see Green and Courant, "The Proton Synchrotron," and L. Smith, "Linear Accelerators," *Handbuch der Physik* **XLIV**: 218 and 341, 1959.)

The principle applies to many other types of systems; in some of these the terms "gradient" and "focusing" are inappropriate. Some of the *periodic-focusing* schemes used in connection with traveling-wave tubes (*q.v.*) and beam-type parametric amplifiers (*q.v.*) are derived from alternating-gradient focusing. Heteroparametric (externally varied parametric) periodic excitation of linear systems is well known in electric circuits and in the study of (usually unwanted) vibrations of mechanical devices. The same mathematical analysis also arises in discussing the stability of periodic behavior in all nonlinear systems (*q.v.*).

In the applications to charged particle optics "quadrupole" fields are used. Consider a particle moving with speed v nearly along the z axis of Cartesian coordinates. A magnetic field $B_x = ky$, $B_y = kx$, derived from $\mathbf{B} = \nabla V$, $V = kxy$, can be generated by four symmetrical magnetic pole faces with hyperbolic cylindrical surfaces $xy =$ constant, the poles in the first and third quadrants being south poles and the other two north poles; k is the magnitude of the magnetic-field gradient. The Lorentz force $q\mathbf{v} \times \mathbf{B}$ produces motions governed by the pair of equations

$$d^2(x,y)/dz^2 \pm (qk/mv)(x,y) \cong 0$$

where the upper sign is associated with x and the lower with y; $z \cong vt$ and m is the particle's relativistic transverse mass $m_0/[1 - (v^2/c^2)]^{1/2}$. (Electric fields produced by four electrodes of hyperbolic cylindrical shape $x^2 - y^2 =$ constant, with alternating polarities, yield similar equations.) If a series of such magnetic regions is provided along the beam path in a periodic array having repetition length L, with successive regions having reversed polarities, the parameter k becomes a periodic function of z; $k(z) = \pm k$ in regions with the stated and reversed polarities, respectively, and $k = 0$ in gaps that may exist between magnets. If, in addition to the periodicity $k(z + L) = k(z)$, the array also has $k[z + (L/2)] = -k(z)$ the behavior in x and y will be the same but displaced in z by $L/2$. In circular accelerators a uniform bending field is superposed on the quadrupole fields, producing an asymmetry between radial and axial motions owing to centripetal force; the asymmetry is small if the resultant focusing is "strong" compared to the "weak" focusing mentioned above. This bending field is obtained by choosing for the path of the central ray a line displaced along the x axis, from the center of symmetry of the field described, far enough so the beam occupies only a region in which B_y is always of one sign. This condition involves opposite displacements of successive regions. The two poles in each region between which the beam does not pass may then be omitted by properly shaping the remaining poles, whose flux returns need only be on one side, leading to a ⊏-shaped magnet cross section.

Floquet's theorem states that for arbitrary periodic $k(z)$ the most general solution of such an equation is the real part of

$$x = A\,e^{j\mu z}P(z) + B\,e^{-j\mu z}Q(z)$$

where A and B are arbitrary complex constants; $P(z)$ and $Q(z)$ have the periodicity of $k(z)$. Great importance attaches to the determination of μ, which depends only on the form of $k(z)$. If the imaginary part of μ does not vanish the motion is unbounded, whereas if μ is real the path consists of a sinusoidal motion of wavelength $2\pi/\mu$ modulated with period L by P and Q.* The value of μ may be real even if $k(z)$ has a negative average value provided the amplitude of its variation is large enough, as is illustrated by the stability of an inverted pendulum whose point of support is forced to oscillate rapidly in the vertical direction.

The virtue of strong focusing for accelerators is that the wavelength $2\pi/\mu$ can be made many times smaller than the machine circumference, whereas for weak focusing it must always be somewhat larger. The transverse aperture required is correspondingly reduced, leading to a much smaller and cheaper magnet for a given particle energy. For the Brookhaven machine mentioned above the number of wavelengths per circumference is about nine; the reduction in aperture area and therefore in stored magnetic energy compared with an equivalent weak focusing machine is by more than a factor 100. This accelerator has a useful gap of $2\frac{3}{4} \times 6$ in., a gradient of 1.3 kilogauss/in. at a peak field of 13 kilogauss, and has 240 magnets containing a total of 4000 tons of steel and 400 tons of copper. The circumference including straight sections is about 0.5 mile.

For containing and transporting particle beams two or three magnets of alternating polarities, called doublets and triplets, are often connected rigidly as a unit. Such arrays have the properties of thick lenses, with the complicating feature that the focal lengths and locations of principal planes will in general be different for trajectories off axis in the x and y directions; i.e., the lenses have astigmatism. However, this property can often be put to good use in experimental arrangements. A typical large-aperture triplet suitable for focusing very-high-energy particles (of order 10^9 ev) has a useful bore of 8 in. diameter, with magnets 16, 32, and 16 in. in length, an over-all length of about 8 ft, a cross section almost 3 ft × 3 ft, and a weight of over 7 tons. Field gradients up to 2.5 kilogauss/in. are used, requiring 350 kw. Such an array would have a focal length of the order of a few feet for particles of these energies; for comparison, the familiar focusing action of a wedge-shaped 10-kilogauss uniform field with the same 64-in. path length would lead to focal lengths of the order of 100 ft. Of course much smaller units are used for particles of lower energies. Here a larger gradient may be employed since it can vary inversely with the aperture.

DAVID L. JUDD

Cross-references: *Accelerators, Electron Optics, Phase-Space Representation*

ALTIMETERS

Electronic altimeters are devices installed in aircraft to determine height above the surface of the earth. They are also known as radar altimeters, radio altimeters, absolute altimeters, and terrain clearance indicators.

The first electronic altimeters were produced in quantity in the late 1930's. Being heavy and consuming a considerable amount of the electric power in aircraft of that day, they saw only limited use. World War II accelerated the need for knowing height above the terrain by the pilot, navigator, weather observer, and the bombardier. Over 50,000 altimeters were produced internationally during that conflict; they operated

* The theory as applied to synchrotrons is developed by Courant and Snyder, *Annals of Physics* **3**: 1, 1958.

in the region of 350–450 Mc. The years following World War II saw emphasis aimed at extending the high-altitude performance to above 50,000 ft, improved accuracy down toward zero feet, improved altitude display, and data pickoff for automatic control and recording. The rf bands of 1600–1660 Mc and 4200–4400 Mc have been assigned for electronic altimeter use, the higher frequency band being exclusively for altimeters.

Techniques. The *capacity* altimeter measures the capacitance between two electrodes mounted on the aircraft, the capacitance between the electrodes varying with aircraft height. The ability to measure small capacity changes limits the use of this technique to about 100 feet above the terrain.

The *sonic* altimeter uses acoustic energy and provides distance information by determining the time between transmitted and received signals. Both pulse and cw modulation methods have been used. The effects of aircraft vibration, low-energy reflection from certain types of terrain, and acoustical noise external to the aircraft limit this technique to about 300 feet above the terrain. Range errors are small at small distances.

The most widely accepted technique uses *electromagnetic energy* in both cw and pulse-modulated forms. One form has not proven more advantageous than the other in terms of size, weight, or characteristics to cover the range of zero to over 50,000 ft. Each form has specific advantages. Frequency modulation of continuous waves has proven more satisfactory from zero to about 2000 ft, whereas pulse modulation has been more satisfactory from about 1000 ft upward.

Uses. The basic need for an electronic altimeter arises because the pilot of an aircraft wants to know his height above the surface of the earth. This information is especially important when he cannot see the earth. In present-day flight operations, where the trend is toward more instrument flying, there is less dependence on visual cues external to the aircraft. The altimeter is used as a height sensor for the dropping of supplies and personnel and for air-sea res-

cues. It finds application in aerial photography for compensating image motion produced by the aircraft speed and for establishing the vertical datum in aerial geodetic work. When used with the pressure altimeter it has found application in obtaining upper air data for meteorological stations as a factor in flight planning. Again in conjunction with the pressure altimeter it is widely used to determine wind patterns during transocean flying. This information can result in minimizing flight time by choosing flight paths that produce tail winds. As various terrains (farm land, mountains, water, etc.) produce differing rf energy-reflection patterns, the air observer can use the altimeter indicator for a rough check of the type of terrain over which he is flying. The altimeter has been useful in giving the pilot a check on his progress along the ILS (Instrument Low Approach System) glide path. Increasing effort is being directed at improving the accuracy and reliability of the electronic altimeter as an aid in blind landing of aircraft.

Design and Performance Characteristics. If all the energy transmitted were received, the inverse-square law ($1/h^2$, where h is the height) of energy attenuation would apply to altimeters. From specular surfaces (like runways and calm bodies of water) this law does hold for heights under several thousand feet. For practical cases, diffuse surfaces can also return all the energy if extremely small heights are involved. For most cases, however, $1/h^2$ tends toward $1/h^3$ as height increases. In addition, techniques of processing the return energy to increase the accuracy of height information discard a considerable quantity of the return energy and lower the height at which the transition to $1/h^3$ begins. Antenna beam width is yet another modifier of the transition region.

Electronic altimeters as a rule use two antennas, one for transmitting and one for receiving. Transmitter power is relatively low and in pulse systems the TR and ATR (*q.v.*) switches so common in higher-power long-range radars add complexity to altimeters. In addition, in pulse systems where ranges under 500 ft are involved, reception essentially takes place during transmission. Separate antennas reduce the direct (transmitter-to-receiver) energy to a greater extent than possible with rf plumbing networks. Separate antennas simplify the design of the rf assemblies. In the portions of the rf spectrum assigned to altimeters, decoupling of the transmitted energy cannot be depended upon to exceed 60–70 db in a practical aircraft installation. Since the reflected energy can be attenuated by 120–150 db, many methods have been devised for processing the return energy to minimize the unwanted direct energy and enhance the desired reflected energy

Antenna beamwidths are generally broad, not only to simplify design but to permit operation during changes in aircraft attitude. Narrower beamwidths are indicated for landing applications to minimize Doppler and capture effects. The restricting limits imposed on aircraft maneuvering during landing permit narrower beamwidths.

Locations of altimeter antennas vary. Where higher altitude performance is required, preferred locations are the acoustically and electrically quiet areas of the fuselage. For landing applications, the antennas are mounted close to the center of gravity (essentially near the main wheels) to minimize altitude and sink-rate errors as the aircraft rotates on its pitch axis during the landing maneuver.

Cw altimeters with zero-frequency IF amplifiers (crystal detectors and audio amplifiers) are limited in capability owing to the microphonics, vibration, and electrical noise in the aircraft. Recent developments in cw altimeters with more conventional IF amplifiers give promise of minimizing these disturbances and bringing with them improved stability and accuracy.

The form in which altitude information is presented depends on the application. The pilot generally performs a visual scanning of his instruments to assess his situation. Direction of motion of his instrument indicators and the rate at which the motion takes place are more significant than the absolute value of the indication. Altimeter instruments for pilots have generally been pointer types whose scales expand as altitude decreases. Other observers such as navigators are interested in precise values and for them digital indicators and other linear presentations are used. There are also applications for altitude recordings and the control of aircraft altitude and attitude.

While a universal electronic altimeter to fulfill all altimeter requirements appears desirable, the need for simplicity, accuracy, and reliability for specific functions dictates otherwise.

ALBERT SEGEN

Cross-references: *Air-Traffic Control, Automatic Pilot, Integrated Instrumentation, Navigation and Navigational Systems, Radar, Radar Displays*

AMMETERS: see INDICATING INSTRUMENTS

AMPLIFIERS

Ac Amplifiers

This article discusses typical transistor (T) and vacuum tube (VT) ac amplifiers used below roughly 500 Mc. Microwave amplifiers, masers, and parametric amplifiers are treated elsewhere.

A typical *lowpass* amplifier is that used for the video signal in a television or radar system. The low frequency limit (which may extend to dc, see below) is a very small fraction of the total 3-db bandwidth.

A VT lowpass amplifier usually employs pentodes characterized by a transconductance g_m and a total shunt interstage capacitance to ground $C = C_{in} + C_{out} + C_{socket\ and\ wiring}$. Triodes may economically be used where the severe limitation on large bandwidths caused by their grid-plate capacitance ("Miller" effect) is not important. The voltage-gain—bandwidth product of one resistance-coupled pentode stage is $g_m/2\pi C$, which for a high performance type such as the E180F (or 6688), is about 200

Mc. By inductive "peaking" techniques, this figure may be improved by a factor of either two, or roughly three to four for 2- and 4-terminal interstages, respectively. The gain of a cascade of n stages goes up as the nth power of the gain per stage, whereas the bandwidth in the absence of peaking decreases by a factor of

$$\sqrt{2^{1/n} - 1}$$

Sufficiently sophisticated peaking techniques can result in the bandwidth remaining approximately constant, but the associated transient response generally has large over-shoot (see amplifiers, pulse).

For extreme bandwidths (> 100 Mc) a distributed amplifier, where the grid and plate capacitances form the shunt elements in lumped transmission lines, may be the only usable VT type. In such an amplifier, the gain-bandwidth product per tube is again approximately $g_m/2\pi C$, but the over-all gain is the *sum* of the stage gains. Above about 100 Mc, tube lead inductances and transit-time input conductance begin to degrade performance and must be taken into account.

A T lowpass amplifier is most simply made with common-emitter stages that provide a current-gain—bandwidth product of

$$f_t/(1 + \sqrt{\omega_t r_b' C_c})^2$$

per stage with the optimum shunt coupling resistor

$$R_L = \sqrt{r_b'/\omega_t C_c}$$

and a current gain of R_L/R_e. Here, f_t is the frequency where the current gain into a short circuit is unity (usually somewhat less than the so-called "alpha cut-off" frequency), r_b' is the ohmic base resistance, C_c is the collector capacitance, and R_e the internal plus external emitter resistances. This gain-bandwidth product is as high as 400 Mc in the type 2N1742. Peaking techniques can increase this to about f_t (600 Mc.). It is worth noting that a simple T amplifier can often out-perform a complex

VT distributed amplifier except in the matter of power output. Distributing a T amplifier generally does not improve gain-bandwidth, but gives greater output capability, since the currents of the distributed transistors add in the load.

Amplifiers of large power output generally are not required over extreme bandwidths. The output circuit and devices are chosen for power dissipation and efficiency considerations. Transistors can currently supply powers of the order of a few hundred watts in the audio range in a class B circuit.

The simplest *bandpass* VT amplifier is made by tuning the pentode shunt capacitance C to band center with a shunt inductor (the interstage is then a parallel RLC circuit) giving the same gain-bandwidth performance as the lowpass resistance-coupled prototype. Much better performance is available with no greater circuit complexity by stagger-tuning. If the bandwidth B is not greater than about one-third of the center frequency f_0, an n-stage maximally flat amplitude response is obtained by tuning the stages to frequencies of $[f_0 + B \cos (\theta/2)] = (1/2\pi\sqrt{LC})$ and making $RC = 1/2\pi B \sin \theta$, where $\theta = (2k - 1)90°/n$, and $k = 1, 2, \cdots n$. Such an amplifier has a gain of $(g_m/2\pi CB)^n$. Double-tuned circuits can give better performance by a factor of 2^n. Where narrow bandwidth is desired, capacitance is added to increase the circuit Q, and multiple resonant circuits may be used for improved selectivity.

Bandpass T amplifiers generally use common-emitter stages. The maximum available power gain is one at a frequency of

$$f_{max} \cong \sqrt{f_t/8\pi r_b' C_c}$$

(For type 2N1742, $f_{max} = 1000$ Mc). The usable power gain at any other frequency is of the order of $(f_{max}/f)^2$ (terminating at some low-frequency limit), and is nearly independent of the bandwidth which is determined principally by the interstage circuit. For $f \gtrsim f_t/5$, the input and output impedances are about r_b' and $1/\omega_t C_c$, respectively. For $f \lesssim f_t/10$, attempts to match input and output impedances will usually result in oscillation; this situation is avoided through neutralization or mismatching, the latter technique being simpler. To insure alignability, the load impedance is chosen small enough so that variations in it do not cause excessive variation in the input impedance. In a typical interstage, the desired impedance ratio is provided by a transformer whose primary inductance is tuned to band center.

Dc Amplifiers

The maximum sensitivity of a dc amplifier is determined principally by drift with time and temperature of the first-stage operating point. This drift is indistinguishable from a signal, and is ordinarily specified as the voltage or current required (with the input nominally short- or open-circuited respectively) at the input to bring the output to zero. Feedback does not reduce the input drift. Voltage drift Δv is the predominant component for a low resistance source, and current drift Δi is important for a high resistance source, where $R\Delta i \gg \Delta v$.

Direct-coupled amplifiers are used where wide bandwidths are important or where the greatest sensitivity is not required. Typical drifts in ordinary tubes are as much as $\Delta v \sim 100$ mv and $\Delta i \sim 10^{-11}$ amp. Special electroscope and electrometer (q.v.) tubes for amplifying very small currents from large source resistances have $\Delta v \sim 2$ mv and $\Delta i \sim 10^{-14}$ amp. Transistors are very temperature sensitive, having $\Delta v \sim 3$ mv/°C and $\Delta i \sim 10$ μa over a 20–50°C range for a germanium alloy unit, and somewhat smaller Δi over a wider temperature range for silicon units. The drift in both tube and transistor amplifiers can be reduced by a factor of from 10 to 100 in a carefully balanced input stage with a series or parallel ("difference" amplifier) configuration. A balanced circuit also substantially reduces the effect of supply-voltage changes.

Amplifiers requiring very low voltage drift usually employ a modulating system such as a chopper, by which the signal is converted to an ac waveform, amplified in an ac amplifier which is free of drift problems, and reconverted to dc at the output. Usually, a detector operating in synchronism with the modulator is employed. Alternatively, such a system may be used to correct the drift of a direct-coupled amplifier. The input signal is compared with an attenuated version of the output, and the difference or error signal is amplified in a low drift chopper amplifier and applied to the direct-coupled amplifier in such a way as to reduce the error. In this way, the inherent bandwidth limitation of a chopper amplifier, about one-half the chopping frequency, is overcome.

Mechanical choppers can provide drift figures of the order of $\Delta v \sim 0.1$ μv, $\Delta i \sim 10^{-11}$ amp. Transistor choppers are lighter, require less driving power, and can operate at higher frequencies (about 10 kc). Values of $\Delta v \sim 20$ μv, $\Delta i \sim 10^{-8}$ amp over a 30°C range have been obtained with germanium transistor switches in an inverted (base drive, emitter facing the load) and balanced configuration. Other modulating schemes employ photoconductors exposed to chopped light ($\Delta v \sim 5$ μv, $\Delta i \sim 10^{-12}$ amp) and magnetic converters ($\Delta i \sim 10^{-9}$ amp).

Feedback Amplifiers

Negative feedback is applied to an amplifier to stabilize its performance against changes in the active elements. In addition, distortion is reduced and control of input and output impedances is available with certain circuits. The price for these advantages is reduced gain and the possibility of instability.

The gain of a feedback amplifier can be written in the classic form $\mu/(1 - \mu\beta)$, where μ is the gain of the amplifier without feedback (μ is negative at low frequencies), and β is the fraction of the output which is returned to the input, usually through a passive network. At frequencies where the loop transmission $T = -\mu\beta$ is much greater than unity, the gain is nearly $-1/\beta$, which can be made a stable quantity. The gain μ

is reduced by $1 + T$, but the sensitivity of the resulting gain to changes in μ is reduced by the same factor. Distortion and other spurious signals originating internally in the μ circuit are also reduced by $1 + T$ when referred to the same output level. However, the signal-to-thermal noise ratio, where the noise arises principally in the first stage, cannot be improved by feedback.

Maintenance of a large feedback factor $1 + T$ over a specified frequency band requires control of the loop transmission (or "return ratio") $T = -\mu\beta$ to much higher frequencies. The natural frequencies of the feedback system are those where $T = -1$; for stability, these frequencies must all lie in the left half of the complex-frequency plane. In the simplest type of single-loop feedback, this requirement is ordinarily satisfied if the plot of imaginary vs real parts of T as frequency is varied from $\omega = -\infty$ to $\omega = +\infty$ does not encircle the point -1. In other words, the phase angle of T must not approach $180°$ where the magnitude of T is greater than unity. It is customary to allow a phase margin of about $30°$ at the frequency where $|T| = 1$, and the relationship between attenuation and phase then requires that $|T|$ must decrease on the average no faster than about 10 db per octave in the range up to an octave or so beyond where $|T| = 1$. For example, if $|T|$ must be larger than 100 (40 db) up to a frequency f_1, the rate of cutoff above f_1 must be controlled for about 5 octaves, or up to $32f_1$. It usually happens that μ cuts off too rapidly, which can be partly compensated by introducing a rising characteristic in β. The limit is set by the ultimate cut-off rate of μ. For example, in an n-stage VT amplifier, the gain magnitude ultimately behaves as $(g_m/2\pi Cf)^n$, and the maximum $|T|$ obtainable over a bandwidth of f_1 is roughly $|T|_{max} \cong (g_m/\pi Cnf_1)^{1.6}$.

R. M. Scarlett

Pulse Amplifiers

A pulse may be characterized in the time domain as the sum of two step functions in

the excitation $E(t) = U(a) + U(b)$. The first step function, $U(t = a)$, is the leading edge of the pulse; the second, $U(t = b)$, the trailing edge. These step functions in the time domain correspond to a continuous spectrum in the frequency domain, all frequencies are required to represent the step function in time as a summation of signals in the frequency domain.*

A pulse amplifier must be capable of uniform amplification over the total frequency spectrum to reproduce a square-shaped pulse of excitation accurately. This characteristic insures that all components, independent of frequency, appear at the output, multiplied by the constant (with amplitude and frequency) gain. This is a linear amplifier.

Such an ideal pulse amplifier must also possess a phase characteristic that is linear over its total passband of frequencies, an infinite passband for this ideal. The linear phase characteristic insures a constant delay at all frequencies and therefore for all components, as delay is the negative of the derivative of the phase characteristic.

The effect of realizing a linear gain only over a portion of the frequency spectrum, and outside of the band of frequencies forcing the amplification to decrease uniformly, is to produce a finite rise time in the output response instead of the square-shaped pulse of the excitation. This degradation is due to the absence of the high-frequency terms that contribute to the steep wavefront. When the amplification is a function of the input pulse height, or amplitude nonlinearity occurs, the determination of the effect on the output usually requires a difficult analysis.

If the phase characteristic departs from a linear quality, the corresponding nonuniform delay of different frequency components produces some "bunching" effects at the output, with high-frequency terms usually arriving earlier than they should owing to reduced delay. This early arrival of high-

---

* Fourier-integral relationships exist between time domain and frequency domain for discrete pulses.

frequency components gives rise to over-shoot.

An amplifier with perfect linearity in gain and phase over an infinite passband is not realizable. However, the amplifiers that can be realized by relaxation of these two constraints are still very useful.

A useful pulse amplifier must produce step functions that correspond in time to the excitation step functions within predictable tolerances of linearity, rise time, and delay. Nonideal rise and fall times are measured between the 10- and 90-percent levels of final final value (Fig. 1). The delay is measured between time zero and the rise to the 10-percent level.

Errors in linearity are characterized by over- or under-shoot, sag, and overloading. Overshoot or undershoot is the amount of error in linearity occurring just after the first step function, expressed in percentage of the output-signal pulse amplitude. Sag or droop is the error in linearity occurring just before the second step function, it is always a decrease in pulse amplitude and expressed as a percentage of the output-signal pulse amplitude. Another error in linearity occurs when pulses arrive at the input so large in magnitude that the amplifier is driven into a nonlinear region of operation. This is called overloading. The time required for the amplifier to recover to a linear mode is called overload recovery time.

When pulses arrive at the input so close together in time that the amplifier output has not recovered from the first before the second pulse arrives, a shift in the base line (dc level) results. This is called "pile-up." Pile-up is not necessarily an excursion into a nonlinear region but the result of coupling capacitances not fully discharging after each pulse.

In many applications the amplifiers used for pulse work are the RC coupled type with maximally flat magnitude characteristics. This form of design gives a good amplification linearity over the passband, essentially 0 to the cutoff frequency ω_c. But the phase characteristic is linear only to approximately half the cutoff frequency $\omega_c/2$ (see, for instance, H. W. Bode, *Network Analysis and Feedback Amplifier Design*, Van Nostrand, New York, 1945). At frequencies above $\omega_c/2$ the phase is increasing at a slower rate (i.e., the slope is decreasing) and the corresponding delay is decreasing, resulting in unwanted and perhaps unpermissible overshoot. Bode has shown that for any general amplifier with maximally flat magnitude response the resulting phase characteristic is always linear only out to about half the magnitude-cutoff frequency.

The technique to circumvent this difficulty is to design the amplifier to have a linear phase characteristic out to a given cutoff frequency ω_c. The amplification response drops off earlier in frequency but not as steeply as the design with maximally flat

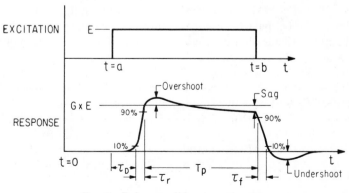

FIG. 1. Pulse-amplifier waveshapes.

magnitude. This nonlinearity does not produce as serious a distortion as the nonlinear phase.

The frequency range of the amplifier extends from a lower cutoff frequency ω_0 to a higher, ω_c. The low-frequency response determines the amount of sag in the output pulse: % sag $= (\omega_0)(\text{pulse width}) 100\%$. The rise time of the output pulse is determined by the high-frequency cutoff: $\text{tr}_{10\text{-}90\%}$ is approximately $0.35/\omega_c$. The cutoff frequencies are defined as those frequencies at which the magnitude response is 0.707 of its midband value or the ordinary -3 db points. For a minimum of sag, ω_0 approaches 0 cps and to achieve the shortest rise times ω_c is as high as possible, hence the frequent need to design for broadbanding. An amplifier with this type of response is often called a *video amplifier*, because of their use for pulse amplification in television systems.

For most applications a broadbanding technique is useful whether one uses tubes or transistors, to obtain linear phase and amplification over a large bandwidth. The majority of feedback schemes for broadbanding depend on a reactive element in the feedback loop, either a capacitance or inductance. This reactive element requires time to discharge at the end of a large pulse and seriously affects the overload recovery of the amplifier. For that reason an interstage technique such as shunt-peaking is a more favorable broadbanding scheme in applications requiring high pulse-repetition rates. However, the stability and linearity requirements can usually be realized easier in a feedback design than in an interstage scheme of broadbanding.

Design criteria to achieve pulse amplification are maximally flat delay or linear phase over a bandwidth from ω_0 (approximately 0) to ω_c, as high as necessary to achieve a desired output rise time; overload recovery time that is short and coupling time constants short enough to prevent interaction of the pulses at the highest repetition rate (shortest spacing). Other requirements of stability, linearity, etc., are the same as ordinary amplifiers.

LARRY SCOTT

Cross-references: *Analyzers, Coupled Circuits, Equivalent Circuits, Feedback System, Network Synthesis, Network Theory, Nonlinear Circuits, Oscillators, Pulse Generation, Systems*

AMPLITRON

The amplitron is a new microwave electron tube which is a practical realization, as an amplifier, of efficient crossed-field interaction. Structurally, it differs from the conventional magnetron only in its rf anode circuit. This circuit is a nonreentrant split ring coupled at its ends to input and output terminals, which are the external features distinguishing the amplitron from the magnetron.

The amplitron is a nonlinear high-level amplifier. It may be regarded as a saturated amplifier or as a locked oscillator. The input signal must exceed a threshold, or locking level, for operation. The rf output power then increases only slightly with increasing input power. The gain thus decreases from its maximum (typically 15 to 20 db) at the threshold state to perhaps 10 db at the operating level. Amplitrons generally are more efficient than magnetrons of similar design; plate efficiencies as high as 85 per cent have been attained. The higher efficiency arises mainly because of lower rf circuit losses, the recirculation of rf energy on the anode system having been eliminated in the amplitron.

Internal operation of the amplitron is governed largely by the reentrant nature of the electron stream. Although the rf potentials on the anode electrodes are not all the same as in the magnetron, but increase from input to output, the interaction space potential can nevertheless be resolved into a set of Fourier component rotating waves, $\Sigma_k V_k \exp j(k\theta - \omega t)$. Traveling-wave interaction occurs when electrons are synchronous with one of these waves—that for which the electronic velocity is $d\theta/dt = \omega/k_0$. The other wave components are asynchronous and have no appreciable effect. The electron motion is thus the same as in the magnetron oscillator. The space-charge is likewise the same—a set of k_0-identical, equispaced spokes rotating in synchronism with the k_0th Fourier component traveling wave of potential.

The differences between the amplitron and magnetron—in particular, the presence of gain in the amplitron when the space charge exhibits none—can be explained in terms of the properties of the rf anode circuit. First, the ability to excite the rf structure externally allows some degree of control of the interaction fields, which in the magnetron are solely the result of space-charge effects within the tube. Second, the space-charge spokes generate rf waves on the anode system at each electrode; these waves propagate in both directions. If the propagation rate of the anode system is proper, these disturbances reinforce each other in the direction of signal flow (the forward direction) and destructively interfere in the opposite direction. This property of directivity is the same as that of an end-fire antenna array ($q.v.$); it is also to be found in the saturated regions of traveling-wave tubes.

The rf potential distribution within the amplitron is determined by the input signal and the space charge-induced traveling waves described above. The result is an essentially linear distribution, governed in details by the magnitude and phase of the input signal relative to the space charge-induced waves. These potentials can be analyzed to determine the synchronously traveling wave, the phase of which is determined by magnetron interaction considerations (dc anode potential, Hartree potential, etc.). This phase relation may be regarded as a self-consistence criterion; it determines the phase relation between the rf input signal and the space charge. When this is established the gain and phase shift through the amplifier can be calculated.

From the simple analysis outlined above, it is found that the amplitron has an operating bandwidth limited by the electron stream reentrance and by internal feedback on the anode system (the backward-traveling space charge-induced waves). The band is widest at high rf level, the gain-bandwidth product being nearly independent of the input level. Theoretically, infinite gain (self-oscillation) is possible at a single frequency. Practically, noisy operation results when no input power is applied, indicating that this oscillation is unstable.

Amplitrons are generally operated in a backward-wave (not to be confused with backward-traveling waves) mode, in which the electron flow is in the direction opposite that of the rf energy. Forward-wave operation is also possible.

Some practical considerations arise from the fact that the amplitron is transparent to backward-traveling energy. Load reflections are transmitted through the amplifier to the driver, frequently requiring the use of an isolator. On the other hand, reflective elements can be arranged in both input and output branches to provide regenerative amplification and/or oscillation. A practical form of this arrangement, using a high-Q cavity, is known as the stabilotron; it has much greater stability than does the magnetron.

GEORGE E. DOMBROWSKI

Cross-references: *Backward-Wave Tubes, Characteristic Frequencies, Crossed-Field Interactions, Magnetron, Space Charge, Traveling-Wave Magnetron, Traveling-Wave Tubes*

ANALOG COMPUTERS

Computing devices in which the instantaneous magnitude of a measurable physical quantity or property represents a variable in the problem to be solved are usually called analog computers. They may be contrasted with digital computers, which solve problems by numerical computation. Prior to World War II a number of mechanical analog computers were in use, but as used today the term applies almost exclusively to electrical computers with variables represented by a value of current or potential. In general, analog computers are less flexible and precise than large digital computers, but they are usually less complicated, more easily programmed, and more readily adapted to the quick comparison of a large number of solutions as various parameters in the problem may be altered by the operator. Analog computers have perhaps been used most extensively in studying the performance of dynamical systems involving complex feedback loops, but they have also been applied to a wide variety of other scientific problems.

A modern analog computer consists of a collection of basic components that may be interconnected to form an analog of the problem to be solved. Only when the various voltages or currents are related to each other in the manner determined by the mathematical equations, can the complete computer circuit achieve a stable state. Measurement of the proper voltages then yields values of the desired solution for the instant of measurement. The major components are operational amplifiers, summing amplifiers, integrators, sine-cosine resolvers, multipliers, and function generators. From these elements a wide variety of other mathematical functions can be obtained.

Computer systems, and the operation of the components mentioned in the section above in such a system, can be illustrated by considering a typical analog computation for solving the differential equation

$$\frac{d^2x}{dt^2} + d\,\frac{dx}{dt} + kx = A \sin y \qquad (1)$$

where y is an input having an arbitrary variation with time. A block diagram of the method of interconnection of the basic elements to solve this equation is shown in Fig. 1. The arrangement shown requires the use of two integrators I, one straight operational amplifier O, one summing amplifier S, and one sine resolver R. In actual practice each of these elements reverses the phase of the input voltage, and this fact is taken into account in the labeling on the diagram of the

points in the circuit where the potential is proportional to x or its various derivatives. That the entire circuit fulfills the conditions of Eq. (1) may be seen from the fact that the output of the summing amplifier S, which we label $\ddot{x}$, is equal to the negative of the sum $d\dot{x} + kx - A \sin y$, if the scale factors on the inputs to the summing amplifier are correctly set. The two initial conditions are represented by setting the initial integrator outputs. Recordings of the values of the potentials corresponding to x would yield a plot of x as a function of time—the desired solution of the differential equation (1).

Solution of the equation in its integral equivalent rather than by using electrical differentiators is standard analog computer practice because of electrical "noise" problems that arise when a real electrical signal is differentiated. However, the use of integrators introduces the possibility of significant errors owing to integration of electrical offsets in the outputs of any of the computing elements, if the problem continues for a time long in comparison to the integration scale factors. The actual time of running of a problem may be altered from that of the solution of the original equation by a change of integrator scale factors. In fact, the selection of a proper time scale is part of the problem of using a particular computer so as to obtain the most accurate solution to a given set of equations.

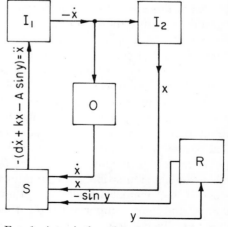

Fig. 1. A typical analog computer circuit.

In addition to selecting the optimum time scale, the programmer of an analog computer must also pay attention to stability criteria that must be met, particularly if the problem to be solved is a complicated one and results in many closed feedback loops in the computer. Each of the computing elements itself, of course, possesses both amplitude and phase errors in the output, which can result in spurious system oscillation if care is not taken, and any initial system transients must decay in an interval of time that is short compared to the time scale of the problem. In actual practice deliberate compensating phase shifts may be introduced to take effect at frequencies outside those involved in the problem solution proper.

Programming of analog computers may be accomplished by a number of ways of interconnecting the required computing elements. The simplest method involves the use of patchcords. The time required for programming may be separated from time consumed by the computer in actual computation by the use of separable patchboards which may be connected up apart from the computer and then plugged into the computer as a complete unit. More compact programming units may be obtained by the use of punched cards, which the programmer prepares by punching holes in the proper places. Insertion of these cards into the computer allows the creation of the proper circuit connections in one quick operation. Such cards are also convenient for storing programs for future reuse and may not only interconnect the proper units but set scale factors and initial conditions as well. Other automatic arrangements may also be used for setting scale factor controls.

The task of programming increases with the size of the computer. Small commercial computers may contain only 20 or so operational elements. Large universal computers, such as those which have been extensively used in missile simulation, may contain up to 1000 such elements. A brief description of some of the more important operational elements is given below.

Operational amplifiers are usually very high gain dc amplifiers employing inverse feedback to provide the desired value of effective external gain. The use of precision input and feedback resistors permits gain precision of 0.01 per cent or better. The connection of more than one input resistor permits the operational amplifier to be used as a "summing" amplifier, which produces an output equal to the algebraic sum of the voltages applied to the various input resistors.

The high internal gain of the basic amplifier permits very linear operation of the operational amplifier when used with normal feedback ratios of 1000 or more, but feedback alone does not eliminate slow variations in amplifier output due to grid voltage drift. For most precision equipment the input voltage offset is reduced to a value of 100 μv or less by "chopper stabilizers" that sense grid voltage drift and introduce a compensating feedback. The choppers may be mechanical or purely electrical photoconductive devices actuated by a pulsating light source.

Integrators usually are formed by taking the same high-gain dc amplifier used to form operational or summing amplifiers and connecting a condenser as the feedback element rather than the feedback resistor used to provide simple gain. Such integrators yield an output proportional to the time integral of the input voltage. Integrating amplifiers are also usually provided with relays for connecting start-stop and initial condition setting circuits. Input-grid drift, which may provide a relatively small and slowly varying output error in a simple amplifier, causes a continually rising output in an integrator, because of the continued integration with time of the input error. Hence stabilizers are also important in integrator usage. The integration scale factors may be set to precisions as high as 0.01 per cent.

Sine-cosine resolvers may either employ electromechanical servos or a form of electrical function generator. Servo resolvers probably require fewer parts than electrical resolvers and are straightforward in use and concept. A shaped potentiometer whose electrical output is proportional to the sine or cosine of shaft rotation forms the basis of dc resolvers. Ac resolvers using variometers have been extensively used in earlier fire-control computers. The chief disadvantages of electro-mechanical resolvers are the inherently slow speed of response, and the reliability problems and wear associated with moving frictional contacts.

All-electronic resolvers may employ nonlinear elements to produce an output voltage proportional over one quadrant to the sine or cosine of an input voltage. Operation over all four quadrants requires special switching means. Electrical resolution may also be performed by various feedback loops, particularly in the special case in which it is necessary to obtain inverse trigonometric functions, such as when two components x and y of a vector are the given inputs. These feedback loops in effect solve the equation represented by a relation such as $\tan \theta = x/y$. Electrical resolvers are in general much faster than electro-mechanical ones and are free from mechanical problems.

Multipliers for electronic analog computers represent a much more difficult design problem than purely linear computing elements such as summing amplifiers and integrators. As is the case for resolvers, multiplication is usually accomplished by either electro-mechanical servomechanisms or by purely electronic means. The servo multipliers are simple in concept and in circuit use, but they are relatively slow and subject to mechanical wear. They consist basically of a linear potentiometer driven by a motor in a feedback loop which sets the potentiometer shaft angle to represent one input. The driving voltage of the multiplier potentiometer represents the other input, so that the voltage output from the potentiometer arm contact is the desired product. Such multipliers can be used for either ac or dc computers.

Electronic multipliers have been built using a wide number of different effects. A fairly simple but low-accuracy (of the order

of 5 per cent) multiplier may be obtained by using a multigrid tube and applying the two input voltages to each of two grids respectively. Other multipliers have been built by using nonlinear elements to obtain "quarter square" multipliers, which use the algebraic relation $xy = (\frac{1}{4})[(x + y)^2 - (x - y)^2]$. Modern multipliers using function generators (as described below) for obtaining the square terms may operate at very high frequencies (up to 20 kc) and with precision approaching 0.05 per cent. Another type of modern high-precision electronic multiplier makes use of "time division" to obtain a voltage whose average value is proportional to the desired product. In these multipliers one of the inputs, say x, is used to determine the on-off ratio or duty factor of a rectangular wave; as x increases, for example, the duration of the "on" part of the wave increases with respect to the "off" part. This rectangular wave is used to operate an electronic switch which is driven by the other input, say y. The output of the switch is thus a rectangular wave whose duty factor is proportional to x and whose amplitude is proportional to y. The average value of such a wave is then xy. It is evident that the repetition rate or frequency of the rectangular wave must be high compared to the frequencies to be handled by the over-all computer, if filtering of the rectangular wave is to be possible without introducing excessive time delays in the resulting product. Repetition rates normally used are of the order of 20 kc to 100 kc. In some types of multipliers this rate may be a function of one input variable. Time division multipliers giving precisions of the order of 0.01 per cent of full scale have been built, although 0.1 per cent is probably a more representative figure for precision commercial products.

Function generators are devices whose output voltage must vary as a prescribed mathematical function of the input voltage. They may employ nonlinear elements such as thyristors, but the more common type contains networks of diodes and resistance elements, such that a given arbitrary function can be approximated by a number of straight line segments. Setting biases and resistor values determines the junction points and slopes of each segment of a plot of the output voltage as function of the input voltage.

Partial differential equations are not readily solved, except in special cases, by analog computers using the discrete operational elements mentioned above. Certain partial differential equations may be solved by analog computers using extended networks of resistances or other impedance elements to permit both spacial and time derivations. Such computers are well adapted to solution of heat-flow problems, for example.

EDWIN C. HUTTER

Cross-references: *Computer Applications, Computer Programming, Digital Computers*

ANALYZERS

Waveform Analyzers

Two basic types of instruments are available for investigating complex waveforms: wave analyzers and distortion analyzers. These instruments were at first designed to allow careful study of audio amplifiers, etc., in the early days of radio. However, their use is not limited to the audio-frequency spectrum. Modern instruments are available with frequency ranges from 1 cps or less to tens of megacycles.

Wave Analyzers. Wave analyzers are basically selective-frequency voltmeters. Typically they contain a very narrow bandpass filter that permits signals of one frequency (or small band of frequencies) to reach the indicating voltmeter. A typical block diagram of a wave analyzer is shown in Fig. 1. The system operates as follows: The local oscillator is tuned to $f + f_1$ and mixed with f_1 as shown. The two sidebands ($f + 2f_1$ and f) are applied to the bandpass filter, which is centered around f. This filter passes f, but rejects $f + 2f_1$. The desired frequency f is then amplified and observed on an indicating meter. Two attenuators are usually provided to prevent overloading the mixer with a large signal while attempting to meter a low level signal at a different frequency. Suppose, for example, that in addition to f_1, a frequency component f_2 were also present in the input waveform. Assume, further, that the amplitude of f_2 is only 1 per cent of the amplitude of f_1. If the local oscillator were tuned to $f + f_1$ and the two attenuators arranged so that a full-scale indication appeared on the meter, and then the local oscillator were tuned to $f + f_2$, the meter would indicate only 1 per cent of full scale. If the attenuation were removed from attenuator 1, the high level signal at f_1 would surely overload the mixing circuits. Therefore, the sensitivity of the device must be increased after the mixing has taken place. Attenuation can be removed from attenuator 2 since the mixing products generated by f_1 and $f + f_2$ will lie outside the pass band of the filter and therefore cannot saturate the amplifier following it. Attenuator 2 is often denoted as "Range" switch since it determines, in effect, the dynamic range of amplitudes that can be observed.

Wave analyzers are available with many bandwidths and frequency ranges. They are used by engine manufacturers to determine sources of vibrations in rotating machines; in the communications industry to measure

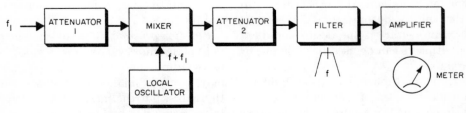

FIG. 1. Wave analyzer.

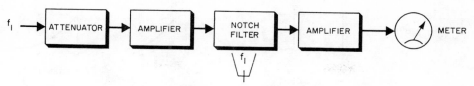

Fig. 2. Distortion analyzer.

noise and other unwanted signals present in carrier channels; to measure stop-band characteristics of filters; and for many special purposes.

Distortion Analyzers. Distortion analyzers are also tuned voltmeters. However, rather than a narrow band-pass filter, they employ a very narrow notch filter. Their principle of operation is to reject the fundamental frequency and to pass all other frequencies. These remaining frequency components are then applied to an indicating voltmeter. The block diagram of a typical distortion analyzer is shown in Fig. 2. The notch filter is normally a tunable bridge network. Any fundamental signal in the operating frequency range may be nulled by being passed through the bridge network. Amplifiers and negative feedback are often employed to improve the actual null selectivity.

Distortion analyzers are still used for measuring over-all distortion in amplifiers, oscillators, and other systems. They give a quick look at the total distortion generated in a system. For more specific information on any particular frequency component, a wave analyzer must be employed.

STANLEY E. MCCARTHY

Spectrum Analyzers

Radar applications of short rf pulses resulted in the development of analyzers for rf spectra. Much of the work originated at the M.I.T. Radiation Laboratory during World War II.

Originally the spectrum analyzer was used in the design and adjustment of pulsed modulators and transmitters. It has been generally accepted as a laboratory instrument suitable for testing of oscillators, amplifiers, attenuators, frequency meters, modulators, couplers, detectors, harmonic generators, filters, etc. It measures frequency, frequency deviations, relative amplitude of voltage or power, attenuation, modulation side bands, distortion, and spurious signals. Analyzers with very wide frequency coverage are better known as *panoramic receivers*, which are used in countermeasures or spectrum surveillance.

The analyzer output is normally displayed in graphic form with amplitude on the vertical axis presented as log voltage, linear voltage, or linear power. Most analyzers display the absolute magnitude without phase information. Frequency is displayed on the horizontal axis in either linear or logarithmic form. For scanning speeds of less than 1 cps, X-Y recorders are necessary to record the output. For higher scanning rates, presentation on a cathode-ray tube is more effective.

The time function $f(t)$ describes the amplitude versus time; it is normally viewed by oscilloscopes, rf-envelope viewers, (synchroscopes) or rf sampling oscilloscopes. The corresponding frequency function $F(\omega)$ as viewed by a spectrum analyzer presents the amplitude versus frequency. They are related by the Fourier transforms:

$$F(\omega) = \int_{-\infty}^{\infty} f(t)e^{-j\omega t}\,dt \quad \text{(direct transform)}$$

$$f(t) = \frac{1}{2\pi} \int_{-\infty}^{\infty} F(\omega)e^{j\omega t}\,d\omega \quad \text{(inverse transform)}$$

Three common sets (the rectangular, Gaussian, and differentiated pulses) are shown in Fig. 3.

The idealized spectrum analyzer can be described as a tunable narrow-band filter which is frequency tuned in synchronism with the horizontal deflection of a cathode-

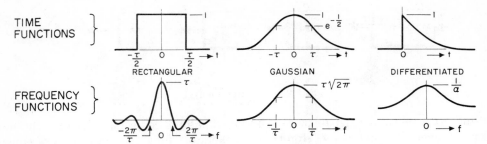

FIG. 3. Time and frequency functions.

ray tube. The sweep speed is slow enough to allow the filter response to the signal to build-up to its steady-state value and to decay entirely before the next signal occurs. The output of the detector describes the envelope of the spectrum energy distribution.

CONTINUOUS–
WAVE
SPECTRUM

|A| VS f

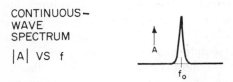

FIG. 4. Spectrum-analyzer display (cw).

PULSE
SPECTRUM

|A| VS f

FIG. 5. Spectrum-analyzer display (pulse).

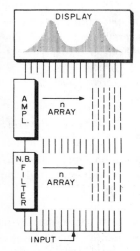

FIG. 6. Filter array.

As the analyzer slowly sweeps through a cw signal the transient appearing on the screen is merely the plot of the pass band of the filter (Fig. 4).

For a *pulse signal* the analyzer is frequency swept at a speed of 1/50 or less than the pulse repetition rate. The filter responds to a very narrow section of the pulse spectrum; for practical purposes this is the value of the function at a single frequency. As the filter progresses in frequency, pulses appear at intervals corresponding to the period of the repetition rate. The amplitude of each pulse indicates the relative amplitude of the spectrum at that frequency. The envelope of the peaks is the relative amplitude distribution of the spectrum. Note that the negative lobes of the $(\sin x)/x$ envelope are reversed because an ordinary AM detector does not perceive phase (Fig. 5).

Sampling rate of a signal is determined by the repetition rate of the pulse. For adequate envelope resolution, at least 50 pulses should appear on the screen, so that the sweep speed should be less than 2 per cent of the pulse repetition rate. The maximum number of pulses per sweep are dictated by the resolution of the spot diameter of the cathode-ray tube or the pen width of the recorder. For negligible loss in sensitivity, the optimum bandwidth (cps) of the filter should be approximately equal to the square root of the frequency sweep rate (cps/sec).

The degree of sophistication depends on the sensitivity requirement, type of spectrum, analysis speed, frequency stability, dynamic range, suppression of suprious signals and output presentation. Any of the

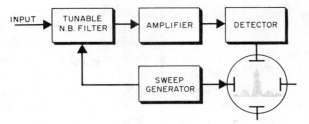

FIG. 7. Sweep-frequency filter.

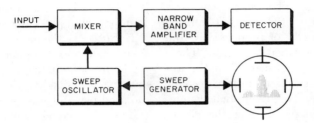

FIG. 8. Sweep local oscillator.

following systems can utilize heterodyning to extend the frequency range.

Filter Array (Fig. 6). This type of analyzer can be used to record a single event in addition to cw and repetitive pulses. All the components of a transient are accepted by the individual filters simultaneously and recorded. Cost for this type of analyzer is high because 50 to 100 narrow-band filters are necessary for analysis of a pulse spectrum.

Sweep-Frequency Filter (Fig. 7). This type is suitable only for cw or repetitive pulses. It requires a narrow-band filter that can be tuned electronically or mechanically in synchronism with the cathode-ray-tube sweep. Cost for this type is moderate.

Sweep Local Oscillator (Fig. 8). This type is suitable for continuous or repetitive pulses. It is simple to build and is inherently a sensitive device. It requires only one fixed frequency filter in the IF amplifier. With the advent of voltage-tuned semiconductor capacitors and ferrite inductors the sweeping local oscillator can be simple and inexpensive. It does suffer from the interference problems of image signal as do all heterodyne systems. Response of the system to harmonics and mixed components of both the

signal and local oscillator can also be a problem.

ARTHUR FONG

Cross-references: *Indicating Instruments, Modulation and Demodulation, Pulse Generation*

ANTENNAS

The subject of antennas is discussed below under several subheadings, as follows: General Considerations, Arrays, End-Fire Antennas, Frequency-Independent Antennas, Horn Antennas, Lenses, Reflectors, Electronically Scanned Antennas, Slotted Guide Antennas, and Special Types.

General Considerations

An antenna is a device or group of devices used either to excite electromagnetic waves (transmitting antenna) or to be excited by electromagnetic waves (receiving antenna). It is usually constructed of metals possessing good conductivity but may include dielectric and permeable materials. Its size can range from a fraction of a wavelength of the electromagnetic wave to hundreds of wavelengths. The wavelength, in turn, can range from several millimeters to hundreds of feet.

The electromagnetic waves that link the transmitting and receiving antennas propagate through the intervening medium in a manner controlled by the medium. Often this is neutral air, in which case the product of frequency and wavelength equals the velocity of light. However, in many applications the waves must travel over ground or water, or through the ionized upper layers of the atmosphere. These media introduce complex propagation phenomena that can include attenuation, polarization effects, changes in the velocity of propagation, and bending of the propagation path. These effects are frequency sensitive and the antenna engineer must take them into account to optimize the design of an antenna system.

The fundamental problem in the design of a *transmitting* antenna is to minimize its radiation of electromagnetic energy in directions that are not useful. The currents that flow in the antenna and the excited waves are connected by an integral of Maxwell's equations,

$$\mathbf{A}(P) = \int_V \frac{\mathbf{i}(P')e^{-jkR}}{4\pi R} \, dV \qquad (1)$$

in which $\mathbf{A}$ is the magnetic potential, P is a point at which the potential is being computed, P' a point on the antenna, and R the distance between P and P'; $k = 2\pi\lambda^{-1}$, $\mathbf{i}$ is the time-sinusoidal current density in the antenna, and V is a volume large enough to encompass the entire antenna. The electric and magnetic components of the excited waves are found by taking simple space derivatives of $\mathbf{A}$.

When P is a great distance from the antenna, $\mathbf{A}$ takes on the nature of spherical waves which diminish as R^{-1} and one can write

$$\mathbf{A}(P) = \frac{e^{-jkr}}{4\pi r} \mathbf{A}(\theta,\phi) \qquad (2)$$

in which (r,θ,ϕ) is a spherical coordinate system centered at an arbitrary reference point in the antenna. The power density in these spherical waves is related to the product of the electric and magnetic field

components and is thus related to the square of the magnitude of $\mathbf{A}$. In a practical application, the power density is specified as a function of direction and Eq. (1) can be used to deduce the necessary current distribution to give the requisite $\mathbf{A}(\theta,\phi)$.

The currents induced in ground, water, or ionosphere must be included in Eq. (1) for an accurate prediction of the directional distribution of the waves. When the current distribution is not a simple sinusoid in time, Fourier techniques can usually be employed.

If $P(\theta,\phi)$ is the power radiated per unit solid angle and P_t is the total power radiated, the *gain* function of the transmitting antenna is defined as the ratio of the power radiated per unit solid angle in the direction (θ,ϕ) to the average power radiated per unit solid angle:

$$G(\theta,\phi) = 4\pi \frac{P(\theta,\phi)}{P_t} \qquad (3)$$

$G(\theta,\phi)$, which is also called the radiation pattern, can be interpreted as the increase in power radiated by the antenna in the direction (θ,ϕ) over what would be radiated in that direction by an isotropic antenna having the same total power output. It is thus a highly useful yardstick of design. The maximum value of $G(\theta,\phi)$ is called the gain of the antenna.

The fundamental problem in the design of a *receiving* antenna is to maximize its sensitivity to waves arriving from the most useful directions in space. The power absorbed by the antenna can be expressed as the product of the power density in the incident wave and the absorption cross section $C_r(\theta,\phi)$ of the antenna. It is possible to exhibit a reciprocity theorem for Maxwell's equations, one consequence of which is that

$$C_r(\theta,\phi) = \frac{\lambda^2}{4\pi} G(\theta,\phi) \qquad (4)$$

and thus the design problem for receiving and transmitting antenna patterns is identical.

The orientation of the electric field in space determines the polarization of the waves excited by a transmitting antenna. If, as the wave progresses, the direction of the electric field remains constant, the polarization is said to be linear, and modifying adjectives such as horizontal or vertical are often included. If, as the wave progresses, the direction of the electric field rotates steadily, but the amplitude remains constant, the wave is said to be circularly polarized, and the modifying adjectives right-handed and left-handed are used to denote the sense of rotation of the electric field. More generally, the wave can be elliptically polarized.

From Eq. (1) it is apparent that there is a connection between the vector orientation of the current distribution and the polarization of **A**, and thus of the electric field. The reciprocity theorem reveals that there is also a connection between the polarization of an incident wave and the strength of the currents induced in a receiving antenna. For these reasons, polarization is an important factor in antenna design, and any changes in polarization caused by the intervening medium must be considered. A wave arriving at a receiving antenna with improper polarization might not induce any signal in the antenna. Receiving antennas with a polarization diversity feature are sometimes employed to protect against this possibility.

The feeding network that connects the antenna to the transmitter or receiver must be designed to insure that the current distribution required in Eq. (1) is achieved. The design procedure involves a knowledge of the impedance of the antenna or the impedances of its constituent parts if it is an assembly of radiators. These impedances have a resistive part owing to ohmic losses in the antenna materials plus a radiation resistance to account for the power radiated. They also have a reactive part owing to nonradiating fields set up by the antenna current distribution, which store energy in a region adjacent to the antenna and return it to the antenna every cycle. In addition to self-impedance, there can be mutual impedence between elements owing to interac-

tions of their fields. All of these impedance effects are usually frequency sensitive. The powerful techniques of network synthesis (*q.v.*) and analysis can often be used in designing feeding systems which are optimized in the presence of antenna impedance.

The bandwidth of an antenna can be defined as the frequency range over which its radiation pattern and/or impedance is within a prescribed tolerance of specification.

R. S. Elliott

Antenna Arrays

An array is an ordered collection of radiators which can be excited simultaneously. Arrays may be classified according to their geometrical arrangement, radiation characteristics, interelement spacing, methods of feeding, etc.

Geometrical Arrangement. Arrays may be linear (elements along a line); planar (elements in a plane); circular (ring arrays); cylindrical; volume; etc.

Radiation Characteristics. Linear arrays may be omnidirectional (as in broadcasting); directional (as in point-to-point communications); broadside (radiate perpendicular to the line of elements); or end-fire (radiate in the direction of the line). Circular or ring arrays may be omnidirectional (as in beacons); or directional (as in Wullenweber or direction-finding antennas).

Inter-Element Spacing. Arrays may have uniform spacing between elements; or nonuniform spacing. Uniformly spaced arrays usually have spacings between $\lambda/2$ and λ. Closer spacings may theoretically realize greater gain for a given antenna length, but have higher resistive losses, less bandwidth, and stronger mutual-coupling effects; larger spacings result in periodic high sidelobes ("grating" lobes). Nonuniformly spaced arrays can achieve less mutual couplings by larger interelement spacings without producing grating lobes, thus yielding greater directivity for a given number of elements; but the over-all sidelobe level is relatively high.

Method of Feeding. The individual radiators in an array may all be separately fed; or only a few elements may be fed, the rest being parasitic (see End-Fire Antennas below).

The radiation power (or amplitude) pattern of an array of isotropic radiators is called its array (or space) factor (respectively). If the isotropic radiators are replaced by directive elements having a pattern of their own, and if all are pointed in the same direction, then the resultant antenna (power) pattern is the product of the element (power) pattern and the array factor. Each element may itself be an array. The array factor of an array of arrays is the product of the array factors.

Uniform Array. In a uniform array, all the elements are coupled equally to the common input or output. Such an array is also called "uniformly illuminated," and is shown in Fig. 1. Its normalized array factor is given by

$$A(\theta) = \frac{\sin^2\left[\dfrac{n}{2}\left(\dfrac{2\pi a}{\lambda}\sin\theta + \phi\right)\right]}{n^2\sin^2\left[\dfrac{1}{2}\left(\dfrac{2\pi a}{\lambda}\sin\theta + \phi\right)\right]}$$

Dolph-Tchebyscheff Arrays. By controlling the power distribution to the elements of a broadside linear array, it is possible theoretically to reduce all sidelobes

below any specified level. The theory of this was first given by C. L. Dolph, using Tchebyscheff polynominals (*Proc. IRE*, June 1946). It gives the optimum power distribution in the sense that (a) if the sidelobe level is specified, the beam width between first nulls is as narrow as possible; or (b) if the first null is specified, the sidelobe level is minimized. The sidelobes are then all of equal height. Extensive numerical tables have been published by the Naval Ordnance Laboratory, Corona, Calif. (NAVORD Report 4629, 28 February 1958). The theory is restricted by the assumptions of scalar diffraction and neglecting mutual couplings. A plot of relative field strength against angle θ of an 8-element Dolph-Tchebyscheff array of isotropic sources a half-wavelength apart is shown in Fig. 2.

Ring Arrays. In ring arrays the elementary radiators are arranged in a circle. Suppose the plane of the circle to be horizontal. Circles may be stacked vertically to give increased vertical directivity. This purpose can also be served by placing an antenna at the center of the circle, or other elements in the plane of the circle, or a shaped circular reflector behind the elements. If the antenna is omnidirectional in azimuth, increased vertical directivity can be achieved by progressive phase increase around the circle.

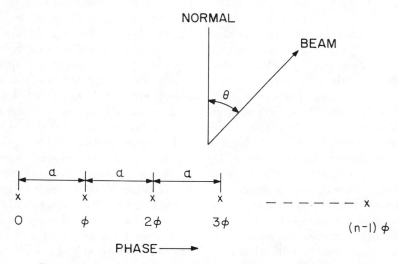

Fig. 1. Uniformly spaced linear array with linear phase taper.

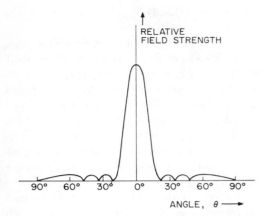

FIG. 2. Pattern of 8-element Dolph-Tcheby-scheff array with $\alpha = I^2$.

Ring arrays can be made directional by using beam-co-phasal excitation of the elements, i.e., phasing them so as to produce a plane wavefront. Such arrays are used for direction finding and other applications requiring a narrow beam that can be swung rapidly in any direction in azimuth.

Arrays used in Electronic Scanning. As antennas have increased in size, and data rates have increased, electromechanical and electronic (inertialess) scanning systems have become more important. Arrays are well suited to such techniques.

The beam formed by the linear array of Fig. 1 points in the direction $\theta = \text{arc sin}$ $(\phi\lambda/2\pi a)$. By controlling the linear phase taper of ϕ radians per element, the beam can be moved from side to side. By extending this principle to a planar array and controling two separate linear phase tapers, the beam can also be swung up and down. Such a beam can never move outside a hemisphere of space, and its gain decreases as the projected aperture decreases. Several such antennas are therefore needed to cover all or most directions. The phase change can be introduced by mechanical or electronic phase shifters or delay lines, or a combination of them. Similar electronic scanning is possible with ring and other arrays.

LEO YOUNG

End-Fire Antennas

An end-fire antenna consists of an array of radiators arranged along a straight line, so excited that maximum radiation intensity occurs along the axis of the array. An end-fire array is usually unidirectional; however, if it is so designed that major lobes of radiation occur in both directions along the axis, it is called a double end-fire array. The term "end-fire" was originally applied to arrays of discrete radiators, but it is now used to denote a wider class of antennas, all of which have a central axis, with major radiation directed along this axis. Thus the rhombic antenna, the V-antenna, the dielectric rod antenna, the Beverage antenna, and the helical antenna may all be regarded as end fire types. The Yagi array and various forms of log-periodic structures are also end-fire antennas.

The simplest end-fire array consists of two nondirectional radiators, separated a distance d, and excited with currents of equal amplitude, but a relative phase displacement of kd radians, where $k = 2\pi/\lambda$, λ being the free-space wavelength. If the radiators are located as shown in Fig. 3, then with $d = \lambda/4$, and with the phase of the current in the left radiator leading that in the right by 90°, the normalized radiation pattern in the plane of the figure is given by

$$E(\theta) = \cos\left[\frac{\pi}{4}(\cos\theta - 1)\right] \qquad (1)$$

This is the equation of a cardioid with its maximum value at $\theta = 0°$ and a null at $\theta = 180°$. This is a popular antenna for broadcast applications in cases where it is necessary to radiate minimum energy in a given direction, yet provide as broad coverage as possible in all other directions.

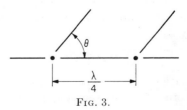

FIG. 3.

The normalized field pattern of n identical point sources spaced a distance d apart along a line, and excited with equal amplitudes but with a uniform phase lag of kd radians between successive radiators from left to right, is given by

$$E(\theta) = \frac{\sin\left[\dfrac{nkd}{2}(\cos\theta - 1)\right]}{n\sin\left[\dfrac{kd}{2}(\cos\theta - 1)\right]} \qquad (2)$$

where θ = angle with respect to the axis of the array.

If each of the n radiators has an identical radiation pattern, $F(\theta,\phi)$, then the over-all pattern of the array is given by $F(\theta,\phi) \cdot E(\theta)$.

Equation (2) gives the pattern of an ordinary or "classical" end-fire array. The pattern is of the "pencil-beam" type, with rotational symmetry about the $\theta = 0$ axis, and the main lobe in the direction $\theta = 0$. When n is large (10 or greater) the beamwidth of the main lobe, between first nulls, is given approximately by

$$\text{Beamwidth} \cong 2\sqrt{\frac{2\lambda}{l}} \text{ radians} \qquad (3)$$

where l is the total length of the array.

The beamwidth between half-power points is approximately half of the above value.

The main lobe of the above array may be considerably sharpened, and the gain increased by about 2 db if the phase shift between adjacent radiators is increased to approximately $kd = \pi/n$. This is referred to as the "Hansen-Woodyard" condition (*Proc. IRE*, March 1938). The new beamwidth between first nulls is given by

$$\text{Beamwidth} \cong 2\sqrt{\frac{\lambda}{l}} \text{ radians} \qquad (4)$$

If the length l is greater than a few wavelengths, the directivity is given approximately by

$$D \cong 7.9l/\lambda \qquad (5)$$

Equation (5) is generally useful for all types of uniformly excited end-fire antennas that satisfy the Hansen-Woodyard condition.

The maximum sidelobe amplitude for long, classical end-fire arrays is about 22 per cent of the main-lobe amplitude, and about 35 per cent in the case of the Hansen-Woodyard design. Lower sidelobe levels can be obtained at the expense of greater main lobe width by imposing an amplitude distribution over the elements of the array, just as in the case of broadside arrays designed for low sidelobes.

The field pattern of continuously excited or traveling-wave end-fire antennas, such as the dielectric rod antenna, is given by

$$E(\theta) = \frac{\sin\left[\dfrac{l}{2}(k\cos\theta - \beta)\right]}{(k\cos\theta - \beta)\dfrac{l}{2}} \qquad (6)$$

where β = phase constant in radians per unit length of the wave exciting the antenna, assumed to be of constant amplitude

$k = 2\pi/\lambda$
θ = angle off axis
l = total length of the antenna

The Hansen-Woodyard condition for the continuously excited antenna is given by

$$(\beta - k)l = \pi \qquad (7)$$

The maximum directivity when the Hansen-Woodyard condition is satisfied is given closely by Eq. (5), if l is greater than 3 or 4λ.

When l is very large, such as 50 to 100λ, Eq. (7) requires β to be very nearly equal to k. Such an antenna becomes impractical to excite. However, if either the amplitude of the traveling wave or the phase constant β are cyclically modulated along the axis, useful end-fire patterns are attainable for much larger average values of β. Such an antenna may be regarded as an array of arrays, each cycle of "modulation" being a single end-fire array. Antennas of this type have been successfully made in lengths of the order of 100λ.

DONALD K. REYNOLDS

Frequency-Independent Antennas

It is well known that the characteristics of a lossless antenna of a given shape depend on its dimensions measured in wavelengths. Thus, if an antenna is doubled in size, its input impedance, pattern, and polarization properties are the same at half the operating frequency. For this reason, antennas with several characteristic dimensions are usually limited to operation within a fairly narrow band of frequencies. On the other hand, the behavior of an antenna whose shape is completely described by angles rather than linear dimensions should be in many respects independent of frequency. Of course, such an antenna would be infinite in extent. There is, however, a class of angular shapes which, when truncated to form practical antennas, lead to operation that is essentially independent of frequency for all frequencies above a certain lower limit. The limit is determined by the one linear dimension of the antenna. Such structures were originally proposed by V. H. Rumsey and have been termed *frequency-independent antennas*.

Consider first a plane antenna whose input terminals are located at the origin of a system of polar coordinates (r, ϕ). The requirement that the antenna shape should be entirely specified by angle or, alternatively, that a change in scale should be equivalent to a rotation about the input terminals rather than a change in linear dimensions, fixes the shape of the structure. It must be bounded by curves which are equiangular spirals:

$$r = ke^{a\phi}$$

where r covers the range zero to infinity as ϕ varies from $-\infty$ to ∞. The parameter a determines how rapidly the spiral expands, and the constant k determines its orientation. A practical antenna consists of two or more metal arms emanating from the origin and separated by air gaps of approximately the same angular width as the arms, the outlines of the arms being equiangular spirals. In order that the bounding curves should not intersect, they all have the same value of a and differ only in orientation. The arms are carried out to some convenient distance from the center and terminated, and the input terminals are the tips of the arms in the center. Operation of this type of structure is perhaps best understood by consideration of an example.

The simplest version consists of the balanced two-arm antenna. Its input impedance is essentially constant for all frequencies between two widely separated limits. At the lower limit, the average antenna diameter is approximately one free-space wavelength; at the upper limit, the spacing between the input terminals is a sizable fraction of a wavelength. The lower limit may be lowered by increasing the antenna size, and the upper limit raised by making the input terminal region smaller. There is no radiation along the structure surface, the surface current density dying out rapidly for distances from the center greater than $\lambda/2$. The effect of the ends of the spiral arms is therefore small. This behavior is characteristic of frequency-independent antennas and indicates why they behave as if they were infinite structures above their lower frequency limit. Since a change in frequency is equivalent to a change in scale and a change in scale is equivalent to a rotation for this antenna, its pattern rotates in azimuth with change in operating frequency. However, the pattern is constant with respect to azimuth angle and therefore remains constant with frequency. The pattern consists of one main lobe on each side of the plane with the maxima along the axis. The radiation is circularly polarized with the sense of polarization in the angular direction along which the spiral expands. It is found that frequency independence is enhanced by making the spiral tightly wound, i.e., a small. In practice, bandwidths of 20:1 have been achieved with such an antenna.

Various patterns and input impedances may be obtained by constructing antennas with more than two arms. For example, a four-arm antenna fed such that adjacent arms are out of phase at the input terminals produces a conically shaped pattern on each side of the plane with a null along the axis.

Consider a more general three-dimensional shape described by the spherical polar coordinates (r, θ, ϕ). The form of the bounding surfaces is fixed by the requirement that a change in scale should be equivalent to a rotation in azimuth angle ϕ,

$$r = ke^{a\phi}F(\theta)$$

where $F(\theta)$ is arbitrary. There are infinitely many shapes that fit this formula. A simple example consists of equiangle spiral arms wrapped around a cone with the input terminals at the apex of the cone. It has been found that with proper choice of cone angle and spiral parameter a the two-arm spiral wound on a cone radiates a single circularly polarized lobe along the cone axis in the direction of the cone apex. As in the plane case, the upper frequency limit is determined by the size of the input region and the lower limit by the size of the base of the cone.

An alternative but related approach to the design of frequency-independent antennas makes use of plane shapes that are essentially cross sections (containing the polar axis) of shapes given by the formula above. The electrical properties of antennas designed in this way are not strictly constant with frequency; rather, they repeat periodically with the logarithm of the frequency. Hence, they are termed *log-periodic* antennas. The following plane curve is a simple example of this sort of shape:

$$\theta = k \sin (\ln r)$$

The frequencies for which such structures have the same electrical properties are arranged in a geometrical progression. The practical problem for the antenna is twofold. In the first place, to make the finite structure appear to be infinite for all frequencies above some lower limit, the radiation field must not propagate along the antenna surface. Second, the operating characteristics must change only slightly over one period so that the operation is essentially independent of frequency above the lower limit. As

an example, consider the antenna formed from two curves of the type described by the above equation with their apices close together as input terminals. It is found that if the solid angle between the planes containing the curves is sufficiently acute the pattern is just one lobe in the direction of the apex. An interesting characteristic of this type of antenna is that the radiation appears to arise from one region of the structure (called the "active" region), which moves along the structure as the frequency is changed. When this region comes to the end of the antenna, the lower frequency limit has been reached. As in the case of the spiral antennas, the upper frequency limit is determined by the size of the input terminal region.

A great many different log-periodic antennas have been investigated and found to be capable of large bandwidths, gains in the range of 5 to 20 db, and both linear and circular polarization. It should be noted, however, that frequency-independent operation is not guaranteed by a log-periodic shape; rather, each structure must be individually investigated.

W. J. Welch

Horn Antennas

Electromagnetic horns are one of the simplest means of obtaining moderate antenna gains and beamwidths at microwave frequencies. In general, a horn is fed from a uniform waveguide (*q.v.*) of arbitrary cross section that flares out to an aperture, again with arbitrary cross section, that radiates into free space. This flaring of the waveguide produces a phase error across the aperture of the horn, reducing the directivity and increasing the beamwidth and sidelobe levels in the radiation pattern from the same size aperture with no phase error. In some horns, phase-correcting devices, such as lenses or portions of paraboloidal reflectors whose focus is at the apex of the horn, are used to eliminate this phase error and to reduce the flare length required to produce a given directivity or beamwidth.

Horns perform two functions. First, they

produce a useful radiation pattern in space and, second, they provide a good impedance match between the waveguide and free space. Well-designed horns can perform these functions over frequency bands at least as wide as the feeding waveguide which may be ridge-loaded, if necessary, to cover extremely wide frequency bands. The low-frequency limit is determined by the cut-off frequency of the waveguide, and the high-frequency limit either by higher-order modes in the waveguide or by the permissible beam deterioration or loss in directivity that occurs as the phase error in the aperture increases with frequency.

The commonest type of horn has a rectangular aperture whose dimensions in the E- and H-planes (parallel to the E- and H-fields in the aperture, respectively) are determined by the beamwidths or directivities required in the two planes. Other horns have square or circular apertures, which are particularly useful for arbitrarily polarized or circularly polarized radiation.

The approximate analyses of horn behavior have been found to be quite accurate as long as the aperture is several wavelengths across or larger. The theoretical on-axis directivity g_e of a rectangular horn flared in the E-plane only (called an E-plane sectoral horn) can be found from Fig. 4, in which the directivity is plotted against the normalized frequency, and λ is the free-space wavelength. The dashed line in the figure is the asymptotic value that the curve approaches for small values of the abscissa, and corresponds to the directivity that could be obtained from the aperture of the horn if no phase errors were present.

A study of this figure reveals that there is a maximum of directivity that can be obtained from a horn of given flare length R_e at the point $b^2/R_e\lambda = 2.099$ and $g_e\lambda b/aR_e = 16.72$. This is called an "optimum" E-plane sectoral horn. Superimposed on the figure is an auxiliary grid labeled in decibels from which the difference in directivity of any horn from that of an optimum horn with the same flare length can be read directly.

A similar curve is shown in Fig. 5, from which the on-axis directivity g_m of an H-plane sectoral horn can be determined. Again, an optimum design is found at the point $a^2/R_m\lambda = 3.172$ and $g_m\lambda a/bR_m = 24.95$, and a corresponding grid is superimposed on the figure from which any difference in directivity from optimum can be read.

For a horn flared in both planes simultaneously, called a "pyramidal" horn, the directivity G can be found by noting the flare in each plane, then finding the cor-

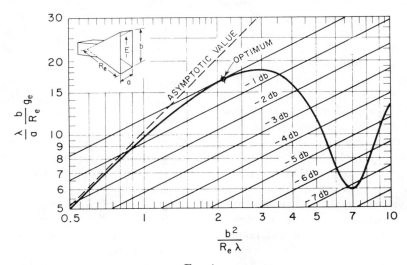

Fɪɢ. 4.

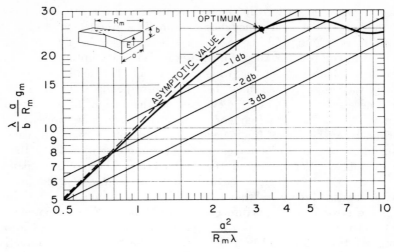

FIG. 5.

responding normalized sectoral-horn directivities, as above, and combining the results by

$$G = \frac{\pi R_e R_m}{32ab} \left(\frac{\lambda b}{a R_e} g_e \right) \left(\frac{\lambda a}{b R_m} g_m \right)$$

For a pyramidal horn optimized in both planes simultaneously, the directivity is given by $G_{opt} = 6.152\ ab/\lambda^2 = 40.96\ R_e R_m/ab$.

Because the abscissas in Figs. 1 and 2 determine the phase errors in the E- and H-planes, respectively, the normalized radiation patterns in the two planes are uniquely determined at each point along each curve, at least within the limits of the theory. The normalized half-power E-plane beamwidths vary from $51\lambda/b$ degrees for small values of the abscissa (zero phase error) to $53\lambda/b$ degrees for optimum E-plane sectoral horns. For H-plane sectoral horns, the corresponding normalized beamwidths vary from $68\lambda/a$ degrees to $80\lambda/a$ degrees.

Horns with circular apertures can be treated in the same way as rectangular horns except that the aperture distributions and radiation patterns in the two planes cannot be treated separately. The gain from such a circular aperture of diameter d with no phase error is $8.3(d/\lambda)^2$, whereas the gain of an optimum conical horn is $5.1(d/\lambda)^2 = 40(l/d)^2$,

where l is the axial length of the horn, given approximately by $l = d^2/2.8\lambda$. The corresponding half-power beamwidths are $60\lambda/d$ degrees in the E-plane and $70\lambda/d$ degrees in the H-plane for the optimum conical horn.

It is, of course, possible to flare a horn more rapidly than prescribed in an optimum design, or to operate an optimum horn at a frequency higher than its design frequency. In addition to the resultant loss in gain, either procedure causes a broadening of the radiation pattern and, in the E-plane, a severe breakup of the main lobe into a number of lobes. Carried to extremes, either procedure produces radiation patterns whose edges are approximately defined by projections of the flared edges of the horn, providing these edges are at least several wavelengths long.

R. C. HONEY

Lenses

The antenna devices considered in this section are those concerned with the refraction of electromagnetic energy. Many are adapted from optics, so that refraction is governed by Snell's law. A smaller group, involving parallel transmission lines, provides refraction independent of Snell's law. A third group utilizes wave propagation along geodesics in parallel-plate media where a generalized form of Snell's law can be applied. These three types of lens materials will be considered in turn.

Dielectrics. The simplest lens material involves a direct adaptation from optical lenses in which a *natural dielectric* material, having a real permittivity (low-loss material), is used. The dielectric constant of most materials considered is relatively independent of temperature for a normal range of temperatures. Exceptions are materials of high dielectric constant, such as barium titanate, which is a function of temperature as well as a function of an applied electric field. In practical applications, it should be recognized that each dielectric material is capable of absorbing a small percentage of water; this is particularly true of the loaded-form dielectrics manufactured for microwave applications. Since the microwave dielectric constant of water is 80, a small percentage of water can produce noticeable changes in dielectric constant. Lenses must be sealed against normal atmospheric conditions.

The next lens material, *void dielectric*, is one directly related to the natural dielectric. It has been found that spherical or cylindrical voids in the natural dielectric yield a material of lower dielectric constant. The analysis of this material is related to that of the natural dielectric by a consideration of the voids as molecules capable of being polarized. Because of the great disparity in size, this would appear to be a gross assumption; however, experimental evidence shows that voids, even as large as one-quarter wavelength in diameter, serve effectively in a void dielectric. As anticipated, the experiments show scattering typical of X-ray crystal diffraction when the voids have larger diameters. It appears that a void dielectric can be examined on the basis of fractional volume, that is, the ratio of the volume of air in the voids to the total dielectric volume. If F is the fractional volume, the ratio between the dielectric constant of the material and that of the base material is given by $(1 + 2 FC)/$ $(1 - FC)$ where $C = (1 - \epsilon')/(1 + 2\epsilon')$ and ϵ' is the dielectric constant of the base material.

Another important lens material has been designated as the *artificial dielectric*. Its analysis is also based upon the polarizability induced by the incident electric field; in place of the voids considered above, its molecular element is metallic. The metallic elements considered have included every conceivable metallic formation, beginning with spheres approximated by many combinations of latitude and longitude circles and by three mutually perpendicular pins. For certain applications, the sphere has been replaced by a disk which is independent of incident polarization, but dependent upon the direction of the incident ray. Replacement of the disk by a pin provides a structure dependent upon incident polarization, but less dependent upon incident-ray direction. The choice of a given configuration depends upon the application considered. The simple spherical obstacle is not very useful; it increases the effective permittivity ϵ' but decreases the effective permeability μ', so that only a marginal increase in refractive index $n = \sqrt{\epsilon'\mu'}$ over that of air is obtained. One significant characteristic of artificial dielectrics sometimes ignored occurs as higher values of dielectric constant are sought. Closely spaced elements serve to increase the index of refraction but cause considerably more reflection of the incident signal than is accounted for by consideration of the index value alone.

A final lens material governed by Snell's law is the metal-plate medium formed by an array of parallel plates. If the electric field vector is in a plane parallel to these plates, the energy undergoes an increase in its phase velocity as it passes between the plates. The resulting effective index of refraction is less than unity and for plate spacing a is given by the relation $[1 - (\lambda/2a)]^{1/2}$; this might be recognized as the effective index in a waveguide (*q.v.*).

Constrained Media. Another general type of material is represented by constrained media. One form of this medium involves a large number of short waveguide sections stacked like cord wood. Energy incident upon one face is forced to travel through the waveguides rather than along conventional ray paths predicted by Snell's law. Another form of constrained lens is the delay lens made up of transmission-line elements in which the index of refraction is maintained at unity; among elements considered have been parallel-plate structures and coaxial transmission lines. In these lenses, varying lengths of transmission line provide varying delays for different elements of the incident wavefront, so that the wavefront is refracted after the fashion of more conventional lenses. One parallel-plate lens involves a venetian-blind structure in which one lens surface is curved to provide variable lengths of parallel-plate transmission line. Another version involves a serpentine structure for achieving differential delay in the various transmission-line units. In recent years, delay lenses have been achieved with different lengths of coaxial cable whose effective index of refraction is not unity; losses must be taken into account in using this medium. It might be pointed out that the design of constrained lenses is simplified by elimination of Snell's law, but reflection at the lens surfaces can be a practical problem.

Parallel-Plate Media. The final lens medium to be considered is one involving parallel-plate media. They have been called "geodesic lens" and "configuration lens" media. This medium is "parallel in the small"; at any given point, the medium is made up of two surfaces having parallel tangent planes. Energy is assumed to propagate along geodesics of an intermediate surface. As a simple example, one might consider two hemispheres of slightly different radii, placed one on top of the other, and everywhere spaced by the difference in radii. Energy propagated between the two surfaces follows great-circle paths. Effective refraction in this structure can be recognized if one compares a source at the periphery of this medium with a similar source on the periphery of a circle lying in the equatorial plane. Rays contained in the plane provide a circular wavefront with center at the source. Rays carried through the parallel-plate medium follow great circles, so that all intersect at the diametrically opposite point, which also lies in the equatorial plane. A comparison of the two systems shows that the expanding rays of the circular wavefront are replaced by rays which first diverge and then converge to a focal point. In general, the lens surfaces utilized are not spherical, but have a more complex set of geodesic curves and, of course, provide more flexibility in refraction of the incident energy.

Constant-Index Lenses. The lens design available for converting a spherical wavefront into a plane wavefront is obtained by curving a constant-dielectric medium to match a hyperboloid surface on the spherical-wave side and providing a planar surface on the planar-wave side. The eccentricity of the hyperboloid is equal to the index of refraction; the center of the spherical surface coincides with a focal point of the hyperboloid. At times, it is desirable to employ a lens which converts a spherical wave emanating from one point into an image spherical wave converging on another. The design requisite is obtained by employing two of the hyperboloid-plane lenses. The first hyperboloid surface is positioned so that its focal point coincides with the emanating spherical wave; the second lens is positioned so that its plane face is coincident with the plane face of the first and its hyperboloid surface is chosen to provide coincidence between the center of the desired converging spherical wave and the hyperboloid focus.

At times, it is desirable to convert a cylindrical wavefront into a plane wavefront. This conversion is achieved by employing a lens surface which is a hyperbolic cylinder; the second surface is again a plane. (This lens structure is, of course, then the two-dimensional version of the configuration which converts a spherical wave into a plane wave.) The lens structure used to convert a plane wavefront into another plane wavefront represents an adaptation of the optical prism; it does not provide the frequency dispersion associated with an optical prism, but does change the direction of propagation of the plane wave. Lenses that convert cylindrical waves into cylindrical waves represent the two-dimensional variation of the structure that carries spherical waves into spherical waves. In general, no lens design problems appear among the relationships between the plane, cylindrical, and spherical wavefronts.

Variable-Index Lenses. *Maxwell Lens.* Historically, the Maxwell lens represents the first variable-index element. It was described by Clerk Maxwell in 1854, who related its construction to that of the eye of a fish. The lens has a spherical surface and the refractive index varies only with the radial coordinate. In its most general form, it images perfectly a spherical wave into a spherical wave. The best-known version of this lens images a source on the surface of a sphere into an image at the diametrically opposite point on the surface. The rays are circles whose center lies on the perpendicular bisector of the diameter under consideration. It can be seen that an object on one surface produces an inverted image on the opposite side of the surface. If we assume an index of refraction of unity over the surface of a sphere of unit radius, then the radial variation in refractive index is given by the expression $n = 2/(1 + r^2)$.

Luneberg Lens. The Luneberg lens appears to have been first described by R. K. Luneberg in 1944 at a series of lectures given at Brown University. In its most general form, the lens images a spherical wave emanating from a point on the axis of an optical system perfectly into another spherical wave converging at another point on the same axis. The particular form that has received the greatest attention is that in which the source point lies on the surface of a lens of unit radius, and the object point is at infinity. The lens images a spherical wave into a plane wave traveling along the axis towards the point at infinity. It can be seen that this lens has a wide field of view, since an incoming plane wave from any direction will be perfectly focused at a point on the lens surface. If the index of refraction over the lens surface is unity, then the radial variation of index is given by the expression $n = \sqrt{2 - r^2}$.

Eaton Lens. In an extension of the Luneberg-type lenses published by J. E. Eaton in 1953, one design described imaged a point source into a cylindrical wave. This lens, which also has spherical symmetry, is designed so that a point source placed on the surface on the sphere is converted into a cylindrical wave whose axis passes through the center of the sphere and the source point. The unusual feature of this component is that it requires an effective refractive index which is everywhere less than unity; its equation is given by $n = r$. Because of this characteristic, no method is known for constructing a three-dimensional Eaton lens. A two-dimensional version has been constructed in a metal-plate medium and shown to operate according to the geometrical-optics model; however, the wavefront produced in such a restricted model is not a cylindrical surface.

Other Lenses. Besides the three lenses discussed above, which relate spherical with cylindrical and planar waves, other microwave variable-index lenses have included one analyzed by K. S. Kelleher, which transforms spherical wavefronts into conical wavefronts. This lens proves to be a generalization of the three preceding lenses. Additional work on conical-wave lenses, as well as analysis of curved-wave lenses, was carried out by J. R. Huynen. A great deal of effort by various investigators has been expended on developing a Luneberg-lens configuration having a small feed circle. Another area involving variable index lenses is that in which an incident plane wave is reflected as another plane wave. It was shown by A. F. Kay that the spherical form of this lens was impractical, but that a cylindrical configuration could be used to reflect satisfactorily waves arriving from any direction in a plane perpendicular to the cylinder axis. The capability for varying refractive index presents unusual opportunities to the antenna designer and it can be expected that many advances in microwave lenses can be obtained by using this technique.

KENNETH S. KELLEHER

Reflector Antennas

Reflector antennas are commonly of two basic types, pencil-beam and shaped-beam antennas. Shaped-beam antennas are used for searching a volume of space and typically have a narrow beam in one plane with a broad, specially designed "fan" beam in the other plane; e.g., a cosecant variation in elevation which covers a vertical slice of space. Shaped reflectors are often parabolic in one cross section with the other cross sections designed to produce the appropriate broad beam. Pencil-beam antennas are used for radar, microwave-link communications, direction finding, space communications, etc., and usually produce a highly directive spatial pattern in which a single main lobe within a narrow cone contains nearly all the radiated power. Typical patterns are nearly circularly symmetric about the main lobe axis. Reflector pencil-beam antennas are quasi-optical in nature; i.e., they consist of a point source at the focus of an optical type of reflector, a parabola of revolution or "dish." The paraboloidal surface collimates the rays from the point source into a parallel beam of rays, analogous to a searchlight beam.

The pattern may be visualized by considering each point to be constituted of a sum of vectors or rays from various elements of the aperture. If the aperture field is of constant phase, all the vectors add in phase at broadside, producing the main beam. Off the main beam axis, the vectors do not add in magnitude, producing through interference a series of secondary maxima and minima, where the geometrical pathlength phase factor makes best and worst compensation for the aperture phase differences.

The diffraction effects are usually studied by consideration of the phase and amplitude of the electric-field distribution across the aperture, where the aperture is the projected plane of the paraboloid of revolution. Although there is no theoretical lower limit on main lobe width, practical feed (source) considerations limit the phase of the aperture distribution to be at most a slowly varying function. So-called supergain designs, which can realize very narrow beamwidths, require rapid phase alternations over the aperture. For uniform (constant) phase distributions, maximum directivity (defined below) is obtained for uniform amplitude. Such a circular aperture produces sidelobes 17.6 db below the main beam.

The distant pattern of the antenna is the Fourier transform of the electric-field distribution over the aperture plane. Examination of various distributions through this relationship yields the information that amplitude tapers (maximum in center) produce lower sidelobe levels (higher sidelobe ratios) at the expense of slightly wider main beams and lower directivity. Commonly used analytical distributions are Gaussian and $\cos^n$ on a pedestal. Typically the sidelobe ratio can be increased to 25 db with a beamwidth increase and directivity decrease of 25 per cent.

Practical reflector antennas are specified by the directivity (maximum gain), half-power beamwidth, and sidelobe level. Directivity is defined as the ratio of maximum intensity per unit solid angle to the total radiated power. Half-power beamwidth is the width in degrees of the main beam between the two points where the power intensity is half the maximum. This is often called the 3-db beamwidth. Although the shape of the sidelobe envelope is of importance, the principal parameter is the ratio of the main beam maximum to the maximum of the closest sidelobe, and is called the sidelobe ratio.

Aperture efficiency is usually defined as the ratio of actual gain to that calculated for an ideal aperture of the same size with uniform amplitude and phase. The three principal factors that affect efficiency are the amplitude taper over the aperture, the feed spillover, and blockage of the aperture by the feed. Other factors are the energy radiated in the cross-polarized component (because of the double curvature of the reflector, some energy is converted into the undesired polarization), phase errors over the aperture, and copper (heating) losses. All of these result in an empirically derived maximum efficiency of about 65 per cent. Practical antennas usually range from 40 to 60 per cent.

A point-source feed is undesirable and impossible; undesirable because the feed should illuminate only the reflector surface to avoid wasting power, and impossible because a vector source can never simulate an isotropic point source exactly. Typical feeds are dipoles with reflectors, horns, and spiral antennas. All have a characteristic unidirectional pattern consisting of one very wide lobe plus side- or backlobes. In order to reduce the primary radiation that falls outside the reflector (spillover), which decreases efficiency and raises the sidelobes, the primary feed pattern may be made to produce a highly amplitude-tapered distribution over the aperture. The taper, however, increases beamwidth and decreases directivity. A compromise is made between directivity loss from spillover and from aperture amplitude taper.

The presence of the reflector affects the feed input impedance and may result in low efficiency, usually corrected by impedance matching at the feed terminals or by a matching plate at the parabola vertex. (See, for instance, S. Silver, ed., *Microwave Antenna Theory and Design*, MIT Rad. Lab. Series, McGraw-Hill Book Co., 1949.)

A design that eliminates feed blockage is the Cassegrainian system with polarization rotation. Here the feed is replaced by a small primary hyperbolic reflector located symmetrically and coaxially between the focus and the larger parabolic reflector. The small reflector is made of a grid of wires, and is illuminated by a feed through a small hole in the large reflector (Fig. 6). The feed is polarized with the electric vector parallel to the wires of the grid, so that the feed radiation is reflected into the large reflector. The reflector surface is covered with a quarter-wave plate surface layer which produces a total 90° rotation of polarization so the electric vector radiated from the large reflector is now perpendicular to the grid and passes through. Elimination of the aperture blockage allows low sidelobes to be realized, which minimizes the stray energy picked up from the earth and other objects when the antenna is used for receiving. The Cassegrainian system with polarization control is only usable when the wave polarization is under the designer's control.

Parabolic reflector antennas are often used

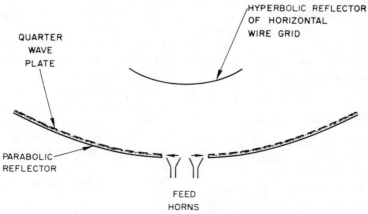

Fig. 6. Lobing Cassegrainian antenna.

for automatic tracking of targets, by a lobe comparison technique. The reflector is fed so as to produce two (or more) main beams slightly skewed on either side of the axis. Comparison of the signal received from each beam enables a servo system to position the antenna so as to make the signals equal, which occurs on axis. Two ways of implementing this are conical lobing and simultaneous lobing. In conical lobing a single feed horn is moved around a small circle whose center is on axis; the main lobe moves around a corresponding circle in space. Comparison of signals is then made on a time-sequential basis. In simultaneous lobing (often called monopulse), four feeds are used to excite the reflector with the comparison being made in two orthogonal planes by hybrid junctions. Both systems result in large aperture blockage; typical aperture efficiencies for lobing antennas are 50 per cent.

Another type of reflector antenna utilizes a portion of a sphere as a spatially fixed reflector: the antenna beam is scanned by movement of the feed structure. However, spherical optics exhibit serious spherical aberration (high sidelobes) when illuminated by a point source. To reduce this effect, a line-source feed located along a radial line must be used. The line source would typically be a slot or dipole array, and would be pivoted about the focus of the reflector. These spherical reflector antennas allow scanning over wide angles with a fixed "dish"; the limitations are in a much lower aperture efficiency, in the narrow frequency-band capabilities of the line-source feed, and in the decrease of projected (effective) aperture with scan away from the axis.

ROBERT C. HANSEN

Electronically Scanned Antennas

An electronically scanned antenna, also known as *phased array*, consists of a mechanically fixed radiating aperture whose phase of excitation can be varied to change the direction of radiation. The antenna phase adjustment can be provided by many techniques such as frequency variation, phase shifters, switching between multiple beams, etc. Some techniques are inertialess by avoidance of components with mechanically moving parts, others may employ mechanical phase shifters or switches.

To achieve high antenna gain and narrow radiation beams, large antennas are needed to communicate over great distances and provide precision direction information. To overcome the difficulty experienced in physical repositioning of antennas with large mechanical inertia, electronic scanning has been developed.

An antenna generates a collimated beam, i.e., produces a radiation maximum in one direction, if each element of the antenna is electrically equidistant from the point of reception. Thus, for large separations between transmitting and receiving antennas, the phasing requirement can be restated as follows: *The rate of phase advance (known as "phase taper") along any line across a plane aperture must be uniform.* Mathematically this means that the beam directions as measured by the angles with x-y coordinates within the plane of the antenna (θ_x and θ_y, respectively) are related to β_x and β_y, the phase tapers along these axes, by

$$\cos \theta_x = \frac{\lambda \beta_x}{2\pi}, \text{ etc.}$$

The above expression permits determination of the relative phase values of each element in the array for a given element spacing.

A phase shifter with 360° phase excursion is adequate even for phase values in excess of 360°, since a phase shift of θ is indistinguishable from a phase shift of $(\theta + 360n)$, where n is any integer.

The scan volume of any electronically scanned antenna is limited by the radiation pattern of the individual element (known as "element factor") and by the separation between elements if ambiguous antenna beams (known as "grating lobes") are to be avoided. The criterion for element spacing is

$$D = \frac{1 - (1/N)}{1 + \sin \theta} \lambda$$

where D is the element separation, N is the effective number of rows or columns of elements, and θ is the maximum off-broadside scan angle. The gain of an electronically scanned antenna can be calculated by using the projection of the actual aperture on a plane normal to the direction of radiation as the effective aperture up to angles of 80° from broadside. Beyond this, gain must be calculated on the end-fire gain basis.

Some examples of electronically scanned antennas are given below.

Frequency-Scanned Antenna. This is the simplest and most compact type requiring, however, a more complex and wideband receiver and transmitter with provisions for accurate frequency control and readout. Frequency scanning is usually limited to a single plane of scan. Because this antenna has no moving parts and no electronically activated circuit components, beam positioning is extremely fast and very accurate. This type of antenna is usually constructed by feeding a large number of elements so that any two adjacent elements are excited through equal phase length differences L (usually a multiple of a wavelength long). The direction of radiation can be expressed as

$$\theta = \sin^{-1}\left[\frac{\lambda L}{\lambda_g d} + N\,\frac{\lambda}{d}\right]$$

where d is the average element separation, N is a negative integer, and λ_g is the guide wavelength.

Phase-Shifter Antenna. This design is more complex, since it requires at least one phase shifter per radiating element. These phase shifters must be driven, either mechanically or electrically, from a central control computer to establish the required phase front for a collimated beam. This computer serves as a beam position readout device, converts beam-pointing angle information into the correct value of phase-shifter excitation, performs phase-taper calculations, determines the phase settings for each phase shifter, and converts phase to excitation current (or voltage) according to

the phase shifter employed. The computer must be sufficiently fast so as not to delay beam repositioning. Phase-shifter antennas possess a slower speed of beam positioning, higher sidelobes owing to greater phase errors, lower gain, and less beam positioning accuracy than frequency-scanned antennas. A complete phase-shifter antenna requires a corporate feed structure to divide the power according to the number of elements and the aperture illumination (e.g., hybrids, directional couplers, or folded pillbox).

The performance of the phase-shifter antenna depends mainly upon the properties of the individual phase shifters, such as: phase dependence upon frequency, temperature, and power level; low insertion loss; high power-handling capacity; low mechanical or electrical inertia for rapid phase changing with low excitation power. Phase changing is accomplished by mechanical means such as line stretching and variable transmission line loading; by ferrites that exhibit variable rf magnetic permeability under varying magnetic-field excitation and thus allow an electronic change of phase velocity; by semiconductors whose transmission and reflection coefficients can be controlled by applied voltage; or by a network of mixers which change a variable frequency input to a variable phase output. The time for beam positioning is limited by the rate at which the stored electrical energy in the electronic phase shifter can be changed with a given driving amplifier power.

Beam-Switching Antenna. These antennas, usually physically the largest, consist of a number of feeds, each corresponding to one beam direction, connected to the same aperture so as to establish the required aperture phase tapers. In addition, a multiport switch is essential for beam-position selection, unless a separate transmitter and/or receiver can be provided for each feed. The speed of scanning depends upon the switch employed. Essentially, this antenna step-scans between predetermined positions.

Multiple phase tapers can be established by exciting a single antenna reflector' (or lens) with a number of primary feeds physically displaced from each other. For a large number of simultaneous beams a network of directional couplers, antenna feed lines, and phase-taper input feed lines is employed. If the antenna feed lines are parallel, with the phase-taper feedlines intersecting them at different geometical angles α, the beam direction θ can be expressed as follows:

$$\theta = \sin^{-1}\left[\frac{\lambda}{\lambda_g}\left(\csc \alpha - \cot \alpha\right)\right]$$

where λ_g is the feed wavelength. Switching between beams can be accomplished by mechanical means, ferrites, gas tubes, or semiconductors.

H. Shnitkin

Slotted-Guide Antennas

In the most general sense, a slot antenna in a flat ground plane is an aperture that transforms guided waves to radiating waves. The method of excitation of the slot generally depends on the impedance characteristic desired and on the restriction imposed by the particular installation. The shape of the slot may take a variety of forms, although the simplest and most common is that of a rectangular slot shown in Fig. 7.

The electromagnetic waves may be introduced at the aperture (terminals T-T) by a two-wire transmission line, a coaxial line, or a direct termination of a waveguide in the ground plane. When the waveguide is short-circuited at the opposite end and fed by a probe, a cavity fed slot is formed. This type of flush-mounted antenna has found special application in aircraft and missiles where low-drag antennas are required.

Slots cut in the walls of a rectangular waveguide is another method of excitation. This method of feed is particularly useful when a number of slots are to be used for an array. The guided wave inside the waveguide "leaks" out of the slot and transforms into a radiated wave.

Half-Wavelength Slot. A half-wavelength slot antenna of width w mounted on an infinite ground plane and excited by a generator V is shown in Fig. 7a. Applying Babinet's principle and replacing the ground-plane by free space and the slot by a metal sheet of width w, the complement of the slot, yields a half-wave electric dipole. Two antennas which are complements of each other have the property that the radiation patterns are identical except that the electric and magnetic fields are reversed.

The radiation from the electric dipole is due to the electric current I_E flowing on the metal conductor, whereas the radiation from the slot is due to the magnetic current I_M flowing in the aperture. The radiation patterns are compared in Fig. 8, with the arrows indicating the direction of the electric and magnetic field. The radiation pat-

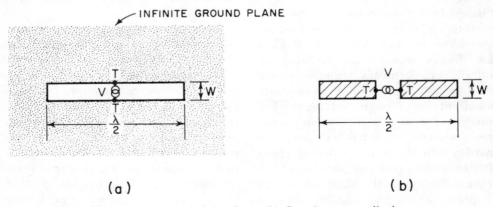

(a)   (b)

Fig. 7. (a) Slot in infinite sheet. (b) Complementary dipole.

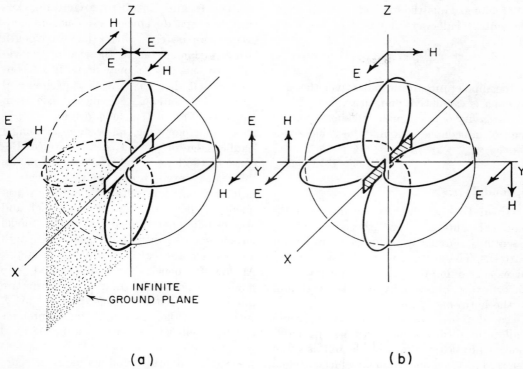

(a)   **(b)**

Fig. 8. (a) Radiation pattern of slot in infinite sheet. (b) Radiation pattern of complementary dipole.

tern is uniform over 360° in one plane and of the form

$$E \frac{\cos\left(\dfrac{\pi}{2}\cos\theta\right)}{\sin\theta}$$

in the other plane.

When the slot on an infinite ground plane is excited by a waveguide or a cavity, the radiation is restricted to one side of the ground. If a finite ground plane is used rather than an infinite ground plane, the radiated waves from the edge of the ground plane cause interference with the direct wave from the slot with the main perturbation occurring at angles away from the normal to the slot. A small amount of energy also diffracts around to the back side of the ground plane. Other configurations of interest are slots in cylinders, spheres, and cones. The field due to the slot (the primary wave) induces currents in the conducting body. The field of the induced currents is called the secondary wave. Since the radiated

field is the resultant of the primary and secondary waves, depending upon the electrical dimension of the body and the slot orientation, considerable perturbation of the original primary pattern of the slot may be obtained.

Annular Slot Antenna. The annular slot antenna is the complement of the loop antenna. Its pattern and polarization are complements of the loop and is thus similar to that of a short vertical stub mounted on a large ground plane.

Impedance of Slot Antennas. The impedance Z_s of a slot antenna is given by

$$Z_s = \frac{Z_0^2}{4Z_d} = \frac{35{,}476}{Z_d} \text{ ohms}$$

where Z_0 is the characteristic impedance of the surrounding medium and Z_d is the terminal impedance of the complementary dipole antenna. Thus the impedance of the slot is proportional to the admittance of the dipole. As an illustration, the impedance of an infinitesimally thin $\lambda/2$ dipole is $73 +$

j 42.5 ohms. Thus the impedance of its complementary half-wave slot is

$$Z_s = \frac{35,476}{73 + j42.5} = 363 - j211 \text{ ohms}$$

If the dipole antenna is inductive, the slot antenna is capacitive and vice versa.

For cavity or waveguide fed slot antennas the slot impedance is double the value given above.

T. MORITA

Special Types

Omni-Directional Antenna. Omni-directional antennas are those possessing essentially circularly symmetric radiation patterns. The vertical pattern (taken in the plane containing the axis of symmetry) may be arbitrary but usually has its maximum in the horizontal plane.

An ideal *isotropic* antenna which would radiate in all directions in a given polarization is physically unrealizable but is often referred to as a standard upon which antenna gain is based. An omni-directional pattern lends itself to "broadcast" applications such as mobile and aircraft communication antennas, ground beacon antennas, and monitor antennas. Typical examples shown in Fig. 9 include the dipole or monopole above the round plane, biconical antenna, a loop antenna, annular slot antenna, and the discone. Additional directivity can be obtained by forming a colinear array of any of these elements or by using phase reversing stubs as in Fig. 9-g to form a Franklin array. A horizontally polarized omni-directional antenna may be formed, for example, from two slotted cylinders as in Fig. 9-h.

An electrically small helix operated in the normal or broadside mode provides a circularly polarized omni-directional antenna. A turnstile antenna is formed by feeding crossed dipoles in phase quadrature as shown in Fig. 9-i. The dipole patterns combine vectorially into a pattern which is nearly omni-directional in the horizontal plane and provides circularly polarized radiation in the vertical direction as well.

Aircraft and Satellite Antennas. Aircraft and space vehicle antennas are considered separately when the wavelength becomes comparable to the size of the vehicle. In this case it may properly be considered that the vehicle itself is excited and forms the antenna. Typical excitation methods (Fig. 10) include driving an isolated tail cap or wing tip, or shunt exciting a leading edge of a wing or tail surface. Because of the large number of current modes that can be excited on a complex structure, radiation patterns of aircraft in this frequency region are difficult to predict and are usually determined by scale model measurements where both the wavelength and vehicle are scaled by a common factor. At low frequencies only dipole and loop modes are possible so that the patterns are predictable. If the vehicle is very much smaller than the wavelength these antennas become inefficient so that trailing or fixed wires are often used, particularly at speeds where the adverse aerodynamic effects are negligible. At all frequencies flush-mounted antennas are usually preferred to minimize drag. At higher frequencies where the radius of curvature of the aircraft skin is very much larger than the wavelength, the antenna patterns can be predicted from a knowledge of the antenna element pattern in an appropriate ground screen taking into account the shadowing effects of remote portions of the aircraft.

Figure 10-c shows a pattern of a uhf monopole mounted on the belly of an aircraft. The distortions in the patterns are due to engine and wing shadows and reflections.

Satellite antennas may employ any of the conventional antennas. Directional antennas may be used if the satellite is inertially stabilized; omni-directional antennas are used when the satellite is spin stabilized; and approximately isotropic antennas, for example a double turnstile (Fig. 10-e) may be used if the satellite is unstabilized.

Satellite and space vehicle antennas differ from conventional airframe antennas in

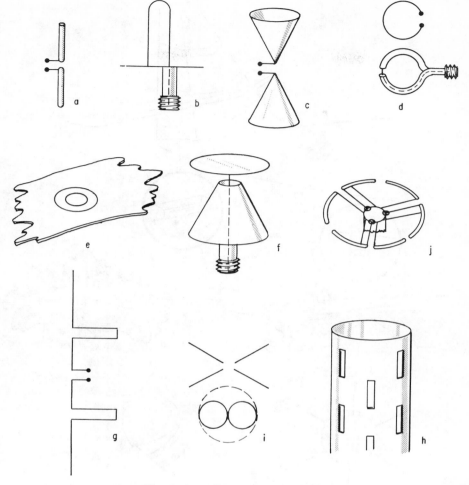

FIG. 9. Omnidirectional antennas.

(a) Half wave dipole.
(b) Monopole antenna.
(c) Biconical antenna.
(d) Loop antenna.
(e) Annular slot antenna.

(f) Discone antenna.
(g) Franklin array.
(h) Slotted cylinder.
(i) Turnstile antenna.
(j) Tri-dipole antenna.

only two respects. Special consideration must be given to the antennas to minimize both the heating effects and the shunting effect of the induced shock-wave ionization on re-entering the atmosphere. Although conventional antenna principles are applied to satellite and space-vehicle antennas, the weightlessness and lack of drag allow other mechanical considerations that permit new configurations. In this way antennas can be inflated like balloons or unfurled after being placed in orbit. Construction need be just rigid enough to withstand the possible stabilization acceleration, micro-meteorites, and solar pressure forces.

Circularly Polarized Antennas. Circularly polarized antennas are often used when the orientation of the incoming polarized energy is unknown or rapidly changing as from a tumbling satellite. Elliptically polarized radiation is produced when perpendicular electric fields are excited in phase

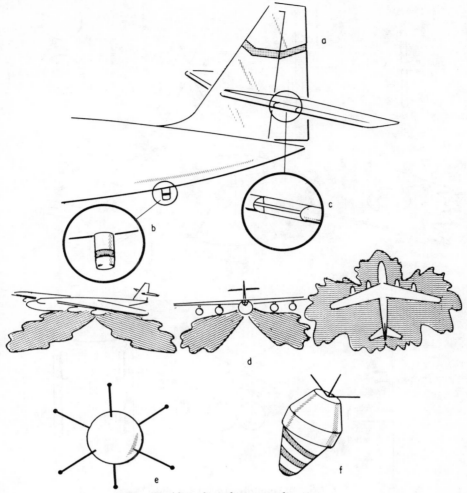

FIG. 10. Aircraft and spacecraft antennas.

(a) Tailcap antenna.
(b) Shunt excited tail section.
(c) Streamlined monopole in belly mounting.
(d) Typical radiation patterns of antenna in 10-c.

(e) Double turnstile satellite antenna.
(f) Unfurled tapered helical satellite antenna.

quadrature. The ratio of the maximum to minimum E field at a given point in the far field is defined as the polarization ratio. The polarization ratio measured on the axis of a beam antenna is known as the axial ratio. Circular polarization may be excited by crossed dipoles as in the turnstile antenna, by a quarter-wave plate in a horn or by a helix or spiral antenna. The quarter-wave plate may consist of a dielectric slab placed in the waveguide feed of the horn in such a

way that it retards one component of the electric field by 90° more than the orthogonal component.

Direction-Finding (DF) Antennas. Direction-finding antennas are designed to measure the angle of arrival of a radio wave, which direction is used for homing or navigation. The angle of arrival is measured either by determining the direction of the maximum (or minimum) response using a known antenna pattern or by comparing the phase received on two nearby antennas. A rotating horn whose output is displayed on an oscilloscope or recorder serves as a crude direction finder. An Adcock array which, in its simplest form, is an array of two parallel dipoles fed out of phase, determines direction more accurately by adjusting for the direction of a null response. The two-way ambiguity of the null response can be resolved by the use of a third antenna. The antennas need not be rotated. A pair of crossed Adcock arrays can be connected to a goniometer so that the array need not be positioned physically to determine the direction of the null response. If the two (or more) elements are widely separated and a phase comparison made, the antenna is called an interferometer. Interferometers provide good resolution, but introduce ambiguities because of their multi-lobed patterns.

A circularly disposed array of elements such as the Wullenweber array in which sectors of elements are switched in turn, provides an alternate means of rotating a beam without physically rotating elements. If an omni-directional antenna element is rotated in the horizontal plane it can be used as a direction finder since the Doppler shift is maximum as the element approaches the incoming wave and minimum as it recedes. The angle of arrival, therefore, lies along the axis of the instantaneous zero Doppler shift points on the circle.

Traveling-Wave Antennas. A half-wave dipole antenna supports a current standing wave. Many antennas, for example a long wire over the earth (Beverage antenna), a long helical antenna operating in the axial mode, or a very long Yagi-Uda array, are more conveniently considered from a traveling-wave point of view. Two general classes of traveling-wave antennas may be distinguished; surface-wave antennas and leaky-wave antennas. A surface-wave antenna is characterized by a traveling wave bound to the exterior of a guiding structure. The guiding surface structure can be a dielectric rod as in the polyrod antenna, an annular corrugated surface, or a periodic

structure as in the Cigar antenna (Fig. 11). These surface waves are characterized by a guide wavelength and have the property that the energy remains essentially in the vicinity of the guiding surface until launched at the point where the surface terminates. Leaky-wave antennas such as the slotted waveguide antenna, Fig. 11-g, or the trough waveguide, Fig. 11-h, are characterized by a traveling wave which radiates progressively along the direction of travel, giving rise to reinforcement and hence radiation at some angle other than the direction of propagation of the wave. In this case, the guiding structure is characterized not only by the guide wavelength but also by its rate of leakage or its attenuation.

Data-Processing Antennas. For special applications appropriate processing of the data received by a particular antenna system can be made to yield results peculiar to another antenna configuration. For example, if the phase received on a linear array is measured, array patterns can be computed corresponding to a variety of amplitude tapers (see antenna arrays). A digital computer could be programmed in such a way to interpret these phases as low-sidelobe arrays, multibeam arrays, or a single broad beam pattern. Since the phase of an rf signal is preserved in heterodyning to a lower frequency, this data processing can be accomplished by IF circuitry and phase shifters to accomplish a variety of simultaneous receiving patterns from a single array. Alternatively, the local oscillators used in the heterodyning process can be programmed to provide phase shifts appropriate to desired array patterns as in other electronically steered beam systems.

Synthetic Antennas. Other data-processing antenna systems are based on the relationship between the space complexity of an antenna and the frequency complexity of the signals to be received. Communication theory provides the relation between pattern information and signal information. A two-element interferometer of fixed spacing can simulate the pattern of a complex array

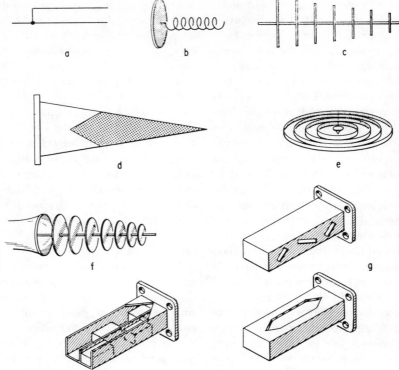

FIG. 11. Traveling wave antennas.

(a) Beverage antenna.
(b) Long helical antenna.
(c) Long Yagi-Uda array.
(d) Polyrod antenna.

(e) Annular corrugated-surface antenna.
(f) Cigar antenna.
(g) Slotted waveguide antenna.
(h) Trough waveguide antenna.

providing sufficient bandwidth in the received signal is allowed. Higher frequency components in the signals correspond to electrically greater spacing of the array elements. One may consider that at the higher frequencies the effective element spacing corresponds to a greater physical separation. Properly weighting the frequency components then corresponds to weighting properly the illumination function of the larger and more complex array of synthetic elements. Similar correlation techniques can be applied to the data received on "incomplete arrays" to "fill in" missing elements. These techniques have been widely applied to antennas for radio astronomy.

Time-Modulated Antennas. Time may be exchanged for bandwidth if the incoming signal is sufficiently stationary. A single element of an array could assume in turn all the positions in a conventional array.

By storing and later combining the information received at the various locations the array pattern could be synthesized. The time domain is thus used as a means of controling receiving antenna patterns. This concept can be applied to continuously moving elements or to other parameters of the antenna system such as aperture size, shape, or illumination to control receiving patterns on a time average basis.

C. E. FAFLICK

Cross-references: *Electromagnetic Theory, Extraterrestrial Radio Sources, Fourier Integrals and Their Applications, Interferometer Method (Optical), Propagation, Radomes, Satellite Communications, Waveguides and Waveguide Components*

ANTIFERROMAGNETISM

Antiferromagnetic materials are those in which the atomic moments are ordered but arranged in such a fashion that the total moment or magnetization at the absolute zero of temperature vanishes. The arrangements of the atomic moments may assume complicated forms such as triangular or spiral but in the simplest form are colinear. The latter form may be visualized as two interpenetrating ferromagnetic lattices in which the atomic moments are oppositely directed. It is thus a ferrimagnetic material (e.g., ferrite) in which the sublattice magnetizations are equal. As the temperature is increased from absolute zero, this arrangement persists until the antiferromagnetic Curie temperature or Néel temperature is reached, above which the material usually becomes paramagnetic. Passage through the Néel temperature is usually accompanied by slight lattice distortions and a change in specific heat. From the simple molecular field point of view the magnetization of each sublattice of an antiferromagnet can be considered to be acted upon by two molecular magnetic fields; the exchange field H_E and the anisotropy field H_A. The exchange field essentially causes the sublattices to line up oppositely and is usually of the order of a million gauss. The anisotropy field H_A determines the direction with respect to the crystalline axis along which the antiferromagnetic ordering takes place. This quantity may vary from a few gauss to hundreds of thousands. The equilibrium positions of the sublattice magnetizations are determined by the exchange and anisotropy fields. In the case where the anisotropy field depends only on the angular displacement of the sublattice magnetizations from their equilibrium position, the antiferromagnet is called uniaxial. The magnetic susceptibility of these materials are of the order of magnitude of the paramagnetic materials.

In the past these materials have been only of theoretical interest. Recently, however, the resonance properties of antiferromagnetics have been suggested for use in devices at millimeter and submillimeter wavelengths. If a uniaxial antiferromagnetic material is placed in a dc magnetic field directed along the axis of symmetry, it absorbs energy from an electromagnetic wave whose magnetic intensity vector is perpendicular to the axis. The resonant frequency (in kilomegacycles) for temperatures well below the Néel temperature is given by

$$f^{\pm} = 2.8(\sqrt{2H_E H_A} \pm H)$$

where H_E, H_A, and H (measured in gauss) are the exchange field, the anisotropy field, and the applied field, respectively. Because of the large exchange field these resonances usually fall in the millimeter to infrared regions of the spectrum. The antiferromagnetic behaves like a ferrite material with a dc magnetic field bias of $\sqrt{2H_E H_A}$. Either branch of the above resonance equation may be used for device application. In practice, a small piece of uniaxial single-crystal material is placed in a waveguide with the axis of symmetry perpendicular to the broad face of the waveguide. If a magnetic field is applied along the axis of symmetry, nonreciprocal resonant absorption of the electromagnetic energy in the waveguide occurs resulting in a resonance isolator. Resonance isolators have been constructed to operate at liquid nitrogen temperatures from 140 to 170 kMc utilizing chromic oxide (Cr_2O_3) which has a Néel temperature of 308°K and a value of $\sqrt{2H_E H_A}$ of 59.6 kilogauss. Ratios of reverse-to-forward attenuations of 20 to 1 have been observed. For an antiferromagnetic resonance isolator the theoretical figure of merit F (defined as the ratio of the reverse to forward loss) is the same as that of a ferrite isolator and is given by

$$F = \left(\frac{4H}{\Delta H}\right)^2$$

where H is the applied dc magnetic field in accordance with the resonance condition and ΔH is the resonance line width. The figure of merit for phase shift type devices such as circulators is also comparable to that of ferrite devices operating below ferromagnetic resonance.

Other antiferromagnetic materials that may be used in devices include manganese fluoride (MnF_2), which has a Néel temperature of 68°K and a zero applied field resonance at about 1 mm. Manganese titanate ($MnTiO_3$), whose Curie temperature is reported to be between 40 and 60°K, exhibits a zero-field resonance at about 3 mm. The additions of small quantities of nonmagnetic materials to antiferromagnetics can change both the exchange and anisotropy fields appreciably so that the possibility of tailor-made materials for particular frequency ranges exists.

G. S. HELLER

Cross-references: *Ferrimagnetism, Ferrites, Ferromagnetism, Magnetism, Millimeter-Wave Generation*

ANTIPARTICLES

The ultimate nature of matter is a problem which has always challenged the profoundest inquiry and the utmost theoretical and experimental ingenuity of scientists. Only 30 years ago, there seemed to be a triumphant solution of the structure of the atom in terms of motions of negatively charged electrons around positively charged nuclei. But as probing of the interior of the nucleus began, an unbelievably complicated jumble of new and unsuspected elementary particles was discovered. The fact that the nucleus is made up of protons and neutrons seemed simple enough, but nuclear properties could not be explained by these particles alone. For when man shatters nuclei with high-energy projectiles newly at his command, a bewildering array of very short-lived particles is created which simply do not exist in atoms of ordinary matter. It has taken quantum theory in its most powerful aspects to predict and account for these particles; but some fit nowhere and the fundamental concept of "strangeness," expressed numerically, has entered the concepts of nuclear physics. Gradually order is appearing out of chaos.

About 25 years ago the four elementary particles building blocks of atoms were the *electron*, the lightest particle, with a rest mass (the basic unit) and a negative charge (the base unit of electricity); the *proton* with a weight of 1836.1 electron masses and a charge of $+1$; and the *neutron* with a mass of 1838.6 and zero charge. The fourth particle was the *photon*, the quantum unit of radiation, or the building block of the electromagnetic field. Since the photon travels with the velocity of light c, it can never be at rest or have a rest mass. Because of its motion, it possesses energy and therefore, by virtue of its motion, it also has mass, expressed by the equation $E = mc^2$. All four elementary particles have characteristic spins (the charged ones then become magnets) expressed by $\frac{1}{2}$ for electrons, protons, and neutrons, which are therefore called fermions (after Fermi); and 1 for photons, which are bosons (after Bose).

The understanding of necessary reactions, or coupling, of particles when they are close together has been a triumph of quantum electrodynamics in recent years. The idea of a virtual process was first exemplified by the coupling of the electron and photon; the continuous emission and absorption of photons by electrons is the means by which electromagnetic field and electron exert a force on each other. This "virtual" photon cannot be observed, and thus the law of conservation of energy is maintained; the virtual photon becomes real only by adding energy by accelerating the electron. Similarly, the proton emits and absorbs virtual photons. In any case, the four elementary particles, with these couplings, seemed sufficient for explaining atomic structures, and the masses and charges of nuclei. Dirac's theory of the electron had predicted some additional particles, including an electron with positive charge, the *positron*. By this theory, a collision of a positive and negative electron would result in annihilation and their mass converted to photons with equivalent energy; or conversely, in a high-speed collision between two particles a positive and negative electron could be created. In this way Anderson discovered the positron, the first antiparticle.

In 1956 came the discoveries of the *antiproton*, with a negative charge, and the *anti-*

neutron, with no charge but with a magnetic moment opposite to that of the neutron. Neutron behavior led to the postulation and finally the experimental discovery of the *neutrino*. Within a nucleus the neutron is stable but outside, after an average of 18 min., it spontaneously ejects an electron (beta-ray) and turns into a proton. The proton and electron together are 1.5 electron masses lighter than the neutron; and this mass, equivalent to 780,000 ev of energy, is lost in the decay. To account for the discrepancy, Pauli suggested that another particle with zero rest mass is formed in the decay and carries the missing energy. Fermi named this particle the neutrino and constructed a theory that the neutron continuously loses and regains an electron and a neutrino by the virtual process which becomes real because the lost mass provides the energy.

There is some confusion in the use of terms, but most physicists prefer the *antineutrino* in this process accompanying electron emission, the antiparticle of the neutrinos which accompany positron emission. Next in order to hold protons and neutrons together in the nucleus, Yukawa postulated the same absorption-emission process by these nucleons for a particle called *meson*, because of intermediate rest mass. After 10 years, the pi-meson or *pion*, positive, negative and neutral, with a weight of 270 electron masses was found, requiring 135 million electron volts of energy to turn a virtual into a real pion; the negative pion is the antiparticle of the positive pion (or vice versa) and the neutral pion, like the photon, is its own antiparticle. The positive pion decays into a neutrino and a positive muon; the negative pion into a negative muon and an antineutrino. The discovery of the *muon* weighing 207 electron masses defeated the so-called dozen-particle theory which was held until its discovery. The muon decays in a millionth of a second into electron (positron for the positive muon, electron for the negative) plus a neutrino plus an antineutrino.

Thus by analysis of particle interactions

Name	Rest mass (electron masses)	
Heavy		
Xi	2585	$\Xi^0\ \Xi^-\ \overline{\Xi^+}\ \overline{\Xi^0}$ (Ξ^0 unknown)
Sigma	2324–2341	$\Sigma^-\ \Sigma^0\ \Sigma^+\ \overline{\Sigma^+}\ \overline{\Sigma^0}\ \overline{\Sigma^-}$
Lambda	2182	$\Lambda^0\ \overline{\Lambda^0}$
Proton	1836.1	$p^+\ \overline{p^-}$
Neutron	1838.6	$n^0\ \overline{n^0}$
Mesons		
K Meson	965	

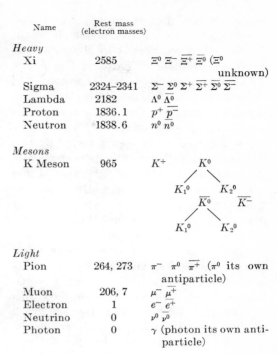

Light		
Pion	264, 273	$\pi^-\ \pi^0\ \overline{\pi^+}$ (π^0 its own antiparticle)
Muon	206, 7	$\mu^-\ \overline{\mu^+}$
Electron	1	$e^-\ e^+$
Neutrino	0	$\nu^0\ \overline{\nu^0}$
Photon	0	γ (photon its own antiparticle)

and the study of tracks made by charged particles in emulsions, Wilson cloud chambers and bubble chambers, the list of particles and antiparticles began to grow, first with *lambda* and *K* particles, and then with other "strange" particles that required theories hitherto undreamed of to account for them; for example, the law of the conservation of strangeness. There are many unanswered questions. It has been well said that "it is likely to be quite a while before the particle physicist finds himself out of a job." Of course there continues to be conjecture concerning the existence somewhere in the universe under stabilized conditions of "inverted" atoms, or antimatter, in which antiprotons and antineutrons and associated antiparticles constitute negatively charged nuclei surrounded by positrons in outer shells.

In the foregoing list, using the convention of Gell-Mann and Rosenbaum (*Scientific American*, July, 1957), the symbols are listed in three groups, and a bar over a symbol stands for the antiparticle.

In April, 1961, new information on the

relationships of protons, neutrons, and mesons in atomic nuclei was presented to the American Physical Society by Hofstadter, de Vries and Herman of Stanford University. The only difference between protons and neutrons is isotopic spin, which can be compared with varying orientations of one magnet in another magnetic field. Each particle has a dense meson core surrounded by two "Yukawa clouds" of mesons. In each particle these clouds match those of the other in size and amount of charge. But the neutron's inner cloud is negative and is a perfect mirror image of the proton's inner positive cloud. Thus, the neutron's positive core charge added to its positive outer cloud exactly equals the negative charge of its inner cloud. Previously the nearly equal magnetic size could not be reconciled with the apparent difference in charge size, with consequent doubt of the validity of the quantum electrodynamics theory.

G. L. CLARK

Cross-references: *Electrons, Ions, Neutrinos, Nucleonics, Positrons, Radiation*

APPLE TUBE: see TELEVISION (COLOR)

APPLEGATE DIAGRAM

Applegate diagram (velocity diagram) is a distance-time diagram useful in the graphical representation of electron-density and velocity modulation in certain microwave tubes.

In a simple case, electrons are assumed to leave a plane at the center of an input structure at equally spaced intervals of time. The velocities of individual electrons are assumed to be a function of the time of departure. Since the slope of a line on a distance-time diagram is a measure of velocity, a series of lines may be drawn starting from points equally spaced along the time axis with slopes corresponding to the individual velocities of the various electrons.

If it is assumed that mutual repulsion

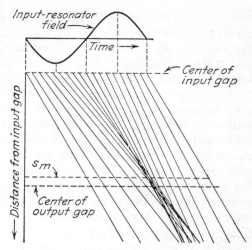

FIG. 1. Velocity diagram.

among electrons is not an important factor and that the electrons drift in a field-free region, each electron retains its original velocity and the diagram is composed of a series of straight lines with various slopes. In general, the lines on the diagram intersect and the intersection of several lines in a small region of the diagram is interpreted as an indication of a concentration of electrons at the time and at the distance from the input structure indicated by the scales on the axes. The Applegate diagram described in the foregoing discussion is an important factor in the theory of operation of two-cavity klystrons.

In reflex klystrons, the electrons drift in a region of direct electric field that reverses the direction of motion, instead of in a field-free region. The lines of the Applegate diagram are then approximated by sections of a parabola instead of by straight lines. The density of lines along a time axis on the complete diagram indicates the degree of density modulation or bunching of electrons.

Use of the Applegate diagram may be extended to include other types of microwave tubes.

J. G. SKALNIK

Cross-references: *Bunching, Klystrons, Velocity Modulation*

ARCS: see ELECTRIC DISCHARGE

ARMSTRONG, EDWIN HOWARD (1890–1954)

Armstrong was born on December 18, 1890 in New York. Following an early intense interest in mechanical toys, primarily trains, Armstrong read *The Boy's Book of Inventions* and *Stories of Inventors* at the age of fourteen, and decided to become an inventor. Using hand-wound spark coils, homemade interrupters, and iron-filled coherers, he started listening to wireless broadcasts while in his teens. He delivered his first technical paper, "Theory of tuned circuits," to the Radio Club of America in May, 1913, and graduated from Columbia University that June with a Bachelor's degree in Electrical Engineering. Even before graduation he had invented a regenerative amplifier circuit using the audion (triode) tube. In 1913 he also realized that the howling noise which sometimes resulted from the regenerative circuit was an rf oscillation, and he filed for a patent on this feedback oscillator circuit.

During World War I he served in Paris as a U. S. Army Signal Corps officer. Besides carrying on his regular duties, he invented and constructed the first superheterodyne receiver while in Paris during the war. This circuit is so basic that it is used in almost every AM radio receiver sold today; in 1918, it was a tremendous step forward, providing much more gain and stability than was previously possible. Armstrong carried on further research on this circuit when he returned to Columbia and a patent was issued to him in 1920 for the superheterodyne circuit, about $1\frac{1}{2}$ years after the application was filed from Paris. While setting up a regenerative circuit for a courtroom demonstration in 1921, he observed a new mode of detection, and following careful experimental investigation, filed a patent application for the superregenerative detector circuit, which was granted in 1922.

Much of his time during the 1920's and later years of his life was spent fighting encroachments on his patents. If this time could have been devoted to research and invention, his technical productivity might have been much higher. Even so, he invented some of the most important circuits of radio, and discovered some of the most important phenomena, such as regeneration, the superheterodyne, and the superregenerative detector. During the midst of his legal battles, from 1928 to 1933, he carried out with little assistance perhaps his finest invention, the development of a wideband frequency-modulation (FM) system, proving that contrary to widespread opinion, wideband FM was essentially free from static and distortion, and far superior as a system of radio broadcasting to AM. On December 26, 1933, four U. S. patents were issued to him on a FM signaling system. As a newly appointed Professor of Electrical Engineering at Columbia University, he announced this invention to the world in characteristic manner, by reading a paper entitled "A method of reducing disturbances in radio signaling by a system of frequency modulation" before the Institute of Radio Engineers in November 1935 and surprising his audience with a demonstration broadcast from an experimental station he had built with the help of a friend. The carrier frequency of 110 Mc was much higher than was considered usable, and the fidelity produced by Armstrong's FM system clearly was far superior to any AM system then in use. However, industry had invested heavily in AM, and much of the rest of Armstrong's life was spent trying to get FM used as the prime radio broadcast system. He refined the system, set up experimental stations, spoke extensively, and spent much of his self-made fortune in this cause, but to little avail.

During World War II, he developed FM mobile units for military communications, demonstrated that long-distance FM communication is possible (by what is now called scatter propagation), and worked extensively on long-range continuous-wave FM radar.

Bedeviled by never-ending patent litigation, he committed suicide in New York on January 31, 1954. Among other honors, he was awarded the first Medal of Honor by the Institute of Radio Engineers in 1918, for his work on regeneration; he received the Franklin Medal in 1941 and the U. S. Medal of Merit at the end of World War II; and he is one of twenty world scientists honored in the Pantheon of the Union Internationale des Télécommunications in Geneva.

T. E. EVERHART

Cross-references: *Historical Background of Electronics*

ARTIFICIAL LINES: see DELAY LINES

ATMOSPHERE: see PROPAGATION

ATMOSPHERICS: see INTERFERENCE; RADIATION (TERRESTRIAL)

ATOMIC CLOCKS

Atomic clocks make use of a property that is generally found only in systems of atomic dimensions: such systems cannot contain arbitrary amounts of energy, but are restricted to an array of allowed energy values E_0, E_1, $\cdots$, E_n. If an atomic system wants to change its energy between two allowed values, it must emit (or absorb) the energy difference, for instance by emission (or absorption) of a quantum of electromagnetic radiation. The frequency f_{ij} of this radiation is determined by the famous relation

$$| E_i - E_j | = \Delta E = h\, f_{ij}$$

(h is Planck's constant). The rate of an atomic clock is controlled by the frequency f_{ij} associated with the transition from the state of energy E_i to the state of energy E_j of a specified atomic system (such as a cesium atom or an ammonia molecule). A high-frequency electromagnetic signal is stabilized to the atomic frequency f_{ij} and a frequency converter relates the frequency f_{ij} to a set of lower frequencies which then may be used to run a conventional electric clock.

The atomic frequency f_{ij} is, according to present knowledge, free of inherent errors; it is in particular not subject to "aging" since any transition which the system makes puts it in a state of completely different energy, where it cannot falsify the measurement. Herein lies the principal advantage over other methods of time measurement. Two atomic clocks have exactly the same calibration as long as they are calibrated against the same atomic transition. Atomic time readings made in Washington, D.C. and Neuchatel, Switzerland between 1957 and 1959 differed by less than 10 msec, whereas the deviation of the astronomically measured time TU_2 from atomic time fluctuated by over 50 msec during the same period. It is to be expected that the unit of time, which is at present based on the orbital motion of the earth, will eventually be defined by an atomic frequency.

The accuracy with which f_{ij} can be measured depends mainly on the degree to which the atomic resonator can be isolated from outside influences such as chemical and electromagnetic forces, and the extent to which Doppler shift can be avoided. Atomic transitions are chosen which have a minimum dependence on electromagnetic fields, and such fields as the magnetic field of the earth are carefully shielded out. Residual fields are nevertheless at present a major source of error in the most accurate clocks. In many of the currently available clocks the atomic systems are moving through vacuum with velocities of the order of 10^4 cm/sec. This motion introduces longitudinal Doppler shifts of the order $\sim 10^{-6}\, f_{ij}$. The transversal velocity causes only second-order shifts of the order $10^{-12}\, f_{ij}$. The transitions have to be observed mostly in the transverse direction, and residual longitudinal components must occur with either sign with equal probability, so as to produce, instead of a shift, only a broadening that is symmetrical about f_{ij}. Whenever the systems collide with each other or are in contact with surrounding material, such as a buffer gas, they are perturbed by chemical forces and f_{ij} undergoes further shifts. Another source of error is the fact that most systems are observed only during a finite time τ. This circumstance gives rise to observation-time broadening of the order $1/\tau$, (typically, 10^2 cps). The error introduced hereby is not given by the broadening δf, but only by $\delta f/r$, where r is the signal-to-noise ratio with which f_{ij} is observed. However, if the phase shift of the observing system varies appreciably over the line width δf, additional errors known as "pulling" are introduced.

Two main problems have to be solved in atomic clocks: the atomic system has to be suspended without perturbation from chemical forces, and the frequency f_{ij} has to be measured. The most radical solution of the first problem is found in molecular-beam devices. The atomic systems are observed in free flight, and only during the relatively short transit time, so that observation-time broadening and Doppler shifts are large. Such devices have nevertheless provided the clocks with the highest accuracy so far, of the order of a few parts in 10^{11}. The problems associated with Doppler shift and observation-time broadening can be alleviated by enclosing the atomic system in a box that is small compared to the wavelength $\lambda = c/f_{ij}$. The problem is to find atomic systems and wall materials such that the radiative process is not interrupted, and the frequency f_{ij} not appreciably influenced, during collision of the atomic systems with the walls. Instead of walls, a buffer gas can also serve as a "container" for the atomic systems. Very long observation times, giving rise to resonances of very high Q, have been produced by this technique. The accuracy of such clocks depends on the degree to which the influence of chemical forces can be neutralized. An indication of the accuracy of which such devices may ultimately be capable can be found in the fact that the measurement of resonance radiation due to Fe^{57} nuclei built into a crystal lattice has made possible frequency determinations with a relative accuracy of some parts in 10^{14}, and effects on time due to general

relativity have been measured by this method. However, very high frequencies ($\sim 10^{20}$ cps) were involved, and no clock has been built for lack of a suitable frequency converter.

The main methods of measuring f_{ij} are the following: In thermal equilibrium, the atomic systems in the lower energy state outnumber the ones in the higher energy state, and radiation of frequency f_{ij} induces more absorption than emission, giving rise to a net absorption signal. Several methods are known by which the population of either energy state is enhanced, giving rise to stronger absorption or emission signals. Particularly elegant is the maser principle. The higher energy state population is sufficiently enhanced so that the emitted radiation itself can sustain the emission process. Often it is preferable to observe the absorption or emission of radiation of frequency f_{ij} indirectly. It is possible to observe microwave absorption via the change in the interaction of the absorbing atomic systems with optical radiation. Another example of indirect absorption is given by the atomic-beam method, where the microwave absorption is monitored by the deflection of the atoms from their trajectory. Indirect observation can be more economical since each microwave transition can be counted, whereas it takes several transitions to make a count by direct observation as long as the quanta to be counted carry less energy than the quanta of thermal radiation.

Detailed descriptions of atomic clocks can be found in the literature. Cesium atomic beams and ammonia masers have controlled the systems of hitherto highest accuracy. An atomic hydrogen maser working between nuclear hyperfine levels may also permit the building of extremely accurate clocks. Hyperfine and optical resonance in alkali metal vapors have been used in the gas-cell-controlled clocks, which may be particularly suited for mobile applications.

MARTIN PETER

Cross-references: *Frequency Standards, Laser, Masers, Molecular-Beam Devices, Radiation, Relativity*

ATOMS

The word "atom" is used universally in chemistry and physics to denote the smallest particle of an element that can exist either alone or in combination with other atoms of the same or of other elements. Breaking up an atom of an element would give us something without the properties of the given element. The size of an atom is about 2 or 3×10^{-10} m. Atoms are the building blocks from which molecules are constructed and they are the particles that occupy regularly spaced positions in the lattices of crystals. The mass of the lightest atom, the hydrogen atom, is 1.67×10^{-27} kg, about 1840 times the mass of an electron.

Historical Development. The name "atom" was derived from the Greek word "atomos" which means uncut or indivisible; the Greek philosopher, Democritus, was the first to propose the existence of such elementary particles. The idea was revived late in the nineteenth century in an effort to explain experimental results. Dalton's law of partial pressures showed that in any mixture of gases or of vapors or of both, each constituent exerted its pressure as though the other constituents were not present. Other studies, such as the development of the kinetic theory of gases and measurements on the combining weights of elements, brought out a more complete atomic theory. In many experiments atoms behaved as though they were tiny solid spheres, in accordance with the ideas of Democritus. However, later developments indicated that the atom was anything but solid and indivisible and that a wave motion was associated with it. These results showed that the atom was far more complex than a simple solid particle.

Many important discoveries in the last half of the nineteenth century had a direct bearing on beliefs about the structure of matter. Studies of electrical discharges through gases and in particular of cathode rays led to the discovery of electrons, and J. J. Thomson (*q.v.*) and others showed that electrons are constituents of atoms. Later, Rutherford carried out elaborate experiments on the scattering of radioactive emanations as these particles passed through metal foils. The results convinced him that the positive charges in matter were concentrated in very tiny regions whose size was about 10^{-14} m. This positively charged core or nucleus was surrounded by an equal amount of negative charge.

The Orbital Model. Einstein invoked the idea of light quanta. This theory proposed that the emission of light energy occurred in certain discrete amounts called quanta or in even multiples of these amounts, but not in other amounts. Bohr tied this concept to processes in individual atoms by developing his orbital model of the atom. He postulated that the negative charge in the atom was carried by electrons which rotated in stable orbits around the positive core or nucleus of the atom. His hypothesis for the hydrogen atom was that there was one stable orbit for the single electron which rotated about the nucleus of this atom. The angular momentum of the electron in this orbit was assumed to have a value equal to $h/2\pi$ where h was the universal constant known as Planck's constant. Bohr also assumed the existence of other orbits in each of which the angular momentum was an integral multiple of $h/2\pi$. If the electron should get out into one of these orbits the atom was in an excited state which was not a stable configuration. All other orbits were considered to be impossible arrangements.

This meant that the atom could exist (at least temporarily) in states in which it had certain definite amounts of energy, but states corresponding to electrons in other orbits or other amounts of energy were ruled out. Hydrogen atoms which were not combined into molecules were found in electrical discharges, and in the discharges the excited states corresponding to electrons in other than stable orbits also appeared. When an electron dropped from one orbit to one in which it was closer to the nucleus, energy was emitted and the atom lost this same amount of energy. Since only certain orbits were considered possible, only certain definite amounts of energy were emitted and these amounts corresponded to Einstein's "packets of energy." Also, energy could be absorbed by the atom in amounts equal to the amounts needed to move the electron out to specific orbits.

Atoms of elements other than hydrogen have more than one electron; these electrons are found in specific orbits when the atoms are in their normal states. Each element is characterized by the number of electrons which makes up its normal complement. This number is also equal to the amount of positive charge contained in the nucleus when that amount is expressed in multiples of the charge on one proton. These numbers, which are called atomic numbers, range up to 103, which corresponds to a recently discovered element for which the name lawrencium has been proposed. For each kind of atom there are certain stable orbits and others which correspond to excited states of the atom. If an atom has either more or less than its normal complement of electrons in orbits around it, the atom is said to be ionized.

Extensions of Bohr's model were proposed that used elliptical orbits or shells of negative electricity to account for the results of some precise experiments. None of these have been entirely successful and Bohr's theory is not considered to be a complete picture of the atom. Nonetheless, the model has retained its usefulness because it provided a picture of the atom which could be visualized and the model is frequently used to describe the conclusions reached by theoretical calculations based on much more complicated models of the atom.

Atomic Weights. The masses of atoms are often expressed as "atomic weights." The atomic weight of an atom is the average mass of the atoms making up a sample of the element when these masses are expressed on a proportional scale on which the average mass of the atoms of a sample of ordinary oxygen is taken as exactly 16. On such a scale, hydrogen has an atomic weight of 1.008. In this scale, the whole number or in-teger nearest to the mass of a particular atom is called the mass number of that atom.

Classification of Elements. Since all the atoms of any one element have the same amount of positive charge on each of their nuclei and this amount is different from the amount on the nuclei of any other element, the elements can be arranged in order of increasing positive charge. When this is done, it is found that these amounts are all even multiples of the charge of the first element on the list—hydrogen. Each element is assigned an atomic number which denotes its position on this list. This number also indicates the number of electrons in the orbits about the nucleus. The arrangement of the electrons, particularly the number of electrons, in the outermost orbit that is occupied, determines the way in which the atom will combine with other atoms to form molecules. In an attempt to classify elements, Mendeléeff found that they could be placed in groups such that those in any one group had similar chemical and physical properties and that various properties showed a continuing trend throughout the group. Names of the elements can be arranged in rows with atomic number increasing from left to right, starting a new row whenever an element is reached which is similar to hydrogen in its chemical properties. This results in a periodic chart of the elements similar to the one proposed by Mendeléeff. Elements in any one column are similar in their chemical properties. These characteristics are determined mainly by the number of electrons in the outermost orbit that is occupied.

Electron Distribution. The electrons in any atom fall into groups or classes in accordance with the amount of energy needed to remove them from the atom; these groups are called the K shell, the L shell, the M shell, etc. Experiments with x-ray photons are used to determine the energies necessary to remove electrons. For each kind of atom the electrons that are hardest to remove are the K electrons, those in the next group are L electrons, etc. The maximum number of electrons in each shell is 2 for the K shell,

8 for the L shell, 18 for the M shell, and 32 for the N shell.

If we start with the lighest atom, the hydrogen atom, and consider each element in turn throughout the periodic table, we find that more and more orbits are occupied. The second element, helium, has two electrons for each atom, which fill the K shell. The next atoms have some electrons in the L shell. It is not always found that any given shell is filled before the next shell receives any electrons. Sometimes a shell is partially filled to a convenient semi-complete stopping place with 8 or 18 electrons in the outermost occupied orbit. Then in the following elements some electrons are placed in the next orbit before any more are placed in the semi-complete orbit. Later, this orbit is filled in. When the outermost orbit which is occupied is full, the atom is inert. There are also inert atoms when the M shell reaches its semi-complete point with 8 electrons and when the N shell has 18 electrons.

The atoms of elements just beyond the inert ones have one and only one electron in the outermost shell that is occupied. This last electron revolves in a field similar to that of the one electron of the hydrogen atom, so that these elements have spectra that are similar to that of hydrogen, and these atoms all have similar chemical properties. Throughout the Periodic Table there are correlations between the chemical properties and the number of atoms in the outer orbit.

One might expect that the atoms which have several occupied shells would be considerably larger than those which have fewer occupied shells. However, the larger attractive forces, which the more strongly charged nuclei of these heavier atoms exert on the electrons, result in the stable orbits being drawn inward so that there is only a comparatively slight variation in size among all the known atoms.

The Nucleus. The nucleus or core of the atom contains all the positive charge associated with that particle. For a long time it was believed that nuclei consisted of protons and electrons. This gave way to the belief that nuclei consisted of protons and neutrons. Elements differ from each other in the number of protons in their nuclei. The lightest element, hydrogen, has only one proton in each nucleus. The next element in the Periodic Table, helium, has two, and so on throughout the table. In addition to the protons present all atoms, except some of those of the very lightest elements, contain one or more neutral particles or neutrons. A neutron has almost exactly the same mass as the proton but differs in that it is uncharged.

It is possible for two atoms to contain the same number of protons in their nuclei and thus be atoms of the same element, but to have different numbers of neutrons and thus have different atomic masses. Such atoms are called *isotopes* (*q. v.*). Some elements are known to exist in as many as seven or eight isotopic forms. The mass number of an atom of a particular isotope can be obtained by adding the number of neutrons in its nucleus to the number of protons in that same nucleus. Different isotopes of an element may differ widely in the stability of their nuclei.

The way in which the components of a nucleus (the nucleons) are arranged is at the present time the object of much study. One hypothesis is that these particles are in much the same form as they are when existing separately but are closely packed together in the atom. Another theory states that they exist more in the form of shells one inside the other. The nucleus is held together by forces which are extremely great when the separations are very small, but which fall off very rapidly as the distances between particles increase. The Japanese scientist, Yukawa, developed a mathematical meson theory that deals with these forces.

The nuclei of all the very heavy elements are unstable in varying degrees and decay spontaneously with the emission of radiations. This process, called *radioactivity* (*q. v.*), was first discovered by Becquerel; it transforms an atom of one element into an atom of another element, the disintegrations following statistical laws. Some isotopes decay so slowly that it takes thousands of years for one-half of the atoms of a given sample to decay and another equal period of time for one-half of the remainder to disintegrate. Others decay so rapidly that one-half of the atoms in a given sample will decay in a tiny fraction of a second. Some isotopes of the lighter elements are also radioactive. The half life for radioactive decay is the length of time it takes for one-half of the atoms in a given sample to decay. At least one radioactive isotope of every element has been found to occur naturally or has been prepared artificially.

Theoretical Interpretation of the Atom. Powerful mathematical methods give quantitative treatments of atomic and subatomic processes. These theories are called quantum mechanics or wave mechanics and are primarily the results of investigations by Heisenberg, Dirac, and Schrödinger. The background for these theories comes from Louis de Broglie's realization that the circumference of the circular orbit of Bohr's atom model for hydrogen in the normal state is equal to the wavelength of the waves that can be associated with the moving electrons. This relationship leads to the idea that in the atom a standing wave is associated with the electron as it moves in its orbit. Erwin Schrödinger proposed that this wavelength be substituted in a classical wave equation and from this beginning he derived a wave equation for the hydrogen atom. This pictures the negative charge of the electrons as a standing wave about the nucleus. The square of the amplitude of the wave represents the probability that the electron can be found at that point.

For other atoms wave mechanics indicates a method for finding the energy values and the electron distributions for stationary states of the atoms. The mathematical difficulties, where many particles are involved, are stupendous, but successes are being achieved. This development is generally

known as the modern orbital theory of atomic structure.

Atomic Energy. Much is being written at the present time about atomic energy, using the expression to refer specifically to the energy obtained from certain changes in nuclear structure. The foundation of this idea of obtaining energy in usable form from atoms can be traced to Albert Einstein who showed that matter seemed to be a form of energy and that it could be changed to other forms of energy. The amount of energy obtained is given by the equation $E = mc^2$. At present only a small fraction of the mass of any given sample can be converted, but this fraction still yields a vast quantity of energy.

Considering two atoms of deuterium, the heavy-hydrogen isotope, each nucleus contains one proton and one neutron. At high temperatures and high pressures these particles combine into one nucleus. This new nucleus has two protons and two neutrons. Thus, it is an atom of helium. However, if we add up the masses of the starting atoms very carefully and compare the sum with that of the helium nucleus, we find that a small amount of mass is missing. It has been converted into other forms of energy. The loss of mass is often referred to as "mass defect."

Considering any other combinations of very light nuclei which result in heavier nuclei, we find that some mass is lost in the process of *fusion* (q. v.). This mass appears as some other type of energy. On the other hand, if we consider the heaviest atoms in the Periodic Table, we find that they can be broken into two nearly equal parts plus some very light particles. The sum of all the masses of the resulting particles is less than that of the original materials. This process is called *fission* (q. v.), and again we have the conversion of mass into other forms of energy.

Chain reactions occur when some of the particles produced in the fission process are ones that are capable of breaking other atoms, and the geometry of the arrangement is such that there is a great enough chance of their breaking other atoms before they are absorbed by competing processes, or are lost oustide of the mass of fissionable material, or are slowed down to the point where they can no longer trigger the fission process.

Atoms should be thought of as entities that are very small but nonetheless so complex that they stagger the imagination and offer rich fields for further research and speculation.

ROBERT M. BESANCON

Cross-references: *Chemical Elements, Electrons, Molecules, Nucleonics, Protons, Radiation*

ATR TUBES: see TR AND ATR TUBES

ATTENUATORS AND ISOLATORS

Attenuators are lossy networks used to reduce voltage, current, or power in controllable and known amounts; they are required in electronic measurements and systems to obtain desired electrical levels for measurement or proper system operation. Attenuators are reciprocal in operation and effect the same reduction in the reverse as occurs in the forward direction. Another related device is the *isolator*, which has low loss in the forward direction and high loss in the reverse direction. Attenuators can be fixed in value, or variable by continuous control or switched steps. The performance of the various forms of attenuators affect their use depending on the frequency range, power level, and accuracy required.

Attenuators

At dc and the lower frequencies, attenuators can be constructed with lumped resistive elements. Unbalanced circuit configurations can be of the T, π, bridged-T, or L forms. Balanced-circuit configurations can be of the same form as above, as well as the lattice form. Source and load impedances are specified to determine the actual attenuation. At low frequencies wire-wound resistors (*q.v.*) are used for high precision. At higher frequencies composition or film-type resistors are used with less precision.

Recent advances in the construction of film resistors allow considerably higher accuracy and use of attenuators at higher frequency with this element. Attenuators using the T or π network with film resistors are constructed in coaxial form for use up to 10 kMc.

A type of attenuator that has found wide use to provide accurate high attenuation is the waveguide (*q.v.*) below cutoff. In this attenuator the attenuation in nepers per unit length is given by

$$(2\pi/\lambda_c)\sqrt{1 - (\lambda_c/\lambda)^2}$$

This type of attenuator relates electrical attenuation to the physical distance between the input and output coupling devices. The absolute attenuation includes the input and output coupler losses, which are not usually known with precision; however, relative attenuation of different attenuator lengths can be determined by precise distance measurement. This type of attenuator is widely used in signal generators.

The most common type of waveguide attenuator uses a resistive film parallel to the electric field. Attenuation is varied by changing the area of the inserted film or moving the position in the waveguide from a region of low to high relative electric-field strength. A precision waveguide attenuator that relates absolute attenuation to another physical parameter is the rotary attenuator. A common form has rectangular waveguide ports at either end, with transition to circular waveguide and a rotating center section with planar resistance film passing through the axis of the circular center section. The attenuation is controlled by the angle θ between the planar resistance in the rotating cylindrical center section and the H plane of the rectangular waveguide. The transmitted amplitude is proportional to $\cos^2 \theta$.

In addition to variable attenuators requiring mechanical control by shaft rotation or linear displacement, others are used that have electrical or magnetic control. Some of these controllable elements or media are: thermistors (*q.v.*), gaseous discharges, ferrites (*q.v.*), and semiconductor and vacuum devices.

Isolators

The most common form of the isolator is the ferrite type. However, considerable progress is being currently made on other forms of unilateral passive devices. The required nonreciprocal coupling usually arises through a kinetic-energy term containing the product of one variable and the time derivative of another. The performance of an isolator is given by the forward and reverse losses and the isolation that is the difference between these losses in decibels.

One type of isolator uses the Hall effect (q.v.) in a semiconductor plate immersed in a magnetic field. This is a major-carrier phenomenon, so that operation over an extremely wide frequency range can be achieved. The only intrinsic frequency limitation on the physical process is the material's dielectric relaxation time, which extends to the infrared range. In passive Hall-effect isolators, resistance elements are also used that cause a minimum forward loss of 6 db. The semiconductor material must have a high carrier mobility (a low energy gap), which results in very high and temperature-dependent conductivity. Practical units with thin and fragile elements have impedance levels of the order of 1 ohm at room temperature. In cooled units with doping to reduce the conductivity, plates of InSb have been fabricated with impedance levels as high as 25 ohms.

Another type of isolator uses a magnetostrictive element mechanically coupled to an electrostrictive element. Current models of this type of isolator are limited in use to the video frequency range and below. Progress in solid-material synthesis will determine the performance of this device.

In many current electronic applications the unilateral property is required. Frequently where passive isolators are not available, active devices are used to construct a unilateral network.

P. D. LACY

Cross-references: *Circulators, Ferrites, Microwave Measurements, Resistors, Semiconductors, Waveguides and Waveguide Components*

AUDIO ENGINEERING: see ELECTROACOUSTICS

AUDIO RECORDING: see SOUND RECORDING

AURORA: see PROPAGATION

AUTOMATIC PILOT

An automatic pilot (autopilot) is a control system that aids or replaces a human pilot in the control of an aircraft, guided missile, or space vehicle. Often called an Automatic Flight Control System (AFCS) it maneuvers and stabilizes the vehicle in accordance with input commands from other systems.

The commands to an autopilot come from many sources. Systems in commercial and military transports commonly receive inputs from the human pilot, the Instrument Landing System, and other types of navigation systems. Bomber and fighter systems must also accept control signals from bombing and fire-control systems. Drones and guided missiles generally require acceptance of signals from ground radio command links, inertial navigation systems, and homing or tracking systems.

The applications of automatic pilots are extremely varied. Most high-performance aircraft require stability augmentation even during manually controlled flight. Here automatic controls add to human-pilot stick maneuvers to offset a tendency of the aircraft to have lightly damped oscillations. Autopilots provide the increased precision demanded by many navigation systems. At the same time, they increase safety by reducing the pilot's fatigue and routine duties. Maneuvering close to the aerodynamic and structural capabilities of the aircraft is accomplished accurately with an automatic pilot.

Automatic pilots date back to before World War I: one type of control was conceived in 1912. By 1933 many types were being introduced and during World War II this device became an important part of every bomber's equipment because it aided accurate bombing. In the age of guided missiles, space travel, and remotely controlled flight, the automatic pilot often replaces the human pilot in all phases of flight.

The automatic pilot manipulates the aircraft controls in response to instrumentation that determines deviations from a prescribed maneuver. The autopilot and aircraft combine to form a multiloop servomechanism.

The components of an automatic pilot can be classified into four functional groups. First, there are the primary data-sensing elements such as directional and vertical gyros, air-pressure sensors for altitude and airspeed control, and radio receivers for navigation. These units measure what the aircraft is doing and convert this measurement into a usable signal. Second, there are the amplifiers and control circuits where the measurement of what the airplane is doing is compared with what it should be doing. The error or difference signal is then modified and amplified to make it suitable to control the servos. The third functional group are the servos that operate the airplane controls for maneuvers. Servo systems receive signals from the amplifiers and control circuits and further increase the power level to operate electric or hydraulic servo-

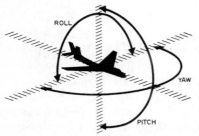

FIG. 1. Aircraft attitudes are defined by these three euler angles: yaw, pitch, and roll.

motors. A fourth group of components is used to insert command or reference signals into the automatic pilot.

Although aircraft have at least 6 degrees of freedom (three in rotation and three in translation, as illustrated in Fig. 1), they are generally controlled by adjusting rotation or attitude. The airplane climbs when the nose pitches up. To cause this pitch up, the elevators are deflected, thereby applying a forcing moment to the airplane. To turn, the aircraft is banked. Since the aerodynamic lift force remains perpendicular to the plane of the wings, a horizontal component is developed by banking. This centripetal force causes a turn, if the rudder is used to keep the airplane heading into the wind (i.e., prevent sideslip). Heading can be maintained constant during level flight by means of the rudder, the aileron, or combined aileron-rudder action.

The operation of one autopilot control loop is illustrated by the single-axis block diagram (Fig. 2). The gyro unit develops an electrical signal proportional to the pitch attitude of the airplane. This signal is then compared with the attitude command. If the pitch angle does not equal the command signal the elevators are deflected. However, before the signal reaches the servo, it is amplified and shaped to provide system stability.

The operation of the automatic pilot is such that it always produces the correct control-surface deflection to return the aircraft to its reference position. For example, if turbulent air causes the vehicle to pitch up, the elevator is deflected downward by an amount proportional to the displacement and rate of deviation. As the airplane returns to

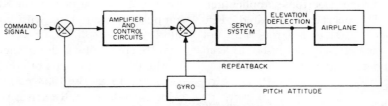

FIG. 2. Autopilot pitch axis.

its reference attitude the elevator returns to neutral.

The control of yaw and bank is similar to pitch. However, in this case coordinated control of both axes is required. The rudder is used primarily to prevent sideslip and the aileron is used to tilt the lift vector.

The analysis of autopilots by means of several separate control loops is useful as a first approximation. However, the equations of the various axes are actually interrelated so that multiloop operation must be considered. Furthermore, these loops have several interconnections with each other, resulting from aircraft dynamics and sensor configuration.

Many types of sensors are used in autopilots. Aircraft attitude is commonly measured with 2-degree-of-freedom gyroscopes. Rate gyros and accelerometers are also used. For many types of control, displacement, rate, or acceleration, sensors can be interchanged with the addition of suitable electronic shaping circuits in the system. Barometric sensors and radio altimeters (*q. v.*) are common for height measurements. Autopilots provide couplers to various radio navigation systems for lateral-position control.

Amplifiers and shaping circuits have generally been conventional. Special requirements are related to the safety and noise-free demands on the autopilot.

E. ROBERT TRIBKEN

Cross-references: *Inertial Guidance, Integrated Instrumentation, Navigation and Navigational Systems, Servo Components, Transducers*

AUTOMATIC TRANSLATION: see TRANSLATION BY MACHINE

AUTOMATION

Industrial Automation. The word automation was first used by the Ford Motor Co. in 1947 to describe transfer machining— a production technique using special-purpose, serially ganged machine tools with automatic transfer of work between them. The concept was not new, but its advent was a sign that mass markets, high wages, large capital structures, and advancing technology would make major new extensions of mechanization profitable.

During the 1950's the word automation acquired a broader meaning, primarily because the introduction of the electronic digital computer as a control device heralded changes which appeared revolutionary rather than evolutionary in nature. Throughout that decade digital applications to control were largely experimental, and the computer impact remained a conceptual one. At the same time, a general application of conventional techniques began in many industries, tending to begin first in continuous processing, next in packaging, and finally in machining, assembling, and inspection. Rapid changes were made in farming, mining, and construction machinery through the application of hydraulic controls.

The decade of the 1950's, adjusted to a standard money basis, was one of low expansion in national productivity. No substantial impact of automation was evident. With some notable exceptions, advances were conceptual, experimental, and promotional rather than economic.

Historically, the emergence of useful sources of power in the 19th century introduced a new productive unit as the basis of economic society—the man-controlled machine. Throughout previous history, the man working with tools had supplied both control and power.

One man and machine could only effect large changes in the local economy of those products requiring a single major operation: flour or lumber, for example. More elaborate products, made for markets continually expanded by transportation and increasing population, required first the use of a set of machines coordinated as a shop, next a set of shops integrated into a factory, and finally a set of factories into an industry. All industrialized nations now are uniting a set of basic industries into some form of unified economy.

The need for men to control individual machines has long been evident. Less recognized as a control function has been the use of additional men to control *sets* of machines. With the successive formation of larger machine aggregates, the white-collar and managerial classes expanded rapidly until their number now often exceeds those directly employed. All levels of indirect control in the past have appeared distinct in nature from direct control but similar to each other. Indirect control at every level has been conducted primarily through the use of paper-borne numbers. At the shop level, control numbers tend to identify items, operations, time, and other matters directly related to operations. At successively higher levels, control numbers increasingly represent money relationships.

The advent of the electronic digital computer eliminates basic distinctions between direct and indirect labor. First, such a computer is capable of controlling the direct productive operations solely by the processing of numbers, thus identifying direct and indirect control processes as a single basic activity. Second, the computer can both process and communicate indirect number systems. It emerges as a device that has application at every level of control, and can replace managerial and clerical as well as direct labor functions.

The application of electronic digital computers to control has been handicapped by the evolution of the computer from a background in scientific computation. This handicap has resulted to date in the extensive development of a special type of computer called "general purpose" which processes numbers one at a time; i.e., it is serially organized. Control applications normally are parallel, involving the processing of a number of simultaneous modes of response. A serial computer applied to a parallel-control operation requires great speed, which in turn, tends to preclude the use of slower, low-cost memories in favor of fast but expensive memories. Such computers normally prove too expensive for decentralized control applications, i.e., direct affiliation with individual production units. Centralized computers, built to process many units from a control center require augmented speed and cost, and experience communication difficulties. Economic payoff has not been substantial. One solution under development, especially for machine tools, is to prepare recorded tapes at a central general-purpose computer, and play them back at the individual unit to produce fixed sequences of operations. Such a solution is not often flexible enough to provide the conditional sequencing required for complete automation.

A new class of parallel computers, extension of digital differential analyzers and modal computers, for example, may resolve this difficulty. By utilizing different forms of internal organization they carry out many modes of operation simultaneously, and thus are able to make use of low-cost memories without sacrifice of control capability. If sufficiently low costs and numbers of components requiring maintenance are achieved, direct computer control of unit operations will become economical.

Military Automation. It has been estimated officially that about 80 per cent of the total money spent nationally for research and development in the field of electronics is spent by governmental agencies, primarily military. Of the 20 per cent of private funds invested, about 10 per cent is spent in anticipation of government business. No discussion of present-day automation is complete that does not include military aspects.

Since World War II three major revolutions in warfare have taken place: the introduction of the A-bomb, of the H-bomb, and of the automated rocket. The long-range guided missile with thermonuclear warhead allows any site on earth to shell any other with explosives of well-known magnitude. Conventional defense has lost its ability to deflect or blunt sudden attack. Instead a deterrent defense based upon threat of punitive counter strike must be employed. A deterrent force is at great disadvantage, since the attack may be directed entirely at the counter attacking system and its communications. To mitigate this disadvantage, defense is forced to employ a much higher degree of automation than is required by the offense. As a nation committed to a defensive posture, we are in the process of evolving an automatic counterattack. The control requirements are multitudinous.

Unit weapons have been introduced which, upon launching, complete automatically all necessary modes of flight to any specified target, utilizing only initial instructions, electronically introduced. Sets of such weapons are being deployed for semiautomatic, simultaneous launching. Weapons at fixed locations increasingly are found to require count down and launching intervals less than the interval between early warning and impact for attacking units. Mobile sets of missiles require less haste in launching, but more locational and targeting automation.

The command of many sets requires the ability to change targeting patterns immediately and on a general scale based on initial damage assessments. Extensive assemblies of instruments, computers, and communications are now under development for this purpose.

Early warning and local radar tracking have become coordinated into monitored-automatic systems. Quasiautomatic processing of intelligence data is needed to furnish an integral part of a complete early warning system. Active defense, now in an experimental stage, will, if successful, require the automatic interception of ICBM's by ground-to-air missiles fully integrated into early-warning and local tracking networks.

A counterattack must have a high percentage of missiles ready at all times, although an attack need not. Automatic checkout systems have been introduced to determine the readiness of each missile unit. These systems have been extended to include preventive maintenance and trouble-shooting capabilities.

To guarantee maintainability, automatic

inventorying has been required. To reduce obsolescence, a number of computer-based planning and scheduling activities are under way in weapons system development which constitute a partially automatic procurement.

In limited warfare, one may characterize the general evolution of weapons and systems as toward an ultimately automatic battlefield.

Military automation systems have already reached a degree of such complexity, as measured by the number of electronic parts, that reliability has become the foremost electronic problem. Major developments are current to increase the reliability of parts by one to two orders of magnitude.

Space systems are beginning to pose greater problems in automation than do terrestrial missiles. The need to carry out more elaborate missions over a longer period of time under more severe environmental conditions is evident. It is probable that the major developmental area for automation during the coming decade will shift from missiles to space weapons systems.

FLOYD GEORGE STEELE

Cross-references: *Cybernetics, Digital Computers, Feedback Systems, Reliability and Quality Control, Systems*

AUTOMOBILE TRAFFIC CONTROL

The present use of electronics in traffic control is almost entirely confined to devices to operate traffic lights or otherwise affect the traffic in some manner, but with considerable time between the measurement and the result. Most systems depend upon detection of vehicles by means of detectors, the main types being doppler radar, ultrasonic radar, switch-actuating treadles, and induction loops buried in the pavement. Currently, the principal use of the detectors is to operate local traffic light controllers; however, there is an increasing use of systems which use many detectors spread over a rather large region (such as many city blocks) and feed the information from all the detectors into a computer. This computer decides and puts into operation the best pattern of traffic lights in order to expedite the flow of traffic in the region involved.

Since the solution to almost any traffic problem starts with the question, "where are the vehicles?," vehicle detectors are usually the basic element in any system. A recent type of induction detector that can be installed entirely below the pavement and is a relatively simple circuit, may find use in systems requiring detection of all vehicles on a road. Such systems would transmit information to individual vehicles by means of one or more methods such as light signals in or alongside the road or by means of antennas buried in the road, so that more precise information could be transmitted to vehicles equipped with suitable receivers.

At present, direct vision is used to indicate a dangerously high closing speed. There is a proposal for alleviating the dangers of rear-end collisions on highways under conditions of poor visibility such as fog. This proposal starts with a series of vehicle detectors in the road so as to detect all vehicles in that lane. Then each detector when activated, initiates a tail of lights back along the road either in the roadbed or alongside. This tail can be made to extend back as far as needed to warn another vehicle in time to make a safe stop; also, the tail can be color-coded such as the first third red, middle third amber, final third green. Thus, a following vehicle need not follow a whole tail length behind, but can follow at the junction of the red and amber lights and will still be warned whenever the lead vehicle changes speed, even though fog may obscure it. In case there is no leading vehicle, the same detector can cause a light to come on in advance of a vehicle to facilitate steering.

Another proposal for use of electronics is to use the vehicle detectors to activate light signals in the opposite lane, around a curve, or over the crest of a hill where there is a restriction in sight distance that would normally prevent the safe passing of a slower vehicle. The lights would permit the driver of a vehicle to pass another vehicle even though there was not sufficient sight distance, if the lane were actually clear on the other side of a hill or around a curve. In many sections of the country where traffic volume only justifies a two-lane road, but many hills and curves prevent safe passing for miles, such an electronic system could add much to safety and convenience.

Ultimately, the same vehicle detectors can operate circuits that radiate signals to vehicles equipped with suitable receivers. Methods are already in the experimental stage in which the road transmits information giving the distance of any vehicle less than a certain distance in front, and (if the vehicle is within this range) also gives the speed of that vehicle. On vehicles equipped with a suitable receiver the speed and distance signals from a leading vehicle can be used to compute whenever a dangerous condition of closing speed and distance is approaching and audible warning given the driver or even automatic brake operation instituted. Experiments to do the same thing have also been conducted using radar on the vehicle to measure the speed and distance of a leading vehicle. Also, the road can transmit voice signals with information on approaching intersections, road conditions, etc., so that the driver need not try to watch traffic and read signs at the same time.

With the need of direct vision so reduced, it becomes profitable to make the steering automatic and demonstrations have been made of standard-size automobiles moving at highway speed steered automatically by means of a signal from a wire buried in the center of the highway lane. Thus, the information needed for completely automatic control is available and not a few observers believe that ultimately much of the driving will be automatic, at least for turnpike operation. An experimental system has been demonstrated that shows the basic practicality of completely automatic control where the vehicle automatically controls steering, speed, and brakes in response to signals from the road.

G. W. GRAY

Cross-references: *Farming (Electronic), Mobile (Vehicular) Communications, Radar*

AUTOTRANSFORMERS (VARIABLE)

The variable autotransformer is an ac control. The transformation ratio is varied to obtain an output voltage less than, equal to, or greater than the supply voltage. Dc operation is not possible, nor can input and output circuits be isolated. In contrast to dissipative controls (rheostats, "potentiometers") of equal rating, efficiency is high and volume low. As compared with resistive or reactive controls, regulation with load change is slight.

The two general types of variable autotransformers are step-variable and continuously variable. Step-variable types are usually designed for a specific function, such as the limitation of motor-starting inrush current, where the transformation ratio is known, and where switching interruptions can be tolerated. Continuously variable types are used if a wide, uninterrupted control range is required, and are available for most common voltage, frequency, and current ratings.

Continuously variable autotransformers usually take the form of a single-layer toroidal wire winding on a doughnut-shaped "iron" core (Fig. 1). Insulation is removed from successive turns of the winding to form a brush track. A graphitic brush traverses the track to vary the transformation ratio. Brush-to-track resistance is high enough to limit short-circuit current to a safe value, as the brush moves from turn to turn; low enough to prevent excessive heating from the passage of useful current (U. S. Patent 2,009,013). The brush track is often coated to prevent deterioration from contamination and temperature effects (U. S. Patent 2,-949, 592).

Other constructions include linear windings on rectangular cores with either circular or linear brush tracks, and helical windings

FIG. 1. Cutaway view of a continuously variable autotransformer showing the core insulated from, and surrounded by, the winding. The brush, upper right, is shown resting on the brush track.

traversed spirally by metal wipers. The latter practice eliminates the brush short-circuit problem, but introduces other costly complexities that limit its use to relatively high-power applications. Still other variations are rolling brushes and multiple, non-shorting metal contacts with external current-limiting resistors.

Variable autotransformers are used to control voltage-sensitive functions. The voltage may be varied to vary the function, or, conversely, the function may be maintained by maintaining a constant voltage from a fluctuating supply. Among such voltage-controlled functions are temperature, illumination, speed, torque, electrolytic film thickness, electrodeposits, rf power and frequency, electron-beam velocity, and magnetic-field strength. Rectifiers are used with variable autotransformers where dc is required. Single and polyphase induction motors, unless especially designed for such service, cannot be controlled satisfactorily by voltage variation. Exceptions are torque motors, wound-rotor motors, and capacitor motors with fan loads.

Variable autotransformers may be ganged

on a single shaft and interconnected for the control of single-phase circuits requiring power greater than the rating of a single unit. Ganged units are also used for polyphase control, either in the open-delta or wye configurations. Series-connected gangs permit operation at voltages above unit ratings.

If input-output isolation is required, a supplementary, fixed, isolating transformer may be used. Although double-wound variable transformers are available, they suffer, in comparison with an adjustable autotransformer of like size, in efficiency and power rating.

GILBERT SMILEY

Cross-references: *Potentiometers,* *Rheostats,* *Transformers*

BACKWARD-WAVE TUBES

Backward-wave tubes are traveling-wave tubes in which the energy velocity of the beam and the energy velocity of the wave guided by the circuit are of opposite sign; this condition involves a continuous positive feedback between the beam and the circuit and consequently the possibility of oscillation. In any traveling-wave tube appreciable interaction is obtained only when equality between the phase velocities of the beam and of the circuit wave is achieved. For backward-wave tubes, this condition means that the circuit has to support a wave of negative phase velocity with respect to its own energy velocity.

The more important behavior of such tubes is the wide variation of the frequency of oscillation when the velocity of the beam is changed, in contrast to the reflex klystron or the traveling-wave tube (in which oscillations might be caused by external feedback, for instance). The frequency of a backward-wave oscillator can vary continuously in a ratio of 1:10 instead of a few per cent characteristic of other tubes. Furthermore, backward-wave tubes are much less sensitive to the load if the wave reflected at the output is absorbed at the other end of the delay line by attenuating material.

For a beam current lower than the starting current, the backward-wave tube behaves like a narrow-bandwidth amplifier, the central frequency of which is changed by the velocity of the beam.

There are two types of backward-wave tubes according to the type of beam employed: the "O" tubes, in which the beam travels near the line at constant dc potential; and the "M" tubes, in which the beam travels near the line in crossed electric and magnetic fields. The main difference lies in the type of energy exchange between the beam and the line: in O type tubes the beam velocity is slowed down by the rf field, synchronism is not insured all along the line, and the efficiency is rather small (less than 20 per cent); in M-type tubes, the velocity of the beam is constant and it may be said that the beam loses its "potential energy"; the efficiency may be as high as 70 per cent.

The backward-wave tube was proposed independently by B. Epsztein and R. Kompfner in 1951.

The Delay Lines of Backward-Wave Tubes

The possibility of negative phase velocities appears is inherent in all periodic structures, proceeding from the Fourier series analysis of the rf field, in contrast with "smooth" structures which cannot support such waves; the geometrical periodicity is called the pitch p.

The propagation of a wave along a line is defined by means of the propagation constant β, which is a function of the angular frequency ω; the group velocity v_g of the wave is equal to $d\omega/d\beta$ as is indicated on a typical characteristic of backward propagation (Fig. 1a). The ratio v_p/v_g will be used also, $v_p = \omega/\beta$ being the phase velocity.

The magnitude of the field is defined by the coupling impedance $K = EE^*(2\beta^2 P)^{-1}$; E is the backward-wave field at the origin of the coordinates used in Fig. 1 when a traveling wave of power P is flowing in the structure. The normalized coupling impedance $R = Kkl/\sqrt{\mu_0/\epsilon_0}$ will be used, l being the width of the circuit and $k = \omega/c$.

Generally the beam flows at a finite distance y from the line; the field of the line is weaker at the beam level than at the line level and correction in K must be introduced.

Figures 1b, c, and d, shows three important structures used in backward wave tubes. Simple results are given below concerning the value of β, v_p/v_g, and R, under the assumption that a wave is traveling along the wires at the velocity of light, except for

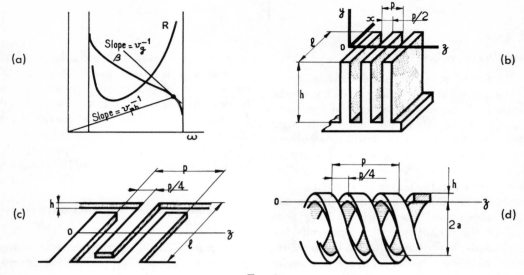

(a) (b) (c) (d)

FIG. 1

the vane line in which case the field in the vanes has to be approximately matched to the field above the vanes.

$V^{1/2}$; the frequency of oscillation, fixed by the synchronism condition, varies less rapidly than $V^{1/2}$ and a frequency range of $1:10$

	β	φ	v_p/v_g	$R(v_g/v_p)$, if ≤ 1
Interdigital line (c) or Bifilar helix (d)	$\dfrac{\varphi - 2\pi}{p}$	$2kl$ or $2\pi ka$	$\dfrac{\varphi}{\varphi - 2\pi}$	$\dfrac{\epsilon_0}{\gamma_0}\dfrac{2}{2\pi - \varphi} J_0{}^2\left(\dfrac{\varphi - 2\pi}{8}\right)$
Vane line (b)	$\dfrac{\varphi - 2\pi}{p}$	$kp\left[1 + \left(\dfrac{\tan kh}{2}\right)^2\right]^{\frac{1}{2}}$		

In these expressions J_0 is a Bessel function and γ_0 is the capacity per unit length between adjacent wires; it may be approximated by $\epsilon_0/\gamma_0 = (p/4h)[1 + (p/4h)]^{-1}$.

The interdigital line is the most commonly used of these lines because of its good heat dissipation in M- and O-type tubes. At the highest frequencies the vane type line is most suitable for O-type BWO by virtue of simplicity of machining.

O-Type Backward-Wave Oscillator (O-Carcinotron)

A tube of this type is shown in Fig. 2; the electrons, accelerated by the anode, travel in the helix at a velocity v_e proportional to

corresponds to a variation of the voltage in the ratio $1:100$, which involves a large variation of the output power. The electronic tuning band of commercially available tubes is approximately $1:2$.

A BWO oscillates only with a current higher than the so-called starting current I_{st}; this current, for a lossless structure of length L and for negligible space charge, is found to be

$$\beta L C_{st} = 2\pi(2^{-5/3}) = 1.97$$

C being the "Pierce factor,"

$$C_{st} = (KI_{st}/4V)^{1/3}$$

In conventional BWO tubes I_{st} is of the

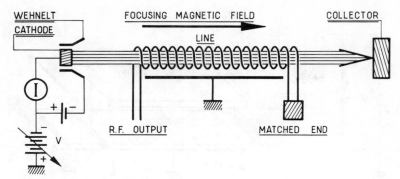

Fig. 2

order of a few milliamperes for a voltage V of a few thousand volts; the operating current may be much higher to increase the output power but it is limited by the higher-order modes of oscillation.

An approximate computation of the efficiency is based on the assumption that the maximum rf current in the beam is equal to twice the dc current. The efficiency would be $\eta_0 = 0.84C$; higher efficiencies have been measured mainly owing to space-charge effects. For very high space charge of plasma angular frequency ω_q, synchronism is achieved between the circuit wave and the slow plasma wave

$$\beta = \frac{\omega + \omega_q}{v_e}$$

This relation gives, in a simple way, the frequency "pushing," which is the variation of the frequency for a variation of the current. An increase of current increases ω_q and β, which corresponds to a decrease in the frequency: pushing is always negative.

Losses increase starting current and oscillations cannot take place for any length of circuit if the attenuation α (neper/m) is higher than $C\beta[2C/Q]^{1/2}$, where $Q = \omega_q/\omega$.

The O-type BWO is commonly used in the usual range of frequencies (0.3 to 30 kMc) as a low-power generator that does not require mechanical tuning and is relatively insensitive to load; its noise is sufficiently low for it to be used in a radar receiver. It seems to be most suitable for the millimeter and submillimeter range; the main limita-

tions arise from the thermal velocities of the electrons and from the current density at the cathode. However, oscillations of a few milliwatts have been obtained up to $\lambda = 1$ mm.

M-Type Backward-Wave Oscillator (M-Carcinotron)

A tube of this type is shown in Fig. 3; it comprises a flat delay line at ground potential and, placed in front of it, a smooth negatively biased plate called the sole; a dc magnetic field is applied perpendicularly to the plane of the paper; the current is injected by means of a "short" gun.

In the absence of rf phenomena the current would flow between the line and the sole up to the collector, the transverse escape of the electrons being avoided by the sole edges; but for $I > I_{st}$, the rf electric field drives the electrons to the line and only a small part of them reaches the collector.

We define distance $d = D[1 + (V_s/V)]^{-1}$; the ratio of the magnetic field to the critical magnetic field B_c in the space of interaction $(B/B_c)^2 = B^2\eta d^2/2V$; the normalized beam impedance $Z = V\eta Bl/Ic\sqrt{\mu_0/\epsilon_0}$; the normalized coupling impedance at the beam level $R' \simeq R \exp(-2\beta d[1 - \frac{1}{4}(B_c/B)^2])$; the circuit gain $(\gamma_c/\beta)^2 = 2(B/B_c)^2 R'/Z$; and the beam gain (diocotron effect): $\gamma_b/\beta = (B/B_c)^2/Z$.

For the M-type BWO in a high-power version the efficiency is the dominant problem; the efficiency η_0 is usually given by

$$\eta_0 = 1 - \frac{1}{4}\left(\frac{B_c}{B}\right)^2$$

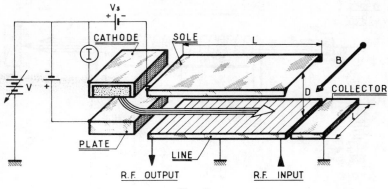

Fig. 3

taking into account the loss of kinetic energy owing only to the mean velocity of the electrons. Measured efficiencies are actually lower, for the following reasons:

(1) The starting current I_{st} is given, if the space-charge effects are neglected, by

$$(\gamma_c/\beta)(\beta L) = \pi/2,$$

L being the length of the line; and when space charge is taken into account, by $\cos([(\gamma_c/\beta)^2 - (\gamma_b/\beta)^2]^{1/2}[\beta L]) = (\gamma_b/\gamma_c)^2$, the starting current being decreased by a factor that is in practice around 3. When the current I is increased, the power increases nearly linearly and saturates when $I/I_{st} \simeq 3$; for lower currents the main part of the beam reaches the collector and the efficiency is reduced.

(2) The space-charge forces cause a rotation of the bunches, which increases the lost kinetic energy.

(3) At very low coupling impedances the beam is intercepted by the line and the sole without any useful interaction with the circuit; this phenomenon arises from the high noise observed in M-type devices. Therefore, the sole has to be negatively biased with respect to the cathode ($V_s/V \simeq 0.2$).

(4) The circuit losses and the irregularities.

At all frequencies investigated to date the interdigital line is the most commonly used structure. At the lowest frequencies R is chosen as high as possible to decrease the size of the tubes; on the other hand, at the highest frequencies the problems of heat dissipation and of cathode-current density lead to low R, high Z, and high line length in spite of the increased circuit attenuation. The following table gives some characteristic values of R, Z, and βL for three existing tubes.

Frequency (kMc)	R	Z	βd	B/B_c	βL	V (v)	I_{st} (amp)	P_{output} (w)	η (%)
0.3	0.1	17	1.8	1.4	65	11,000	1.5	25,000	60
3	0.04	35	2.4	1.3	100	5,000	0.2	1,000	40
30	0.03	35	3.5	1.1	500	2,000	0.03	20	10

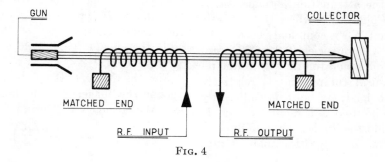

Fig. 4

The frequency of the M-type BWO varies with V, more rapidly than the O-type tube; however, the electronic tuning band is reduced to 30 or 50 per cent because of the noise that appears at the lower voltages. The pushing of this type of tube is small and positive in general. The M type BWO is mostly used in radar jamming.

Backward-Wave Amplifiers

The voltage gain of a backward-wave tube is given by $[1 - (I/I_{st})]^{-1}$. It is too critical to be of practical use. The system (proposed by Currie and Whinnery, *Proc. IRE* **43**: 1617, 1955) using two backward-wave circuits, shown in Fig. 4, gives a more stable gain in O- and M-type tubes.

J. ARNAUD

Cross-references: *Amplitron, Crossed-Field Interactions, Magnetron, Millimeter-Wave Generation, Traveling-Wave Tubes*

BAIRD, JOHN LOGIE (1888–1946)

J. L. Baird was born at Helensburgh in Dumbartonshire on August 13, 1888, the son of a minister. He attended the Royal Technical College in Glasgow and then Glasgow University, but his education was interrupted just short of graduation by World War I. Throughout his life he was plagued by ill health, which interfered with his success in various business ventures. He moved to Hastings in Sussex in 1922 and occupied himself with the development of a practical television system utilizing mechanical scanning. In 1924 in Hastings he transmitted the image of the Maltese cross over a distance of several feet, whereupon he moved his apparatus to London. On January 27, 1925 he demonstrated his system before fourteen members of the Royal Institution, with transmitter and receiver in separate rooms. Scanning was obtained by an ingenious arrangement of lensed disks, gas-filled potassium photocells, and mechanically linked receiver and transmitter motors. By using floodlights and photocells with matching spectral characteristics, he demonstrated that his system would work in the absence of all visible light, with infrared light only; he christened this system "noctovision."

In 1927 he demonstrated a transmission over several hundred miles of telephone line between London and Glasgow. In 1928 he managed to have a telecast from London picked up in New York and also by a ship in mid-Atlantic. During the following few years, he chalked up an astounding number of "firsts," including color television, daylight television, and stereoscopic television (in 1928); regular television service and a transmission of synchronizing impulses (1929); simultaneous transmission of vision and sound, and big-screen television (1930); televising of a public day-time event (the Epsom Derby) and of film (1931); and demonstration of ultra-short-wave transmission (1932).

He was unalterably committed to mechanical scanning, a system that was bound to suffer by comparison with the electronic scanners then being developed. In 1937, after running an all-electronic experimental system alongside Baird's system for two years, the B.B.C. dropped the latter altogether. He continued to work on color, stereoscopic, and big-screen television, convinced that his original idea was the only way to achieve large color displays, until he died at Bexhill in Sussex on June 14, 1946. He was a fellow of the Television Society and of the Physical Society, an honorary fellow of the Royal Society of Edinburgh, and a recipient of the gold medal of the International Faculty of Science (1937).

CHARLES SUSSKIND

Cross-references: *Historical Background of Electronics*

BALUN: see WAVEGUIDES

BANDWIDTH REDUCTION

Compression or reduction of the bandwidth required to transmit an information-bearing signal is possible only by eliminating predictable or superfluous detail in that signal. Such detail may arise from constraints in the generating mechanism, from the properties of the receiver, or from both.[1]

Speech is an example where both are important. Here the generating mechanism is the human vocal tract and vocal cords. In producing vowel sounds, the vocal tract acts as an acoustic tube of nonuniform cross-sectional area.[2] It is excited at its lower end by repetitive pulses of air from the vocal cords and it radiates sound from the lip opening. Analysis shows that below 3000 cps, the transfer response of such a tube can be characterized by three or four simple resonances or *formants*. These are the first longitudinal modes of the tube resonanting as a pipe. Therefore the complex frequency spectrum of the vowel may be written

$$p(s) = k \frac{s}{s + a} \prod_i \frac{s_i s_i^*}{(s - s_i)(s - s_i^*)} v(s) \quad (1)$$

where s is the complex frequency variable; s_i is the ith formant frequency (complex) and s^*, its complex conjugate; $p(s)$ is the complex pressure spectrum in front of the lips; $v(s)$ is the complex volume velocity spectrum at the vocal cords; and k and a are positive real constants. The factor $s/(s + a)$ accounts for the radiation characteristics of the lip opening. The frequencies of the formants are a function of the configuration of the tract which changes with the vowel sound being spoken. Though consonant sounds follow a somewhat different model, the flow of speech can nevertheless be considered a succession of such steady states occurring at a rate of about 20–40 per second.

Nominally, a 3000-cps band is required to transmit a fully intelligible speech time-waveform. One possibility for bandwidth reduction represents the waveform by a sequence of parameters specifying the value of $p(s)$ according to Eq. (1). The necessary parameters are k, the over-all speech intensity; ω_1, ω_2, and ω_3, the imaginary parts of the complex formant frequencies s_1, s_2, and

s_3; and the repetition frequency of the excitation $v(s)$. Since such sets of parameter values need follow each other at only $\frac{1}{30}$-sec intervals, the representation could be transmitted in about 150 cps bandwidth. This principle is the basis of the *resonance*, or *formant*, *vocoder* (from VOice CODER) which consists of an analyzer at the sending terminal plus a synthesizer at the receiving terminal. The analyzer determines the parameter values by analyzing the input speech. After transmission, these parameters are used in the synthesizer to regenerate the speech. The synthesizer is a resonant configuration based upon the model indicated in Eq. (1). The state of the present art does not permit an automatic, yet accurate, parametric speech analysis for both men and women by the same "formant tracker" particularly if the input speech is contaminated by noise or has been amplitude distorted. However, laboratory models have operated to the extent of transmitting highly intelligible speech over a 175-cps bandwidth.

A more modest, but also more successful approach, stems from the quasi-steady-state property of speech previously mentioned. In this view, speech is a succession of distinct spectra joined together smoothly in time. The *channel vocoder* measures input speech spectra dynamically at its analyzer-transmitter and regenerates them at the synthesizer-receiver. Here the representation is,

$$\overline{|S(j\omega_k, t)|} = \left| \frac{1}{2\pi} \int_{-\infty}^{t} S(\tau) h_k(t - \tau) e^{j\omega_k(t-\tau)} \, d\tau \right| \quad (2)$$

$$k = 1, 2, \cdots m$$

where S is the complex short-time spectrum, $S(t)$ is the speech waveform, $h_k(t)e^{j\omega_k t}$ is a filter impulse response, and the ω_k are the m frequencies at which the spectral values are specified. The short-time average value of $|S|$ is the representation used in the channel vocoder. Particular characteristics of human hearing dictate two of its features. First, since the sense is nearly phase deaf, only the magnitude of S need be considered. Second, since auditory frequency discrimination is not precise, only about 20 values of ω_k are sufficient to specify each spectrum. The channel vocoder analyzer is a spectrograph composed of a bank of contiguous bandpass filters, each followed by a rectifier and low-pass smoothing filter. The array of signals from this analyzer specifies $|\,S\,|$. The synthesizer is a similar bank of filters followed by multipliers which superimpose the measured spectral shape upon an artificial vocal cord excitation. Its repetition rate is controlled by a measured value from the transmitter. For some consonant sounds, random excitation is used. Appropriate switching between these excitation sources is controlled also from the analyzer.

Ignoring phase and restricting the number of frequency channels yields a saving of about a 4:1 in bandwidth. Time averaging by the analyzer low-pass filter yields another factor of about 3:1. Thus the total reduction is about 10:1, corresponding to a transmission band of about 300 cps. Channel vocoders have operated satisfactorily for both men and women talkers, and as of today are the best candidate for practical application.

Another speech bandwidth compression scheme is based upon a phonetic representation. The analyzer transmits a sequence of phonetic symbols which are converted by the synthesizer into speech once again. With this scheme a compression on the order of 100:1 or more is theoretically possible, but it is yet to be effectively realized even in the laboratory.

Bandwidth compression of pictorial information has made less progress than in the case of speech. A major difficulty is the specification of generator constraints. One scheme is based upon a perceptual constraint; namely, a satisfactory rendition of apparent motion induced by a sequence of rapidly projected pictures can be had by presenting them about 15 per second. Yet to prevent the presentation from flickering ob-

jectionably requires between 24 and 30 per second. Therefore, a 2:1 compression can be obtained by transmitting only 15 pictures per second, and at the receiver time-compressing them so that each can be repeated twice, giving a 30 per second presentation. However, this scheme calls for storage of an entire picture. Such storage is expensive and difficult to realize.

A second scheme takes advantage of the insensitivity of visual perception to absolute brightness level in regions of abrupt changes in brightness. In such areas, accurate rendition of brightness magnitude is superfluous, while in broad areas of slowly changing brightness even small inaccuracies give objectionable effects. Several methods for converting pictures to sequences of binary pulses for digital transmission utilize fine brightness quantization (equivalent to 1-per cent accuracy or 7 binary digits) in slowly changing areas, and coarse quantization (20-percent accuracy or about 2 or 3 binary digits) for rapidly changing details. Thereby, in comparison to a uniformly quantized picture, a 2:1 or 3:1 reduction in the number of binary pulses is achieved.

The philosophy of capitalizing on generator or perceptual constraints might be applied to other signals, such as handwriting or information from any sensor. In any case, such constraints are not rigorously satisfied and therefore all band-compressed signals incur some amount of perceptual degradation. Bandwidth compression might be viewed basically as an attempt to discard unimportant detail while minimizing degradations. Therefore, a meaningful performance specification of compression schemes must include not only the compression achieved, but the signal-to-noise transmission requirements for the reduced signals and the amount of subjective degradation incurred.

REFERENCES

1. J. R. Pierce and E. E. David, Jr., "Man's World of Sound," New York, Doubleday and Co., Inc., 1958.

2. C. G. M. FANT, "Acoustic Theory of Speech Production," The Hague, Netherlands, Mouton and Co., 1960.

E. E. DAVID, JR.

Cross-references: *Acoustics, Compression and Expansion, Modulation and Demodulation, Vocoder*

BARKHAUSEN, HEINRICH (1881–1956)

Heinrich Barkhausen was born in Bremen on December 2, 1881, and completed his secondary education in that city. He entered engineering school in Munich but soon switched to physics and continued his studies at the Universities of Munich, Berlin, and Göttingen, completing them with a dissertation on "The problem of the generation of oscillations" in 1907. This work, in which he recognized the importance of feedback, attracted a good deal of attention and during the following four years he was a member of the research staff of Siemens Laboratories.

In 1911 he took over the chair of communications engineering in Dresden, where he founded the first institute on this subject in Germany. He made important contributions to the theory of nonlinear switching elements, formulated the electron-tube coefficients (and the equations relating them) that are still in use, and wrote a four-volume text on electron tubes. He also made contributions in the fields of acoustics (the method of subjective measurement of loudness and the employment of the *phon* as a unit of loudness were first proposed by him) and of magnetism (the *Barkhausen effect* is named after him). With his collaborator Kurz, he developed the Barkhausen-Kurz oscillator (*q.v.*).

He was the recipient of many honors in Germany and abroad, notably from Japan and the U.S.A.: the Institute of Radio Engineers awarded him the Morris Liebmann Memorial Prize in 1933. Through his efforts, his institute in Dresden remained one of the outstanding centers of electronics research. The institute was destroyed by bombing in February 1945, but after World War II, Barkhausen returned to Dresden to resume his teaching activities at the age of 63. He remained there, after becoming professor emeritus, until his death on February 20, 1956. The buildings housing the new institute in Dresden are named *Barkhausenbau* in his honor.

CHARLES SUSSKIND

Cross-references: *Historical Background of Electronics*

BARKHAUSEN-KURZ OSCILLATOR

Barkhausen-Kurz oscillations are probably the earliest method employed for generating coherent-wave electromagnetic radiation at fractional-meter wavelengths. If a triode's dc circuit connections maintain its plate at or a little below cathode potential, with the grid held strongly positive, the potential difference between cathode and plate along a path midway between grid wires resembles an inverted parabola with flattened sides—or an inverted "V" with its upward-pointing apex blunted by a fillet. Because electrons "fall uphill" in such a distribution, they will after leaving the cathode oscillate to and fro through the grid many times before striking and entering it, much as a ball oscillates in a bowl. The cyclic period is approximately twice the cathode-to-plate transit time. For an inverted "V" potential model with the fillet influence ignored, this is (for a planar configuration) twice the cathode-to-plate spacing divided by an average velocity that is the same on the two sides of the grid. Thus, approximately,

$$\text{Frequency} = \sqrt{2q_e/m_e} \; \sqrt{V_c}/4S_p$$

$$= 5.93 \times 10^5 \; \sqrt{V_c}/4S_p$$

where q_e/m_e is the ratio of charge to mass for an electron, V_c the dc grid voltage, and S_p the cathode-to-plate spacing in meter units. For Kozanowksi's nonflattened parabolic potential model (*Proc. IRE*, June 1932) the frequency is obtained by using π in place of 4.

If a Lecher-wire circuit designed to resonate at or near this frequency is connected between cathode and plate, and the cathode temperature and grid voltage are adjusted to give a current somewhat below the space-charge-limited value, this oscillation can become a self-sustaining group movement of swarms of electrons. The plate potential is driven cyclically slightly below, then slightly above, its negative dc value by the approaching and receding of successive swarms, thus causing an rf power flow into the Lecher-wire circuit in the absence of dc plate current. This power flow exists because the plate voltage variations cause the swarms to have less kinetic energy as they recede toward the grid than during approach from it. Thus the rf power is associated with a corresponding reduction of grid dissipation below the simple product of dc current and grid voltage.

An oscillating tube has been developed in Sweden (the "strophotron") that employs a similar principle for coupling from an internal oscillating swarm to a circuit, but having a lateral magnetic influence on the trajectories that moves the electrons away from the strongly positive grid to one at a lower dc potential before collection. This action lessens the grid dissipation for given rf circuit power.

WILLIAM G. DOW

Cross-references: *Bunching, Electron Tubes (Conventional), Velocity Modulation*

BARRETER: see BOLOMETERS

BATTERIES

Dry Batteries

A battery is a dc power source consisting of two or more cells. A dry cell is a type of primary cell in which the electrolyte is retained in the separator and chemical mix. The term normally is used only for cells employing the electrochemical system discovered by LeClanché—zinc anode, ammonium chloride and zinc chloride electrolyte, and manganese dioxide cathode. Since carbon is used in the cathode as a current collector, this electrochemical system is often called the carbon-zinc system.

Service Capacity. The voltage of a dry cell (nominally 1.5 v) decreases with use. Therefore, service capacity is greater as the minimum acceptable voltage is lowered. The electrochemical efficiency and milliampere-hour capacity of a dry cell improve as the current density decreases. Over a certain range of current density, service life may be tripled by halving the current drain. A dry battery operates more efficiently on intermittent use. The service capacity of a battery used 2 hr per day will be considerably different from that of a battery used 12 or 24 hr per day. On extremely light current drains or very intermittent use the effect of shelf life becomes important and may reduce milliampere-hour capacity.

Shelf Life and Temperature Limitations. Shelf life is defined as the period of time (measured from date of manufacture) required to reduce battery capacity to a specified percentage (usually 90 per cent) of its original energy content. The storage temperature is considered to be 70°F.

Shelf deterioration is caused by moisture loss in the cell through evaporation and low-level chemical reactions occurring within the cell independent of those due to current drains.

Elevated temperatures hasten wasteful zinc corrosion and other chemical side reactions within the cell; lower temperatures moderate them. Exposure of dry batteries to high ambient temperatures must be avoided. Temperatures in excess of 125°F cause very rapid deterioration and possible leakage. At 70°F, depending on battery size and construction, shelf life may range between 6 months and several years.

Dry batteries are produced in over two hundred different shapes, voltages and electrical capacities. The physical construction of the individual cells as well as the exact composition of the chemical mix is varied to optimize desired characteristics. For example, one manufacturer produces five different LeClanché "D" size flashlight cells, each designed for a particular type of use. Because of the variety of batteries available, most battery manufacturers supply detailed engineering information and recommendations on request.

Mercury Batteries. Since the late 1940's mercury cells and batteries have been commercially available. A mercury cell is a type of primary cell using an immobilized electrolyte of potassium or sodium hydroxide with a powdered zinc anode and a mercuric oxide cathode. The voltage discharge characteristic is more uniform than that of a LeClanché cell and mercury cells provide more energy per unit volume.

Alkaline Batteries. A development of the 1950's, alkaline primary cells, use a powdered zinc anode, gelled potassium hydroxide electrolyte and a manganese dioxide cathode. These cells have a voltage characteristic similar to LeClanché dry cells but they supply greater total energy and operate efficiently under extremely heavy continuous drain conditions where dry cells or mercury batteries are inefficient.

D. B. CAMERON

Rechargeable Batteries

The hermetically sealed, rechargeable nickel-cadmium cell is basically the same as all standard open or vented nickel-cadmium cells. In the charged condition the positive is comprised of nickel hydroxide, the negative of cadmium with a dilute solution of potassium hydroxide (KOH) as the electrolyte, and metallic contact is prevented by a porous separator. As the cell is discharged the positive material is reduced to a lower nickel hydroxide and the negative is oxidized to cadmium hydroxide.

The nominal load voltage of a nickel-cadmium cell is 1.20 to 1.25 v per cell depending on cell type and current density. Unlike other systems, the nickel-cadmium cell has a very flat and stable voltage throughout an entire discharge. The latest developments in these cells have resulted in internal resistance as low as 0.006 ohm for a "D" size cell, permitting extremely high current density discharges.

The nickel-cadmium sealed cell is one of the most efficient systems, with regard to service capacity, commonly used. These cells will supply up to 16 w-hr/lb and 1.5 w-hr/in.[3] They are available in many different sizes and configurations.

The sealed cell differs from the open cell in that the open nickel-cadmium cell electrodes liberate both hydrogen (from the negative) and oxygen (from the positive) when they become fully charged and are then overcharged. When several cells are used in a series-connected battery, it is possible during discharge, because of differences in capacity, for the lower-capacity cells to reverse polarity while the others continue to supply current. These overdischarged or reversed cells also liberate hydrogen and oxygen, but from opposite electrodes, owing to the reversed polarity.

If an open-type cell is hermetically sealed without special precautions, these liberated gases would result in pressure build-up within the cells and eventual rupture of the seal. To effectively seal this cell, precautions must be taken to either prevent gas evolution or to dispose of the gases as they are formed.

Owing to the state of charge of the negative electrode when the cell is sealed and an excess of negative capacity, the evolution of hydrogen is completely suppressed on overcharge.

The oxygen evolved from the positive electrode during overcharge is channeled through the porous separator to the negative electrode and oxidizes the finely divided metallic cadmium available in the charged negative. This cadmium hydroxide is then continuously electrochemically reduced (owing to charging current) to metallic cadmium, which is again available for oxidation, thus preventing a build-up of excess oxygen pressure.

Care must be taken to assure that the

rate of evolution of oxygen gas does not exceed the rate of recombination. Since this rate of evolution is proportional to the rate of charge, the rate of charge must not exceed that specified for any specific cell.

The mechanism of reversal protection functions in much the same manner as that for protection during overcharge. The evolution of hydrogen is completely suppressed, and the oxygen evolved from the negative electrode is recombined. The main difference is that metallic cadmium is made available on the positive and is commonly known as the anti-polar mass. This process does not disturb the normal functions of the positive electrode during charging and discharging, since it exists in this case as electrochemically ineffective cadmium hydroxide.

Here again the rate of evolution of oxygen must not exceed the rate of recombination and is controlled by the rate of discharge of the cell. In cases where the discharge ratings of the cell must be exceeded, it is possible to utilize exterior regulation such as a voltage cut-off to avoid cell reversal.

E. S. GRAHAM

Cross-references: *Electrochemistry, Energy Conversion, Standards*

BEACONS: see NAVIGATION

BEAM-SWITCHING TUBE

The beam-switching tube is a ten-position, high-vacuum, constant-current distributor. It may be made to operate in a variety of distribution or switching modes: (1) the tube may be in a clear or cut-off condition, (2) an electron beam may be formed in any one of the ten positions, (3) the electron beam may be switched sequentially, (4) the electron beam may be switched at random from any one position to any other position, and (5) the electron beam may be switched and cleared (cut itself off).

The tube consists of ten identical "arrays" located radially about a central cathode (Fig. 1). Each array is composed of (1) a

spade that automatically forms and locks the electron beam, (2) a target output that makes the beam current available with constant-current characteristics, and (3) a high-impedance switching grid that serves to switch the beam from target to target. A cylindrical magnet is permanently attached to the outside of the glass envelope to provide a magnetic field which, in conjunction with an applied electric field, forms the crossed fields necessary for the operation of this tube.

The operation may be understood most simply by considering the motion of an electron moving in crossed magnetic and electric fields. An electron placed in such a field tends to move along an equipotential line. Therefore, if one of the spade electrodes is maintained at the same potential as the cathode and the other nine spades are maintained at a positive potential with respect to the cathode, electrons flow from the cathode to the spade that is at cathode potential. As the spade is lowered in potential, the current to it tends to increase until the spade is near cathode potential. The current then tends to decrease as the effects of electrostatic repulsion of the electrons from the spade become predominant. Figure 2 shows the static voltage-current characteristic curve of one spade taken with all other electrodes at the spade supply voltage. This curve contains a negative-resistance slope which, when intersected with a suitable load line, exhibits bistable states.

The spade resistance load line (typical 130 K) shown in Fig. 2 intersects the curve

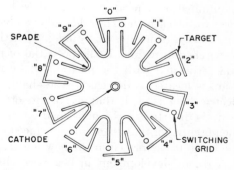

Fig. 1. Cross section of beam-switching tube.

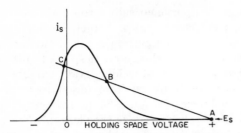

Fig. 2. Spade voltage-current characteristics.

at points A, B, and C. "A" corresponds to the potential of the spades which are at the spade bus potential. "B" is a regenerative point with positive feedback and is unstable since any variation in either current or voltage causes a change of the other in such a way as to increase the original change. Point "C" is a degenerative point with negative feedback and is stable as any variation in either voltage or current causes a change in the other parameter cancelling the original change. With a proper resistor in series with each spade, lowering the potential of one spade to slightly below point B results in the regenerative action that forms and locks the electron beam to the spade at point C. The holding spade requires only sufficient electron current flowing through its resistor to "lock" the spade at stable point C. Approximately 85 per cent of the beam current is passed on to the associated target output electrode where it is available to perform useful work.

Switching of the beam is accomplished by the use of the switching grids. These grids are normally connected in two groups, called the odd grids and the even grids, and are maintained at a positive potential with respect to the cathode. The odd and even pairing of the grids insures that only one position is switched at a time. If the potential of the grid associated with the position where the beam is located is decreased, the change in electric field is such that a portion of the beam is diverted to the next spade, causing the potential of that spade to be reduced and the beam to be formed in the new position.

A recent development in beam-switching tubes is the "BEAM-X" switch in which the external magnet has been eliminated. In this tube type, the external magnet is replaced by ten rod magnets placed inside of the tube envelope. To conserve space and to enable the magnet to be physically located where the resultant magnetic field has the desired strength, the magnets are also used as active electrodes. In one commercial version of the "BEAM-X" switch, for instance, the ten rod magnets replace the targets and act in their stead as the current-collecting electrodes.

Roger W. Wolfe

Cross-references: *Crossed-Field Interactions, Electron Optics*

BETA RAYS: see ELECTRONS; RADIATION (IONIZING)

BETATRON AND CYCLOTRON

Betatrons and cyclotrons belong to a class of accelerators in which particles move along circular or nearly circular paths at right angles to a magnetic field; acceleration is achieved in the betatron by a time variation of the magnetic field, and in the cyclotron, by rf electric fields, as described below.

The betatron or magnetic-induction accelerator was devised by D. W. Kerst in 1940. Its operation has been compared to the action of a transformer (*q.v.*) in which the moving electrons form the secondary winding. The equation relating electric field and magnetic flux, $E\,ds = d\phi/dt$, for this case becomes

$$2\pi RE = \pi R^2\,dB/dt$$

where R is the orbit radius; and since the momentum of a particle traveling in a circular path under the influence of a magnetic field B_0 is given by $mv = qRB_0$, one has for the rate of change of momentum

$$\frac{d}{dt}(mv) = qE = \frac{qR}{2}\frac{dB}{dt} = qR\frac{dB_0}{dt}$$

which yields the basic betatron equation

$$\frac{dB}{dt} = 2\frac{dB_0}{dt}$$

The magnetic circuit must be laminated, because of the losses that would otherwise arise from the varying magnetic fields; the pole pieces may weigh hundreds of tons. The magnetic field is usually varied at 60 cps and a shunt capacitor bank is used to adjust the phase angle between magnet current and voltage. Acceleration takes place during the first quarter cycle. The beam is directed at the target by a perturbation of the magnetic field toward the end of the accelerating period.

Betatrons are mainly used for the acceleration of electrons, which quickly reach the velocity of light owing to their small mass, so that they move at substantially constant speeds during the acceleration period. For protons moving at nonrelativistic velocities, the cyclotron proves to be more advantageous.

The cyclotron (Fig. 1), invented by E. O. Lawrence in 1932, uses a strong magnetic guide field and one or more accelerating electrodes, called dees, to accelerate charged particles to energies of millions of electron volts. The frequency of the dee voltage is chosen to synchronize with that of the rotation of the charged particles, so that the particles are accelerated each time they cross a dee edge. This condition is called cyclotron resonance. The angular frequency ω_r is

$$\omega_r = (q/m)B$$

where q is the charge and m the mass of the particle, and B is the magnetic field intensity. For protons, this relation reduces to

$$f_r = 1530B$$

where B is in gauss and f_r is in cycles per second. As the particles are accelerated, the orbit radius increases until the particles reach the final radius ρ; the momentum p of a particle is then

$$p = qB\rho$$

The particle energy is

$$U = m_0c^2\left\{\left[1 + \left(\frac{p}{m_0c}\right)^2\right]^{1/2} - 1\right\}$$

where m_0 is the rest mass of the particle and c is the velocity of light. For protons, Eq. (4) becomes

$$U = 938\{[1 + 6.61 \times 10^{-13}(BR)^2]^{1/2} - 1\} \text{ (Mev)}$$

where R is the final orbit radius in inches.

The particles to be accelerated start from an ion source which is located near the center of the cyclotron. In the ion source, a gas is ionized by a stream of electrons from a hot filament; these ions escape into the accelerating chamber through a hole in the ion-source housing. The type of gas determines the type of particles available. For example, for protons, hydrogen is used; for deuterons, deuterium; for alpha particles, helium. Heavier ions also may be produced by the appropriate choice of gas.

Usually the particles are extracted from the source by the electric field from the dee. The particles cross the dee edges many times; each time they pick up an amount of en-

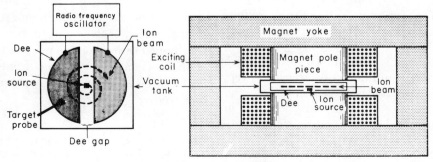

Fig. 1. Cyclotron.

ergy corresponding to the instantaneous potential of the dee at the time of the crossing. Ultimately the particles acquire enough energy to reach the final radius of the magnet. Then they are guided out of the magnet by a deflector.

There are two factors that limit the practical size of cyclotrons. First, as a particle is accelerated to higher energy, its mass increases, and the required rf frequency decreases as shown by Eq. (1). Thus, the frequency required to accelerate particles at small radii is incompatible with that required at large radii. The second factor is the requirement of a magnetic guide field that provides a focusing force for the beam and a centering force for the orbits. This requirement is accomplished by tapering the magnet poles so that the field decreases slightly with increasing radius. This tapering causes the magnetic-field lines to bow outward slightly, producing a component of force on the particles toward the median plane (the plane of equilibrium midway between the magnet poles). Like the relativistic mass increase, this decrease in magnetic field also reduces the required frequency for cyclotron resonance at the larger radii. These two factors limit the beam to about 150 turns and restrict the energy of proton cyclotrons to about 20 Mev.

McMillan and Veksler independently discovered the principle of phase stability. One of the consequences of this discovery was the realization that the energy limitation of cyclotrons could be circumvented by frequency-modulating the dee voltage. Machines of this type are called synchrocyclotrons. The frequency of the dee voltage starts at the particle-starting frequency (i.e., the cyclotron frequency corresponding to rest mass) and is swept down to that which is required for full radius. With each sweep, a group of particles is accelerated to full energy. Many synchrocyclotrons are in operation; the highest-energy machine produces 730-Mev protons.

In 1938, L. H. Thomas found another method of circumventing the two limitations of cyclotrons. He showed that by varying the magnetic field azimuthally according to a certain formula, one could achieve isochronism (equal transit times for all orbit) while maintaining focusing of the beam and centering of the orbits. While Thomas' theory preceded McMillan and Vekslers' theories of phase stability by many years, it was not checked experimentally until 1950 at the University of California Radiation Laboratory in Berkeley. As a result, the synchrocyclotrons preceded the Thomas cyclotrons.

D. W. Kerst in 1955 extended Thomas' theory by showing that forming the magnet-pole hills into spiral ridges results in stronger focusing and more economical use of the magnet steel. Machines of this type are called spiral-ridge cyclotrons. Being cw machines, they produce very large beam currents—several orders of magnitude larger than those of synchrocyclotrons.

In 1954, a second generation of cyclotrons started. At Livermore, Calif., Rochester, N. Y., and Los Alamos, N. M., variable-energy cyclotrons were built so that physicists and chemists could study nuclear reactions in much more detail. These first machines covered the range from 1 to 15 Mev. All of the cyclotrons that have been built since have been variable-energy machines. Those nearing completion at present will extend the range of variable energy beams to 75 Mev.

To produce a variable-energy external beam, the rf frequency and magnetic field must be adjustable so that cyclotron resonance can be maintained. In addition, sufficient precision of the magnetic field must be maintained throughout its range. Production of such magnets has become a fine art and field ranges of 5 or 10 to one are readily produced.

BOB H. SMITH

Cross-references: *Accelerators, Characteristic Frequencies, Synchrotron and Bevatron*

EBVATRON: see SYNCHROTRON AND BEVA-
TRON

BIOELECTRONICS: see BIONICS; MEDICAL
ELECTRONICS

BIOLOGICAL EFFECTS OF RADIATION: see
RADIATION (IONIZING); RADIATION HAZ-
ARDS (NONIONIZING RADIATION)

BIONICS

Bionics is the science, or art, of using living prototypes. The term, by derivation from bion, should refer to the science of systems that function after the manner of, or in a manner characteristic of, or resembling, living systems. The purpose of bionics is to borrow, from living things, principles, processes, and techniques useful in the solution of engineering problems. Though this is an old technique of inventors, its significant widespread application has become feasible only recently as a result of the rapid advance in the electronic art and of modern understanding of life processes. Its major motivation is the rapidly increasing requirement for the automatic acquisition, processing, and utilization of information.

Bionics must be distinguished from bio- and medical electronics. The latter two use electronic theory and techniques in the problems of biology and medical diagnosis and treatment. Bionics is the inverse, being the application of biological knowledge to the advancement of the electronic and other engineering arts. It is more closely related to cybernetics (q.v.), defined by Norbert Wiener as control and communication in the animal and the machine. His application of the same mathematical concepts and techniques to animals and machines shows that their similarity is more than superficial.

Bionics is possible because of the similarity of function existing between living systems and present or proposed synthetic ones. This similarity of function implies potential similarity of constituent processes or techniques. The living system serves first as proof that a particular function may be achieved. Under further analysis it may reveal clues to methods and processes sufficient to accomplish the desired function. As in any copying operation it is necessary, but not always easy, to distinguish essential features from accidental.

Bionic borrowing consists of three steps: analysis, formalization, and synthesis, corresponding to the work of the biologist, the mathematician, and the engineer respectively. Analysis of the living system is adequate when it has resulted in the decomposition of system function into a number of component processes which have existing or achievable engineering counterparts. The synthesis problem is that of designing or selecting hardware for achieving the component processes and combining it into a system having the desired system function.

Formalization is necessitated largely by biological tradition. Except for biochemists and biophysicists, most biologists record their conclusions in a manner that is often relatively vague and imprecise from an engineering point of view. This information must be restated in terms meaningful to an engineer.

The mathematician and logician serve a larger purpose than mere translation. They often start from postulates based on biological data and develop completely new postulational systems. They may, on a purely formal basis, demonstrate that component biological processes not directly achievable in hardware are equivalent to combinations of other steps which are achievable.

A typical example of this three-step sequence is Aristotelian logic formalized by George Boole to Boolean algebra (q.v.) and applied to engineering problems almost simultaneously by Nakasima, Shestakov, and Shannon.

Biological functions suitable for copying

are many. Inhibition of bacterial growth by a mold, observed by Flemming, led to the discovery of the molecular structure of penicillin and then to its synthesis. A coating for ship hulls patterned after the skin of porpoises accomplishes drag reduction through boundary-layer control. A light airplane gains improved lift and yaw stabilization through drooping wingtips, the result of engineering studies inspired by the wing conformation of soaring birds.

Solar-energy fixation by photosynthesis, the generation of electricity through the enzymatic oxidation of organic fuels; these and many other life functions are under study because of their engineering implications. However, at present, the most important area is not mechanics, organic synthesis, or energy conversion. It is utilization of information, the same need responsible for the rapid advance of electronics.

The nervous system is specialized to deal with information. It may be studied and modeled on many levels. The four most significant at present are intelligent behavior, large nerve nets, small nets, and elements.

Problem-solving behavior, as studied and analyzed by psychologists, is inspiring computer techniques such as non-numerical data processing and heuristic programming. Theoretical models of large nerve nets based on psychological and neurophysiological implications, are being applied to such problems as pattern recognition and concept formation. These models are leading both to new programming techniques and to the design of new components and circuits. Among the more significant results of this type of modeling is a growing awareness of the advantages of parallel processing and the possibility of treating both the network and the data it handles on a statistical basis. The living prototype cannot be specified genetically beyond a degree of determinacy statistical in nature. It functions well in spite of this indeterminacy and of continuous variation and failure of its components. This fact has stimulated intense study of the logics appropriate to such systems.

Small nets, cochlea, retina, and spinal reflexes are being studied with such processes as "property filtration," "peripheral processing," and "neighborhood logic" being incorporated in theoretical or actual physical models almost as rapidly as they are observed or proposed. The engineering need is for the preliminary processing of signals such as speech, radar and sonar returns, and photographic images prior to the application of traditional logical operations. These efforts are also significant for the efficient use of communication channels through the elimination of redundant or insignificant data.

Neurone building is probably the most popular bionic activity, the hope being that given enough neurones one can build a brain. On the theoretical level, these models contribute to the development of new logics and on the physical level to the design of new types of computer components.

Molecular electronics is making some engineering aspects of bionics feasible while increasing the need for bionics. The limits of miniaturization are set by the inevitable variability of microcomponents. Living systems have solved the problem of using such elements.

Plagiarism is easier, faster and cheaper than invention. Life offers a wealth of highly desirable, unpatented prototypes to anyone having the skill to use them.

JACK E. STEELE

Cross-references: Cybernetics, Human Engineering, Information Theory, Medical Electronics, Microcircuitry, Neuristor, Neuron

BOLOMETERS

A resistor with a large temperature coefficient (TC), used originally to measure the heat of stars, now also to measure microwave power. The term "bolometer," referring in the past only to positive TC elements, has lately come to include suitable forms of thermistors, with the term "barretter" distinguishing positive TC bolometers.

Thermistors used for power measurement consist of a metallic oxide mixture. Across two parallel fine wires a few mils apart, a semi-liquid drop of the mixture is placed and sintered, forming a ceramic bead. A thin glass coat is fired on and the diagonally opposite wires are cut off. The bead, of about 0.015 in. in diameter, may be used uncapsuled, enclosed in a glass capsule with axial leads, or soldered into a barretter cartridge.

Barretters are commonly made of Wollaston wire, fine platinum wire clad with silver and drawn to about 0.001 in. in diameter. After soldering into position, the silver is etched away, leaving a platinum core about 50×10^{-6} in. in diameter and about 0.1 in. long. Instrument fuses made this way were used early in World War II for measuring power, leading to the development of the "Sperry barretter" specifically for this purpose. A polystyrene sleeve surrounds the wire, which is suspended between brass end contacts, forming a cartridge about 0.8 in. long by 0.2 in. in diameter. Barretters are also made in crystal cartridges and on mica sheets. Small tungsten lamps have been used as barretters at the lower frequencies.

To absorb the power in a transmission line, the bolometer is placed in a terminating line section, or "mount." The mount may hold a removable cartridge or a thermistor soldered in. The impedance is matched to the line as required and a low-frequency connection provided.

In bolometric measurements, equal amounts of microwave power and easily measured dc or low-frequency ("bias" or "substitution") power are usually assumed to affect the bolometer resistance equally. Various studies show that the "substitution error" is negligible up to at least X-band. Another usual assumption is that all power absorbed by the mount is dissipated in the bolometer. Actually, losses may reduce the mount efficiency appreciably. Typical figures at X-band are 95–98 per cent for waveguide mounts, 85–95 per cent for coaxial mounts.

In measurement systems, the bolometer is one leg of a bridge fed with bias power and balancing at, usually, 100 or 200 ohms. The bolometer itself requires about 15 mw. Thermistors are about 2000 ohms cold, barretters about 120 ohms. The microwave power causing a given bridge unbalance after initial balance can be equated to the increase in bias required for the same unbalance. However, since change in the bolometer resistance affects the mount impedance, it is preferable to re-balance the bridge with the unknown applied and equate the unknown to the decrease in bias. Alternatively, dc bias may be adjusted for balance with the unknown applied, then audio power substituted for the unknown and adjusted to re-balance.

The so-called "self-balancing" bridge, basis of most commercial power meters, substitutes power automatically. It is in an amplifier loop, one side providing positive feedback, the other negative. Audio oscillation occurs, at the level necessary to set the bolometer resistance to the value required by the bridge elements and the loop gain. The action is the same as in the lamp-stabilized RC oscillator. When microwave power is applied, the level automatically decreases an equal amount, the decrease being indicated on a meter. Dc bias is used to set the initial level to a reference value (zero-set), regardless of differences in total power requirements at different ambient temperatures or between different bolometers.

Short-time ambient temperature variations set a lower measurement limit of 10 to 100 μw, since a bolometer is affected equally by heat from its surroundings and heat from power dissipation. Temperature compensation, using a double-bridge circuit, can extend the range down to 1 to 10 μw. The second bolometer is placed in the mount, exposed to the same ambient temperature, but not to the power.

Barretters, with time constants of 100 to 400 μsec, make excellent square-law detectors for microwave attenuation measurements. The resistance follows the power variations of a modulated signal. Dc is fed through the barretter, resulting in an audio voltage proportional to the microwave power. Although not as sensitive as crystals, barretters are more closely square law, with a useful range of 20 to 30 db.

Thermistors, with time constants of about 1 sec, are more suitable for measuring the average power of a modulated signal.

B. P. Hand

Cross-references: *Bridges, Fuses, Microwave Measurements, Indicating Instruments, Thermistors, Varistor*

BOOLEAN ALGEBRA AND SYMBOLIC LOGIC

A Boolean algebra[1,2] is a system consisting of a class S of binary valued objects a, b, c, $\cdots$ with two binary operations called logical addition and logical multiplication. The binary values of the objects may be called "true" and "false" or more simply "1" and "0."

Besides the binary operators "AND" and "OR" it is convenient to introduce other connectives. Those most frequently used are given in Table I. They are a unitary operator "NOT" or "$\daleth$", and three relational operators (conditional implication "$\supset$", equivalence "$\equiv$", and exclusive disjunction "$\neq$"). The stroke and dual stroke may be expressed in terms of $\wedge$ and $\vee$ by the formulas $A \mid B \equiv \daleth(A \wedge B)$, and $A \downarrow B \equiv \daleth(A \vee B)$.

From the rules of Table I it is clear that the class S is closed under the given operators. The precedence order for the operators is (1) $\daleth$, (2) $\supset$, $\equiv$, and $\neq$, (3) $\vee$, and (4)

$\wedge$. Expressions inside parentheses are evaluated first and operators at the same level are evaluated in order from left to right. Under these circumstances the operations are commutative, associative, and distributive. Note that $A \wedge (A \vee B) \equiv A \vee A \wedge B \equiv A$.

A formula which is true for all values of its arguments is called a *tautology*. Thus $A \vee \daleth A$ and $1 \equiv 1$ are tautologies. More interesting tautologies are De Morgan's theorems:

$$A \downarrow B \equiv \daleth(A \vee B) \equiv \daleth A \wedge \daleth B$$

$$A \mid B \equiv \daleth(A \wedge B) \equiv \daleth A \vee \daleth B$$

The duality represented by these theorems may be generalized to obtain a *principle of duality*. The dual f_D of a formula f is obtained by interchanging in pairs: 0 and 1, V and $\daleth V$ (for each variable), $\supset$ and $\subset$, $\vee$ and $\wedge$, $\equiv$ and $\neq$, and $\downarrow$ and $\mid$. Thus, the principle of duality says that $\daleth f \equiv f_D$ is a tautology.

The validity of a formula may be checked by constructing a truth table. Table I is a truth table for the arguments A and B. Note that a truth table for n arguments has 2^n lines in order to provide for all possible combinations of zeros and ones for the various arguments. In some applications some cases may be known to not occur. Such nonoccurring cases are called "don't care" cases.

Three classes of Boolean quantities (binary valued) will be considered: (1) *Identifiers*, (2) *Terms*, and (3) *Expressions*. Elements of the class S are identifiers. If i, t, and e are used generically to denote repre-

Table I

A	B	Negation Not A $\daleth A$	Conjunction A and B $A \wedge B$	Inclusive disjunction A or B $A \vee B$	Conditional implication If A then B $A \supset B$	Equivalence A if and only if B $A \equiv B$	Exclusive disjunction A or B but not both $A \neq B$	Stroke Not both A and B $A \mid B$	Dual stroke Neither A nor B $A \downarrow B$
0	0	1	0	0	1	1	0	1	1
0	1	1	0	1	1	0	1	1	0
1	0	0	0	1	0	0	1	1	0
1	1	0	1	1	1	1	0	0	0

sentatives of the respective classes then rules for the generation of terms and expressions may be given as

Terms	Expressions
i	$t, \neg t$
$t \wedge t$	$e \vee t$
(e)	$e \subset e, e \equiv e$

In other words, an identifier is a term and an expression. If A and B are terms then $A \wedge B$ is a term, etc. Consistent with the precedence rules given above, parentheses may be removed or added to Boolean expressions provided the meaning is not changed.

A formula or Boolean expression which is false for all values of its arguments is said to be a *contradiction*. Every expression which is not a contradiction can be expressed as an inclusive disjunction of all those conjunctions (of all the arguments or their negations) for which the expression is true. This form of the expression is called the *disjunctive normal form*.

The extreme reliability required in digital computer circuitry has led to the use of two-state circuits.[3] Thus, Boolean algebra has been extensively used to represent the performance of such circuits. For example, a coincidence circuit (gate) can be presented by a conjunction of its inputs. OR circuits (mixers) can be represented by disjunctions. For example, if A and B are the input binary digits of the operands, and C is the input carry, then the digit of the binary sum in that position and the output carry are given by

$$S \equiv A \wedge B \wedge C \vee A \wedge \neg B \wedge \neg C$$
$$\vee \neg A \wedge B \wedge \neg C \vee \neg A \wedge \neg B \wedge C$$
$$C_{out} \equiv A \wedge B \wedge C \vee A \wedge B \wedge \neg C$$
$$\vee A \wedge \neg B \wedge C \vee \neg A \wedge B \wedge C$$

These expressions are in their disjunctive normal forms. This form is of particular importance in the process of simplification of such expressions. By use of the tautology $P \vee \neg P$ the expression for C_{out} may be simplified to

$$C_{out} \equiv A \wedge B \vee B \wedge C \vee C \wedge A$$

Venn diagrams may be used to represent Boolean expressions. For example, the function $F = \neg A \wedge B \wedge C \vee A \wedge B \wedge \neg C \vee \neg A \wedge \neg B \wedge C$ is represented by the crossed squares in Fig. 1:

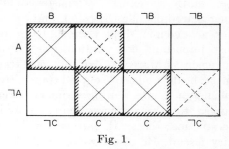

Fig. 1.

If $A \wedge B \wedge C$ and $\neg A \wedge \neg B \wedge \neg C$ are nonoccurring or "don't care" terms in the expression (represented by dashed crosses) then it is easy to see that $\neg A \wedge C \vee A \wedge B$ is equivalent to F under the circumstances.

By introducing the concept of delay and considering time as consisting of discrete intervals, computing machines (finite state machines) may be completely described using the above language.

REFERENCES

1. I. M. COPI, "Symbolic Logic," The Macmillan Co., New York, 1954.
2. W. V. QUINE, "Methods of Logic," Henry Holt and Co., New York, 1950.
3. H. D. HUSKEY AND G. A. KORN, "The Computer Handbook," McGraw-Hill Book Co., New York, 1961.

HARRY D. HUSKEY

Cross-references: *Computer Logic, Computer Programming, Digital Computers, Logic Circuits*

BRAUN, KARL FERDINAND (1850–1918)

K. F. Braun was born on June 6, 1850 in Fulda, Hesse in Germany and studied at the Universities of Marburg and Berlin. After various teaching positions in several German cities he became professor of experimental physics at the University of Tübingen in 1885, where he set up an Institute of Physics and worked in the fields of electrolysis and electrical measurements. In 1895 he moved to Strasbourg, where he made his most important contribution to electronics, the cathode-ray-tube oscillograph. The original tube employed a cold cathode, two collimating apertures, magnetic deflection, electrostatic screening (by moistened filter paper placed outside the tube), and a phosphor-covered mica display screen. His second most important contribution was an improvement of Marconi's damped-wave transmitter: he devised the "coupled transmitter" utilizing a nonresonating primary circuit coupled to a secondary circuit containing the antenna; the spark gap was in the primary circuit. He also developed a coupled receiver on similar principles. It was principally for this contribution that Braun received the Nobel Prize (jointly with Marconi) in 1909.

He continued to work in the field of radiotelegraphy, developing the idea of directional transmitting and receiving antennas, applying the results of some of his earlier work with crystals to the utilization of such materials for detection (replacing the coherer), and proposing the use of radio transmissions as beacons for navigation. He visited the U.S.A. in 1909, and again after World War I broke out to testify in a patent suit, the principal result of which would be to close down the radio station at Sayville, Long Island, which was being used for communication with Germany after the disruption of the transatlantic cable. The suit was postponed, and when America entered the war, Braun had to remain in the U.S.A., living at his son's home in Brooklyn, N.Y., where he died on April 20, 1918. His name survives in the German designation for the cathode-ray-tube oscillograph, *Braun'sche Röhre.*

CHARLES SUSSKIND

Cross-references: *Historical Background of Electronics*

BRAZING COMPOUNDS: see SOLDERS AND BRAZING COMPOUNDS

BREMSSTRAHLUNG

An electron can suffer a very large acceleration in passing through the Coulomb field of a nucleus, and in this interaction the radiant energy (photons) lost by the electron is called bremsstrahlung[1,2] (also, bremsstrahlung sometimes designates the interaction itself). If an electron whose total energy $E_0 \gtrsim 800/Z$ Mev traverses matter of atomic number Z, the electron loses energy chiefly by bremsstrahlung. This case is considered here. Protons and heavier particles radiate relatively little because of their large masses (radiation rate is proportional to the square of the acceleration and inversely proportional to the square of the mass). If an energetic electron traverses one radiation length (X_0) of any matter, bremsstrahlung reduces the electron's energy to $1/e$ of its incident value on the average. Some examples are:

Element	Air	C	Al	Fe	Cu	W	Pb
Radiation length X_0 (cm)	29800	20	9.1	1.7	1.42	0.32	0.51

A beam of energetic electrons incident upon a radiator produces a bremsstrahlung beam that is directed sharply forward. Angular distributions for typical "thick" tungsten targets are shown in Fig. 1. Curves for other heavy metals are similar if all radiator thicknesses are measured in units of the radiation length. In such thick radiators, the incident electrons scatter before radiating appreciably, making any observed distribution actually an average over electron scattering angles of the corresponding basic distribution. The basic angular distribution has a zero at $\alpha = 0$, which is quite different from the curves of Fig. 1. The basic spectral shape is a weak function of photon angle and, in thick radiators, electron scattering modifies this shape slightly (Fig. 2). Examples of thick radiator spectra (bremsstrahlung cross sections) are shown in Fig. 3 for various incident electron energies. The bremsstrahlung spectra depend upon screening of the nuclear Coulomb field by atomic electrons through the parameter $\gamma = 51k/[E_0(E_0 - k)Z^{1/3}]$, where k = photon energy in Mev. For complete screening ($\gamma \approx 0$), the thick radiator spectrum is given by

$$\frac{d\sigma_b}{dk} = \frac{4Z^2r_0^2}{137k} \left\{ \left[1 + \left(\frac{E}{E_0}\right)^2 - \frac{2}{3}\frac{E}{E_0} \right] \right.$$

$$\left. \cdot \ln\,(183Z^{-1/3}) + \frac{1}{9}\frac{E}{E_0} \right\} \text{ cm}^2/\text{Mev}$$

where E is the final electron *total* energy in Mev and $r_0 = 2.82 \times 10^{-13}$ cm. For no screening ($\gamma \gg 1$),

$$\frac{d\sigma_b}{dk} = \frac{4Z^2r_0^2}{137k} \left[1 + \left(\frac{E}{E_0}\right)^2 - \frac{2}{3}\frac{E}{E_0} \right]$$

$$\cdot \left[\ln\frac{2E_0E}{0.51k} - \frac{1}{2} \right] \text{ cm}^2/\text{Mev}$$

Intermediate screening ($2 < \gamma < 15$) leads to much more complicated formulas.

The absolute number of bremsstrahlung photons in the photon energy interval dk radiated by a single electron of energy E_0 traversing a radiator of thickness dt and n atoms/cm³ is given by $(d\sigma_b/dk)n\,dt\,dk$, where $d\sigma/dk$ can be found from Fig. 3.

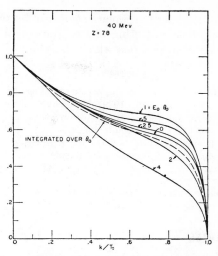

Fig. 2. Dependence of the spectral shape (Schiff's calculation) on the photon emission angle, θ. k is the photon energy in Mev. These curves are from Ref. 1. T_0 is the incident electron energy in Mev.

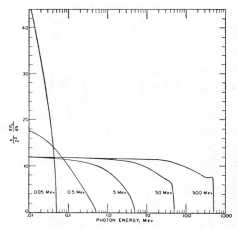

Fig. 3. Dependence of the Born-approximation absolute cross section integrated over the photon directions on the photon and electron energy. These curves are from Ref. 1.

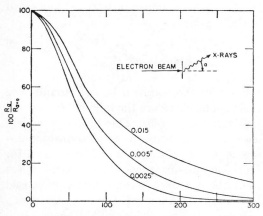

Fig. 1. Theoretical bremsstrahlung angular distributions from thick tungsten targets for relativistic energies. These data are obtained from the National Bureau of Standards Handbook 55. $R\alpha$ is defined as the fraction of the total incident electron kinetic energy that is radiated per steradian at the angle α.

It must be noted that photon-electron showers begin developing in approximately one radiation length and these formulas and curves apply only to the basic bremsstrahlung interaction itself or to radiators somewhat thinner than one radiation length. Bremsstrahlung beams are partially polarized only from extremely thin radiators ($< 10^{-3}$

radiation lengths). Polarization is obliterated by electron scattering and is unimportant in beams from practical thick radiators.

REFERENCES

1. H. W. Koch and J. W. Motz, *Rev. Modern Phys.* **31**: 920, 1959. Extensive survey of formulas and excellent presentation of curves for numerical calculation.
2. "Bremsstrahlung"—German; *bremsen*, to brake, and *Strahlung*, radiation.

Robert W. Kenney

Cross-references: *Radiation (Ionizing)*

BRIDGES

A bridge circuit is a network widely used for measurement purposes in which, when a voltage is applied to the network, the voltage appearing across one network branch can be brought to zero by adjustments of the parameters of other branches. Since at balance a mathematical relationship exists between the parameters of the balance-determining branches, the parameters of an unknown placed in one branch can be determined from the parameters of other branches. In a bridge, the balance condition is independent of the impedances of the voltage source and null detector, and the same balance point is obtained when the source and detector are interchanged. In some cases a more limited definition of a bridge is used, which specifies a network form similar to that shown in Fig. 1 in which the detector is "bridged" across equal potential points in the network.

Bridges are well suited for measurement purposes, since an unknown can be measured in terms of standards to a high degree of accuracy, independent of the voltage calibration or impedance of the source or detector. Since the balance condition is indicated by a null in the bridge output, very-high sensitivity detectors can be used to obtain resolutions of 1 part in 10^8 or better. Bridges are commonly used for measurements of frequency, rf power, resistance, inductance, capacitance, impedance, and admittance over wide frequency ranges. The majority of bridges are designed for use below a few hundred megacycles, but coaxial-line and waveguide forms of bridges have found many applications in the microwave region.

The most common form of bridge is the four-arm bridge shown in Fig. 1. The fundamental form of this bridge, in which all arms are resistive, is called the Wheatstone bridge. It was discovered by S. H. Christie in 1833, but its potentialities were not recognized until 1843, when Sir Charles Wheatstone called attention to them. The general balance equation which expresses the relationship between the impedances in the arms of a general four-arm bridge at balance is:

$$\frac{Z_x}{Z_C} = \frac{Z_B}{Z_A}$$

If an unknown impedance Z_x is connected in the x arm, then at balance,

$$Z_x = \frac{Z_B}{Z_A} Z_C$$

Some of the common bridge circuits and their applications are the following:

Wheatstone Bridge. This bridge is widely used for general-purpose resistance measurements. However, it is not well suited for precision measurements of resistances of less than about 1 ohm because of errors caused by lead and contact resistances.

Kelvin Double Bridge. This bridge is a four-terminal resistance bridge which is generally used for dc measurements of very low resistances. In it the effects of lead and contact resistances are eliminated.

Maxwell Inductance-Comparison Bridge. This ac bridge has inductors in two adjacent

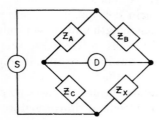

Fig. 1. General four-arm bridge.

arms and resistors in the other two arms, and is used for the comparison of inductances.

Maxwell Bridge (Maxwell-Wien). This ac bridge is used for the measurement of series inductance in terms of resistance and capacitance (Fig. 2).

Hay Bridge. This ac bridge is similar to the Maxwell bridge except that the loss-balancing resistor is connected in series with the standard capacitor rather than in parallel with it, and parallel inductance is measured directly.

Anderson Bridge. This ac inductance bridge is a modification of the Maxwell bridge.

Owen Bridge. This ac inductance bridge is frequently used for the measurement of series or parallel inductance in terms of capacitance and resistance. The inductance balance is usually made by means of a precision-variable resistor.

Schering Bridge. This bridge (Fig. 3) is widely used for measurements of capacitance and dissipation factor at low frequencies and also at very high voltages, and for capacitance, inductance and resistance at frequencies up to a few hundred megacycles. For high-frequency use, it can be modified to use only variable capacitors for the adjustable elements, which is an important feature since high-frequency variable resistors are inaccurate.

Bridges frequently used for mutual-inductance measurements are the Carey-Foster bridge, the Maxwell Mutual-Inductance bridge, the Heaviside Mutual-Inductance bridge, and the Heaviside-Campbell Mutual-Inductance bridge.

A relatively new type of general-purpose bridge is the transformer-ratio-arm bridge. In its basic form, this bridge is a four-arm bridge in which two of the arms are replaced by two very closely coupled coils, as shown in Fig. 4. The ratio arms are usually secondary windings of a transformer whose primary winding is connected to the signal source. At balance, the ratio between the standard and the unknown is almost exactly equal to the turns ratio n of the two coils. Balance

can be obtained by adjustments of the standards, by changing taps on the transformer, or by a combination of both. The bridge ratio can be increased by the use of a second tapped transformer in the detector circuit, in which case the effective ratio is the product of the turns ratios of the two transformers. In well-designed transformers, ratio errors are usually less than a few parts per million, and since the ratio is practically invariant with time, highly accurate bridges can be

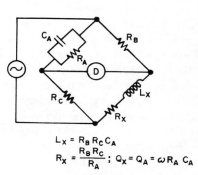

$$L_x = R_B R_C C_A$$
$$R_x = \frac{R_B R_C}{R_A} \; ; \; Q_x = Q_A = \omega R_A C_A$$

Fig. 2. Maxwell bridge.

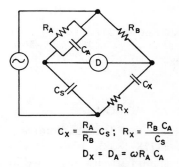

$$C_x = \frac{R_A}{R_B} C_S \; ; \; R_x = \frac{R_B C_A}{C_S}$$
$$D_x = D_A = \omega R_A C_A$$

Fig. 3. Schering bridge.

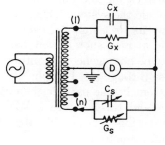

$$G_x = n G_S \; ; \; C_x = n C_S$$
$$n = \text{TURNS RATIO}$$

Fig. 4. Transformer bridge.

built using this circuit. One important feature of the bridge is that it is practically unaffected by impedances from either unknown terminal to ground, and hence, measures only the *direct* admittance or impedance appearing between the unknown terminals. This type of bridge can be used for measurements on all types of components and is particularly well suited to measurements on small capacitors. Transformer bridges have been built for use from the low audio frequencies to a few hundred megacycles.

Other types of null circuits which have been used for impedance measurements are the *Twin-T* circuit and the *Bridged-T* circuit. Both of these circuits fit the general definition of a bridge circuit, but have not usually been called true bridges because they lack the diamond network form often associated with bridge circuits. At vhf and microwave frequencies, various types of hybrid circuits, which are also null networks, have found many applications in impedance-measuring instruments.

R. A. SODERMAN

Cross-references: *Errors in Measurement, Impedance Measurements, Microwave Measurements, Standards*

BROWNIAN MOTION

In 1827 the British botanist, Robert Brown (1773–1858), discovered that extremely small particles suspended in a liquid perform a chaotic zigzag movement, seemingly never ceasing and uninfluenced by any factor outside the system. This movement is now known as *Brownian molecular motion.*

A liquid at rest, such as water in a glass, appears to be homogeneous, continuous, and motionless throughout. If a powder consisting of extremely fine particles is mixed with the water and this mixture is stirred well, again no motion is noticeable after the dispersion has come to rest. Microscopic studies have revealed, however, that this is actually not the case and that the fine particles which have been placed in water, or any other fluid,

do not sink if they are of colloidal size, but are endowed with a very vigorous motion that is quite haphazard and irregular. The particles, even though of colloidal dimensions, reflect enough light to be detectable in an ultramicroscope.

In 1863 C. Wiener said: "The movement does not originate in the particles themselves, nor in any cause exterior to the liquid, but must be attributed to internal movements characteristic of the fluid state." He also expressed the opinion that, according to thermokinetics, the movement of the dispersed particles is due to the irregular bombardment they receive from the surrounding molecules of the dispersion medium. His purely theoretical deductions were supported by a large number of very carefully conducted experiments carried out by Gouy and Cantoni.

Somewhat later, M. von Smoluchowski worked out the theory of the Brownian motion from a molecular-kinetic point of view. According to him, the middle kinetic energy of a particle, which is moved about by the impact of the surrounding molecules of the liquid, must in stationary condition be equal to the kinetic energy of these molecules. Therefore, the particle must behave as if it were a molecule of a dissolved substance. A similar deduction was drawn by Einstein, who assumed that particles which can be made visible in a microscope and which show Brownian motion must exert on an impermeable membrane exactly the same osmotic pressure as an identical number of molecules would.

ERNST A. HAUSER

Cross-references: *Noise*

BUNCHING

Bunching is the formation of a concentration or "bunch" of electrons. The concept of bunching has application to a wide variety of microwave tubes.

In a tube of conventional construction, the bunches are formed by means of Class C operation. In such a tube, a gating voltage applied to a control electrode prevents electrons from approaching the output region except in short intervals of time.

In two-cavity and reflex klystrons, the bunches are formed as the result of a difference of velocity imparted to electrons traversing the input region of the tube at different times in the signal cycle. In the drift space between the input and the output, the faster electrons overtake the slower ones. The original velocity difference or modulation consequently results in density modulation or bunching.

Similar phenomena in other microwave tubes such as traveling-wave tubes and magnetrons lead to a corresponding density modulation. In general, the combined action of static and dynamic electric and magnetic fields upon the electron stream results in the bunching within the stream.

In principle, knowledge of the bunching process allows calculation of the signal components of beam current at the output region of the device. This knowledge, in conjunction with information concerning the output coupling circuitry, allows calculation of the power output and related performance characteristics of the microwave tube. In practice, the calculations usually involve considerable analytical complexity and are only an approximation.

J. G. SKALNIK

Cross-references: *Applegate Diagram, Klystrons, Magnetrons, Traveling-Wave Tubes, Velocity Modulation*

C

CAPACITORS

Basic Relations. Capacitors are storage elements for electrical energy, the amount of energy being

$$(\tfrac{1}{2})V^2C \qquad (1)$$

where C is capacitance (or capacity) measured in f (farad) $= 10^6$ μf (microfarads) $= 10^{12}$ $\mu\mu$f or pf (picofarads). If V is measured in volts, the energy stored is in watt·sec. The capacity is defined by the quotient of the current flowing into (or out of) the capacitor and the rate of change of the voltage at the capacitor.

$$C = i/(dv/dt) \qquad (2)$$

For sinusoidal excitation of circular frequency ω, the reactance of the lossless capacitor is

$$jX = 1/j\omega C \text{ [ohm]} \qquad (3)$$

For uniform fields

$$C = \epsilon_0\,\epsilon' A/l \text{ [f]} \qquad (4)$$

with ϵ_0 = dielectric constant of free space = $(36\pi\cdot 10^9)^{-1}$[f/m] and ϵ' = relative dielectric constant (= 1 for vacuum), A = area of electrodes in m² and l = distance of electrodes in m.

For most dielectrics, a linear relationship exists between the electric flux-density D [coul − m^{-2}] and the electric field strength E [v − m^{-1}].

$$D = \epsilon_0\epsilon E \qquad (5)$$

Losses in the dielectric may be expressed by a complex dielectric constant

$$\epsilon = \epsilon' - j\epsilon'' \qquad (6)$$

where $\epsilon'/\epsilon'' = Q_e$ determines the dielectric quality factor. For $Q_e > 10$, the loss resistance of the capacitor is given by

$$(1/\omega C)/r_s = Q_e = \mathrm{R}_p/(1/\omega C) \qquad (7)$$

where r_s is the equivalent series and $R_p =$ the corresponding parallel loss resistance. $Q_e = 1/DF$ (DF = dissipation factor). The power factor is related to the DF by

$$PF = DF\sqrt{1/(1 + DF^2)} \qquad (8)$$

The loss factor $= (DF)\cdot\epsilon$ is proportional to the energy loss/cycle/voltage²/volume.

The transient behavior of a capacitor C in series with a resistor R is characterized by the time constant

$$CR = \tau \qquad (9)$$

For capacitor discharge (E_0 = starting voltage)

$$e_c/E_0 = e^{-t/\tau} \qquad (10)$$

and for capacitor charge (E_b = battery voltage)

$$e_c/E_b = 1 - e^{-t/\tau} \qquad (11)$$

Dielectrics and General Structure. The objective of developing a good *fixed* capacitor is to have the largest capacity in the smallest possible volume for a given operating voltage. Ideally, the capacitance is not to change with voltage, temperature, time, mechanical stress, humidity, and frequency, and (in most cases) is to have a minimum of losses.

The reliability of a capacitor is predominantly determined by the dielectric and the seal of the housing. One has to distinguish between failure value and withstand value. The failure value of dielectric strength is the voltage at which the material fails and is conventionally given as the average failure voltage. In contrast, the withstand value is a voltage below which no failure can be expected. The greatest capacity can be achieved by maximizing (a) ϵ and (b) A and minimizing (c) l cf. Eq. 4).

Typical for Case (a) are *ceramic* capacitors made in discoidal or tubular form (and now recently also as rolled capacitors). There are four classes of ceramic dielectrics:

(1) Semiconducting, so-called layerized, ceramics have a dielectric constant above 10^5. They can be used only for very low voltages (transistor circuits), are quite lossy, and have a strong dispersion of ϵ in the megacycle range.

(2) High-ϵ' dielectrics (mostly barium titanates) with ϵ' in the order of 6,000. They are quite temperature- and voltage-sensitive (nonlinearity and hysteresis) and are used as guaranteed-minimum-value capacitors (GMV).

(3) So-called stable dielectric capacitors with an ϵ' of 2,000 or, if doped with rare-earth materials, with an ϵ' of 3,000 to 4,000. They are much less dependent on temperature and applied dc voltage.

(4) Linear, high-Q (in the order of several thousand) temperature-compensating capacitors made with a prescribed (P positive, N negative, or NPO) temperature coefficient of the capacity for incorporation in temperature-stable tuned circuits (compensation of the temperature coefficient of the inductance). The ϵ of such materials is betwene 10 and 100.

Case (b) (large A) is exemplified best by stacked plates [silvered mica (for military use; excellent Q, T.C. about -100 ppm) or ceramic (monolithic)] or rolled dielectric strips [polystyrene; (excellent Q; commercial use; also about -100 ppm T.C.); Mylar; oil-impregnated paper; teflon, etc.].

Case (c) (small l) is represented by polarized capacitors (to make them unpolarized, two capacitors are connected in series in polarity opposition, usually in the same housing), and include the older, larger, and cheaper types are the aluminum foil electrolytics. The newer, more costly, but much smaller, types (having much less leakage current) are tantalum-oxide capacitors. Ti_2O_5 stands continuously the extraordinary field strength of 3×10^6 v/cm with an ϵ' of 25, l being measured in angstroms. The Q is of the order of 100. There are four distinct forms of tantalum capacitors: (1) tantalum wire anode (smallest size); (2) tantalum foil anode (in all voltage ranges; low and high temperature; edged to increase capacity; polarized and unpolarized); (3) sintered tantalum pellet anode (sometimes bulky to contain volatile electrolytes); and (4) solid electrolyte tantalum capacitors (not yet fully developed).

Continuously *variable* capacitors are applied for tuning purposes; ϵ, A or l, may be changed. Most common is change of A in an air capacitor by rotating one set of electrodes against the other. Shape of electrodes determines whether the angle of rotation gives linear change of capacity, frequency, or wavelength.

Applications and Special Capacitors. Capacitors are used for: (1) frequency determining or selective networks (LC circuits and filters; cf. Eq. 3); (2) energy storage (Eq. 1), for instance, the capacitor being slowly charged and quickly discharged (Eqs. 9 and 10) in a short burst of energy; and (3) integrators and differentiators (in conjunction with R; cf. Eq. 2).

A few practically significant particulars should be mentioned:

(1) For high voltage, the edges of the capacitor electrodes have to be formed according to the Rogowski profile to prevent corona and breakdown by field concentration at the edge. For very high voltages and high Q, either low-loss ceramics or vacuum capacitors are recommended.

(2) The lead inductance of shunt capacitors causes a series resonance above which the capacitor acts like an inductor (for instance, large-capacity tantalum capacitors may have a series resonance in the 10-kc range; small ceramic disc capacitors with a C of the order of 5,000 pf with extremely short leads may resonate in the 10-Mc range).

(3) For low-pass filters in the vhf, uhf, and microwave ranges, feed-through capacitors are required. They must be considered as fourpoles. Not only must the lead inductance (2) in the shunt branch be eliminated but the input and output end of the fed-through center conductor must be shielded from one another by mounting the outer electrode in a metallic shield and, in addition,

the transfer impedance of the capacitor must have no "suck-out" points. These parallel resonances in the capacitor proper represent a high impedance. They are just the opposite of what is required for an rf short circuit needed for feedback and interference elimination at these very high frequencies. Ceramic feed-through capacitors are preferred for their small size at these frequencies. The older, plain tubular feed-through capacitors have detrimental resonances in the vhf and uhf ranges. Much better feed-through capacitors for these very high frequencies are of the discoidal, cross-slotted tubular, and cascaded (with ferrite beads) tubular types.

(4) For microminiaturized circuits in integrated semiconductor networks, a capacitor dielectric can be formed by oxidizing the surface of the silicon to form SiO_2 (quartz).

(5) The dielectric of highly nonlinear capacitors is the depletion layer formed at the p-n junction by application of proper bias. These back-biased diodes have a reasonable Q and are widely used as nonlinear reactances in parametric amplifiers for vhf and high frequencies. Nonlinear ceramics are less suitable for this purpose because of their high losses and great temperature dependency.

H. M. SCHLICKE

Cross-references: *Dielectric Theory, Filters, Refractive Index*

CARCINOTRON: see BACKWARD-WAVE TUBES

CATHODE-RAY TUBES (DISPLAY)

This form of thermionic, vacuum tube ("CRT") consists of a minimum of five functional parts:

(1) An electron-beam source with means for varying beam current (gun).

(2) A focusing device to constrict the electron beam (lens).

(3) A system of deflection or beam positioning (electrostatic deflection plates or magnetic deflection coils).

(4) A thin layer target of phosphor upon which the beam impinges to produce cathodoluminescence or visual display (screen).

(5) An evacuated envelope enclosing the electron gun and phosphor screen (bulb).

Typical gun structures are shown with a cathode, a control or modulating "grid," and an accelerating or anode structure. Indirectly heated electron sources are common practice. The emitter or cathode is usually a nickel cylinder with a flattened end facing the phosphor screen. The flattened end is coated with a mixture of barium and strontium oxides to achieve a low work function (*q. v.*); i.e., a surface from which electrons escape at relatively low energy levels. The heater is usually tungsten wire, coated with an insulating layer of aluminum oxide.

The control electrode (grid) is usually a disk with a small aperture positioned centrally and parallel to the emitting area.

Another disk with a similar aperture is frequently used with a potential of several hundred volts positive with respect to the cathode, and this electrode is called "a screen grid." A high positive potential is applied to a cylindrically shaped electrode and a conductive interior bulb coating. This electrode furnishes the final accelerating potential field for the beam. Most practical electron guns exhibit cylindrical symmetry.

In most cathode-ray tubes the beam should be confined to a minimum dimension at the screen. The normal tendency of electron beams to spread as they emanate from the cathode source is counteracted by a convergent action of the focusing lens.

Electrostatic focusing lenses involve at least one cylindrical electrode with a potential considerably lower than the final anode potential.

The required beam-converging action may be obtained by the use of a magnetic focusing structure. Both permanent magnets and solenoid focusing units are used. A relatively efficient "thin-lens" form is preferred for low cost and efficiency of power.

The electron beam may be positioned by either electrostatic or magnetic means. Electrostatic deflection plates (Fig. 1a) are mounted on the interior of the bulb with connections "feeding through." In magnetic

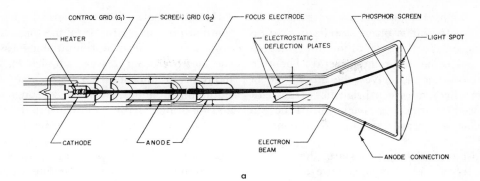

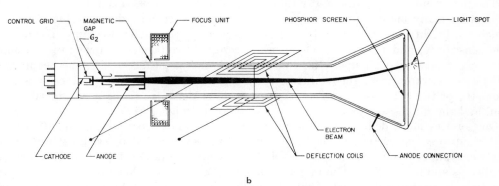

Fig. 1. Cathode-ray-tube deflection systems. (a) Electrostatic, (b) Magnetic.

deflection systems (Fig. 1b), the coils or solenoids are usually placed exterior to the tube.

The approximate formula for deflection displacement at the screen for the electrostatic deflection is as follows:

$$D = \frac{LpV_d}{2SV_a} \qquad (1)$$

The corresponding approximate expression for magnetic deflection is:

$$D = \frac{LpB}{3.4 \times 10^{-6}\sqrt{V_a}} \qquad (2)$$

In the foregoing formulas D is the displacement at the phosphor screen; V_d is a difference in deflection plate potential; V_a is the voltage equivalent of the beam velocity; L is the distance of the electron beam travel from the deflection center to the phosphor screen; p is the effective length of the deflection zone; B is the magnetic field in

webers per square meter; and S is the separation of deflection plates. (All lengths in the magnetic formula are in meters.)

It will be noted from the formulas that the deflection displacement is a direct function of the electron velocity (anode voltage) for the electrostatic case and the square root of the anode voltage for the magnetic case. This factor accounts in part for the wide use of magnetic deflection in television receivers where a high anode voltage is used.

The phosphor screen is usually a thin layer of inorganic, cathodoluminescent material. The material converts a part of the impinging beam energy into light. The material is thin to permit efficient penetration by the electron beam and to permit a maximum of contrast and brightness. It is common practice to use a thickness of approximately 2 microns per kilovolt of anode supply.

Since phosphors by nature are essentially insulators or semiconductors and have relatively high secondary-emission ratios, the screen potential is often stabilized by thin conductive coatings of aluminum, magnesium, or some other light metal. The thin metal coating also gives the advantage of higher effective screen brightness (the light that would normally go back toward the gun is reflected forward) and improved contrast ratio.

Most cathode-ray tubes are "hard" vacuum tubes and usually require a vacuum reading of 10^{-6} mm of Hg or better.

The performance of a cathode-ray tube is defined by many factors, prominent among which are brightness, contrast ratio, deflection sensitivity, and resolution. These performance factors depend upon the characteristics of electron gun, the voltages, the geometry of the bulb, focus, deflection system, and the fluorescent screen.

One of the most definitive measures of performance is the current intensity of the electron beam or resolution for given level of brightness and size of field. The majority of the cathode-ray tubes used today have been designed to meet the specified needs of domestic television. A resolution of 500 to 1000 lines in the total screen has been satisfactory for television purposes.

Recently, because of the advances in industrial and military electronics, high-resolution cathode-ray tubes have been designed and used. When high resolution is required at a high brightness, the electron gun must produce more current per unit area and the phosphor screen must be of fine, dense texture, and relatively thinner than conventional types.

N. F. FYLER

Cross-references: *Cathodoluminescence, Charactron, Dark-Trace Tubes, Electron Guns, Electron Optics, Electron-Tube Manufacture, Flying-Spot Scanning, Iconoscope, Image Intensifier, Image Orthicon, Monoscope, Radar Displays, Television (Color), Vidicon*

CATHODOLUMINESCENCE

Cathodoluminescence is luminescence arising from the excitation of phosphors by a cathode-ray beam. For commercial purposes the phosphor in microcrystalline form is deposited in a layer of optimum thickness for the electron-beam voltage applicable. The more usual phosphors are zinc and zinc-cadmium sulphides, zinc silicate, tungstates, and fluorides, with suitable impurity activators. A zinc phosphate is used as red component in color television tubes. In such screens linearity between beam voltage and light intensity may be obtained but a power-law relation is more usual (Fig. 1a). A sublinear relation is usual between emission and beam current density (Fig. 1b). Poor screen preparation can cause a 'dead' or threshold voltage effect owing to contamination on the surface facing the beam. However, 3-ev electrons can produce emission in zinc oxide. Intrinsic light output efficiencies may be higher than 25 per cent for zinc sulphides but usually center on 10 per cent. Some power is lost by backscattering of the primary beam. Secondary electron emission (*q. v.*) must be adequate to prevent screen charging and for tube potentials of about 6 or 7 kv or above aluminizing of the free sur-

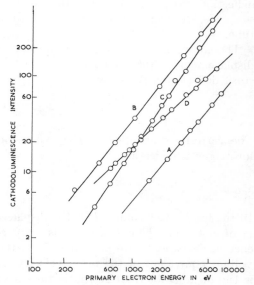

Fig. 1a. Variation of cathodoluminescence emission intensity with primary electron energy.

A. ZnS-Ag (10 μa/cm^2), B. ZnS-Ag (550 μa/cm^2), C. Zn$_2$SiO$_4$-Mn (5 μa/cm^2), D. ZnS-Mn (10 μa/cm^2).

face of the layer is necessary. If properly deposited the metal layer increases the forward light emission. Phosphors show a wide range of afterglow (persistence, phosphorescence) lasting from microseconds to many seconds of two main types, exponential or hyperbolic with time (or a mixture of the two), this being an important factor in choice of phosphors for specific applications.

Under extensive cathode-ray bombardment deterioration in efficiency occurs, which is more severe at low tube potentials since electron penetration is small and excitation densities high. The nature of this "electron burn" is not clearly understood and more systematic research is required. It is unlikely to be caused by ballistic disruption of the phosphor but is probably caused by intense ionization.

Fundamental mechanisms of cathodoluminescence are best understood by study of single-crystal phosphors. Linearity between electron energy and light output is usually found. The Thomson-Widdington law for penetration distance x vs electron energy

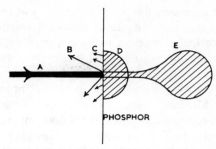

Fig. 2. Schematic diagram of electron penetration and scattering in a phosphor crystal.

A. Primary electron beam. B. Scattered primary electrons. C. Low-velocity secondary electrons. D. Excitation volume for low primary electron energy. E. Excitation volume for high primary electron energy.

can be assumed to be approximately true $E_0^2 - E^2 = bx$ where E_0 is incident electron energy, E that remaining at penetration distance x, and b is a constant). Recent work shows a marked dependence of decay constant on penetration depth, nonradiative loss of beam energy being prominent near the crystal surface. Scattering and excitation profiles appear to vary with the primary electron energy in the way shown in Fig. 2.

Substantial improvements in cathodoluminescence efficiency seem improbable but even small reductions in nonradiative transitions would permit higher beam powers (e.g., projection crt's) without undue phosphor heating. Transparent phosphor screens currently available give higher resolution and freedom from scattered room glare. Infrared and ultraviolet controlled cathode-ray-tube screen characteristics are still being explored.

Most of the above descriptions also apply to other cathodoluminescent devices, e.g., to photoelectric image intensifiers (*q. v.*).

G. F. J. GARLICK

Cross-references: *Cathode-Ray Tubes, Color Television, Electroluminescence, Fluorescence, Secondary Emmission*

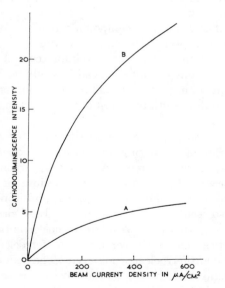

Fig. 1b. Variation of cathodoluminescence emission intensity with electron beam current density for a Zn_2SiO_4-Mn phosphor.

A. 4-kev electron energy, B. 10-kev electron energy (after Strange and Henderson: *Proc. Phys. Soc.* **58**: 369–401, 1946.

CERAMICS

There are three main classes of ceramic materials for electronic applications: insulator ceramics, dielectric ceramics, and magnetic ceramics. Insulator ceramics are used where high electrical resistivity and/or low dielectric losses are needed. Dielectric ceramics are useful because of their ferroelectric, antiferroelectric, and piezoelectric properties. Magnetic ceramics are useful because of their ferrimagnetic and antiferromagnetic properties. Typical materials, their properties at room temperature, and applications are given below.

Insulator Ceramics. Insulator ceramics of greatest importance are electrical porcelains, steatites, forsterites, aluminas, and beryllias. Electrical porcelains exist in a variety of compositions, but are mostly mullite with varying amounts of soda, potassia, calcia, magnesia, and zircon. These additive oxides combine with alumina and silica to form complex aluminum silicates or glass. Steatites are mainly enstatite with soda, potassia, and silica as additives. Forsterites are composed mainly of the mineral forsterite in a glassy matrix. Other oxides are not deliberately added, but occur as raw material impurities. Alumina ceramics are composed chiefly of 80–100 per cent alpha alumina. Silica, magnesia, and calcia are the most common additives to alumina ceramics; however, chromia and titania are also used. Additives may exist as complex aluminum silicates, spinel, glass, mullite, or in solid solution with the alumina. Beryllia ceramics contain beryllium oxide as their principal constituent. The beryllium oxide content of beryllia ceramics is commonly 95–100 per cent. Silica, magnesia, calcia, and alumina are common additives.

High electrical resistivities (10^{12} to 10^{18} ohm-cm) characterize insulator ceramics. Dielectric constants and dissipation factors of 6–10 and 0.010–0.00005, respectively, are common in the 1 to 10,000-Mc range. Dielectric strength for $\frac{1}{4}$-in.-thick specimens is generally 200–300 v/mil at 60 cps. Flexural strength can range from 9,000 to 60,000 psi, with aluminas the strongest and electrical porcelains the weakest materials. Thermal expansions (25–700°C) range from

5 to 11 $\times$ 10^{-6} per °C, and thermal conductivities from 0.002 to 0.07 cal/sec-cm²-cm-°C for all materials except the beryllias, for which the thermal conductivity can be as high as 0.53 cal/sec-cm²-cm-°C. The materials described are normally vacuum tight.

Typical uses of insulator ceramics are high-frequency insulators, high-temperature electrical insulators, vacuum-tube envelopes and spacers, circuit boards, antennas, substrates for miniature circuits, microwave windows, and radomes.

Dielectric Ceramics. Dielectric ceramics generally have titania as a basic ingredient. There are four classes of dielectric ceramics.

(1) Temperature - compensating bodies with dielectric constants between 15 and 900.

(2) Intermediate-dielectric-constant bodies, where $\epsilon' < 2000$.

(3) High - dielectric - constant ceramics, where $\epsilon' > 2000$. These ceramics are principally barium titanate and strontium titanate.

(4) Piezoelectric ceramics with dielectric constants between 1000 and 1500. Calcium titanate and lead titanate are piezoelectric materials.

The following compounds exhibit ferroelectric properties similar to the titanates: cadmium columbate, sodium columbate, potassium columbate, lead columbate, lithium columbate, sodium tantalate, potassium tantalate, lithium tantalate, and tungstic oxide.

Common additives to titanates for purposes of modifying ferroelectric properties are barium zirconate, calcium zirconate, strontium zirconate, and magnesium zirconate. Compounds of tin, copper, and iron are also used as property modifiers. Lead zirconate is a material with antiferroelectric properties. Dielectric ceramics are ferroelectric and antiferroelectric materials. The magnetic analogs of these materials are to be found in the magnetic ceramics, where one encounters the ferrimagnetic and antiferromagnetic materials.

Dielectric ceramics have volume resistivities of 10^8–10^{15} ohm-cm. The dielectric-constant range for dielectric ceramics is 15–10,000. These materials are subject to induced polarization, so that dielectric constant can be a function of electric field strength. Hysteresis curve shape for dielectric constant as a function of field strength can be varied by use of the forementioned additives. Dissipation factors of dielectric ceramics are usually 0.050–0.0002 at 1 Mc. Dielectric strength for $\frac{1}{4}$-in.-thick specimens is generally 50–300 v/mil at 60 cps. Thermal expansion (25–700°C) is 7–10 $\times$ 10^{-6} per °C. Thermal conductivity is 0.008–0.01 cal/sec-cm²-cm-°C. The Curie temperature range for dielectric ceramics is −260° C to +600°C (Barium titanate has a Curie temperature of 120°C.) Dielectric ceramics which have a wide variety of polarization properties are available. Dielectric ceramics are used in capacitors, transducers, memory devices, switching-devices, nonlinear circuit elements, attenuators, pick-ups, and piezoelectric devices.

Magnetic Ceramics. There are four classes of magnetic ceramics or ferrites: "soft" ferrites, "hard" ferrites, information-storage ferrites, and gyromagnetic ferrites. All exhibit ferrimagnetism or antiferromagnetism. "Soft" ferrites are nickel-zinc ferrite, and manganese-zinc ferrite, with the oxides of copper, magnesium, and cobalt commonly used as property-modifying additives. The "hard" or permanently magnetized ferrites are most frequently barium ferrite. Alumina, silica, lead oxide, copper oxide, and bismuth oxide can be used as additives. Information-storage ferrites are magnesium-manganese ferrite, copper-manganese ferrite, and lithium-nickel ferrite. Common additives for property modification to this group are nickel oxide, copper oxide, zinc oxide, calcium oxide, and lead oxide. Magnesium-manganese ferrite, nickel ferrite, and yttrium-iron garnet are gyromagnetic materials.

The properties of "soft," information-storage, and gyromagnetic ferrites are similar. They have volume resistivities between 1 and 10^9 ohm-cm. Their range of permeability is 1 to 5000 gauss per oersted. Saturation magnetization can be as high as 5000 gauss with 1500–3000 gauss as common values. A residual magnetization of 2700 gauss would commonly be associated with a saturation magnetization of 3000 gauss. The coercive field for "soft" ferrites is in the 0.17- to 5-oersted range. The Curie temperature ranges from 70–500°C for these materials. Information storage ferrites have square loop hysteresis curves which make them useful in memory storage devices where their switching times of 0.5–5 μsec are useful. The gyromagnetic ferrites have the property of microwave beam rotation and polarization over the frequency range of 0.5 to 30 kMc.

"Hard" ferrites can be permanently magnetized. A measure of permanent magnetization is the energy product B (gauss) $\times$ H (oersteds) which can be as great as 3.5 $\times$ 10^6. Volume resistivity of barium ferrite is 6×10^{10} ohm-cm. Permeability of the material is approximately 1 gauss per oersted. For a residual magnetization of 2200 gauss a coercive field of approximately 1700 oersteds is required. The Curie temperature of barium ferrite is approximately 400° C.

The "soft" ferrites are used for transformer cores and antenna rods. They are also used in filter coils, telephone circuits, and IF transformers. The information storage ferrites are used principally as magnetic memory cores in information storage systems. "Hard" ferrites are used as permanent magnets in many mechanical devices and as speaker magnets. Gyromagnetic ferrites are used in microwave gyrators.

LAURENCE E. FERREIRA

Cross-references: *Antiferromagnetism, Ferrimagnetism, Ferrites, Ferroelectrics, Magnetic Cores, Piezoelectricity and Pyroelectricity*

CERENKOV RADIATION

The Russian physicist Cerenkov first discovered experimentally that electrons moving with large constant velocity through polarizable media emit electromagnetic radiation. The correct theoretical explanation of the phenomenon was given by I. Frank and I. Tamm. It is essential for the medium to be optically dense, i.e., the velocity of light in it must be less than the velocity of light in vacuum. Let the velocity of light in the medium be denoted by u and the velocity of a charged particle moving through the medium by v. It is then easy to show that the radiation is emitted in directions making an angle θ given by

$$\cos \theta = u/v \qquad (1)$$

It is thus emitted along the generators of a cone of opening θ. In Fig. 1 let OP be the direction of movement of the charged particle. The passage of the charge polarizes the medium. The passing particle is equivalent to a pulse of current which, by its electromagnetic action, disturbs the movement of the orbiting electrons of the medium and causes them to radiate.

It is clear that the wavelets emitted by the medium along the path of the particle interfere with each other and the direction of radiation is the one where constructive interference takes place.

Let this direction, OQ, make an angle θ with the direction OP. While the electron has moved through a distance v the radiation has moved through a distance u. The points P and Q are thus points of equal radiation phase and the direction PQ is parallel to a wavefront. One sees that u must be smaller than v so that one obtains a real angle from

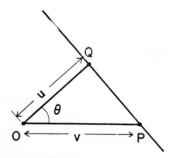

Fig. 1. Wave kinematics of Cerenkov radiation.

(1). One can show that the number of quanta N of radiation with angular frequency between ω and $\omega + d\omega$ is

$$N = \frac{1}{137} \left(1 - \frac{\mu^2}{v^2} \right) \frac{d\omega}{c}$$

The radiation extends over the frequency range for which $u < v$. One can show that in a waveguide the Cerenkov radiation forms a discrete spectrum and moves parallel to the axis of the guide. The velocity of the waves can be smaller than that of the electrons only if the guide is filled with a dielectric medium or when it incorporates a slow-wave structure. From the point of view of physics one may classify the amplifying action of an electron beam in a slow-wave structure such as a traveling-wave tube as a process of emission of Cerenkov radiation.

H. Motz

Cross-references: *Traveling-Wave Tubes*

CHANNEL CAPACITY

The capacity of a channel is defined as the maximum rate at which information can be transmitted over a channel. This maximization is to be taken over all sources that can be connected to the channel.

Channel capacity is given significance by Shannon's Coding Theorem (see his *Mathematical Theory of Communication*, University of Illinois Press, Urbana, 1949), which, in nonrigorous terms, states that the output from any source of rate R can, by suitable encoding and decoding, be transmitted over a channel of capacity $C > R$ with arbitrarily small error.

Since the channel in a communication system can usually be defined in several different ways, the channel capacity of a system is meaningless unless a particular channel is defined. For example, in a digital-data system, a coding theorist might define the channel to extend from the digital-data transmitter input to the digital-data receiver output, whereas a modulation expert might define the channel as the physical medium, thus getting a different capacity.

Although evaluation of the capacity of arbitrary channels is in general extremely difficult, explicit formulas are available in a few special cases. The simplest case is that of a noiseless channel for which the input accepts one symbol from an alphabet of k symbols each unit of time and for which the output is identical to the input. The capacity of this channel is $C = \log_2 k$ bits per symbol or bits per unit time, achieved by a source using the k symbols independently and equiprobably. More generally, the capacity can be computed for noiseless discrete channels even though the symbols are of unequal duration and constraints exist between the symbols.

A technique also exists for evaluating the capacity of a fairly broad class of noisy channels known as discrete constant channels (see, for instance, R. M. Fano, *Transmission of Information*, Technology Press, Cambridge, Mass., 1961), although the technique will not be described here. A discrete constant channel is specified by a finite alphabet of input symbols, x_i, $1 \leq i \leq n$; a finite alphabet of output symbols, y_j, $1 \leq j \leq m$; and a set of transition probabilities, $P(y_j \mid x_i)$. Each unit of time the channel input accepts one of the x_i and the output produces y_j with probability $P(y_j \mid x_i)$. A binary symmetric channel is a discrete constant channel with the same two symbols for input and output, and a probability p of the output differing from the input. Its capacity, achieved by a source of independent equiprobable binary digits, is

$$C = 1 + p \log_2 p + (1 - p) \log_2 (1 - p)$$

bits/symbol

The additive white Gaussian noise channel is an important example of the relatively few nondiscrete channels for which channel capacity is known. The inputs for this channel are assumed to be restricted to signals within a frequency bandwidth of W cps with an average power of at most S. White Gaussian noise with an average power per

unit frequency of N_0 is added to the channel input to obtain the channel output. The capacity of this channel is

$$C = W \log_2 \left(1 + \frac{S}{WN_0} \right) \quad \text{bits/sec}$$

When $S/WN_0 \gg 1$, the channel capacity increases almost linearly with W and logarithmically with S, whereas when $S/WN_0 \ll 1$, C increases almost linearly with S and is almost independent of W.

Robert G. Gallager

Cross-references: *Congestion and Waiting Systems, Information Theory, Noise, Statistical Communication Theory, Transmission Reliability*

CHARACTER RECOGNITION

Character recognition is a process by which a reading machine automatically identifies the digits, letters, or symbols in a printed or hand-written text. It is a new branch of science in its initial stages of development. This problem is of interest not only from the viewpoint of effective engineering applications but also because it reflects the modern tendency in engineering of assigning a machine an ever increasing number of functions that have been hitherto performed solely by a human being.

In character recognition, it is essential that a certain definite limited set of characters is used. The difficulty of character recognition usually arises from variations in characters, such as variations in size, shape, ink intensity, contrast gradient, positions, movements, and distortion. As a consequence, instead of a set of single characters, the recognition system deals with a set of classes of patterns. The classes of patterns or their characteristics are known to, or designed into, the machine. The aim of recognition is to identify the character presented to the machine by putting the character into an appropriate class according to some criterion. Many criteria for classification have been used. The recognition process is a many-to-one mapping.

The machine may err. However, it is possible to reduce the error rate by setting up the machine in such a way that in doubtful cases it refuses to identify, and rejects the character and/or notes the ambiguity of the results. The relative numbers of misrecognitions and rejections serve as a reliability measure of the recognition system. The over-all performance of the recognition system depends not only upon its capabilities but also upon external factors, such as numbers of characters to be recognized, character styles, and noise statistics.

Any character-recognition system consists of three basic operations: (a) presenting and sensing, (b) information processing, and (c) decision making. The pattern that is presented is first excited, such as by illumination or magnetization, and then applied to a certain transducer (usually photoelectric or electromagnetic) that generates an electric signal corresponding to the pattern. The signal is standardized (for example, converted into a sequence of discrete values). Some preprocessing of signals is often employed to reduce spurious noise or distortion, such as making the lines finer, smoothing the contours, eliminating small defects in the print, reducing the grainy effect of the print, eliminating small spots of extraneous origin, increasing the contrast, etc. The next stage is information processing, which is generally a data-reduction process, as classification puts the specific signal into a general class, often eliminating some of its specific characteristics in the process. Abstraction of information is performed according to some criterion that is most appropriate for the purpose of recognition. There are many forms of and approaches to the information abstraction. They are frequently variants of the abstracting schemes using one or more of: (a) geometrical; (b) topological; (c) statistical or probabilistic properties. In principle it is also possible and sometimes desirable to combine a part or all of the information processing with the sensing process. The decision process consists of comparing the results of the information abstraction with *a priori* knowledge of the classes of character patterns and in some optimum fashion identifying which of the possible characters is present, or rejecting if the observed data are ambiguous. The *a priori* knowledge of the character classes, characterized by the noise and signal structure, or standards, are stored explicitly in one or another form of memory or implicitly in the connections of logical elements of the recognition system. The process of registration and normalization is often included in recognition systems. This process is needed to register the character pattern properly into a standard position and to scale the pattern to a standard size. All these operations are interrelated and mutually dependent; one influences the other. An integrated approach to the recognition system design is required.

The recognition problem is essentially statistical in nature, and can be considered as a problem of testing multiple hypotheses in statistical inference. The concept of maximum likelihood or minimum risk in the statistical decision theory can be properly used as a criterion for optimum recognition.

Generally speaking, a decision rule for recognition partitions the signal space into disjoint regions and the recognition is performed by detecting in which region the unknown pattern lies. The basic problems in the character recognition are proper choices of the signal space, its coordinate system, and the decision rule. One of the dominating factors that influence these choices is the noise and signal structure, or the statistical data of the character variations with which the recognition machine is faced.

There are many existing or proposed reading machines. In the sensing schemes, the character field may be traversed continuously, selectively sampled at particular points, or sensed simultaneously. The sensors are either one-dimensional or two-dimensional in nature, as typified by a conventional magnetic read head and a television-type scanner. Other types are: polar scanning system following an initial centering of the character; tracing or curve-following scanner; parallel array of scanners; and mosaic sensing systems that let an entire character image fall upon and excite simultaneously a mosaic of photosensitve devices.

Many recognition techniques are employed in the present reading machines, including matching techniques and feature recognition. In the matching techniques, the signal derived from the pattern is compared with the reference characters stored in the machine, and the recognition is based on degrees of closeness in matching. The matching may be made on the entire character or on parts of the characters, where various parts may be properly weighted. Or, the image derived from the character pattern may be analyzed point by point over the entire image field to determine the features, or characteristics, of the input character. Most designers prefer to use criterion features derived from their experience with geometry, topology, or other fields. Ingenuity enters in choosing the features. Some examples of the features used in various systems are the number and location of horizontal or vertical strokes; concavity of the geometrical pattern; radius of curvature; number and nature of intersections of line segments.

The reading systems can be further classified according to the use of probability criteria; some systems take into account one or more probabilities in their computing and logic and others, because of simpler problems, require no probability factor.

Some machines, in addition to their recognition capability, have been designed to assimilate the statistical data based upon sample characters presented to them and to store the results or to modify locigal connections of the machines as standards for recognition. These machines are examples of "learning" or "adaptive" devices.

C. K. CHOW

Cross-references: *Computer Logic, Computer Printout and Reading, Decision Theory, Probability*

CHARACTERISTIC FREQUENCIES

In the study of the motion of charged particles, the following four terms are often encountered; plasma frequency, cyclotron (or gyro-) frequency, Larmor frequency, and collision frequency. Many of these concepts and their physical applications in the field of radio propagation are discussed by J. A. Ratcliffe.[1]

Plasma frequency is the natural frequency of oscillation of a plasma of equal and oppositely charged species of particles. The formula for plasma radian frequency is (in MKS units)

$$\omega_p = \left[\frac{\rho q}{\epsilon m^*} \right]^{1/2} \tag{1}$$

and the plasma frequency is $f_p = \omega_p / 2\pi$; ρ is the charge density of each species, q/m^* is the sum of the charge-to-mass ratios for the two species, and ϵ is the dielectric constant of the environment. Often the term is applied to electrons in a stationary neutralizing background, so that q/m is just 1.76×10^{11} coul/kg. In that case, the plasma frequency is $f_p = 9\sqrt{n}$ cps, if n is the electron density per cubic meter.

Analytically, the plasma frequency arises from a consideration of the electric field generated when the two species of charge are slightly displaced from one another by an amount x. A simple slab of plasma is considered.

$$E = -\frac{\rho}{\epsilon} x \tag{1}$$

The accleration thus produced is

$$\frac{d^2 x}{dt^2} = \frac{q}{m^*} E = -\frac{\rho}{\epsilon} \frac{q}{m^*} x \tag{3}$$

Since the solution to Eq. (3) is sinusoidal at a frequency f_p, the plasma is resonant at this frequency.

Cyclotron frequency (gyro-frequency) is the frequency of rotation of a charged particle in a steady magnetic field, given by $f_c = (q/2\pi m)B$ in MKS units. The corresponding radian frequency is $\omega_c = (q/m)B$. In these expressions q is the charge carried by the particle, m is its mass, and B is the magnetic field strength (flux density). In practical units, the cyclotron frequency for an electron is 2.80 Mc/gauss, and for a proton it is 1.52 kc/gauss. This is the frequency at which a cyclotron (q.v.) must be operated in order to accelerate charged particles synchronously, hence the name. In some other branches of physics, and in the study of radio propagation, this quantity is called the gyro-frequency.

The analytical significance of the cyclotron frequency may be seen from consideration of the force equation for an electron in a steady magnetic field

$$dv/dt = \frac{e}{m}\, v \times B \tag{4}$$

If the electron velocity is initially perpendicular to the field, this equation has as a solution a velocity vector rotating in direction with a frequency f_c, and a constant magnitude.

The cyclotron frequency has a practical significance in any problem where charged particles in a magnetic field are exposed to alternating electric fields, as the motion of the particles resonates with a circularly polarized electric field at this frequency.

Larmor frequency is one half the cyclotron frequency, $f_L = (q/4\pi m)B$ for electron motion in a steady magnetic field. The corresponding radian frequency is $\omega_L = (q/2m)B$. The Larmor frequency has significance in the field of mechanics, as it is the frequency with which a rotating charged particle precesses about a steady magnetic field. The concept was originally introduced by Larmor[2] and is discussed in modern terms by Brillouin.[3] The mechanical significance of the Larmor frequency can conveniently be seen in a uniform magnetic field. Particle motion across the field lines is considered. The generalized momentum $\hat{p}$ of a particle is given by $\hat{p} = p - qA$ in MKS units were A is the vector potential and p the mechanical component of momentum,

mv. The generalized angular momentum about the axis of the magnetic field is then $\hat{p}_\theta = m\omega r^2 - qrA$. If the field is uniform, the total flux is $\phi = 2\pi rA$; thus one can write

$$\hat{p}_\theta = m\omega r^2 - q\,\frac{\phi}{2\pi}$$

$$= m\omega r^2 - qr^2\,\frac{B}{2}$$

It is now seen that a particle rotating with angular velocity $\omega_L = (q/2m)B$ has zero generalized angular momentum. Then ω_L is the mean angular frequency of a particle that started its trajectory outside the magnetic field and has had no transverse forces acting on it other than magnetic. Note that $\omega_L = \frac{1}{2}\omega_c$, and thus a particle arbitrarily injected into a magnetic field has an irregular motion such that its average angular velocity is ω_L while the particle describes a local circular motion in addition, so that the rate of rotation about the guiding center is ω_c.

Collision frequency is an average rate at which particles collide with others. There is in principle a collision frequency for each type of atomic collision process. Furthermore, since collision rates may depend on velocity, a measured collision frequency may depend on the particular experiment used. In spite of the limitations, it is a useful concept, as the effect of collisions may be put into the force equation for a particle as follows:

$$m\,\frac{dv}{dt} = \text{Force} - m\nu_c v$$

where ν_c is the collision frequency. In the analysis of propagation in ionized media, the collision frequency in this form explains the observed dissipative processes.

REFERENCES

1. J. A. Ratcliffe, "Magneto-Ionic Theory," Cambridge University Press, 1959.
2. J. Larmor, "Aether and Matter," Cambridge University Press, 1900; Ch. 4.
3. L. Brillouin, Phys. Rev. **67**:260, 1945.

D. G. Dow

CHARACTRON

The Charactron shaped-beam tube is a special-purpose cathode ray tube used to display letters, numbers, and symbols at rates compatible with the output from digital computers. The information displayed on the tube face may be viewed directly to obtain "real-time" information or may be recorded on film or other media for later use.

Several methods have been developed for the display of alphanumeric information. Whereas most of the techniques involve complex waveforms, a matrix of dots or straight line segments to form the character, much as one would with a pencil, in the Charactron method the character is formed by controlling the cross section of the electron beam, by directing the electron beam to one of a series of stencil-like openings to shape the beam cross section into the desired character.

Figure 1 shows the relative location of the elements in one type of tube. In operation an electron beam is formed using a standard electron gun. The beam diameter is adjusted to equal the center-to-center spacing of the characters in the matrix. Selection of the desired character is accomplished by use of a set of electrostatic plates, called selection plates, located between the electron gun and the matrix. Selection of the character to be displayed is accomplished by means of a 6-bit code from the computer or programming source. The information is fed into selection decoders, 3 bits for the X coordinate and 3 for the Y coordinate. The decoders convert the input information into X and Y deflection voltages which, after passing though amplifiers, are applied to the deflection plates. These voltages cause the electron beam to be deflected to one of the character positions in the matrix. Since the matrix consists of a two-dimensional array, the selection of a character requires deflecting the electron beam away from the tube axis. If the beam is not returned to the optical axis, a nonuniform display results when the beam is deflected to the screen. To overcome misregistration, two elements are added. One of these, the convergence coil, is merely a solenoid. The magnetic field of the coil redirects the electron beam toward the optical axis. A conjugate set of electrostatic plates, called reference plates, supplies the correction necessary to redirect the beam along the optical axis.

Deflection of the shaped beam to the desired position on the tube face is accomplished in the conventional method, using either electrostatic or magnetic deflection. One difference from the usual cathode-ray

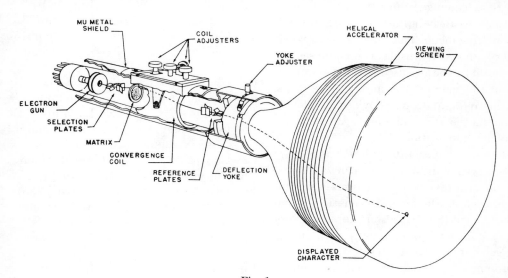

Fig. 1.

tube is that deflection occurs in a step-like fashion rather than as a scan. That is, selection, reference, and deflection voltages are established to display the desired character at the required position on the screen; the electron beam is then unblanked, after which a new set of conditions are established. Positioning of the beam at the tube face is achieved using a digital input from the computer with the number of bits determined by the accuracy required. Often 10 bits for X and 10 bits for Y positions are used.

This type of display is capable of very high speeds. The ultimate speed is determined by the application and choice of components. As an example, if magnetic deflection is employed, a compromise must be made between yoke sensitivity and speed of response. In general, 15 to 50 μsec are allowed for the establishment of equilibrium deflection currents. Depending upon the requirements, 10 to 50 μsec unblanking time is allowed for displaying the information. This yields recording speeds of 10,000 to 40,000 characters/sec. If electrostatic deflection is used the deflection voltages can be established in 2–3 μsec. Using a display time of 7–8 μsec per character yields display rates of 100,000 characters/sec or higher.

In addition to its use as a character display, by changing the focus voltage the electron beam can be adjusted to operate in a spot writing mode. This mode allows regular raster scan or PPI displays to be presented. The beam can be also used with the computer output to generate grid lines, graphs, maps, or other data, and thus provides an all-electronic means of combining graphical and character information.

The most important applications to date for this type of display have been varied and include such diverse uses in aircraft surveillance, such as the Semi-Automatic Ground Environment (SAGE) system; air traffic control ($q.\ v.$), an aid to computer programming, the generation of engineering drawings on microfilm, and the high-speed printout of magazine address labels, billing, and high-speed data transmission.

SHERMAN H. BOYD

Cross-references: *Cathode-Ray Tubes (Display), Computer Printout and Reading, Electrostatic Printing, Facsimile*

CHEMICAL ELEMENTS

In the following list of chemical symbols, the atomic weight appears in parentheses. Elements 57 to 71 constitute the lanthanide series (rare-earth elements), and 89 and above, the actinide series.

Ac	Actinium (9)	Eu	Europium (63)
Al	Aluminum (13)	Fm	Fermium (100)
Am	Americium (95)	F	Fluorine (9)
Sb	Antimony (51)	Fr	Francium (87)
A	Argon (18)	Gd	Gadolinium (64)
As	Arsenic (33)	Ga	Gallium (31)
At	Astatine (85)	Ge	Germanium (32)
Ba	Barium (56)	Au	Gold (79)
Bk	Berkelium (97)	Hf	Hafnium (72)
Be	Beryllium (4)	He	Helium (2)
Bi	Bismuth (83)	Ho	Holmium (67)
B	Boron (5)	H	Hydrogen (1)
Br	Bromine (35)	In	Indium (49)
Cd	Cadmium (48)	I	Iodine (53)
Ca	Calcium (20)	Ir	Iridium (77)
Cf	Californium (98)	Fe	Iron (26)
		Kr	Krypton (36)
C	Carbon (6)	La	Lanthanum (57)
Ce	Cerium (58)	Lw	Lawrencium (103)
Cs	Cesium (55)		
Cl	Chlorine (17)	Pb	Lead (82)
Cr	Chromium (24)	Li	Lithium (3)
Co	Cobalt (27)	Lu	Lutetium (71)
	Columbium (see Niobium)	Mg	Magnesium (12)
		Mn	Manganese (25)
Cu	Copper (29)	Md	Mendelevium (101)
Cm	Curium (96)		
D	Deuterium	Hg	Mercury (80)
Dy	Dysprosium (66)	Mo	Molybdenum (42)
Es	Einsteinium (99)	Nd	Neodymium (60)
Er	Erbium (68)	Ne	Neon (10)

Np	Neptunium (93)	Se	Selenium (34)
Ni	Nickel (28)	Si	Silicon (14)
Nb	Niobium (41)	Ag	Silver (47)
N	Nitrogen (7)	Na	Sodium (11)
No	Nobelium (102)	Sr	Strontium (38)
Os	Osmium (76)	S	Sulfur (16)
O	Oxygen (8)	Ta	Tantalum (73)
Pd	Palladium (46)	Tc	Technetium (43)
P	Phosphorus (15)		
Pt	Platinum (78)	Te	Tellurium (52)
Pu	Plutonium (94)	Tb	Terbium (65)
Po	Polonium (84)	Tl	Thallium (81)
K	Potassium (19)	Th	Thorium (90)
Pr	Praseodymium (59)	Tm	Thulium (69)
		Sn	Tin (50)
Pa	Protactinium (91)	Ti	Titanium (22)
		W	Tungsten (74)
Pm	Promethium (61)	U	Uranium (92)
		V	Vanadium (23)
Ra	Radium (88)	Vi	Virginium (87)
Rn	Radon (86)		Wolfram (see Tungsten)
Re	Rhenium (75)		
Rh	Rhodium (45)	Xe	Xenon (54)
Rb	Rubidium (37)	Yb	Ytterbium (70)
Ru	Ruthenium (44)	Y	Yttrium (39)
Sm	Samarium (62)	Zn	Zinc (30)
Sc	Scandium (21)	Zr	Zirconium (40)

CHARLES SUSSKIND

Cross-reference: *Abbreviations*

CHOKES: see COILS; WAVEGUIDES

CHROMATRON: see TELEVISION (COLOR)

CIRCLE DIAGRAM: see SMITH CHART

CIRCUITS: see NETWORK THEORY

CIRCUIT BREAKERS

A circuit breaker is a device for interrupting a circuit between separable contacts under normal or abnormal conditions. Proper selection of a circuit breaker for any particular application requires that the circuit breaker shall (1) withstand the maximum voltage stress to which it may be subjected; (2) carry rated current continuously without damage; (3) have sufficient interrupting capacity to interrupt fault currents, of any magnitude within its rating, a designated number of times and subsequently to remain closed on normal load current; (4) be suitable for operation in the intended environment with due consideration to ambient temperature, atmospheric pressure, relative humidity, contaminants in the atmosphere (sand, dust, explosive gases, corrosive substances), and to mechanical shock and vibration; and (5) provide the protective function or combination of protective and control functions as may be required.

Circuit breakers using the hydraulic-magnetic principle of delayed tripping on overload are used extensively for protection of electronic components and circuitry because (1) they may be precisely rated for protection of components, (2) their small physical size minimizes panel-space requirements, (3) they require less operating energy than other direct-acting overload protective devices, and (4) their mechanical and electrical design features may be varied to suit particular application requirements and to perform multiple protective and control functions.

The circuit-breaker mechansim consists of the magnet frame, the coil-and-tube assembly, a toggle linking the handle with the moving contact, and the armature and tailpiece assembly. The magnet frame is positioned and supported within the molded case.

Fault sensing is accomplished by the coil and-tube assembly consisting of a movable iron core surrounded by a tube of nonmagnetic material, the remaining space being filled with hydraulic fluid (silicone or other fluid). The core is normally held at the end of the tube opposite the pole face by a light compression spring; the magnet coil surrounds the other end of the tube. Under short-circuit conditions, sufficient magnetic flux is developed to attract the armature and trip the circuit breaker instantly without affecting the position of the core. On smaller fault currents, the initial magnetic flux is insufficient to produce tripping and the iron core is attracted by solenoid action toward the pole face, its velocity governed by the magnitude of the current and the retardation effect of the hydraulic fluid. The entry of the iron core into the magnetic circuit reduces the reluctance to a point at which the magnetic flux is sufficient to trip the circuit breaker. The core spring then returns the iron core to its initial position and, after correction of the condition that caused the overload, the circuit breaker may be immediately reclosed.

If time-delay tripping is not required, the magnetic circuit may have a fixed rather than a variable reluctance; circuit breakers may be constructed to provide instantaneous tripping at overload values of 120 per cent of continuous current rating.

Silicone fluid is the most usual damping medium, although other types of hydraulic fluids are also used; the time delay depends on the viscosity.

Mechanical Design Modifications

Either normally open or normally closed circuit-breaker contacts may be provided. A locking device may be applied to the circuit-breaker handle which, although not affecting the automatic operation, prevents manual operation until its removal. Single-pole, double-throw, snap-action auxiliary switches may be applied (to any pole having no more than two terminal studs) for interlocking purposes or to provide remote indication of the condition of the circuit. By special design of the magnetic circuit, it is possible to produce circuit breakers for operation up to 400 cps.

For operation under conditions of varying ambient temperature and high humidity, cadmium-plated ferrous parts may be further protected by a chromate dip treatment. Phenolic-resin molded parts may be treated with fungus-resistant lacquer, or special molding materials may be used that are inherently fungus resistant.

Standard circuit-breaker construction employs a latch mechanism that is inherently "trip-free": the latch mechanism operates independently of the handle under overload or short-circuit conditions. In certain applications (aircraft landing-gear control, control of traverse and elevation motors of machine-gun mounts), protection of the equipment is less important than the performance of the function that the equipment provides. To suit such needs, the toggle mechanism may be modified to provide "non-trip-free' operation, enabling the operator to maintain the circuit closed under overload conditions.

Circuit breakers intended for airborne use, or for other applications in which mechanical vibration and shock may be encountered, incorporate counterbalances on the armatures and on the latches to render them vibration-proof and shock-resistant.

Multiple functions can be provided within one device (two-pole or three-pole circuit breaker) by selection of the proper combination of mechanical and electrical features.

Electrical Design Modifications (Fig. 1)

(1) *Series-overload* construction is the most commonly used type in which the coil

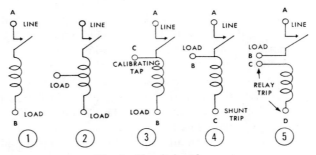

Fig. 1. Circuit breakers.

is in series with the contacts and there are two terminals per pole, a line terminal and a load terminal.

(2) *Dual-rating* construction is similar to series-overload type except that an additional terminal is provided connected to a tap on the overload coil. This construction permits one circuit breaker to be used alternatively on loads of two different current ratings.

(3) *Calibrating-tap* construction is similar to series-overload type except for the addition of a third terminal electrically connected at the junction of the coil and contacts. This construction employs three terminals per pole and permits two electrical loads to be connected to one circuit breaker and controlled by it, responsive to overloads only in the circuit that is supplied through the overload coils of the circuit breaker. Calibrating-tap construction also affords a ready means of supplying a dual-voltage load through a simple link-switching arrangement where the voltage ratio (and hence current ratio) is 2:1. Calibrating-tap construction may be employed to provide an adjustable trip point by shunting the coil with a variable resistor. This scheme is usually applicable only on circuit breakers rated under 1 amp. Addition of a diode in series with the resistor provides a simple method of reverse-current protection, with adjustable trip point for overloads in the forward direction.

(4) *Shunt-trip* construction employs three terminals per pole. In this construction, no overload protection is provided and the coil is designed to operate from the line voltage. The coil may be energized from a remote point by means of a pushbutton or by contacts on one or more relays or other devices used to sense any measurable function (temperature, pressure, water level, accumulation of products in a conveyor system, etc.) that may be affected by the electrical circuit served by the circuit breaker. It should be noted that the coil is self-protected in that tripping of the circuit breaker will de-energize the coil.

(5) *Relay-trip* construction employs four terminals per pole, as the contacts and the coil are electrically separate. This construction is most versatile, as it permits the coil to be wound for operation at specified current values or for use at voltages and frequencies different from those of the power supply of the circuit breaker. Either instantaneous or time-delay tripping may be specified and high-voltage insulation may be secured to insulate the coil from the circuit breaker frame and permit the coil to be used, in some instances, in circuits at 1,000,000 v.

General Considerations

The various coil constructions described above use single bobbins and single coils. Additional versatility in design and application is obtained by the use of two coils wound either on one or on separate bobbins.

New problems arise from the use of transistors in computer circuits, in which dc voltages up to 1000 v (appreciably higher than the nominal dc voltage ratings of circuit breakers) are used; proper functioning of the computers requires that these voltages must be held to their design values within close limits. The incorporation of a multiturn blowout coil in the stationary contacts permits successful operation on circuits up to 1000 v dc, and the use of silver inlays on the contacts and silver-plating of contacts and terminals reduces the terminal-to-terminal voltage drop to acceptable limits.

Immediate restoration of power, following removal of fault condition, is made possible by the incorporation of a check valve in the iron core. During the overload sensing phase the valve remains closed and the hydraulic fluid is caused to flow between the surface of the core and the wall of the tube. After the circuit breaker trips, the core spring forces the core away from the pole face and the pressure of the hydraulic fluid causes the valve to open, allowing the hydraulic fluid to flow through the longitudinal hole in the core. In some applications it is desirable that the circuit breaker shall "remember" recently occurring overload conditions and an integrating effect may be provided by using a solid core or, in some instances, by using a valve type of core with an inverted check valve so that overload sensing (accompanied by extension of the core re-set time) may be accomplished more rapidly.

F. M. Ballou

Cross-references: *Contacts, Relays, Switches*

CIRCULATORS

Microwave ferrite circulators are three-port or four-port transmission-line structures designed so that rf power entering at port 1 appears at port 2, power entering at port 2 appears at port 3, etc. This basic circulator characteristic may be achieved for all load impedances and rf power levels.

The principle of operation of a typical ferrite circulator is based on either of two nonreciprocal effects: (a) Faraday rotation of the plane of polarization in circular waveguide propagating the dominant TE$_{11}$ mode through the use of axial magnetic fields, or (b) nonreciprocal phase shift in rectangular waveguide oeprating in the dominant TE$_{10}$ mode. A third method employed is (c) field displacement in TE$_{10}$ mode rectangular waveguide using transversely biased ferrites. In all cases the circulator characteristic is achieved through the difference exhibited by the real component of the complex permeability tensor of the ferrite material when the ferrite is exposed to positive or negative circularly polarized microwave fields.

Microwave Circulators Employing Faraday Rotation. Figure 1 shows a typical X-band waveguide (RG-52/U) three-port ferrite circulator (or polarization rotator) employing nonreciprocal rotation of 45° in the plane of polarization of the E_y component of a wave propagating in the dominant TE$_{11}$ circular waveguide mode. A variation of this basic design utilizes a fourth arm adjacent to arm 3 but oppositely polarized, which is decoupled from the circular waveguide structure by a structure similar to that shown for arm 3. The advantage of this design is that in a radar receive-transmit duplexer any power reflected from the receiver arm (3) is absorbed by a matched load in the fourth arm, thereby preventing any reflected power from entering the transmitter arm (1).

In operation, rf energy traveling from port 1 to port 2 is rotated clockwise by +45° so that it emerges with minimum loss from arm 2; and conversely, rf energy traveling from arm 2 toward arm 1, after experiencing a polarization rotation of 22.5° in passing through port 2 and being unaffected by the ferrite section, is oriented so that it does not couple to port 1, but passes into the output arm of the rectangular waveguide structure arm 3. Energy entering at port 3

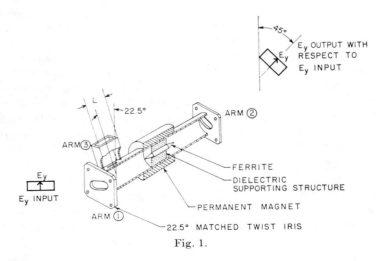

Fig. 1.

travels toward port 2 and is rotated 45°. It is then reflected from port 2 to emerge from port 1, and so on.

The primary limitations of this circulator form are that (1) difficulty is experienced in covering a broad frequency range owing to the variation in Faraday rotation as a function of frequency, (2) the power handling capacity is limited to approximately 50 w cw owing to the inability of the ferrite rod in this structure to dissipate the heat generated by resistive losses, and (3) since this circulator uses an unsaturated nonoriented anisotropic ferrite material, its low-frequency limit is about 3 kMc.

The primary advantage of Faraday rotation circulators is that for narrow-band medium-power switching or duplexing applications in the frequency ranges 8 to 75 kMc, it is possible to construct extremely compact circulators. For example, an X-Band circulator with 25 db isolation over a 400-Mc bandwidth may be 2 in. long by 1.5 in. in diameter.

Ferrite Circulator Employing Nonreciprocal Phase-Shift Transverse Field Principle. A nonreciprocal phase shifter, having different phase shift in opposite direction of propagation, is the heart of this type circulator. One or two ferrite slabs are placed symmetrically with respect to the waveguide center of two adjacent parallel waveguides as shown in Fig. 2. When the ferrites are biased with opposite magnetic fields, the structure exhibits known nonreciprocal changes in phase constant. For the loading shown, the transcendental equation describing the phase characteristics is obtained by

solving the propagation equations in accordance with the boundary conditions within the ferrite loaded section.

For a single slab of ferrite, if one dimension of the slab is small compared with the incident signal wavelength the amount of differential phase shift may be approximated by expanding the phase velocity v_g in a Taylor series in powers of the ferrite thickness t about the point $t = 0$ (corresponding to propagation in an infinitely thin layer section of ferrite). Determined by experimentation, the relative phase shift for a given frequency occurs when the ferrite material is spaced from the waveguide wall approximately $\frac{1}{8}$ to $\frac{1}{4}$ of the waveguide broad dimension. This region also occurs within the region of planes of positive and negative circular polarization in unloaded rectangular waveguide propagating the TE_{10} mode. In operation the rf power flow for a signal incident at port 1 would be as follows: The rf power splits into two equal parts, in the adjacent transmission-line sections shown in Fig. 2. With the external biasing dc fields applied as shown in Fig. 2, the portion of the rf signal propagating in the left-hand transmission-line section experiences a velocity propagation phase delay of $-45°$ (electrical) with respect to the phase of the original signal incident at both ports of the duplexing section initially. This phase change is due to the resonance absorption and ferromagnetic tensor permeability change induced in the ferrite material in the left arm of Fig. 2 by the direction and density of the external dc field. Through the use of the proper input and output 90° shunt hybrids, it is now

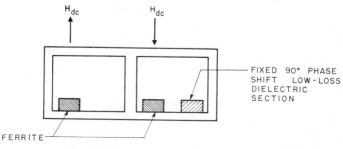

Fig. 2.

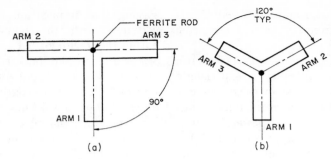

Fig. 3.

possible to have all the rf power incident at port 1 emerge at port 2.

In a typical pulsed radar system, one antenna may be used for both transmitting and receiving. This type of duplexer may also be used as a high-speed switch by reversing the magnetic field in the ferrite loaded portions of the differential phase shift section. The power flow is then reversed and the port order becomes 1, 4, 3, 2, 1. Extending this approach, if the load is replaced by another antenna, the source may be switched between the two antenna outputs and provide both receive-transmit functions for both antennas by reversing and dc field.

Three-Port Field Displacement Y and T Ferrite Circulators. This type of ferrite circulator employs a technique in which the field in a waveguide is displaced by a ferrite. The major difference between Y and T circulators, as shown in Fig. 3, is that the ferrite-loaded Y circulator is geometrically symmetrical looking into any of its ports; whereas the T type is asymmetrical with respect to junction signal phase characteristics. This basic asymmetry inherent in the T structure limits the bandwidth and application of T-type circulators because of the necessity of matching input ports to the transmission-line junction. For this reason this particular portion of the discussion shall be confined to symmetrical Y-type circulators.

The basic Y circulator consists of an H-plane (shunt) junction of three identical rectangular waveguides. The junction region contains a symmetrical loading of ferrite material at the linear plane of polarization (at the center of the waveguide). This ferrite is transversely magnetized by an external field. A signal incident to any arm of the structure appears at an adjacent arm. The ferrite element serves two functions. One is to induce an asymmetric electrical field at the common junction, so that differential rf propagation characteristics are achieved by distorting either the positive or negative circularly polarized plane inherent in the TE_{10} mode configuration. The other function is to provide a method of matching reactance at the junction by appropriate selection of the permeability and dielectric constant of the ferrite rod and correct transverse dc field. The use of this technique causes all the power to be diverted into an adjacent waveguide by inducing the asymmetric electric-field configuration and matching out any reflection introduced by the ferrite loading at the junction. The principal advantages of application of the Y circulator are:

(1) The circulator may be operated without the matching devices and is insensitive to load impedance.

(2) Wide bandwidth.

(3) Low insertion loss and high isolation of all ports.

(4) Minimum size, since matching considerations are eliminated.

(5) High power application, since a minimum of energy is absorbed by the ferrite element. Waveguide systems employing Y type circulators are capable of handling 100 kw peak and 100 w average power.

(6) Extremely high-speed switching of incident rf signals may be accomplished by

switching the transverse biasing field, since the transverse field required is extremely small: e.g., 60 gauss at S-band frequencies in RG-48/U waveguide. Switching speeds of less than 1 μsec have been achieved in a TEM-mode strip-line (*q.v.*) version of the Y type circulator.

D. S. ELKORT

Cross-references: *Attenuators and Isolators, Faraday Effect, Ferrites, Microwave Measurements, Waveguides and Waveguide Components*

CLASS A, AB, B, C OPERATION

Power amplifiers are classified as Class A, Class B, or Class C according to the location of the operating point on the plate current-grid voltage characteristic as indicated in Fig. 1.

Class A: An amplifier in which the grid bias and ac grid exciting voltage are such that plate current in the tube under consid-

eration flows for the entire 360° of the grid exciting voltage cycle when this voltage is applied.

Class B: An amplifier in which the grid bias is approximately equal to the cutoff value so that the plate current in the tube under consideration is approximately zero when no ac grid exciting voltage is applied, and flows for essentially 180° of the grid exciting voltage cycle when this voltage is applied.

Class C: An amplifier in which the grid bias is considerably greater than the cutoff value so that plate current in the tube under consideration is approximately zero when no ac grid exciting voltage is applied, and flows for appreciably less than 180° of the grid exciting voltage cycle when this voltage is applied.

Class AB: An amplifier intermediate between a Class A and a Class B in operation. In this amplifier the grid bias is such that plate current in the tube under consideration flows for considerably more than 180° but

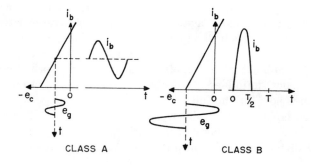

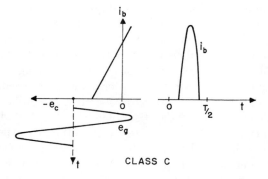

Fig. 1. Class A, B, and C operation.

less than 360° of the grid exciting voltage when this voltage is applied.

Class-A power amplifiers are used almost exclusively at audio frequencies. The waveform of the plate current in a Class-A amplifier is a good replica of the grid signal and there is little distortion in the output.

Class-B power amplifiers are used as audio-frequency amplifiers and as rf amplifiers. Since in this type of operation the plate current flows for only 180° of the grid exciting signal it is necessary to use push-pull operation when audio frequencies are being amplified. Push-pull operation is not required in rf operation as the amplifier is then always used with an appropriate resonant output circuit, which discriminates against undesired harmonic components in the plate-current pulse.

Class-C power amplifiers are used as rf amplifiers only. The duration of the plate current pulse being considerably less than 180° of the grid exciting signal makes this type of amplifier completely unsuited for audiofrequency operation. This amplifier is always used with an appropriate resonant output circuit, which discriminates against undesired harmonic components in the plate current pulse.

Class-AB power amplifiers are mainly used as audio-frequency amplifiers. Since plate current does not flow for the full 360° of the grid exciting signal these amplifiers, like Class-B amplifiers, must be operated in push-pull if serious distortion in the output is to be avoided.

Class-A power amplifiers provide relatively large power amplification but the available power output is low. The theoretical maximum plate circuit efficiency is 50 per cent. Actual practical operating efficiencies of 20 to 30 per cent are attained. Attempts to obtain higher efficiencies result in excessive distortion in the output signal.

Class-B power amplifiers provide relatively low power amplification but the available power output is much larger than in Class-A operation. The theoretical maximum plate circuit efficiency is 78.5 per cent. Actual

practical operating efficiencies of 50 to 65 per cent are attained.

Class-C power amplifiers provide relatively low power amplification but the available power output is high in comparison with Class-A operation. The theoretical maximum plate efficiency is 100 per cent. Actual practical operating efficiencies of 70 to 85 per cent are attained.

Class-AB power amplifiers provide power gains and efficiencies between those obtained for Class-A and Class-B operation.

H. J. Scott

Cross-references: *Amplifiers, Modulation and Demodulation, Oscillators, Pulse Generation*

CLEAN ROOMS

Clean rooms serve as work areas in which control is exercised over contaminating materials subject to airborne transport. The extent of control required depends on the particular operations performed in the area. For operations requiring localized small area control, the clean room can be simply a dust-excluding box pressurized with filtered air. For operations requiring more than localized control, it is necessary to build clean rooms that incorporate principles and practices that assure the degree of control required by the work to be done.

Experience has shown that the following principles and practices are pertinent to setting up and maintaining clean rooms.

(1) Materials of construction must not generate particulate matter. Nonvolatile, nonchipping, crack-free, hard finish materials should be used.

(2) Construction design should stress smooth flowing surfaces so as to avoid dust collecting overhangs and ledges, sharp corners, and surface configurations difficult to wipe clean. Installations for services and supplies should be designed to permit the related functions to be performed without the need for entering the clean room.

(3) The clean room can be no cleaner than its air supply. Therefore, the room must be

pressurized with air filtered free of all particles of a size considered harmful. Absolute filters are rated 99.95+ per cent efficient on particles 0.3 μ in size. In addition to air filteration, temperature and humidity should be controlled.

(4) Clean-room air is degraded by the presence of people in the area and by activities and materials that generate particulate matter. Population density, transient, and internal traffic in clean rooms must be minimized. Intercom systems and through wall ports for transfer of parts stored in clean containers should be used to full advantage. Clothing worn by people in the clean room should not shed lint, fibers, or any other material. Outer clothing should be made of continuous filament material sealed at the cut edges to prevent shedding. No material or activities that generate particulate matter should be allowed in the clean room. When this cannot be avoided, arrangements for compartmentalizing should be made to assure isolation of less clean from cleaner operations.

(5) A dust-excluding box pressurized with properly filtered air serves as a very effective miniature clean room. Box volume should be kept to a minimum. Closed boxes with sealed arm ports provide more effective control than boxes open across the front. If open-front boxes are used, the pressure across the front must be adjusted to minimize contaminating backdrafts. Chance of such contamination is reduced when the box is located in a clean surrounding.

(6) Access to the clean room should be through an air lock pressurized negatively with respect to the clean room but positively with respect to the outside area. The air lock should contain facilities for washing and air-drying hands, equipment for shoe cleaning or changing, and apparel for covering street clothes or changing into special clean-room clothing.

(7) Good housekeeping practices should be in force at all times. Periodic house-cleaning should be done by trained personnel during hours when work in the clean room has stopped.

The effectiveness of the clean room depends on how adequately it is set up originally and on how carefully good practices are observed at all times thereafter. The best criterion of the effectiveness of the clean room is the performance of the devices made in the area. It is wise to correlate device performance with measurement of airborne particle concentration and size distribution. Once this correlation has been done, periodic measurements by a reliable method should provide the necessary information that signals satisfactory or unsatisfactory clean room conditions.

P. R. PONDY

Cross-references: *Electron-Tube Manufacture, Semiconductor Manufacture*

COAXIAL LINES

A coaxial line is a type of electrical transmission line consisting essentially of two concentric cylindrical conductors separated by a dielectric insulating region. The larger or outer conductor completely encloses the inner conductor and the insulating region. Electromagnetic waves propagate through the dielectric medium bounded by the coaxial cylinders.

The inner, or center conductor, may consist of a hollow metal tube, a single wire or rod, or a stranded configuration of several wires made of electrically conductive material such as copper. Precious-metal plating and laminated construction of the conductors are also employed.

The materials comprising the dielectric region are usually required to support and align the center conductor, in addition to providing the necessary electrical insulation. The dielectric region may be homogeneous, as in flexible solid-dielectric coaxial cables, and in rigid coaxial lines using quarter-wavelength stub supports. On the other hand, a heterogeneous construction may consist of a helically spiralled filament of dielectric material, such as polyethylene or teflon, as the supporting member, with air or a more desirable gas or liquid filling the remainder of the dielectric region. Regularly spaced dielectric beads are also used in conjunction with suitable dielectric fluids. Many different types and combinations of dielectric materials are to be found in present-day coaxial transmission lines.

The outer conductor is typically a solid metal tube or a braid of fine metal wires. In addition to being a return or second conductor, it also serves as a barrier to electromagnetic waves, and is, therefore, often referred to as a shield. It is effective both in confining a signal within a cable, and in isolating the cable from external interfering signals. A jacket may be applied over the outer conductor, and is commonly employed over the braided conductor of flexible coaxial cables. Coaxial Transmission Lines are used throughout the rf spectrum, ranging from the audio or very low through the microwave frequencies.

Three categories are commonly used to classify coaxial transmission lines: (1) flexible, (2) semi-flexible, and (3) rigid.

Other designations indicative of the intended application are sometimes used, such as high-temperature, pulse, low-noise, underwater, radiation-resistant, etc. Electrical characteristics are an important basis of classification, particularly the characteristic impedance, the capacitance, the velocity ratio, the maximum operating voltage, the attenuation, and the useful range of frequencies.

The electrical characteristics used to describe the performance of coaxial transmission lines are commonly understood to relate to the principal (TEM) mode of propagation, unless otherwise specified. Higher-order modes can also exist, similar to the TE and TM modes in waveguides. The TEM mode will transmit a signal of any frequency, whereas the higher order modes will propagate only if excited at the frequency above their cutoff (critical) frequency. When used at the higher frequencies,

the transverse dimensions of the coaxial line are generally restricted so that energy can be transmitted only in the TEM mode.

The *primary electrical parameters* of a coaxial line are the inductance L per unit length; the capacitance C per unit length between the conductors; the resistance R per unit length due to the conductors; and the conductance G per unit length due to losses in the dielectric. The characteristic impedance is then calculated from the formula

$$Z_0 = \sqrt{\frac{R + j\omega L}{G + j\omega C}}$$

where $\omega = 2\pi f$ and f is the frequency of operation. When R/ω is considerably smaller than L, and G/ω smaller than C, this formula is approximated by the expression

$$Z_0 = \sqrt{\frac{L}{C}} = 138\sqrt{\frac{\mu'}{\epsilon'}}\log\frac{b}{a} = 60\sqrt{\frac{\mu'}{\epsilon'}}\ln\frac{b}{a}$$

where μ' is the relative permeability of the medium separating the conductors (unity for free space), ϵ' is the dielectric constant of that medium (unity for free space), a is the outer radius of the inner conductor, and b is the inner radius of the outer conductor.

The *propagation characteristics* of a coaxial line are given by the attenuation constant α and phase constant β. The total attenuation is the sum of the attenuations due to conductor losses and losses in the dielectric.

The phase constant is related to the wavelength λ along the transmission line by the formula

$$\beta = \frac{2\pi}{\lambda}$$

The velocity of propagation v is then given by

$$v = \frac{\omega}{\beta}$$

Voltage breakdown occurs when the electric field gradient between conductors exceeds the limiting value. For an air-filled line under normal atmospheric conditions the limiting gradient is about 30,000 v/cm.

The maximum power that can be transferred to a matched load by a coaxial transmission line is determined by its maximum voltage rating and characteristic impedance. Power-handling capability can be expected to vary with radial dimensions, frequency, temperature, altitude or gas density, and the mismatch (standing-wave ratio, q.v.) between the line and the load. The power-handling capacity of a coaxial cable is usually limited by the heating of the center conductor.

Periodicity is a type of anomalous behavior occurring in flexible cables at different frequencies or frequency bands· and their harmonics. It is characterized by a high standing-wave ratio (VSWR) and increased attenuation. The sources of this effect are periodic variations in the physical construction of the cable.

Flexible coaxial cables have been used extensively where flexibility, light weight, small size, and ease of handling were essential requirements. These cables may be flexed many times with no significant change in electrical, mechanical, or physical characteristics. The center conductor is ordinarily stranded and the outer conductor is of braided construction. Both solid and heterogeneous dielectrics are commonly used.

Semi-flexible coaxial transmission lines afford a more rugged construction with improved electrical performance. They are constructed with a solid metal outer conductor in place of the braid of the flexible cable, thereby affording lower attenuation. The outer conductor is relatively thin and made of materials such as aluminum or copper to permit bending. Over-all diameters smaller than the corresponding flexible cable are possible, since the solid outer conductor is a more efficient shield and does not ordinarily require additional jacketing.

Rigid coaxial transmission lines are best suited for permanent installations requiring high voltage and power ratings, and optimum efficiency. These lines usually employ

a gas as the principal dielectric insulation, thereby minimizing the losses occurring in the dielectric region and affording higher voltage ratings. Use of highly conductive materials for the rigid inner and outer conductors minimizes the losses of the conductors and allows increased power ratings.

RICHARD C. BECKER

Cross-references: *Delay Lines, Interference, Standing-Wave Ratio, Strip Lines, Waveguides and Waveguide Components*

COCKCROFT-WALTON ACCELERATORS

Voltage-multiplying rectifiers produce a high dc voltage from a lower ac input voltage. One of their principal uses is the acceleration of charged particles, to produce nuclear reactions. If n stages (n rectifier tubes or diodes and n capacitors) are used, the no-load dc voltage is n times the peak ac voltage applied to the input of the rectifier; n may be even or odd. Such rectifiers are also called *cascade rectifiers* because the output of each stage is connected to the input of the next stage (Fig. 1). All voltage-multiplying rectifiers are based on the circuits first published by H. Greinacher in 1921. Such a circuit, with the addition of an ion source and evacuated tube, was used by

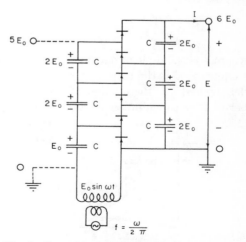

Fig. 1. Cascade rectifier shown for 6 stages or 5 stages.

J. D. Cockcroft and W. Walton to produce the first artificially created nuclear reactions by acceleration of protons (Proc. Roy. Soc. **129**: 477, 1930).

To understand the voltage-multiplying action for zero dc load current, consider only the lowest diode and condenser, which are in series across the ac voltage source. The steady voltage E_0 exists across the first condenser. The voltage across the first diode is thus the sum of a dc voltage and an equal ac peak voltage, so that the diode inverse-peak voltage is $2E_0$. This voltage may be rectified by the addition of a second diode and condenser in series connected across the first diode as shown, so that a steady voltage $2E_0$ appears across the second condenser. By applying Kirchhoff's second law around the proper path, it is seen that the voltage across the second diode is identical with the voltage across the first. A third-stage diode and condenser may be added and so on, with the result that there is a steady voltage of $2E_0$ across each condenser except the first, which is E_0. Therefore the no-load dc output voltage is nE_0. By omitting the top diode and condenser and connecting the output as shown by the dotted lines, the voltage multiplication factor n becomes an odd number.

The no-load dc voltage $E = nE_0$ derived above is reduced by an amount ΔE when a dc load current I is drawn, where

$$\Delta E = \frac{I}{fC}\left(\frac{1}{12}\,n^3 + \frac{3}{16}\,n^2 + \frac{1}{24}\,n\right)$$

where I is the dc load current, f is the input frequency, C is the capacitance of each condenser, and n is the number of stages (number of diodes or number of condensers). The

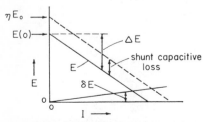

Fig. 2. Voltage relations in a cascade rectifier as a function of load current.

amplitude of the ac ripple voltage δE superimposed on the dc voltage is

$$\delta E = \frac{I}{fC}\left(\frac{1}{16}\,n^2 + \frac{1}{8}\,n\right)$$

By amplitude is meant half the peak-to-peak value (as it is usually defined for a sine wave).

The above analysis of voltage under load conditions is correct only when the stray shunt capacitance C_s associated with each diode is zero. There is an additional load-current-independent voltage loss, which can be very important in practice when n is large. It is easily shown by use of transmission-line theory that, when $n \gg 1$,

$$\frac{E(0)}{nE_0} = \frac{\tanh x}{x}$$

where $E(0)$ is the dc output voltage at no load, and $x = n\sqrt{C_s/C}$. The two voltage losses and ripple amplitude are shown as functions of I in Fig. 2.

Circuits like the one shown in Fig. 1 are often referred to as half-wave voltage multipliers because the ripple frequency is equal to the line frequency rather than twice the line frequency as in a full-wave rectifier. By connecting another string of condensers and rectifiers with opposite polarity across the transformer in parallel with the network shown, a full-wave voltage multiplier is obtained. However, the full-wave circuits lack the common dc and ac terminal of the half-wave circuits. The well-known full-wave voltage doubler is the full-wave version of Fig. 1 reduced to the minimum of two diodes and two condensers.

Typical supply frequencies are 60 cps, 480 cps, and 100 kc. High-frequency input has the advantage that smaller values of C may be used, but stray shunt capacitance is a source of trouble. If hot-cathode rectifiers are used, as is often the case, then complications arise because of the necessity of supplying filament-heating power at high dc potentials above ground. High-frequency filament heating is sometimes used. Typical dc voltages are between 100 and 1000 kv, although voltages up to 3000 kv have been produced.

The cascade rectifier has the advantages over the electrostatic (Van de Graaff) generator that no moving belt is required, the dc voltage is easily regulated without the need of corona devices, and intermediate voltage points are available for voltage-dividing electrodes on an evacuated accelerating tube. The rectifier usually has the disadvantage of requiring filament-heating power at high voltage above ground. If an inexpensive cold-cathode rectifier with an inverse voltage rating of 100 kv or more were developed, the cascade rectifier might supplant the electrostatic generator for many purposes.

J. R. Woodyard

Cross-references: *Accelerators, Cold-Cathode Tubes, Rectifier Tubes, Van de Graaff Accelerator*

CODING AND CODING CIRCUITS

The problem of coding from finite alphabets is merely that of selecting signals for some communication channel where the signals are represented as sequences of symbols such as $a_i a_j a_k \cdots$. The most familiar code of this type is probably the Morse code, which maps the English letters and some other symbols into sequences of dots and dashes.

Three interrelated criteria exist that must be used in selecting a code for data transmission: (a) compatibility, (b) efficiency, and (c) reliability. The first is certainly the most important. Yet it is also the one about which the least can be said.

(a) The message of a data transmission-system arises as the output of one system (or subsystem) and it must be appropriate as the input to some other system (or subsystem). The code therefore is the language by which two systems communicate. As such it must be capable of expressing all of the information we wish to get out of the first system, and also be capable of delivering the information to the second system (including start, stop, and synchronization signals). These requirements are often easily met (e.g., coding English letters into dots and dashes) but in some more sophisticated systems—such as the vocoder (*q.v.*), which encodes voice signals directly—the coding problem is much more difficult. Another aspect of the compatibility problem for codes is the desirability of standardizing codes that transport information from system to system. One recent attempt at standardizing binary data transmission codes is FIELDATA, a code for converting alphanumeric symbols into sequences of six binary digits (binits).

(b) The ultimate limits of efficiency for a code transmitting information from some information source are provided by Shannon's noiseless coding theorem. In order to explain this theorem we must first define certain properties and subclasses of codes.

Definition: Let the symbols comprising a given alphabet S be called

$$\{s_1, s_2, \cdots s_n, \cdots\}$$

Then we define a *code* as a mapping of all possible sequences of symbols of S into sequences of symbols of some other alphabet $X = \{x_1, x_2, \cdots x_r, \cdots\}$. We call S the *source alphabet* and X the *code alphabet*.

The definition of a code as given above is much too general to be of use. We shall therefore restrict the codes we are willing to consider to those codes having certain additional properties. The first of the properties we shall require is that the code be a *block code*.

Definition: A *block code* is a code which maps each of the symbols of the source alphabet S into a fixed sequence of symbols of the code alphabet X. These fixed sequences of the code alphabet (sequences of x_i) are called *code words*. We shall denote the code word corresponding to the source symbol s_i by X_i. Note that X_i denotes a sequence of x_j's.

Definition: A block code is said to be *nonsingular* if all the words of the code are distinct.

Definition: the nth *extension* of a block code which maps the symbols $\{s_i\}$ into the code words $\{X_i\}$ is the block code which maps the sequences of symbols $s_{j_1}s_{j_2} \cdots s_{j_n}$ into the sequences of code words

$$X_{j_1}X_{j_2} \cdots X_{j_n}$$

Definition: A block code is said to be *uniquely decodable* if, and only if, the nth extension of the code is nonsingular for every finite n.

Definition: An uniquely decodable code is said to be *instantaneous* if it is possible to decode each word in a sequence without reference to succeeding code symbols.

The concept of a prefix and the concept of an instantaneous code are closely related. To show this we make the following definition.

Definition: Let $X_i = \{x_{i_1}x_{i_2} \cdots x_{i_m}\}$ be a word of some code. Then the sequence of code symbols $x_{i_1}x_{i_2} \cdots x_{i_j}$, where $j \leq m$, is called a prefix of the code word X_i.

The relation we seek may now be stated.

A necessary and sufficient condition that a code be instantaneous is that no complete word of the code is a prefix of some other code word.

For this reason instantaneous codes are sometimes referred to as "prefix codes." We can summarize the subclasses of codes we have defined as follows:

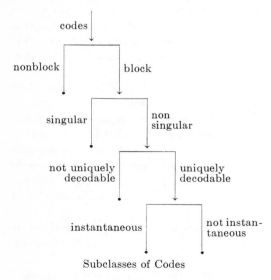

Subclasses of Codes

The efficiency of a code is a measure of the average number of code symbols needed when the code is used to transmit source symbols from some information source. In general, we should like to use a small number of code symbols to transmit each source symbol. An important restriction on the lengths (number of code symbols) of code words is given by the *Kraft Inequality*.

A necessary and sufficient condition for the existence of an instantaneous code with word lengths $l_1, l_2, \cdots l_k$ is that

$$\sum_{i=1}^{k} r^{-l_i} \leq 1$$

where r is the number of different symbols in the code alphabet.

For $r = 2$ (binary coding) the Kraft Inequality is just

$$\sum_{i=1}^{k} 2^{-l_i} \leq 1$$

The Kraft Inequality provides certain restrictions on the lengths of the individual code words in a code. The over-all efficiency of a code, however, must depend upon the probabilities with which the various code words are sent—or on the statistics of the information source being encoded. The most important result in the theory of noiseless coding (coding for efficiency) is *Shannon's Noiseless Coding Theorem* which we shall state in two parts.

Let L be the average number of code symbols used per source symbol in an instantaneous code. Then

(i) $$L \geq \frac{H(S)}{\log_2 r}$$

where $H(S)$ is the entropy (in bits) of the source being encoded and r is the number of symbols in the code alphabet.

(ii) By encoding symbols from the source n at a time, it is possible to make the difference between L and $H(S)/(\log_2 r)$ less than any positive number.

From (ii) of the Noiseless Coding Theorem, we see that we may define the efficiency of a code when used for a particular information source as

$$\text{efficiency} = \frac{H(S)}{L \log_2 r}$$

For a given information source, we may

not be able to find a code which yields an L approximately equal to $H(S)/(\log_2 r)$ (unless we encode n source symbols at a time). A coding method, due to Huffman, however allows one to synthesize the optimum (i.e., minimum-L) code for a given source.

(c) In section (b), we were concerned with codes that used as few digits as possible in order to transmit a message. While such efficiency considerations may be appropriate when the probability that an error in transmission will occur is negligible, they are often not appropriate when errors occur with appreciable frequency. In fact it may be said that efficiency and reliability are conflicting critera for codes. *A good ilustratin of that pont is povided by this sentnce.* Even though several letters were omitted from the sentence, the reader is still able to determine its meaning. This of course is true because of the natural redundancy (inefficiency) of the English language. It is possible to insert redundancy into a sequence of code symbols by adding additional symbols to the sequence. This redundancy may then allow us to correct (or perhaps merely detect) some errors that occur in transmission.

The most direct method of inserting redundancy is to repeat the message being transmitted. That is, instead of the message 110 we might transmit 110110110 and if any single error occurred in transmission, it could be corrected easily by the receiver. Repetition of this sort however usually reduces the efficiency much more than is necessary to achieve a given reliability. Shannon's fundamental coding theorem tells us that if we are willing to encode messages in very long blocks we do not have to continue to decrease efficiency indefinitely in order to increase reliability. In fact this theorem states the surprising result that *any* required degree of reliability can be achieved as long as we transmit information at a rate less than channel capacity (*q.v.*) by using long block lengths.

Codes designed to improve the reliability of data transmission are usually rated in terms of their error detection or error correction capability. For example, a double error

correcting code will allow the receiver to determine the correct message in a block of digits if no more than two errors occurred in the transmission of those digits. A triple error *detecting* code will allow the receiver to determine that some part of the message is in error if no more than three digits of the message are received in error. There are also codes designed to combat bursts of errors rather than general errors. For example, a quadruple burst error-correcting code will allow the receiver to correct any four or fewer errors in a block of digits if they occur in a burst of maximum width four. Various combinations of the above are of course possible.

Historically the first error-correcting and detecting codes obtained were the single-error-detecting, single-error-correcting, and the single error-correcting-double-error detecting Hamming codes. Since then a large number of classes of error-correcting and detecting codes have been found. The two most important classes are the Bose-Chaudhuri codes which may be used for error detecting and correcting arbitrary error patterns and the Fire codes which may be used for correcting and detecting bursts of errors in a block of digits.

The codes mentioned above are all block codes. Some recent work has indicated that nonblock codes (recurrent codes or sequential codes) may offer certain computational advantages over block codes when very long block (or inter-symbol constraint lengths) are used. In such codes the data digits are fed continuously into the channel instead of being broken into blocks for transmission. A particularly effective method of increasing reliability in data transmission is to combine any one of the various methods mentioned above with a feedback channel when one is available. The use of a feedback channel when possible is certainly one of the most reliable methods of eliminating errors.

Coding Circuits

In this section, we shall mention some of the primary considerations in the design of coding circuits for error-correcting and error-detecting codes. Since the reason for employing such codes is to increase the reliability of data transmission, it is clear that the reliability of the circuits used to implement the codes must be much higher than that of the communication channel. This fact limits the effectiveness of some of the more complicated coding schemes that have been proposed. In particular sequential codes and high order Bose-Chaudhuri codes will require some sort of computer in order to decode the transmitted message. This requirement severely limits the usefulness of such codes for many applications. The Fire codes however (which include a modified form of the Hamming code as a special case) can be instrumented with remarkable simplicity. These codes are subclasses of cyclic codes. Several investigators have shown how these codes may be instrumented using little more than a shift register for both error detection and error correction.

NORMAN ABRAMSON

Cross-references: *Computer Programming, Information Theory, Pulse-Code Modulation, Transmission Reliability*

COERCIVE FORCE: see MAGNETISM

COILS

A coil is a conductor wound in cylindrical or spiral form or variants of these, to obtain a concentrated magnetic field parallel to the axis of the coil. The method used in winding the coil, the number of turns of the coil, and the dimensions of the windings all contribute to the specific electrical characteristics of the coil, as does the absence or presence of an iron or ferrite core.

The coil characteristics considered in circuit design are the inductance (or *self* inductance) of the coil, the distributed capacitance of the windings, the figure of merit, and the losses in the coil. The inductance of the coil can be defined as:

(a) the flux associated with the coil when the current flows in the conductor;

(b) the back electromotive force generated in the coil by a unit rate of change of the current; or

(c) twice the work done in establishing the magnetic flux associated with a unit current in the conductor.

These definitions describe identical values of the inductance if the coil is surrounded by and contains only material of constant permeability, and provided the rate of change of the current is not so great as to cause nonuniform distribution of the current in the conductor.

The distributed capacitance of the coil results from the potential difference on adjacent windings. Losses in the coil include the joule heating of the conductor; eddy currents in the conductor; the increased apparent resistance of the conductor owing to skin effects (*q.v.*); dielectric losses in the material surrounding the coil and contained within the coil; hysteresis losses in iron or ferrite cores if present in the coil and hysteresis losses in ferrous shielding surrounding the coil, where used.

The skin-effect losses result from the tendency of the magnetic field to concentrate the current in the conductor on the inner surface of the turns and the magnetic field created *within* the conductor to concentrate the current on the surface of the conductor.

The inductance of an air-cored coil varies proportionally to the square of the number of turns and to a constant related to the length and diameter of the coil, the winding configuration, and the dimensions of the conductor. The constant is empirically derived for various winding configurations.

The self-capacitance of the coil has also been empirically derived for various coil forms and for single-layer coils varies very nearly as the radius of the coil.

The self-capacitance of the coil can be varied by including within the coil a nonferric core. The inductance of the coil can be greatly increased by inclusion of a ferric or ferrite core that does not form a closed magnetic circuit. In coils containing ferric cores forming a closed magnetic circuit the inductance is determined by the configuration of the current through the conductor. The inductance in such coils depends on the *incremental* permeability of the core, which varies with the dc component of the current through the conductor; with a larger dc component the incremental inductance is smaller and at the point of saturation of the core the inductance becomes vanishingly small.

The figure of merit of the coil is the quotient of the inductance of the coil and the apparent resistance of the coil under the particular conditions of application.

Principal application of coils in electronic circuits is in resonant circuits, with or without external capacitors, which at the resonant frequency exhibit either maximum or minimum impedance to the current through the circuit.

Coils are wound in single or multiple layers. Typical single-layer coils are the cylindrical solenoid and the basket-weave coil, the latter designed to minimize self capacitance. Typical multilayer coils are the multilayer solenoid, the bank-wound coil, the honeycomb coil, the duolateral coil, and the spiral coil which contains one turn per layer, as does the spider-web coil. Most prevalent at high frequencies are the single-layer solenoids. Most prevalent at moderately high frequencies are the duolateral coils, in which the windings zig zag back and forth between the sides of the coil. The duolateral coil is a compromise of the honeycomb coil, which was designed for minimum self-capacitance.

A special form of coil is the toroidal coil, generally wound on a ringform core with circular cross section. The toroidal coil has the special advantages of high inductance with low leakage fields.

The behavior of coils was first investigated extensively by Faraday and by Henry, for whom the unit of inductance is named. These investigators dealt exclusively with solenoid type coils. Special coil designs were not formulated until well after the introduc-

tion of radio communications in the early 20th century.

THOMAS JASKI

Cross-references: *Magnetic Cores, Magnetism, Permanent Magnets, Transformers*

COLD-CATHODE TUBES

MgO Cold Cathode. This type of cathode operates in a vacuum and is a type of self-sustained emission. Like other types it is not self starting and requires a current limiter, usually in the form of a series resistance.

The cathode consists of a porous layer of magnesium oxide on a nickel or other metal base. Heating in oxygen or air during the processing is such as to provide a stoichiometric excess of oxygen that seems to be necessary for stable operation and long life. During operation the outer surface has a positive charge which maintains the surface potential near but below that of the nearest positive electrode. This potential maintains a high electric field within the layer. A typical value for the surface potential is 150 v. Current densities of a few milliamperes per square centimeter are usual although much higher currents can be obtained for short periods or with cooled cathodes. High current densities heat the layer to the point where the resistivity of the magnesium oxide coating is greatly reduced, which seems to "short circuit" the layer and stop emission.

In operation, the cathode exhibits a distinctive blue glow that is believed to be due to cathodoluminescence (*q.v.*) excited by the electrons as they pass through the layer. The emission mechanism is not completely understood. Since the current-vs-voltage relationship follows the formula for an electron avalanche it is believed that electrons released at the MgO-nickel interface are multiplied by avalanches in the layer and that the removal of the electrons from the surface by the external field maintains the surface potential and hence the electric field in the layer. One theory holds that the initial electrons at the interface are liberated photoelectrically.

Since the positive surface potential is necesary for operation, the starting means must produce this potential. Ultraviolet light or bombardment by electrons to produce secondaries may be used.

The application of this cathode in its present state of development is limited by the wide distribution of velocities of the emitted electrons, the higher noise level of the current in comparison with that of the thermionic cathode, and the need for starting. No commercial application has been made to date.

Gas Tubes. The *glow discharge* has several features that make it useful for cold-cathode operation. The spreading of the glow over the surface of the cathode as the current is increased without substantial voltage increase provides a means for voltage regulation. After the glow has covered the cathode, the voltage rises steeply. A tube with one electrode having a small surface and the other having a large surface thus serves as a rectifier. Such rectifiers, because of their high voltage drop, have generally been replaced by thermionic and semiconductor types. Special types, however, are still used.

This type of discharge is self sustaining and requires a current limiting means such as a series resistor. It requires starting by the application of a break-down voltage that is substantially higher than the operating voltage. Lowest voltage operation is obtained with cathodes covered with alkali or alkali earth elements and with the lighter noble gases or mixtures thereof. Many commercial tubes of this general type operate in the range of 65 to 150 v and pass currents up to 50 ma.

A third electrode, or "grid" is used in the cold cathode thyratron. It is designed so that a relatively small voltage breaks down the gap between the "grid" and cathode and the discharge transfers to the cathode-anode region.

For voltages from 300 to over 40,000 v the *corona-discharge* tube provides voltage regulation. It consists of a pair of coaxial cylinders of ordinary metal in an atmosphere, usually of hydrogen, at pressures ranging from 50 to 760 mm of Hg.

The inner cylinder is the anode about which stabilization takes place by virtue of a positive-ion space charge. Currents range from a few microamperes to several milliamperes.

Besides the many mercury vapor rectifiers and thyratrons there are several *arc discharge* thyratrons with cold cathodes of either cesium chloride or potassium chloride mixed with aluminum. Designed for pulse operation, they pass currents of hundreds of amperes. Special anode shielding provides hold-off voltages as high as 2000 v and the "grid" element gives triggering. They are generally filled with neon or helium at pressures of from 5 to 40 mm of Hg, with cesium or potassium vapor added by the arc. The strobotron, krytron, and an automotive ignition tube are examples.

A. M. SKELLETT

Cross-references: *Electric Discharge, Rectifier Tubes, Secondary Emission, Thyratrons*

COLOR CODES

Color codes are used to indicate the values of small resistors and capacitors. The values corresponding to the several colors are given in Table 1. Note that the colors red through violet follow the sequence of the colors of the rainbow.

TABLE 1. COLOR CODE FOR RESISTORS AND CAPACITORS

Color	Significant figure	Decimal multiplier	Tolerance (%)	Voltage rating*
Black	0	1	—	—
Brown	1	10	1*	100
Red	2	100	2*	200
Orange	3	1000	3*	300
Yellow	4	10,000	4*	400
Green	5	100,000	5*	500
Blue	6	1,000,000	6*	600
Violet	7	10,000,000	7*	700
Gray	8	100,000,000	8*	800
White	9	1,000,000,000	9*	900
Gold	—	0.1	5	1000
Silver	—	0.01	10	2000
No color	—	—	20	500

* Applies to capacitors only.

Resistors

Composition resistors and small wire-wound resistors packaged in molded cases carry color marks as shown in Fig. 1. Radial-lead resistors are colored as shown at the top, and the second drawing shows the color-

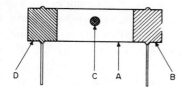

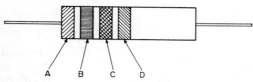

Fig. 1. Color markings for resistors. *A*, first significant figure (ohms); *B*, second significant figure; *C*, decimal multiplier; *D*, resistance tolerance in per cent (no color means ±20%). Color code is given in Table I.

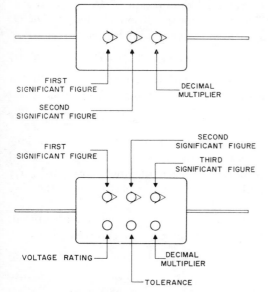

Fig. 2. Color markings for mica, molded-paper, and tubular ceramic capacitors. Three-dot code is used in 500-v, ±20% capacitors only; other capacitors use the six-dot code. (In older capacitors, the six-dot code may have a different meaning, as described in the text.) Color code is given in Table I.

TABLE 2. COLOR CODE FOR CERAMIC CAPACITORS

Color	Significant figure	Decimal multiplier	Capacitance tolerance		Temp. coeff. ppm/deg C
			More than 10 μμf (in %)	Less than 10 μμf (in μμf)	
Black	0	1	±20	2.0	0
Brown	1	10	±1		−30
Red	2	100	±2		−80
Orange	3	1000			−150
Yellow	4				−220
Green	5		±5	0.5	−330
Blue	6				−470
Violet	7				−750
Gray	8	0.01		0.25	30
White	9	0.1	±10	1.0	500

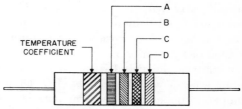

Fig. 3. Color markings for ceramic capacitors. Dots may be used instead of the narrow bands. *A*, first significant figure; *B*, second significant figure; *C*, decimal multiplier; *D*, capacitance tolerance in per cent. Color code is given in Table II.

band location for axial-lead resistors; in the latter, the color of the body has no significance.

Conventional Capacitors

Mica, molded-paper, and tubular ceramic capacitors carry color marks as shown in Fig. 2. Two schemes are used: three-dot and six-dot markings. [Older capacitors, notably surplus from World War II, carry six-dot markings in which the top row indicates, from l. to r., (1) mica (black) or paper (silver), (2) first significant figure, (3) second significant figure; and the bottom row, (1) characteristic, (2) tolerance, (3) decimal multiplier.] The three-dot code is used only for capacitors with 500-v ratings and ±20% tolerance.

Ceramic Capacitors

The color code for ceramic capacitors is shown in Table 2, and the markings are indicated in Fig. 3. The narrow bands are sometimes replaced by dots.

CHARLES SUSSKIND

Cross-references: *Capacitors, Resistors*

COLORIMETRY: see TELEVISION (COLOR)

COMMUNICATION THEORY: see STATISTICAL COMMUNICATION THEORY

COMPLEX NOTATION

Suppose there exists a dynamical variable such as a time varying voltage or magnetic field whose real instantaneous value is Q_a. In the early part of this century, C. P. Steinmetz (*q.v.*) demonstrated the utility of representing such a variable by a complex number or "general number," as he called it. In a manner similar to that of Steinmetz, we define a *complex representation* of Q_a as any complex number a whose real part is just Q_a, viz.,

$$Q_a = \mathrm{Re}\{a\} \tag{1}$$

Then, a^* (a conjugated) or $a + ju$ ($j = \sqrt{-1}$) where u is any real number, are also complex representations of Q_a. The choice of the real part of a to represent Q_a is arbitrary, and the imaginary part could equally well have been chosen. We proceed to develop two arithmetic rules for complex representations.

1. *Rule of Addition.* If a, b, c, $\cdots$ are the complex representations of Q_a, Q_b, Q_c, $\cdots$, then a complex representation of $Q_a + Q_b + Q_c$ is

$$a + b + c + \cdots \tag{2}$$

2. *Rule of Multiplication.* If a and b are complex representations of Q_a and Q_b, $Q_a Q_b = (\mathrm{Re}\{a\})(\mathrm{Re}\{b\}) = \mathrm{Re}\{\frac{1}{2}a(b + b^*)\}$, so that a complex representation of the product of Q_a and Q_b is

$$\tfrac{1}{2}a(b + b^*) \tag{3}$$

Dynamical Variables Described by a Unique Frequency. We apply these rules

to the frequently encountered set of dynamical variables Q_μ, where.

$$Q_\mu = A_\mu(\mathbf{r}) \cos [\omega t + \theta_\mu(\mathbf{r})], \ \mu = a, b, c \cdots$$

The A_μ are real amplitudes, the θ_μ are real angles, and ω is the unique angular frequency, common to each dynamical variable of the set. For example, in a network composed of linear lumped elements, the Q_μ are voltages and currents and the θ_μ are constants. For the propagation of electromagnetic waves in the z direction in a homogeneous, isotropic medium, the Q_μ are electric and magnetic field components and $\theta_\mu = \pm\beta z + (\mathrm{const})_\mu$, where β is the phase constant.

1. *Addition.* A complex representation of Q_μ is

$$\mu = V_\mu e^{j\omega t}, \qquad V_\mu = A_\mu(\mathbf{r})e^{j\theta_\mu(\mathbf{r})}$$

Then, a complex representation of the sum of Q_a and Q_b is $a + b = V_a e^{j\omega t} + V_b e^{j\omega t}$ or equally well $a + (b^* + ju_b) = V_a e^{j\omega t} + (V_b^* e^{-j\omega t} + ju_b)$ where u_b is a real number. It is convenient to *choose* representations in which the $u_\mu = 0$ and the sign of $j\omega t$ in the exponential is the same for all the Q_μ as in the first representation of $Q_a + Q_b$ above. Then the representation of the sum of Q_a and Q_b at a given point in space is

$$a + b = (V_a + V_b)e^{j\omega t} \tag{4}$$

One thus is able to write in general that a complex representation of $\sum_\mu Q_\mu$ at a given point in space is $\sum_\mu V_\mu e^{j\omega t}$ where $\sum_\mu V_\mu$ is the vectorial sum of the V_μ. For representations chosen in this manner, the V_μ are called *phasors.* Note that the angle between $V_a(\mathbf{r}_1)$ and $V_b(\mathbf{r}_1)$ in the complex plane is the *time phase* between Q_a and Q_b.

2. *Multiplication.* The complex representation of the product of Q_a and Q_b is

$$\tfrac{1}{2}a(b + b^*) = \tfrac{1}{2}V_a V_b e^{2j\omega t} + \tfrac{1}{2}V_a V_b^* \tag{5}$$

where V_a and V_b are phasors. It is frequently of interest to compute the *time average* of $Q_a Q_b$. The complex representation of this is easily seen to be

$$\tfrac{1}{2}V_a V_b^* \tag{6}$$

where V_a and V_b are phasors, so that the time average of $Q_a Q_b$ is $\frac{1}{2}\text{Re}\{V_a V_b{}^*\}$. Thus, if Q_a is the voltage across a two-terminal network with $V_a = V$ as the corresponding phasor, and Q_b is the current flowing into the network with $V_b = I$, then the time average of the power flowing into the network is

$$\text{ave. power} = [Q_a Q_b]_{\substack{\text{time}\\\text{ave.}}} = \text{Re}\,\{\tfrac{1}{2}VI^*\}$$

Dynamical Variables Described by Discrete Frequencies. In multifrequency systems, such as modulators, parametric amplifiers, and masers, in general, the dynamical variables are described by frequencies that are discrete though possibly infinite in number. A complex representation of a dynamical variable of the system can still have the form

$$V_\mu e^{j\omega_\mu t}$$

where now angular frequency depends on μ. It is convenient to choose the sign of $j\omega_\mu t$ that appears in the exponential so that all representations corresponding to the same frequency have the *same* sign. Then we can depend upon all complex representations of dynamical variables *of the same angular frequency* to combine as above. In particular the total time-averaged power at all frequencies flowing across a plane through the device consists of a sum of terms each of the form $\frac{1}{2}\text{Re}\{V_a V_b{}^*\}$.

R. N. CARLILE

Cross-references: *Network Theory*

COMPRESSION AND EXPANSION

Successive sections or passages of signals such as speech and music may differ in intensity by many decibels. These fluctuations can be reduced by selective amplification of the weaker intervals. This operation boosts the average power in the signal without increasing the peak power, thereby increasing the resistance of the compressed signal to noise. A device to achieve this end is called a *compressor* and is commonly incorporated in the transmitter of a communication system for protection against noise in the transmission channel. At the receiver, the compression is removed by a complementary device, namely an *expandor*. Together these devices are commonly known as a *compandor*. The same principle can serve to prevent overmodulation of a carrier while keeping low-level portions of the signal well above the noise.

To accomplish its function, a compressor-expandor must change its gain in accordance with its input signal amplitude. Two generic types of compandors can be distinguished according to the property of the input utilized to control the gain. A *syllabic* or *volume* compressor is a linear amplifier whose gain is controlled by the mean-square value of the input, averaged over some milliseconds. An *instantaneous* compressor transforms each instantaneous amplitude value of the input to an output value specified by a nonlinear characteristic. The associated expandors operate on the corresponding principles.

A block diagram of a volume compandor is shown in Fig. 1. The compressor is negative-feedback arrangement that suppresses volume variations of the input by increasing the gain whenever the output volume decreases. This amplification of weak portions of a signal prior to their exposure to the channel noise provides an increase in the transmitted signal-to-noise ratio. The mixture of signal and noise is attenuated by the expandor to restore the original relative level, but the signal-to-noise advantage remains. The effect of companding, therefore, is to keep the effective noise level low when the signal level is low, allowing it to increase only in proportion to the signal level. If there is no input, the output noise is drastically reduced by the expandor.

The advantage provided by a compandor can be specified from its compression characteristic, which relates input volume E to output volume V. The advantage is merely the difference in decibels between V and E. A typical characteristic employed in speech-transmission systems reduces the volume

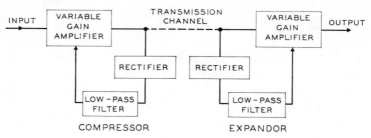

Fig. 1.

range of the input to half the number of decibels over a 60-db range. Such a system reduces the subjective effect of transmission noise by as much as 20 db.

Successive speech sounds and musical notes can vary widely in volume. Therefore, volume compression is often used for speech and music before applying them to recording media or radio and wire transmission systems. Expandors may or may not be used. Point-to-point transmission of high-quality material would use an expandor, whereas one is not usually employed in commercial radio receivers and phonograph reproducers. Volume compression introduces rather little nonlinear distortion since gain changes are slow (2–5 msec) compared to individual undulations of the signal, but rapid compared to syllabic or note intervals (100–500 msec). The absence of an expandor, therefore, leaves only the volume range, and not the tonal quality, distorted.

An extreme form of volume compression is *peak limiting*. Here the input signal volume is the same as the output volume until the former rises beyond a critical value. Above this input volume the output volume remains fixed. Peak limiting cannot be reversed by an expandor. Limiting is commonly used by broadcast stations to prevent overmodulation of their output while keeping low-level portions of program material well above the noise level. Typically, peak limiters are fast acting. Signal peaks are attenuated in less than 100 μs after they first appear. Subsequent relaxation is usually much slower; 0.5–2 sec is typical.

Instantaneous compandors are used most often in pulse-transmission systems. An instantaneous compressor is a passive, non-linear, zero-memory circuit whose input-output characteristic has a greater slope (greater gain) at low signal amplitudes than at high. Because it changes the signal waveform, an instantaneous compressor produces significant nonlinear distortion components both within and outside the input signal band. If the compressed signal is again limited to the input bandwidth for transmission, all of the distortion cannot be removed by merely passing the transmitted signal through a complementary expandor. Rather a complicated and exacting iteration procedure is required. In analog (unquantized) pulse systems such as time-division pulse-amplitude modulation, however, the transmission band for time samples of the compressor output is much wider than that of the unsampled input signal. Therefore, the problems inherent in bandlimiting the compressor output no longer arise, and a simple complementary expandor suffices. Instantaneous companding in analog pulse systems serves the same function as volume compression.

In quantized pulse systems, the compressor serves to decrease the effects of quantizing noise. Here compression has no relevance to transmission noise, its effect being determined solely by the digital coding of the quantized signal. Rather, the compressor is designed so that weak signals are finely quantized, stronger signals less so. Thus the quantizing noise is less for weak signals.

A usual logarithmic quantizing characteristic is:

$$V = \frac{V_{max} \ln \left[1 + (\mu E/V_{max})\right]}{\ln (1 + \mu)} \quad \text{for } 0 \leq E \leq V_{max}$$

$$V = -\frac{V_{max} \ln \left[1 - (\mu E/V_{max})\right]}{\ln (1 + \mu)} \quad \text{for } -V_{max} \leq E \leq 0$$

where V_{max} is the maximum quantized excursion from zero, E is the input value, V is the output value, and μ is a constant. The larger μ, the greater the compression achieved. Values between 30 and 100 are typical for speech, giving subjective gains equivalent to 2 or 3 binary digits. Again, a simple expandor is appropriate.

In practical applications, it may be difficult to make the instantaneous compressor and expandor exactly complementary because of temperature and aging effects in the circuit elements. Specially selected diode elements in a constant-temperature oven are necessary to keep distortion below a satisfactory level.

An extreme form of instantaneous compression *for speech* is merely peak clipping. The instantaneous signal peaks are removed and the resulting signal bandlimited for transmission. Though such clipping may yield as much as a 12 db increase in transmitted signal power without materially decreasing intelligibility, the distortion incurred may be objectionable for many applications and cannot be removed by any currently practical method.

E. E. DAVID, JR.

Cross-references: *Bandwidth Compression, Modulation and Demodulation, Noise, Signal Fluctuation and Noise*

COMPUTER APPLICATIONS

Many digital computers are designed to handle one particular application and are of the "special-purpose" type. Examples include small airborne computers used for missile guidance (*q.v.*), as well as the large central computers that form part of a national air-defense system. In many cases these computers have capabilities that would enable them to handle many other applications.

There are also many "general-purpose" computers in use by industry and government. Less than half of them are used primarily for the solution of scientific and engineering problems; the remainder are used largely for commercial and government data processing (*q.v.*).

Most of the applications performed on computers can be grouped in the following categories.

1. *Commercial Applications.* Such applications include many of the business operations that in the past were often performed by staffs of clerks, sometimes using desk calculators. Commercial applications that can be handled effectively on a digital computer include such items as the computation of a company's payroll, raw materials and stock inventory maintenance, billing, accounts receivable processing, sales analysis, production scheduling and control, budget preparation and expense control, cost and general ledger accounting, financial statement computations, premium accounting, the preparation of summarizing reports from large files of information, and numerous banking operations. In these applications the data-handling abilities of a computer are usually (but not always) more important than the ability to perform high-speed arithmetic.

2. *Engineering and Scientific Applications.* Many mathematical problems arising in the sciences and engineering involve the solution of differential equations or the performance of various matrix operations. The latter, which also appear in frequently used methods for solving differential equations, include matrix multiplication, inversion, the solution of simultaneous linear equations, and the computation of eigenvalues and eigenvectors. For example, the use of multiple linear regression analysis in statistics involves, essentially, matrix multiplication and inversion.

By way of illustration, engineering and scientific applications include: the computation of the stresses in an airplane wing, the solution of a partial differential equation with boundary conditions arising in hydrodynamic theory, orbital calculations, distillation calculations, cut-and-fill problems in highway construction, the setting up and use of econometric models, electric network calculations, heat exchanger calculations, and the simulation of an oil refinery. Many statistical procedures, including forecasting techniques that involve formidable computations, are often applied on high-speed computers. A complete list of scientific and engineering applications would include examples from every science and branch of engineering.

The availability of high-speed digital computers has stimulated the further development of classical numerical analysis in a search for methods that can be successfully applied on this equipment. New methods such as in the theory of linear programming (*q.v.*) are feasible, in part, because of the availability of high-speed digital computers.

3. *Real-Time Applications.* In an increasing number of applications, information obtained from various external devices is transmitted directly to a computer without human intervention. On the basis of the information it receives, the computer makes certain analyses and decisions. It may then signal controlling information to external devices that take appropriate action. An example of such a system is in automatic process control where a computer may control the operations of an entire chemical plant. Another illustration would be the use of a computer in controlling the path of a missile or in fire control. The input information might be obtained by telescopes or a rangefinder and the output information from the computer would determine the guidance of the missile.

4. *Government Applications.* This category includes the handling of census information, military logistics, tax auditing, and the maintenance of Social Security files, which involves considerable computer usage.

Many miscellaneous applications cannot be included in the above categories. For example, there is a considerable amount of interest and activity in automatic language translation. While fluent translations of complicated text material cannot yet be obtained, the progress in this area seems to be very promising. Examples of other miscellaneous applications include: the preparation by a computer of a concordance of the Bible, an airlines reservation system, the automatic translation from written English to Braille,

the formation of all pronounceable five-letter strings, the playing of checkers or chess, and the playing of management "games" and even "war games." Election predictions by the large radio and television networks have attracted considerable attention.

Computers are beginning to find increasingly frequent use in the study of complex situations by means of simulation techniques. For example, it is possible to study the behavior of a gas under certain prescribed conditions by considering the gas to be made up of a large number of individual particles. The computer can prescribe, in a random way conforming to the physical situation, the motion of an individual particle and then determine its future behavior. By repeating the calculation many times, and averaging the behavior over a large number of particles, the computer can "simulate" the behavior of the gas.

In determining whether or not an inventory is adequate the computer might, from past experience that implies the distribution of demand with respect to time for a given item, follow a long sequence of artificial transactions and thus simulate the real life situation. In many of these situations the Monte Carlo Method (*q.v.*) is employed, as in the random selection by the computer of values for stochastic variables in accordance with their frequency distributions. A simple example would be the determination of the expected length of a queue in front of an airlines ticket window from information that includes the distribution of passenger arrival times and the distribution of servicing times.

It appears quite possible that there will be, in the future, computers with multimillion-word random-access memories and the capability to perform arithmetic and logical operations in less than 1 μsec. In considering the potential use of such machines it is clear that there will be always some mathematical problems—such as the solution of certain partial differential equations of hydrodynamics—that require these speeds. There are in fact many mathematical problems that cannot be attacked by classical methods even if the arithmetic operation time is reduced to 1 ns. The potential use of such computers in nonmathematical problems is not at all clear. It is hoped that they may be programmed to perform complex "analytical" processes more closely rivalling those of the human mind than is possible with existing computers. New types of computer storage ("associative" memories) may also aid in this development.

F. S. BECKMAN

Cross-references: *Digital Computers, Medical Electronics, Translation by Machine*

COMPUTER LOGIC

The logical functions of computers fall into four categories: addressing, sequencing, execution and input-output control.

Addressing. Memory cells and occasionally arithmetic and logic unit registers, or cells, are assigned fixed, unique numeric addresses. Thus, stored program instructions conventionally refer to other instruction words and data words (operands) by the address of the cell where they are stored.

Three significant variations on the conventional method of addressing are *immediate*, *indirect* and *abbreviated* addressing. In *immediate* addressing an instruction word contains the operand itself, in lieu of the address of that operand. An *indirect* address is the address of the *address* of an operand. (Note that the second address might also be indirect, and so on for as many steps as desired.) Indirect addressing often simplifies programming. *Abbreviated* addresses are partly implicit. For example, the operation code may implicitly specify that one operand is found in a set of special storage cells. The abbreviated adress would explicitly specify which of the set.

Instructions may be operated upon as data to perform *address modification*, enabling the computer itself to compute the variations on a base program for iterative processes. Address modification is simplified in most modern computers by the provision of some *indexing* logic, which usually consists of

special registers to contain the modifying values to be added to (or subtracted from) addresses; means of adding the modifying value to the operand address without additional instructions; special operations for modifying the value itself; and some means of keeping track of the number of times a value has been modified, e.g., by decrementing the value, or by counting down, and testing for zero.

The number of addresses provided for in the instruction word format varies from one address to as many as four. The most efficient format is a variable-length instruction word, which provides for a variable number of addresses depending upon the requirements of the operation to be executed (e.g., one address for a branch instruction; three addresses for an arithmetic operation in which the result is to be stored in a new location).

Sequencing. In most computers instructions are executed in the sequence that they are stored in memory, unless a branch to another sequence is specified. An instruction counter (IC) is automatically advanced to the next higher memory location, after the present instruction has been fetched.

Branch instructions normally contain an address that replaces the address in the IC, if the branch is to be effected. This address may be modified by indexing. In many computers the IC is itself addressable or usable as an index value.

Many branches are to program subroutines for processes used repeatedly—for example, a square-root routine. These branches require a procedure for saving the present content of the IC in order to return to the main program at the right point after completing the subroutine. In many computers the content of the IC is automatically stored in a fixed memory location in conjunction with any branch instructions.

The normal sequence of instructions is also often *interrupted* by special conditions that arise, such as machine failure, a specified overflow condition, or an external signal. When multiple interrupts are possible, priority, subroutine selection, and re-entry to normal instruction sequence require elaborate control procedures that vary from computer to computer.

In early computers nearly all operations, and substeps within operations, were done sequentially. In modern computers an effort is made to overlap wherever practicable. For example, memory accesses are overlapped with previous instruction executions; input-output operations with internal operations; and address modification or indexing with memory accesses and execution. In a few cases execution of arithmetic and logic is overlapped by providing concurrently operating arithmetic or logic units.

Sequencing is further complicated by *time-sharing*, a process in which a unit shares its use among several other units. For example, a memory unit may share its access cycles among several slow input-output units and the fast arithmetic unit.

Execution. Conventionally, the computer can execute a fixed set of arithmetic, logic, and control operations. The operation code in the instruction word defines which of the set of operations is to be executed and initiates the appropriate built-in subprogram of simple logical steps to accomplish the specified operation. A typical instruction set would include add, subtract, multiply and divide; a few logical operations such as compare, logical multiply, and shift right or left; control operations such as branch and branch on zero or overflow; and several input-output operations.

In a few computers provision has been made for altering, or *microprogramming*, the subprogram of steps which make up an operation—either by an easy physical change, or by a stored program of the substeps.

The tendency in recent computers has been toward larger instruction sets and toward the use of modifiers to operation codes (e.g., modifiers that cause signs to be ignored, reversed on one operand, etc.). Modifiers, in effect, increase the size of the instruction set. Typical additions to instruc-

tion sets include built-in floating-point arithmetic, Boolean functions, editing operations and a variety of additional input-output operations.

Input-Output Control. The functions of input-output control are to specify the I/O device; buffer the usually slow, non-synchronous, data flow with the fast computer; organize the data into computer words; develop addresses where data are to be stored or fetched; and handle all exception signals.

The early computers required most I/O control to be programmed. The main arithmetic registers served as buffers. No overlapping was possible.

Major increases in efficiency have been obtained by the development of elaborate I/O control units. These units are essentially small computers with buffer registers, logic to organize data into input or output words, arithmetic to compute memory addresses; and built-in procedures for the exception signals. The main program supplies a control word which specifies, typically, the I/O unit, a starting memory address, and the number of memory words. The I/O unit executes the program defined by the control word. The memory accesses required by the I/O program are typically time-shared with the main arithmetic unit.

W. J. LAWLESS, JR.

Cross-references: *Boolean Algebra and Symbolic Logic, Digital Computers, Logic Circuits*

COMPUTER PRINTOUT AND READING

Computer printout and reading, as used here, is that large set of input-output problems involving the man-machine interface. Automatic sensing of the environment as a computer input, as well as computer output for automatic control—e.g., missile guidance and industrial process control—are excluded from this definition. In many business and scientific digital computer applications, certain raw data can come only from the manual effort of an operator, and the results of computations must be in a form readable by interested persons.

In the data coding and collection, or input, area, operators read handwritten or printed data, count items, measure quantities, etc., and based on this information, activate keys, buttons, levers, etc., in a predetermined manner to prepare a record intelligible to a computer or to a computer input device.

Two common manually prepared records are punched tape and punched (or Hollerith) cards. Punched tape uses five or more holes per character at a typical packaging density of 10 characters/in. Punched cards have various formats, one of which involves eighty 12-position columns where one or more holes per column identify the alphanumeric or special character. Other means of coded data collection include mark-sense cards, magnetic strips on cards and ledgers, special font character printing for automatic character recognition, etc.

Except for relatively low-speed computers, cost of computer operating time demands efficient flow of input-output data. A common mode of operation to achieve such a flow centers around the use of magnetic tape as a buffer between the computer and various input-output devices. Magnetic tape heads, read-write circuitry, and tape transport mechanisms have been refined to a point where data can be transferred to and from the computer at an acceptably high rate. A computer often has several magnetic-tape units associated with it so that at least one unit is always available for reading into or recording from the computer. Thus stopping to rewind, to change reels, to search, etc. does not produce computer idleness.

In lower- and medium-speed computer applications, punched tape is frequently used as the buffer. Punching rates of over 100 characters/sec and reading speeds of 1000 characters/sec are available. Furthermore, punched tape can be used directly with teletype systems, making possible a wide separation between the computer and its input-output equipment. Computers in business

and scientific applications nearly always use printing in one form or another as their outputs. Where the computer deals directly with the printer and/or its buffers, the printing is said to be on-line. Where the output of the computer is sent first to a temporary storage, such as magnetic tape, and the data are later transferred to a printer at a more leisurely pace, the printing is said to be off-line.

Mechanical serial printers, such as teletype and automatic typewriters, are suitable (as the main print-out) only for the lowest cost computers. Mechanical printers—parallel (or ganged) rack or sector—have a higher character rate, but are still too slow (up to 3 lines/sec) for on-line work with the large computers.

The wheel, or drum, printer, where a font of all characters is placed on the circumference of the drum at each horizontal print position, can achieve a higher printing rate than the rack printers. Up to 1800 lines per minute have been printed with this type of printer, although, for reliability, rates below 1000 lines per minute are typical.

Although the fully formed character used in the above printers presents an esthetically desirable print, an improvement in speed is realizable with a matrix wire printer. This technique employs a rectangular array of wires, or pins, at each horizontal print position. The ends of these pins are perpendicular to the paper and can be thrust forward independently so that each can print a dot. The character shape is formed by activating the appropriate wires in the matrix.

To achieve high speeds, the present trend in computer output printing is in the non-impact area, including electrostatic, electromagnetic, electrochemical, and thermal processes. In one electrostatic process, for example, static charges are impressed on an insulated, coated paper in a few microseconds per charge. A powdered ink is then applied to the paper and adheres to only the charged surface. The ink is then permanently fixed by heat and/or pressure. The matrix approach is utilized to achieve character

Fig. 1. Sample of Burroughs electrostatic printing.

printing. An electromagnetic process employs a magnetizable drum on which characters are magnetically formed. This drum is then inked by magnetic ink which is later off-set by means of a hot transfer drum to the recording paper. Other printers produce marks (characters) on special paper by chemical or thermal means.

PAUL R. HOFFMAN AND
ROBERT J. O'CONNELL

Cross-references: *Character Recognition, Digital Computers, Electrostatic Printing, Storage*

COMPUTER PROGRAMMING

Digital-computer programming involves formalization of techniques usually learned intuitively by most human beings in the solution of problems of all sorts. The closest direct approach in the past has probably been the formal calculation, using pencil and paper or a desk calculator, of results described by a sequence of operations. The act of describing such a formal calculation, when applied to the solution of problems using a high-speed digital computer, is one example of "programming." Other examples include the formalization of the process for differentiating standard algebraic functions for use by a stored program digital computer, formalization of procedures for balancing an assembly line, calculating individual pay items and printing out the corresponding pay checks, calculating and maintaining information on the geographical position of aircraft, and making decisions as to when two of them may collide.

The key to programming is first the learning and use of various formal languages for the description of problem solution. Behind this, of course, lies a knowledge of the theory that underlies the solution of whatever problem is being attacked. A computer program-

mer combines both of these factors to produce an operational description of a problem solution. This description, the program, is then (at present) manually keyed into machine-readable material (punched cards, paper tape, magnetic tape) which is later fed into the stored program digital computer for actual performance. The machine follows each step of the programmer's written program description, providing the system is properly designed and working.

Computer *languages* are command languages, containing individual verbals (instruction operations), nominals (addresses used as operands) and certain language modifiers of an adjective- or adverb-like characteristic. These languages describe a sequence of steps or instructions to the machine. Descriptive elements may be included in such a language: statements concerning the nature of the problem, characteristics of the computer, restrictions on speed, information-handling requirements, or on the language itself that aid in interpreting the problem description as written in the language.

The most familiar of computer languages are the scientifically oriented, algorithmic languages, of which the proposed international standard language, ALGOL, is an example. ALGOL is a language based on the usual notation of elementary algebra, using the idea of variable, the common operations $(+, -, \times, /)$, and the commonly used functions (sin, cos, exp, log, power, etc.). An example of a portion of a program in ALGOL notation is the following:

Example 1.

DISPLACEMENT := K × SIN (OMEGA × TIME)

which might ordinarily be written in completely mathematical notation as

$$D = K \sin \omega T$$

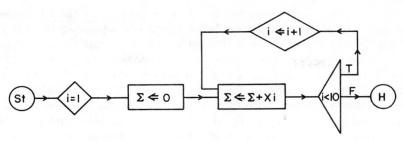

Fig. 1.

The symbol combination ":=" represents one symbol, a "substitution" symbol that indicates that the value, obtained upon performing the operations described on the right-hand side of this instruction, is to be substituted for the previous value whose name is given on the left-hand side.

Another near-familiar language might be the "common business-oriented" language, COBOL, in which the basic operations and operands represented by English verbs and nouns are combined to produce a computer performable version of Basic English.

Example 2.

FILE WITHHOLDING TAX IN PAYROLL FILE UNDER EMPLOYEE

These two languages, like many others more specialized in usage among various computers (such as FORTRAN, IT, UNICODE, MAD, etc.), enable a human programmer to describe a sequence of computer operations in a language that is somewhat familiar to him.

Users of computers—programmers, as they are often called—also use a diagrammatic language; the language of flow diagrams, to describe a problem-solution procedure. A flow diagram consists of a sequence of ordered, directed lines connecting boxes in which a description of individual operations (perhaps couched in one of the two languages above) is included. An example of a flow-diagram to add the 10 numbers: $X_1, \cdots, X_{10}$ is given in Fig. 1.

A translation into the ALGOL language of Example 1 would require the following lines of instructions to describe this sequence:

> *begin*   *integer* I; *real* SIGMA; *array* X [1:10];

> I: = 1;
> SIGMA: = 0;

> SUM: SIGMA: = SIGMA + X [I];
>   *if* I < 10 *then go to* REPEAT *else go to* FINISH;

> REPEAT: I: = I + 1;
>   *go to* SUM;

> FINISH: *end*

Successive lines would set the initial value of the index I to 1, set the initial value of the summation location "SIGMA" to 0, add the next x_I to the summation, and then test to see if the task is finished. There are two possible sequences following the "IF I < 10 ..." sequence, one merely to *end* when this is not true, the other to the line labelled REPEAT. At that point the statement "GO TO SUM" carries the flow of the sequence back to the line labelled SUM; this continues until the statement "I < 10" becomes false.

Translation of these languages into activity on the part of a specific computer is the task of a computer program, stored in the machine, which takes the coded symbol strings of the external language (ALGOL or COBOL, for example) as input. There are two general classes of such programs. The first class, more general in their abilities, is called the interpretive program, or "interpreter," which scans the sequence of coded material, performing the operations required on the stored information as each appears. Such interpretive procedures allow the program being input (being performed) to be of a most general character. For example, programs being interpreted may alter their own structure, in the input language, or indeed alter the syntax of the language in which they are described, during the actual problem-solution process. With present-day computers, such techniques are very powerful; but they are also inefficient as far as time and storage are concerned. Such interpreters have been used to interpret algorithms (programs) for proving of theorems, balancing of assembly lines, integration of algebraic expressions, for example, all of which would have been far more difficult to describe without this interpretation technique.

The alternative method for handling external problem-oriented languages is the "translater," a program that makes a direct, running translation from the external language into the language of the digital computer. Only after the translation is concluded does the actual performance of the problem solution begin. Thus, in this case, the structure of the language describing the problem and the problem solution are virtually isolated. Most uses of the ALGOL, COBOL, and other standard external languages for computers make use of this translation technique, followed by execution of the translated set of commands. In some cases, elaborate systems combine both of these techniques. The entire area of machine aid to the programming process is generally called "automatic programming."

In the solution of large problems, with complex volumes of data and intricate procedures, the technique of separating the over-all program into separate functional blocks, often called "subroutines" or "subprograms," becomes very important. By using this technique, a large algorithm may be broken down into smaller constituent parts, each of which may be individually constructed (programmed) and tested for correctness of the representation. Such subroutines are generally constructed so that when they are used, they may be used semi-automatically or completely automatically, just as the mathematical analyst uses the standard functions of trigonometry and algebra in a consistent fashion, without

having to analyze their behavior at every stage. Such large programming problems as the SAGE (Semi-Automatic Ground Environment) program for continental air defense of the United States were planned and executed in this fashion, with smaller groups of programmers working on pieces of the over-all problem, and a centralized group working to combine the pieces in the required fashion.

The ordinary problem solver programming the solution of his problem on a computer in general need not know very much about the structure of the automatic programming aids (translaters, interpreters, or subroutines) that he uses. Professional programmers, working on the construction of such devices for specific machines, in many cases will already have programmed them. Addition of a "compilation" feature to the standard translater, for example, done preceding regular usage, will allow the ordinary programmer to call on standard functions, or standard routine computer procedures (input of information via punched cards, magnetic tape, paper tape; input and output to secondary storage; output to printers) by a simple listing of the operation he wants performed. Without the background effort involved in this vast construction of pre-written, pre-tested programs, present general ease of problem solution would not be possible.

Inside a computer or data processor, storage and handling of information is usually based on some primitive information element. Such individual data elements may generally be representations of numerical digits in some number system (binary or decimal, for example) or of a larger alphanumerical symbol set or fixed- or variable-length sequences of such elements. In addition, sequences of such primitive elements also serve as instructions to the computer itself, inserted from outside via some external representation by the computer user or programmer.

Alphanumeric computers like the RCA 501 and the IBM 705 use *characters* as the individual data-elements. Scientific computers like the IBM 7090, UNIVAC 1107, CDC-1604, and Philco S-2000 use strings of binary digits (ranging from 36 to 64 binary digits) as the fundamental word unit.

Example 3. COMPONENT123

(A Univac II computer word contains 12 alphanumeric characters, and is fixed in length.)

10110111000101011011111001011101

(A Bendix G-20 computer word contains 32 binary digits, again fixed in length.)

Such fixed- or variable-length sequences (the former occur most often) are used as integral units in themselves when processed by the machine, and are called *words*. Pieces of such units, sub-words ("bytes," "fields," half-words, etc.), may also be used as integral primitive elements.

Thus, in most machines receiving information from and returning it to human beings (not completely tied in only with other machines, as in a process-control system), information used will relate in some fashion to notations ordinarily used by humans. Numerical and alphanumerical data may be handled within the computer in a code that relates common external symbology (most often limited only to the character-set on the computer's input-output equipment) to the internal computer primitive element. Words can be either data or instructions. Usually this characteristic of a word is ambiguous; only its context and actual usage determine whether it is datum or instruction.

JOHN W. CARR III

Cross-references: *Boolean Algebra and Symbolic Logic, Coding and Coding Circuits, Computer Logic, Computer Printout and Reading, Digital Computers, Linear Programming, Translation by Machine*

CONDENSERS: see CAPACITORS

CONDUCTION

Electrical Conduction

Most homogeneous solids obey Ohm's law for sufficiently small electric fields. The elec-trical resistance of an isotropic, uniform sample is given by the product of the resistivity ρ of the sample and its length parallel to the current direction, divided by the area of the cross section perpendicular to the current direction. If the resistance is in ohms and the distances are in centimeters, the resistivity is in ohm cm (called practical units). The conductivity σ is the inverse of the resistivity, and is measured in (ohm cm)$^{-1}$ or mho/cm. Single crystals of materials which do not have cubic structures may be anisotropic, i.e., the resistivity depends upon current direction.

Solids are usually classified as metals, semiconductors, or insulators. Metals are characterized by an increasing resistivity with increasing temperature. Resistivities of metals at room temperature range from about 10^{-6} to 10^{-4} ohm cm. Semiconductors are characterized by a decreasing resistivity with increasing temperature (impure semiconductors may show this behavior only at high temperatures). Resistivities of semiconductors at room temperature range from about 10^{-3} to 10^{9} ohm cm. Insulators share the same temperature behavior of resistivity as semiconductors, so that the difference between the two classes of materials is one of degree only. Generally, materials with room temperature resistivities greater than 10^{9} ohm cm are called insulators. Resistivities as high as 10^{18} ohm cm have been observed. There are some materials intermediate between metals and semiconductors. For example, the resistivity of manufactured carbon decreases with increasing temperature at low temperatures, and increases at high temperatures. The room temperature resistivity is also intermediate, varying from 10^{-3} to 10^{-2} ohm cm depending upon conditions of manufacture.

Modern quantum mechanics has shown that not all the electrons in a solid are free to carry current. The conductivity is proportional to the number of free carriers n, and to their ease of motion in the electric field. This latter factor is expressed by the mobility μ, which is the ratio of the drift velocity to the electric field strength. The conductivity can be expressed as

$$\sigma = ne\mu$$

where n is in cm^{-3}, e is the magnitude of the electronic charge (1.6×10^{-19} coulomb), and μ is in cm^2/volt sec. Quantum mechanics has also shown that the mobility in a pure, perfectly regular crystal would be unlimited. The mobility is limited by scattering of the electrons by deviations such as the thermal vibrations of the atoms, impurity atoms, or irregularities in the crystal structure (including vacancies, dislocations, and grain boundaries).

In good metals, n is of the order of the number atoms per cm^3, and is independent of temperature. As the amplitude of the atomic vibrations increases with increasing temperature, the scattering effect increases, and the mobility and conductivity decrease. At high enough temperatures the resistivity of a typical metal is proportional to the absolute temperature. At lower temperatures the effects of impurities and other imperfections are important, and the resistivity is approximately the sum of the temperature dependent part and a temperature independent part which is proportional to the defect concentration (Matthiessen's rule). At very low temperatures (1 to 18°K) some metals become superconductors and all measurable resistance disappears.

Pure semiconductors at absolute zero of temperature have no free electrons. As the temperature is increased, some electrons are excited to current-carrying states (in the "conduction band"). The states that are left unoccupied (in the "valence band") are also free to carry current, and are called free holes. The concentrations of electrons and holes increases very rapidly with temperature, causing the resistivity to decrease. Extra carriers may also be provided by impurity atoms, "donors" contributing electrons, and "acceptors" trapping electrons and producing holes. Very small impurity concentrations may make very large changes in resistivity. If most of the free carriers

come from impurities the material is called "extrinsic," and is n(negative) type if electrons predominate or p(positive) type if holes predominate. If most of the carriers come from thermal excitation the concentration of electrons and holes are about equal, and the material is called "intrinsic." The rate of change with temperature of the mobility of a semiconductor is generally less than the rate of change of carrier concentration. The mobility is often represented by $\mu = c\,T^r$, where r varies from about -2.2 to 1.5 depending upon the particular material, concentration and type of defects, etc. Mobility values at room temperature range from about 1 to 10^5 cm^2/volt sec. The conductivity of intrinsic material can be expressed as

$$\sigma = g(T)e^{-\Delta E/2kT}$$

where T is the absolute temperature, k is Boltzmann's constant, $g(T)$ is a slowly varying function of T. and ΔE is the energy "gap" between the valence and conduction bands. This equation is often used to analyze experimental data and find ΔE.

When the mean free path of the carriers between collisions is of the order of the distance between atoms, the carriers are regarded as being localized, and the current is carried by "hopping" from atom to atom. This phenomenon is currently being investigated and is not completely understood. A case of "hopping" conduction that is well understood is that of conduction by ions in solids such as the alkali halides. The resistivities of such solids are of the order of 10^6 to 10^{12} ohm cm at room temperature, but are as low as 10 to 10^4 ohm cm at elevated temperatures.

J. W. McClure

Thermal Conduction

Thermal conduction is the transfer of heat, in the form of kinetic energy, from one part of a system to another, without appreciable displacement of the particles involved. The relationship governing unidirectional conduction of heat in continuous bodies is expressed by Fourier's law which states that

$dQ/dt = -kA(dT/dx)$ where dQ/dt is the instantaneous rate of heat flow in calories per second through the area A at right angles to the flow direction, dT/dx is the temperature gradient at the position x in degrees per unit length, and k is the thermal conductivity in calories per second, centimeter, degrees Centigrade. The minus sign in Fourier's law indicates that heat flows in a direction opposite to the thermal gradient. For the case of a bar or cylinder of cross section A and length L, with ends maintained at temperatures T_1 and T_2, Fourier's law reduces to $dQ/dt = (kA/L)(T_1 - T_2)$. This relation assumes an average value of k for the temperature range employed. In cases where the temperature dependence of k is large for the temperatures under consideration, Fourier's law must be integrated with the proper temperature dependence of k taken into account.

Thermal conductivity k is a property of the material and its physical state. It may vary by several orders of magnitude from one material to another. In a given system the conductivity depends on temperature, pressure, and porosity. Typical room temperature values of k, in units of cal/sec cm °C, are 0.00003 and 0.0004 for gases such as carbon dioxide and hydrogen; 0.00002 for porous, insulating solids such as flannel; 0.002 for nonporous insulating solids such as glass; 0.1 to 0.5 for normal metals; and 1.0 for metals such as copper and silver. Molten metals and fused salts, because of the electronic contributions, usually exhibit thermal conductivities similar to those of the metals.

Fourier's law applies to liquids as well as to gases and solids. Because of the smaller k values in liquids and gases, and because convection effects are generally not negligible in such systems, caution must be exercised in applying the relation to areas where heat transfer by convection or radiation may be operative. With the exception of water and several other aqueous solutions, the thermal conductivities of most nonmetallic liquids decrease with increasing temperatures. Increased pressures, on the other hand,

cause only slight increases in liquid thermal conductivities. The viscosity of a gas plays an important role in determining its thermal conductivity. From kinetic theory, Maxwell showed in 1860 that the dimensionless term $k2\mu c_v$, where μ is the absolute gas viscosity and c_v is the specific heat at constant volume, is essentially independent of temperature and pressure. In modern practice the dimensionless relation $c_p/k = N_{Pr}$ is used for a closer estimate of k, where c_p is the specific heat at constant pressure and N_{Pr} is the Prandtl modulus.

In electrically insulating solids the heat energy is transferred by mechanical coupling of the individual atomic vibrations, a concept first introduced by Debye in 1914, and presently referred to as lattice conductivity. In electrically conducting solids the thermal conductivity is increased by the presence of the conduction electrons which are free to move and can transfer energy through mutual collisions. In good metals the electronic contribution usually dominates the conductivity process. In poor metals such as bismuth, or in alloys, where the alloying elements cause local lattice distortions, the lattice conductivity may dominate.

Scattering processes, which limit the transfer of thermal energy, determine the thermal resistivity of solids. In insulating solids, scattering by the crystal boundaries is effective at low temperatures resulting in low thermal conductivity. Scattering by anharmonic coupling, the so-called "Umklapp" process, is effective at both very low and at high temperatures with resultant low thermal conductivity in these regions. Imperfections in the crystals and impurities, in the form of alloying materials or foreign elements, also result in scattering, particularly in the low and medium temperature range. Thus, the thermal conductivity of insulating materials increases from a low at low temperatures, reaches a maximum, and then decreases again as the temperature is further increased.

In metals, energy transfer by the conduction electrons rapidly overtakes the lattice contributions as the temperature is increased, resulting in a thermal conductivity which increases monotonically with temperature. In the high-temperature range the conductivity is primarily electronic and is approximately related to the electrical conductivity by the Wiedemann-Franz law, $k/\sigma T = L = 2.7 \times 10^{-13}$ cgs units where σ is the electrical conductivity, T is absolute temperature in degrees Kelvin, and L is the Lorenz number.

R. T. DOLLOFF

Cross-references: *Semiconductors, Statistical Mechanics, Superconductivity, Thermodynamics, Thermoelectricity*

CONGESTION AND WAITING SYSTEMS

Congestion (blocking) is the situation when arriving "units" (signals, calls, customers, orders, etc.) which demand the service (the use) of a group of "servers" (channels, switches, clerks, goods, etc.) cannot be served *immediately* because the demand is too heavy for servers; the servers are then *blocked*, and the units suffer either *delay* (must wait) or *loss* (are rejected), or both.

Congestion Theory (CGT) is a mathematical discipline concerned with the study of losses and delays encountered by the *traffic* of units flowing through a communication system. Owing to the probabilistic character of congestion phenomena, CGT is a branch of theory of stochastic processes, but it has its own aims and its results are of importance in diverse fields concerned with the mass behavior of human beings, animals, and machines. In view of its object of study, CGT constitutes a part of operations research (*q.v.*); in particular, it embraces queueing theory.

Applications of CGT are growing in number, and range from simple waiting lines (composed of people or machines) through analysis of all kind of traffic (e.g., telephone, road, air), to the study of congestion properties of complicated communication networks. There are also close connections, conceptual and formal, with the theory of

counters, storage theory, inventory problems, scheduling, and management sciences.

A *Congestion Process* is a stochastic process whose random variables represent some attributes of congestion situations (e.g., number of units in the system, waiting time, busy period, etc.); the *waiting (or queueing) process* and the *loss process* refer to delays and losses, respectively. The mathematical methods of CGT range from elementary probability theory to the most advanced aspects of theory of stochastic processes.

CGT originated from the pioneering work of A. K. Erlang (in 1909) on telephone traffic; significant contributions have been obtained by E. C. Molina and by F. Pollaczek. Their names are associated with fundamental results in CGT; the unit of traffic is called an erlang (abb. *e*). CGT has enjoyed a revival in the last two decades, gaining firm scientific standing and solving many challenging problems and presenting new ones; CGT is now in the state of intensive growth.

A typical system in which congestion may occur consists of a group of *n sources* (which originate demands for service—*input*), a group of *s servers*, and the *waiting room* of size *r* which accommodates waiting (delayed) units. When there is at least one accessible free server, then the waiting room is empty, and the incoming unit reaches the free server and occupies it for a certain time, known as *service time*; after completion of service, the unit leaves the server, and the server becomes free to accept a new engagement. When all accessible servers are engaged, the arriving units are put into a *queue* (waiting line), or queues, formed in the waiting room, and are forced to wait for free accessible servers (maximum number of waiting units is *r*). When the waiting room is full (and all accessible servers engaged), the arriving units are rejected (lost).

Systems with $0 < r < (n - s)$ are known as *waiting systems with losses* (or combined loss-delay systems); $r = 0$ and $r = n - s$ correspond to the pure loss system and pure waiting system, respectively. The system is said to be a *full-availability* system when any unoccupied server can be used by any arriving unit; the system is said to have *limited (restricted) availability* when the incoming unit has access only to some of the servers. Simple systems include a single queue in front of one group of servers; complicated systems with several stages in series and in parallel have been also considered. The structure of the system considerably influences its congestion properties.

The arrival of units (the stochastic *input process*) is usually described in terms of *interarrival times* T between two consecutive arrivals. The most frequently considered is the *regenerative (renewal) input* in which all T's are nonnegative random variables (r.v.'s) with a common distribution function (d.f., q.v.) $U(t) = pr(T \leq t)$; special cases include Poisson (random, pure chance) input and regular input. Other inputs considered include: scheduled arrivals, group arrivals, combined input from finite number of sources, dependent arrivals, etc. Service times L's are also nonnegative r.v.'s, with the d.f. $F(t) = pr(L \leq t)$, usually the same for all units. The most typical L's are the exponential service time and the constant service time.

The manner in which a queue is formed and dispersed, and the behavior of units during the period of waiting, is known as *queue discipline*. The most common is the strict order servicing (ordered queue, "first come-first served" discipline) in which units are served in the order of their arrival; random servicing is of great interest. Other possibilities studied include: bulk service (units served in batches), balking (early departures from a queue before being serviced), "last come-first served" discipline, queues with *priorities* (e.g., preemptive service), etc. In systems with losses, rejected units may repeat their demands.

The time W which elapses between the instant of arrival of a unit and the instant at which this unit starts to be serviced is known as *waiting time*. W is a nonnegative r.v. with the (complementary) d.f. $W^c(t) = pr(W > t)$, and the *mean waiting time M*. $W^c(t)$ has a peak component at the origin, of magnitude $W^c(0)$, known as *probability* (pr.) *of delay*. The function $V^c(t) = W^c(t)/W^c(0)$ is the (complementary) d.f. of the waiting time when nonwaiting units are excluded.

The periods B's of time during which all (or some) servers happen to be engaged are referred to as *busy periods*; their d.f. $B(t) = pr(B \leq t)$.

The pr. that at an arbitrary instant of time the system is fully blocked (waiting room full, all servers engaged) is known as the *pr. of blocking S* (time congestion). The pr. that at the instant of arrival, the incoming unit will find the system fully blocked (and thus will be lost) is known as the *pr. of loss P* ("unit" congestion). S and P differ in general, but are equal for Poisson input.

The state of the system is described by the r.v.'s $Y(t)$ which represent the total number of units in the system at time t, $0 \leq Y(t) \leq r + s$; the *pr. of state* is then $P(j,t) = pr[Y(t) = j]$, or $P(j)$ in the ergodic case. The number of waiting units (*queue length*) is $D(t) = \max[Y(t) - s,0]$. The averages $E[Y(t)]$ and $E[D(t)]$ are called *traffic carried* by the system and *waiting traffic*, respectively. *Traffic offered A* is the average number of units incoming during the average service time, and the *traffic lost R* is the average number of rejected units. All traffic is measured in erlangs.

Any typical congestion problem is specified by the assumptions on: (i) input and service time, (ii) queue discipline and the fate of congested units, and (iii) structure of the system. On this basis a stochastic model of actual situation is formulated, and from it all required properties can be deduced (by the solution of appropriate integro-differential difference equations for distributions or their transforms). The principal objects of study include: (i) number of units in the system and queue length, (ii) waiting time of units, and (iii) busy periods of servers; other characteristics of interest have been also investigated. The results are expressed usually in terms of various *congestion functions* (e.g., pr. of special situations; distributions, their moments) whose magnitude is a measure of losses and delays.

The most frequently used tools are provided by *Markov processes* (*q.v.*; especially *birth and death* process). As congestion processes are in general non Markovian, and the departure from Markovian character leads to serious difficulties in the analysis, special methods have been used to generate for each process its Markovian analog; e.g., *regeneration points* technique (extraction of the imbedded Markov chain), inclusion of *supplementary variables* (enlarging the description of a state), etc.

Equilibrium (time-independent) solutions for probabilities of interest (or their functions) are obtained from the analysis, and are sufficient for practical applications, but recent theoretical work is concerned with *transient* (time dependent) solutions which are much more difficult to find; in particular in relation to diverse queue disciplines. Numerical analysis and stimulation procedures are also frequently used, especially for systems non amenable to theoretical analysis.

R. SYSKI

Cross-references: *Channel Capacity, Information Theory, Markov Processes, Operations Research, Probability, Random Processes, Statistical Communication Theory*

CONNECTORS

A connector is a device for joining, uniting, or linking single or several electrical circuits. It is composed of mating halves identified as "plugs" and "receptacles." Each of these halves consists of a coupling member and electrical contacts separated by an insulating medium. This combination provides a means of joining electrical transmission lines.

Connectors are used where installation of electrical circuits necessitates frequent and convenient connecting and disconnecting of single or multiconductor cables, in junction or connection to electrical equipment. Standards for connectors are established covering many sizes and configurations with contact arrangements to meet many varieties of applications. Contacts are designed in sizes to cover a range of current-carrying requirements. Their spacing is arranged to provide for various voltage ratings. For circuit combinations, multicontact connectors are available that accommodate power contacts of various rating, shielded, and constant-impedance coaxial (as well as thermocouple) contacts, when required.

Connector types are commonly classified in four groups: (1) Cable to cable, for joining of cables; (2) Cable to chassis, for cables to equipments; (3) Feed-through connector, for cabling through bulkheads; (4) Rack and panel, where removable equipment must be connected or disconnected from a supporting structure or frame.

Types (1) and (2) are of circular configuration equipped with threaded, quick disconnect or bayonet-lock couplings to facilitate ease of mating plugs with receptacles containing large numbers of contacts. Type (3) a feed-through adapter for type (1), serves the purpose of providing a means to install multiconductor cables through bulkheads where pressure sealing is a requirement or where cables cannot directly be pulled through bulkhead openings. Type (4) is of rectangular configuration for connections to removable electronic equipment of modular construction.

Contacts are mostly of the pin-and-socket type; however, other types are employed in connectors for the electronics industries, depending upon applications. There are a variety of designs utilizing strip, ribbon, or wire materials with flexing qualities to assure adequate contact pressure. Of unique design are hermaphrodite contacts which have the advantage that the mating contacts are alike and both equally provide contact pressure.

Latest developments in connecting devices are connectors adaptable for printed-wire circuitry. In some cases the conductors on the printed or etched board are utilized as the contact members, and thus form the plug that directly engages into the corresponding receptacle. These are "edge-board connectors." Other versions have a plug attached to the edge of the board and mate with a receptacle. These are similar to rack-and-panel connectors. Connectors for "printed-wire-cables" are connecting devices in which the conductors of the tape-cable are used as contact members. In these cases pressure fingers are employed to provide uniform contact pressure between overlapping conductors.

In the trend toward subminiaturization, "micro-miniature" connecting devices are available. The accomplished size reduction represents volume ratios of 1:16 as compared to standard connectors of its type. The corresponding current rating has been reduced by only 1:10 and the voltage rating only by 1:4. Rf coaxial connectors apply where electromagnetic energy is confined within a shielded transmission system. These connectors provide constant-impedance characteristics to match applicable coaxial rf cables for efficient transfer of electrical energy. The four general connector types, for power connectors as outlined above, apply to rf connectors also and are classified into a series according to their functional use. They are arranged generally in accordance with the cable sizes to which they are attached. Small cables use BNC, SM, and UHF series connectors. Medium cables use C, HN, QDS, and N series connectors. Large cables use QDL, LC, LT, UHF, and LN series.

The BNC series are rated: 10,000 Mc maximum frequency, 50 ohms impedance, and 500 v maximum, per MIL-C-3608. The C series are rated: 10,000 Mc maximum frequency, 50 ohms impedance, and 1,500 v per MIL-C-3989. Rf connectors, when assigned a "UG" nomenclature by the Military Services, are required to be in conformance with applicable Military Specifications. As with military standardization for power connectors, the Services, with the aid of industry, instituted connector speci-

fications and MS drawings to assure connector uniformity and conformance to meet requirements. Connectors produced to these specifications, when approved and qualified by the Services, can be identified by their MS nomenclature. A few applicable specifications, outlined here, cover requirements and features to meet a variety of applications.

MIL-C-5015D covers regular aircraft connectors, AN-type of circular configuration. These connectors are available in five classes, twelve shell sizes, and a variety of five contact sizes having current carrying capacities from 22 to 245 amp. The connectors have a selection of contact spacings for operating voltages up to 3,000 v rms (sea level), or one fourth of the ratings at altitudes of 50,000 ft. MIL-C-26500 covers environmentally improved connectors, circular and miniature, to meet severe environmental conditions as encountered in space flight for missiles and supersonic aircrafts, operating in high ambient temperatures of 200°C. These connectors, with quick disconnect, bayonet, or threaded couplings are produced in seven shell sizes and three crimp-type, poke-home contact sizes, rated at 7.5, 13, and 23 amp, with contact spacings for operating voltages up to 1,500 v rms at sea level and 110,000 ft altitude. They are submersion-proof at changing pressure differentials without detrimental effects in performance.

MIL-C-26518 covers miniature rack and panel connectors, rectangular, and are available in three shell sizes. The electrical as well as environmental requirements are identical to those spelled out in MIL-C-26500 above. Their contacts are identical and interchangeable. Other military connector specifications are: MIL-C-8384, for internal rack and panel connectors and sockets; SCL-6001 (Signal Corps), connectors for ground equipment (Q-Connector); and MIL-C-22248 (Ships), hermetically sealed connectors.

CURT W. KLOSTERMANN

Cross-references: *Contacts*

CONTACT POTENTIAL

When two differing conducting or substantially semiconducting solid or liquid substances come into electrically conducting contact, being otherwise electrically isolated, there appears an electrostatically measurable "contact potential difference" between them. This difference persists unchanged if the elements become part of a closed circuit containing electric power sources and carrying current, as long as the circuit as a whole remains in thermal equilibrium. Contact potential differences add to zero around such a closed circuit, so that they do not cause any contribution to the current flow, and cannot be measured by voltmeters responsive to current flow. Between metals, the contact potential difference is the difference between the "work functions" of the metals, work function being the electron-volt energy that must be given—as by a photon of light—to one of the highest-energy and most favorably situated free electrons within the metal to cause its escape from the metal, in a zero-absolute-temperature model. Contact-potential-difference magnitudes, such as this relationship to work functions for metals, are governed by a flow equilibrium and a potential energy requirement, which are best understood in terms of an otherwise electrically isolated contacting pair of substances.

The isolation compels zero net charge interchange, which is provided by the presence (when equilibrium is achieved) of an internal potential barrier at the contacting interface. This fact limits to the higher-energy electrons the random-motion electron flow through the interface in one or the other direction, to the extent necessary to equalize the flows. In metals the electrons have, nearly enough, the zero-temperature Fermi-Dirac random energy distribution, the maximum kinetic energy being the Fermi-level energy. The internal barrier required is easily shown to be the difference between the Fermi-level energies.

For any substance individually, an electron must experience a definite potential-energy change in passing from the interior through a noncontacting surface to the outside, because of surface-related forces and fields, as for example the image force on an electron escaping from a metal, and the space-charge-sheath field just interior to the surface of an n-type or p-type semiconductor material. The potential energy requirement affecting contact difference of potential is that an electron must experience zero net change of potential energy if carried around a closed path from one of the interiors across a contacting interface into the other interior, then back to its starting point via noncontacting surfaces of the two materials and the intervening contact potential difference field. For a metal, the least escape energy (work function) is of course the difference between the surface transit potential energy and the maximum interior kinetic energy—the Fermi-level energy. Simple bookkeeping, recognizing that the internal barrier is the difference between the Fermi-level energies, then shows the contact potential difference to be the difference between the two work functions, for a metal-to-metal contact.

For an n-p or p-n semiconductor junction, involving electron and hole densities customary for junction transistors and semiconductor diodes, electrons and holes have, nearly enough, the Maxwell-Boltzmann random energy distribution. This circumstance permits equilibrium-flow evaluations of the internal barrier potential and the space-charge-sheath potentials, which dominate the surface-transit potential energy change.

W. G. Dow

Cross-references: *Contacts, Distribution Functions, Work Function*

CONTACTS

An electric contact is a releasable junction between two conductors that is apt to carry an electric current. The conductors are called contact members, or anode and cathode, respectively, and sometimes simply contacts.

Contact area. One distinguishes the load bearing area A_b, and the metallically or quasimetallically (see below) conducting area A_c. With clean members A_b equals A_c. But members more or less covered by an insulating film have A_c constituting a part of A_b, thus A_c smaller than A_b. The contact between a sphere and a flat member or between two perpendicularly crossed cylinders with equal radii has A_b practically circular if the surfaces are smooth. Between two practically flat members (for instance in the carbon-brush copper-ring sliding contact) A_b consists of several discrete load bearing areas. There also A_c consists of several areas, so-called a-spots.

The load bearing area A_b is a function of the mechanical contact load P Nw, often called contact force, and of the yielding property of the contact metal. At small P (say, less than 0.5 Nw) the common contacts may yield elastically. At high P the yield will be more or less plastical, according to the hardness H Nw/m^2, of the material. A computation of A_b can be based on the formula

$$P = \xi H A_b$$

where the shape factor ξ equals 1 in crossed rod contacts with a relatively large P, and often lies between 0.2 and 0.5 in practically flat contacts.

The determination of A_c must be based on the measurement of constriction resistances (see below) and requires knowledge of the shape and number of the a-spots.

Films. One distinguishes two major types of contact films: (1) practically insulating films and (2) films penetrable by the tunnel effect. All visible films (thickness greater than 10^{-8} m) are practically insulating. However, the contact often appears conducting because either the film has been mechanically ruptured at contact make, or it has been fritted (see below). Films with a thickness smaller than 2×10^{-9} m are well penetrable for the tunnel effect. They often consist of adhering oxygen or constitute a first layer of oxide (sulfide, etc.).

Fritting is a kind of electrical breakdown of an insulating contact film resulting in metallic contact spots or metallic bridges between the members. The fritting of a visible film requires a field strength within the film of about 10^8 v/m, independent of the film thickness.

The tunnel effect (explicable on the basis of the quantum theory as a consequence of the wave property of the electrons) appears at very thin (invisible) films, through which electrons "tunnel" independent of whether the film would be insulating according to the classical theory. The tunneling of a certain current density requires a voltage across the film that increases strongly with the film thickness and with increasing work function of the metal. The tunneling current density J can be expressed as $J = \sigma/A$ amp/m^2, where σ is the "tunnel resistivity" per unit area of the film and A is the contact area through which the tunneling takes place. Although σ has the dimension of a resistance the tunneling electrons lose energy first when they enter the anode but not in the film through which they tunnel.

Monolayers of oxygen or other deposits have so low a σ that, except for microcontacts, their tunnel resistance is comparable with or smaller than the constriction resistance of the contact. Spots with such films are called quasimetallic.

Contact resistance. There is no measurable "transition resistance" in clean metallic contacts. Nevertheless, between probes on both sides of the contact one measures an evident resistance. It is a constriction resistance R_c, resulting from the flow lines being tightly bent together through the small contact spot. Figure 1 illustrates the current constriction between two cylinders in a butt-contact, with one single central a-spot. The figure indicates current flow lines and equipotential surfaces. The constriction begins practically at the equipotential surfaces marked by A_e. Evidently the constriction resistance is located within the contact mem-

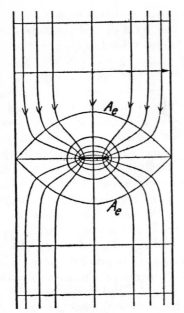

Fig. 1. Lines of current flow and equipotential surfaces of a current constriction. The contact spot is marked by a heavy line.

bers on both sides of the contact spot, essentially in the vicinity of the contact spots. A film may add a film resistance R_f, so that the total contact resistance R becomes

$$R = R_c + R_f \qquad (1)$$

With I being the current through the contact, the contact voltage is $V = RI$ and the constriction voltage $V_c = R_c I$.

If a conducting spot is approximately a circle and all parts of the corresponding equipotential surface A_e have distances from the center of the contact spot (radius a) which are many times (say more than 10 times) greater than a, then the constriction resistance associated with this spot is close to

$$R_c = \frac{\rho_1 + \rho_2}{4a} \text{ ohms} \qquad (2)$$

where ρ_1 and ρ_2 are the resistivities (in ohm-m) of the members; for instance for copper $\rho_1 = 1.75 \times 10^{-8}$ ohm-m. The constriction resistance belonging to a spot with the area πa^2 but having a noncircular shape is smaller than according to Eq. (2). For example, if the spot is an ellipse with the

semiaxes $3a$ and $a/3$, the constriction resistance is $0.75(\rho_1 + \rho_2)/4a$.

Contact supertemperature θ above the bulk temperature[1] of the members. The current heats the constriction, i.e., produces θ-values. In a symmetric contact the highest supertemperature, $\theta = \Theta$, appears in the contact surface. Because electric and thermal currents follow the same paths, a simple relation exists between Θ and the constriction voltage V_c. One speaks of the melting contact voltage, which is the voltage that appears across a symmetric constriction (at any spot shape) when, with room temperature in the bulk, the temperature reaches the melting point in the contact; see the following table.

Material	Al	Ni	Cu	Ag	W	Pt	Au	C	
Melting voltage	0.3	0.65	0.43	0.37	1.1	0.65	0.43		(5)

Sliding Contacts. The passage of the current through a contact spot is independent of the sliding velocity (including zero velocity) but the size of the spot may be influenced by the movement. Therefore a sliding contact may exhibit a contact resistance that differs from the resistance of the stationary contact.

The contact between a carbon-brush and a metal ring or commutator has particular features. During sliding the so-called collector film is formed, consisting of carbon and oxides. It entails a two-fold effect. First, it provides a kind of favorable lubrication. Second, the undamaged film is practically insulating against very small voltages, but in practice fritting provides conducting a-spots that are adapted to the current, and a contact voltage of about 1 v is acquired to drive the current through the contact. This relatively high voltage is valuable since it constitutes the means for the so-called resistance commutation adding to the commutation effect of the interpoles. Defectiveness

[1] The temperature and also its gradient in a constriction decreases with increasing distance from the contact area. The bulk temperature exists where the gradient is negligible.

of the commutation causes arcing and thus detrimental wear.

Contact difficulties. Failure of the contact making means more or less insulation. The failure may be caused by tarnish films (oxides, sulfides, etc.) or by alien material as dust or deposits (for instance polymerized organic vapors) for the fritting of which the applied voltage is too small. To avoid tarnish one uses noble metals. To avoid alien material in the contact one has to keep the ambient air clean.

Failure of the contact opening, i.e., sticking, is usually a consequence of welds. The weld can be caused by arcs during bouncing at contact make. But also so-called cold welds appear between very clean contact members. They result from a cohesion in the contact where metal directly meets metal.

Other failures issue from the deformation of the contact members by material transfer, particularly produced by arcing during contact opening. The arc evaporates material that partly deposits on new places on the members. The material transfer G (m^3) per operation may be expressed as $G = \gamma\ q$, where q (coulomb) is the quantity of electricity transported by the arc and γ is a coefficient of the order of 0.5 to 10 $\times$ 10^{-12} m^3/coul. Even without arcs a small so-called bridge transfer occurs.

RAGNAR HOLM

Cross-references: *Circuit Breakers, Connectors, Relays, Switches*

COOKING (ELECTRONIC)

Electronic cooking is a means for preparing food by heating it with microwave electromagnetic power. This is a process similar to broiling but is done at much lower frequencies.

The primary advantage of electronic cooking arises from the dielectric properties of food. Microwave power penetrates deeply into food. In comparison, electromagnetic energy in the infrared portion of the spectrum, as is used in broiling, is substantially dissipated at the surface of the food and cooking is performed by the thermal conduction (*q.v.*) of heat into the food. Electronic cooking may be, therefore, done at much higher power levels with a corresponding reduction in cooking time.

The depth of penetration of microwave power into foods (which may be considered nonmagnetic) may be calculated from the following equation:

$$P_x = P_0 \exp\left\{ -\frac{4\pi}{\lambda_0}\left[\frac{\epsilon'}{2}\left(\sqrt{1 + \left(\frac{\epsilon''}{\epsilon'}\right)^2} - 1\right)\right]^{1/2} x \right\}$$

where P_0 = incident power entering surface of the food

P_x = power level at depth x in the food

λ_0 = wavelength of radiation in free space

ϵ' = dielectric constant of the food

ϵ'' = loss factor of the food

x = distance below surface of the food

The dielectric properties of certain foods at 1,000 Mc are shown in Table I. The properties of beef are such that the depth of penetration is very nearly a linear exponential relationship to frequency. Consider, for example, the depth at which the power level has been attenuated to $1/e$ (36.8 per cent) of its incident value. The depth of penetration in beef is of the order of 10 in. at 10 Mc, 1 in. at 1 kMc, and 0.1 in. at 100 kMc.

Little is known about the dielectric strength of foods. Tests run with a 27-Mc dielectric heater, however, produced an observed electrical breakdown and arcing in beef and in potatoes at voltages as low as 1 kv/in. These foods could not be cooked at this frequency with the low power level required to avoid electric breakdown. In comparison, standing rib roasts of beef have been cooked with a 915-Mc cavity heater at microwave power levels in excess of 4 kw without electrical breakdown in food. Successful cooking results have also been obtained with a 2,450-Mc cavity heater at high power levels.

TABLE I. DIELECTRIC PROPERTIES OF FOODS AT 1,000 Mc

Food	State	Temperature (°F)	Dielectric Constant (ϵ')	Loss Factor (ϵ'')
Beef	Frozen	5	5.0	.8
Beef	Fresh	75	62.0	18.6
Beef	Roasted	75	28.0	5.6
Pork	Frozen	5	6.8	8.2
Pork	Fresh	75	33.0	42.2
Pork	Roasted	100	23.0	55.2
Potatoes	Raw	75	50.0	35.0
Potatoes	Steamed	75	38.0	11.4
Rice	Dry	75	4.0	0.8
Rice	Boiled	75	57.6	9.8
Rice	Boiled	140	78.0	32.0
Peas	Frozen	5	2.5	0.5
Peas	Steamed	75	9.0	4.5
Spinach	Frozen	5	13.0	6.5
Spinach	Steamed	75	34.0	27.2
Squash	Frozen	5	5.0	1.5
Squash	Steamed	75	58.0	32.6
Biscuits	Dough	75	42.0	25.2
Biscuits	Baked	125	7.5	3.0
Milk	Homogenized	75	72.0	14.4
Water	—	10	3.3	0.005
Water	—	75	77.0	4.2
Water	—	150	64.0	1.5

Since electronic cooking requires fairly high power levels and might otherwise interfere with communications, the Federal Communications Commission has assigned seven bands for this purpose. These bands have mid-frequencies at approximately 14, 27, 41, 915, 2,450, 5,850, and 18,000 Mc.

Microwave generators for electronic cooking may use any one of a number of different types of oscillators. The most popular generator uses the magnetron (*q.v.*) since its frequency of oscillation is relatively stable with respect to varying loads and the magnetron can be subjected to severe mismatches without damage. The electric field for the magnetron may be furnished from a dc power supply, from an unfiltered full-wave ac rectifier, or from raw ac, in which case the magnetron provides its own rectification. The magnetic field for the magnetron may be furnished by an electromagnet with a separate power supply, by an electromag-net connected in series with the plate supply, or by a permanent magnet.

Electronic cooking is usually done by placing the food in an enclosed cavity or oven in order to prevent leakage radiation from causing bodily harm, loss of power into space, and harmonic interference to communication. This cavity may have openings or perforations for observation or ventilation, but these perforations must generally be smaller in each dimension than one-eighth the wavelength of the fundamental frequency and any important harmonics. Power is coupled from the microwave generator to the food through a suitable probe or loop antenna. If the microwave generator is remotely located with respect to the heating cavity, the coupling may be done through a waveguide or coaxial line. Since the heating cavity is usually only a fraction to a few wavelengths long in each dimension, large standing waves may exist in the cavity and cause uneven heating in the food. More uniform heating can be produced by rotating the antenna, by revolving the food, or by mechanical motion of a parasitic antenna or reflector.

Since microwave power penetrates deeply in food, little if any browning on the surface of the food occurs. Surface browning may, however, be provided by adding conventional electric heating elements together with a suitable temperature control to the microwave heating cavity. This assembly is called an Electronic Oven.

Recent developments in the art of electronic cooking indicate that it holds great promise for extensive industrial, commercial, and residential applications.

GEORGE W. SCHROEDER

Cross-references: *Heating (Electronic), Interference, Radiation Hazards (Nonionizing Radiation)*

CORES: see MAGNETIC CORES

COSMIC RAYS

Cosmic rays are fast-moving charged particles of extraterrestrial origin. At the present time two types are distinguished on the basis of their origin.

One variety of cosmic ray contains very high-energy particles in its spectrum and is always present at the earth although they undergo rather large time variations imposed by phenomena in the solar system. These particles are believed to originate in our galaxy and to be distributed throughout it. These are frequently referred to as *galactic cosmic rays*. Their upper energy limit is still unknown but particle energies up to at least 10^{17} ev have been measured. The chemical composition of the radiation is well known, and contains 85 per cent hydrogen nuclei, 14 per cent helium nuclei, and 1 per cent heavier nuclei which are mostly carbon, nitrogen, and oxygen, but includes iron (and even higher-atomic-number nuclei) as well.

Solar cosmic rays originate on the sun in connection with chromospheric eruptions called solar flares. These cosmic rays are thus sporadic but occur much more frequently during peaks of the 11-yr sunspot cycles. The solar cosmic rays may be present at the earth in extremely high fluxes although their average energy is far below that of the galactic cosmic radiation. On rare occasions, however, the sun may emit particles with energies up to 3×10^{10} ev. The energy spectrum of the solar cosmic rays is usually very steep in contrast with the much flatter spectrum of the radiation from the galaxy. The solar cosmic rays have also been found to contain helium, carbon, nitrogen, and oxygen nuclei but in much less abundance than the galactic cosmic radiation.

When the high-energy galactic radiation strikes the earth's atmosphere, nuclear and electromagnetic interactions take place that alter the radiation and reduce its intensity. However, even at ground level the presence of the secondary particles can be readily detected. The intensity of the secondaries depends on geomagnetic latitude. The intensity increases as one moves away from the equator up to about 50°, where there is a flattening and no further increase. This latitude effect is caused by the action of the earth's magnetic field on the primary charged particles. Since particles arriving in the equatorial plane must cross more lines of magnetic force they are deflected more than particles directed at the polar regions. Thus particles below a critical, or cutoff, energy cannot arrive at the earth's atmosphere near the equator but may do so over the polar regions.

The means by which particles are accelerated to cosmic ray energies are not known. Their origin in supernovae has been discussed and Fermi has proposed an elegant theory, which calls for their acceleration to come about gradually over millions of years through successive collisions with moving interstellar gas clouds.

KINSEY A. ANDERSON

Cross-references: *Radiation (Ionizing)*

COSMOTRON

Although the name Cosmotron was first used to denote the 3-Bev proton synchrotron completed in 1952 at the Brookhaven National Laboratory, it has been applied since that time as a generic term to other proton accelerators with C-shaped magnets, small weak-focusing magnetic gradients, and generally similar design. As in other synchrotrons, the magnets are arranged in a ring with a magnetic field perpendicular to the plane of the ring to guide the particles in an approximately circular path of constant radius inside a ring-shaped vacuum chamber. At one or more locations on this circular orbit, the particles are given a small increment in energy by an rf electric field and keep circulating past these accelerating stations many hundreds of thousands of times until the final energy is reached. During each accelerating period, the frequency of the accelerating field must continuously increase to many times its initial value, since the velocity of the particles is increasing. At the same time, the magnetic guiding field must also increase to keep the ever-more-energetic particles inside the constant-radius ring.

In the Brookhaven cosmotron, protons are pre-accelerated to about 3.5 Mev in a horizontal Van de Graaff accelerator (q.v.) before injection into the synchrotron in a direction tangent to their circular orbits. The injected pulse is about 100 μsec long and circulates in the synchrotron for about 1 sec. There is one accelerating station which provides about 1000 ev to the protons at each traversal and its frequency varies from about 370 kc at injection to 4.2 Mc during the 1-sec period of acceleration. The pulses are repeated every 5 sec.

The magnet ring is about 75 ft in diameter and 8 x 8 ft in cross section. This ring is broken into four quadrants separated by four field-free regions about 10 ft long which accommodate the injection box, the acceleration unit, and various targets and ejection systems. The magnetic guiding field, which rises to a maximum of 14 kilogauss, is maintained across a gap about 3 ft wide and about 9 in. high that is cut in from the outside of the ring to give a C-shaped cross section. This shape is particularly advantageous since it allows the emergence of particle beams around large portions of the periphery of the machine and provides easy access for tests and maintenance. The jaws of the magnet are slightly tapered to produce a small radial decrease in the magnetic field that is usually described by the "n-value"

$$[(-dB/dR)(R/B)]$$

which for this machine is about 0.6. This gradient provides restoring forces to keep the protons inside the vacuum chamber that fills the magnet gap. For good operation the pressure in this chamber must be kept below 5×10^{-6} mm of Hg. The power supply for the magnet consists of a 1750-hp induction motor, a 45-ton flywheel, and a 12-phase alternator of 21,000 kva rating.

Since the protons' energy must keep in step with the rising magnetic field, the radio frequency providing the energy increments is controlled from the magnetic field. A signal proportional to the magnetic field is the input for an electronic computer whose output is the frequency-control voltage for an electrically tuned oscillator. The frequency is correct at all times to an accuracy of 0.1 per cent. The oscillator then impresses the correct frequency schedule on the acceleration system which is, essentially, an rf transformer whose secondary voltage appears at an insulated gap in the vacuum chamber. A large ferromagnetic ferrite core surrounds the particles' orbits that act like one-turn secondary windings linking the transformer core.

At present, about 10^{11} particles are accelerated in each pulse. At the end of the acceleration period, ejection systems can be activated to bring about half this number out of the synchrotron to study various types of nuclear interactions. Other experiments examine the secondary particles produced when the internal circulating beam strikes targets inserted into the vacuum chamber. The machine is operated continuously 24 hr per day, with periodic shutdown days for maintenance and rearrangement of experimental equipment.

Other proton synchrotrons of the cosmotron type include one very similar to the Brookhaven cosmotron that operates up to a maximum of 2.8 Bev at the Nuclear Energy Centre, Saclay, France, and a 1-Bev machine at the University of Birmingham, Great Britain, which has a continuous ring magnet with no field-free sections, a pre-accelerator of only 0.46 Mev energy, and a rather different accelerating system. Under construction are a 7-Bev synchrotron at the Rutherford High-Energy Laboratory, Harwell, Great Britain, and a 3-Bev machine that will provide pulses 20 times per second and is being built at Princeton, New Jersey, under the joint auspices of Princeton University and the University of Pennsylvania.

M. HILDRED BLEWETT

Cross-references: *Accelerators, Alternating-Gradient Focusing*

COUNTER AND SCALER CIRCUITS

A *counter* is a device capable of changing from one to the next of a sequence of distinguishable states upon each receipt of an input signal. The output of a counter may be either an indication of state or an impulse produced at a particular state transition. An ordinary counter steps through its sequence of states in a continuous cycle, and usually has provision for being set to at least one reference state by some special means.

An ideal counter changes state instantly. Changing the state of a real counter takes time, known as *dead time*. Input pulses appearing during a counter's dead time are not counted, but in some applications, a correction may be estimated.

In construction, counters range from simple, mechanically driven, geared wheels, whose output is observed visually, to electronic devices, operating at hundreds of megacycles, emitting a multiplicity of electrical signals. They are employed widely for measurement, control, and calculation.

Some examples of measurement applications follow. A counter may be used to produce a signal whose frequency is a submultiple of that of the input signal; in this application it is said to *divide* or *scale down* the input signal. If the counter is permitted to count only during a measured interval of time, the number of state changes is a measure of the frequency of the input impulses. A *preset counter* is one set to emit a signal after receiving an externally chosen number of input pulses, thus it may be used to demarcate groups of events or things. A *reversible* or *bidirectional* counter can step through its states in either order; thus the net change in state is the difference in number of counts of two different input sources or of the two modes of a single input source. If a number of counters are connected in cascade, such that the output pulse of one is the input pulse to the next, the number of pulses needed at the first input for an output at the last counter is the product of the numbers of states in the individual counters (assuming continuous recycling). When the state of the counters must be read by a person, the number of states assigned to each counter usually is ten, so that a given over-all state may be read in decimal notation. Such counter modules are called *decimal scalers*. Since, in cascades, the frequency of operation of successive counters is not the same, a grading of speed capabilities may be employed for economy.

In addition to measurement, a counter may be used to control a number of concurrent processes. Most counters are composed of individual components capable of assuming several discrete states, and the various states of the counter consist of some combinations of the individual states. Counters may be built so that separate outputs may be taken from the individual components. For example, a counter may be used to control the currents on the wires of a magnetic core memory. As successive parts of the memory are needed, an input pulse steps the counter; some individual stages will be turned on, others off, and new wires will be selected. The control of the lines may be effected by direct connection to the counter components, or indirectly by gating elements that produce the desired combinational functions of the components' states.

Counters are naturally suitable (although not the only means) for constructing arithmetic organs in digital calculating machines, and are used in both decimal and binary number systems. Some unconventional arithmetical operations have been designed in which the state of one counter controls the cycle length of another. The outputs of such counter networks may be used for generating various mathematical functions.

For reliable operation, a component stage of an electronic counter usually is designed to assume only two states, variously labeled "ON" and "OFF," "1" and "0," etc. Not all possible combinations of component states may be employed. For example, the four binary stages of a conventional decimal scaler have sixteen possible configurations, but only ten are allowed by the construction of the counter. The order in which the stages of a counter change in response to an input signal differs considerably in various kinds of counters. In a *ring counter*, only one stage is "ON" at a time. In counting according to the rule known as the Gray code, only one stage changes at a time. In a *binary counter*, the number of input pulses required to change the state of a given stage is some integral power of two. There are many other rules of change, appropriate for special uses in calculation, code conversion, process control, analog-digital conversion, etc.

JACK GOLDBERG

Cross-references: *Analog Computers, Digital Computers, Digital Instrumentation, Frequency Multipliers, Sequential Circuits, Switching Circuits*

COUNTERMEASURES

Electronic countermeasures (ECM) is the technique of nullifying, limiting, or disrupting the use by an enemy of electromagnetic-wave propagation for communications, detection, measurement, and control. For every measure depending on electromagnetic-wave propagation, there is countermeasure, given the time and money to find it. In turn, for every countermeasure, a counter-countermeasure can be found. This endless chain is limited only by our imagination, inventiveness, and the finiteness of our gross national production and service.

Uses for countermeasures can be reduced to three in number: detection, deception, and denial.

Detection. One of the uses of ECM is the detection, location, examination, and analysis of electromagnetic radiation. From them, useful information of strategic and tactical importance can be derived. For example, the element of surprise can be lost if electromagnetic radiation can be used as a warning of the impending action. Detection can also be used as a method of evaluating the strength and deployment of enemy forces.

Deception. ECM is used to produce signals simulating real signals in such a manner as to mislead the user of the electro-magnetic system into thinking that the situation is different from what it actually is. The purpose of the deception may be to give the alert when there is no alert, to indicate activity where there is no activity, and to divert forces from one objective to another less valuable one.

Denial. All actions that serve to deny the use of the electromagnetic spectrum, by the introduction of signals designed to mask the real signals required by the system for satisfactory operation, fall in the category of "denial." Denial may be rudimentary, partial, or complete. It may be restricted in specific coordinates and/or in time.

The following are the classification of typical countermeasures: Detection: Ferrets, ground monitor receivers, reconnaissance receiver, passive tail warning, search receivers, direction finders, passive radar warning. Deception: Passive reflectors, repeaters, decoys, absorbing material, target simulators, chaff. Denial: Jammers, chaff.

Equipment. The detection equipments are desired to provide various combinations of capabilities for location and measurement of the characteristics of the received electromagnetic wave. Among the possible parameters are direction of arrival, signal frequency as a function of time, signal amplitude as a function of time, polarization, and fine structure details of the signal characteristics in addition to the information contained in the signals.

Deception equipment is designed to produce two general effects: the introduction of signals simulating expected real signals, and the elimination of signals that would normally result without specific ECM action. Absorbing materials used against radars are in this latter category. They serve to eliminate a signal by preventing the reflection that the target would normally produce, so that the target is no longer visible to the radar. The remaining deception items are intended to generate signals. Passive reflectors, decoys, chaff, and target simulators are designed to produce, when actively illuminated by a radar, realistic signals normally associated with real targets of a specific character. Repeaters and signal simulators can be used to generate signals deceptive both in character and information content.

Equipments associated with denial fall in two categories: they either produce signals designed to mask the real signal on the basis of relative power, or they hide targets behind large reflecting surfaces.

The general category of ECM includes all activities designed to reduce the value of the use of electromagnetic-wave propagation to an enemy. ECM is a weapon of a battle which is fought in the coordinates of frequency and time.

An alternate division of ECM electronic countermeasures is in terms of the equipment used. Countermeasures can be divided into two forms, both closely related:

(a) Active: Deceiving or denying enemy electromagnetic transmissions are active countermeasures.

(b) Passive: Detection and interception of enemy electromagnetic radiations to learn his deployment, future battle plans, and/or to determine the enemy techniques, equipment characteristics, and operating frequencies for use in the development and employment of our countermeasures are in the area of passive devices.

ECM requires a close relationship between signal intercept and jamming and deception. A knowledge of the enemy signals is an essential factor in the effective use of jamming and deception. The intercept of enemy signals and the degree of accuracy with which the characteristics are determined are a function of the operational objectives of the system. In general, intercept of enemy signals involves the determination of pulse width, pulse repetition frequency, polarization, and direction of arrival for radar signals; and frequency, type of modulation, direction of arrival, polarization, and message content for communications signals. From direction of arrival information and geographic geometric considerations the radiating sources may be located.

The requirement for coverage of broad frequency bands and many directions necessitates the use of frequency scanning receivers and scanning antennas. Since the signal to be intercepted also varies in time and space, the probability of intercept is a major factor in determining the receiver parameters. The indicating and recording equipment are determined by the characteristics to be measured and the total number of signals in the operational environment. They are in the form of oscilloscopes with photographic recording devices, magnetic-wire or tape recorders, oscillographic records on paper charts, and human observation with manual data recording.

Jamming and deception systems can be divided into two categories: radiators and nonradiators. In the latter category are included the target-modifying devices such as corner reflectors, chaff, and absorbing materials. These devices are completely passive in themselves and function only in the presence of enemy electromagnetic signals by interacting with the signal in a prescribed fashion. The corner reflector acts as a directional reflector and enhances the reflected signal. Chaff, which is made up of numerous metallic dipoles each contributing statistically to the reflected signal, is also used to enhance signals or introduce reflections where there would normally be none.

The active jamming and deception devices are transmitters of electromagnetic signals. Their effectiveness is a function of the geographic geometry of the jamming situation. A jammer is effective if the combination of its power output and its distance from the enemy receiver is such as to provide to the receiver a signal of sufficient strength to mask real operational signals.

ECM is a weapon in a battle for control of the electromagnetic spectrum.

JOSEPH H. VOGELMAN

Cross-references: *Radar*

COUPLED CIRCUITS

When two or more circuits interact so that the behavior of one is influenced by the

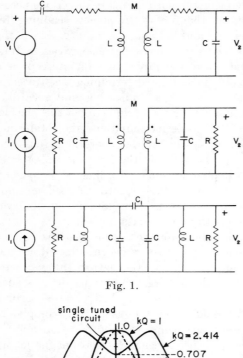

Fig. 1.

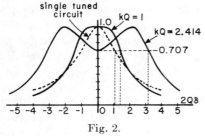

Fig. 2.

presence of the other the circuits are said to be coupled. The coupling is said to be *tight* or *loose* depending on the degree of interaction. The coupling is *conductive* when there is a direct connection between the circuits; it is *inductive* when the coupling is magnetic.

Figure 1 shows three coupled circuits which are widely used as interstage circuits in IF amplifiers. The first two are inductively coupled tuned circuits, the third a capacitively coupled tuned circuit. The frequency responses of the three circuits can be made almost identical with proper choice of the elements. A frequency response can be achieved that is sharper and has a wider bandwidth than that of a single tuned circuit.

Figure 2 shows the frequency response curves (magnitude of the transfer impedance

or voltage ratio as a function of frequency) for two values of coupling. Q has its usual significance of $\omega_0 L/R$ and the Q's of both sides are assumed to be the same; k is the coupling coefficient of the transformer in the first two circuits, and is the ratio $C_1/(C + C_1)$ in the third; δ is the fractional frequency deviation from the center frequency: $\delta = (\omega - \omega_0)/\omega_0$; and ω_0 is the resonant frequency of L and C, assumed to be the same for both sides.

At very low values of coupling the response is similar to a single resonance curve. As the coupling is increased the response tends to become wider and flatter at the top until at $kQ = 1$ the *critically coupled* or *maximally flat* response is obtained. For larger coupling the response curve acquires a ripple and the circuit appears to have two resonant frequencies $\omega_0/\sqrt{1 + k}$ and $\omega_0/\sqrt{1 - k}$. At $kQ = 2.414$ the valley in the ripple is 3 db below the peak; this is referred to as the *equal ripple* case. The bandwidth of the equal ripple response is increased by a factor of about 3 over that of the single tuned circuit.

If the Q's of the primary and secondary are not identical the response shows some minor differences from that shown in Fig. 2. For example, the ripple in the response does not occur for $k > k_c$ but for

$$k > k_c \sqrt{[(Q_1/Q_2) + (Q_2/Q_1)]/2}$$

where Q_1 and Q_2 are the Q's of the two sides of the coupled circuit. Similarly, if the two sides are tuned to slightly different frequencies, then the two peaks in the response will not be of the same height.

Other types of coupled circuits may combine inductive and capacitive coupling.

NORMAN BALABANIAN

Cross-references: *Equivalent Circuits, Network Synthesis, Network Theory*

COUPLED-MODE THEORY

Practically every branch of science involves the study of mutually coupled oscillating or wave-propagating systems. By considering the features that are common to such systems, such as conservation of energy, reciprocity, linearity, etc., it is possible to obtain a unified theory of many seemingly unrelated phenomena.

In general, the problem of coupled lossless systems is insoluble except by numerical techniques. However, there are many cases in which the coupling is weak and an approximate solution becomes possible by standard perturbation methods. A few examples of weakly coupled lossless systems in microwave electronics are traveling-wave tubes, directional couplers, backward-wave amplifiers, and parametric devices. The perturbation technique applied to the field of microwave electronics has become known as the theory of coupled modes. Its groundwork was laid by 19th Century mathematicians.

Conceptually, the coupled-mode approach is quite simple and may be best understood by an example. Consider two lossless waveguides weakly coupled by small holes in a common wall between them. One is interested in finding the effect of the coupling on the normal modes that can propagate in the uncoupled guides. To treat such a problem, the normal modes that propagate in the guides in the absence of coupling (the familiar TE and TM modes) are first found. If the coupling is weak, it causes only slight perturbation of the uncoupled fields in the guides. An approximate solution then becomes feasible in terms of a slight alteration of the uncoupled solutions.

Such a technique usually leads to a better physical understanding of coupled systems as well as to a mathematical simplification. As an example, it is found that uncoupled modes having opposite phase velocity in the two guides are practically unaffected by weak coupling. This result reduces the order of the coupled equations that must be solved to a half. It is also found that waves having large differences in phase velocity are little affected by coupling. Thus, one need only consider coupling between waves having approximately the same phase velocities. This result

yields a further reduction in the number of coupled equations which need be solved.

Consider again the two coupled waveguides that are assumed to be identical for simplicity. It is apparent from the above observations that corresponding modes in the two guides will be most strongly coupled. If the lowest-order mode is excited in guide 1, it couples primarily to the lowest-order mode in guide 2. If the uncoupled phase velocities of these modes are the same, power is periodically transferred completely between the two guides. By ending the coupling after a suitable distance any fraction of the power in guide 1 may be transferred to guide 2. Owing to reciprocity, power applied only to guide 2 periodically transfers to guide 1. This is one example of a directional coupler.

If the two uncoupled guides have different phase velocities, only a partial power transfer takes place, whereas if they are far enough out of synchronism, there is no power transfer between these modes, in agreement with the general observations above.

The technique is also applicable to active media which propagate waves. A very good example is a traveling-wave tube, which involves coupling between a transmission line (helix) and an electron beam. This problem may be handled by first finding the modes of a helix which guides electromagnetic waves. By adjusting the pitch of the helix the phase velocity may be slowed down to a velocity comparable with the dc velocity of an electron beam, say a tenth the speed of light in free space. It is found that the lowest-order mode has an axial electric field at the center of the helix that can propagate in either direction. Next, the modes that can propagate on a cylindrical electron beam in free space are found. It is found that there is one space-charge mode that travels with velocity slightly greater than the dc beam velocity and one that travels with velocity slightly smaller than the dc beam velocity. These waves are now coupled by allowing the beam to flow axially down the center of the helix. The electric field of the helix couples the beam and circuit and the strength of the coupling depends on the space-charge density. By adjusting the dc beam velocity, to be in approximate synchronism with the circuit phase velocity, one need only consider coupling between the forward lowest-order circuit mode and the two lowest-order space-charge modes. It is easy to show that gain results when the slow space-charge mode is in approximate synchronism w th the circuit mode, whereas periodic power transfer between beam and circuit takes place when the fast space charge mode is in synchronism with the circuit mode. The latter case provides a means of coupling power from the circuit to the beam and is the *Kompfner dip directional coupler*. The problem has obviously been simplified since the coupling between only three modes need be considered instead of the infinite number which appear in the exact problem. J. R. Pierce essentially used the coupled-mode approach in his first treatment of the traveling-wave tube and his later work provided impetus to the coupled mode approach that has proved to be extremely useful in the theory of parametric amplifiers.

In many problems, the theory of coupled modes has been used only after the problem was solved by more conventional techniques. There are problems, however, that have been solved initially using coupled-mode theory, and it is believed that as the technique becomes more familiar, conventional solutions to a large class of coupled systems will be unnecessary since coupled-mode theory provides a unified approach to all weakly coupled systems.

To summarize, when tackling a new problem, it must first be decided which of the uncoupled modes are most likely to be coupled. Next, the coupling coefficients must be evaluated. (Techniques used to accomplish this goal may be found in the literature.) Finally, the coupled equations must be solved by standard techniques. The simplifications occur because, in general, only a few modes need be considered rather than the infinite set.

The unified approach of coupled mode theory makes earlier analyses of coupled propagating systems almost obsolete. It leads to a physical understanding of such phenomena as well as considerable mathematical simplification.

REFERENCE

W. H. LOUISELL, Coupled-Mode and Parametric Electronics, Wiley, New York, 1960.

W. H. LOUISELL

Cross-references: *Backward-Wave Tubes, Coupled Circuits, Parametric Amplifiers, Space-Charge Waves, Traveling-Wave Tubes, Waveguides and Waveguide Components*

COUPLERS: see WAVEGUIDES

CROOKES, SIR WILLIAM (1832–1919)

William Crookes was born in London on June 17, 1832, and at the age of 15 entered the Royal College of Chemistry in London, then directed by A. W. von Hofmann, the great organic chemist. He was an assistant in the college from 1850 to 1854, working principally on selenium compounds. After a couple of years spent at Oxford and Chester, he moved to London in 1856 and remained there until his death, working largely independently. He was the founder (1859) of the *Chemical News* and its editor for many years. He was primarily an experimentalist in chemistry and physics. He discovered thallium in 1861 and was elected a Fellow of the Royal Society in 1863. His attention next turned to the properties of highly rarified gases and the rare earths. He devised the Crookes radiometer, in which a set of vanes blackened on one side and polished on the other is caused to turn by radiant energy; however, he did not provide the correct explanation of its operation.

Perhaps the most important of his researches were those concerned with electrical discharges in rarified gases; he noted the dark space around the negative electrode (now named for him) and investigated the properties of the "cathode rays" emanating from it. He conceived of these rays as made up of gaseous molecules carrying electric charges and spoke of a "fourth state" of matter that he termed "radiant matter." Although this explanation proved to be mistaken when J. J. Thomson showed the particles to be of sub-atomic size (electrons), the experimental work of Crookes turned out to be of lasting value. Moreover, he immediately recognized that Thomson's explanation of his work was correct.

During the remainder of his life he occupied himself with spectroscopy and compounds of the elements of the rare earths, as well as radioactivity; his observation that the impact of alpha particles is accompanied by a scintillation is the fundamental principle on which scintillation counters (q.v.) are based.

Crookes was knighted in 1897. The breadth of his interests can be judged from the fact that he was at various time president of the Chemical Society, the Institution of Electrical Engineers, the Society of Chemical Industry, the British Association, and the Royal Society. He died in London on April 4, 1919.

CHARLES SUSSKIND

Cross-references: *Historical Background of Electronics*

CROSSED-FIELD INTERACTION

The phenomenon of rf build-up in clouds, beams, or streams of charged particles (electrons or ions) when subjected to dc electric and magnetic fields mutually at right angles manifests itself in oscillators (magnetrons), amplifiers (traveling-wave magnetrons) and, probably, some kinds of gaseous plasmas. It is also known as the "diocotron effect."

In crossed fields all charged particles perform a steady drift motion at velocity E/B at right angles to both fields. Upon this drift is superimposed a circular motion with cyclotron frequency eB/m, resulting in cycloidal paths. Deviations from uniformity in either field create deviations from perfect cycloids; in the magnetron, where the dc field is radial, the mean drift is in circles about the cylindrical axis with an angular velocity such that the centrifugal force, the electrostatic force, and the "Lorentz force" $\mathbf{v} \times \mathbf{B}$ just balance.

Under some conditions, such as in the very early low-density magnetrons, the rf interaction is merely a kind of cyclotron resonance at frequency eB/m, with careful arrangement of electron interception so that some of their dc energy is converted into rf energy. A mere resonance is not enough to explain spontaneous build-up (two tuned pendula do not begin to swing by themselves) and in general crossed-field interaction is more than a resonance. Indeed, under many conditions, and in some of the most powerful tubes, the operating frequency and the cyclotron frequency may differ by factors of two or more (without being exact multiples of each other). They are merely of the same order of magnitude.

In another extreme situation, the traveling-wave magnetron or M-tube carrying a thin beam, the build-up occurs almost in the same manner as in an ordinary traveling-wave tube, through synchronism between beam and circuit wave rather than cyclotron resonance. The crossed fields then have the function of establishing and guiding the dc beam and do not play any obvious part in the dynamical phenomena.

In both these extremes the resonant circuits are essential to the mechanism of rf build-up. However, strong high-frequency power can arise spontaneously in crossed fields without circuits. Unless channeled into a preferred frequency by some (loosely coupled) external resonator, this generation manifests itself in noise: crossed-field devices are notoriously noisy.

Crossed-field interaction of charged particles with each other, rather than with a circuit, presupposes appreciable space-charge forces. If the dc configuration carries space-charge, the dc electric field cannot be uniform along its direction. Hence the drift velocity is sheared across its direction. Such a sheared flow is known as "Brillouin flow" or as a "slipping stream." Even in ordinary traveling-wave tubes, with the magnetic field along the (cylindrical) beam, there is a radial space-charge electric field across the beam and hence a peripheral sheared Brillouin rotation. When the beam is hollow, one observes break-up of the beam, which is yet another manifestation of crossed-field interaction.

The mean Brillouin drift may be accompanied, to a lesser or greater extent, by gyrations of the particles about the mean with frequency eB/m. The over-all pattern may still be static, and in equilibrium. The particle motions and the dc fields must then be "self-consistent." The general self-consistent equilibrium configuration is difficult to analyze for stability, but a state in which the Brillouin drift is dominant and the gyrations may be treated as perturbations with zero average can be tested by standard methods.

The result of these tests is that Brillouin flow is inherently unstable. Typically, oscillations arise that are "negatively damped," i.e., growing, like $\exp{(0.06\,eBt/m)}$ in amplitude, over a wide frequency band. One way of interpreting this growth is to observe that in Brillouin flow many streams are running parallel with different velocities so that the two-beam interaction can take place, between any pair of streams.

In magnetrons, the spontaneous growth accounts for noise as well as for start-up into the mode which is encouraged (and experiences a faster growth rate than the others) by the resonating circuit. In the absence of a circuit the high noise fields allow electrons to break through to the anode in violation of Hull's cutoff formula. The latter is based on the assumption that a symmetrical steady state is preserved, and it describes the confining action of the magnetic field under such ideal conditions.

In the traveling-wave magnetron (M-tube, crossed-field tube, diocotron) the spontaneous growth is exploited for the purpose of amplifying rf from one end to the other. The diocotron derives its name from the situation held responsible for the interaction, namely the fact that different streams pursue each other (Greek διωκειν = pursue).

The instability of the Brillouin flow, and the growing oscillations resulting from it, were first calculated for the particular density distribution which is appropriate to the magnetron, both in its planar and in its cylindrical version. The analysis amounted to a small-signal theory and demonstrated the initial stages of the spontaneous rotating spoke formation. This theory was, after World War II, extended to more general crossed-field situations, such as those prevailing in crossed-field beam tubes. In each case, the ballistic equations for the electrons were combined with the field equations and a certain amount of numerical integration eventually led to the results.

The growing wave travels somewhat more slowly than the fastest-drifting electrons (which feed the wave with energy), but not as slowly as a "slow plasma wave" would travel. When, in a beam tube, the drift does not change by more than about 50 per cent from one edge of the beam to the other, the wave keeps step, more or less, with the average drift.

The limiting case of a very thin undulating sheet-beam can be analyzed without explicit reference to the characteristic velocity shear of crossed-field systems. With certain plausible assumptions about the self-field of such an infinitesimal sheet one can then explain the build-up of undulations in terms of the action of one part of the beam on another part that follows or precedes it. Such longitudinal effects are, of course, also present and important in the appreciably sheared flow, and they participate in the build-up there. The two models give the same quantitative answers wherever both are valid.

The small-signal behavior of beams or charge clouds in crossed fields is understood, but the large-signal problem remains, as yet, unsolved. In an oscillating magnetron one believes that a fairly ordered rotating-wheel pattern of space charge is set up. When a wide-band noise spectrum is amplified by crossed-field interaction, on the other hand, statistical considerations can be applied and one can endow the particles with an abnormally high temperature. This can explain, for instance, the currents to the negative "sole" in a traveling-wave magnetron, as it explains, qualitatively, the high currents in a "cutoff" magnetron diode.

O. Buneman

Cross-references: *Amplitron, Characteristic Frequencies, Magnetron, Space Charge, Traveling-Wave Magnetron, Traveling-Wave Tubes*

CROSSTALK: see INTERFERENCE

CRYOGENICS

Cryogenics, or low-temperature physics, is that branch of science that is concerned with the investigations and the elucidation of natural phenomena that occur at extremely low temperatures. The origin of this phase of science dates back to the time when the so-called "permanent gases," oxygen, nitrogen and hydrogen, were first liquefied. The interest in these gases at the present time has passed largely from physics to industry. In the modern research laboratory they have become essentially 'stock' items.

Today's scientific research at the lowest possible temperatures depends mostly on the availability of liquid helium (b.p. $-452.0°F$ or $4.2°K$). The liquefaction of helium gas was accomplished for the first time in 1908 by H. Kamerlingh Onnes (1853–1926) at the first organized Low Temperature Laboratory located at the University of Leiden, Holland. By pumping the vapors away from the surface of the liquid helium, thus cooling the latter by evaporation, Onnes ultimately reached a temperature within $0.7(°K)$ of absolute zero ($-459.7°F$ or $0°K$). This still represents the lowest temperature that can be attained without resorting to the newer techniques of adiabatic demagnetization, first suggested independently by Giauque and Debye. By

this method temperatures close to $0.001°K$ have been obtained both at the Clarendon Laboratory at Oxford and the Leiden Laboratory. More recently N. Kurti of the Clarendon Laboratory, Oxford, has attained temperatures close to $0.000001°K$ by nuclear cooling techniques.

In addition to liquefying helium for the first time, Onnes discovered the phenomenon of superconductivity (*q.v.*) in 1911. This revealed one of the most impressive of all phenomena that occur within a few degrees above absolute zero. Since Onnes' discovery other materials have been known to become superconductors. Certain metals such as tantalum, mercury, lead, tin, aluminum, etc.; certain alloys such as $PbTl_2$, Au_2Bi, $PbSb$, $PbAsBi$, etc.; and compounds such as $VN, NbN, CuS, V_3Si, Nb_3Sn*$, become superconductors at temperatures close to absolute zero. Below a particular temperature, which is different for each substance, a wire of the material loses all its measurable resistance to the flow of electric current. A sheet or disk of the same material below this temperature (transition temperature*) becomes a good screen against magnetism. This observable fact in these various substances is today certainly the most intriguing and the most challenging both from the scientific and practical point of view.

In addition to the existence of the phenomenon of superconductivity, there is one equally fascinating that occurs in liquid helium itself. Below $2.19°K$ helium enters a new state, which does not resemble a solid, a liquid or a gas. For this reason it has been termed a "fourth state" of matter. The liquid in this "super fluid" condition can creep up the sides of the containing vessel. It has a very high coefficient of thermal conductivity, loss of inertia (quantum fluid), etc.

Some metals, instead of becoming superconductors at these low temperatures, show an increase in resistance with decreasing

---

* The material with the highest transition temperature is Nb_3Sn. It becomes super conducting at $18°K$ ($-427.4°F$).

temperature (resistance minimum). Small amounts of chemical impurities seem to cause this behavior. Resistance minima have been observed in such substances as copper with small amounts of tin as impurity. In still other substances, such as copper with small amounts of manganese as impurity, not only is a minimum in resistivity exhibited, but at still lower temperatures a maximum is observed. Specific heats of all materials show a decided decrease when compared to their room temperature values. For common metals this low-temperature value may be less than 1/1000 of that at room temperature. Rapid changes in resistance with temperature, and these extremely small values of specific heats of a particular substance, may be combined in a controlled manner to make the material an extremely sensitive bolometer (i.e., a detector of radiant energy). Magnetic properties of matter are greatly changed at these low temperatures. Insulators like sapphire or diamond become nearly perfect in the liquid-helium temperature region. These are but a few of the many interesting phenomena that occur at extremely low temperatures.

There are a number of ways of attaining them. The most widely used method in the past has been that called the Joule-Thomson regenerative cycle. This technique is simply a sequence of compression, heat exchange and expansion. The gas cooled by this process is used to cool the incoming gas, so that as the process goes along the gas gets colder and colder until it finally liquefies. In case of helium the Joule-Thomson effect becomes operative only after the gas has been cooled to the temperature of liquid hydrogen.

The second method of liquefaction, which has only recently become commercially successful, is to allow the helium gas to drive an engine so that a portion of its thermal energy is converted to mechanical energy. Helium at room temperature is very much like water when the latter exists far above its boiling point. Such an helium-engine type of apparatus has been developed by S.C.

Collins of M.I.T., appropriately called the Collins Helium Cryostat. The availability and wide use of this machine has greatly accelerated low-temperature research activity. In addition to the development of this liquefier, large metal thermos containers or Dewars have recently been designed and constructed and by their use, liquid hydrogen and liquid helium can be stored for several weeks. For maintaining these low temperatures during an experiment, apparatus (or cryostats) have been designed to accommodate standard electrical and mechanical research equipment.

The techniques developed for the measurement of temperature in these low-temperature regions give a precision in measurement still unattainable in research carried out at higher temperatures. Detection of temperature differences of the order of 0.0001°K is quite commonplace. Temperatures can be measured conveniently by the utilization of the electrical resistance-temperature characteristic of fine metallic wires (platinum, gold) or the change in the same characteristic of small commercially available carbon resistors. These types of thermometers are usually referred to as resistance thermometers. They are only useful after their resistance characteristics have been carefully correlated with the absolute scale of temperature. The most convenient thermometer is the thermocouple. However, at extremely low temperatures its sensitivity falls off rather rapidly. Over limited temperature regions the measurement of the vapor pressure of the refrigerant liquid itself serve as a convenient thermometer. For example in the temperature region 0.9 to 4.2°K (-458.1 to $-452.0°F$) the vapor pressure thermometer appears to be the most satisfactory. The primary thermometer that gives the absolute temperature is the gas thermometer. The pressure variation with temperature of a known amount of gas (e.g., helium) kept at a constant volume is carefully measured. From the equation of state of the gas relating pressure (P) and volume (V), temperature (T) can be evaluated. The gas thermometer, however, represents a rather elaborate piece of apparatus. Only a few laboratories in the world are equipped with such a unit. The apparatus is used mostly to calibrate secondary thermometers such as the resistance thermometers or thermocouples.

WARREN DE SORBO

Cross-references: *Cryotronics, Superconductivity*

CRYOTRONICS

The cryotron is a two-port, superconductive device in which current in the input circuit, or control, magnetically controls the superconducting-to-normal transition in the output circuit, or gate. A cryotron is therefore a magnetically controlled switch similar to a relay, in which the closed state is zero resistance (infinite conductance) and the open state is some finite resistance. Since the control element is made of a superconductor having a critical field higher than that of the gate, the control remains superconducting at all times. Thus in normal operation, the major part of cryotron circuits has zero resistance. The only resistances present are in those cryotron gates whose controls are energized.

Circuits are usually operated in a current-steering mode. A number of parallel paths are available; current from a constant-current source flows in the path or paths of zero resistance. The current is excluded from a path by the quenching (making resistive) of a cryotron gate in that path. Energy is only dissipated during this switching process. Any current distribution is stable when all circuit resistances are removed, since the circuit loop equations, of the form

$$L(di/dt) + Ri = 0,$$

then have the solution $di/dt = 0$, $i =$ constant. Circuit capacitances are usually negligible because of the low impedance level of cryotron circuits, and circuit speeds depend on L/R time constants.

Switching functions may be realized with cryotrons by techniques similar to those for relay contact networks. Series connection of cryotron gates results in an *and* gate; parallel connection of cryotron gates results in an *or* gate. Nonseries-parallel or bridge connections can often be used advantageously.

Memory. Information may be stored in superconducting circuits by the presence or absence of a persistent current (0/1 mode) or by the direction, clockwise or counterclockwise, of a persistent current (±mode). Once established, current continues to flow indefinitely, since there is no energy dissipation. The basic memory cell consists of a superconducting loop with an easily quenched region. A persistent current is stored in the loop as follows: A writing is established in the loop, either conductively or inductively; this current is disturbed or destroyed by the quenching of part of the loop; and then the source of the current is removed. The stored current is proportional to the degree of disturbance due to the introduced resistance and can easily be made equal to the writing current. Information may be read destructively, by quenching part of the loop and detecting the resulting transient: or nondestructively, by using the persistent current to quench an output cryotron gate.

A number of different memory cells can be made by varying (1) the storage mode (0/1 or ±); (2) the manner in which resistance is introduced into the loop (self-quenching due to current, or external quenching, i.e., a cryotron); (3) the manner of establishing the writing current (inductively or conductively); and (4) the method of readout (destructive or nondestructive). Still further variety in memory organizations is possible in the manner in which the cells are interconnected and selected.

Cryotrons. Early cryotrons (1955–56) were made of superconducting wires. A typical wire-wound cryotron was about 0.25 in. long and consisted of a 0.003-in. niobium wire (the control) wound on a 0.009-in. tantalum wire (the gate). The comparatively high control inductance and low gate resistance of this form of cryotron resulted in slow switching speed. Typically, a flip-flop made of wire-wound cryotrons had a 0.5-msec complement time.

At the present time cryotrons are made by the vacuum deposition of lead and tin or indium films for the controls and gates, respectively. A shield or ground plane is used to reduce circuit inductances. Silicon monoxide is usually used to insulate the various metallic layers. Film cryotrons are made in two configurations. In the crossed-film cryotron, the gate and control cross each other; in the in-line cryotron, they are parallel, one above the other.

Gain—Bandwidth. The current gain G of a cryotron is defined as the ratio of the maximum gate current I_{gc} that does not quench the gate, to the minimum control current I_{cc} that does quench the gate. Since these currents are proportional to the gate and control widths w_g and w_c, respectively, the current gain is proportional to the ratio of these widths: $X = w_g/w_c$. The constant of proportionality, $\eta = G/X$, is a figure of merit for the gate material; typical values range from 0.02 for thin or poor gates to 0.6 for thick or good gates.

Another important parameter of the gate material is the area resistivity, ρ/t. Typical values range from 0.05 to 0.1 ohm for 1000-Å tin films to about 0.002 ohm for 5000-Å tin films. The resistance R_g of a quenched gate of a crossed-film cryotron is

$$R_g = \frac{\rho/t}{X} \text{ (ohm)}$$

and the inductance of a cryotron control is given by

$$L_c = 4\pi \times 10^{-9} X d = K_L X \text{ (henry)}$$

where d is the effective separation between the control and ground plane and K_L is the area inductivity. The cryotron time constant L_c/R_g is therefore

$$L_c/R_g = \frac{K_L X^2}{\rho/t} \text{ (sec)}$$

and a constant gain-squared—bandwidth product.

$$G^2 R_g/L_c = \frac{\eta^2 \rho/t}{K_L} = M_2/K_L \text{ (sec}^{-1})$$

may be defined. The area inductivity K_L is of the order of 10^{-12} henry, and the composite figure of merit M_2 has a maximum value of about 10^{-3} ohm for 4500-Å thick tin gates at an operating temperature of 3.4°K; thus gain-squared—bandwidth products of 10^9 sec^{-1} are obtainable. Still higher gain-squared—bandwidth products can be obtained by using high-resistivity alloy gates or lower operating temperatures, or by increasing the cryotron gain through the use of a control current bias. Circuit speeds on the order of 10 Mc have been obtained.

The gate resistance and control inductance of an in-line cryotron are both proportional to the length of the cryotron. Therefore, a comparatively high impedance level can be obtained by the use of long in-line cryotrons. The gain of these cryotrons is limited by the ratio η, and can be greater than unity only if the cryotrons are operated with a control-current bias. Different characteristics are obtained for an in-line cryotron if the gate and control currents are parallel rather than antiparallel. Higher incremental gain, $\mu = \partial I_g/\partial I_c$, is obtained with the antiparallel connection. There is also an appreciable amount of mutual inductance between the control and the gate.

Power and Energy. The energy dissipated in switching a current I from one path to another is

$$W = \tfrac{1}{2} L I^2 \text{ (joule)}$$

where L is the sum of the inductances of the two paths. This total inductance is low ($\approx 10^{-10}$ henry) so that even for currents as large as 1 ampere, it takes 10^{10} switching operations per second to produce 1 w of heat.

Of more significance are the instantaneous power densities in the cryotron gates during a switching operation given by

$$D_i = (\rho/t)(I/w_g)^2 \text{ (w/cm}^2)$$

Typical values of 1 w/cm² (for $\rho/t = 10^{-2}$ ohm and $I/w_g = 10$ amp/cm) result in appreciable heating. In fact, the maximum repetition rate of many circuits may be limited by the thermal time constants rather than by the electrical time constants.

MARTIN L. COHEN

Cross-references: *Cryogenics, Superconductivity, Switching Circuits*

CUTOFF FREQUENCY: see CHARACTERISTIC FREQUENCIES

CYBERNETICS

Variously described as *the science of automatic control* or *the science for explanation of the functions of the human brain*, cybernetics is more accurately a near-pentology of interdisciplinary character originally dealing with the problems of automatic fire control for the interception of military aircraft. Because of the complexity of such control the originators of the discipline turned to organisms capable of performing analogous functions and through scientific description of the activities of the organism attempted to derive the necessary mathematical formulation for their automata.

The word cybernetics originated from the Greek *kybernetike*, the Latin *gubernator*, the French gouvernail and the English governor, all meaning, in one sense or another, "control." In 1834 the French physicist Ampère used the word cybernétique in his *Essay on the Philosophy of the Sciences* to describe the study of the means of government. More recently Norbert Wiener at M.I.T. has used the word to name his volume, which deals with the activity of a group of scientists engaged in the solution of the above-mentioned wartime problem, and some of the mathematical concepts involved.

Since the original work by Wiener's group the word has become associated with the solution of problems dealing with purposive activities for computers, necessitating consideration of providing computers with perception, synthesis, and flexibility of approach. As such, the discipline must rely on the skills and knowledge of the practitioners

of the exact sciences as well as life sciences such as biology, psychology, biochemistry and biophysics, neurophysiology, and anatomy.

The contributions of the life scientists to the progress of cybernetics consists of the evaluation, measurement, and description of the capabilities and of the structural and functional attributes of living organisms. Such studies involve the methods of communication, feedback, and control in the living entity. Hence an important aspect of the work in cybernetics in the province of mathematicians deals with the mathematical theory of communication, as propounded by Claude Shannon and Warren Weaver since 1948.

In terms of computer development, cybernetics is concerned with the design and construction of electrical or electronic analogs capable of performing processes carried out within living entities (including the selection and evaluation, as well as the storage, of information) and resulting in appropriate activity based on the information in accordance with assigned purpose.

In terms of understanding the operation of the human nervous system cybernetics is expected to contribute new insight into a wide range of processes, such as learning, discrimination, regulation, physiological and psychological malfunction, and the emotional behavior of individual human beings as well as societies. Specifically the problems of decision making, thinking and synthesis, imagination and creative endeavor of people comes under the scrutiny of cyberneticists.

It is anticipated that the future developments of automated industries and societal functions will be based on the theorems developed from cybernetics which thus far has made significant contributions to the technology of guided missiles, business and scientific computer applications, active prosthetics, communications, and automatic control.

THOMAS JASKI

Cross-references: *Automation, Bionics, Statistical Communication Theory*

CYCLOTRON: see BETATRON AND CYCLO-
TRON

CYCLOTRON FREQUENCY: see CHARACTERIS-
TIC FREQUENCIES

CYCLOTRON-RESONANCE TUBES

Cyclotron-resonance detector tubes utilize the cyclotron motion of electrons as a resonant system that can be either electronically tuned at a rapid rate or form a system whose resonant frequency depends upon a spatial relationship. The resonant system is composed of an electron beam, a static magnetic field parallel to the beam, and a perpendicular rf electric field. Detection and frequency determination of rf signals occurs within a single vacuum envelope; i.e., a cyclotron-resonance detector tube is a complete receiver by itself.

One type of cyclotron-resonance tube is shown in Fig. 1. A pencil-type electron beam is directed between the inner and outer conductors of the coaxial line. When an rf signal is applied, an alternating electric field perpendicular to the beam is excited. A velocity component transverse to the axial magnetic field is thereby imparted to the electrons. This rf-induced transverse velocity component causes the electrons to spiral about the beam axis at the cyclotron frequency. The electron trajectory may be visualized as a helix of constant pitch with an axis parallel to the static axial-magnetic field. The number of revolutions performed each sec-

ond by the spiralling electrons (the cyclotron frequency) is uniquely determined by the static magnetic-flux density. If the frequency of the transverse rf field, as viewed by an observer moving at the axial velocity of the electrons, is equal to the cyclotron frequency and if the phase relationship of the spiralling electrons and the rf field is optimum, the electrons continuously gain energy from the rf field. The path radius of the spiralling electrons then continuously increases as the beam moves through the interaction structure.

If the observed rf frequency differs from the cyclotron frequency, the electrons gain less energy, and their path radius is less. Hence, the spiralling electrons form a resonant system, i.e., the amplitude of the spiral motion depends upon the relationship of the applied signal frequency and the electron cyclotron frequency.

Resonance is detected by shooting the spiralling electrons through a honeycomb mesh grid; the current intercepted by the grid is greatest at resonance and is proportional to the rf signal power. A wire-wound solenoid is normally used to generate the required magnetic field for the tube. The resonant frequency of the device is then a linear function of the current flowing in the solenoid windings. The tube can be tuned over a wide frequency range (at least 10:1) with a single control.

The useful low-frequency limit of these tubes appears to be approximately 100 Mc; the upper frequency limit is in practice de-

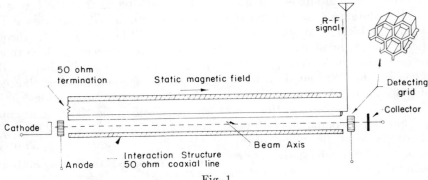

Fig. 1.

termined by the magnetic-field requirements. For example, a magnetic flux density of 1000 gauss is required to attain a resonant frequency of 2800 Mc.

A second type of cyclotron resonance detector tube utilizes the same basic principle, but rather than being resonant at only one frequency at a given time, it is simultaneously resonant at many frequencies. This type may be visualized if one imagines that the beam is shot between the faces of a TE_{10}-mode rectangular waveguide (so that the rf electric field is transverse to the beam) rather than between the coaxial-line conductors. Instead of a single pencil beam and detector grid, a sheet beam and a number of detecting grids mounted along the narrow face of the waveguide are used. The magnetic-flux density is made to vary spatially, is a known manner, across the sheet beam so that electrons in different sections of the beam have different resonant frequencies. The frequency of an unknown signal is then determined by observing (with a detector grid) which section of the beam is in resonance with the signal. Such a tube is then a wide-open receiver capable of instantaneous frequency resolution.

Both the rf acceptance bandwidth and sensitivity of these tubes depend upon the transit time of the electrons through the rf electric field. A tube having a 10-in. interaction structure of the type illustrated and operated with a 4-v beam would typically have a 3-db bandwidth of 4 Mc and could detect an rf signal having a strength of $1/100 \ \mu$w.

F. M. Turner

Cross-references: *Characteristic Frequencies, Waveguides*

D

DARK-TRACE TUBES

Dark-trace tubes are cathode ray tubes whose screens absorb light when bombarded by an electron beam and produce dark spots or traces. The screen materials are called "scotophors" rather than "phosphors." The term "skiatrons" has also been used for dark-trace tubes.

Light absorbing alkali-halide crystals, usually potassium chloride, are deposited on the face of the tube or on a carrier directly behind the face. The crystals contain faults consisting of potassium and chlorine ions, randomly distributed and having an energy level somewhere between that of the occupied band and that of the nearest conducting band. When bombarded with high-energy electrons, many internal secondary electrons are excited from the occupied band into the conducting band, leaving holes in the occupied bands. Most of the holes are trapped by potassium ions, whereupon an electron in the conducting band loses its mobility and becomes susceptible to trapping by a chlorine ion. A light absorption center forms, which is reasonably stable and can be dissolved only by further excitation. The absorption center of potassium chloride is in the F band (about 5600 Å). When bombarded by an electron beam the dark spots or traces reflect magenta coloration under white light illumination. Removal or "erasure" of the dark "writing" of the beam may be accomplished by increasing the energy of the electrons trapped in the chlorine vacancies until they have sufficient mobility to move out of the traps. This energy may be supplied by heating the screen, bombarding it with flood electrons, with light, or by a combination of these means. The contrast and persistence of the dark trace depend upon the intensity of the bombarding beam, the time a beam remains on one spot (writing speed) and also upon the ambient light and temperature, which have continual erasing effect.

Advantages of dark trace tubes over bright-trace tubes are:

(1) Extremely long persistence—up to days and weeks.

(2) Capability to integrate signal pulses, giving tonal range and signal-to-noise discrimination.

(3) Traces can easily be observed in high ambient light.

(4) The dark trace may be used as a "light valve" to modulate a lamp and produce a large projected display.

Disadvantages are:

(1) Difficult to erase, requiring time and external heat or complex tube elements.

(2) Persistence affected by ambient heat and light.

(3) External light source required to illuminate the screen.

(4) Inherently poor contrast of the dark trace, which is the most detrimental factor.

History. The action of cathode-ray beams on ionic crystals was discovered by E. Goldstein in Germany about 1894. In Britain, shortly before World War II, dark-trace tubes were used in experimental television. Unsatisfactory images were received owing to poor contrast and too long a persistence. In 1941 the British started to use the tubes for radar. During the war an extensive study of dark-trace screens was carried out at the Radiation Laboratory of MIT, from which was developed information on physical characteristics, test procedures and measurements, and psychological aspects. The ensuing Type 4AP10 tube was used in a type VG Projection Radar Indicator with Schmidt reflective optics, external illumination, and infrared lamps for erasing. The 48-in. diameter screen on which the display was projected became a plotting table. These indicators had wide U. S. Navy use during the war and subsequently were turned over to the FAA for airport traffic control, where some are still used.

Visibility of dark traces under bright light make these tubes potentially attractive for daylight viewing of radar and other displays in aircraft cockpits. The 4-in. 4AP10 is too small and too hard to erase for airborne use. In 1948 the U. S. Navy initiated a new research program to develop larger tubes with fast erasure. The resulting 7-in. diameter Type NU-2112 has the scotophor mounted on a very thin internal mica disk whose low thermal capacity allows rapid heating and cooling. An internal tungsten filament erases the trace in 7 sec. However, it, too, suffers from poor contrast at high writing rates and unwanted erasure from ambient heat and light. The Navy discontinued development in 1955 because newly developed charge storage tubes appeared to offer more promising performance potential in aircraft indicators. Some commercial development of dark-trace tubes is still under way. These tubes are used in storage-type oscilloscopes both in the United States and Germany in addition to the radar display function.

FRANCES R. DARNE

Cross-references: *Cathode-Ray Tubes (Display), Electroluminescence, Radar Displays, Storage Tubes*

DATA PROCESSING

Data processing, as used in this article, refers to systems that automatically acquire physical data, convert them into digital form, record them, display them, and perform simple editing and computation upon the data. This class of data processing is often called *data acquisition.*

The physical data are usually the measured parameters of a process plant (e.g., a chemical manufacturing plant) or a test facility. Typically the information is obtained in the form of analog (nondiscrete) voltages from a variety of transducers (e.g., thermocouples, strain gages). It is then converted to digital form, edited to elim-

inate redundancy or unwanted data, manipulated to provide it in understandable parameters, and then recorded or displayed.

These equipments are closely related to digital computers. The internal machine operations are performed by the same type of logical elements used in the computers. However, it is in the analog area that the significant contributions have been made by the data acquisition systems. Through techniques described below, it has been possible greatly to improve the methods by which physical measurements are made on complex devices. These techniques make it possible to sample simultaneously many different parameters at high speed with high accuracy, and to have the data available immediately in a form usable for display or further computation.

This type of data processing is best understood by examining an example of this type of system, such as a high-speed, solid-state, data processing unit for a test facility (Fig. 1).

Functionally it operates as three separate subsystems:

    (1) input
    (2) converter and control
    (3) output

It amplifies and scans the low-level analog voltages, converts this information into digital form, records the data on magnetic tape in computer format, and provides visual representation of the data on an oscilloscope.

Analog inputs to the system come from transducers measuring such variables as velocity, temperature and pressure. Low-level signals from 1 to 500 mv full scale are accurately amplified to 5 v full scale by high-input-impedance differential amplifiers. High-level signals bypass this amplification stage and are attenuated by precision dividers to 5 v full scale. All analog signals are then scanned by a transistor commutator at the rate of 5,000 channels per second. The scanning order is determined by a sequence patchboard. The analog signals are then converted to digital form by a

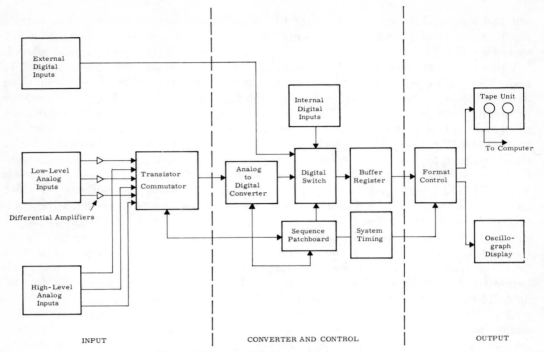

Fig. 1. High-speed data acquisition system.

weighted decision type of analog-to-digital converter.

The digital switch, under control of this sequence patchboard, selects one of several digital signals for recording. In addition to the output of the analog-to-digital converter, such numbers as time, run, block, and frame number can be automatically entered. The information from the digital switch is read in parallel into a buffer register. It is read out of the buffer in the character-serial—bit-parallel form which is required for writing on magnetic tape. The format control adds parity information and puts the information on the tape in the word and block lengths compatible with the particular computer used in further processing. Simultaneously the digitalized signals are fed into the oscillographic display unit where selected channels are presented in bar graph form.

The factors that make this equipment particularly valuable to test facilities and industrial plants are:

(1) It is an isolated probe.

(2) It provides nearly simultaneous measurements of all inputs.

(3) It is highly accurate.

(4) It is highly reliable.

Isolated Probe. There usually exist, between the location of a transducer and the data system, ground potential differences of 0.1 to 5 v. These differences consist of power-frequency and dc voltages. They are known as common-mode voltages, as they are common to both transducer leads.

Transducers are often grounded or have low leakage impedance to ground. Therefore it is a necessity to isolate the data system input from ground or the resultant current flowing in the transducer and line impedances would create errors larger than the input signal.

Common-mode voltage errors have been eliminated by the use of isolating amplifiers. Typically the signal information is converted to ac and inductively coupled to the grounded side of the data system. Use of multiple electrostatic shields, one of which is connected to transducer ground, reduces the common-mode voltage error to less than $1:10^6$.

The amplifiers have high closed-loop gain

and are in a potentiometric configuration. Typical input impedances are 100 megohms.

The ground isolation and the high input impedance make the data system a nearly perfect probe.

Simultaneous Measurements. The high speed of measurements, up to 20,000 readings per second, make the readings essentially simultaneous. The exact time of each is also known. Thus it is possible to interpolate in order to obtain a "slice in time." Data systems are also available that sample and hold all channels in parallel and then digitalize them serially.

Accuracy. Data acquisition systems have been made that have short-time (8-hour) errors of less than 0.02 per cent of full-scale ± 2 μv referred to the input. Long-term (6-month) errors of less than 0.05 per cent of full scale ± 2 μv referred to the input have been obtained. The high accuracy is attributable to four items:

(1) System acts like an isolated probe.

(2) Amplifiers with high closed-loop gain and precision feedback resistors have long-term accuracies of better than 0.9999.

(3) The development of weighted decision type of analog-to-digital converters capable of accuracies of 0.9999 at speeds of 15,000 readings per second.

(4) The development of special wiring techniques and equipment that minimize the noise susceptibility of the data-acquisition system. Errors owing to moderate noise environments and internally generated noise are essentially eliminated. The significance of this development is apparent when one realizes that current changes of several amperes, and voltage level changes of several volts, occur in fractions of microseconds and in the same cabinet with microvolt signals.

Reliability. The systems are constructed of modular building blocks, each of which is very carefully designed and toleranced. Thus, it is possible to make custom equipment with very high reliability.

TAYLOR C. FLETCHER

Cross-references: *Analog Computers, Digital Computers, System Identification, Systems*

DECISION AND GAME THEORY

Decision Theory

Let $\mathcal{S} = \{(X_t, Y_t), t \epsilon T\}$ be a stochastic process over the discrete nonnegative time set T including 0 and with range spaces $\mathcal{X}_t$, $\mathcal{Y}_t$ of the random variables X_t, Y_t, and such that for each t the random variables X_t and Y_t are conditionally independent given the past. Let $\mathcal{F}$ be a certain class of distribution schemes μ for the X_t : each μ consists of (i) a distribution μ_0 for X_0, and (ii) for each $t > 0$ and each set of values $x_\tau \epsilon \mathcal{X}_\tau$, $y_\tau \epsilon \mathcal{Y}_\tau$ for all $\tau < t$, a distribution $\mu_t(\cdot \mid x_\tau, y_\tau ; \tau < t)$ for X_t. Similarly let $\mathcal{G}$ be a certain class of distribution schemes ν for the Y_t. The actual distribution scheme of the X_t is some particular, fixed element $\mu^* \epsilon \mathcal{F}$, and the marginal process $\{X_t, t \epsilon T; \mu^*\}$ is usually called "nature." Let $\mathcal{X}$ denote the direct product of all the spaces $\mathcal{X}_t$, $t \epsilon T$, and $\mathcal{Y}$ that of all the $\mathcal{Y}_t$. The points (x, y) of $\mathcal{X} \times \mathcal{Y}$ comprehend all the possible actualizations of $\mathcal{S}$. Present-day decision theory supposes that there is given, corresponding to each $\mu \epsilon \mathcal{F}$, each $x \epsilon \mathcal{X}$, and each $y \epsilon \mathcal{Y}$, a number $W(\mu, x, y)$ which denotes the loss incurred if the "true state of nature," μ^*, is actually μ, and if (x, y) actualizes in the evolution of $\mathcal{S}$. $W(\mu, x, y)$ incorporates costs and penalties that depend solely on the actualizations x and y (e.g., costs of experimentation in investigative processes, stockout penalties in inventory processes, etc.), but also penalties that are suffered due to making the set of selections x when μ^* is μ (e.g., a particular component of x may be the designation of a definite $\mu' \epsilon \mathcal{F}$ to be taken as an estimate of μ^* for some future work, in which case a positive penalty might be incurred if μ^* is μ and μ' is different from μ.) For specified μ and ν, the probabilities in $\mathcal{S}$ are completely determined, and one may evaluate the expectation of the *loss function W*. This expectation is a function, $\rho(\mu, \nu)$, of μ and ν, and is called the *risk function*. The problem confronted by the statistician is to select a $\nu \epsilon \mathcal{G}$, the random variables Y_t referring to acts in his behavior or in that of some system whose interests he represents. The ν's are called *decision functions*. A ν is called a *nonrandomized* decision function if it has the following property: for some particular point $x_0' \in \mathfrak{X}_0$, $\nu_0(\{x_0'\}) = 1$, and for each $t > 0$ and each set of values x_τ and y_τ for all $\tau < t$, there is a particular point $x_{t,[x_\tau,y_\tau;\tau<t]} \in \mathfrak{X}_t$ such that $\nu_t(\{x_{t,[x_\tau,y_\tau;\tau<t]}\} \mid x_\tau, y_\tau ; \tau < t) = 1$. Otherwise, ν is called a *randomized* decision function.

The guiding principle, according to current decision theoretic ideas, for the statistician's selection of a decision function is that the risk should be minimized insofar as possible. If μ^* is known, then $\rho(\mu^*, \nu)$ may be directly minimized with respect to ν, in accordance with this principle. But if μ^* is unknown, then in general $\rho(\mu, \nu)$ varies with μ and the "optimization" principle does not give a definitive prescription; therefore, various concepts are introduced for the classification of decision functions. ν' is said to be *uniformly better* than ν'' if (i) $\rho(\mu, \nu') \leqq \rho(\mu, \nu'')$ for all $\mu \in \mathfrak{F}$, and (ii) $\rho(\mu, \nu') < \rho(\mu, \nu'')$ for at least one $\mu \in \mathfrak{F}$. ν is said to be *admissible* if there is no $\nu' \in \mathcal{G}$ which is uniformly better than ν. If one is basing oneself on the risk function, one would certainly not want to adopt a nonadmissible ν. A class C of decision functions is said to be *complete* if for any ν not in C there is a ν' in C such that ν' is uniformly better than ν. A complete class is said to be *minimal* if no proper subclass of it is complete. A minimal complete class exists if and only if the class of all admissible ν's is complete, and then the latter is the unique minimal complete class. If λ is a probability distribution over $\mathfrak{F}$, and $\rho^*(\lambda, \nu) = \int_{\mathfrak{F}} \rho(\mu, \nu) d\lambda$, then ν' is called a *Bayes decision function relative to the prior distribution* λ if $\rho^*(\lambda, \nu') \leqq \rho^*(\lambda, \nu)$ for all $\nu \in \mathcal{G}$. Under certain conditions, the class of all Bayes decision functions is a complete class. Let $\hat{\rho}(\nu) = \sup_{\mu \in \mathfrak{F}} \rho(\mu, \nu)$; then ν' is said to be a *minimax decision function* if $\hat{\rho}(\nu') \leqq \hat{\rho}(\nu)$ for all $\nu \in \mathcal{G}$. Let $\bar{\rho}^*(\lambda) = \inf_{\nu \in \mathcal{G}} \rho^*(\lambda, \nu)$; then λ' is called a *least favorable prior distribution* if $\bar{\rho}^*(\lambda') \geqq \bar{\rho}^*(\lambda)$ for all prior distributions λ. Under certain conditions, a minimax decision function is a Bayes decision function relative to a least favorable prior distribution.

Game Theory

Let $\mathcal{S} = \{X_t, Y_t, Z_t ; t\epsilon T\}$ be a stochastic process that is to evolve, with t varying over the discrete nonnegative time set T including 0, with range spaces $\mathfrak{X}_t$, $\mathcal{Y}_t$, $\mathcal{Z}_t$ of the random variables X_t, Y_t, Z_t, respectively, and such that, for each t, X_t, Y_t, Z_t are conditionally independent given the past. Let $\mathfrak{F}$ be a certain class of distribution schemes, μ, for the random variables X_t: each μ contains a probability distribution μ_0 for X_0, and for each $t \epsilon T$ and each selection of values $x_\tau \epsilon \mathfrak{X}_\tau$, $y_\tau \epsilon \mathcal{Y}_\tau$, $z_\tau \epsilon \mathcal{Z}_\tau$ for all $\tau < t$, μ contains $\mu_t(\cdot \mid x_\tau, y_\tau, z_\tau; \tau < t)$ which is a conditional distribution for X_t given $X_\tau = x_\tau$, $Y_\tau = y_\tau$, $Z_\tau = z_\tau$, $\tau < t$. Similarly, let $\mathcal{G}$ be a certain class of distribution schemes, ν, for the random variables Y_t. For the random variables Z_t there is a unique, fixed distribution scheme ζ. Let $\mathfrak{X}$ denote the direct product of all the $\mathfrak{X}_t$, $t \epsilon T$; $\mathcal{Y}$ that of the $\mathcal{Y}_t$, $\mathcal{Z}$ that of the $\mathcal{Z}_t$; let $\Omega = \mathfrak{X} \times \mathcal{Y} \times \mathcal{Z}$. W and V are real-valued functions on Ω.

$\{\mathcal{S}, \mathfrak{F}, \mathcal{G}, W, V\}$ is called a *two-person game*; the marginal processes $\{X_t, t \epsilon T; \mathfrak{F}, W\}$, $\{Y_t, t\epsilon T; \mathcal{G}, V\}$ and $\{Z_t, t\epsilon T; \zeta\}$ are called *player I*, *player II* and "chance," respectively. X_t, Y_t, Z_t are called *moves*. A point of Ω that is a possible actualization of $\mathcal{S}$ is called a *play*. W is called the *pay-off function to player I*, that player receiving an amount $W(\omega)$ if the play ω actualizes. V is the *pay-off function to player II*. The elements μ of $\mathfrak{F}$ (ν of $\mathcal{G}$) are called the *behavior strategies for player I (II)*. For given μ and ν the expectations of W and V may be evaluated, say $\rho(\mu, \nu)$ and $\sigma(\mu, \nu)$, respectively. The object is that players I and II, knowing all the above data, shall select "optimal" strategies μ and ν in the light of the expected pay-off functions ρ and σ.

A strategy μ is called a *pure strategy for player I* if it has the following property: there is a particular point $x_0' \epsilon \mathfrak{X}_0$ such that

$\mu_0(\{x_0'\}) = 1$, and for each $t > 0$ and each selection of points $x_\tau \in \mathfrak{X}_\tau$, $y_\tau \in \mathfrak{Y}_\tau$, $z_\tau \in \mathfrak{Z}_\tau$ for all $\tau < t$, there is a particular point $x_{t,[x_\tau,y_\tau,z_\tau;\tau<t]} \in \mathfrak{X}_\tau$ such that

$$\mu(\{x_{t,[x_\tau,y_\tau,z_\tau;\tau<t]}\} \mid x_\tau, y_\tau, z_\tau; \tau < t) = 1.$$

The *pure strategies for player II* are defined correspondingly. Let $\mathfrak{F}^p$ and $\mathfrak{G}^p$ denote the subclasses of pure strategies. A probability distribution over $\mathfrak{F}^p(\mathfrak{G}^p)$ is called a *mixed strategy for player I (II)*. If

$$\rho(m,n) + \sigma(m,n) = 0$$

for all $m \in \mathfrak{F}^p$, $n \in \mathfrak{G}^p$, the game is *zero-sum*, $\rho(m,n)$ being the *(expected) pay-off function from II to I*.

As detailed above, the game is said to be given in *extensive form*. The nature of the spaces $\mathfrak{X}_t$, $\mathfrak{Y}_t$, $\mathfrak{Z}_t$ and of the distribution scheme ζ, and the structure of the classes $\mathfrak{F}$ and $\mathfrak{G}$, imply the *playing rules of the game*.

The stochastic process consisting of just two independent random variables, with range spaces $\mathfrak{F}^p$ and $\mathfrak{G}^p$, is called the *normalized form* of the above game; $\rho(m,n)$ and $\sigma(m,n)$ are its pay-off functions. A game of this simple structure is called a *rectangular two-person game*, and if $\mathfrak{F}^p$ and $\mathfrak{G}^p$ are countable, it is called a *matrix game*. Let p,q be mixed strategies for players I and II, respectively, in a zero-sum rectangular game, and $\rho^\circ(p,q) = \int_{\mathfrak{F}^p \times \mathfrak{G}^p} \rho(m,n) dp dq$. I can assure himself of expected return up to $v_1 = \sup_p \inf_q \rho^\circ(p,q)$. II can secure himself against expected loss greater than $v_2 = \inf_q \sup_p \rho^\circ(p,q)$. Always $v_1 \leqq v_2$. If $v_1 = v_2 = v$ the game (and any extensive game of which it is the normalized form) is *strictly determined*, and v is the value of the game. If p' and q' are such that $\rho^\circ(p,q') \leq \rho^\circ(p',q') \leq \rho^\circ(p',q)$ for all p and q—in which case (p',q') is called a *saddle point*—then $v_1 = v_2$. The components of a saddle point are called *optimal strategies* for the two players. A finite matrix game always has a saddle point. If it is the normalized form of a game with *perfect information* (e.g., tick-tack-toe, chess, etc.) then it has a saddle point in pure strategies.

Nonzero-sum games and n-person games (n random variables in place of the two, X_t and Y_t) are studied as well, but there is not as sharply determined a definition of "optimal" strategies in these cases.

E. W. Barankin

Cross-references: *Probability, Statistical Communication Theory*

DE FOREST, LEE (1873–1961)

Lee De Forest was born in Council Bluffs, Iowa, on August 26, 1873. He attended the Sheffield Scientific School at Yale University, graduating in 1896, and served with the 1st Yale Battery in the Spanish-American War. He returned to Yale University and earned a Ph.D. degree in 1899. After making important contributions to the new field of radiotelegraphy, he unveiled what was to become his most important invention, the three-electrode vacuum tube, in 1906. His discovery that an electric current in a vacuum tube can be controlled by means of an interposed grid was one of the most crucial to the development of radio communications, since it made the amplification of weak signals possible for the first time.

After participating actively in the development of the radio industry in New York for several years, De Forest went to work for the Federal Telegraph Co. in Palo Alto,

Lee de Forest

Calif., where he developed a feedback circuit for his triode amplifier. He made California his permanent residence and continued to make inventions at an astonishing rate; he was granted more than 300 patents in his lifetime, in all phases of electronics. The list includes a radio knife for use in surgery, the high-frequency feedback circuit, radio-telephony, radio signaling system, radio receiving system, communications system for trains, a loudspeaking device, a photoelectric cell, soundproofing of picture cameras, television apparatus, apparatus for reproducing sound on film, radio scanning television system, color television, and an apparatus for bunching electrons.

In 1912, De Forest collaborated with a number of colleagues in founding the Institute of Radio Engineers. He received numerous honors in his lifetime, including the IRE Medal of Honor (1915) and the Cross of the French Legion of Honor. He was regarded by many as one of the last of the great individualistic inventors, spending several fortunes in fighting over patent rights in courts. He had a deep appreciation of the cultural opportunities inherent in mass communications and as the "father of radio," once berated the executives of the radio industry: "What have you gentlemen done with my child? The radio was conceived as a potent instrumentality for culture, fine music, the uplifting of America's mass intelligence. You have debased this child, you have sent him out in the streets in rags of ragtime, tatters of jive and boogie-woogie, to collect money from all and sundry."

Despite his distaste for the uses of radio, he believed strongly in the future of electronics and participated in its development almost to his death, with work on improving magnetic tapes and in thermoelectricity. He died in Hollywood, Calif., on June 30, 1961. The organization of long-time electronics industry executives, the De Forest Pioneers, is named in his honor.

CHARLES SUSSKIND

Cross-references: *Historical Background of Electronics*

DELAY LINES

A delay line, also called artificial transmission line, is a continuous or periodic structure designed to delay the arrival of an electrical or acoustical signal at a given point by a predetermined period of time.

Acoustical delay lines generally are structures inserted between electrical circuits when the relatively slow propagation of sound must be employed to delay electrical signals for greater periods of time than can be achieved electrically. Common media for acoustical delay are mercury, water, oils, or solids such as quartz rods, depending on the bandwidth demanded of the line. In all cases electrical-acoustic transducers are required at the beginning and end of the delay path.

Electrical delay lines take a variety of forms depending on the bandwidth, cutoff frequency, and delay specified. For frequencies up to approximately 400 Mc lumped inductance and capacitance delay lines can be employed. Delays of the order of a microsecond can be achieved with such a delay line if a sufficient number of circuit elements are used, bearing in mind that with a large number of elements the phase distortion created in the line will be the limiting factor rather than the cutoff frequency.

The structure of the lumped-constant delay line is that of a repetitive constant-k low-pass filter with series inductances and parallel capacitances. Stray capacitance in the associated circuits must be considered as contributory to the capacitance of the line. The lumped-constant delay line has a characteristic impedance (often called the iterative impedance) which, within the passband, is purely resistive, but dependent on frequency.

Standard and specially constructed coaxial cables and waveguides can serve as delay lines, but have the inherent disadvantage that to obtain useful delays very long sections may have to be used. Propagation velocity of signals along coaxial cables or waveguides vary with the frequency. Attenuation in coaxial cables becomes a significant factor above 1000 Mc and becomes excessive for delays of the order of 1 μsec.

A special form of delay line is the spiral delay line, which is a coaxial cable with helical inner conductor. It has the advantage that longer delays can be obtained with relatively short lengths of cable and the disadvantage of relatively large variation of inductance with variation of frequency, and hence is suitable for a relatively narrow passband if phase distortion is to be maintained within acceptable limits.

In principle any transmission line can serve as a delay line within its limitations of passband, cutoff frequency, attenuation, phase distortion, losses, and physical dimensions. The suitability of the line depends on the delay desired and the space available for storage of the requisite length of line.

Delay lines were initially used principally in telephone communications applications to restore the character of signals transmitted over long lines, suffering phase distortion in the process. The application of such compensatory delay lines became of greater importance with the transmission of video information over telephone circuits.

Since the advent of radar, delay lines have been more intensely applied for a variety of purposes such as pulse formation and pulse discrimination. Delay lines of many different types also play an essential role in electronic data-processing systems.

THOMAS JASKI

Cross-references: *Acoustics, Coaxial Lines, Filters, Pulse Generation, Strip Lines*

DETECTION: see MODULATION AND DEMODULATION

DIAMAGNETISM

Diamagnetism may be visualized in terms of the motion of orbital electrons. An atom having no magnetic moment is not orientated by an external magnetic field, but the orbital electrons, being equivalent to circulating currents, are accelerated or decelerated by a field. This constitutes a microscopic induction effect directed in opposition to the applied field. The electromagnetic equations describing orbital motion under the influence of a field turn out to be identical with those relevant to observing the motion from a system of coordinates rotating about the field as axis. In this way, it can be shown that, in the direction of the field, the induced magnetic moment of one orbital electron is $(-e^2/4mc^2)\overline{r^2}H$, where e and m are respectively the charge and mass of the electron, H is the applied field, and πr^2 is the projection of the orbital area on to a plane perpendicular to the field. Hence the magnetic susceptibility per mol is

$$\chi_m = -(Ne^2/6mc^2)\sum \overline{r_i^2},$$

where $\overline{r_i^2}$ is the mean square orbital radius and the summation extends over all orbital electrons.

This result, first obtained in 1905 by Langevin, is substantially unchanged by quantum mechanics. Susceptibility should thus be independent of temperature and of field strength, and further should be exhibited by all matter. In many substances, paramagnetism, generally two orders greater in magnitude, masks the underlying diamagnetism.

As the theory applies strictly to mononuclear systems in which all interaction effects are ignored, it is fair to say that experimental results support the theory. Observed temperature dependence is attributed to interaction effects, e.g., polymerization in liquids, etc.

Theoretical estimates of $\Sigma\overline{r_i^2}$ require the use of quantum mechanics and in any comparison between theory and experiment this is the most difficult part. Attempts to allow for screening of the nuclear charge from one electron by others have been made by Pauling, Van Vleck, Stoner, Slater, and Angus, of whom the last two have produced results in best agreement with experiment. Refractive indices and ionization potentials may also be estimated by these methods and compared with experiment.

Gases and ions provide the closest approach to assumptions made in the theory, and consequently many measurements have been made. The most accurate measurement is usually by a Gouy-type experiment in which a specimen supported in a strong magnetic field experiences a measurable force. Diamagnetism is generally assumed to be an additive property; for example, the susceptibility of an aqueous potassium chloride solution might be calculated from a knowledge of the susceptibilities of water, potassium, and chlorine ions. This is only approximately true, but by suitable choice (e.g., similar solute ions in dilute solution) additivity may be applied with fair success. In this way, it is also possible to derive susceptibilities of atoms and ions and to compare with theoretical values. Agreement amongst experimental results is about $\pm\frac{1}{2}$ to 1 per cent, whereas the various theoretical estimates often diverge by more than 5 per cent. Deviations from additivity are sometimes used as a method of detecting interaction effects, changes in chemical bonding and the like.

Diamagnetism in metals may also arise from the thermal motion of free electrons. Interaction with an applied magnetic field leads to a temperature-dependent susceptibility, which can sometimes be of the same order as that arising from orbital electrons.

W. R. MYERS

Cross-references: *Electromagnetic Theory, Ferromagnetism, Magnetism, Paramagnetism*

DIELECTRIC CONSTANT: see REFRACTIVE INDEX

DIELECTRIC RODS AND SINGLE-WIRE TRANSMISSION

The dielectric line and the single-wire transmission line (usually called Surface-Wave Transmission Line or G-Line) employ a dielectric rod and a dielectric-coated wire,

respectively, as the wave guiding means. The energy is propagated in a nonradiating surface-wave mode with plane phase fronts and a phase velocity that depends on the cross-sectional dimensions of the guide and is smaller than the velocity of light. The cross-sectional field distribution outside the guide is mathematically described by Hankel functions with imaginary argument, and approaches an exponential decrease at large distances from the guide. Though the field extends theoretically without limits, the energy is substantially confined to a cylindrical space whose diameter increases with increasing phase velocity. Both guides have a spectrum of surface-wave modes. Only the dominant modes, which have no cutoff frequency, are utilized for the transmission lines since their attenuation from internal guide losses is very small.

The dominant mode of the dielectric rod, the so-called "dipole mode," is a hybrid mode with longitudinal components of both the electric and magnetic fields. For rods with circular, rectangular, and other symmetrical cross sections, the electric and magnetic fields each have a plane of symmetry. These planes intercept at right angles along the axis of the guide. Typical field lines are shown in Fig. 1. As the rod is made thinner or as the frequency is decreased, an increasingly greater fraction of energy is found outside the rod.

The dominant mode of the dielectric coated wire is a TM mode with a small longitudinal electric-field component. The field has axial symmetry. Electric and magnetic field lines are shown in Fig. 2. The fraction of energy inside the dielectric coat is usually very small and decreases with decreasing coat thickness or frequecny.

Dielectric lines and single-wire lines have special terminations for launching and receiving the surface waves and for connecting the lines to standard waveguides or coaxial cables. Dielectric rods are energized through a rectangular or circular metal waveguide operating in the dominant transverse electric mode since the transverse electric field con-

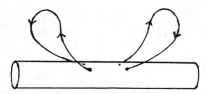

Fig. 1. Typical field lines of the hybrid mode on a dielectric rod.

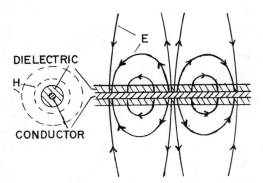

Fig. 2. Electric (E) and magnetic (H) field lines on a dielectric coated wire.

figuration of this mode is roughly similar to that of the dipole mode. The ends of the dielectric rod are usually tapered and extend into the end of the waveguide, which is continued by a metal horn with an aperture commensurate with the radial extension of the field of the surface wave (Fig. 3). The standard termination for a single-wire line consists of a coaxial-line section, the center conductor of which is connected to the dielectric-coated wire, with the outer conductor continued by a metal horn of adequate aperture (Fig. 4).

The loss of both transmission lines consists of the following components:

(a) The internal guide loss caused by dissipation of energy within the dielectric and conducting materials; this loss increases with frequency, and at a given frequency, is greater if the field is concentrated closer to the guide.

(b) The termination or launching loss caused by simultaneous excitation of radiating waves on the guide; it ranges from 0.1 to 0.5 db per termination, depending on the design.

(c) Additional radiation loss occurs if there are bends in the guide. This loss is smaller if the field is more concentrated. For small bends the loss increases with the square of the deflection angle of the guide at the bend.

The practical frequency range for the dielectric line is above 20 kMc, where the loss is smaller than that of standard rectangular waveguides. Short teflon rod lines of relatively high field concentration are used as a flexible link in waveguide assemblies. The practical frequency range of the single wire line extends from 80 Mc to above 10 kMc. Within the microwave range, copper wires of 2–3 mm in diameter with a polyethylene or Teflon coat of a few tenths of a millimeter have approximately the same losses as standard rectangular waveguides. At lower frequencies, where dielectric layers of a thickness up to that of the wire are used, the loss is less than $\frac{1}{5}$ of that of coaxial lines whose inner conductor is of the same size as the conductor of the single-wire line. Of course, these comparisons are valid only for longer lines where the termination loss is a small fraction of the total loss. Single-wire lines are used as antenna feed lines, and, within the frequency range 80 to 300 Mc, for wideband transmissions (community TV) over distances of several miles. In this case they are supported from crossarms of telephone poles by slings of nylon cord to

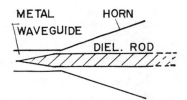

Fig. 3. Termination of dielectric line.

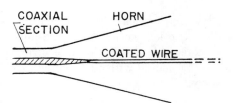

Fig. 4. Termination of single-wire line.

provide the required clearance for the surface wave field at a minimum of field distortion by the supports.

GEORG GOUBAU

Cross-references: *Antennas, Coaxial Lines, Waveguides and Waveguide Components, Wire (Multiconductor)*

DIELECTRIC THEORY

A dielectric is a material having electrical conductivity low in comparison to that of a metal. It is characterized by its dielectric constant and dielectric loss, both of which are functions of frequency and temperature. The dielectric constant is the ratio of the strength of an electric field in a vacuum to that in the dielectric for the same distribution of charge. It may also be defined and measured as the ratio of the capacitance C of an electrical condenser filled with the dielectric to the capacitance C_0 of the evacuated condenser:

$$\epsilon' = C/C_0$$

The increase in the capacitance of the condenser is due to the polarization of the dielectric material by the applied electric field. When a condenser is charged with an alternating current, loss may occur because of dissipation of part of the energy as heat. In vector notation, the angle δ between the vector for the amplitude of the charging current and that for the amplitude of the total current is the loss angle, and the loss tangent, or dissipation factor, is

$$\tan \delta = \frac{\text{loss current}}{\text{charging current}} = \frac{\epsilon''}{\epsilon'}$$

where ϵ'' is the loss factor, or dielectric loss, of the dielectric in the condenser; and ϵ' is the measured dielectric constant of the material.

At low frequencies of the alternating field the dielectric loss is normally zero and ϵ' is indistinguishable from the dielectric constant ϵ_{dc}' measured with a static field. Debye has shown that

$$\frac{\epsilon_{dc}' - 1}{\epsilon_{dc}' + 2} = \frac{4\pi N_1}{3}\left(\alpha_0 + \frac{\mu^2}{3kT}\right) \tag{1}$$

where N_1 is the number of molecules or ions per cubic centimeter; α_0 is the molecular or ionic polarizability, that is, the dipole moment induced per molecule or ion by unit electric field (1 e.s.u. = 300 v/cm); μ is the permanent dipole moment possessed by the molecule, k is the molecular gas constant, 1.38×10^{-16}, and T is the absolute temperature. An electric dipole is a pair of electric charges, equal in size, opposite in sign, and very close together. The dipole moment is the product of one of the two charges and the distance between them.

In the above equation $\mu^2/3kT$ is the average component in the direction of the field of the permanent dipole moment of the molecule. In order that this average contribution should exist, the molecules must be able to rotate into equilibrium with the field. When the frequency of the alternating electric field used in the measurement is so high that dipolar molecules cannot respond to it, the second term in the parentheses of Eq. (1) decreases to zero and we have what may be termed the optical dielectric constant ϵ_∞', defined by the expression

$$\frac{\epsilon_\infty' - 1}{\epsilon_\infty' + 2} = \frac{4\pi N_1}{3}\alpha_0 \tag{2}$$

ϵ_∞' differs from n^2, the square of the optical refractive index for visible light, only by the small amount due to infrared absorption and to the small dependence of n on frequency, as given by dispersion formulas. It is usually not a bad approximation to use $\epsilon_\infty' = n^2$. The general Maxwell relation $\epsilon' = n^2$ holds when ϵ' and n are measured at the same frequency.

Anomalous dielectric dispersion occurs when the frequency of the field is so high that the molecules have not time to attain equilibrium with it. One may then use a complex dielectric constant

$$\epsilon^* = \epsilon' - j\epsilon'' \tag{3}$$

where $j = \sqrt{-1}$, Debye's theory of dielectric behavior gives

$$\epsilon^* = \epsilon_\infty' + \frac{\epsilon_{dc}' - \epsilon_\infty'}{1 + j\omega\tau} \tag{4}$$

where ω is the angular frequency and τ is the dielectric relaxation time. Dielectric relaxation is the decay with time of the polarization when the applied field is removed. The relaxation time is the time in which the polarization is reduced to $1/e$ times its value at the instant the field is removed, e being the natural-logarithm base.

Combination of the two equations for the complex dielectric constant and separation of real and imaginary parts gives

$$\epsilon' = \epsilon_\infty' + \frac{\epsilon_{dc}' - \epsilon_\infty'}{1 + \omega^2\tau^2} \qquad (5)$$

$$\epsilon'' = \frac{(\epsilon_{dc}' - \epsilon_\infty')\omega\tau}{1 + \omega^2\tau^2} \qquad (6)$$

These equations require that the dielectric constant decrease from the static to the optical dielectric constant with increasing frequency, while the dielectric loss changes from zero to a maximum value ϵ_m'' and back to zero. These changes are the phenomenon of anomalous dielectric dispersion. From the above equations, it follows that

$$\epsilon_m'' = (\epsilon_{dc}' - \epsilon_\infty')/2 \qquad (7)$$

and that the corresponding values of ω and ϵ' are

$$\omega_m = 1/\tau$$

and

$$\epsilon_m' = (\epsilon_{dc}' + \epsilon_\infty')/2$$

The symmetrical loss-frequency curve predicted by this simple theory is commonly observed for simple substances, but its maximum is usually lower and broader because of the existence of more than one relaxation time. Various functions have been proposed to represent the distribution of relaxation times. A convenient representation of dielectric behavior is obtained, according to the method of Cole and Cole, by writing the complex dielectric constant as

$$\epsilon^* = \epsilon_\infty' + \frac{\epsilon_{dc}' - \epsilon_\infty'}{1 + (j\omega\tau_0)^{1-\alpha}} \qquad (8)$$

where τ_0 is the most probable relaxation time and α is an empirical constant with a value

between 0 and 1, usually less than 0.2. When the values of ϵ'' are plotted as ordinates against those of ϵ' as abscissas, a semicircular arc is obtained intersecting the abscissa axis at $\epsilon' = \epsilon_\infty'$ and $\epsilon' = \epsilon_{dc}'$. The center of the circle of which this arc is a part lies below the abscissa axis, and the diameter of the circle drawn through the center from the intersection at ϵ_∞ makes an angle $\alpha\pi/2$ with the abscissa axis. When α is zero, the diameter lies in the abscissa axis, there is only one relaxation time, and the behavior of the material conforms to the simple Debye theory. When, as may arise from intramolecular rotation, a substance has more than one relaxation mechanism, or when the material is a mixture, the observed loss-frequency curve is the resultant of two or more different curves and, therefore, departs from the simple Debye or Cole-Cole curve.

If the dielectric material is not a perfect dielectric, and has a specific dc conductance k' (ohms^{-1} cm^{-1}), there is an additional dielectric loss

$$\epsilon_{dc}'' = \frac{1.8 \times 10^{12}k'}{2\pi\omega} \qquad (9)$$

In a heterogeneous material, interfacial polarization may arise from the accumulation of charge at the interfaces between phases. This accumulation occurs only when two phases differ considerably from each other in dielectric constant and conductivity. It is usually observed only at very low frequencies, but if one phase has a higher conductivity, the effect may increase the measured dielectric constant and loss at frequencies as high as those of the radio region. This so-called Maxwell-Wagner effect depends on the form and distribution of the phases as well as upon their real dielectric constants and conductances. For a commercial rubber, for example, the observed loss may be

ϵ'' (observed) $= \epsilon_{dc}'' + \epsilon''$ (Maxwell-Wagner)

$$+ \epsilon'' \text{ (Debye)} \qquad (10)$$

CHARLES P. SMYTH

Cross-references: *Dipole Moment, Electromagnetic Theory, Optics, Refractive Index*

DIGITAL COMPUTERS

The digital computer has become an important scientific, business, and military tool in the short span of 10 years. From its beginning in the universities during World War II, it has grown to a 1.5 billion dollar per year business. The digital computer can be characterized as an extremely high-speed information handling device that has a memory for storage of data and operating instructions. The computer can alter the data stored, including the instructions, and contains the logic necessary to make elementary decisions (for example, that two quantities are equal, or that a quantity is greater than another) and to alter its actions depending upon these decisions.

All general-purpose electronic digital computers have five major system components, or functional sections: input, output, memory, arithmetic, and control. Input is that part of the system that is used to enter information into the system; output is used to receive results; memory is used to store data and instructions for a problem; arithmetic performs the operation specified by the instruction; and control interprets the instruction to direct the arithmetic operations. The arithmetic, memory, and control sections are the computer proper (the *central* computer). Figure 1 illustrates the typical organization of a general-purpose digital computer.

Number Systems and Representation of Information

The radix or base of a number system describes the number of unique symbols employed by the number system. Thus, the decimal system (base 10) employs the digits 0, 1, 2, 3, 4, 5, 6, 7, 8, and 9 to represent all numbers. The binary system (base 2) employs only two digits, 0 and 1, to represent any number. Numbers (N) are related to the digits (d_i) and the base or radix (R) of a system as follows:

$$N = d_0 + d_1R + d_2R^2 + d_3R^3 + \cdots + d_nR^n$$

It is the usual practice to write the digits in reverse order, thus:

$$N = d_nR^n + \cdots + d_3R^3 + d_2R^2 + d_1R + d_0$$

As an example, the decimal number 1743 would be written:

$$1 \times 10^3 + 7 \times 10^2 + 4 \times 10 + 3 = 1743$$

The same number in the binary system is:

$$1 \times 2^{10} + 1 \times 2^9 + 0 \times 2^8 + 1 \times 2^7 + 1 \times 2^6$$
$$+ 0 \times 2^5 + 0 \times 2^4 + 1 \times 2^3 + 1 \times 2^2$$
$$+ 1 \times 2 + 1 = 11011001111 = 1743$$

The binary system was chosen for most computers because of the economy of storage possible, and the ease of constructing circuits representing only two stable states as opposed to ten. One such circuit, known as a flip-flop, is found in all computers regardless of type. It is an elementary device capable of storing a 1 or a 0. Groups of flip-flops serve as registers and to control the logic of computers. Other logical elements are AND gates and OR gates.

Because people use decimal numbers and alphabetic symbols to describe quantities and qualities of objects, computers have been made that treat groups of binary digits (*bits*) as codings of the decimal and/or alphabetic symbols. These computers, called decimal or alphanumeric, have the advantage that conversion from decimal or alphanumeric coding to binary and back again is unnecessary.

In performing scientific calculations, or in handling non-numeric data, the number of symbols used to describe the data may be arbitrarily long. In computers, however, it is

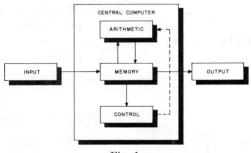

Fig. 1.

convenient to fix the unit of data that the computer operates upon, and to use as many of these units as are necessary to contain the actual information being operated upon. This unit is called a *word*, and represents the amount of information the computer can manipulate in a single operation. Word size is described either in bits (binary digits) or in characters (in alphanumeric computers). Words in modern computers range in size from 6 bits (one character, as in the IBM 705) to 64 bits (as in the IBM 7030 STRETCH).

General and Special Purpose

It is convenient to distinguish special-purpose and general-purpose computers. Special-purpose computers have one or more of the following characteristics: (a) they are generally limited to a single problem or problem class; (b) they frequently employ special input-output equipment; and (c) the command list is frequently small and encompasses only enough operations to solve the problem. An example of a special-purpose computer is the Burroughs D-202, an airborne navigation computer, in which the inputs are radar returns, position and velocity of the computer vehicle, and human decisions, whereas the outputs are steering commands and displays. Another kind of special-purpose computer is one developed by Remington Rand UNIVAC (card punching printer) to print and punch customers' bills. This machine has magnetic tape input (only) and punched card output (only), has no multiply or divide instructions, and is used for customer billing exclusively. Although many aspects of special-purpose computers are quite interesting, the discussion below is in general limited to stored-program general-purpose computers.

Major Systems Components

Input and Output Sections. As noted previously, the computer input and output sections insert data and receive results. The input equipment may include magnetic tapes, punched card readers, punched paper tape readers, analog-to-digital converters, and the like. The output equipment may include magnetic tapes, card punches, paper tape punches, typewriters, line printers, digital-to-analog converters, cathode-ray-tube displays and the like. The choice of a particular set of input-output equipment is dictated by the design objective for the computer. Most manufacturers provide a variety of input-output equipment and permit the customer to select that configuration which is most suitable for his application.

Memory Section. The memory section provides the data and the program storage for the computer system. High-speed memories of magnetic ferrite cores (*q.v.*) are part of most present-day computer systems, although the magnetic-drum memory still enjoys popularity because of the economy it affords. Information is recorded in a magnetic-core memory by setting the cores (corresponding to bits in a word) to a positive magnetization for 1's and to a negative magnetization for 0's. Reading is accomplished by switching the cores and sensing the voltage induced by the flux change. The magnetic drum holds information recorded as magnetic "spots" on the surface of the rotating drum. Magnetic-drum techniques are similar to those employed in recording information on magnetic tapes. In general, large-scale data-processing systems employ magnetic-core memories, whereas magnetic drums are found as the main memory system in some medium- and small-scale equipment.

Other devices used as computer memories include cathode-ray tubes (IBM 701) and delay lines (UNIVAC I). Recomp II and the IBM 305 RAMAC employ magnetic disks for memory; however, this is in principle the same memory element as a magnetic drum.

Some special-purpose computers have been built using various forms of photographic storage as well. A greater variety of novel approaches to the computer storage problem are under development; one or more of these will probably replace all present techniques in most applications.

Arithmetic Section. The arithmetic section is that portion of the computer which performs the arithmetic and logical operations on the data. Generally, there are several registers associated with the arithmetic section that are used as temporary storage during the execution of a command. The accumulator is one such register, which holds one of the operands in arithmetic operations, and also receives the result of the operation performed. Because operations such as multiplication can create numbers with more digits than either of the two operands, an extension to the accumulator is provided in most computers so that this information is not lost.

In addition to the usual arithmetic operations, the arithmetic section performs operations usually classified as logical. The logical operations generally do not transform data, but are included to provide a primitive qualitative measure of the data. Thus, the comparison of two computer words to determine which contains the larger quantity is considered a logical operation. As a result of such comparisons, decisions are made between alternate paths of computation. The logical operations in computers contribute heavily to the wide application and generality of the machines.

Control Section. The control section of the computer interprets the instructions that make up the program and causes specified operations to be carried out in the arithmetic section. The arithmetic and control sections of a computer are frequently combined as a single unit. The instructions stored in the memory generally consist of two parts, an operation code and an address, as in Fig. 2. Instructions are obtained from memory under the control of a special register, known variously as the sequence counter, program counter, or control counter, which contains the address of the next instruction to be executed. As each instruction is obtained, a 1 is added to the sequence counter, thus providing for the orderly execution of the individual steps of the program. An alternate sequence of instructions may be initiated (usually as a result of logical operations) by placing an entirely new address in the sequence counter. The instruction word entering the control section is placed in another register, known as the control register, where the address portion of the instruction is used to obtain (fetch) the word located at that address and to send the word to the arithmetic section. The individual bits of the operation code are interpreted to effect the operation specified (for example, addition, multiplication, etc.) on the data word fetched and the contents of the accumulator. The control section also initiates input/output operations.

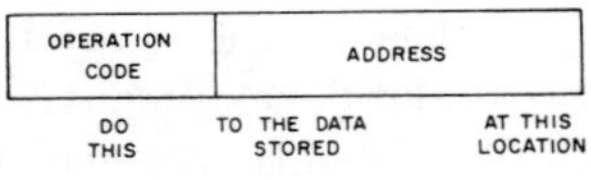

Programming. The preparation of a problem to be run on a given computer is known as programming. Programming places the problem in a form from which it can be rapidly translated, by an essentially rote process, into the language devised for the particular computer. The resulting sequence of coded instructions is the computer program, and is usually stored in a fixed pattern in the computer memory section. Details of computer construction can affect the form a program will take, yet this process is to a large extent independent of the computer, since it is concerned with the *procedure* to be employed in the solution of a problem, and the sequence of events that must take place to effect the procedure.

Recently, there has been an intensive effort to develop techniques that permit computers to assist automatically in the preparation of their own programs. This process, known as automatic coding, has evolved to a high degree of importance; complex programs, written in a stylized English or algebraic form, may now be converted directly into machine operating instructions. Examples of English-language coding schemes include COBOL (Common Business Oriented Language, which is to be implemented by most

OPERATION CODE	ADDRESS	
DO THIS	TO THE DATA STORED	AT THIS LOCATION

Fig. 2.

computer manufacturers), FACT (Honeywell 800), Commercial Translator (IBM 705 and 7080), and FLOWMATIC (UNIVAC I, II, and the solid-state 90). Algebraic coding systems include ALGOL '58 (Burroughs 220), ALGO (Bendix G-15), the FORTRAN series (the IBM family of computers), and AT-3 (the UNIVAC computers). Great reductions in coding costs are made possible by such systems; hand-coded programs range in cost from $2 to $5 per instruction, whereas compiler-produced programs range from $0.10 to $0.50 per instruction.

JAMES P. ANDERSON

Cross-references: *Analog Computers, Coding, Computer Logic, Computer Printout and Reading, Computer Programming, Computer Applications, Counter and Scaler Circuits, Digital Instrumentation, Logic Circuits, Storage, Switching Circuits, Translating Machines*

DIGITAL INSTRUMENTATION

Digital circuitry represents information in code or digital form by the state of a group of circuit elements, each element having only a few possible states. Each possible state of a circuit element is considered to represent a number. The state of a group of elements then represents a series of numbers, which may represent the magnitude of a variable or a code having an assigned meaning.

For example, each of a group of three wires may be considered to represent the number zero when negative of ground, and the number one when positive of ground. These three wires may then indicate any of the following eight possible codes.

000
001
010
011
100
101
110
111

These codes represent numbers 1 through

7 in the binary system of numbers and therefore could be used to represent the magnitude of a variable. If the binary number 111 (decimal number 7) represents full scale of the variable, then the variable may be represented to the nearest unit value, but not exactly. The difference between the actual value and the nearest code value would constitute a limit of accuracy. In the worst case the number would differ from the actual value by $\frac{1}{14}$ of full scale, which is a possible inaccuracy of about 7 per cent. Of course, more wires could be used allowing full scale to be represented by a higher number, thereby improving the accuracy of indication.

It is generally true that the accuracy of digital circuitry may be improved to any degree by increasing the complexity of the circuitry. However, most digital instruments involve some analog circuitry, which limits their possible accuracy. Also, some instruments require a longer period of time to make a more accurate measurement.

It should be noted that the actual voltage of the three wires could vary ±50 per cent or more without obscuring the number. It is always possible to design digital circuitry so that large variations in circuit parameters can take place without obscuring information or in any way altering the correctness of operation. This lack of sensivity to drift of component parameters is a great advantage of digital circuitry over analog circuitry. Analog circuitry represents a variable by a proportional electrical quantity, usually voltage. If this quantity drifts 50 per cent, the represented number changes by 50 per cent. A wide variety of analog instruments are available, which will remain within 0.1-per cent accuracy for extended periods of time. However, it is generally necessary to use digital instruments to achieve higher orders of accuracy or to achieve 0.1-per cent accuracy in a system involving several instruments.

Digital-Circuit Elements. Most digital devices are made up of various combinations of only a few circuit types. Table 1 lists the

TABLE 1. COMMON DIGITAL CIRCUITS

Notes: —▷ = Dc signal; —▶ = Ac signal; Shaded transistor is conducting in reset state. Polarities are based on pnp transistors.

Name and Symbol	Action
Binary, flip-flop, or bistable multivibrator 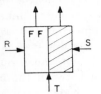	The circuit has two stable states. Each state has one transistor saturated and one transistor cut off. States are designated as the set state and the reset state. The T input switches states. The S input causes the binary to swtich to, or remain in, the set state. The R input causes the binary to swtich to or remain in the reset state. Inputs require a positive pulse or step.
One-shot multivibrator, delay multivibrator, or mono-stable multivibrator	The circuit has two states. One state with one transistor conducting is stable. The other state with the other transistor conducting is quasi-stable. When pulsed the circuit triggers to the quasi-stable state and remains for a period of time dependent on the RC value. At the end of this time, the circuit triggers back to the stable state.
Free-running multivibrator or astable multivibrator	The circuit has two quasi-stable states. It continues to trigger between these states remaining in a condition of one transistor conducting for a time determined by a circuit time constant and remaining in a condition of the other transistor conducting for a time determined by another circuit time constant.
Schmitt trigger circuit	The circuit has two stable states. The circuit is in the state having one transistor conducting when the input voltage is more negative than a voltage V_1. The circuit is in the other state when the input is positive of a voltage V_2 which is more positive than V_1. When the input is between voltages V_1 and V_2, the circuit retains its state. $V_2 - V_1$ is called hysteresis.
Inverter $A = \bar{a}$	Input is inverted
Three-input inverting gate Note. The symbol for a non-inverting gate lacks the circled output:	
Negative logic $A = \overline{(a + b + c)}$	With negative inputs signals this circuit is an "or" circuit producing a positive-going output when any input is negative.
Positive logic $A = \overline{(abc)}$	With positive input signals this circuit is an "and" circuit producing a negative-going output when *all* inputs are positive.

most common digital circuit types with an explanation, symbol, and action. Many systems of symbols have been devised for digital circuits, but none of these has been generally accepted by the electronics industry. The symbols shown should be considered only as symbols for the circuits and not as elements of logic diagrams. Otherwise, ambiguity in interpretation may result.

Various memory devices are also important elements of digital instruments. These devices include magnetic tape, magnetic drum, punched tape, punched card, magnetic core, magnetic shift register and others. The first four circuits of Table 1 utilize positive feedback in a manner that causes the circuits to have two and only two stable or quasi-stable states. The transit time between stable states depends on the gain bandwidth product around the positive feedback loop, while the circuit is in the transient condition between states. It also depends on storage time of the transistors and the magnitude of the input signal. The maximum repetition rate of consecutive circuit triggering is limited if excessive RC time constants exist in the coupling networks to the transistor bases.

Counting. Binary circuits count input pulses according to the binary system of numbers when interconnected as shown in Fig. 1. The binaries reset state represents the number zero and the set state represents the number one.

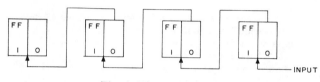

Fig. 1. Binary counter.

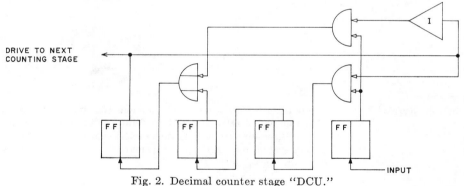

Fig. 2. Decimal counter stage "DCU."

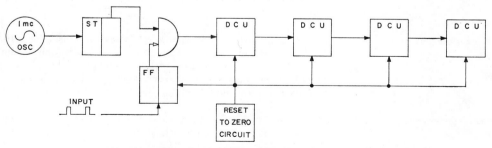

Fig. 3. Decade counting stages.

TABLE 2. SAMPLE DIGITAL INSTRUMENTS

Class Name	Quantities Measured	Available Outputs	Typical Specifications
Digital voltmeter or analog-to-digital converter	Dc volts Ac volts Ohms Voltage ratio	Digital display Printer Code (The code output may be used to drive a card or tape punch or other recording device.)	Indicate 5 decimal digits Accuracy of dc voltage reading is $0.01\% \pm 1$ digit. Range $= 0.0001$ to 1010 v with automatic ranging. Input impedance $= 10$ megohms.
Universal counter and timer	Events per unit time or frequency Total count of input cycles Frequency ratio Period of wave Width of pulse Time between pulses	Digital display Printer Code	Accuracy of frequency and time measurement is 3 parts in $10^7 \pm 1$ digit
General-purpose digital computer	A program of operations to be performed is fed into the computer in code form. Capability of the computer includes addition, subtraction, multiplication, utilizing tables, and utilizing results of previous operations.	Usually punched tape and automatic typewriter	

TABLE 3. SAMPLE DIGITAL SYSTEMS

Class	Function
Data-reduction system	Input is data from a test such as magnetic-tape recordings from a missile flight. Data are converted into a digital form, which may be utilized directly or fed into a digital computer. The data-reduction system may perform mathematical operations to derive the output data.
Tachometer system	Conditions of an engine under test are sensed by transducers and converted to meaningful numbers which may be remotely indicated and recorded.
Missile-checkout system	The system operates according to a set of instructions, generally on IBM cards or punched tape. These instructions cause the system to apply electrical stimulus to control equipment on the missile and to measure voltages and resistances at specified points. The system records any value outside of specified tolerances.
Time-code generator	On demand this instrument generates a signal which is modulated to a digital code that very precisely states the time of day.

Pulses In	Indication			
0	0	0	0	0
1	0	0	0	1
2	0	0	1	0
3	0	0	1	1
4	0	1	0	0
5	0	1	0	1
6	0	1	1	0
7	0	1	1	1
8	1	0	0	0
9	1	0	0	1
10	1	0	1	0
11	1	0	1	1
12	1	1	0	0
13	1	1	0	1
14	1	1	1	0
15	1	1	1	1

Gates or feedback circuits may be added to a group of four binaries causing the indication to return to zero at each tenth input pulse. The circuit then has ten stable states and may be used as a decade counter. Additional circuitry is required to convert the output code into a ten line code, which is suitable for driving a decimal indicator (Fig. 2).

Pulses In	Indication			
0	0	0	0	0
1	0	0	0	1
2	0	0	1	0
3	0	0	1	1
4	0	1	0	0
5	0	1	0	1
6	0	1	1	0
7	0	1	1	1
8	1	0	0	0
9	1	0	0	1
0	0	0	0	0

Figure 3 shows an example of a circuit utilizing decade counting stages to measure elapsed time in microseconds between two input pulses. Sample digital instruments and digital systems are listed in Tables 2 and 3, respectively.

F. W. Jenkinson

Cross-references: *Analog Computers, Computer Printout and Reading, Counter and Scaler Circuits, Digital Computers, Indicating Instruments, Sampled-Data Systems*

DIODES (SEMICONDUCTOR)

Pn Junction Diodes

Semiconductor diodes are two-electrode elements having a nonlinear voltage-vs-current characteristic. The nonlinearity has been attributed to one of the metal-to-semiconductor contacts, or entirely to the semiconductor, which is the model we discuss here. If the doping in a region of semiconductor changes rapidly enough, the mobile charge carriers introduced by the impurities try to equalize the carrier distribution by diffusing, and in so doing cause a separation of charge and an electric field that ultimately limits further diffusion. Carriers are now able to cross the region, in one direction, only if their kinetic energy exceeds the potential energy of this barrier. In the interior of the semiconductor, carriers obey Maxwell-Boltzmann statistics, so that the number having energy E, and therefore able to climb a barrier of this height, is proportional to $e^{-E/kT}$. If a forward voltage V is applied to the barrier, the height is lowered by an amount qV, where q is the electronic charge, and the number able to climb the barrier is $e^{-(E-qV)/kT}$ or $e^{-E/kT}e^{qV/kT}$. The term $e^{-E/kT}$ can be lumped into a constant, I_0, called the saturation current, and q/kT is conveniently abbreviated by α, which equals 38.44 v^{-1} at 300°K. However, some carriers slide back down the barrier, causing a back current not dependent on voltage. The net current at equilibrium (zero voltage) must be zero, so that the back current is also equal to I_0. The total current through the diode, which is the difference between the forward and back current, is therefore given by $I = I_0(e^{\alpha V} - 1)$.

This equation provides the basis for most ordinary applications such as rectification, mixing, switching, etc. It should be noted that the nonlinearity exceeds that of vacuum-tube diodes. The saturation current is due to the continuous thermal generation of carriers, and also depends on how the carrier moves once it has crossed the barrier. In practice, I_0 is not constant in the back direction, but increases owing to leakage, breakdown, and perhaps other reasons. If the breakdown is abrupt, the diode is useful in voltage regulation (*Zener diode*). The saturation current can be increased by generating carriers in the semiconductor through exposure to radiation, or to energetic particles. A back-biased diode therefore functions as a detector. In the forward direction, there are also deviations from the simple diode equation. Thus α and I_0 may depend on voltage, and even if α is constant, it may be anywhere between $q/2kT$ and q/kT. The discrepancies have been attributed to carrier generation in the barrier, as well as to voltage drops across regions of semiconductor between the metal electrodes and the barrier, the so-called base regions. The base voltage drop can be minimized by heavy doping, but this cannot be carried too far, for the barrier width also decreases with doping. For a narrow enough barrier, carriers may tunnel through, and the diode behavior becomes totally different (tunnel diode, *q.v.*). As the forward bias is increased, and if the diode does not burn out, the voltage-current characteristic eventually becomes linear, owing to unavoidable resistances of the contacts and the base regions (spreading resistance). At high frequencies, various reactive elements can affect the diode behavior. Perhaps the most important is the barrier capacitance, which arises because the removal of mobile carriers from the barrier region exposes the fixed charge of doping impurities. Since the width of this region depends on the applied voltage, the amount of exposed charge varies with the voltage (although not linearly), and the region acts as a capacitance that bypasses the barrier with a displacement current. One way of preventing this effect is to reduce the area drastically, which may explain the effectiveness of catwhisker or point-contact diodes. Other reactances arise in the base region of diodes. After climbing the barrier, carriers move by diffusion or drift until they are collected at the electrodes, or recombined in the interior of the material. Because of the slowness of the diffusion process there is some charge which cannot be withdrawn when the voltage changes; it is stored in the base, and manifests itself as a capacitance. If there is drift as well, then an inductance can arise in the base, because the current does not instantaneously rise to its final value. The nonlinear reactances of these diodes can be used in parametric amplifiers (*q.v.*), although at present only the barrier capacitance is so used. Semiconductor diodes suffer from temperature sensitivity, which is not unexpected in view of the exponential dependence on T. However, I_0 is also a function of temperature, so that the total dependence is complicated, and can even be useful (e.g., in a thermometer).

I. LADANY

Point-Contact Microwave Diodes

Point-contact diodes are used in superheterodyne receiving converters for microwave frequencies from 300 Mc to 70 kMc. They are also used as detectors of these frequencies by simple rectification. Formerly, they were widely used as frequency multipliers, modulators, and switches; they are now being supplanted in these uses by microwave junction diodes (see above).

Most units are made from p-type silicon doped with boron or aluminum. The active surface is polished and given a heat treatment consisting of oxidation at about 1000°C. The oxide is removed with hydrofluoric acid. It is believed that the treatment produces a high-resistivity surface layer, which results in lowering the barrier capacitance of the finished diode. A pointed "whisker" (tungsten wire) is brought in contact with the silicon surface to form the rectifying barrier. The diameter of a contact is about 0.0003 in. in diodes made for 9,000 Mc mixers. Smaller diameters, obtained by lighter pressure, are used at higher frequencies. The diode may be subjected to mechanical shock ("tapping") as a final processing step to obtain desired electrical performance and mechanical stabilization.

Microwave point-contact diodes have been made with n-type germanium and n-type gallium arsenide. For these types, the tapping process is replaced with a "forming" operation, consisting of controlled electrical overload.

The basis for the use of these diodes is their nonlinear current-voltage characteristic, as shown in Fig. 1. In a mixer, a local-oscillator signal is applied. The small-signal conductance, defined by the slope di/dv, accordingly varies at the local oscillator frequency and permits conversion of an input microwave signal to an intermediate frequency (usually 30, 60, or 70 Mc). These intermediate frequencies are chosen, rather than lower frequencies, to avoid low-frequency noise ("1/f noise") attributed to the flow of rectified current through the small contact area. When the noise figure of the intermediate frequency amplifier is 1.5 db, such superheterodyne receivers can have noise figures of 7.0 db at 9,000 Mc. For 70 kMc typical results are 15 to 20 db. These figures include the impairment of sensitivity owing to image response; 1 to 3 db improvement is possible in circuits which reflect the image.

The impairment of response at higher frequencies can be understood in terms of the equivalent circuit shown in Fig. 2. The nonlinear current-voltage characteristic of the barrier represented by a variable resistance, shunted by the barrier capacitance and in series with the series resistance. Series resistance attenuates conversion efficiency and increases noise at high frequencies.

The point-contact diode is available in a variety of packages according to frequency, usually being a cartridge for easy replacement. At frequencies above 40 kMc, the diode is built directly in a section of waveguide. The package is an inherent electrical part of the device. Test circuits have carefully specified configurations.

Similar diodes are used (without local oscillators) as detectors. For low signal levels, the diode functions as a "square-law" detector; that is, the output *current* into a

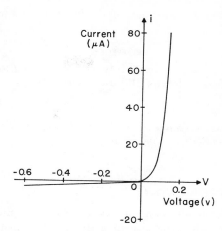

Fig. 1. Nonlinear current-voltage characteristic of silicon point-contact microwave diode.

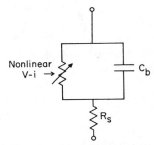

Fig. 2. Equivalent circuit of point-contact diode; C_b is somewhat voltage dependent.

specified load is proportional to the incident *power*. For signal bandwidths of the order of 10 Mc, such detectors are approximately one million times less sensitive than superheterodyne receivers. They are, nevertheless, widely used in countermeasures receivers where the exact input frequency cannot be predicted and also in many laboratory applications where maximum sensitivity is not required.

Because of the small contact area, the principal thermal time constant is a small fraction of a microsecond. For this reason, the contact may be destroyed or deteriorated by electrical pulses of short duration that might not otherwise be noticed. Static discharge during handling and leakage of transmitter power through radar duplexers are the main causes of such "burnout." The diodes should be shielded from transients caused by switches and electromechanical devices.

REFERENCES

H. C. TORREY AND C. A. WHITMER, "Crystal Rectifiers," McGraw-Hill, New York, 1948.

A. UHLIR, JR.

Cross-references: *Rectifier Tubes, Rectifiers (Solid-State), Tunnel Diode*

DIPOLE MOMENT

A dipole moment is a vector quantity measuring the size of a dipole. An electric dipole consists of a pair of electric charges, equal in size but opposite in sign and very close together. The dipole moment, sometimes called the "electric moment," is the product of one of the two charges by the distance between them. A magnetic dipole is a magnet of very short length and infinitesimal width and its moment, commonly called the "magnetic moment," is the product of the strength of one pole by the distance between the two.

The electric dipole moment is normally a molecular property arising from asymmetry in the arrangement of the positive nuclear charges and the negative electronic charges in the molecule. A very small moment is induced in a molecule by an electric field, which displaces the positive and negative charges relative to one another. A permanent moment arising from permanent electrical asymmetry is usually much larger. Its order of magnitude is that of the product of an electronic charge, 4.80×10^{-10} electrostatic units, times an atomic radius, 10^{-8} cm, that is, 4.80×10^{-18}. The moment values are, therefore, expressed in 10^{-18} e.s.u. cm, which is sometimes called a "debye."

In polyatomic molecules, the molecular dipole moment is the vector sum of the moments of dipoles associated with bonds or groups of atoms in the molecule. Dipole moments are widely used to determine the geometric structures of molecules and also to investigate the distribution of electronic charge

Dipole moments are usually calculated from the results of dielectric-constant measurements on gases, dilute solutions, or pure liquids. Values have been obtained for simple molecules from microwave spectroscopic measurements. A few, usually approximate values have been obtained for molecular moments by means of molecular beam measurements and for bond moments by means of infrared intensity measurements.

In a molecular dielectric material, the permanent dipole moment is responsible for the dielectric loss and for any part of the dielectric constant in excess of the small contribution of the induced charge shift. It is, therefore, a quantity of theoretical importance in determining electrical forces in matter and of practical importance in determining the properties of insulating materials. The induction of small dipole moments by the electric field of a light wave is responsible for the refraction of light by matter and the induction of small dipoles in molecules by the electric fields of neighboring molecules gives rise to intermolecular attraction.

Magnetic moment arises from the spin and orbital motions of unpaired electrons in atoms, molecules, and ions. The experimental values are obtained from measurements of magnetic susceptibilities by means of the Langevin equation, on the analogy of which the Debye equation was developed for the calculation of electric dipole moment from dielectric constant. When the unpaired electrons are not screened by other electrons, the contribution of the orbital motion becomes unimportant in comparison with that of the spin. For many cases, the moment is then $\sqrt{n(n + 2)}$ Bohr magnetons, where n is the number of unpaired electrons. The magnetic moment is often particularly useful in the investigation of complex ions and coordination compounds of transition metals, where determination of the number of unpaired electrons may determine the nature of the bonds and even the molecular shape.

CHARLES P. SMYTH

Cross-references: *Dielectric Theory, Electromagnetic Theory, Refractive Index*

DISTRIBUTION FUNCTIONS

The statistical mechanical distribution laws describe the average behavior of a system of weakly interacting elements which are in thermodynamic equilibrium. Typical examples are the molecules of a gas, the free electrons in a metal, and the photons in a blackbody radiation cavity. For a one-component system the mean number of elements in quantum state a is

$$n_a = \frac{1}{e^{\alpha + \beta \epsilon_a} - r} \tag{1}$$

The energy of the state is ϵ_a; $\beta = 1/kT$, where T is the absolute temperature in °K and $k = 1.38 \times 10^{-16}$ ergs/°K is Boltzmann's constant; α is related to the chemical potential μ by $\alpha = -\beta\mu$. The index r characterizes the statistics.

Fermi-Dirac $(r = -1)$

$$n_a = \frac{1}{e^{\alpha + \beta \epsilon_a} + 1}, \tag{2a}$$

Maxwell-Boltzmann $(r = 0)$

$$n_a = e^{-\alpha - \beta \epsilon_a} \tag{2b}$$

Einstein-Bose $(r = +1)$

$$n_a = \frac{1}{e^{\alpha + \beta \epsilon_a} - 1}. \tag{2c}$$

If there is a fixed number of elements N, then the parameter α is determined by the equation

$$N = \sum_a \frac{1}{e^{\alpha + \beta \epsilon_a} - r} \tag{3}$$

The energy ϵ_a generally depends on the external parameters such as the volume V, external fields, and on the motion of the container. The following discussion is re-stricted to the case of elementary particles in a stationary, field-free, container. In this case the quantum state a is described by the momentum $\mathbf{p}$ and internal quantum numbers which refer to the intrinsic spin s of elementary particles ($s = \frac{1}{2}, \frac{3}{2}, \cdots$ for fermions; $s = 0, 1, 2, \cdots$ for bosons) or to the polarization state of photons (and phonons). The energy depends only on the magnitude of the momentum $\epsilon = \epsilon(p)$, so that for each momentum there are g states, where $g = 2s + 1$ for particles and $g = 2$ for photons.

It is usually possible to convert sums over quantum states into integrals by allotting each quantum state a volume h^3 in phase space ($h = 2\pi \hbar$ is Planck's constant):

$$\sum_a \rightarrow g \frac{1}{h^3} V \int d^3p \tag{4}$$

The average value of a function of energy is thus

$$\bar{A} = \int_0^\infty d\epsilon \rho(\epsilon) f(\epsilon) A(\epsilon) \tag{5}$$

where

$$f(\epsilon) = \frac{1}{e^{\alpha + \beta \epsilon} - r} \tag{6}$$

and ρ is the density of states per unit energy interval. For particles $\epsilon = p^2/2m$ and

$$\rho = g \frac{V}{(2\pi h)^3} 4\pi \frac{(2m)^{3/2}}{2} \epsilon^{1/2} \tag{7}$$

whereas for photons with $\epsilon = cp$

$$\rho = \frac{8\pi}{c^3} \frac{V}{(2\pi\hbar)^3} \epsilon^2 \tag{8}$$

Thermodynamic properties may be obtained from the internal energy

$$U = \int_0^\infty d\epsilon \rho(\epsilon) f(\epsilon) \epsilon. \tag{9}$$

A useful relation, valid in quantum as well as classical statistics if $\epsilon = p^2/2m$, is $PV = \frac{2}{3} U$; the analogous rule for photons is $PV = \frac{1}{3} U$.

If the thermal De Broglie wavelength

$$\lambda = \sqrt{\frac{h^2}{2\pi m kT}}$$

is small compared to the particle separation, then $n_a \ll 1$ and the quantum distributions go over into the Maxwell-Boltzmann law, Eq. (2b). The most famous application of the classical distribution is Maxwell's velocity distribution of 1859. The probability for finding a particle with velocity in the range from v to $v + dv$ is

$$n_0(v)\ dv = \left(\frac{m}{2\pi kT}\right)^{3/2} 4\pi v^2 e^{-(1/2)mv^2\beta}\ dv \qquad (10)$$

The basic thermodynamic formulae here are $PV = NkT$ and $U = N\frac{3}{2}\,kT$. (The last relation is a special case of the classical equipartition principle.) The specific heat per particle at constant volume in this case is $\frac{3}{2}\,k$.

The most important application of the Fermi-Dirac statistics is to electrons in a metal. At absolute zero the distribution law, Eq. (2a) becomes

$$f(\epsilon) = \begin{cases} 1 & \epsilon < \mu \\ 0 & \epsilon > \mu \end{cases} \qquad (11)$$

The equation for μ (usually called the Fermi energy) is Eq. (3) which becomes

$$N = \int_0^\mu d\epsilon \rho(\epsilon) f(\epsilon) \qquad (12)$$

or

$$\frac{N}{V} = \frac{2}{(2\pi\hbar)^3} \frac{4\pi}{3}\ p_F{}^3 \qquad (13)$$

where p_F is the Fermi momentum

$$\frac{p_F{}^2}{2m} = \mu \qquad (14)$$

With $p_F = \hbar k_F$ and $V/N = r_0{}^3$ there is the useful numerical rule, $k_F r_0 \cong 3$. Further analysis shows that at low temperatures ($kT \ll \mu$) the specific heat at constant volume is linear in T.

Another familiar application is to phonons and photons for which $\epsilon = cp$ and

$$f(\epsilon) = \frac{1}{e^{\beta\epsilon} - 1} \qquad (15)$$

The specific heat in this case is proportional to T^3.

At very low temperatures, the transcription of Eq. (4) is not always valid for Bose-Einstein particles because the low-lying states have very high occupation ($n_a \gg 1$), whereas the density of states in Eq. (7) becomes very small for $\epsilon \to 0$. A more accurate treatment leads to the Bose-Einstein contenstation phenomenon in which the ground state has a *macroscopic* occupation below the transition temperature T_c:

$$n_0 = N \begin{cases} 1 - (T/T_c)^{3/2} & T < T_c \\ 0 & T > T_c \end{cases} \qquad (16)$$

The formula for the transition temperature is $(\lambda_c r_0)^3 = 2.612$, where λ_c is the corresponding thermal wavelength. It is generally thought that this property of the ideal boson gas is related to the superfluidity of liquid helium, for which $T_c \approx 3°$K.

A. E. Glassgold

Cross-references: *Statistical Mechanics, Thermodynamics*

DOPPLER NAVIGATION

The principles and applications of the Doppler shift to navigation may be conveniently illustrated by the description of a satellite Doppler navigation system, known as the Transit Navigation System, now under development for the U. S. Navy at Johns Hopkins University (Guier and Weiffenbach, *Proc. IRE* April 1960). This system is based upon measurements of the radio Doppler shift produced by transmissions from satellites in precisely known orbits about the earth. The system is all-weather with true global coverage and passive. The navigator need not have knowledge of local vertical or the direction of north. Since no angle data are taken, special antenna arrays are not needed nor do the problems of antenna bore-sighting or stabilization arise. Depending upon the accuracy desired, the navigator can employ various degrees of sophistication in his instrumentation and computing equipment. Development is aimed at establishing the system in operational use with an initial accuracy of 0.5

nautical mile and an eventual accuracy of
0.1 nautical mile. It is applicable to both
ships and aircraft and will be made available to all nations of the world.

The Doppler shift of a constant-frequency
cw radio transmitter when received by the
navigator's equipment is proportional, except
for refraction effects, to the time rate of
change of the instantaneous slant range between the satellite and the navigator. Consequently, when corrected for refraction,
accurate measurements of the time dependence of the Doppler shift uniquely specify the relative position of the satellite and
navigator. When the navigator is given an
accurate specification of the trajectory of the
satellite he can determine his absolute position. In the Transit system, the orbit parameters are determined by a fixed ground
Doppler tracking system using the same cw
transmissions that the navigator uses. The
orbit parameters are computed for each
satellite every 12 hr and transmitted to the
satellite. Upon receipt of the orbit parameters by the satellite, a digital memory stores
the parameters and, as the satellite orbits

the earth, continually retransmits the new
orbit parameters. Since the satellite's stable
oscillator can function as a clock, accurate
time can be also supplied by the satellite.
The Transit satellites will transmit the
calibration of this clock along with the orbit
parameters. The navigator will receive the
orbit parameters and the time calibration
as a simple phase-advance/phase-retard
modulation of the same transmissions used
to generate the Doppler shift. New orbit
parameters are injected into the satellite as
frequently as every 12 hr to limit the
build-up of error in the satellite trajectory
to a negligible amount. The operational
Transit system envisions the maintenance of
four satellites in polar orbits that are nominally circular at altitudes of about 600 nautical miles with ascending nodes roughly 45°
apart. These orbits will allow a navigation fix
at least once every 2 hr anywhere on the
earth's surface. Figure 1 shows a schematic
view of the operation of the Transit system.

From the point of view of the navigator's
equipment, the accuracy of the navigation
fix is principally determined by the accuracy

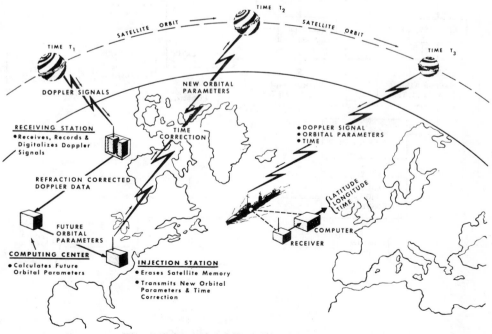

Fig. 1. Schematic of Transit system operation.

of the Doppler frequency measurements, the degree to which ionospheric refraction effects are eliminated, and the sophistication of the computing procedure to determine position. Frequency stability of the navigator's local oscillator should be a few parts in 10^9 over a 1-hr time interval and measurement of the time-varying Doppler frequency should be made to an accuracy of about one part in 10^4, e.g., about 0.5 cps (RMS) for a transmitter frequency of 200 mc. The error due to ionospheric refraction can be eliminated by simultaneously measuring the Doppler shift on two harmonically related frequencies. The frequency dependence of the ionosphere's index of refraction is known sufficiently accurately to make possible a reliable interpolation between the two measured Doppler shifts to produce a "vacuum" Doppler shift at each instant of time. The Transit satellites will radiate a minimum of two harmonically related frequencies in the

region of 100–400 mc to allow for such a refraction correction.

The computing procedure that produces the most accurate navigation fix is one that performs a least-squares fit of the theoretical Doppler shift to the entire time history of the received Doppler shift using the navigator's position as variables in the theoretical curve. In this way the large redundancy of position information contained in the Doppler shift is fully utilized. This least-squares computation requires a small special-purpose digital computer. If less accuracy is desired, simplified computing procedures can be used where most of the redundancy of information is ignored.

Figure 2 indicates schematically the functions of the Transit navigation equipment for a surface ship that desires to obtain high navigation accuracy. Figure 3 indicates the expected operational navigation error resulting from such equipment. The navigation

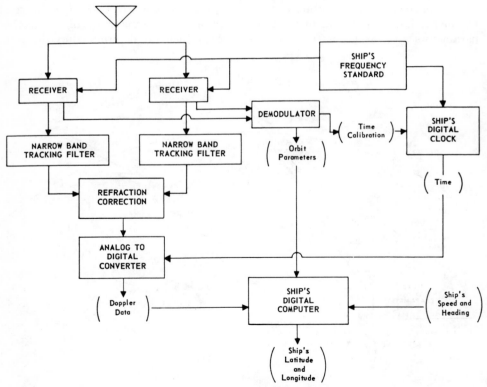

Fig. 2. Schematic of accurate ship Transit navigating equipment.

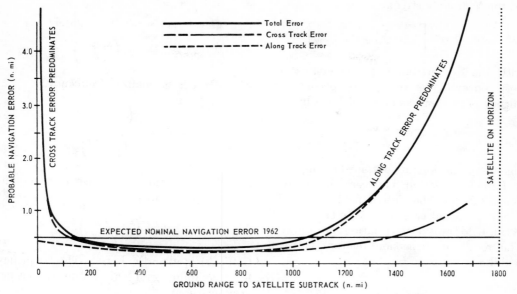

Fig. 3. Expected error from accurate ship Transit navigating equipment.

error becomes large for overhead satellite passes (small ground range) because a change in the cross-track coordinate of the navigator's position produces a very small change in the slant range to the satellite.

WILLIAM H. GUIER

Cross-references: *Missile Guidance, Navigation and Navigational Systems, Radar, Satellite Communications, Satellite Electronics, Telemetry*

DOSIMETRY: see RADIATION (IONIZING)

DOUBLE-STREAM AMPLIFICATION

Electron (or ion) streams, where mixed, may amplify a disturbance or become unstable. A perturbation from uniformity in one stream induces changes in the other stream so as to reinforce the initial perturbation. The rate of growth of the perturbation depends on the relative velocity of the two streams, their densities, and the frequency or wavelength of the perturbation.

This interaction may occur with two or more streams having discrete velocities or with a collection of particles having a mul-

tiply peaked velocity distribution (time averaged). In the latter, the interaction ceases if the random motion becomes too large compared with the directed motion. In the analyses to follow, it is assumed that the streams are discrete, without random motion.

The analytical approach given here is that of Eulerian hydrodynamics, following the electrons as if they formed a jellied-out stream of charge-to-mass ratio e/m the same as electrons, considering only zeroth and first-order solutions. The model analyzed consists of two electron streams of zeroth order, uniform drift velocities v_{01}, v_{02}, and charge densities ρ_{01}, ρ_{02} in a neutralizing background of positive ions which are massive and considered immobile; the streams are constrained to motion along coordinate z by a strong magnetic field B_{0z}. The first-order variables depend on the coordinate z and time t; the solutions for all variables are of the form exp $j(\omega t - \beta z)$. Assuming this z and t dependence, the displacement plus convection current density is

$$J_1 = j\omega\epsilon_0 E_1 \left[1 - \frac{\omega_{p1}^2}{(\omega - \beta v_{01})^2} - \frac{\omega_{p2}^2}{(\omega - \beta v_{02})^2} \right]$$

or, for N discrete streams,

$$J_1 = j\omega\epsilon_0 E_1 \left[1 - \sum_{n=1}^{N} \frac{\omega_{pn}^2}{(\omega - \beta v_{0n})^2} \right]$$

with the exponential term understood on both sides; ω_{p1} is the radian plasma frequency of stream one and is defined by

$$\omega_{p1}^2 = \frac{e}{m} \frac{\rho_{01}}{\epsilon_0}$$

The wave solutions are obtained by imposing a (circuit) relation between the current density J_1 and the electric field E_1. In the one-dimensional case here, $\nabla \times \mathbf{H} = \mathbf{J} = 0$ because no transverse variations are allowed. The resultant dispersion relation between ω and β is

$$\frac{\omega_{p1}^2}{(\omega - \beta v_{01})^2} + \frac{\omega_{p2}^2}{(\omega - \beta v_{02})^2} = 1$$

This is an algebraic equation with real coefficients, quartic in ω (given β) or quartic in β (given ω); the roots may be all real (no growth) or appear in complex conjugate pairs indicating growth and decay in time or in distance.

Case I. Streams Drifting in the Same Direction. In this case, with the streams excited by a stationary source at real frequency ω, the phase constant β may be complex. The growth rate (power ratio) is exponential

with distance, as

$$\text{growth rate} = 8.68 \, (\text{Im } \beta) \, \text{db/m}$$

$$= 8.68 \left(\frac{\omega_{p1}}{v_{01}} \frac{\omega_{p2}}{v_{02}} \right)^{1/2} G(W, B)$$

where W is a normalized frequency,

$$W \equiv \omega \frac{\left(\dfrac{1}{v_{02}} - \dfrac{1}{v_{02}} \right)}{\left(\dfrac{\omega_{p1}}{v_{01}} \dfrac{\omega_{p2}}{v_{02}} \right)}$$

and B is the ratio of the plasma wave numbers (or perveances),

$$B \equiv \left(\frac{\omega_{p1}}{v_{01}} \bigg/ \frac{\omega_{p2}}{v_{02}} \right)$$

$G(W, B)$ is given in Fig. 1. The frequency for maximum gain (maximum G) occurs very nearly at

$$W_{opt} = \frac{B + 1}{\sqrt{B}} \cong \sqrt{B} \left(\text{or} \cong \frac{1}{\sqrt{B}} \text{ for } B < 1 \right)$$

which is the frequency for synchronism between the slower wave of the faster stream and the faster wave of the slower stream of the uncoupled streams. For $B = 1$, maximum gain occurs where the streams slip past each other one stream wavelength in one cycle of the plasma frequency.

Experimentally, these results have been checked very closely for excitation by cav-

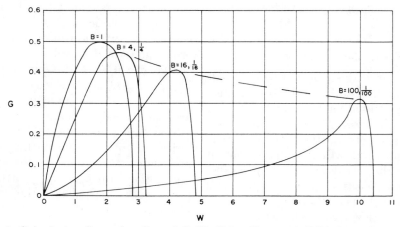

Fig. 1. Gain factor G as a function of B, W. (After Nergaard, *RCA Rev.*, Dec. 1948.)

ities and slow-wave circuits at low signal levels. Large total gains (>30 db) have been obtained owing to double streaming. With increased excitation, the gain decreases and a maximum occurs in power output, usually on the order of a few per cent of the total stream power. The apparent reason for the early saturation (at this writing) is the use of weak streams, $\omega \gg \omega_p$, with attendant velocity separations of only a few per cent. The growth tends to decelerate the faster stream and to accelerate the slower stream on the average, thus tending to destroy the very means of growth. However, it is more likely that the velocity distributions initially broaden as the excitation grows, lessening the growth rate, yet without much net transfer of energy between streams or to the fields (or currents) that drive the output gap (or helix). With experiments using ω near ω_p, and attendant large velocity separations, improvement in efficiency to some tens of per cent may be realized.

Case II. One Stream Drifting, One Stream Stationary. For $v_{01} \neq 0$, $v_{02} = 0$, and real ω the solution for β is

$$\beta = \frac{\omega}{v_{01}} \pm \frac{\omega_{p1}/v_{01}}{\sqrt{1 - \frac{\omega^2}{\omega_{p2}^2}}}$$

Gain is available $0 < \omega < \omega_{p2}$. The infinite gain peak at ω_{p2} does not exist in reality, ruled out by random velocities in stream two, or by collisions, or by the fact of finite diameters of the streams. However, large gains have been observed experimentally arising from interaction between electrons in stream one injected into a plasma and interacting with the electrons of the plasma.

Case III. Opposing Streams. For this case the possibility of growth remains; however, with small or zero net convection, the disturbance does not propagate, but stays localized and grows with time. Small-signal theory may be used to predict the initial rate of growth; for $v_{01} = -v_{02}$, $\omega_{p1} = \omega_{p2}$, growth occurs for

$$0 < \frac{\omega_{p1}}{v_{01}} < \sqrt{2}$$

with a maximum growth rate of

$$(\operatorname{Im} \omega)_{maximun} = \frac{\omega_{p1}}{2}$$

The growth rapidly builds up large fields that may either reflect the streams or trap them, converting the initial drift velocities to random velocities. The final state depends on the initial conditions.

C. K. BIRDSALL

Cross-references: *Bunching, Characteristic Frequencies, Space-Charge Instabilities, Space-Charge Waves, Traveling-Wave Tubes, Velocity Modulation*

DUPLEXER FOR RADAR: see TR AND ATR TUBES

DYNODE: see ELECTRON TUBES (CONVENTIONAL)

E

EARPHONES

An earphone is an electroacoustical transducer, designed to be worn against the ears, singly or in pairs, and which serves to convert variations of electrical currents or voltages into vibrations audible to human ears. Originally earphones consisted of a metal diaphragm in close proximity to one pole of a permanent magnet. The magnet carried a coil wound with very fine wire. Variations of current in the coil altered the attraction between magnet and diaphragm, setting the latter into motion.

Earphones were an adaptation of the original musical telephone suggested by Charles Bourseul of France, and independently conceived by Philip Reis in Germany. Reis, in the course of investigations in the transmission of sound, constructed a musical telephone, which could however not carry human-voice vibrations. On February 14, 1867 Alexander Graham Bell applied for a patent on the first practical telephone for human speech. On the same day a caveat was filed on behalf of Elisha Gray of Highland Park, Ill. Elisha Gray, inventor of many electrical devices, claimed the telephone as his invention, but the record shows that his proposed device was based on an erroneous principle.

Modern earphones are evolved from the original concept, with many improvements in construction and design, or embody different principles. One variation makes use of piezoelectrical properties of certain materials. In these earphones the diaphragm is moved as the result of distortions caused in the material by the application of varying voltages to electrodes bonded to the piezoelectric slabs. Rochelle salts were used early, but have been replaced by a ceramic material, barium titanate, which is more efficient and economical. Another variation is the dynamic earphone, in which the coil is carried by the diaphragm and is free to move laterally in a circular airgap in the magnet structure. Variations of current applied to the coil through thin flexible leads, cause the coil to move in accordance with these variations.

Earphones generally have a limited response range unless specially constructed to reproduce music faithfully. Generally earphones reproduce vibrations between 300 and 3000 cps. Special provisions are made where earphones are subjected to the weather, and where their vibrations must be heard under conditions of extreme noise, as on aircraft carriers. In the latter case special pads surrounding the entire outer ear provide better than 90 dbm reduction of ambient sound.

THOMAS JASKI

Cross-references: *Electroacoustics, Hearing Aids, Loudspeakers and Microphones*

ECM: see COUNTERMEASURES

ECONOMICS OF THE ELECTRONICS INDUSTRY

The electronics industry is credited with being one of the major manufacturing industries in the United States today with a sales volume in excess of $10 billion annually. Growth rate is expected to double that of the gross national product during the next decade. In other countries an equal growth rate can be anticipated as new ideas, techniques, and applications stimulate the demand for electronic products and processes. This rapid growth is expected to have an economic effect equivalent to that produced by the automobile industry in the past three decades through universal usage of its products as well as an employer of a vast number of people.

A broad product classification within the

U. S. electronics industry based on current dollar volume of sales is as follows in order of importance:

Military. Currently the largest user of electronic equipment with a projected substantial growth in dollar sales but with a smaller percentage of total of all electronic production anticipated.

Consumer. Second largest segment but highly competitive field lacking in stimulus to sustain its sales growth.

Industrial. Most rapidly growing of the four classifications with impetus from products developed for the military.

Replacement Parts and Components. Are important contributors to volume but depend upon the development of new products and consequent obsolescence of older ones.

Having taken their place among the leading industries, electronic-product manufacturers may expect to be troubled with problems confronting all other industries respecting supply and demand, business cycles, wage bargaining, taxes, and other cost increases as well as price competition. Plotting the financial course of a company engaged in this field is difficult: technological change can upset the best considered planning. Because of the current rapid growth of the industry, tremendous amounts of capital have been required to finance costs that are recovered very slowly. Research and development, technical personnel, and specialized manufacturing facilities require advance expenditures long before product sales materialize.

Military-product manufacturers have had the stimulation of development and production contracts to support their expenditures to a large extent. These contracts can facilitate extension of credit or investor interest providing the ability to perform under the contract terms is apparent. "Certificates of necessity" provide special rules regarding rapid depreciation of facilities, which have the effect of reducing indicated profits and therefore taxes, thus encouraging the investment of risk or lender capital.

A relatively few companies in the United States account for the majority of dollar volume of sales at present, since they have been able to provide the tremendous cash outlay needed in development. Their successes have, nevertheless, attracted the flow of capital from other sources. It is not uncommon for new products or technological ideas to be developed into substantial industries through sound nourishment by proper management of risk capital, borrowed funds, and continued research and development.

Risk capital as used in this context may mean an investment in cash, time, or knowledge contributed toward the production of goods or services with the anticipation of its return in value coupled with an increment of profit or gain. It may be contributed by an individual (such as an inventor or businessman), by a group of individuals acting on their behalf, or by a legal entity (such as a corporation, syndicate, joint venture or partnership, to name the most common forms). Unsecured loans provided by interested parties, institutions (such as banks), or private lenders may be considered risk capital when no tangible asset underlies such credit to an unseasoned venture. The amount of risk capital required in any given enterprise of course depends entirely upon the sales potential of the product or service. For example, a simple electronic device that could be produced for $100 and sold for $150 at the rate of 1,000 units per year to a limited number of users purchasing these devices at regular intervals during the year would not require any substantial capital investment. However, a more complicated device, which cost $1,000 to produce for sale at $1,300 to a large number of users who purchased in quantity only at certain seasons on the basis of the lowest bid price, could cause its manufacturers a considerable investment.

Many successful electronics companies can trace their origin from an investment of only a few hundred dollars parlayed into millions of dollars through prudent expansion and reinvestment of profit. More often, however, the business finds a need for more substantial additional capital than can be produced from current earnings in order to meet an expansion requirement. Certain plants and equipment by their universal application may be acquired with the assistance of a lender or lessor in the form of a mortgage loan or a long-term lease; such financing may be available through banks, insurance companies, leasing concerns, or private sources.

An electronics manufacturer may find that his sales growth far exceeds the ability of his company's invested capital to cover overhead and production costs owing to the time interval between costs incurred and collection of sales receivables. This period may extend anywhere from 1 to 180 days or longer depending on the manufacturing period, delivery date, and settlement of billing. The solution to this problem may be in obtaining an unsecured term loan (payable monthly, quarterly, or annually from projected profit) from banks or other institutional lenders, or by public sale of debentures. Pledging of receivables or factoring provide another source of replenishing operating funds. However, costs of handling are generally higher, and if competitive conditions are severe, they could be prohibitive.

The above borrowing situations depend necessarily upon a proven ability and experience of the company and although somewhat expensive have the benefit of maintaining the vested control of the business; nevertheless, because of the substantial financing requirements of certain businesses, a broader ownership is often a necessity and the public offering by investment bankers through an underwriting agreement may provide the solution. Such underwritings are strictly governed by regulatory authorities and many company confidences must then be made available to the general public and therefore to the competition. The beneficial factors of additional capital planning on a long-range basis may more than offset the loss of privacy. Pooling of interests and facilities through merger, consolidation, or acquisition of related or complimentary businesses may be arranged in such a way as to benefit growth. In recent years venture capital and small business-investment companies have met the expansion requirements of many concerns, although managerial representation is usually expected.

The electronics industry is subject to the economic fluctuations caused by national and international conditions as well as intrinsic problems within its own sphere. It is therefore advisable to have available adequate financial planning for both growth and development. Failures and insolvency are not uncommon along the way regardless of the technical superiority of a product. The key to a successful electronics company is the flexibility of management to grasp quickly the need and profit potentiality of a product, swiftly produce and merchandise it in quantity and quality, and then divert its major effort to the next product or development.

JOHN PILLSBURY

Cross-references: *Patents*

EDDY CURRENTS: see MAGNETISM

EDISON, THOMAS ALVA (1847–1931)

T. A. Edison was born in Milan, Ohio, on February 11, 1847; his father was a Canadian of Yankee Loyalist stock. He had little formal schooling but amused himself with a home-made chemical laboratory since the age of ten. After five years as an itinerant telegrapher, during which he made a few labor-saving devices to increase his spare time, he became a telegrapher at Boston, and devoted himself to inventing seriously, mostly in the field of automatic telegraph indicators. In the following year, he came to New York and continued to make inventions, of which the most important are quadruplex telegraphy, the carbon microphone, the phonograph, and the first practical incandescent lamp. During this period, he also made two less appreciated contributions to the development of technology: in 1869 he formed (with Franklin L. Pope and James N. Ashby) the first firm of consulting electrical engineers; and in 1876, he founded the first industrial research laboratory at Menlo Park, N. J., which became the prototype of all such institutions.

During his work on the incandescent lamp in 1883 he discovered the *Edison effect*, foreshadowing the discovery of electrons and thermionic vacuum tubes. He noted that carbon particles blackened the inside surface of the glass bulb near the positive end, and that a white streak appeared behind the positive wire. He inserted an added electrode and was surprised to find that a current flowed through an external circuit connecting it to the positive end of the filament, although the added electrode was not internally connected. Edison applied for a patent on this electrical indicator (granted in 1884) for "the utilization of this discovery for indication or regulating variations in electromotive force." He exhibited a model of his voltage regulator at the International Electrical Exposition in Philadelphia in the same year, and E. J. Houston gave a paper on it (*Trans. AIEE* **1**: 1–8, 1884). The discovery aroused widespread scientific interest; among others, William H. Preece, then the chief engineer of the General Post Office of Britain, saw a demonstration and lectured on the Edison effect before the Royal Society the following year; so did J. A. Fleming (*q.v.*). Additional work on the effect was done at the Edison laboratory by J. W. Howell and A. E. Kennelly (after whom a layer of the ionosphere is named), in 1897.

Contrary to widespread belief, Edison did not merely discover the effect and then forget about it because he had not the mental equipment to explore it; he publicized it, he described it in a patent, he proposed an application, and he caused it to be described in contemporary technical literature. Fleming's discovery of the diode 20 years later is directly traceable to his appreciation of the Edison effect. It is not difficult to see why Edison could not devote his full attention to an exploitation of his discovery. In 1882 he had opened the Pearl Street Station in New York, the world's first generating plant, for which he had to invent, design, and construct the generators, distribution lines, meters, switches, fuses, and lamp sockets. He also had to do a considerable amount of trouble-shooting after the plant opened and take a hand in the management of the company organized to promote the new system.

In 1887, the Edison laboratory was moved to West Orange, N. J., and continued to supply many inventions. Edison also organized a number of commercial firms, which were consolidated into the Edison General Electric Company; later, by a merger with the Thomson-Houston Company, the firm became the General Electric Co. In the 1890's, Edison proposed a process for magnetic separation of iron from ore, in which he invested heavily, but lost most of his investment because the process was applied to low-grade ores and could not compete with the high-grade ores mined elsewhere. He continued to make a great many other inventions on devices such as storage batteries, railway signaling, train and mine lighting, dictating machines, mimeographing, and alternate sources of rubber. He received the Rumford Medal from the American Academy of Arts and Sciences, and in 1927 he was elected a member of the National Academy of Sciences. He deprecated the designation of "genius" applied to him by his well-known epigram that "genius is two per cent inspiration and ninety-eight perspiration." Throughout his adult life he suffered from deafness, which makes his many contributions to audio engineering the more remarkable, and perhaps explains his interest in that field. He died in West Orange, N. J., on October 18, 1931.

CHARLES SUSSKIND

Cross-references: *Historical Background of Electronics*

ELECTRIC DISCHARGE

When we speak of electric discharge in gases, we mean the passage of electric current through the gas; usually this is accompanied by the emission of light, heat, and various chemical effects. Current is carried by free electrons, positive ions (molecules that have lost an electron), and negative ions (molecules that have gained an extra electron). All are in rapid random motion.

Collision of electrons with atoms or molecules leads to excitation, radiation of visible or UV light, dissociation of molecules, ($O_2 \rightarrow 2O$; $H_2 \rightarrow 2H$, etc.) and to ionization: $e^- + M \rightarrow M^+ + 2e^-$, where M is any atom or molecule. A certain amount of ionization is necessary for the discharge, in order to replace ions and electrons that are lost by diffusion to the walls, migration to the electrodes, and recombination with oppositely charged ions. The velocity of the electrons is enormous compared with that of the positive ions; the latter produce very few effects.

Different types of gas discharge have been distinguished: the *arc* is characterized by relatively low voltage, high current density, and the fact that the electrodes become very hot. The vaporization of the electrode material has made the arc important in chemical spectroscopy; and there are important technical applications in welding and electrothermics.

The *spark* discharge requires relatively high voltage to produce, and is completed in an extremely short time (a millionth of a second or less). The initially very high resistance of the gap drops nearly to zero, so that any attempt to prolong the process leads to some form of low-voltage discharge, usually an arc. Except for lightning, which may be regarded as a spark discharge on a grand scale, sparks were doubtless first observed in the "discharge" of electrostatically charged bodies.

The potential required to produce a spark through a gas is called the *breakdown* potential; it depends on the nature of the gas, its pressure (and temperature), and on the distance between the electrodes and the form of the electrode. According to *Paschen's* law, so long as the nature of gas and the geometry of the electrodes is unaltered, the breakdown potential is a function of Pd/T (P = pressure, T = absolute temperature, d = electrode spacing). The typical *glow discharge* is produced at low pressures (0.1 to 10 mm of Hg). Voltages are much lower than required for a spark of equal length. The familiar "neon sign" tube may be several meters in length and employ as much as 15,000 v.

If the tube is operated with direct current, certain alternating bright and dark bands appear. The length of the cathode region (comprising the bands from the cathode through the negative glow) depends on the gas and varies inversely with its pressure. The voltage drop across this region (100–400 v.) depends only on the gas and on the metal of the electrode. This cathode region is essential to the maintenance of the discharge; the positive column merely fills up the rest of the tube.

The positive column actually contains large numbers of free electrons and positive ions in active motion: the motions of the electrons and their collision with the atoms or molecules of the gas lead to excitations (hence radiation), dissociation of molecules, etc. The positive column is important for its luminosity; various chemical reactions in the positive column have been studied. When the glow discharge tube is operated with alternating current, each electrode is cathode half the time and anode half the time, and the banded structure is obscured. If provision is made for heating the electrodes, the tube becomes a "hot cathode" tube; technically this is classed as an arc.

If there are two electrodes, at least one of which is a *wire* or *point*, and we apply a sufficiently high voltage (either ac or dc) across them, we get the *corona* or *brush* discharge. It is characteristic of this discharge that it is seen only around the point (or wire). If the voltage is raised sufficiently to make it extend across the gap, a spark results.

It has been found that if air containing suspended particles (dust, etc.) is passed near a dc corona discharge, the dust particles acquire electric charges that cause them to be attracted to, and deposited on, the opposite electrode. This is the basis of the very important *electrostatic precipitation* process (*q.v.*) of dust and fume removal.

In an arrangement consisting of two electrodes, separated by at least one layer of insulator (such as glass) in addition to an air space, under a high alternating voltage, the air space is filled with a more or less uniform glow, called the *silent electric discharge* or *ozonator discharge*. This is a uniform purple glow in dry air, if the spacing is not too wide. If the air contains more than a trace of water vapor, or if the spacing is too large, a large number of bright spark-like discharges are seen. The discharge in *nitrogen* has the same appearance as in air; in *oxygen* it is white in appearance, and is streaky rather than uniform. The discharge in *hydrogen* produces little or no visible radiation. In ammonia gas it is greenish-yellow, and full of bright streaks. The "corona" and the "ozonator" discharges have common features, in that both have a bluish color in air and both produce ozone (O_3).

To obtain this "ozonator" or "silent electric" discharge, certain things are required: (a) the layer of dielectric (insulator) is absolutely essential since without it, only a spark discharge occurs; (b) alternating current is necessary, since no current can actually pass through the dielectric, which merely collects charges (electrons or ions) on its surface during one half-cycle of the alternating current, and gives them off again when the polarity reverses. An apparatus for producing the silent electric discharge and collecting the chemical products produced, is called an *ozonator*.

T. C. MANLEY

Cross-references: *Ions, Plasma*

ELECTRIC SHOCK

Safety from electric shock is achieved by isolation, insulation, current limitation, and grounding. It is only when one or more of these safety measures fail that there is an electric-shock hazard.

The following are the four methods of achieving electrical safety.

(a) Achieving safety by *isolation* means that high-voltage wires are placed overhead high above reach, and dangerous equipment is behind guards or inside of cabinets. This means is frequently nullified by the booms of overhead cranes contacting the wires, operation of electric equipment with the guards removed, or safety doors circumvented.

(b) *Insulation* is universally used to provide safety from low and intermediate voltages. However, all insulations can be ruined by excessive temperature, usually from overloading the equipment; by mechanical damage caused by abuse, neglect, or carelessness; or by water. All insulations deteriorate with age; such defects are often visible and can serve as a warning before a hazardous condition develops.

(c) The principle of current *limitation* means that safety is assured by purposely limiting the shock intensity from a device to a value known to be reasonably safe. This means is used in home radios and TV sets.

(d) *Grounding* achieves safety by providing a low-resistance path between the chassis and the neutral of the supply system, which is grounded. This means provides two distinct safety measures. First, providing a low-resistance path from the normally non-current-carrying parts of the device to the electric power source assures that any electrical failure inside the device that energizes the frame (and hence the handle or metal parts grasped by the hand) results in instantly opening the circuit overcurrent protective devices such as the fuses or circuit breaker. Second, connecting the frame of the device to ground assures that regardless of the kind of defect the voltage of the frame remains too low to become hazardous. The ground wire does not affect normal operation of the device; its sole purpose is to provide safety when a defect occurs. It is therefore obvious that the integrity of the ground wire must receive the highest priority.

Practical Thresholds of Electric Shock

Lethal Shock Hazard: Ac and dc circuits capable of passing through a 500-ohm resistor an uninterrupted ac current in excess of 100 ma, an uninterrupted dc current in excess of 500 ma, or an impulse discharge in excess of 50 joules; for complex output waveforms, such as from a dc power supply, a total of 50 joules or more through a 500-ohm resistor for 1 sec.

Shock Hazard: Ac and dc circuits capable of passing through a 500-ohm resistor an uninterrupted ac current in excess of 9 ma, an uninterrupted dc current in excess of 62 ma, or an impulse discharge in excess of $\frac{1}{4}$ joule.

Negligible Shock Hazard: Shocks of an intensity less than those producing "shock hazard" defined above, or equipment and circuits operating at 25 v or less.

Effects of Electric Shock

In case of an electric-shock accident, the victim must be freed *promptly* from contact with the circuit. Immediately break the circuit by removing the extension cord from its convenience outlet, or by opening the switch. If you do not know which switch to open, open all of them. If the victim is still receiving a shock, use a dry stick, dry rope, dry clothing, or any nonconductor and separate the victim from the energized conductor. Move either the conductor or the victim. Do not touch any part of the victim's body with your body or unprotected hands as long as he is electrified.

Muscular contractions and sensations of heat increase as the current is increased. Sensations of pain develop and voluntary control of the muscles in the current pathway becomes increasingly difficult. Finally, a value of current is reached for which the victim cannot release his grasp of the conductor. The maximum current a person can tolerate while holding an electrode in the hand and still let go of the energized conductor by using muscles directly stimulated by that current is called the "let-go current." Let-go currents are important as experience has shown that an individual can withstand, with no ill aftereffects, his let-go current for at least the time required to release the conductor. Currents in excess of one's let-go current are said to "freeze" him to the circuit. Such currents are very painful, frightening, and hard to endure for even a short time. Failure to interrupt the current promptly is accompanied by a rapid decrease in muscular strength caused by the pain and fatigue associated with the accompanying severe involuntary muscular contractions.

The most dangerous effect of electric shock is a derangement of heart action known as ventricular fibrillation. In the fibrillating condition, the pumping action of the heart stops, and death is likely in about 5 min. Unfortunately, such cases do not respond to resuscitation, and the skill and equipment needed to apply the only known remedy, a controlled counter-electric shock, are not generally available. Establishing the minimum electric current likely to produce ventricular fibrillation in man is important, as no man should knowingly be subject to shocks of this magnitude. Such knowledge is gradually being incorporated in improved designs of an increasing number of electrical installations.

The minimum current required to produce unconsciousness lies somewhere between the let-go and fibrillating thresholds. Currents passing through the chest or vital nerve centers may produce paralysis of the breathing mechanism (respiratory inhibition). Much higher currents, such as those used in electrocution of criminals, may raise the body temperature sufficiently to cause immediate death. Currents sufficient to blow fuses and trip circuit breakers often create awesome destruction of tissue, and may produce very severe shock and irreparable damage to the nervous system.

Although the deleterious effects of electric shock are caused by current actually flowing through the human body, in accidents the voltage of the circuit is usually the only electrical quantity known with certainty; yet variations in skin and contact resistances are so great that let-go voltages are relatively meaningless. On very-high-voltage circuits, the skin and contact resistances break down instantly and play only a minor role in limiting the current received by a victim. However, on lower voltages the resistances at contact locations become of increasing importance; and these resistances are of paramount importance on very-low-voltage circuits. Obviously, wet contacts create a most dangerous condition for receiving electric shock, and it is for this reason that persons must never use electrically powered appliances or equipment in wet locations without first taking precautionary measures such as wearing dry gloves, standing on dry boards, using rubber overshoes, etc.

Burns suffered in electrical accidents are of two types, electric burns and thermal burns. Electric burns are the result of electric current flowing through the tissues. Typically,

electric burns are slow to heal, but they seldom become infected. Thermal burns, on the other hand, are the result of high temperatures in close proximity to the body, such as produced by an electric arc, vaporized metals, or hot gases released by the arc; or by overheated conductors caused by short circuits. These burns are similar to burns and blisters produced by any high-temperature source. Currents of the let-go level, if they flow for an appreciable time, are more than sufficient to produce deep burns, and both types of burns may be produced simultaneously. Any serious burn should receive prompt medical attention.

No discussion of electric shock would be complete without at least mention of rescue and resuscitation for victims of serious electric-shock accidents. In many cases, the victim may remain in contact with the circuit because of his inability to let go of the energized conductor, or because of unconsciousness. Immediately rescue the victim from the circuit, and apply an approved method of artificial respiration if the victim is not breathing or appears not to be breathing. Dispatch an assistant for medical assistance and a mechanical resuscitator. Continue resuscitation without interruption until the victim revives, until rigor

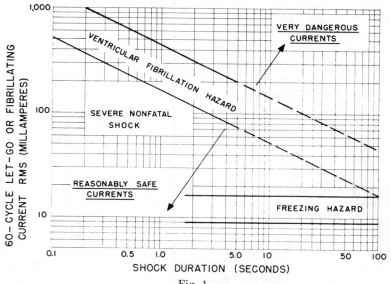

Fig. 1.

mortis sets in, or until he is pronounced dead by a physician. Many victims of serious electric accidents recover, perhaps after extensive burns are healed, but with no serious permanent aftereffects.

Figure 1 illustrates in graphical form the freezing hazard and the hazard from ventricular fibrillation. The lowest line of each hazard represents the theoretical response of 0.5 per cent of an infinite group, whereas the upper line represents the response of 50 per cent of the group. Currents in excess of the 50-percent lines must be considered to be very dangerous.

C. F. Dalziel

Cross-references: *Circuit Breakers, Fuses, Medical Electronics, Radiation (Ionizing), Radiation Hazards (Nonionizing), Safety*

ELECTROACOUSTICS

Electroacoustic systems generally consist of coupled electrical, mechanical, and acoustical elements reacting with each other and, normally, with an extensive acoustic medium. Their frequency- and transient-response characteristics are often conveniently investigated by means of equivalent electric circuits on which either numerical or experimental studies can be speedily, easily, and economically made. Adjustments made in the characteristics of the elements in the *equivalent circuits* (q.v.) or in their circuit connections are readily transferred to the corresponding elements and connections in the original system. This equivalent-circuit technique has proved itself a powerful tool in the design of electromechanical and electroacoustic transducers and systems.

Equivalent Circuits. The foundations of the equivalent-circuit relations are the laws of continuity and equilibrium, which state that the following sums are zero: (1) the sum of the voltage drops around an electrical loop, (2) the sum of the currents at an electrical node, (3) the sum of the velocity changes around a mechanical loop, (4) the sum of the forces acting at a mechanical node, (5) the sum of the pressure drops

around an acoustic loop, and (6) the sum of the volume currents at an acoustic node.

For simple single-loop and single-node lumped-constant circuits these sums are, in order,

$$L\frac{di}{dt} + Ri + \frac{1}{C_E}\int i\,dt = e(t) \qquad (1)$$

$$C_E\frac{de}{dt} + \frac{1}{R}e + \frac{1}{L}\int e\,dt = i(t) \qquad (2)$$

$$C_M\frac{df}{dt} + \frac{1}{R_M}f + \frac{1}{M_M}\int f\,dt = v(t) \qquad (3)$$

$$M_M\frac{dv}{dt} + R_Mv + \frac{1}{C_M}\int v\,dt = f(t) \qquad (4)$$

$$C_A\frac{dp}{dt} + \frac{1}{R_A}p + \frac{1}{M_A}\int p\,dt = U(t) \qquad (5)$$

$$M_A\frac{dU}{dt} + R_AU + \frac{1}{C_A}\int U\,dt = p(t) \qquad (6)$$

where, in the order of the equations,

i = instantaneous current in the electrical loop

$e(t)$ = variable externally-applied voltage

L, R, C_E = series inductance, resistance and capacitance in the electrical loop

e = instantaneous voltage drop between node and ground

$i(t)$ = variable externally applied current

L, R, C_E = paralleled inductance, resistance, and capacitance between node and ground

f = instantaneous force in the mechanical loop

$v(t)$ = variable externally applied velocity in loop

M_M, R_M, C_M = series-connected mass, resistance and compliance of mechanical system

v = instantaneous velocity of mechanical node

$f(t)$ = variable externally applied force at node

M_M, R_M, C_M = paralleled mass, resistance, and compliance of mechanical system between node and ground

p = instantaneous pressure in the acoustic loop

$U(t)$ = variable externally applied acoustic volume current in loop

M_A, R_A, C_A = series-connected mass, resistance and capacitance of acoustic system

U = instantaneous volume current at acoustic node

$p(t)$ = variable externally applied acoustic pressure at node

M_A, R_A, C_A = paralleled mass, resistance and capacitance of acoustic system between node and ground.

The equivalent forms of Eqs. (1) through (6) serve as the bases for representing any one of the circuits by any one of the remaining five. Thus, electroacoustic systems, which in practice generally employ a mechanical circuit to couple an electrical circuit to an acoustical one, may, by appropriate conversions revealed in these equations, be represented by an equivalent all-electrical, all-mechanical, or all-acoustical circuit of either type (i.e., on a loop basis or on a nodal basis).

All-electrical equivalent circuits are by far the most convenient to analyze and to test. Such circuits are invariably used in simulating not only the combination systems found in electroacoustic transducers, but also in simulating pure mechanical, pure acoustical, or combined mechanical-acoustical systems. It should be noted that in common with all the other mechanical components, mass is a two-terminal element, except that *one* of its terminals is *always* referred to *ground*. This is a very important concept in mechanical circuit diagrams; it is always essential to indicate a dotted connection from one side of a mass to ground to avoid errors otherwise easily made in setting up mechanical dual circuits or equivalent electrical circuits.

Although in the simple systems repre-

sented by Eqs. (1) through (6) there are no restrictions on the simulation of one circuit by another, in the more complex practical situations, for which equivalent circuit techniques are most useful, restrictions of two types occur. On the one hand only *planar* systems may be directly converted to their duals; i.e., equations of the type (2), (4), and (6), may be converted to the types (1), (3) and (5), respectively, without complication, if no avoidable crossovers occur in the original circuit diagram.

It is possible to convert nonplanar systems to planar systems through the use of suitable transformers, and then to convert the planar system so obtained to its dual. This procedure, however, has not found wide acceptance because of practical difficulties and the force current analogy is invariably used for nonplanar systems.

On the other hand, the character of the mechanical coupling force between the electrical and the mechanical components of a transducer also determines the admissible equivalent circuit, as shown below.

Coupling. In electromagnetic transducers (such as dynamic microphones, loudspeakers, etc.) the force developed in the coupling element (e.g., the voice coil) is proportional to the current through it, and alternatively the voltage induced in the coupler is proportional to its velocity across the magnetic field. This means that in the equivalent circuit for the mechanical system, force must be represented by current and velocity by voltage, leading to the analogy represented by Eqs. (1) and (3), the so-called *mobility* analogy. Thus, if a voice coil having the blocked impedance $Z_c = R_c + j\omega L_c$ drives a system having the mechanical impedance $Z_M = R_M + j[\omega M_M - (1/\omega C_M)]$, the impedance seen by the driving voltage applied at the coil terminals is $Z_E = Z_c + (D^2/10^7 Z_M) = Z_c + Z_m$, where Z_m is the *motional impedance* of the system. Here, $D = 0.2\pi r N B$ dynes/amp is the electromagnetic coupling constant, with r = the radius of the voice coil, N = the number of turns, and B = the magnetic flux density in gauss of the radial magnetic field. The paralleled components R_m, L_m, C_m of the motional impedance are related to the series components R_M, M_M, C_M of the mechanical impedance as follows:

$$R_m = \frac{D^2}{R_M} 10^{-7}; \quad L_m = D^2 C_M 10^{-7}; \quad C_m = D^{-2} M_M 10^{-7}$$

In plane electroacoustic elements such as condenser microphones, pieozelectric transducers and electrostatic speakers, the displacement current is proportional to the rate of change of spacing (i.e., velocity) between polarized plates and the force between plates is proportional to the voltage existing across them. Thus, the equivalent circuit for the mechanically coupled electroacoustic system must be represented by Eqs. (1) and (4), the so-called "impedance analogy."

Thus, a parallel-plate electrostatic transducer having for its movable plate a mechanical impedance $Z_M = R_M + j[\omega M_M - (1/\omega C_M)]$ and subjected to a time-varying force $f(t)$ is represented by an equivalent electrical circuit of impedance $Z_E = R_E + j[\omega L - (1/\omega C_E)]$ subjected to a time-varying voltage $e(t)$. The relations between the mechanical and equivalent electrical elements are given by $R_E = (d^2/C^2 E^2) R_M$, $L = (d^2/C^2 E^2) M_M$, $C_E = (C^2 E^2/d^2) C_M$, $e(t) = (d/CE) f(t)$, where d = dielectric thickness, C = transducer capacitance, and E = polarizing voltage across the transducer plates.

Lumped Representation of Mechanical and Acoustical Systems. For steady-state studies of electroacoustic systems containing distributed mechanical or acoustical elements the impedances of the distributed components may be represented by equivalent lumped impedances at each frequency. The transient response of such a system may, in principle, be obtained from the Fourier transform of its frequency response. However, for practical numerical or experimental studies of the transient response of distributed systems, and even for frequency-response studies of systems of mathematically intractable geometric form, the continuous distribution of system properties may be conveniently approximated by a finite number of lumps. Reasonably accurate results are obtained so long as five or more lumps are used per quarter-wavelength of the shortest wave of interest. For example, tone arm bending-torsion vibrations may introduce spurious effects in the electrical output of a phonograph pickup. Studies of the effect of tone arm compliance and damping may be made by means of a lumped-parameter equivalent circuit in which the arm may be represented by 10 or 20 rigid lumps elastically interconnected. A 20-lump system should give a good approximation to the first three or four bending-torsion modes and frequencies of the tone arm.

In dealing with acoustical elements, not only may lumping procedures be required for extended systems, but also corrections for acoustic medium entrainment and acoustic energy radiation may be necessary. For example, in designing loudspeakers and bass reflex cabinets the effective mass of the speaker cone is increased by the surrounding air which it moves back and forth, while the effective mass of the plug of air in the resonator port is similarly increased by the surrounding air. Radiation of sound from both elements adds to the over-all damping of the system. Similar corrections are involved for orifices in the walls of pipes and for open ends of pipes and horns transmitting sound.

W. W. Soroka

Feedback Elimination

Acoustic feedback in public-address (p.a.) systems occurs when sound energy from the loudspeaker(s) reaches the microphone. If the gain around the feedback loop (microphone, amplifiers, loudspeaker, room, microphone) exceeds +1 (0 db) at any frequency, acoustic feedback results in instability of the p.a. system (howling).

The first step to minimize feedback is to eliminate any response peaks (resonances) in the electroacoustic equipment, particularly the loudspeakers, as may be done by electrical equalizing filters. Electrical filters can also be used to suppress any troublesome frequency components that do not add to speech intelligibility, notably frequencies below 300 cps.

The second step consists of reducing as much as possible any *direct* sound transmission between loudspeaker and microphone. This goal is achieved by proper placement of loudspeakers and microphones and, if necessary, the use of directional microphones and loudspeakers.

The third step consists of minimizing the effect of *indirect* sound transmission between loudspeaker and microphone via reflections from the wall, ceiling etc., which is the most difficult task of all. The multiple reflections in rooms lead to very irregular frequency responses. A p.a. system operating over such a response curve will be unstable when the peak loop gain g_{max} exceeds 0 db. If the room had a flat frequency response with the same average gain, the gain of the p.a. system could be raised by about 10 db before instability would occur.

Unfortunately, there is no practical method to "equalize" the irregular frequency responses of rooms. However, the unstable build-up of signal amplitude of a frequency component falling on a peak of the room's frequency response can be avoided by inserting an electronic frequency shifter between microphone and loudspeaker, shifting all frequency components of the microphone signal by a constant amount. An optimum frequency shift corresponds to the distance between large peaks of the frequency response and the nearest valleys. In this manner a signal component having experienced excessive gain at one of the response peaks encounters a very low gain at its next trip around the feedback loop and thus is quickly eliminated from the feedback process. The average distance between large peaks and adjacent valleys is reciprocally related to the reverberation time of the room; for reverberation times of the order of 1 sec a (not very critical) optimum frequency shift is about 5 cps. A shift of this magnitude is inaudible for speech and most types of music.

A preferred method of implementing the frequency shift is single-sideband modulation and demodulation as shown in Fig. 1. The microphone signal, after amplification, is first modulated unto a 20-kc carrier from a crystal-controlled oscillator. After rejecting the lower sideband by a single-sideband filter, the signal is demodulated with a 19.995-kc carrier from a second crystal-controlled oscillator. The resulting signal has all its frequency components shifted upward by 5 cps.

The subjectively acceptable extra stable gain realizable by frequency shifting (over that without frequency shifting) is about 6 db for continuous operation. Even larger gains can be "absorbed" for short periods. This feature improves the over-all reliability of p.a. systems considerably and eases their operation in complex installations such as are used at large conventions. Even if no extra gain is desired, frequency shifting can be used to advantage to eliminate un-

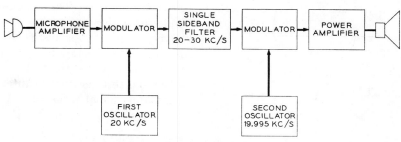

Fig. 1. Feedback elimination.

pleasant "ringing" of p.a. systems operating below but too close to the instability point.

Artificial Reverberation

Artificial reverberation is used extensively by record manufacturers (to improve the subjective quality of their recordings); by broadcasters (to add the proper amount of reverberation to their programs—for instance, a symphony recorded during an open-air performance at a summer music festival and for special effects); by manufacturers of electronic organs (to make them sound less mechanical), and by room acousticians (to change the "acoustics" of auditoriums).

There are two basic kinds of artificial reverberators: (1) two- or three-dimensional analogs of rooms, and (2) electronic reverberators using amplifiers and delay (realized by acoustic tubes, magnetic tape or disk, mechanical waves on helical springs, etc.) in closed feedback loops.

Examples of the first kind are reverberation chambers (a rather trivial case), small reverberation boxes using scaled-up frequencies, and reverberation plates excited to bending waves. Reverberators of this kind can be rather expensive (especially a full-scale chamber) and are not as flexible as electronic reverberators.

The simplest example of a reverberator of the second kind is a delay and an amplifier in a feedback loop as shown in Fig. 2 (without the dashed line). The impulse response of this device is shown in the lower part of the figure. It consists of exponentially decreasing echoes at integer multiples of the delay τ. This simple reverberator has two fundamental defects: (1) It does not produce as many echoes as a three-dimensional room, resulting in a "fluttery" response. (2) Its amplitude-frequency response is not flat; in fact, it has the appearance of a "comb" with rather sharp peaks. As a result, the reverberated sound is "discolored"—as if transmitted through a hollow barrel (which indeed has a similar echo response).

Many attempts have been made to overcome these defects but none, until recently, has met with complete success. The basic difficulty can be traced to the fact that rooms are three-dimensional resonators, whereas a delay in a feedback loop is the equivalent of a one-dimensional resonator.

Recently, it has been discovered that by adding to the reverberation the undelayed sound with opposite sign and proper amplitude (dashed line and shaded area in Fig. 2), the frequency response of the reverberator becomes *flat*.

Thus, the problem of sound discoloring is completely avoided. Also, reverberators with flat frequency responses can be connected in tandem. In this manner the echo densities of the individual reverberators *multiply*, thereby producing the high echo density necessary for high-quality artificial reverberation. This kind of reverberator is called *all-pass* reverberator because it passes all frequency components equally well.

A typical all-pass reverberator consists of three to five feedback loops, shown in Fig. 2, with different delays connected in tandem. The longest delay is $\frac{1}{20}$ of the desired reverberation time. The shortest delay depends upon the application and may vary between 1 msec (for pistol shots) and 10 msec (for slow music). The remaining delays are chosen to divide the ratio of the longest to the shortest delay into intervals of approximately equal ratios of 3:1.

M. R. SCHROEDER

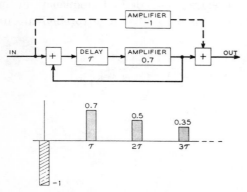

Fig. 2. Artificial reverberation.

Cross-references: *Acoustics, Compression and Expansion, Earphones, Hearing Aids, Larynx*

(Electronic), *Loudspeakers and Microphones, Music (Electronic)*, *Musical Instruments (Electric)*, *Sonar, Sound Recording, Stereophonics, Transducers, Ultrasonics, Underwater Sound, Vocoder*

ELECTROCHEMISTRY

Definitions. Electrochemistry is concerned with the relation between electrical energy and chemical change. In dealing with electrochemistry, several terms are commonly employed that require definition at the outset. The international ampere is defined as the current strength, which flowing for 1 sec, causes the deposition, under specified conditions, of 1.11800 mg of silver from a silver nitrate solution. The international ohm is the resistance at 0°C of a column of mercury of uniform cross-section 106.3 cm long; such a column of mercury weighs 14.4521 g. The international volt can then be defined by the equation, $E = IR$, where E is the international volt, I is the international ampere and R is the resistance in international ohms. This equation is Ohm's law. The volt cannot easily be established by this definition, and by international agreement the saturated standard Weston cell is taken to have a voltage of 1.0183 at 20°C; and this cell is used as a standard by government agencies in establishing the volt. A coulomb is the quantity of electricity passing when 1 amp flows for 1 sec. Current density is commonly expressed as amperes per square foot or amperes per square centimeter.

Types of Conductors. In metallic or electronic conductors, current is carried by a flow of electrons from atom to atom, the atomic nuclei remaining stationary. This type of conduction is common to all metals and alloys, carbon and graphite, and certain solid compounds of which manganese dioxide and lead sulfide are examples. In electrolytic or ionic conductors, current is carried by ions. Such conduction is found in solutions of acids, bases, and salts and in many fused compounds. In electrolytic conduction, as in metallic conduction, heat is generated and

a magnetic field is formed around the conductor, but in addition, matter is transferred. In a few materials, such as solutions of alkali and alkaline earth metals in anhydrous liquid ammonia, both types of conduction take place simultaneously; such conductors are called mixed conductors.

Electrolysis. When current is passed through an electrolyte, electrolysis takes place. The current enters the solution through an electronic conductor called an anode and leaves through another electronic conductor called a cathode. The container, with its electrolyte and electrodes, is called an electrolytic cell. Whenever current passes through an electrolytic cell, chemical changes, specifically called electrochemical changes or reactions, take place at the interface between electrodes and the electrolytes. The electrolyte strictly refers to the solution of ionized substances, but is frequently applied also to undissolved acids, salts and bases because, when dissolved, they produce electrolytes.

Electrolytic Dissociation. In 1887 S. A. Arrhenius (1859–1927) formulated a theory to help explain some anomalies in physical chemistry not satisfactorily explained theretofore. It had been known that for osmotic pressure the gas law $PV = nRT$ applied to aqueous solutions of nonelectrolytes (like alcohol or glucose in water) but did not apply to dilute solutions of electrolytes. In this equation P is the osmotic pressure, V the volume of the solution, n represents the number of moles in the solution and R is the gas constant. It was also well known that solutes of nonelectrolytes produced a "normal boiling-point elevation" in the solvent, amounting to 0.51°C/g-mole solute/ liter water and a "normal freezing-point depression" amounting to 1.860°C/g-mole solute/liter water. However, in aqueous solutions of weak electrolytes the osmotic pressure, boiling-point elevation and freezing-point depression are greater than these "normal" values. For instance, for hydrochloric acid, alkali chlorides and hydroxides, these values are nearly doubled: for potassium sulfate and oxalate, and for barium hydroxide, the values are even greater. In 1886 J. H. van't Hoff (1852–1911) published his classic paper on the theory of solutions in which he introduced an empirical factor i into the gas law equation for electrolytic solutions, to make the equation agree with observed data; thus, $PV = inRT$. The value of i is equal to the ratio of experimental osmotic pressure to the theoretical value based on the ideal gas laws.

Arrhenius, in order to explain these deviations of osmotic pressure, freezing-point depression and boiling-point elevation, formulated his famous theory of electrolytic dissociation. According to this theory, the molecules of electrolytes break up into positively and negatively charged ions spontaneously when dissolved in water. In very dilute solutions, the breaking up or ionization, properly referred to as dissociation, is complete; in more concentrated solutions, only some of the molecules are dissociated. Arrhenius apparently assumed that the process of solution formed the ions. There is now evidence that the ions exist in the crystals before solution, and that during the process of solution some of these ions dissociate. It is the free ions and not the undissociated molecules that carry the current in electrolytic solutions, but according to Arrhenius, it is the total number of particles in solution, molecules plus ions, that determine the osmotic pressure. Therefore, electrolytic solutions, in which there is dissociation, have a higher osmotic pressure for equal concentrations than do nonelectrolytes, like a glucose solution. Dissociation is commonly represented in the following manner:

$$KCl \rightleftharpoons K^+ + Cl^-$$

$$BaCl_2 \rightleftharpoons Ba^{++} + 2Cl^-$$

$$NaOH \rightleftharpoons Na^+ + OH^-$$

If α is taken to represent the degree of dissociation, that is, the fraction of molecules dissociated into ions, n the number of ions into which each molecule can dissociate,

and m the number of molecules, then

$$i = \frac{m - m\alpha + nm\alpha}{m} = 1 - \alpha + n\alpha, \quad \text{and}$$

$$\alpha = \frac{i - 1}{n - 1}$$

The van't Hoff factor i is obtainable from freezing-point or analogous measurements; the value for α, the so-called degree of dissociation, can then be calculated. Arrhenius showed that α can also be evaluated from conductance measurements and that the results by the two methods are in good agreement. This agreement was accepted as strong evidence of the validity of the theory of electrolytic dissociation. It is now known that this agreement was largely fortuitous, but with some modifications the theory is now universally accepted.

In the case of salts, strong acids or bases dissolved in water, the degree of dissociation is very considerable and these compounds are called strong electrolytes. Weak acids and weak bases and a few salts dissociate only to a small extent, unless the dilution is very great, and they are called weak electrolytes. Although water is the most common solvent for the preparation of electrolytes, organic solvents also serve the purpose, but the solubility of inorganic compounds in them is very low and the degree of dissociation is very small.

Electrochemical Reactions. When a direct current is passed through an electrolyte, electrochemical reactions take place at the junction between the electrolyte and the electrodes. In such reactions there is always a transfer of electrons. Reactions that take place at an anode are of the following types:

(1) Atoms of the anode in contact with the electrolyte give up one or more electrons to the circuit and become anions (negative ions). Examples are represented in the following equation in which e represents an electron:

$$Ag - e \rightleftharpoons Ag^+$$

$$Cu - 2e \rightleftharpoons Cu^{++}$$

$$Al - 3e \rightleftharpoons Al^{+++}$$

When reactions of this type take place, the anodes are said to be soluble.

(2) Anions in contact with the anode give up one or more electrons to the anode and become atoms or combine with water to form compounds:

$$Cl^- - e = Cl$$
$$2OH^- - 2e = H_2O + O$$
$$SO_2^{--} - 2e + H_2O = H_2SO_4 + O$$

When reactions of this type take place, the anodes are said to be insoluble.

(3) Ions of a lower degree of oxidation give up one or more electrons to the anode and become oxidized to a higher degree:

$$Fe^{++} - e = Fe^{+++}$$

All reactions at the anode are oxidizing reactions and any gases liberated appear first in the nascent state. Anodes cannot be classified into soluble and insoluble, for an anode may be soluble in one electrolyte and insoluble in another. A lead anode acts as a soluble anode in a nitrate or acetate solution but as an insoluble one in a sulfate solution. Carbon always acts as an insoluble anode and platinum does so under most conditions and these two materials are commonly classed as insoluble anodes.

At the cathode the following types of reaction take place:

(1) Cations (positive ions) in contact with the cathode receive one or more electrons from the cathode and become atoms:

$$H^+ + e = H$$
$$Ag^+ + e = Ag$$
$$Cu^{++} + 2e = Cu$$
$$Cr^{+++} + 3e = Cr$$

(2) Ions of a higher degree of oxidation in contact with the cathode receive one or more electrons from the cathode and become reduced:

$$Fe^{+++} + e = Fe^{++}$$

All reactions at the cathode are reducing reactions.

Several different reactions may take place simultaneously at an electrode. Electrolysis of a dilute hydrochloric acid solution yields a mixture of chlorine and oxygen at the anode. In a solution of stannic salts there may appear simultaneously at the cathode, liberation of hydrogen, deposition of tin and reduction of stannic ions to stannous ions.

Faraday's Laws of Electrolysis. During 1833 and 1834 Michael Faraday (*q.v.*) published the results of much of his research, among which are his famous laws, since called Faraday's laws, which can be expressed as follows: (1) The amount of chemical change produced at the electrodes in an electrolytic cell is directly proportional to the quantity of electricity passing through the electrolytic solution. (2) The amounts of various substances liberated at the electrodes by the same quantity of electricity is directly proportional to their chemical equivalent weights.

The quantity of electricity required to produce one equivalent of change at an electrode is independent of the nature of the change and is called the faraday, F, and is equal to 96,500 coulombs. The weight of an element or group of elements set free by the passage of 1 coul of charge is called the *electrochemical equivalent* of that element or group.

The specific resistance of an electrolyte may be defined as the resistance of a cube of the electrolyte, measured between opposite faces. The reciprocal of the specific resistance is called the specific conductance, L. The units of specific conductance are ohm^{-1}cm^{-1}.

The equivalent conductance Λ is the conductance of a solution containing 1 g equivalent of a dissolved electrolyte placed between two flat and parallel electrodes 1 cm apart. The equivalent conductance depends upon the degree of dilution and the temperature. The equivalent conductance increases with dilution until a point called "infinite dilution" is reached, after which the conductance remains constant with further dilution; at infinite dilution dissociation of the molecules is complete

$$\Lambda = \frac{100L}{c} \text{ cm}^2 \text{ equiv}^{-1} \text{ ohm}^{-1}$$

TABLE 1. SINGLE ELECTRODE POTENTIALS*
(ELECTROMOTIVE SERIES)

Based on standard hydrogen electrode = 0
All ions are at unit activity, temperature = 25°C

Single Electrode Potential, $E°$	Electrode Reaction at the Anode (Oxidation Reaction)
3.045	$Li = Li^+ + e$
2.925	$K = K^+ + e$
2.87	$Ca = Ca^{++} + 2e$
2.714	$Na = Na^+ + e$
1.66	$Al = Al^{+++} + 3e$
1.18	$Mn = Mn^{++} + 2e$
0.763	$Zn = Zn^{++} + 2e$
0.74	$Cr = Cr^{+++} + 3e$
0.50	$Fe = Fe^{++} + 2e$
0.41	$Cr^{++} = Cr^{+++} + e$
0.403	$Cd = Cd^{++} + 2e$
0.3363	$Tl = Tl^+ + e$
0.277	$Co = Co^{++} + 2e$
0.250	$Ni = Ni^{++} + e$
0.136	$Sn = Sn^{++} + 2e$
0.126	$Pb = Pb^{++} + 2e$
0.00	$H_2 = 2H^+ + 2e$
−0.15	$Sn^{++} = Sn^{++++} + 2e$
−0.153	$Cu^+ = Cu^{++} + e$
−0.2802	Normal calomel electrode
−0.337	$Cu = Cu^{++} + 2e$
−0.521	$Cu = Cu^+ + e$
−0.771	$Fe^{++} = Fe^{+++} + e$
−0.7991	$Ag = Ag^+ + e$
−0.987	$Pd = Pd^{++} + 2e$
−1.0652	$2Br^- = Br_2(1) + 2e$
−1.3595	$2Cl^- = Cl_2 + 2e$
−1.50	$Au = Au^{+++} + 3e$
ca −1.68	$Au = Au^+ + e$
−2.8	$2F^- = F_2 + 2e$

* Values of potentials taken with permission from Wendell M. Latimer, "Oxidation Potentials," 2nd ed., Prentice-Hall, Inc., 1952.

where c is the number of gram equivalents per liter.

The type of cell mentioned above would be inconvenient for making equivalent-conductance determinations. They are made in more convenient cells having small platinum electrodes and using a small volume of solution. The cell constant is determined by obtaining the conductance of a known solution in the cell, usually a 0.0200-molar potassium chloride solution.

Electromotive Force. When an electronic conductor is placed in an electrolyte, a voltage is set up spontaneously between the electrode and the electrolyte. This volt-age cannot be measured directly. It is a function of the species of ions, their concentration, the temperature, and (for gaseous electrodes) the pressure. Since the absolute voltage of the single electrode cannot be measured, an arbitrary datum value is used, just as an arbitrary datum plane is used for measuring heat content or terrestrial elevations. For electrode potentials, the voltage of the hydrogen electrode is taken as zero. With this voltage as a basis, the familiar electromotive series is established. For such a series the numerical value of the voltage, $E°$, is based on the metal dipping into a solution of its own ions at unit activity, this electrolyte being connected by a salt bridge to a hydrogen electrode in a solution of hydrogen ions at unit activity; the whole system at a pressure such that the hydrogen gas in contact with the platinum black electrode is at one atmosphere pressure and the whole system is at 25°C. The results obtained are actually the combined voltage of two electrodes, one of which is the hydrogen electrode. Nevertheless, the resultant value is commonly referred to as the single electrode potential.

In such a series the absolute numerical values of the single electrode potentials have no significance in themselves; the importance lies in the numerical difference between any two electrode potentials. Table 1 gives the single electrode potentials of some metals; such a table is called the electromotive series. The algebraic signs are on the basis that the reaction involved is an oxidation reaction:

$$Zn - 2e = Zn^{++}, \quad E° = 0.762$$

In much of the literature the reaction is taken to be a reduction reaction:

$$Zn^{++} + 2e = Zn, \quad E° = -0.762$$

When such a convention is used, the signs are opposite to those given in the table.

Electrolysis Cells. Electrolysis cells are cells used to produce electrochemical changes at the electrodes by passing through the cell a direct current derived from an external source such as a dynamo or a battery. They include cells for producing chlorine, caustic soda, hypochlorites, cells for electroplating and for refining of metals.

Voltaic Cells. Voltaic cells are cells that generate a voltage spontaneously and which will therefore produce a current if the electrodes are connected by a metallic conductor. Voltaic cells convert chemical energy into electrical energy. They comprise the primary cells or batteries of common use; strictly speaking the term "batteries" should be applied only to a group of primary cells connected to act electrically as a unit, but by common usage, the term is also applied to single cells. The open-circuit voltage of a voltaic cell depends upon the nature of the electrodes and of the electrolyte or electrolytes; this voltage cannot be predicted accurately from data in the electromotive series, because the conditions in the voltaic cell are not the same as those on which the electromotive series is based.

Strictly speaking, any pair of dissimilar electrodes immersed in any electrolyte, or different electrolytes in contact with each other, yield a voltaic cell. However, economics, voltage, capacity and useful life of a cell limit the combinations to only a few. Most voltaic cells employ only one electrolyte, and zinc is the most common metal used for anodes; copper and carbon are the most common materials used for cathodes.

These voltaic cells are called primary cells; when their useful life has been exhausted the cells are discarded or the reactive materials are replaced. In voltaic cells the anode reactions are usually nearly reversible, but the cathode reactions are not. That is, the reaction cannot be reversed at the cathode by passing a current through the cell in an opposite direction to the discharge current.

In **secondary** or **storage cells** the reactions at both electrodes are reversible. Such cells, when discharged, can be brought back to the charged state by passing a charging current through the cell in a direction opposite to the discharge current.

Standard Cells. The saturated cadmium cell is accepted as the standard for measuring voltage. Two glass tubes closed at the bottoms are connected by a horizontal tube, the whole forming a letter H. Platinum electrodes are sealed through the bottoms of the tubes. A cadmium amalgam, containing 10 to 13 % cadmium in mercury is placed in one tube. Pure mercury is placed in the bottom of the other tube on which is placed a paste of mercury and mercurous sulfate. Crystals of cadmium sulfate, $3CdSO_4 \cdot 8H_2O$, are placed over the materials in each tube, and the remaining space is nearly filled with a saturated solution of cadmium sulfate and the tops of the tubes are sealed. The voltage of the cell is 1.0183 v at 20°C.

In place of the crystals of cadmium sulfate and saturated solution, a solution of cadmium sulfate saturated at 4°C may be employed. At room temperature the solution is unsaturated and the voltage of the cell is 1.0186 v. The voltage of the unsaturated cell is virtually independent of the temperature under normal laboratory conditions.

Polarization. Whenever a current passes through an electrolytic cell, changes are produced at the electrodes, and these changes produce a countervoltage, both in electrolysis cells and in voltaic cells. This countervoltage is called the polarization voltage of the cell, but actually, polarization is a phenomenon taking place at each electrode, the polarization of the cell being the combined polarization effects. If two copper electrodes are placed in a $CuSO_4$ solution and a current is passed through the cell, there is an accumulation of copper ions adjacent to the anode and an impoverishment of copper ions adjacent to the cathode. This change in concentration of ions in that part of the electrolyte adjacent to the electrodes causes polarization. This type of polarization is so common that it has been given the name of concentration polarization. In electrolysis cells the effect of polarization is to reduce the current through the cell under a fixed applied voltage; in a voltaic cell polarization reduces the operating voltage of the cell. The charging of a storage cell is actually a case of polarization of an electrolysis cell.

Overvoltage. Overvoltage, in simplest terms, may be considered as a special case of polarization in which a gas is evolved on an electrode. It is the difference in the equilibrium voltage for that gas and the voltage under actual operating conditions. Hydrogen overvoltage is the most common overvoltage encountered. The actual overvoltage for a specific gas evolution depends upon the nature of the electrode, its surface texture, the current density, and other factors. Therefore, a rigid list of numerical values of overvoltages for a particular gas cannot be given.

Decomposition Potential. When two platinum electrodes are placed in an electrolytic solution and the voltage is gradually increased, beginning with zero voltage, there is no appreciable flow of current until a certain critical voltage is attained when a large current begins to flow and then increases in magnitude directly as the voltage is increased. The voltage at which the current strength increases abruptly is called the decomposition potential, and varies for different salt solutions, their concentrations and temperatures. The decomposition potential for several normal salt solutions between platinum electrodes are as follows, according to LeBlanc:

Copper sulfate	1.92 v
Lead nitrate	1.52
Nickel sulfate	2.09
Nickel chloride	1.85
Potassium sulfate	2.20
Silver nitrate	0.70

The decomposition potential of most strong acids and bases that give off oxygen and hydrogen upon electrolysis is 1.7 v.

W. A. KOEHLER

Cross-references: *Batteries, Ionization, Ions, Standards*

ELECTRODEPOSITION

Electrodeposition, as distinguished from electroplating, is sometimes called electrophoretic deposition. It covers those electrolytic processes in which electrically charged particles other than ions are deposited at either the anode or the cathode. Although such processes are not so extensively employed as electroplating techniques, they have interesting industrial applications; they are also used in gravimetric analysis. Oxide coatings may be applied to the cathodes used in electron tubes by electrodeposition of carbonates of the alkaline earths precipitated from their nitrates by sodium carbonate and maintained in a slurry containing about 10 g of solids per liter. Electrolysis of the slurry deposits the carbonates on the cathode in a uniformly thick film that can be baked to obtain the oxides, which comprise the active cathode of the electron tube.

The advantage of electrodeposition over spraying or other mechanical methods of application is the uniformity of thickness of the film obtained. The conditions of electrolysis vary widely depending upon the material being deposited and the nature of the electrolyte used. The voltage required may range from 1.5 to more than 100 v, although industrially a potential of over 15 v is seldom encountered. In general, the lower voltages prevail in inorganic systems and the higher voltages in organic electrolytes. Current densities also are quite variable but commonly are about 10 to 20 $amp/ft.^2$.

The current density which may be employed is determined mainly by side reactions and byproducts at one or both electrodes. Excessive anodic current densities result in the evolution of oxygen in aqueous electrolytes, usually with harmful results. The product formed at the anode may either be distorted by the evolution of the oxygen or it may be oxidized chemically.

Discharge of hydrogen at the cathode is commonly encountered in industrial processes, and usually causes foaming of the electrolyte. This effect is prevented ordinarily by interposing a semipermeable diaphragm between the electrodes. Although the voltage drop across the cell is increased, it is the easiest solution of the foaming problem.

In many cases the electrode at which the product is obtained must be selected with great care. Often a slight solubility of the anode will greatly affect the product; for example, a copper anode would never be used for rubber deposition because of the unfavorable affect of small amounts of copper on many rubber compositions. Stainless steel and lead are often used in practice.

HAROLD J. READ

Cross-references: *Electroforming, Electron-Tube Manufacture*

ELECTROFORMING

Electroforming is a critically controlled electrolytic process of metal deposition on a photomatrix. Several basic steps are necessary to prepare the electroforming photomatrix. An etched and filled glass ruling or a photographic master positive is printed onto a sensitized conductive plate with a highly passive surface. After reducing the unexposed portion of the sensitized photo resist this matrix is immersed in a plating bath as a cathode and metal is deposited on all conductive (unexposed) areas. All exposed areas of the photo resist are nonconductive and represent the open areas in the resulting metal part. The finished metal part is stripped off the matrix, and the process can be repeated.

The electroforming process is used for the fabrication of fine electroformed mesh, as used in storage tubes (*q.v.*). The storage target is electroformed mesh (up to 1000 crossed lines or 1,000,000 holes/in., Fig. 1). The mesh is coated with dielectric material on one side. Thickness of the mesh ranges from 0.0002 in. depending upon the brightness required in the tube. Other applications for electroformed mesh is in camera tubes such as the vidicon (*q.v.*) and the image orthicon (*q.v.*), where high resolution is important. Cross line rulings up to 22 x 22

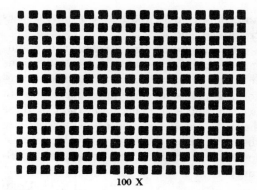

100 X

Fig. 1. 1000-line-in. mesh approximately 125 ✕ enlarged.

in. have been prepared to produce large pieces of mesh for 21 in. radar storage tubes.

Electron microscopes use fine (250 or 500 lines/in.) electroformed copper and gold grids as a measuring scale for microstructures. Another area in the electronics industry where the electroforming process has helped to solve a difficult manufacturing problem is in semiconductor manufacture (*q.v.*). High-frequency mesa transistors are now almost exclusively massproduced with the aid of electroformed nickel evaporation masks featuring slits of 0.0003 x 0.0015 in. or the more exotic types of horseshoe patterns of similar size. Other electroformed evaporation masks are used to fabricate various solid-state and infrared devices with a maximum tolerance of 0.0001 in. Pre-positioned gold wires 0.0003 ✕ 0.0008 in. and smaller are electroformed on top of a 0.002-in.-thick nickel carrier to serve as multiple connectors for an automated manufacturing process of the mesa transistor in the micromodule assembly. Subminiaturized electroformed gold circuits are deposited on anodized aluminum conductors to serve as shaft encoder commutators in miniaturized airborne computers.

An electroformed micro-meteorite counter was recently developed. Fine electroformed gold wires (0.0002 x 0.0003 in. in cross section) were bonded to a 0.001-in.-thick mylar insulator in a micropotentiometer type of circuit. This device covers the area of an equilateral triangle with 4.25-in. sides and contains over 150 ft of continuous electroformed gold wire.

Reliable particle size distribution of granular materials in the range of 1 to 150 microns in diameter can be measured with electroformed precision micromesh sieves to an accuracy of $\pm 2\mu$. The application of these sieves to the determination of particle size distribution has been of particular interest in chemical industry and in powder metallurgy.

FRANZ UCKO

Cross-references: *Electrodeposition, Miniaturization, Modular Construction*

ELECTROLUMINESCENCE

Electroluminescence is luminescence excited by electric fields or currents in the absence of bombardment or other means of excitation. Two quite different types of electroluminescence must be distinguished.

The first observation of what is now known as "recombination electroluminescence" was made in 1923 by Lossew, who found that when point electrodes were placed on certain silicon carbide crystals and current passed through them, light was often emitted. Explanation of this emission has been possible only with the development of modern semiconductor theory. If minority charge carriers are injected into a semiconductor, i.e., electrons are injected into p-type material or "positive holes" into n-type material, they recombine spontaneously with the majority carriers existing in the material. If some of these recombinations result in the emission of radiation, electroluminescence results. Minority-carrier injection may occur not only at point contacts but also at broad area rectifying junctions; in this case the junction must be biased in the forward or "easy-flow" direction, and the electric field in the junction is lower when the voltage is applied than in its absence.

The recombinations in this type of electroluminescence may occur directly between energy bands of the host material or by means of impurity or activator centers. In general, the emission intensity is a linear function of the injected current; the emission is "current-controlled." This type of emission has now been observed in a wide variety of materials, including SiC, diamond, Si, Ge, CdS, ZnS, ZnO, and many of the so-called III-V compounds such as AlN, GaSb, GaAs, GaP, InP, and InSb. The emission of many of these materials lies in the infrared region of the spectrum. In all cases, with the possible exception of InSb, the efficiency is very low, values of one emitted quantum per million injected carriers often being observed. For this reason, this type of electroluminescence has not yet found practical application.

The second kind of electroluminescence was first observed in 1936 by Destriau. He observed the emission of light from a specially prepared zinc sulfide phosphor suspended in an insulating oil and subjected to an intense alternating electric field by means of capacitor-like electrodes; the emission is "field controlled." Today the phosphor powder is usually embedded in a solid organic (plastic) or inorganic (glass) medium. Thin films of tin oxide or of metal are used to provide transparent electrically conductive electrodes. Such "cells" can be made with a base of glass, metal, or flexible or rigid plastic material.

This type of electroluminescence, which has been called the "Destriau effect" or "acceleration-collision electroluminescence" has also been observed in Zn_2SiO_4:Mn, $BaTiO_3$, TiO_2, BN, and some organic materials. The best electroluminescent phosphors, however, are still ZnS and related materials; copper is the most common activator, although ZnS:Cu, Mn is also used. The emission or recombination process in these materials is the same as for excitation by ultraviolet radiation or by cathode rays. The excitation process, however, is quite different. It has been found that to prepare good electroluminescent phosphors it is necessary to make the material very nonuniform electrically by introducing, on the surface or in defects in the interior of the ZnS particles, segregations of a relatively good conductor, such as ZnO or Cu_2S. The local electric field strength in the neighborhood of these segregations may be a hundred or more times the applied field strength, which is already of the order of 10^4 to 10^5 v/cm. Under the action of these intense local fields, aided perhaps by thermal action, electrons in donor levels or "traps" may be liberated and accelerated to acquire considerable energy from the field; field emission of electrons from the segregations may also occur. Some of these energetic electrons may collide with and excite or ionize the activator or luminescence centers.

The intensity of electroluminescence increases rapidly as the applied alternating voltage is increased, and also increases slightly less than linearly as the frequency is increased until a region of saturation is approached at frequencies of the order of 100,000 cps. Very high brightness may be achieved (2500 ft-lamberts or more at 20,000 cps). Maximum efficiency is not achieved at the same conditions as maximum brightness. The efficiency of electroluminescence (2.5-3.0 per cent) is yet low compared to other light sources. Some comparative figures are: electroluminescence, 10 lumens/w; incandescence, 16 lumens/w; fluorescent lamp, 65 lumens/w. Electroluminescence, however, is an area source of light, in contrast to an incandescent lamp, which is essentially a point source, or a fluorescent lamp, which is a line source. Electroluminescent lamps may be made only a fraction of an inch in thickness and of any size or shape. Some electroluminescent phosphors also exhibit a change in emission color as the frequency of the applied voltage is varied.

Another feature of electroluminescent phosphors of practical importance is the decrease in output during operation. This deterioration is strongly influenced by humidity, temperature, and operating frequency. High temperature and high frequency greatly accelerate the deterioration; the time required to produce a given loss is essentially inversely proportional to the frequency. Moisture must be carefully excluded. The time required for the output to "buildup" after application of a sinusoidal voltage is of the order of a few cycles and hence decreases as the frequency is increased; this time may be decreased by application of a dc bias. The decay time after excitation is independent of frequency.

Phosphors with controlled brightness-voltage characteristics may be prepared for specialized electronic applications. In addition to powder phosphors, continuous films of ZnS a few microns thick may be prepared. These films operate on ac as well as dc and at comparatively low voltage (of the order of 20 v). Superposition of ac and dc can lead to interesting interaction and control of ouput by small signals.

In electronic applications electroluminescent phosphors ("electroluminors") may be advantageously used in conjunction with other solid-state components such as nonlinear resistors, photoconductors, magnetic devices, and ferroelectrics (q.v.) for voltage distribution and control. Uses range from single-element control circuits to complicated logic circuits, multielement storage devices, shift registers, light and x-ray image amplifiers and storage panels, and thin large-area image display devices for radar or television. Specially segmented lamps for display of numerical, alphabetical, or other types of information are also available.

In addition to electroluminescence proper, other interesting effects occur when electric fields are applied to a phosphor which is concurrently, or has been previously, excited by other means. Such effects are usually termed *electrophotoluminescence*. One such phenomenon is the "Gudden and Pohl effect," discovered in 1920. Here the phosphor is first excited (by ultraviolet radiation, for example) and then an electric field is applied during the afterglow or phosphorescence, or even after the emission has decayed below the limit of detection. A burst of emission is observed with some materials, even those which do not exhibit electroluminescence. In this case the field acts on electrons in traps that are responsible for the phosphorescence.

Most phosphors, if continuously excited by ultraviolet radiation, X-rays, or cathode rays, show a decrease in emission if an electric field is simultaneously applied. This "field quenching" was first observed by Déchêne in 1935. In 1954 Destriau discovered that some ZnCdS:Mn phosphors excited by x-rays show the opposite effect; i.e., their emission is increased by the application of an electric field. Since that time a similar enhancement effect has been observed for excitation by light, ultraviolet radiation, cathode-rays, and α-particles. These effects may find application in radiation converters, light amplifiers, and particle detectors.

HENRY F. IVEY

Cross-references: *Cathodoluminescence, Fluorescence, Fluorescent Lights, Semiconductors*

ELECTROLUMINESCENT DISPLAYS: see SOLID-STATE DISPLAYS

ELECTROLYSIS: see ELECTRODEPOSITION

ELECTROMAGNETIC THEORY

Electrostatics

The electric force on a charge q in an electrostatic field E is $\mathbf{F} = q\mathbf{E}$. The field is proportional to q/r^2, where r is the distance. The proportionality constant is $1/4\pi\epsilon$; thus for discrete charges, $E = (1/4\pi\epsilon)\sum(q/r^2)$, where $\epsilon = \epsilon'\epsilon_0$ is the permittivity, and ϵ' is the dielectric constant ($= 1$ for vacuum); $\epsilon_0 = 8.85 \times 10^{-12}$ farad/m is the permittivity of vacuum.

The field at a distance r from a line carrying a charge q_l per unit length is $q_l/2\pi\epsilon r$; from a surface carrying a charge q_a per unit area, $q_a/2\epsilon$.

The force between two charges q_1 and q_2 is given by *Coulomb's law*, $F = q_1q_2/4\pi\epsilon r^2$. The work done on a unit charge in moving it from A to B is $_A\phi_B = -\int_A^B \mathbf{E}\cdot d\mathbf{l}$, and is

called the potential difference. Integration yields $\mathbf{E} = -\nabla\phi$, where ϕ is the potential. It follows that $\nabla \times \mathbf{E} = 0$ for an electrostatic field.

The potential of a charge q is $\phi = -(1/4\pi\epsilon)\int(q/r^2)\,dr = q/4\pi\epsilon r$, and for a continuous charge distribution of charge density ρ, $\phi = (1/4\pi\epsilon)\int_v(\rho/r)\,dv$. The potential of a line charge is $\phi = -(q_l/2\pi\epsilon)\ln r$; between parallel plates a distance d apart, $\phi = q_ad/\epsilon$; between coaxial cylinders of radii a and b, $\phi = (q_l/2\pi\epsilon)\ln(b/a)$; between concentric spheres, $\phi = (q/4\pi\epsilon)[(1/a) - (1/b)]$; and between equal parallel cylinders of radius a separated a distance D on centers, $\phi = (q_l/\pi\epsilon)\cosh^{-1}(D/2a)$.

The capacity between two conductors carrying equal and opposite charges is the charge on one of the conductors divided by the potential difference between them: $C = q/\phi$.

Two equal and opposite charges $+q$ separated by a distance d constitute a dipole. For small d, the potential of a dipole at $r \gg d$ is $\phi = (qd/4\pi\epsilon r^2)\cos\theta$; $q\mathbf{d} = \mathbf{m}$ is called the dipole moment, and θ is the angle between d and r.

When a dielectric is placed in an electric field, dipoles are induced in the dielectric (by one of two means: one, in media having nonpolar molecules, each molecule becomes a dipole because of electron displacement; two, in media with molecules possessing permanent dipole moments, existing randomly oriented dipoles line up). Total dipole moment per unit volume is called the polarization $\mathbf{P}$, which is proportional to $\mathbf{E}$.

Let q_p and ρ_p denote the charge and volume charge density, respectively, appearing automatically as a result of polarization; let the real charge and charge density placed on the body be q_r and ρ_r, respectively. Note that $\rho_r = 0$ inside a dielectric, and $\rho_p = 0$ in vacuum.

Gauss's law states that the surface integral of the normal component of E over a surface equals the total charge enclosed by the surface, divided by ϵ_0, or $\int_a \mathbf{E} \cdot d\mathbf{a} = (1/\epsilon_0)\sum (q_r + q_p)$. For a continuous charge distribution, this is $(1/\epsilon_0)\int_v (\rho_r + \rho_p)\,dv$, and from Gauss's (divergence) theorem, $\int_a \mathbf{E} \cdot d\mathbf{a} = \int_v \nabla \cdot \mathbf{E}\,dv$, so that $\nabla \cdot \mathbf{E} = (\rho_r + \rho_p)/\epsilon_0$. Since $\nabla \cdot \mathbf{E} = -\nabla^2 \phi$, we have $\nabla^2 \phi = -(\rho_r + \rho_p)/\epsilon_0$, which is *Poisson's equation*. If $\rho_r + \rho_p = 0$, $\nabla^2 \phi = 0$ (*Laplace's equation*).

The surface integral of the normal component of $\mathbf{P}$ over a surface equals the total polarized charge flowing out; i.e., for a continuous charge distribution, $\int_a \mathbf{P} \cdot d\mathbf{a} = -\int_v \rho_p\,dv$. Again from Gauss's theorem, $\nabla \cdot \mathbf{P} = -\rho_p$, which when substituted in $\nabla \cdot \mathbf{E}$ gives $\epsilon_0 \nabla \cdot \mathbf{E} = (\rho_r + \rho_p) = (\rho_r - \nabla \cdot \mathbf{P})$, or $\nabla \cdot (\epsilon_0 \mathbf{E} + \mathbf{P}) = \rho_r$.

Define $\mathbf{D} \equiv \epsilon_0 \mathbf{E} + \mathbf{P}$ as the electric displacement, so that $\nabla \cdot \mathbf{D} = \rho_r$. Also, since $\mathbf{P}$ is proportional to $\mathbf{E}$, so is $\mathbf{D}$; the proportionality constant is ϵ, so that $\mathbf{D} = \epsilon \mathbf{E}$.

The dielectric constant is thus $\epsilon/\epsilon_0 = 1 + (P/\epsilon_0 E) = \epsilon' = 1 + \chi_e$, where $\chi_e = P/\epsilon_0 E$ is called the electric susceptibility.

At a boundary, the normal component of D is continuous (unless a surface charge density ρ_s exists there, in which case $D_{n1} - D_{n2} = \rho_s$), and the tangential component of E is continuous. Since $E = 0$ inside a conductor, $E_t = 0$ outside the surface of the conductor, and $D_n = \rho_s$.

Magnetostatics

Magnetic forces are produced by magnetized bodies (e.g., permanent magnets), or by charges in motion (electric currents). The magnetic force on a single charge q (not isolated, but part of a procession of charges) moving with a velocity $\mathbf{v}$ in a magnetic field $\mathbf{B}$ is $\mathbf{F} = q\mathbf{v} \times \mathbf{B}$. The field $\mathbf{B}$ is proportional to qv/r^2, where r is the distance, and is normal to both $\mathbf{v}$ and $\mathbf{r}$. The proportionality constant is $\mu/4\pi$; thus for a discrete moving charge forming part of a current distribution independent of time,

$\mathbf{B} = (\mu/4\pi)q(\mathbf{v} \times \mathbf{r})/r^3$ or, since $q\mathbf{v} = I'\,d\mathbf{l}'$ (where I' is the current flowing in a conductor element of length $d\mathbf{l}'$), $\mathbf{B} = \int \mu I'(d\mathbf{l}' \times \mathbf{r})/4\pi r^3$. Here $\mu = \mu'\mu_0$ is the permeability, and μ' is the relative permeability ($= 1$ for vacuum; <1 for diamagnetic and >1 for paramagnetic materials; $\gg 1$, and depends on B, for ferromagnetic materials; is a tensor whose components depend on the direction and magnitude of B for ferrites); $\mu_0 = 4\pi \times 10^{-7}$ henry/m is the permeability of vacuum.

The field at a distance r from a straight wire carrying a current I is $\mu I/2\pi r$; on the axis of a circular loop of wire of radius R at a distance z from the plane of the loop, $\mu I R^2/[2(z^2 + R^2)^{3/2}]$; at the center of this loop, $\mu I/2R$; and inside a solenoid (n turns), $\mu n I$.

The force between two elements of current is given by *Coulomb's law*, $d\mathbf{F} = \mu I_1 I_2 [d\mathbf{l}_1 \times (d\mathbf{l}_2 \times \mathbf{r})]/4\pi r^3$. Since lines of B form closed curves, $\nabla \cdot \mathbf{B} = 0$ always, but $\nabla \times \mathbf{B} = 0$ only in special cases, and B cannot be written as $\nabla \phi$ in general; we can, however, define a vector potential $\mathbf{A}$ such that $\mathbf{B} = \nabla \times \mathbf{A}$.

A small loop of area a carrying a current I' constitutes a magnetic dipole. The scalar potential due to it at a distance r is $\phi = (\mu I'a/4\pi r^2)\cos\theta$; $m = I'a$ is called the dipole moment, and θ is the angle between the normal to the surface and r.

When a magnetic material is placed in a magnetic field, dipoles are produced by one of two means: (1) in diamagnetic media, currents are induced in the atoms and the resulting magnetic dipoles are directed opposite to the field; (2) in paramagnetic media (i.e., possessing permanent dipole moments which arise both from electrons circulating within atoms and from the magnetic moments of the individual electrons), existing randomly oriented dipoles line up. (In ferromagnetic media, the permanent dipoles have a tendency to line up even in the absence of an external magnetic field.) Total dipole moment per unit volume is called the magnetization $\mathbf{M}$, which is proportional to $\mathbf{B}$.

Let I_m and $\mathbf{J}_m$ denote the current and current density, respectively, appearing automatically as a result of magnetization; let the real current and current density resulting from current flow be I_r and $\mathbf{J}_r$, respectively. Note that generally $\mathbf{J}_r = 0$ in magnetic media, and $\mathbf{J}_m = 0$ in vacuum.

Ampère's law states that the line integral of the tangential component of $\mathbf{B}$ over a closed contour equals μ times the total current threading through the contour, or $\int \mathbf{B} \cdot d\mathbf{l} = \mu_0 \sum (I_r + I_m)$. Current and current density across an area a are related by $dI = \mathbf{J} \cdot d\mathbf{a}$, and from Stokes's theorem, $\oint \mathbf{B} \cdot d\mathbf{l} = \int_a \nabla \times \mathbf{B} \cdot d\mathbf{a}$, so that $\nabla \times \mathbf{B} = \mu_0(\mathbf{J}_r + \mathbf{J}_m)$. But $\mathbf{B} = \nabla \times \mathbf{A}$, and if we specify that $\nabla \cdot \mathbf{A} = 0$, we have $\nabla^2 \mathbf{A} = -\mu_0(\mathbf{J}_r + \mathbf{J}_m)$.

The current density resulting from magnetization is given by $\nabla \times \mathbf{M} = \mathbf{J}_m$, which when substituted in $\nabla \times \mathbf{B}$ gives $(1/\mu_0) \nabla \times \mathbf{B} = (\mathbf{J}_r + \mathbf{J}_m) = (\mathbf{J}_r - \nabla \times \mathbf{M})$, or $\nabla \times [(\mathbf{B}/\mu_0) - \mathbf{M})] = \mathbf{J}_r$.

Define $\mathbf{H} \equiv (\mathbf{B}/\mu_0) - \mathbf{M}$ as the magnetic field intensity, so that $\nabla \times \mathbf{H} = \mathbf{J}_r$. Also, since $\mathbf{M}$ is proportional to $\mathbf{B}$, so is $\mathbf{H}$; the proportionality constant is μ, so that $\mathbf{B} = \mu \mathbf{H}$.

The relative permeability is thus $\mu/\mu_0 = 1 + (M/H) = \mu' = 1 + \chi_m$, where $\chi_m = M/H$ is called the magnetic susceptibility.

At a boundary, the normal component of $\mathbf{B}$ is continuous, and the tangential component of H is continuous [unless a surface current density $\mathbf{J}_s$ exists there, in which case $(\mathbf{H}_{t1} - \mathbf{H}_{t2}) \times \mathbf{a}_n = \mathbf{J}_s$, where $\mathbf{a}_n$ is a unit vector normal to the boundary].

Maxwell's Equations and Wave Equation

The relationship between electric and magnetic fields is governed by *Faraday's law* $\int_a \mathbf{E} \cdot d\mathbf{a} = -(d/dt) \int \mathbf{B} \cdot \mathbf{a}_n \, da$, which (for the case of a stationary circuit) can be transformed through Stokes's theorem to $\nabla \times \mathbf{E} = -\partial \mathbf{B}/\partial t$; and by Ampère's law $\nabla \times \mathbf{H} = \mathbf{J}$. The latter applies only when $\mathbf{J}$ is a steady current density; in the time-varying case, the equation of continuity $\nabla \cdot \mathbf{J} = -\partial \rho/\partial t$ and $\nabla \cdot \mathbf{D} = \rho$ yield instead $\nabla \times \mathbf{H} = \mathbf{J} + \partial \mathbf{D}/\partial t$. *Maxwell's equations* are

$$\nabla \cdot \mathbf{B} = 0$$

$$\nabla \cdot \mathbf{D} = \rho$$

$$\nabla \times \mathbf{E} = -\partial \mathbf{B}/\partial t$$

$$\nabla \times \mathbf{H} = \mathbf{J} + \partial \mathbf{D}/\partial t$$

to which may be added *Ohm's law* $\mathbf{J} = \sigma \mathbf{E}$, where σ is the specific conductivity; and the constitutive equations and force equation

$$\mathbf{D} = \epsilon \mathbf{E}; \quad \mathbf{B} = \mu \mathbf{H}; \quad \mathbf{F} = q(\mathbf{E} + \mathbf{v} \times \mathbf{B})$$

Magnetic vector potential $\mathbf{A}$ is still given by $\mathbf{B} = \nabla \times \mathbf{A}$, but now $\nabla \cdot \mathbf{A} = \epsilon \mu \, \partial \rho/\partial t$ and $\mathbf{E} = -\nabla \phi - \partial \mathbf{A}/\partial t$, where ϕ is the electrostatic scalar potential.

Then $\mathbf{A}$, ϕ, $\mathbf{E}$, and $\mathbf{H}$ are all governed by the *wave equation*

$$\nabla^2 \mathbf{E} - \sigma \mu \, \partial \mathbf{E}/\partial t - \epsilon \mu \, \partial^2 \mathbf{E}/\partial t^2 = 0$$

which has as one solution $E = E_0 e^{j\omega t - \gamma x}$, representing a sinusoidally time-varying wave (frequency $f = \omega/2\pi$) propagating in the x direction. The propagation constant is complex, $\gamma = \alpha + j\beta = \pm[j\omega\mu(\sigma + j\omega\epsilon)]^{1/2}$, where α is the attenuation and β is the phase constant.

When conductivity $\sigma = 0$, the wave equation reduces to the undamped form $\nabla^2 \mathbf{E} - \epsilon \mu \, \partial^2 \mathbf{E}/\partial t^2 = 0$ and the propagation constant is $\beta = \omega(\mu\epsilon)^{1/2}$. The velocity of propagation is $v = \omega/\beta = (\mu\epsilon)^{-1/2}$, which in free space becomes $c = (\mu_0\epsilon_0)^{-1/2}$, the velocity of light ($\approx 3 \times 10^8$ m/sec); $v = c/n$, where $n = (\mu'\epsilon')^{1/2}$ is the index of refraction.

CHARLES SUSSKIND*

Transmission-Line Formulation

The wave equation for the propagation of plane waves in the direction of the x axis governing the behavior of wave functions for

* The above material is reproduced by permission of San Francisco Press, © 1961.

the electric and magnetic field $E_y(x,t)$ and $H_z(x,t)$ is

$$\frac{\partial^2 E(x,t)}{\partial x^2} - \mu\epsilon\,\frac{\partial^2 E}{\partial t^2} = 0$$

where μ and ϵ are the permeability and permittivity of the medium in which the waves propagate ($\mu = \mu'\mu_0,\ = \epsilon'\epsilon_0$).

An identical wave equation has been found to govern the distribution of the voltage $v(x,t)$ and current $i(x,t)$ along a transmission line,

$$\frac{\partial^2 v(x,t)}{\partial x^2} - LC\,\frac{\partial^2 v(x,t)}{\partial t^2} = 0$$

plane:

$$Z(x) = \frac{E_y(x)}{H_z(x)}$$

This impedance varies with distance when the wave functions $E_y(x,t)$ and $H_z(x,t)$ are combinations of waves traveling both in the positive and in the negative direction of the x axis. Waves propagating in opposite directions are found when reflections exist at an interface of two media with different intrinsic impedances.

Corresponding quantities for a transmission line and a plane wave are listed in the table below:

Transmission Line		Plane Wave	
Voltage $v(x,t)$	v	Electric field $E(x,t)$	v/m
Current $i(x,t)$	amp	Magnetic field $H(x,t)$	amp
Propagation constant $\beta = \omega\sqrt{LC}$	m^{-1}	Wave number $k = \omega\sqrt{\mu\epsilon}$	m^{-1}
Velocity of propagation $c = \dfrac{1}{\sqrt{LC}}$	m-sec^{-1}	Velocity of propagation $c = \dfrac{1}{\sqrt{\mu\epsilon}}$	m-sec^{-1}
Characteristic impedance $Z_0 = \sqrt{L/C}$	ohm	Intrinsic impedance $\eta = \sqrt{\mu/\epsilon}$	ohm

where L and C are the distributed inductance and capacitance per unit length.

The general solution to this wave equation, given by D'Alembert, is

$$E(x,t) = e_1(x - ct) + e_2(x + ct)$$

where e_1 and e_2 are arbitrary functions and c is the velocity with which the waves propagate; $c = 1/\sqrt{\mu\epsilon}$ or $c = 1/\sqrt{LC}$, respectively.

The voltage $v(x,t)$ and the current $i(x,t)$ are integral forms of the electric field $E(x,t)$ and the magnetic field $H(x,t)$. Close analogies to plane-wave propagation exist among the transmission-line phenomena. In addition to the corresponding velocities of propagation, it is possible to define a quantity analogous to the characteristic impedance of a line $Z_0 = \sqrt{L/C}$, the characteristic wave impedance or intrinsic impedance $\eta = \sqrt{\mu/\epsilon}$, which has the same dimension as Z_0. At a plane x the field or wave impedance $Z(x)$ is defined as the ratio of total electric field to total magnetic field at that

The value of wave impedance $Z(l)$ a distance l in front of an interface normal to the direction of propagation at which the value of the wave impedance is known (e.g., Z_L) is given by the corresponding transmission-line formula:

$$Z(l) = \eta\,\frac{Z_L \cos\left(\dfrac{\omega}{v}\,l\right) + j\eta \sin\left(\dfrac{\omega}{v}\,l\right)}{\eta \cos\left(\dfrac{\omega}{v}\,l\right) + jZ_L \sin\left(\dfrac{\omega}{v}\,l\right)}$$

Consequently the Smith chart (q.v.) is also useful in reflection problems. A change in intrinsic impedance of the medium corresponds to a change in the characteristic impedance in a transmission-line model. The above formula can be applied successively when propagation of waves through more than two different media separated by parallel interfaces is analyzed. These analogies are convenient in making conclusions regarding the reflections of plane waves at interfaces between various media. The above formula shows that there are no reflections when the *ratio* of μ'/ϵ' of the two media is the same.

A dielectric slab that is some multiple of half wavelengths thick causes no reflections for waves of that wavelength; in other words, it is completely transparent. It corresponds to a transformation of impedance through a half-wavelength long section of a transmission line. A layer a quarter-wavelength thick inserted between two dielectrics of different intrinsic impedances eliminates all reflections when its intrinsic impedance is equal to the geometric mean of the intrinsic impedances of the outer two dielectrics. This property is used in the coating of lenses to reduce reflections and is exactly analogous to the method of interposing a quarter-wavelength line section of a characteristic impedance that is the geometric mean of the two sections to be matched. Elimination of reflections means that an object has been made invisible for waves of a given wavelength.

Another example of the usefulness of the transmission-line analogy to electromagnetic wave propagation is found in the method for elimination of wave reflections from good conductors. It is known that in a shorted transmission line an impedance equal to the characteristic impedance of a line is placed a quarter wavelength before the short circuit. The line appears perfectly terminated to the generator (the quarter-wavelength section represents an infinite impedance shunted across the perfect termination).

Likewise it is possible to eliminate reflections from a perfectly conducting wall by placing a quarter wavelength before it a thin film of conducting material whose resistance is equal to the intrinsic impedance of the medium in which the waves propagate.

VLADISLAV BEVC

Cross-references: *Coupled-Mode Theory, Dielectric Theory, Energy, Historical Background of Electronics, Magnetism, Relativity Theory, Statistical Mechanics, Stress Tensor, Thermodynamics, Vector Algebra*

ELECTROMETER: see ELECTROSCOPE AND ELECTROMETER

ELECTRON DIFFRACTION AND SCATTERING

Diffractometry is the well-established instrumental technique based on the diffraction by crystals, acting as three-dimensional gratings, of x-rays, electrons and neutrons. With a crystal of known grating constant, or interplanar spacing (for example, the atomic planes parallel with the cleavage face of calcite), it is possible in spectrometry to evaluate wavelengths in the spectra of x-rays, which like light consist of photons guided by a train of waves, and of electron and neutron beams that have wave properties, even though primarily corpuscular in nature. On the other hand, with beams of known wavelengths of all three radiations, it is possible to analyze from diffraction patterns the previously unknown structures and interplanar spacings of crystals. (See **X-rays.**)

It is the purpose here to describe briefly the techniques and applications of electron diffraction analyses of crystalline solids and the closely related analysis based on electron scattering from noncrystalline as well as crystalline surfaces.

The de Broglie Theory and Its Verification. In 1921, while studying the intensity of scattered electrons as a function of the angle of scattering, Davisson and Kunsman observed certain unexplained maxima of intensity. This study of anomalous scattering intensities continued for some time without an adequate explanation. These results were not recognized as diffraction phenomena simply because no existing conception of electrons could comprehend such behavior. In 1924, quite independent of these scattering studies, de Broglie proposed a wave theory of matter which was soon thereafter found to explain the problems of electron scattering as well as many others. On examining the properties of this wave system, we deduce the very important relationship

$\lambda = h/mv$, where λ is the wavelength of the wave associated with a mass m, traveling with a velocity v. Neglecting the relativity change in mass of the electron with velocity, we obtain for the kinetic energy $\frac{1}{2} mv^2 = Ve$, where V is the accelerating potential and e the electron charge. Substituting for v yields

$$\lambda = \frac{h}{mv} = \frac{h}{\sqrt{2meV}} \sqrt{\frac{150}{V}}$$

approximately. This λ for the electron beam at $V = 30$ kv (a satisfactory range for diffraction) is 0.0695 Å.

Experimental evidence accumulated rapidly in favor of the de Broglie theory. Davisson and Germer in 1927 first showed that the heretofore anomalous scattering intensities of electrons reflected from a nickel crystal agreed fairly well with the expected maxima when the electrons of wavelength h/mv are considered to be diffracted as are x-rays. Further proof of the validity of the wave theory came with the experiments of Kikuchi on mica, and of Ponte; using powdered metallic oxide specimens, such as ZnO and MgO, he was successful in verifying de Broglie's law to within 3 parts per thousand. These early experiments were sufficient to establish the truth of de Broglie's conclusions. The diffraction of electrons was considered a fact, and immediately was applied to the study of many different types of substances, such as thin films of high molecular weight compounds, cellulose and its derivatives.

Apparatus. Full details regarding many kinds of construction can be found in the literature. There are, however, certain fundamental requirements which any apparatus for this work must meet: (a) a monochromatic beam of electrons; (b) a good vacuum; (c) manipulation of the specimen within the evacuated apparatus; (d) electrical or photographic registration of diffraction maxima; and (e) a reliable measurement of the electron wavelength by sphere gap, standard substance, or otherwise. It is not surprising that modern electron microscopes (*q.v.*) pro-

vide the necessary requirements of a beam of electrons finely collimated with magnetic lenses and a constant voltage and wavelength for electron diffraction analysis of selected areas of specimens as microscopically observed.

Scattering of Electrons by Free Atoms and Molecules. Considerable light has been thrown upon the distribution of charge within an atom by the diffraction of electrons by free atoms. That such diffraction studies are capable of revealing something about the atomic structure is due to the fact that the atomic size and wavelength of the electrons are of the same order of magnitude, and hence interference between wavelets scattered from various parts of the atom is to be expected at certain angles. One cannot, therefore, assume the atom to be merely a point of scattering, and the amplitude of the diffracted ray to be independent of scattering angle. The studies pertaining to the scattering of electrons by single atoms are not numerous. They do show a close analogy between electron and x-ray scattering.

It is well to remember, however, that the efficiency of electron scattering is about 10^{-7} times that of x-rays. Debye developed the theory governing the scattering of x-rays by the molecules of gases and vapors. The apparatus is simply a modification of that used in working with solids. A jet of vapor passes through the electron beam and is condensed on a surface cooled with liquid air in order not to disturb the vacuum in the apparatus. Good patterns are obtainable in a few seconds, or even in a fraction of a second in some cases. Fast electrons are usually employed because their use obviates any consideration of inelastic collisions.

The method of interpreting the photographs differs quite considerably from that employed in the cases of solid or crystalline diffracting substances. Essentially it involves the assumption of a certain molecular structure and interatomic distances within the molecule, the calculation of the interference intensities expected from such a structure, and a comparison of the calculated with the observed intensities to establish the identity of the assumed model with the actual molecule. Pauling and Brockway have studied the merits of the various methods for evaluating the intensities in a photograph, and point out that visual methods are accurate to within about 1 per cent. Many and various are the molecules that have been subjected to this type of analysis. De Laszlo has pointed out that any substance having a vapor pressure of at least 10 cm of Hg at 750°C can be examined by electron diffraction.

Scattering of Electrons by Crystalline and Semicrystalline Substances. As in the previous cases of electron scattering by free atoms or molecules, so too in the theoretical treatment of the interaction of an electron with a crystal, one inserts the proper ψ value in the Schrödinger wave equation, solves for the scattered wave and deduces from it the angular distribution of scattering intensity. In the first cases of electron diffraction by crystalline substances, the simple method of substituting the de Broglie wavelength in the Bragg equation was used. Many subsequent investigations followed this precedent, and generally the agreement with experiment was good so long as fast electrons were employed. This method has been found a reliable one in the hands of such men as Kikuchi, Kirchner, Ponte, Rupp, Thompson, and others who usually employed electrons of at least 15 kv.

The first attempt at a more accurate approach to the problem was made by Bethe, who considered the crystal lattice to possess a potential that determines the ψ value in the wave equation. If the energy of the incident electron beam is not very great, the average inner potential of the crystal exerts a refractive effect upon the electrons, which is very appreciable in comparison with the refractive index of x-rays. Many interesting effects have been observed in single-crystal investigations for which sharp spots are normal, but black and white lines called Kikuchi lines also appear. In most cases the

ordinary methods used in x-ray analysis have also been applied in this type of work with electrons; that is, the de Broglie wavelength has been substituted in the Bragg equation for diffraction, such effects as inelastic scattering, refractive index, and so forth being ignored. This procedure introduces but very little error because of the high speed of the electrons usually employed.

Metallic specimens to be used for transmission of electrons must be very thin and can be prepared by various methods: etching of metal leaf or foil by floating it on a suitable solvent; sublimation of the metal by heating in vacuum; chemical deposition (e.g., Ag from an ammoniacal solution); anodic thinning in an electrolytic cell; and various others. Ordinary commercial gold leaf needs only very little thinning with KCN to make it suitable for diffraction by transmission. In general, these powder or fiber patterns made from extremely thin specimens or layers compare with the x-ray diffraction patterns on thicker specimens, though there are evidences occasionally in very thin layers of unusual crystallographic forms. A wide variety of specimens exposed to air for some time may yield identical electron diffraction patterns from the organic films (grease, etc.) adsorbed from the air. Thus, electron diffraction supplements x-ray diffraction in its capacity for determining structures in very thin surfaces, through which x-rays would easily penetrate.

Much interest has centered about the question of an amorphous layer on the surface of polished metals. Naturally, in this type of study, diffraction is by reflection only. The polished surfaces of all metals give rise to the same two broad diffraction rings, neither of which is related to the metal's crystal-lattice dimensions. This observation confirms the existence of a liquid, or Beilby, layer of metal, so-called after Beilby, who first postulated it on the basis of microscopic evidence. Investigators failed to detect such a layer when using x-rays to study the surfaces of polished metals, doubtless because the x-rays penetrated to, and revealed, the metal underneath it. Lubrication with graphite and with long-chain molecules, catalysis, passivity of metals, particle size in the colloidal range, and crystal structure determination with extremely small specimens (for example, with 10^{-7} g of polonium) are other applications.

Analysis by Electron Backscattering. The most recent application of electrons (β-particles) to analysis is the remarkable demonstration at Los Alamos that the backscattering is a discontinuous function of atomic number, but is strictly linear in respect to atomic number within each period of the Periodic Table; hence backscattering from compounds can thus be predicted with high precision. The very simple apparatus consists of a collimated source of β-particles from strontium-90 which impinges on the sample (solid, liquid, or solution) after screening to transmit only the 2.18-mev betas from the daughter element yttrium-90; and a Mylar window admits the back-scattered particles into a methane proportional counter.

A calibration plot of relative backscattering shows that discontinuities or changes in slope appear precisely at atomic numbers 10, 18, 36, and 54 corresponding to rare-gas configuration of neon, argon, krypton, and xenon; with linear equations over each range ($BS = aZ + b$, where BS is back-scattering in per cent, Z is atomic number, and a and b are constants), it is possible to calculate the values for remaining elements that are closely in agreement with experimental values. Hydrogen exhibits negative backscattering, so that carbon in hydrocarbons accounts for more backscattering than the compounds, the difference being directly proportional to the hydrogen content. Similarly, corrections can be made for hydrates.

The difference in backscattering between hydrogen and deuterium has considerable theoretical importance. Measurements have been made very successfully on a number of organic compounds in single and multiple component systems using the following BS values in percent: 6C, 5.230; 7N, 6.461; 8O,

7.692; 9F, 8.923; 16S, 15.953; 17Cl, 16.920; 35Br, 29.560; 53I, 36.208. Isomers scatter identically, but halogenated compounds for example, are distinguished with high precision. It is obvious that β-particle backscattering as well as absorption can be used in continuous monitoring of process streams by use of a count-rate meter and recording potentiometer.

It is highly significant that surface analysis is also made with high precision by scattering of ions such as protons.

GEORGE L. CLARK

Cross-references: *Electrons, Ion Scattering, Neutron Diffraction, Protons, Radiation (Ionizing), X-rays*

ELECTRON GUNS

It is convenient to classify electron guns in terms of their *perveance*, a parameter that remains invariant when the gun is geometrically scaled. The commonly used unit of perveance is the microperv, where the perveance in micropervs is $P =$ (beam current in microamps)/(anode voltage)$^{3/2}$. High-perveance guns, ones with perveances greater than 0.1 microperv, are used to produce well-defined electron beams for injection into traveling-wave tubes, klystrons, and other beam-type devices. The condition of high perveance requires that space-charge fields must be considered in the design of the gun and that at high potentials the current density is high, so that high convergence of the beam is needed to limit the current density at the cathode.

The Pierce gun design method makes use of a space-charge-flow solution, a portion of which is to be the finite beam in the gun. Laplace's equation exterior to this finite beam is solved with the boundary condition that the potentials and fields are those given by the space-charge solution at the beam edge. The equipotential surfaces of this Laplacian solution are then suitable gun electrodes, which can form a finite beam that flows as if it were part of an infinite space-charge flow. An example given by Pierce is the strip beam gun of Fig. 1 which

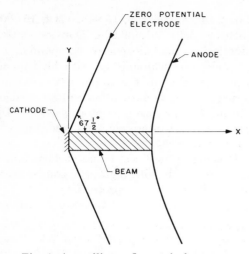

Fig. 1. A rectilinear-flow strip-beam gun.

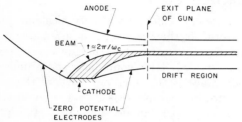

Fig. 2. A crossed-field, curvilinear-flow electron gun.

uses the rectilinear flow solution from a plane cathode in which the potential varies as $V = Ax^{4/3}$, and the electric field normal to the direction of flow is zero. If one beam edge is $y = 0$, it follows from complex-variable theory that the expression $V = \mathrm{Re}A(x + jy)^{4/3} = $ constant determines the equipotentials outside the beam, any one of which can be an electrode. The electrodes can also be determined in an electrolytic tank by using a dielectric strip to synthesize the boundary condition that the electric field normal to the beam edge is zero.

Until recently, the only analytic space-charge flow solutions used in the design of the guns for klystrons and traveling-wave tubes were those for rectilinear flow between two planes, two cylinders, or two spheres. With a spherical cathode, for instance, the electrons flow along the radii of the cathode towards the center of the sphere, and the

beam can be highly convergent. The lens effect due to the hole in the anode through which the beam passes then focuses the flow into a parallel beam.

A new development in gun design is the use of space-charge-flow solutions with curved electron trajectories. An example of this type of gun (Fig. 2) is one that emits a parallel electron beam in balanced flow into uniform crossed electric and magnetic fields. For this crossed-field gun, the cathode is taken to be the plane $y = 0$, the current density J_y at the cathode is taken to be uniform, the electric field E_y is to be in the y direction and to vary only with y, and the magnetic field B is to be uniform and in the z direction. It may be shown that for a space-charge-limited flow the potential, electric field, and all other parameters at the point x, y can be stated parametrically in terms of the transit time t of an electron from the cathode to x, y; in particular, the electron trajectory starting from a point on the cathode $x = x_0$, $y = 0$, is

$$x = x_0 + \frac{eJ_y}{m\epsilon_0\omega_c^3}\left[\frac{(\omega_c t)^2}{2} + \cos\omega_c t - 1\right]$$

$$y = \frac{eJ_y}{m\epsilon_0\omega_c^3}(\omega_c t - \sin\omega_c t)$$

where $\omega_c = -eB/m$ is the cyclotron frequency.

The trajectories of this flow are curvilinear; they leave the cathode at right angles, and at the points $\omega_c t = 2n\pi$ pass through points of inflection where they are parallel to the cathode. Two such trajectories ended near the point $\omega_c t = 2\pi$ can form the boundaries for a suitable finite convergent beam to be used in a gun. As all the potentials and fields within the beam are known in analytic form, electrodes for the gun may be found by an extension of the complex variable method of analytic continuation already described. Such guns have been constructed and tested, and their performance is in close agreement with the theoretical predictions.

A general class of curvilinear space-charge-flow solutions suitable for gun design may be found by the use of the method of separation of variables. With no magnetic field, it follows from the equation of motion of an electron that, for the flow from a unipotential cathode, the velocity is irrotational, i.e., $\nabla \times \mathbf{v} = 0$, a condition known as normal congruent flow. The velocity can therefore be expressed in terms of a scalar potential function, called the action function W, by writing $\mathbf{v} = \nabla W$. For instance, to find the flow from a circular cylindrical cathode, W is written in the separable form $W = e^{nz}W_2(r)$, where n is an arbitrary real constant. From the equation of conservation of energy, $v^2 = -2eV/m$, it follows that the potential V may also be expressed in the separable form

$$V = -\frac{me^{2nz}}{2e}\left[\left(\frac{\partial W_2}{\partial r}\right)^z + n^2 W_2{}^z\right]$$

On examination of Poisson's equation, the equation of conservation of charge, and the relation between current and charge, it may be seen that all parameters of the flow may also be expressed in separable form, and can be related to $W_2(r)$. In general a nonlinear, fourth-order partial differential equation for $W_2(r)$ can be derived, which with the insertion of the correct boundary conditions at the cathode, yields a solution for the flow. The trajectories of the electrons may then be found by writing

$$\frac{dr}{dz} = \frac{v_r}{v_z} = \frac{(\partial W_2)/(\partial r)}{nW_2}$$

and integrating this equation. The trajectories are curvilinear in form unless $n = 0$; one trajectory may be derived from another by a simple translation in z.

Other solutions for the flows from conical cathodes, planar cathodes, and cathodes which form part of an equiangular spiral have been derived by similar methods.

The method of separation of variables may be adapted to take account of magnetic field by using the Lorentz equation of motion in the form

$$m\mathbf{v}\cdot\nabla\mathbf{v} = e(\mathbf{E} + \mathbf{v}\times\mathbf{B})$$

In a spherical polar coordinate system (r,θ,ϕ), the velocity $\mathbf{v}$ is expressed in the separable form

$$\mathbf{v} = r^n[v_r(\theta),v_\theta(\theta),v_\phi(\theta)]$$

where n is an arbitrary real constant. It may be shown that all the other parameters of the flow and the magnetic field may also be expressed in similar separable forms. From the resulting set of differential equations in θ, a large class of flow solutions from conical cathodes can then be derived. Similar solutions are also obtainable in other coordinate systems; they require, in general, that the magnetic field should be nonuniform.

The solution in spherical polars with $n = 1$ and B uniform has provided a basis for the design of a magnetron injection gun to produce a well-defined high perveance (>10 micropervs) hollow beam for injection into a drift tube. A similar design has also been arrived at by use of an extension of the crossed-field gun theory already discussed.

The conformal transformation procedures mentioned above can be adapted to the design of electrodes for all strip beam guns. However, for a circularly symmetric gun, these procedures break down because the solution of Laplace's equation cannot be expressed as the real part of an analytic function.

One possibility would be to integrate numerically Laplace's equation away from the beam boundary. But, because Laplace's equation is elliptic, the integration is unstable, and leads to inordinately large errors. Nevertheless, the potentials produced by electrodes designed this way would still be very little in error at the edge of the beam. But, for a high perveance gun in which the beam thickness may be comparable to its length, the errors in potential at the middle of the beam would be large. Such difficulties would also occur even if an electrolytic tank could be used.

A solution to this problem is to generalize the coordinate system itself and make it complex. Thus for the simple example of a strip beam, the x coordinate is replaced with a new coordinate $x + j\bar{x}$. Laplace's equation in this new coordinate system can then be written in the hyperbolic form

$$\frac{\partial^2 V}{\partial \bar{x}^2} - \frac{\partial^2 V}{\partial y^2} = 0$$

which is stable, as is the wave equation.

The numerical procedures used in deriving a space-charge-flow solution can be generalized, solved in a complex coordinate system of this type, and complex boundary conditions generated at a complex beam surface. It is then possible to work away from this surface numerically and find the required equipotentials, the electrodes, in real coordinates.

G. S. Kino

Cross-references: *Characteristic Frequencies, Crossed-Field Interactions, Electron Optics*

ELECTRON MICROSCOPES

The electron microscope (EM) is an instrument employing electron beams for the purpose of producing magnified images of minute objects. The feasibility of such an instrument became apparent as the result of the work of H. Busch who demonstrated in 1926 that axially symmetrical electrostatic and magnetic fields would focus electron beams in the same fashion that glass lenses focus beams of light. At about the same time L. de Broglie advanced the hypothesis, later confirmed experimentally, that the wavelength in Å units (10^{-8} cm) associated with a beam of mono-energetic electrons is given by the equation $\lambda = (150/V)^{1/2}$ where V in volts is the potential through which they have been accelerated from rest. Since the wavelengths for moderate accelerating potentials (50 − 100 kv) are very short compared to the wavelength of visible light the possibility was foreseen that electron microscopes could exceed the resolving power of the best optical microscopes whose resolving power, as shown by Abbé in 1867, is about one-half the wavelength of the light employed. The ultimate resolving power obtainable with existing electron microscopes is limited by

lens aberrations (in particular spherical aberration) as well as wavelength, and is between 5 and 10 Å for the best instruments. Since spherical aberration reaches an irreducible minimum for focusing fields that can be produced at present there is little hope that this performance can be improved, although the possibility exists that an instrument employing proton beams with their shorter wavelength for the same accelerating voltage might improve the resolution to the order of 1 Å, i.e., to the order of atomic dimensions.

Electron lenses. Magnetic lenses for electron microscope application consist of a magnetic circuit symmetrical about an axis along which the electrons are to travel, energized by windings as indicated diagrammatically in Fig. 1. Permanent magnets instead of windings are sometimes employed. Electrostatic lenses for high resolution electron microscopes are of the "unipotential" type consisting of three coaxial circular apertures, the outer two being of the same diameter and at the same potential and the inner one being at a negative potential with respect to the outer two and with a bore which may be greater or less than the outer two. A schematic of a typical electrostatic microscope with circuitry is shown diagrammatically in Fig. 2.

If the magnetic lens consists of a gap length l cm which is large compared to the axial bore through which the electrons pass, the focal length is given by the equation:

$$1/f = 1/l \cdot \frac{0.187NI}{\sqrt{\bar{V}}} \sin \frac{0.187NI}{\sqrt{\bar{V}}} \text{ cm}^{-1}$$

where f is in cm, V is in volts and NI is the ampere-turns. The image is rotated by an angle $\Theta_i = \pm 0.187 NI/\sqrt{V}$ radians in addition to the usual 180° inversion resulting from the formation of a real image. Many lens fields may be represented by the symmetrical bell-shaped function $H_z = H/[1 + (z/a)^2]$ where H_z is the component of the field in gauss along the lens axis (z-axis), H_0 is the maximum value of H_z and $2a$ is the breadth of the bell-shaped function at half-

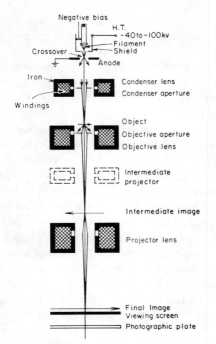

Fig. 1. Diagram showing the optics of a magnetic electron microscope.

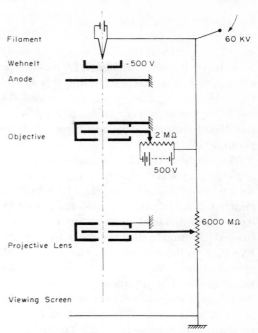

Fig. 2. Diagram showing the optics and circuitry for an electrostatic electron microscope. (H. Bruck and P. Grivet.)

intensity. The focal length is then given by the formula:

$$\frac{1}{f} = 0.77 \times \frac{0.15}{\sqrt{V}} H_0 \sin 2a \frac{0.15}{\sqrt{V}} H_0 \text{ cm}^{-1}$$

and the angle of rotation

$$\theta_i = \pm 0.15 \pi a H_0 / \sqrt{V}.$$

Both these formulas assume that the object is at a point where the field is of negligible magnitude. An approximate formula for the focal length of the unipotential electrostatic lens is given by the equation:

$$\frac{1}{f} = \frac{3}{16} \int_{-\infty}^{+\infty} \left(\frac{dV/dz}{V}\right)^2 dz \text{ cm}^{-1}$$

where the z-axis is the lens axis. No rotation occurs as in the magnetic lens. Minimum focal lengths for electron microscope lenses are in the range 1–5 mm.

Electron lenses are afflicted with the same geometrical lens aberrations that occur with uncorrected simple glass lenses. Chromatic aberration can be minimized by using mono-

chromatic beams. Pincushion distortion may occur under certain conditions, though it may not be perceptible to the eye, and causes a variation in magnification from one part of the field to another. The most important aberration is spherical aberration, which leads to an unsharpness in the image $d_{sph} = C_s \alpha^3$ where α is the half-angle of the cone of illumination (aperture angle) leaving a point at the object. C_s is from 0.2 to 2 cm for most microscope objectives. A second source of unsharpness in the image is due to the wave nature of the electron beams and is given by the Airy formula $d_{\text{diff}} = 0.6\lambda/\alpha$ where λ is the wavelength and α is the aperture angle. Comparing the formulas for the spherical aberration error and the diffraction error we see that they depend on α in inverse proportion so that the combined effect of the two is a minimum where the two are approximately equal. This minimum occurs for $\alpha = (\lambda/C_s)^{1/4}$. Typical numerical values for λ and C_s require α to be in the range 10^{-3} to 10^{-2} radian which is extremely small compared to the apertures of optical microscopes.

For the optimum α, the image defect or resolving power becomes $d_0 = C_s^{1/4}\lambda^{3/4}$. It would appear from this that d_0 could readily be reduced by reducing λ, i.e., by raising the accelerating potential. Actually this is not the case since C_s also depends on λ and the resolving power is very little affected when the beam voltage is raised upward from about 50 kv.

Magnetic EM. The optical system of a typical magnetic electron microscope is shown schematically in Fig. 1. Electrons emitted from the tip of a hot tungsten filament (ca 5 mil in diameter) are accelerated toward the anode and focussed by a negative bias on the surrounding shield (Wehnelt cylinder) to form a crossover at some distance below. The negative bias may be produced by a resistor between shield and filament or by a variable impedance such as can be obtained by a diode in this position. The condenser lens with one aperture or a set of interchangeable apertures 4 to 10 mils in diameter is used to control the intensity of illumination and the aperture of illumination at the object. With the crossover focused at the object plane as indicated in the figure, the intensity and aperture of illumination are a maximum and the area illuminated is a minimum. Two condenser lenses are frequently employed to obtain a greater variation in aperture, intensity and area illuminated.

Objects to be examined by transmission electron microscopy should transmit an appreciable fraction of the beam relatively unscattered and so should be in general less than about 1000 Å in thickness. Electrons scattered through angles larger than the optimum for image formation can be removed from the beam by an objective aperture which thus controls relative intensities or contrast in the image.

Image contrast in very thin specimens is also a function of phase effects produced by the object. Scattering is mainly due to atomic nuclei and the scattering cross section per atom is closely proportional to $Z^{4/3}$. If I_0 is the image intensity through an opening in the specimen and I is the intensity at an area where the mass is w g/cm^2, then $I/I_0 = e^{-Sw}$ where S is the scattering cross section per g. S is relatively independent of atomic number but depends on the spherical aberration constant of the lens, the focal length, the beam potential, and the size of the objective aperture. Its numerical value is usually in the interval 2 to 10×10^4 cm^2/g.

The image formed by the objective lens is remagnified by two or more projector lenses to produce a final image on a fluorescent screen which can be observed at higher magnifications by means of an optical magnifier. Though it is possible to photograph the image on the screen, recording is usually accomplished by allowing the beam to strike a photographic plate or film. Magnifications may be from a few hundred to two hundred thousand but with fine-grain plates further useful enlargments up to 1 million can be obtained. Most electron microscopy is done by transmission but reflection microscopy can also be carried out on opaque objects with angles of incidence between beam and surface of about 15° and less.

Besides the power supplies, which must be held steady to one part in about two hundred thousand over short periods of time, the instrument consists of a pumping system for maintaining a vacuum of less than 10^{-4} mm of Hg, controls for lens currents, photographic mechanisms, controls for moving the specimen in the vacuum, and adjustments for optical alignment of the beam and lenses. The length of the column may be about 4 ft from gun to viewing screen or a total height of about 6 ft above the floor.

Electrostatic E.M. A typical electrostatic electron microscope is shown schematically in Fig. 2. The unipotential lenses are energized by the same supply that provides the accelerating potential. The range of useful focal lengths for the projector lens is limited, but multiple projector lenses can be used to extend the range of magnification. Although the theoretical resolving power of an electrostatic EM is practically the same as for the magnetic type and the circuitry is simpler, the electrostatic EM has not been widely successful in practice owing to tendency to arc-over between lens electrodes and sensitivity to contamination at the lens apertures.

Emission Microscopy. In an emission microscope the objective lens is generally electrostatic and produces the accelerating field as well as lens action. A flat cathode heated by a noninductive winding or by electron bombardment from behind as in Fig. 3, emits electrons that are formed into a real image showing the relative emission intensities over the surface. Subsequent lenses can be electrostatic or magnetic. Resolving power is a function of the field gradient at the emitting surface and is of the order of several hundred Å. Emission microscopes have been useful for the study of thermionic emission and for the study of crystal structure and phase transitions occurring at emitting surfaces.

Field-Emission Microscope. In this device, invented by E. W. Muller, electrons are drawn out of a pointed filament (which may or may not be heated) with a radius of curvature of the order of 0.1 μ (micron) and accelerated toward a fluorescent screen at high positive potential. A projected image of the emission pattern of the filament tip appears on the screen with a magnification R/r where R is the distances from tip to screen and r is the radius of the tip. Magnifications of the order of 10^6 can be obtained with a tube of small dimensions. The theoretical resolving power is a function of the wavelength of the electrons at the emitting surface and is 10 to 20 Å. Muller has operated this device as an *ion microscope* by reversing the accelerating potential and admitting a trace of either hydrogen or helium into the envelope. The gas adsorbs on the anode tip and is drawn off as protons or alpha particles whose wavelength is much shorter than electrons of the same velocity. When the anode is cooled to liquid-hydrogen temperature to suppress thermal agitation, the shorter wavelength of the alpha particles

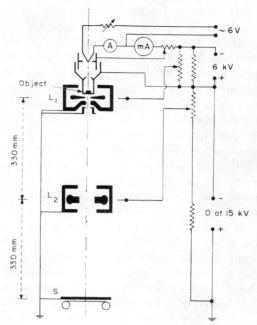

Fig. 3. Emission electron microscope. (M. Gauzit and A. Septier.)

makes it possible to resolve single atoms in the emission pattern.

Electron Mirror Microscope. A novel reflection electron microscope for the observation of metallic surfaces has been made by L. Mayer. In this microscope the electron beam is directed toward the specimen at nearly perpendicular incidence. A high negative charge is applied to the specimen which allows the electrons to approach very close to the surface but eventually turns them around and reflects them as if from a mirror. The reflected beam is focused by a lens to form an image in which the relative intensities are a function of the topography of the reflecting surface. Resolution is about 2000 Å.

Electron Probe Instruments. Closely allied to conventional electron microscopes are devices in which electron lenses are employed to produce demagnified images of an electron source to probe the structure of an object. Such a demagnified image occurs at the back focal plane of a lens of short focal length and a series of such lenses demagnifies in the same ratio that they would magnify an object placed near the first focal point, as in conventional microscopy. The minimum dimensions of such a probe are fixed by the aberration constants of the lenses and by the space charge. Probes as small as about 100 Å have been produced but usually they are the order of 1–5 μ. If a conventional electron microscope specimen is placed in front of a fine probe a magnified shadow image is projected by rectilinear propagation. The magnification is the ratio of distance to the screen from the probe divided by the distance from probe to specimen. The resolving power is approximately equal to the diameter of the probe.

If an electron probe is caused to impinge on a thin metal target, X-rays are emitted from a small region and the X-ray source can be utilized to produce a projected X-ray image of an object. The same magnification and resolving power relations hold as for the electron shadow microscope but the size of the X-ray source is increased by scattering of electrons in the target and the resolving power so far obtained is about 0.1 μ.

Electron scanning microscopes consist of an electron beam probe that can scan an area of the object or a static probe with a movable object. Microanalysis of the object is achieved by analyzing the secondary electrons emitted or X-rays emitted or by both of these effects together.

Cecil E. Hall

Cross-references: *Electron Guns, Electron Microscopy, Electron Optics, Field Emission, X-rays*

ELECTRON MICROSCOPY

Because of the low penetrating power of electrons it is obvious that sample preparation for electron microscopy is of vital importance. Such specimens then must be extremely thin. They are mounted on thin films of collodion, parlodion, or "Formvar" or coherent evaporated films of alumina, silica, silicon monoxide, silicon or beryllium, which in turn are supported on grids of very fine wire, so that micrographs are made through one mesh of the gauze. The specimen must be not only very thin, but also stable in the high vacuum of the microscope (thus eliminating water-containing materials) and in the powerful electron beam which will in some cases vaporize or disintegrate organic or biological specimens. The process of preliminary freeze-drying will often preserve without distortion the form of a specimen (especially biological) on water removal. The design of microtomes to slice very thin sections has been greatly improved to meet this challenge, but the production of suitable *replicas* of many specimens that are unsatisfactory for direct electron transmission has become a highly developed technique.

Surfaces are usually etched differentially in order to produce relief, which is replicated by coating with a thin layer of plastic from solution or evaporated metals or oxides already mentioned, or best of all a film of carbon from an arc. The thin replica is then peeled off, or the substrate is dissolved away, and then introduced into the specimen chamber of the microscope. In many cases the scattering of electrons in the specimen may not be sufficiently different to disclose fine detail. The specimen may then be "stained" (analogous to color staining of biological specimens) with heavy metal salts, which may also be fixatives such as OsO_4.

The specimen or replica may be shadowcast. This technique was devised by an astronomer, R. D. Williams, who observed that the mountains of the moon were clearly observed by the shadows they cast in oblique light of the sun. A beam of vaporized metal is made to impinge on the specimen in an evacuated chamber at a grazing angle, so that metal piles up on the near side of elevated portions of the specimen. Then when this shadowcast specimen is examined by a vertical beam of electrons transmitted through the film, greatly enhanced details of structure are evident.

Variations on the microscope with electromagnetic or electrostatic lenses in which electrons are scattered from a specimen to produce magnified images have been recently devised. These variations are the emission microscope, in which electrons emitted by the specimen upon irradiation produce an image of the source; the shadow microscope; the point-projection or field-emission microscope, in which electrons from a cold-cathode point produce an image; and the scanning microscope, in which a fine electron probe is used to scan a specimen point by point.

To produce micrographs at 40,000 diameters magnification directly in the electron microscope, which may be further photographically enlarged if so desired up to 200,000 or more, is obviously to open up an entirely new vista of observation and evaluation of fine structure almost to the limit of atoms themselves: the sizes and shapes of particles too small for the best optical microscope, such as viruses and the usually much larger bacteria; the finest carbon blacks; and the photographs of many kinds of larger molecules which constitute living matter of synthetic polymers; the minutest details of structure and texture of tissue sections (including teeth and bones, both normal and pathological, thus providing a new tool for medical science); entirely new information from replicas on structures and deformation effects on metals and alloys, on clays and soils, and on such difficult problems as the structure of highly porous specimens such as storage battery plates and a host of other problems. In the electron microscope laboratory, as nowhere else, by the same techniques may be found under investigation the converging interests of the chemist, physicist, engineer, botanist, physiologist, zoologist, virologist, bacteriologist, ceramist, agronomist, mineralogist, geologist, metallurgist, pathologist, and many types of medical research workers. For extensive coverage of all phases of electron microscopy in 38 articles by international authorities the reader is referred to the Encyclopedia of Microscopy (Reinhold, 1961).

GEORGE L. CLARK

Cross-references: *Electron Microscopes, Electron Optics*

ELECTRON OPTICS

Electron Motion and Electron Optics. The study of the paths of electrons through electromagnetic fields began with the first experiments on cathode rays, towards the end of the last century. Electron optics, however, can be said to have started in 1926 when H. Busch showed that the motion of electrons in fields of circular symmetry can be studied by the application of optical laws.

It is of great practical importance that all electrostatic or magnetic fields, with either circular or with "two-dimensional" symmetry, possess the properties of optical lenses—i.e., they can project electron optical images. This fact implies that important parts of an electron trajectory can be obtained by applying the laws of geometric-optical image projection. There, we require a knowledge of only six points in the field, namely the well-known cardinal points of geometrical optics; we can disregard any complicated structure of the lens field through which the electrons are projected.

In order to find the cardinal points of an electron lens, we can—just as in light optics—trace a few significant rays through the lens field. In some cases this has been done by following up the orbits of electrons with the help of the laws of electrostatics or of magnetism, respectively. In other cases, typically optical methods of ray tracing have been proved to be of great advantage. Instead of considering the shape of the orbits caused by accelerations due to electrostatic or magnetic forces, these orbits are imagined to be the result of refractions of electron rays through a series of refracting surfaces such as equipotential surfaces in the electrostatic field.

The Refractive Index in an Electrostatic Field. The field of an electrostatic lens is set up between any arrangement of electrodes of circular symmetry maintained at constant potentials. It is convenient to imagine this field to be divided by a number of surfaces of equal potential. Let us now make the assumption that the potential between two successive surfaces is constant and of the potential value of the surface through which the electron travels first. Hence at each equipotential surface, the potential jumps a given step.

Consider an electron traveling with uniform speed u through a space of constant potential V. Let this electron be transmitted through a potential step into a space with another homogeneous potential $V'(>V)$.

The velocity component at right angles to the step is increased. The tangential velocity component u_{tan}, however, remains unchanged. Hence the electron suddenly changes its direction when it passes through the step, i.e., the electron ray is refracted. The angle of incidence α and the angle of refraction α' are given by

$$\sin \alpha = u_{tan}/u$$
$$\sin \alpha' = u_{tan}/u'$$

so that

$$u \sin \alpha = u' \sin \alpha' \qquad (1)$$

Since the electron velocity is proportional to the square root of the voltage through which the electron has been accelerated, Eq. (1) can be written

$$\sqrt{V} \sin \alpha = \sqrt{V'} \sin \alpha' \qquad (2)$$

This equation is identical with Snell's law of refraction if the refractive index is taken to be

$$N \propto \sqrt{V} \qquad (3)$$

where V is zero at a point of zero electron velocity. It has become a convenient practice in electron optics to measure the refractive index in an electrostatic field directly in units of square root of volts.

The sudden change of refractive index, which we have introduced above in order to apply light-optical methods, seems to be a rather forced assumption for fields that change continuously along the path of the electron. However, it is always possible to simulate a continuously changing potential by a finite number of potential steps between layers of constant potential so that the path of an electron can be traced by a

repeated application of Snell's law. Results of high accuracy can be obtained if the field is divided into a sufficiently large number of steps and if a sufficiently accurate method for determining the angles of refraction is applied.

A plot of equipotentials can be obtained with the help of an electrolytic tank, or by means of a resistor network analog. The relaxation method can be also used for a computation of the field, based on an application of Laplace's equation. Only in very simple cases is the potential distribution accessible to analytical treatment. For the study of any of these methods the reader is referred to the specialized literature.

After a determination of the required system of equipotential surfaces various methods can be applied for the ray tracing.

The application of Snell's law by a repeated plotting of the angles of incidence and refraction at every equipotential is cumbersome and not very accurate. In practice an application of numerical methods or the use of automatic ray-tracing machines is preferred, but here again we have to refer to the specialized literature.

Electrostatic Electron Lenses. The most important electrostatic lenses are the two-tube lenses and the three-aperture lenses. Two-tube lenses are produced by the field between two coaxial tubes at different potentials. Figure 1a represents a cross-sectional drawing of two coaxial tubes T_1 and T_2 of equal diameter. The equipotentials shown in the figure, are marked in percent of the total potential difference between the tubes. If these electrode potentials V_1 and V_2 are such that $V_1 < V_2$ then ray tracing shows that the field between T_1 and the midplane M converges the rays like a convex glass lens L_1 (Fig. 1b). On the other hand, the field between M and T_2 diverges the beam like a concave glass lens L_2. However, for every value of V_1 and V_2 the converging lens is always of greater power than the diverging lens.

In this way, the over-all effect of any two-electrode lens is to converge the electron

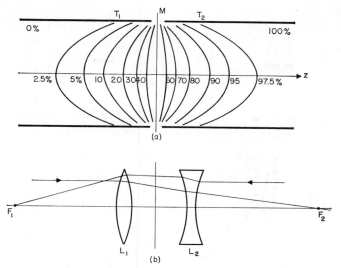

Fig. 1. Two-tube electrostatic lens: (a) field plot, (b) light-optical analogy. (After Klemperer, "Electron Physics.")

beam. Moreover, both focal lengths of any two-electrode lens are found to decrease with increasing voltage ratio [$(V_2/V_1) > 1$]. The ratio of the two focal lengths f_1 and f_2 of every lens is well known to be equal to the ratio of refractive indices N_1 and N_2 in front and in the rear of the lens. Hence, by using Eq. (3) we have for any two-electrode lens the relation

$$f_1/f_2 = (V_1/V_2)^{1/2} \qquad (4)$$

Without going into details about the location of foci and principal planes, we present in Fig. 2 a diagram containing practical information about the symmetrical two-tube lens. After Spangenberg and Field, there are plotted the object distances p from the midplane M against the image distances q from M, both measured in terms of tube radii R. Two sets of curves are shown; one set is drawn for given fixed voltage ratios [$2 < (V'/V) < 11$], and the other set of curves is drawn for given magnifications ($0.05 < M < 5$).

Another important class of lenses comprises the aperture lenses in which the electrostatic field is set up between plane parallel diaphragms containing coaxial apertures. In the simplest case, a single-apertured

diaphragm of a given potential V_0 is arranged between two charged conducting planes. There, the apertured diaphragm separates two spaces with approximately homogeneous fields E and E', respectively. The focal length of this aperture can easily be calculated. It is given by the useful and simple formula of Davisson and Calbick, namely

$$f = \frac{4V_0}{E - E'} \qquad (5)$$

For practical purposes, however, it is required that the diaphragms in front and behind the considered aperture contain apertures too, so that electron beams traveling along the axis can enter and leave the system. Equation (5) is, in this case, no longer applicable but three-diaphragm lenses of this kind have become of technical importance, especially when the two external diaphragms are at a common positive potential with respect to the intermediate diaphragm. Such lenses are known as "saddle-field" lenses or as "einzel lenses." In Fig. 3 is shown a saddle-field lens which has been used in electrostatic electron microscopes. The two outer electrodes A and B are at ground potential; the central diaphragm C,

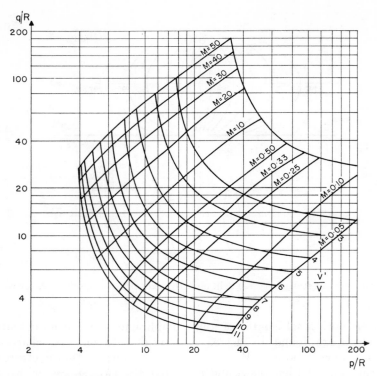

Fig. 2. Mid-object against mid-image distances for symmetrical two-tube lens. (After Klemperer, "Electron Optics.")

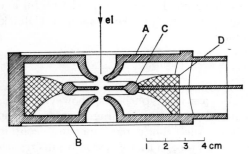

Fig. 3. Three-diaphragm electrostatic lens. (After Klemperer, "Electron Physics.")

which is supported by a strong insulator D, is at the potential of the cathode which emits the electrons and which may be at a high negative voltage (e.g., 40 kv).

Magnetic Lenses. Consider first the focusing properties of a homogeneous field. If an electron is moving through this field with a velocity u at a small angle θ with the flux density vector $B = B_z$, this velocity can be imagined to consist of two components. The first component $u_z = u \cos \theta$ is

parallel to the field and is not influenced by the field. The action of the field on the other component $u_y = u \sin \theta$, which is perpendicular to the field, does not depend on the existence of the first component. Thus the projection of the electron path on a plane perpendicular to B is a circle, and the path of the electron itself is a helix lying in the wall of a cylinder.

The pitch of the spiral path is given by the distance z_f which the electron moves in the longitudinal direction while performing just one circle with the cyclotron frequency

$$\omega_c = \frac{e}{m} B \tag{6}$$

where e/m is the charge-to-mass ratio of the electron. Hence

$$z_f = u_z \left(\frac{2\pi}{\omega_c}\right) = u \cos \theta \, \frac{2\pi m}{eB} \tag{7}$$

Suppose a bundle of electron rays of a given velocity u crosses at a point J some given

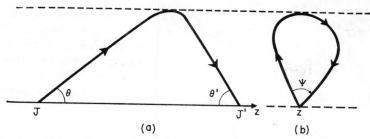

Fig. 4. Electron orbit through a magnetic lens: (a) in the meridional plane, (b) in the equatorial plane.

line of force at various angles θ. (All angles θ are assumed to be so small that $\cos \theta \approx 1$.) These electrons again cross the same line of force at another common point J' as soon as the component perpendicular to the line of force has performed just one full revolution within the cyclotron period. Thus it appears that a homogeneous magnetic field can project—point by point—an electron-optical image of unit magnification at the distance $JJ' = z_f$ or a multiple thereof, where

$$z_f = \frac{2\pi}{B} \frac{mu}{e} \qquad (8)$$

The lens properties of a short magnetic field of circular symmetry can be derived from the equation of motion in the in-homogeneous field. This leads first to the "paraxial magnetic-ray equation"

$$\frac{d^2r}{dz^2} = \frac{-e}{8m} \frac{B_z^2(r,z)}{V} r \qquad (9)$$

which states that the curvature of the path at any point is proportional to its distance r from the z-axis of symmetry, proportional to the square of the axial component B_z of the flux density at this point, and inversely proportional to the energy V (in electron-volts) of the electron. Equation (9) is of practical importance for the problem of ray tracing through magnetic lenses.

The motion of an electron through the lens may be visualized with the help of Fig. 4, where one electron orbit is drawn in two different planes. Figure 4a refers to a meridional plane which contains the axis (z) of

the lens and rotates with the electron about this axis. Figure 4b refers to an equatorial plane at right angles to the z-axis; this plane moves with the electron in the direction of the z-axis.

The electron emerges from the object-point J at an angle θ with the z-axis. It moves along a straight line until it enters the magnetic field where it is bent. After leaving the field, the electron path is again a straight line which cuts the z-axis at an angle θ', at the image point J'. Figure 4b shows that the orbit starts from the z-axis and returns to it as a straight line, but that it is twisted about the axis in an helical motion while it is passing through the field. The total angle of twist ψ (indicated in Fig. 3b) is of practical interest since every image projected by a magnetic lens is rotated with respect to the object.

Equation (9) yields by integration the famous Busch formula for the focal length f of the thin magnetic lens, namely

$$\frac{1}{f} = \frac{e}{8mV} \int_{-\infty}^{+\infty} B_z^2 \, dz \qquad (10)$$

Equation (10) agrees well with experimental results as long as the width of the field distribution is small in comparison with both object and image distances.

The magnetic field of practical electron lenses is produced by coils. To increase the field intensity, these coils are frequently enclosed by an iron shield that leaves only a short, circular magnetic gap. Pole pieces can be used for increasing the field concentration. An example of such a lens with the extremely short focal length of about 1 mm

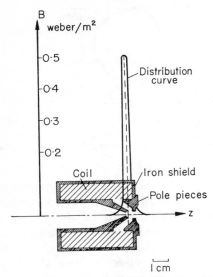

Fig. 5. Magnetic microscope objective with flux density distribution. (After Klemperer, "Electron Physics.")

is shown in Fig. 5. The flux density reaches values up to 5000 gauss.

Emission Systems. An emission system consists of a cathode and of an arrangement of electrodes which is necessary for projecting the electron rays into a substantially field-free space. Two very simple emission systems are shown in Fig. 6. Each of these systems consists of a cathode C, a control electrode (sometimes called grid electrode, beam-forming, or Wehnelt electrode) G, and an anode A.

The system in Fig. 6a has been used in electron guns of simple cathode-ray tubes. There C is a plane oxide-coated cathode. The anode A is a conducting surface on the inside of the neck of the tube. In order to focus the divergent bundle projected by the system into a spot on the fluorescent screen, an electron lens is required, for instance a magnetic coil on the outside of the tube neck.

The system shown in Fig. 6b has been used in electron microscopes. The cathode C is a hairpin-shaped tungsten wire which emits electrons from the tip of the hairpin only, where the temperature is highest. The anode is a diaphragm containing a relatively small aperture through which the electrons are projected into the field-free space. A condenser electron lens is used to focus the emission onto the microscopical specimen.

The most essential electrical properties of an emission system can be defined by two simple relations:

(i) The perveance G, which is given by:

$$G = I/V_A{}^{3/2}$$

where V_A is the voltage applied to the anode and I is the space-charge-limited emission current at zero grid bias. In a well-designed emission system, no current should be intercepted by either the grid electrode or by the anode.

(ii) The penetration factor, given by

$$D = \frac{V_{g0}}{V_A}$$

where V_{g0} is the negative-grid bias which is just sufficient to cut off the emission, and D corresponds approximately to the reciprocal voltage amplification factor of a valve.

V_{g0} cannot be defined accurately since the emission current decreases exponentially when the field between cathode and grid electrode is increased; however, the cut-off is sharp enough to make for a practically useful definition. Both G and D depend essentially on the configuration of the system, e.g., on the distances between grid and cathode or grid and anode; these distances must be adjusted accurately according to the requirements of emission current or of grid base at the given voltage. The electron-

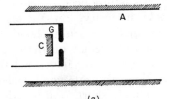

(a)

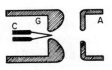

(b)

Fig. 6. Electron emission systems.

optical efficiency of an emission system is measured by the value of the "directional beam intensity" which is given by the ratio of emission density to the solid angle over which the emitted beam is spreading (amp m^{-2} sterad^{-1}).

Specialized Developments in Electron Optics. Electrostatic lenses show the same five geometrical aberrations as glass lenses, namely spherical aberration, field curvature, astigmatism, coma, and distortion. Magnetic lenses suffer from three additional aberrations: spiral distortion, anisotropic coma, and anisotropic astigmatism. However, despite the anisotropic errors, magnetic lenses are often found to be superior to the best electrostatic lenses; the disadvantage of anisotropic errors is not serious enough to reverse the general judgment.

In addition to the geometrical errors some other errors are produced by particular properties of the electron beams. Unavoidable inhomogeneities in electron velocity lead to chromatic aberration. The mutual repulsion of the electrons in sufficiently intense beams leads to a space-charge error. The de Broglie wavelength of the electron leads to a diffraction error.

There are also line-focus electron lenses, which have no circular symmetry. Electrostatic lenses of this kind are produced, for instance, by charged diaphragms containing slit apertures or by coaxial cylinders terminated in a lip-like structure.

Some magnetic line-focus lenses have found a large field of application, for instance, for focusing electron or ion beams in high-energy particle accelerators. These lenses consist of four mutually perpendicular pole pieces energized in an alternating sense by solenoids and mounted like the spokes of a wheel about the axis of the beam. Two "quadrupole lenses" of this kind, mounted one after the other in such a way that their line foci are crossed at right angle, form a "strong-focusing" pair that can cause an electron beam to converge in two mutually perpendicular directions. Under suitable conditions the quadrupole lenses could converge a beam into a point focus by using far fewer energizing ampere-turns than could be done with magnetic lenses of circular symmetry.

Finally we should not omit to mention that electron optics has been successfully applied to the study of deflecting fields. Electrostatic deflecting condensers and magnetic deflection coils of particular shape have been developed for wide-angle deflection with the least distortion of the deflected beam. Such deflection fields have found much application in the scanning systems of cathode-ray tubes.

Some other important progress in the electron optics of deflecting fields has lead to a substantial progress in the design of velocity-analyzing spectrometers and of particle accelerators.

O. KLEMPERER

Cross-references: *Accelerators, Cathode-Ray Tubes (Display), Electromagnetic Theory, Electron Diffraction and Scattering, Electron Guns, Electron Microscopes, Electron Tubes (Conventional), Phase-Space Representation*

ELECTRON PARAMAGNETIC RESONANCE (EPR)

Paramagnetic resonance in solids was first suggested and attempted by C. J. Gorter, but due to some rather poor luck in choosing materials and the detection scheme, he failed to detect a resonant absorption. The first successful experiment was carried out by Zavoisky (1945), followed closely by reports from Cummerow and Halliday (1946) and Bleaney and Penrose (1946). In essence, the resonance condition occurs when the rf frequency satisfies the equation $\omega = g\mu_B H/\hbar$, where g is the spectroscopic splitting factor (often a number close to 2.0), μ_B is the Bohr magneton, H is the static magnetic field perpendicular to the rf field, and $\hbar$ is Planck's constant divided by 2π.

Whenever a substance has one or more magnetically unpaired electrons, it is possible to observe EPR. Under good conditions, a billionth of a gram of paramagnetic material can be detected. The resonance is generally observed by imposing a large static magnetic field on the material and observing microwave energy absorptions of the atomic electrons as they make transitions in the magnetic field. In many crystalline solids, the atomic electrons are almost "free," and the orbital motion does not take part in the magnetization. When these substances are placed in a magnetic field, the atomic magnetic moment assumes certain orientations with respect to the field direction. The energy associated with the orientation is $MH \cos \theta$, where θ is the angle between the magnetic moment M and the field H. The rules of quantum mechanics allow only certain orientations for the spinning electrons. In the case of an atom having exactly one electron spin which is not paired with others in an opposing direction, only two positions are permitted; either the spin is parallel or antiparallel to the field. With two unpaired electron spins, the number of orientations is three. In general, the number of allowed positions in the field is $2S + 1$ where S is the total electron spin value of the atoms in units of $\hbar$. The allowed positions correspond to different energy levels. Therefore the number of energy levels of atoms with a net spin of S units is also $2S + 1$. Paramagnetic resonance in these materials is simply the absorption of microwave energy as atomic

transitions occur from lower energy levels to higher ones. These transitions are not entirely canceled by the emission from atomic transitions downward in energy because the latter occur less frequently, owing to the fact that fewer spins occupy the upper energy levels than the lower.

Most of the materials in which EPR may be observed may be divided into the following categories:

(1) crystals containing bonded atoms of the transition elements;

(2) crystals having broken bonds or defects such as F centers where free electrons occupy atomic sites;

(3) semiconductors containing electron donor impurities;

(4) metals and semiconductors in which conduction band electrons provide resonance absorption;

(5) free radicals; and

(6) ferromagnetic materials.

Elements of the apparatus needed for observation of the resonance condition are a stable source of microwave energy, a tuned cavity to contain the crystal, and a rectifier-amplifier-indicator system. A simple arrangement is shown on Fig. 1. Microwave energy is generated by a klystron and stabilized at the same frequency as the resonant cavity

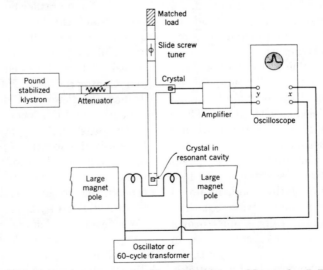

Fig. 1. A typical EPR measurement system. (Reproduced from *Masers*, by J. R. Singer, by permission of the publishers, John Wiley & Sons, New York, 1959.)

loaded by the sample. The magic tee is essentially a bridge. The microwave energy divides, half goes to the sample cavity, and half towards the matched load. Tuning of the slide screw tuner so as to balance the bridge, results in no energy appearing at the crystal detector. Now, let the magnetic field be changed by the oscillator coils so that the resonance condition

$$\omega = g\mu_B H/\hbar = \gamma H \qquad (1)$$

is satisfied. The bridge is then unbalanced because more energy is absorbed in the cavity. Power appears at the detector which after amplification traces out a resonance curve in the oscilloscope. This description is somewhat oversimplified. The resonant frequency ω also depends upon the crystalline electrical fields acting upon the paramagnetic atoms through the coupling of the magnetic spins to the atomic orbits. Thus the resonant frequency of Eq. (1) is altered by the nature of the crystal and additional terms appear in the energy equation. The study of crystal structure using EPR methods has been advanced greatly by Bleaney, Griffith, Pryce, Abragam, Stevens, Elliot, Judd, and others. The description is generally formulated in terms of a phenomenological "spin Hamiltonian" to describe the magnetic-energy levels.

Electron paramagnetic resonance studies have greatly increased our knowledge of the structure of both crystalline and noncrystalline matter. Free radical investigations provide insight into atomic bonding configurations. Metallic and semiconductor (cyclotron-resonance) investigations show the nature of the Fermi surfaces. Some biological studies utilize free spins to investigate photosynthesis and cancer. The field of paramagnetic resonance constantly encompasses more possibilities, and will probably continue in this direction for some time.

J. R. SINGER

Cross-references: *Microwave Spectroscopy, Nuclear Magnetic Resonance*

ELECTRON SCATTERING: see ELECTRON DIFFRACTION AND SCATTERING

ELECTRON-TUBE MANUFACTURE

The manufacturing procedures to be described apply particularly to the receiving type of vacuum tube; however, the same general principles apply to the manufacture of such other tubes as transmitting tubes, cathode-ray tubes (q.v.), magnetrons (q.v.), traveling-wave tubes (q.v.), and gas-filled tubes (q.v.). The process of making receiving tubes includes: (1) mounting (assembling the tube parts and welding the electrodes to the stem leads); (2) sealing-in (sealing the envelope to the stem); (3) exhaust and activation (evacuating and degassing the tube and simultaneously bringing the cathode to an emitting state); (4) aging; and (5) testing.

Mounting. The parts of a tube (Fig. 1) are usually held in precise alignment by means of spacers punched from thin sheets of mica which are placed at the top and bottom of the tube structure. Other classes of tubes may use ceramic spacers or, if the tube parts are rigid enough to maintain the interelectrode spacings, no spacers at all. Ordinarily, one spacer is set in place over a mandrel. The electrodes, including the cathode, grids, and plate, are inserted into holes previously punched in the spacer; then a second spacer is placed over the electrodes to hold the structure in place. The heater, usually an insulated tungsten or tungsten-molybdenum wire, is inserted into the cathode sleeve. The completed unit is known as the cage assembly. The electrodes themselves or thin metal connectors called tabs are then welded to the stem leads. A getter structure is welded to a suitable tube part to complete the mount. Although tube mounting has been done by hand for many years, automatic mounting machines, which eliminate much of the variability inherent in hand mounting, are coming into use.

Sealing-In. Most receiving tubes are sealed-in and exhausted on a rotary machine,

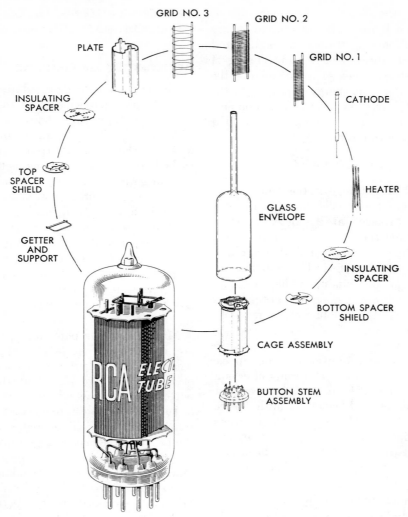

Fig. 1. Parts of a miniature pentode.

usually a circular unit with a number of working positions. The mount, consisting of the cage assembly welded to the stem, is inserted into the machine and the glass envelope is placed over the assembly. As the mount and envelope move around the machine from position to position, a series of flames plays on the envelope just above the stem and seals the glass to the stem. After it has been sealed, the tube is ready to be evacuated.

Exhaust and Activation. To prepare it for exhaust and activation, the tube is removed from the sealing section of the ma-

chine and the exhaust tubing is inserted into a rubber port which is connected to a series of vacuum pumps. As the port moves around the machine, several operations take place:

(1) The air is pumped out of the tube by high-capacity mechanical pumps, alone or in combination with diffusion pumps.

(2) The metal parts inside the tube are degassed by heating them with rf power or, for metal tubes, flames.

(3) Voltage is applied to the heater of the tube to bring the cathode to the temperature at which the coating (a mixture of alkaline earth carbonates) on the nickel cathode de-

composes to form the alkaline earth oxides and carbon dioxide gas. The gas is pumped out of the tube.

(4) The cathode is activated by reaction of barium oxide in the coating with a portion of the reducing elements in the nickel to form some free barium.

In the later positions on the machine, the getter structure is first degassed by heating with rf power or, in certain cases, by a flame or by direct electric heating. Then, just before the exhaust tubing is sealed off, the getter is "flashed" by heating it to a temperature at which a chemical reaction takes place; free barium metal is produced and is deposited on part of the tube envelope as a thin mirror-like metallic film. After the exhaust tubing has been sealed off, this barium acts as a chemical pump that will adsorb or react with any gases evolved during the life of the tube. (Gas-filled tubes are filled with mixtures of inert gases after the air has been pumped out and the getter has been flashed.) If a separate tube base is used, it is cemented on after the tube is sealed.

Aging. After exhaust, the cathode activity usually has not reached the level required for maximum emission. As a result, an additional procedure called aging is almost always required. In aging, the tube is operated under specified conditions to complete the activation reactions; the cathode is operated at a higher-than-normal temperature to allow the reducing agents in the nickel of the cathode sleeve to diffuse to the surface where they can react with some of the barium oxide in the coating to bring the cathode to its maximum emission capability.

The heat generated during aging helps to drive gases from other tube parts (e.g., the grids and plate) onto the surface of the getter. These gases are held by the getter during the life of the tube so that they cannot reduce emission by reacting with ("poisoning") the cathode coating. An aging schedule, which is chosen to meet the needs of each tube type, may take from several minutes to more than an hour.

Testing. Every tube is tested after ag-

ing and must meet specifications before it is released for sale. The characteristics tested depend upon the tube type, and may include transconductance at normal and low heater voltage, plate current, screen-grid current, control-grid cutoff voltage, and heater current.

In addition to 100-percent testing for characteristics, a sample of each week's production of each tube type is life-tested. The life test involves operation of the tubes under normal or severe conditions for several weeks or months, during which the characteristics of the tubes are measured at fixed intervals. Several different types of life tests may be made on a tube type to bring out any possible defects. The decision to release the week's production for sale is based upon accumulated life test results. These results are also useful in guiding the constant improvement of the product.

I. F. STACY

Cross-references: *Clean Rooms, Materials Used in Tube Technology, Semiconductor Manufacture, Vacuum Techniques*

ELECTRON TUBES (CONVENTIONAL)

A conventional electron tube is one in which the electron stream is supplied by a thermionic cathode, operates at low power levels—say, not much higher than 1 kw—and is operated in such a way that electron transit time has no critical effect on performance. Examples are tubes used in radio and television receivers, low-power transmitters, and industrial equipment.

Tube Nomenclature. In general, tubes can be classified according to the number of electrodes that influence a single electron stream. For example a diode has two electrodes—cathode and anode—a triode has three electrodes, etc. A tube in which there is more than one independently controlled electron stream is commonly designated by the number of electrodes influencing the separate electron streams; thus a tube containing two triodes is a double triode—not a hexode. Tubes are also classified as receiving or high-power tubes, as well as according to the functions for which they are intended such as oscillators, amplifiers, rectifiers, converters, etc. A distinction should be made between a tube and the unit in which it operates. For example, an *amplifier* may include an *amplifier tube*, a socket, biasing resistor, and one or more impedance-matching devices.

The electrodes and support elements of small tubes are usually made of nickel or nickel alloys. An important factor in manufacture or experimental production is the cleaning of these parts. In most applications cleaning in a solvent such as trichlorethylene, followed by firing in hydrogen at 1000°C, is adequate. Where better cleaning is needed acetone is substituted for the chlorinated hydrocarbons. In critical applications ultrasonic cleaning in any of several detergents is preferred, followed by washing in distilled water, then treating for about one minute in a solution of hydrogen peroxide 45%, formic acid 10% and distilled water 45% at 65–70°C, followed immediately by thorough rinsing in distilled water and drying in warm air; the firing is usually done in hydrogen having a very low dew point.

Cathodes. Oxide-coated cathodes are commonly used in tubes where the output power is less than about 100 w. Tubes used for amplification and transmission of signals at higher power levels usually employ thoriated tungsten filaments if continuously operated, whereas many modern tubes, such as traveling-wave tubes, use dispenser cathodes. Only the oxide-coated cathode is discussed in this article.

The oxide-coated cathode, discovered by Wehnelt in 1903, has been developed to the point where reliable performance can be had at an average current density of more than 100 ma/cm², and peak current densities of more than 10 amp/cm² when pulse operated. For continuous operation the cathode is usually maintained at a temperature of about 1000°K; for pulsed operation requiring large peak current densities the average temperature is usually considerably higher.

Early oxide-coated cathodes were of the directly heated or filament type; platinum, platinum-irridium and platinum-nickel wire or ribbon was used. In the early 1920's nearly pure nickel ribbon came into general use. The indirectly heated cathode, in which a nickel cylinder is heated by an alundum-coated tungsten wire, largely replaced the directly heated cathode in tubes for broadcast receivers about 1928, and in most other low-power applications, except for battery operation, shortly thereafter.

The nickel used for cathodes usually contains controlled amounts of selected impurities such as tungsten, chromium, aluminum, titanium, and magnesium. Some serve to provide mechanical strength by inhibiting grain growth; others serve as activators by reacting with the oxide coating to form atoms of the alkaline earths, mostly barium, which serve as donors of electrons to the conduction band of the coating.

The oxide coating commonly consists of about equal parts of BaO and SrO with the addition of 5 to 10 per cent of CaO. The coating is applied as a slurry of the carbonates in nitrocellulose highly diluted with organic solvents such as amyl acetate. The texture of the sprayed coating is dictated by the kind of tube for which the cathode is to be used; for example, a smooth surface is usually best for rectifier tubes and a rough surface is best for amplifier tubes. The carbonate is prepared by precipitation from a nitrate solution by adding a solution of Na_2CO_3 or $(NH_4)_2CO_3$ under carefully controlled conditions that are highly standardized to control purity and particle size.

Diodes

A diode is a thermionic tube having a cathode and an anode. It may be either a high-vacuum or a gas-filled device; both kinds are used as rectifiers of alternating current, but tubes containing gas—usually argon or mercury vapor—are used mostly in large installations. High-vacuum diodes are used as rectifiers in low-power installations such as in power supplies for radio and television receivers, and in numerous applications where use can be made of the non-linearity of the current-voltage relation, the most familiar example being the second detector stage of a radio receiver.

When the anode voltage in a high-vacuum diode is at least a few volts positive with respect to the cathode, and the current is smaller than its temperature-limited value, the current varies with the three-halves power of the voltage. For parallel-plane electrodes the relation is

$$I = \frac{2.33 \times 10^{-6} V_a^{3/2}}{s^2} \qquad (1)$$

amperes per unit area; V_a is the anode voltage and s the spacing between the electrodes. For coaxial cylinders the current per unit length is

$$I = \frac{14.65 \times 10^{-6} V_a^{3/2}}{r_a \beta^2} \qquad (2)$$

in which r_a is the anode radius and β is a function of r_a/r_k, r_k being the cathode radius. The table below shows values of β for same values of r_a/r_k to illustrate the numerical relation.

r_a/r_k	β	r_a/r_k	β
1.0	0.000	5	0.767
1.5	0.119	7.5	0.907
2.0	0.279	10.0	0.978
3.0	0.517	∞	1.000

When r_a/r_k is not much larger than unity, it is convenient to use Eq. (1) with $s = r_a - r_k$. For tubes having cathodes that are approximately circular in cross section and anodes that are of arbitrary shape, the relation between current, voltage, and electrode configuration is given with fair accuracy by Eq. (2) if r_k is the average cathode radius and r_a is taken to be the radius of a coaxial cylinder having the same capacitance to cathode as the actual anode.

With V_a less than a few volts, Eqs. (1) and (2) are not strictly applicable; the influence of initial electron velocity and the existence of a contact potential (q.v.) differ-

ence normally result in currents larger than the simple equations would indicate.

In gas-filled diodes the anode voltage when the tube is conducting under normal operating conditions is usually not much larger than the ionization potential of the gas.

Triodes

Ordinarily, a *triode* consists of a thermionic cathode, an anode, and a grid interposed between them to control the magnitude of the current. The name is usually restricted to a high-vacuum device; gas-filled tubes containing three electrodes, of which several varieties exist, are designated by specialized terminology.

The characteristics of major importance are the anode or plate current, the electronic mu and the transconductance. At high frequency the capacitances between the electrodes are also important.

When a tube is operated under normal voltage conditions the total current to anode and grid can be expressed with useful accuracy by the relation

$$I = 2.33 \times 10^{-6}[V_g + (V_b/\mu)]^{3/2}/s_1^2 \qquad (3)$$

amperes per unit area if the electrodes are parallel planes. Here V_g is the grid voltage, V_b is the anode or plate voltage, μ is the amplification factor, and s_1 is the cathode-grid distance. If the term in brackets is less than about 1 v, (3) can be considerably in error unless corrections are made in that term for the potential minimum, due to initial electron velocity, and contact potential difference. The accuracy of (3) can be further improved by substituting for s_1 the distance from the potential minimum to the plane at which the potential is that given in the brackets of (3); this is approximately s_2/μ beyond the grid, where s_2 is the grid-anode spacing.

For cylindrical electrodes Eq. (3) is modified as was explained for the parallel-plane case to yield a useful expression for the current; here r_g, the grid radius, replaces r_a in (2) and β is the function of r_g/r_k exemplified in the table following that equation.

The grid-anode transconductance is the quotient of change in anode current by change in V_g when the latter change is small and V_a remains constant. For a tube operating with V_g negative, Eq. (3) is the anode current I_b, and the transconductance is the derivative of that equation with respect to V_g. The resulting expression is especially useful if the physical dimensions are eliminated by combining (3) with its derivative; one then has for the transconductance

$$g_m = \frac{\partial I_b}{\partial V_g} = \frac{(3/2)I_b}{V_g + (V_b/\mu)} \qquad (4)$$

When the denominator of (4) is smaller than about 1 v, this expression must be corrected for initial electron velocity and contact potential difference. The combined effect usually increases the term in parentheses by a few tenths of a volt in a tube that has been in service for 50–100 hr, or sometimes as much as 0.5 v in tubes that have not been used.

The amplification factor can be defined as $\mu = g_m r_b$, in which r_b is the dynamic plate resistance. The meaning of this relation is made somewhat clearer by writing $\mu = g_m/g_b$, where anode conductance g_b is simply the reciprocal of r_b. This dimensionless ratio varies with electrode voltage and cathode temperature, even in a tube having all spacings constant; it is especially noticeable when V_g is so negative that I_b is reduced to a small fraction of normal operating value. For these reasons, mu, when so defined, cannot be expressed accurately in terms of the physical dimensions of the tube. However, the amplification factor of a tube operated with V_g a few volts negative and having grid wires equally spaced, and with all dimensions large compared with the diameter of the grid wire, is very nearly the same as the electrostatic mu, which can be expressed in terms of electrode dimensions. The electrostatic mu is simply the ratio of the grid-cathode capacitance to the anode-cathode capacitance, exclusive of the contributions to the capacitances by leads, base, etc., when the cathode is cold. Several formulas for this term have

been published. The simplest one that is of useful accuracy is

$$\mu = \frac{2\pi n s_2 - \ln \cosh \pi n d}{\ln \coth \pi n d} \qquad (5)$$

in which n is the number of grid wires per unit distance in the plane of the grid, s_2 is the grid-anode distance, and d is the grid wire diameter. While this expression is not precise for very small spacings, it is generally used in tube design.

In a *remote cutoff* tube the control grid is made with the control grid having short sections with the spacing $1/n$ different from that of its neighbors; consequently, the electronic mu varies steeply with control grid bias. Such tubes are usually tetrodes or pentodes (see below), but it seems appropriate to discuss briefly the variable mu aspect at this point.

The electronic mu of these tubes at a selected value of control grid bias can be predicted with fair accuracy. For each short section of constant grid wire spacing or pitch, the current is determined by (3) or its equivalent for cylinders, the electrostatic mu is determined by (5) and the transconductance by (4). In (3) and (4) the plate voltage V_b is replaced by the screen grid voltage. Then if I_b is the total current and g_m is the total transconductance for all of the sections, the electronic mu for the tube as a triode is given by re-arranging (5) to the form

$$\mu = \frac{g_m V_b}{(3/2)I_b - g_m V_g} \qquad (6)$$

For a tetrode or pentode, I_b is the total current to the anode, but V_b is still the screen grid voltage. For a tetrode, Eq. (6) is multiplied by the electronic mu relation between screen grid and anode; this is usually smaller than the corresponding electrostatic relation, primarily because of secondary emission. With tetrodes the mu is given approximately by (6) when multiplied by the product of the screen grid-to-suppressor grid mu and the suppressor grid-to-anode mu, both of these mu's being the electronic values. These values cannot very well be predicted by formula because of space change in the region of the suppressor grid. Nevertheless, Eq. (6) is still very useful in design work because of the ease with which the screen grid-anode mu can be determined experimentally.

A *dynatron* is a kind of triode that has been of interest for many decades, but has not been widely used because of its erratic behavior. In its simplest form it consists of a thermionic cathode, a grid operated at a positive voltage, and a third electrode called a *dynode*. The dynode is operated at a potential smaller than that of the grid, and its surface is treated to enhance its secondary emission. When properly treated, the dynode has a negative resistance characteristic; thus the tube can be made to serve either as oscillator or amplifier. Most of the secondary electrons emitted by the dynode are collected by the grid, because few of them have sufficient energy to reach the cathode. Several modifications of this physical arrangement, all of them employing dynodes, have been described in the technical literature. The principal reason why the dynatron has not been fully exploited is that the secondary-emission ratio, hence the negative resistance, deteriorates rapidly in operation. It is widely anticipated that some of the more recent solid-state inventions, notably the tunnel diode (*q.v.*) which in a way is analogous to the dynatron in that it is a two-terminal negative resistance device, will prove to be more reliable.

Multigrid Tubes

A *tetrode* is a tube with four electrodes making use of a single electron stream. Usually these electrodes are a thermionic cathode, a control grid, a second or "screen" grid, and an anode. The screen grid permits higher gain than can be had with a triode and reduces the control grid-anode capacitance. Secondary electron emission from the screen grid produces wide variations in performance at high anode voltage; secondary emission from the anode renders the tube almost useless for the amplification of large

signals. For these reasons it was, for most applications, superseded by the pentode soon after its introduction in 1928.

A *pentode* is a tube with five electrodes and a single electron stream. Most pentodes are similar to the tetrodes described in the preceding paragraph except that an additional electrode between screen grid and anode provides for the suppression of secondary electrons. The additional electrode may be in the form of a grid with widely spaced wires, in which case it is called a "suppressor" grid. Alternatively, especially in output tubes designed to work with a peak signal that may be as large as the control-grid bias, the suppressor grid may be replaced by a pair of "beam-confining" plates.

Suppressor grids and beam-confining plates are usually connected to the cathode inside the tube. Their effectiveness depends upon the fact that a region of electrostatic potential lower than that of either the screen grid or anode is formed between those two electrodes. Most secondary electrons are emitted with energies smaller than a few electron volts; therefore they cannot pass through the region of low potential. The most noticeable results of the addition of the fifth electrode are a high degree of uniformity of performance characteristics during life; high plate resistance, therefore high gain, in small-signal tubes; and in output tubes the ability to provide power as large as 50 per cent of the anode dissipation without excessive distortion.

Most *hexodes*, which are tubes containing six electrodes associated with a single electron stream, are designed for use as frequency converters. Usually the first grid is used for injection of the local-oscillator signal and the third grid for injection of the modulated signal. The second and fourth grids have a positive voltage and serve to maintain low capacitance between the two input grids and between signal grid and anode; the second grid also provides the field required to draw an electron current from the cathode.

A *heptode* is a tube with seven electrodes and one electron stream. Practically the only heptode in common use is the *pentagrid converter*, which is used as a first detector in superheterodyne receivers. Of special interest is the fact that it provides its own local-oscillator signal; the two grids nearest the cathode serve as the grid and anode of a triode oscillator. Of the remaining three grids, one is used for injection of the modulated signal and the others are screen grids used for the same purposes as a screen grid in a pentode amplifier.

An *octode* is a tube with a cathode, anode, and six grids for a single electron stream. Most octodes are used as frequency converters, and differ from a pentagrid converter in that a suppressor grid is placed between fifth grid and anode.

GEORGE D. O'NEILL

Cross-references: *Beam-Switching Tubes, Cathode-Ray Tubes (Display), Cold-Cathode Tubes, Electron Optics, Electron-Tube Manufacture, Ignitron, Klystron, Magnetron, Rectifier Tubes, Secondary Emission, Thermionic Emission, Thyratrons, Traveling-Wave Tubes, Work Function*

ELECTRONS

The electron is the elementary unit of negative electrical charge, the value of which has been found to be 1.60×10^{-19} coulomb. The electron has the smallest mass of any of the stable elementary particles—9.1066×10^{-31} kg. Electrons appear to revolve around the nucleus of an atom in more or less well defined orbits, the number of electrons in each orbit being governed by the Pauli exclusion principle. Thus, 2 electrons are allowed in the innermost orbit or shell, 8 in the second, 18 in the third, and in the nth orbit $2n^2$.

The number of electrons surrounding the nucleus of a neutral atom is equal to the atomic number of that atom. The tendency for atoms to form complete shells accounts for the valence of that atom. For instance, sodium, which has atomic number 11, normally has its 11 electrons distributed with 2 electrons in the first shell, 8 in the second, and 1 in the third. When the outermost electron is removed, the atom is said to be *ionized*. This leaves the atom with a positive charge of one unit and accounts for the valence of $+1$ in the case of sodium.

Similarly, fluorine has its 9 electrons arranged with 2 in the first orbit and 7 in the second. Its tendency is to accept one more electron to complete the second shell, giving the atom a charge of -1. Therefore, fluorine is said to have a valence of -1. All the halogens have a shortage of one electron to form a closed shell, but they also could get rid of seven electrons and thereby form a closed shell. This phenomenon accounts for the valence of $+7$ in such a compound as $KClO_4$.

Electrons can be removed from metal or other surfaces in various ways such as heating the surface (thermionic emission, *q.v.*), allowing light of appropriate wavelength to strike the surface (photoelectric effect, *q.v.*), placing the surface in a strong electric field (field emission, *q.v.*), or bombarding the surface with charged particles (secondary electron emission, *q.v.*, or positive-ion bombardment).

Although the name "electron" is usually reserved for a particle carrying a negative charge, there can be produced, by gamma rays of sufficient energy, pairs of electrons, one of which is an ordinary electron while the other is similar in all respects except that it carries a positive charge. These positive electrons, or *positrons*, have only a momentary existence, after which they combine with a negative electron to form a pair of gamma rays.

R. T. ELLICKSON

Cross-references: *Alpha Particles, Antiparticles, Atoms, Electron Diffraction and Scattering, Ions, Positron, Radiation*

ELECTROSCOPE AND ELECTROMETER

An electrometer is an instrument capable of detecting or measuring a small electric charge. Direct-indicating electrometers utilize the force of attraction or repulsion existing between two electrically charged bodies to produce a physical displacement of one or both members of the system. Such movement serves as an indication of the presence of an electric charge and, if calibrated, provides a measure of the magnitude of the charge. In recent years vacuum-tube-amplifier technology has made possible instruments which amplify the power level of the phenomenon being observed to levels suitable for indication on conventional meters, for continuous recording on strip chart recorders, for remote read-out by wire or radio telemetry link, and for automatic control systems.

The gold-leaf electroscope employs two thin strips of gold-leaf attached to a conducting rod which serves as support and as a means of imparting the electric charge to the gold-leaf. Figure 1a illustrates the position of rest of the gold-leaf system. If an electric charge is placed on the metal ball (Fig. 1b), the charge distributes throughout the ball, rod, and leaves; if the charge is negative, each excess electron is repelled by all other excess electrons and assumes a position of equilibrium within the bounds of the conducting system. Around each leaf an electric field exists, and since the charges on the two leaves are of like sign, the force between them causes them to stand apart. Some electrostatic voltmeters operate on the same principle as the gold-leaf electroscope and are used to measure voltages as low as millivolts and as high as hundreds of kilovolts. The electroscope may also be used to detect a charge on another body as in Fig. 1c. The negatively charged rod repels electrons from the ball into the leaves, causing them to stand apart.

The quadrant electrometer, Fig. 2, utilizes both the force of attraction between charged bodies of unlike sign and the force of repulsion between charged bodies of like sign. A movable vane v, free to rotate against the torsion of a suspending wire, is connected to quadrants 1 and 3. If an electric potential is connected between terminals A and B the vane is attracted toward quadrants 2 and 4

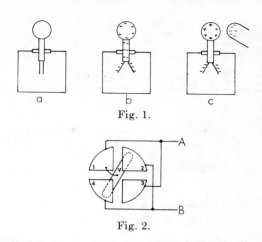

Fig. 1.

Fig. 2.

and is repelled by quadrants 1 and 3. A measure of the angular displacement of the vane indicates the magnitude of the potential.

The string electrometer uses a conducting fiber supported between two oppositely charged plates as the moving element. A charge imparted to the fiber causes it to deflect toward the plate of opposite charge and away from the plate of like charge. Versions of the string electrometer are made in fountain-pen sizes and are used as X-ray and radioactivity dosimeters.

The vacuum-tube electrometer detects and measures electric current by measuring the voltage drop produced by the current in a known resistance. In the basic circuit of Fig. 3, R_b is adjusted to balance the plate current of the vacuum tube to establish a zero reading on meter M with zero input current. An input current produces a change in grid voltage, $e_g = I_{in}R_g$, and meter M reads the resulting change in plate current. If R_g is chosen as 10^{12} ohms and the vacuum tube has a transconductance of 100 μmhos, an input current of 10^{-13} amp produces a meter reading of 10 μa. The circuit therefore provides a current gain of 10^8. However, only especially designed vacuum tubes are capable of operation in electrometer applications. The electrometer-type of vacuum tube is designed to have low control grid current and to have a high degree of stability. The low grid current requirement dictates a very

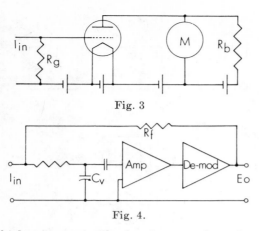

Fig. 3

Fig. 4.

high vacuum inside the glass envelope, low conductance in the glass envelope, coating of the glass surface to minimize surface leakage, operation of the tube in darkness to minimize photoelectric emission (*q.v.*) on the grid, and the use of low potentials on the plate and screen grid to prevent ionization of the gas remaining in the tube. Modern electrometer tubes achieve grid currents of 10^{-13} to 10^{-15} amp routinely and, with somewhat more care, 10^{-17} amp may be achieved. Rugged, subminiature tubes are available and require only 12 mw of filament power and 6 to 15 v plate and screen grid supply. Although the circuit of Fig. 3 is adequate for many applications, it proves to have limitations in response time and drift which make more complex circuits desirable. Most instruments employ additional stages of amplification, degenerative feedback, and, often, balanced amplifier circuitry. Commercially available, multirange instruments have maximum sensitivities of the order of 10^{-14} amp with drift rates equivalent to less than 5×10^{-15} amp/day.

The vibrating-reed electrometer is illustrated in Fig. 4. An electric charge flowing into C_v produces a potential on C_v of $e_{cv} = Q/C_v$. If the capacity is then changed by altering the spacing of the plates of C_v, e_{cv} changes to satisfy the relationship $e_{cv2} = Q/C_{v2}$. In practice, C_v is made of a reed assembly forming one plate and a stationary member for the other plate. The reed is made to vibrate several hundred times a second by an electromagnet. Thus an alternating voltage is developed across C_v that is proportional to the charge Q. An ac amplifier may be used to raise the signal to the desired level with considerable reduction in the grid current and drift problems encountered in the dc amplifiers. A demodulator circuit restores the signal to dc. Degenerative feedback is provided through R_f. If the over-all amplifier gain is large (of the order of 1000), I_{in} is equal to the output voltage divided by R_f. The desired current sensitivity is established by selection of R_f. Currents as small as 10^{-15} amp may be measured in this manner. For smaller currents R_f is removed and the instrument becomes an integrating electrometer. As current flows into C_v, the charge on C_v rises with time. The input current may be inferred by observing the rate of rise of the output voltage. The ultimate sensitivity in this mode of operation is limited to currents of the order of 10^{-17} amp by the inherent drift rate of the instrument.

Breaker amplifier. Vacuum-tube electrometers and vibrating reed electrometers lend themselves most readily to measurement of current from high-resistance sources such as ion chambers. The breaker amplifier may be used to measure low-level voltage from low-resistance sources such as thermocouples (*q.v.*). The current to be measured is connected to a transformer primary winding through a rapidly operating switch contact. The ac voltage resulting in the secondary is amplified in an ac circuit to a suitable level. Sensitivity is limited to currents of about 10^{-10} amp by the noise level in the breaker.

WILLIAM A. NICHOLS

Cross-references: *Indicating Instruments, Integrating Instruments*

ELECTROSTATICS: see ELECTROMAGNETIC THEORY

ELECTROSTATIC PRECIPITATION

The function of the Electrostatic Precipitator or Separator is to remove dust and droplets from gases. In its simplest form it consists of a vertical pipe (Fig. 1) in which a metallic, insulated wire is suspended axially. The laden air or gas travels up the pipe and escapes clean, at the top. The pipe is grounded. A unidirectional high voltage current, varying from 15 to 100 kv in the different installations, is fed to the wire, so that a powerful electric field is created. As the dusty air or gas travels up the pipe, the electric field ionizes the air or gas; the ions in turn charge the suspended particles by contact. The charged particles travel to the relatively uncharged wall, there depositing the negatively charged particles. Periodically the pipe is rapped (such as at half minute intervals) so that the deposit drops down into a container box. Suspended droplets are similarly deposited on the pipe wall, where they coalesce and travel downward as a liquid to a suitable outlet. The cleaned air or gas leaves at the top of the pipe.

The full-scale electrostatic precipitator for smelter or factory installation is more often designed to provide narrow rectangular passages between flat plates, which are then the collecting electrodes, with a series of spaced wires suspended in the center plane of the space; these are now the emitting or discharge electrodes. The distance the charged particle travels is 3 or 4 in. before it strikes the collecting electrode. The unipolar corona discharge is secured by impressing the negative polarity on the wire; the negative corona permits higher voltages and currents to be carried. The choice of the negative corona is now a general rule to which the only exception is the installations for air-cleaning where the positive polarity is impressed on the wire, because of the lower ozone generation.

The unidirectional high-voltage current is produced in the modern installations by means of the electron tube or, increasingly, by the solid-state silicon transformer-rectifier, with askarel as insulating liquid [a nonflammable liquid].

Both the collecting electrode and the discharge electrode are rapped, but differently. Wire rapping is achieved by the use of elec-

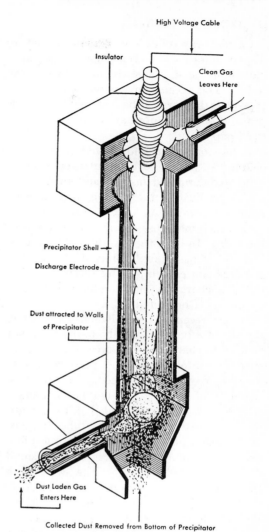

Fig. 1. The precipitator chamber. (Courtesy Research-Cottrell, Inc.)

tric vibrators, whereas plate rapping is performed by recently developed magnetic impulse gravity impact (MIGI) rappers. This latter rapper includes a plunger raised by an electric solenoid and dropped by gravity.

The action of the electrostatic separator is on the two-phase system; it collects the disperse phase. The electrostatic separator is powerless in the separation of two gases.

E. RAYMOND RIEGEL

Cross-references: *Electric Discharge, Ionization. Static (Tribo-) Electricity*

ELECTROSTATIC PRINTING

Cathode-ray tubes have long been used to display information. Television, radar, and alphanumeric displays are in common use today. The recent development of a new type of cathode-ray tube now permits direct printout of video information onto nonsensitized paper.

It has long been known that patterns of charge can be placed on insulating surfaces in a predetermined fashion and then made visible by dusting the surface with an electroscopic powder. At least two printing systems which make use of this principle are in use today. In both the "Xerograph" process and the "Electrofax" process the charge patterns are established by discharging an initially charged, photoconducting surface by means of projected light.

It has recently been demonstrated that the electron beam of a cathode-ray tube can be used to charge selected areas on a moving strip of coated paper and produce visible images at very high speed. This process, called "Videograph,"* operates as follows: A special faceplate is sealed onto a high-resolution cathode-ray display tube. In place of the usual phosphor screen, the faceplate has a large number of wires of very small diameter sealed into it. The wires run through the faceplate to permit the electron beam to strike the inside ends of the wires; the outside ends are placed near or in contact with a moving dielectric surface—paper, for example. The wires are arranged in a single row or in a two-dimensional array. The electron beam is accelerated toward the wires, at the same time being deflected and intensity modulated as in a kinescope.

While being struck by the beam, the wire accumulates charge and begins to approach the potential of the cathode. In normal operation, the ultor voltage of the electrostatic writing tube is maintained at ground,

* "Videograph" is the registered trade name of the A. B. Dick Company, 5700 West Touhy Avenue, Chicago 48, Illinois. Equipment employing tubes described in this section is manufactured by them.

with the cathode potential being held at about −15 kv. The paper is pressed against the tube face by means of a grounded electrode. The writing surface is coated with a very thin dielectric layer; in addition, the paper is itself slightly conducting. Thus, a potential gradient develops across the dielectric coating between the negatively charged wire and ground. Under these conditions, charge is transferred to the paper coating. It is unnecessary for the wires to be in contact with the paper. Charge transfer occurs even when a small air gap is present. In this case, the mechanism of transfer is different and it is somewhat analogous to a spark discharge. Usually, charge is transferred at a lower voltage and more reliably when the paper contacts the wire ends than when there is a significant air gap.

The following tube parameters determine resolution and writing speed: beam diameter, current density, wire packing density, wire-to-wire capacity, and wire-to-ground capacity.

The rate at which the voltage of a given wire rises, with respect to ground, depends upon the current flowing to the wire and the capacity of the wire. Beam diameter and current density are determined by the characteristics of the electron gun. Wire capacity is minimized both by keeping the wires as short as possible and by making use of low-dielectric-constant faceplate material.

Typical tube characteristics are as follows: ultor voltage, −15 kv; nominal beam diameter, 0.003 to 0.005 in.; peak wire current, 150 μa; wire density, 250 per inch; wire diameter, 0.001 in.; wire length, 0.030 in.; beam writing speed, 250,000 in./sec. Tubes with these characteristics are capable of producing images that have a resolution of about 100 picture elements per inch, in both X and Y directions, and at a rate of ten square feet of copy per second.

To assist in adjusting the tube, a phosphor strip that can be viewed through the bell of the tube is laid down adjacent to wires. The beam can be positioned and focused on the phosphor strip and then displaced downward, onto the wire ends, by means of the centering controls. Once on the wires, the beam may be further monitored by viewing the voltage developed across a resistor that is placed between ground and the electrode holding the moving paper against the wires.

Electrostatic printing tubes may be operated in either of two modes: line-by-line scan, as in television; or character-by-character printing, as required for computer printout.

In the first example, the tube is supplied with video and sync from some scanning device. The scanner may be a television camera or an electronic or mechanical flying spot scanner. High-resolution operation, such as facsimile reproduction of printed material, demands a spot size and intensity generally beyond that available from cathode-ray tubes. Special scanners have been built for this application that sweep a spot of light across the copy by means of a rotating mirror.

Normally, the beam is intensity modulated by applying a signal to the control grid in the usual fashion. Since the gun is at high negative potential, the video must be applied across this voltage gap. An alternate modulation scheme, which operates without high-voltage difficulties, is one in which the beam is deflected off the wires to prevent it from writing by means of an auxiliary set of deflection electrodes inside the tube. These electrodes operate at ground potential rather than cathode potential.

In the second example, character-by-character printing, the tube face contains a number of parallel rows of wires rather than the single row which is adequate for television-type reproduction. The electron beam is scanned in both X and Y directions, and intensity modulated as before. The video pattern for the characters is generated in an auxiliary circuit that makes use of a monoscope (q.v.) having a target with the required characters printed on it. In response to digital input, the monoscope beam is directed at the appropriate character and scans it with a small raster. The secondary-electron signal taken from the collector electrode in the monoscope is applied to the control grid of the electrostatic printing tube. The beam in the printing tube scans in synchronism with that in the monoscope. Characters can be formed and printed at a rate of 20,000 per second with this system.

Electrostatic printing tubes of the type described above are used in high-speed facsimile systems and in computer output printers.

PHILIP RICE

Cross-references: *Cathode-Ray Tubes (Display), Charactron, Computer Printout and Reading, Facsimile*

ELEMENTS: see CHEMICAL ELEMENTS

ENERGY

Energy is a fundamental physical property that may be defined as *the capacity to do work*. Energy may exist in many forms such as mechanical, thermal, chemical, electrical, radiant, nuclear, etc. It may be readily changed from one form to another, but the law of the conservation of energy—a basic law of classical physics and the first law of thermodynamics—states that energy cannot be either created or destroyed, i.e., the total amount of energy in an isolated region remains constant.

Most of the familiar forms of energy may be classified as either potential or kinetic. *Potential energy* is energy due to the position or shape of a body. For example, we add potential energy to an iron ball when we raise it from the floor to a table top, to a watch spring when we wind the watch, and to a mass of gas when we compress it. When the ball falls to the floor its potential energy is transformed into energy of motion, called *kinetic energy*; when it strikes the floor the kinetic energy is transformed into heat energy.

Water at the top of Niagara Falls possesses potential energy, which is transformed into kinetic energy as it falls, and finally into enough heat to warm the water about 0.2°F. Some of the water may impinge upon the vanes of a water turbine, and so do useful work, but in this case there is less temperature increase. An electric cell has potential energy in chemical form which may be transformed into electric current and then into heat in a wire or a lamp filament. The potential energy of gasoline and oxygen is transformed into heat and then into kinetic energy in the cylinder of a motor car. The energy of a swinging pendulum is potential at each end of the swing and kinetic at the central point of the swing. All forms of energy tend to be transformed into heat, which is the least available form of energy. In no machine can friction be entirely eliminated and the energy which disappears in friction ultimately appears as heat.

The unit of energy in the cgs system of units is the *erg*. It is defined as the energy expended when a force of one dyne moves its point of application one centimeter in the direction of the force. The unit in the British system is the foot-pound and it is similarly defined. Very careful measurements have shown that the number of units of mechanical energy required to produce one unit of heat is always the same. This ratio is called the *mechanical equivalent of heat*: 4.18×10^7 ergs = 1 calorie of heat; 252 calories = 1 British thermal unit of heat; 778 foot-pounds = 1 Btu of heat. Hence there are about 1.35×10^7 ergs in 1 ft-lb of energy. The MKS unit of energy is the *joule*, which is equal to 10^7 ergs.

Chemical energy is a form of potential energy due to the attraction of the atoms of one element for those of another. When conditions are such that they are free to combine they do so, sometimes quietly, as in the leaves of trees, sometimes explosively, as in a bomb. Chemical attraction appears always to be due to exchanging or sharing of electrons between atoms.

One form of transmission of energy is by means of waves. These may depend upon gravity, as on the surface of water, or upon the elastic properties of the medium transmitting the waves. Waves may be transverse, like water waves, or longitudinal, like sound waves in air. In any case the energy is transmitted by only a to and fro motion of the particles of the transmitting medium, across the direction of propagation of the wave in case of transverse waves, in the direction of propagation in case of longitudinal or compression waves. In either case the energy, as in the case of a vibrating pendulum, is constantly changing from potential to kinetic and back again. Light, radio broadcasts, and radiant energy in general, behave like transverse waves when they enter measuring instruments; but mechanical transverse waves are transmitted only by elastic solids and there is no such solid in empty space, such as between the sun or stars and the earth.

To account for the transmission of light and heat from the sun to the earth a "hypothetical medium" called ether, was at one time assumed to pervade all space and was given the necessary properties which proved to be fantastic and mutually contradictory. In the 1860's and 1870's Maxwell proposed his theory that these waves consisted of rapidly vibrating electromagnetic fields. Edison is reported to have said that he did not know what electricity is, but he did know what he could do with it. The same may be said about electric and magnetic fields, and Maxwell's theory was universally adopted.

The progress of science in the past has been built upon two laws of conservation, the conservation of energy, already mentioned, and a similar law of conservation of mass. These laws state that neither mass nor energy can be created or destroyed. They apply perfectly to measurements of mass and energy made by means available before the beginning of the present century; but more recent researches on atomic structure and mutations have led to the discovery that mass may disappear while radiant energy appears in its place. The reverse change, i.e., from energy into mass, is also known to take place. Einstein has shown that when this takes place the relation between mass and energy is

Energy (in joule) = mass (in kilograms) $\times c^2$

where c is the velocity of light, i.e., 3×10^8 m/sec. This relation has been abundantly verified by experiment. Since mass can be converted into radiant energy we must now consider mc^2 joules to be part of the energy of a body.

The mass of an atom of helium is slightly less than the sum of the masses of the two protons and the two neutrons which make up the helium atom. When an atom of helium is formed the lost mass appears as radiant energy. For every gram of helium formed, the radiant energy developed equals that developed in burning about 20 tons of coal. One theory to account for the enormous amount of energy the sun is radiating continually is that the hydrogen of the sun is being built into helium by a series of atomic reactions with a consequent emission of radiant energy—that is, the sun is actually radiating away its mass.

In 1939 another important discovery was made. Atoms of one isotope of uranium split spontaneously into two approximately equal parts with a comparatively large loss of mass and equivalent gain in radiant energy. This process is called *fission*. Since 1939 other atoms have been found, and still others made artificially, which undergo fission. The energy into which this lost mass is transformed can now be controlled and may be used for atom bombs or for the production of power for peaceful purposes.

NORMAN E. GILBERT

Cross-references: *Energy Conversion, Fission, Plasma, Thermodynamics*

ENERGY CONVERSION

Photoelectric

The solar photovoltaic converter, the principal device used in photoelectric conversion, consists of a semiconductor crystal, usually silicon, containing a composition gradient termed a p-n junction. At this junction the impurity type changes in a distance of 10 microns from acceptor to donor. Since donors are ionized positively and acceptors negatively, an electrostatic field is established that opposes the tendency of the chemical potential gradient of electrons or holes to cause diffusion of such charge carriers and thus prevents any net charge flow at equilibrium. This electrical potential difference is just the familiar contact potential difference present whenever a composition gradient exists within a system, e.g., a system containing two different metals.

Energetic photons from the sun create hole-electron pairs by removing electrons from valence bonds. These pairs are separated by the field at the junction causing a current to flow. Equilibrium is restored by some of the charges flowing through and delivering energy to an optimum external resistor.

The efficiency of this converter is determined by the following:

(1) The solar spectrum is composed of photons distributed in energy similar to a blackbody at about 5800°K. Therefore, only a part of the energy of the high-energy photons is used in creating a pair, the remainder being dissipated as heat.

(2) Conversely, photons of insufficient energy to create a pair are unabsorbed. Because of these two opposing effects, there is an optimum band gap that can utilize the maximum energy from the solar spectrum. The band gap for silicon is 1.1 ev, which approaches the optimum of approximately 1.25 ev.

(3) Some pairs recombine before they can be separated by the junction field, since each must diffuse a finite distance to the junction-field region. Materials with longer lifetimes will improve this situation.

(4) Fortunately, the preparation of the highly-doped p-type layer on which the solar energy is incident produces an almost nonreflecting surface and, hence, negligible reflection losses.

(5) The potential developed across an optimum load is far below the average energy per photon. The potential would increase, but only slowly, if the light were increased by a lens or mirror system.

(6) To permit light transmission, contact is made only to the edge of the p-type layer. This configuration introduces a series resistance, and hence a loss, which can be reduced by increasing the thickness of the p-type layer, necessitating a longer diffusion path, increasing the loss under (3). Here, an optimum must be effected.

Practical silicon solar converter efficiency is now 10 to 15 per cent. In principle, InP and GaAs converters with band gaps near the optimum should be of higher efficiency; actually, basic fabrication difficulties preclude its achievement. An efficiency of 50 per cent might be obtained in a three-semiconductor "sandwich" assembly, with the widest-gap semiconductor on top utilizing the highest-energy photons, the medium gap the next lower energy, etc. Other schemes, utilizing converters with continuously varying band gaps, have been proposed; they have not been realizable because of limitations in the technology and economics of compound semiconductors.

Silicon solar converters are employed in both terrestrial and celestial applications. Such converters are used in conjunction with storage batteries since, in both applications, there is insufficient light at times.

For terrestrial use, the converters are oriented for maximum insolation at the winter solstice and an economic balance between the number of converters and storage batteries is made consistent with power requirements.

For satellite power supplies, the design is concerned principally with the optimum dispersal of solar converters on or about the satellite, the determination of the necessary energy storage and the translation of these requirements into an assembly of minimum mass.

R. L. Cummerow

Thermoelectric

If two wires of different metals are connected together at both ends and the two junctions are maintained at different temperatures, a voltage is developed in the circuit. The thermoelectric effect was first discovered by T. J. Seebeck (1770–1831) in the early 19th century. The use of thermocouples (q.v.) to measure the temperature at a given location is based on this phenomenon. The open-circuit thermoelectric voltage is given by $\alpha_{12}\Delta T$ where ΔT is the temperature difference of the junctions and α_{12} is the thermal emf or Seebeck coefficient which depends upon the metals used and on the mean operating temperature of the junctions. For common metals, α_{12} is in the range of several microvolts per degree (Kelvin) of temperature difference; therefore, metals are used only for measuring purposes as in thermocouples but they are not capable of delivering power as required in energy conversion.

The thermal emf coefficient α of semiconductors is in the range of several hundred microvolts per degree Kelvin. Semiconductors are thus capable of supplying voltage about one hundred times and power ten thousand times larger than metals. Industrial thermoelectric converters are all made of semiconducting materials. The physical process which is responsible for thermoelectricity in semiconductors is as follows. If metal contacts are made at both ends of a semiconductor rod and one end is kept at a higher temperature than the other, majority carriers tend to diffuse from the hot to the cold junction, thus setting up a potential difference between the two ends. To enhance the output voltage, a thermoelectric generator usually consists of two arms, one made of n-type and the other made of p-type of the same semiconductor. The open-circuit voltage of such a unit depends upon the difference of the chemical potentials (or the Fermi levels) of the n- and p-type semiconductor.

Recent advances in semiconductor technology not only have improved the operating efficiency of thermoelectric generators but have reduced the cost of such units sufficiently so that soon they will be able to compete economically with the conventional turbo- or engine-machinery type of energy-conversion units. Besides costs, thermoelectric generators have many distinct advantages over conventional units: they have no moving parts so that their maintenance cost is lower; and they occupy less space and weigh much less per kilowatt output power. As an example, a lead telluride cell of laboratory scale (say, 1 cm^2 cross section) maintained at a temperature difference of 600°C is capable of delivering electric power of about 1 w. To increase output power, a great number of thermoelectric cells may be staggered together and industrial units providing power in the kilowatt range are now feasible. The future practical possibilities of thermoelectric energy conversion depend on how successful the search for new materials operating efficiently at high temperatures will be.

Theoretically, if a thermoelectric generator has no internal losses due to thermal and electric conduction, its conversion efficiency approaches that of a Carnot engine. In a practical unit, the conversion efficiency is further limited by thermal and electric losses in the thermoelectric element. The most important quantity used as a basis for comparison of different thermoelectric materials is the figure of merit Z, defined as $\alpha^2 \sigma / K$ where α is the Seebeck coefficient, σ is the electrical conductivity, and K is the thermal conductivity. The higher the value of Z, the higher the operating efficiency of a thermoelectric element. The value of Z for the best thermoelectric element is around $3 \times 10^{-3}/$ deg K, which gives a conversion efficiency of about 10 per cent.

Among thermoelectric materials, compounds of lead (or bismuth) with selenium (or tellurium) have been most extensively investigated and widely used. Regarding choice of thermoelectric materials, the following remarks should be made. Each thermoelectric material operates most efficiently

and economically as an energy converter only within a certain temperature range. For larger temperature differences, it is necessary to design a multistage generator with each stage operating within its optimum temperature range. At very high temperatures several technical problems must be considered. First, the material must have a sufficiently large energy gap in order to assure that it will remain extrinsic, i.e., that the hole or electron concentration will be determined by the impurity concentration. Second, diffusion in solids becomes quite rapid above 600°C; consequently extreme care must be taken to prevent diffusion of undesirable impurities (from soldered joints or electrical contacts, for example) into the thermoelectric material. Precaution should also be made against oxidation of the material. Search for high-temperature thermoelectric materials to overcome the above technical difficulties is still in progress.

Solid solutions of intermetallic compounds (for example, lead telluride with lead selenide) are often used to optimize the ratio of electric conductivity to thermal conductivity. The Seebeck coefficient and electrical conductivity of a thermoelectric material are both functions of doping (that is, electron or hole concentration in n-type or p-type semiconductor, respectively). Therefore, the figure of merit of a thermoelectric cell can be optimized by proper choice of the right amount of impurities and proper mixing with other compounds. Other theoretical considerations that may serve as criteria for the choice or improvement of materials are the following. The phonon thermal conductivity is usually low in semiconductors of large atomic or large molecular weight. A further reduction is possible by a disordering of the lattice structure through the introduction of grain boundary or impurity atoms having sizes different from the regular constituents of the material. The electron or hole mobility is usually high in semiconductors of large atomic or large molecular weight.

Thermoelectric generators are essentially low-voltage, high-current devices. It is important that the contact resistance at both junctions of a thermoelectric cell should be negligibly small compared to the resistance of the thermoelectric elements. At low temperatures, soldered contacts are commonly and satisfactorily employed. At high temperatures, pressure contacts are used to avoid diffusion of undesirable impurities into the thermoelectric element.

In the actual design of a thermoelectric energy conversion unit, other engineering considerations besides the choice of material arise, e.g., to determine the number of stages required, to minimize the heat loss other than conduction loss in the thermo-electric element, to minimize the ohmic loss at contacts, and to convert the low-voltage dc power into ac power efficiently. Thermoelectric generators of small output power are already extensively used. Power plants using thermoelectric energy converters have already been given enthusiastic consideration and will be in operation in the not too distant future. For completeness, one should also mention thermoelectric *refrigeration*, based upon the Peltier effect, the opposite of Seebeck effect. It is safe to say that thermoelectric refrigerators and air-conditioners will become common household appliances before long.

SHYH WANG

Thermionic

Thermionics has been the basis of many electronic devices and circuits used in communication, radar, radio, etc., for many years. The thermionic diode has been used for over 50 years; during this period of time, several scientists indicated the possibility of using this diode for direct conversion of heat to electrical power, but rejected its practicality on the basis of negligible attainable efficiencies. Only since 1955 has a serious effort been undertaken by engineers to use a thermionic type of device to convert thermal energy directly into useful electrical power with reasonable values of thermal efficiency and of current density.

Thermionic emission (*q.v.*) is the process of evaporation of electrons from a hot surface of a conductor into a space which may be a vacuum, a low-pressure gas, or a plasma. The thermionic energy converter comprises the hot electron emitter and a colder electron collector, separated by a vacuum, or a low-pressure gas, or a plasma. The electron cloud tends to build up a negatively charged region outside the emitter (the space charge). Only a few of the evaporated electrons, the high-energy electrons that can pass through the space-charge region, are collected at the colder anode or collector without the aid of an external battery supplying work. The electrons flow directly through the external load and return to the hot emitter to complete the circuit.

The simplest thermionic energy converter is the closed-spaced vacuum diode, which consists of a hot emitter placed very close to a colder collector in a high vacuum of the order to 10^{-6} mm of Hg. This type of diode has been analyzed successfully by scientists such as Langmuir, Fry, and others; its electrical characteristics have been known for many years. The transformation of this type of diode into a practical energy converter was made possible by engineers, such as Hatsopoulos, Kaye, and others, for two main reasons: first, by careful examination of the methods of reducing the large heat-transfer losses, and second, by developing the mechanical means of attaining very close spacings of the order of 0.001 cm. It now appears likely that such energy converters can attain thermal efficiencies of the order of 10 to 20 per cent.

There are other types of thermionic energy converters under study that depend on various means of controlling the space charge between the emitter and collector surfaces. The close-spaced diode controls the space charge by bringing the emitter and collector surfaces very close together. The magnetic triode is a vacuum diode in which the space-charge effects are controlled by the use of electrical and magnetic fields to guide the electronic trajectories; the physical arrangement of the emitter and collector surfaces is such that a large reduction in heat-transfer losses is also accomplished simultaneously. The magnetic triode offers, in the long run, an improvement in thermal efficiency over that of the close-spaced diode for the same values of high and low temperatures. The third type of energy converter is the gas-filled diode, which operates in several different modes depending on the nature of the gas (e.g., cesium vapor) and on the pressure of the gas. The cesium diode and the plasma diode appear to offer large potential gains in power density in the higher temperature range of operation of such thermionic energy converters. (Detailed analyses of these types of thermionic energy converters may be found in the book by J. Kaye and J. A. Welsh, *Direct Conversion of Heat to Electricity*, Wiley, 1960.)

The future prospects of thermionic energy converters appear very promising with respect to attaining thermal efficiencies of 20 to 30 per cent, power outputs of 10 to 100 w/cm^2 of emissive surface, small size per unit output, and high reliability. The applications of such converters will probably be: first, for specialized uses, such as for space and military devices and systems, and for cathodic protective devices; second, for standby power sources for remote areas; and third, in competition with currently available power devices of small sizes and of all types. Furthermore, the thermionic energy converters may be readily combined with other types of power plants that require lower input temperatures, so that in effect the thermionic device becomes a topping unit for the other power plants. Examples of such combinations are: first, a thermionic converter with its highest input temperature of 2000°K, which rejects heat at 1000°K to a thermoelectric generator, and the latter rejects its heat to the atmosphere or to space as a low-temperature sink; second, the combination of a plasma thermionic diode in the center of a nuclear reactor and rejection of the heat from the diode to the normal cooling fluid of the nuclear reactors, and then passing the cooling fluid through the ordi-

nary turbo-machinery type of power plant customarily used; and third, the combination of the thermionic unit with another power producer as for a solar-powered space device, in which the heat from the thermionic converter is rejected to a Stirling heat engine, and the latter rejects its heat to space. It is evident that different forms and variations of the thermionic energy converter will appear in the power plants of the future.

JOSEPH KAYE

Cross-references: *Contact Potential, Photocell, Photovoltaic Effect, Semiconductor Manufacture, Thermal Detectors, Thermionic Emission, Thermocouples, Thermoelectricity, Work Function*

ENVIRONMENTAL TESTING

Vibration. In vibration testing, alternating forces are generated, usually by external means, at frequencies up to 15,000 cps. These forces can excite a part at its resonant frequency or frequencies. The objective of such testing is to reveal progressive fracture, undesirable contact between parts, misalignment of internal parts, leakage through deformation, and other defects prohibited by the requirements of a particular application.

The two major types of tests are: (1) sinusoidal vibration, both at fixed frequencies and swept over a band of frequencies at a predetermined rate; and (2) random vibration.

Equipment used may be either mechanically, electrically, or hydraulically driven tables. Mechanical exciters are usually limited to low frequencies (less than 100 cps); hydraulic exciters can be operated up to about 2000 cps; electrodynamic exciters are available that operate as high as 20,000 cps. Automatic cycling can be incorporated in all systems, but only electrodynamic and hydraulic systems can maintain either constant displacement *or* constant acceleration.

Electrodynamic vibration systems have been developed within recent years that can generate random vibration at constant energy levels for selected bandwidths. The energy transmitted to the specimen is referred to variously as power-spectral density, acceleration density, mean-square-acceleration density, all of which mean the same. The energy level is expressed in units of the square of the acceleration caused by gravity, divided by the frequency of the bandwidth in cycles per second. This method of vibration testing is used extensively in missile and rocket programs.

Shock Tests (Impact). Shock or impact tests are designed to reveal malfunctioning or catastrophic failure in components and equipments over a short period of time (usually in micro or milliseconds) by the imposition of a large acceleration force in a controlable force-time pattern. A shock pulse, either by applying brute force through mass-acceleration means (as in the case of a large mass supported off its center of gravity) or by exciting parts at their natural frequencies, can produce defects similar to those encountered in vibration tests.

Several types of equipment are used. High-force, short-duration shocks, intentionally replete with harmonic distortions arising from table resonances, are generated by a type that incorporates a swinging hammer impacting against a table free to slide.

More precisely controlled pulse waveforms are produced by the sand-drop machines. The test specimen is attached to a table which is free to fall between guide bars onto sand of a specified composition. Pulse duration is reasonably well controlled by changing the number of wood rails attached to the underside of the specimen table.

More refined versions of the sand-drop method that have been developed recently utilize rubber pads and lead pellets. The rubber pads produce half-sine waves; the lead pellets produce sawtooth and square-wave pulses. Pulse duration and waveform are precisely controlled and repeatable.

Another refinement is a pneumatic machine, which can produce almost any pulse form and duration by use of properly designed metering pins and orifices.

Linear Acceleration (Centrifuge). Centrifuge tests are required to determine the limits of linear acceleration which a component part or equipment can withstand without catastrophic failure or malfunctioning either during or after the test. Parts may bend into undesirable contact, be either crushed or pulled loose from their attachments, crack from overstressing, or suffer other deleterious effects.

Equipment used to perform these tests can range from the physically small (2- to 3-ft diameter) to the huge (30- to 40-ft arms), depending upon the size of the specimen to be tested. Equipment capabilities range from a few gravities to several thousand gravities.

Temperature Tests. Thermal tests are divided into three major categories; (1) high temperature, (2) low temperature, and (3) thermal shock (i.e., rapid shifts between temperature extremes). The classes of defects encountered include insulation failure, material strength loss, performance degradation, dimensional tolerance changes, destruction of finishes and coatings, and the like.

Equipments are available with varying degrees of complexity for controlling and recording chamber ambient temperatures.

Humidity. Humidity tests are designed to assure reliable operation in humid areas or after prolonged storage in such areas. Humidity normally causes such detrimental effects as material decay with resultant loss of structural strength, insulation breakdown, and short circuits.

Equipment must generally be capable of varying the humidity from 5 to 100 per cent and controlling associated temperatures.

Salt Spray. In the salt-spray test, fog of a standard salt solution is introduced into a chamber containing the test specimen. Corrosion is produced primarily by electrolytic action, and creates short and open circuits, arcing, overheating, and subsequent effects causing malfunctioning of electronic equipment.

Altitude. Altitude chambers are capable of attaining barometric pressures as low as those which exist at extreme altitudes. These tests produce such effects as corona, insulation breakdown, arcing, seal leakage, seal rupture, overheating owing to reduced air density, and other defects.

Acoustic Excitation (Air-Induced). These tests subject a part to a specified sound quality and level in an acoustic chamber for a required period. Parts fail when either the operation deteriorates outside given limits or undesirable physical damage occurs.

Immersion. In immersion testing, the specimen is exposed to successive cycles of immersions in hot and cold baths of either fresh or salt water, and subsequently tested for leaks and electrical operation.

Explosion. A device may be subjected to either or both of two kinds of explosion tests. One test operates the part in a controlled explosive atmosphere to determine its potential to *cause* an explosion; the other test subjects the part *to* an explosion and determines particularly its tendency to fragmentize.

Nuclear. Parts that depend upon the properties of ionization are operated in environments of nuclear radiation which produce neutron, gamma, and thermal bombardment. Such parts must function without damage or deterioration during and after such bombardment.

These tests are normally conducted by government agencies, although some companies have started testing their products privately in independent laboratories licensed by the U. S. Atomic Energy Commission.

Rain, Sunshine, Sand and Dust, and Fungus. Although important, these tests do not normally present complications either in their conduct or in the ability of the part or component to pass. Protection, if necessary, is easily afforded by coating or housings.

R. H. KIRKLAND, JR.

Cross-references: *Electron-Tube Manufacture, Modular Construction, Packaging, Radiation (Ionizing), Semiconductor Manufacture*

EPOXY MOLDING COMPOUNDS

Epoxy molding compounds are new, high quality thermosetting materials. They have been developed primarily because the electronics industry has needed the useful characteristics of epoxy resins in a form suitable for use in high speed molding operations. Epoxy molding compounds are finding their main applications in the encapsulation of resistors, capacitors, chokes, delay lines, etc., and in the formation of casting cups, transformer cans, brush blocks, potentiometer housings, and the like. In general, epoxies are used where their quality and performance characteristics offset the price advantages of such materials as phenolics, alkyds, ureas, and melamines. The most valuable characteristics of epoxy molding compounds are their excellent adhesive properties; high electrical, chemical, and moisture resistances; soft flow during molding, low mold shrinkage, and their 100-percent reactivity (nonoutgassing). Typical values for molded epoxies are shown in the following table:

Compressive Strength	20,000 psi
Coefficient of linear thermal expansion	2.5×10^{-5} in./in.-deg C
Volume Resistivity at 73°F	Over 10^{15} ohms-cm
Dielectric strength at 73°F	325 v/mil
Dielectric constant at 73°F	6.0
Mold shrinkage	0.003 in./in.

Epoxy molding compounds are normally single-package materials which include epoxy resin, curing agent, filler or reinforcement, pigment, and release agent. Within this definition there is a tremendous variety of materials. There are many available epoxy resins, for instance, including the bisphenol-epichlorohydrin, epoxy novolak, and peroxidized polyolefin types. There is also a wide variety of useful curing agents, such as diamines, dibasic acids, acid anhydrides, inorganic salts, and organo-metallic compounds. In addition, the fillers and reinforcing materials can be of high or low density, conductive or nonconductive, metallic or nonmetallic, organic or inorganic. The pigment, or dye, and release agent can be varied also. Obviously, epoxy molding compounds of extremely diverse types can be formulated to meet the exacting requirements of particular applications. Also, self-extinguishing compounds can be formulated through the use of particular resins, curing agents, and fillers.

Epoxy molding compounds are suitable for both transfer and compression molding. Usual molding temperatures are in the range of 275 to 325°F. Molding pressures can be as low as 50 psi or, for highly reinforced materials, they may be as high as several thousands of pounds per square inch. The low-pressure applications are often ones in which delicate or complex inserts are being encapsulated and where care must be taken not to distort or displace them. High-pressure applications are usually encountered in the manufacture of structural components in which extreme mechanical strengths are required, in addition to the regular qualities of epoxies.

Normal transfer and compression molding equipment is usually employed for epoxies. However, low-pressure applications and short production runs have occasionally led to reduced equipment requirements, particularly with regard to molds. Aluminum and plastic molds have been used with epoxies, as have built-up molds made of nonhardened steel. Such molds have led to a great reduction in the cost of short run and prototype work. Lower cost, low-pressure molding presses, designed especially for epoxy applications, are also available.

PAUL E. JACOBSON

Cross-references: *Materials Used in Tube Technology, Packaging*

EQUIVALENT CIRCUITS

If the electrical behavior (the relationship between the voltages and currents) of one circuit or device is identical with that of another circuit or device at a specified number of terminals, the two are said to be *equivalent* at the specified terminals. It should be noted that two equivalent circuits can differ radically in their internal structure, number of components, type of components, etc., while still being equivalent at the specified terminals.

Electrical devices can be analyzed by representing them by means of equivalent circuits. Such circuits can be arrived at through two different routes. In the first place, an explanation of the operation of the device based on the pertinent physical laws leads to relationships among the terminal voltage and current variables. Following this path, a circuit consisting of passive and active components is sought whose external behavior approximates that of the physical device.

Alternatively, from measurements of the external behavior of the device a set of empirical curves are obtained. These curves are approximated by equations relating the terminal voltages and currents, and circuits are synthesized having these equations as their voltage-current relationship.

Figure 1 shows an equivalent circuit of a pnp transistor. This circuit is obtained from an analysis of the physical operation of the transistor. In the expression for the dependent source, α is the current gain; C_{te} and C_{tc} are the junction capacitances of the emitter and collector junctions, respectively, and so on. Each of these elements in the equivalent circuit can be expressed in terms of the fundamental device parameters; e.g., $\alpha = \operatorname{sech} (1 + j\omega\tau_m)^{1/2}/L_m$, where τ_m is the minority carrier lifetime and L_m the diffusion length in the base region of the transistor.

In an equivalent circuit of a device developed in this fashion, there is a close correlation between the elements of the equivalent circuit and the fundamental physical parameter of the device. On the other hand, when an equivalent circuit is derived from empirical characteristics, the elements in the circuit do not necessarily correspond to any physical properties of the device.

It is clear from the preceding discussion that a given physical device has more than

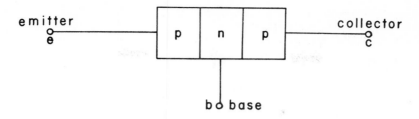

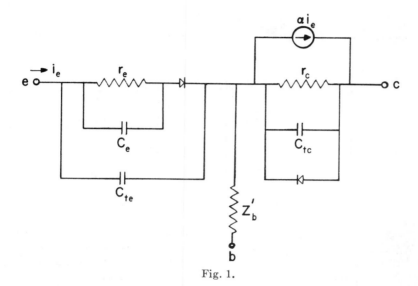

Fig. 1.

one equivalent circuit. The basis for choosing one particular equivalent circuit from many is its intended use. If the objective is the analysis of circuits containing the physical device, any equivalent which facilitates analysis and interpretation is appropriate. Thus, the equivalent circuit of the transistor shown in Fig. 1 with only one dependent source might be more appropriate than another equivalent containing two dependent sources. If the intended use is the accurate experimental measurement of device parameters, then a different equivalent circuit —in the case of the transistor, the h-equivalent because its parameters can be measured with greater ease and accuracy—may be more appropriate. If the intended use is to acquire a better understanding of the internal mechanism of the device, then that equivalent circuit is preferable whose elements are closely related to the physical parameters of the device.

The range of validity of equivalent circuits is finite both in terms of voltage or current amplitudes and in terms of frequency. The use of linear circuits to represent physical devices is limited to the "small-signal" region. Furthermore, one equivalent circuit may be valid for a particular device at low frequencies, and another when the frequency is increased. Thus, in the small-signal equivalent circuit of a triode vacuum tube shown in Fig. 2, the inter-terminal capacitances must be taken into account at high radio frequencies, but can be omitted from the equivalent circuit at low frequencies. Often the equivalence between two circuits may be required for but a single frequency.

Equivalent circuits find application in network synthesis. Sometimes a synthesis technique yields a network with element values that are either unobtainable in practice or which are too close to the values of stray elements unavoidably present in any

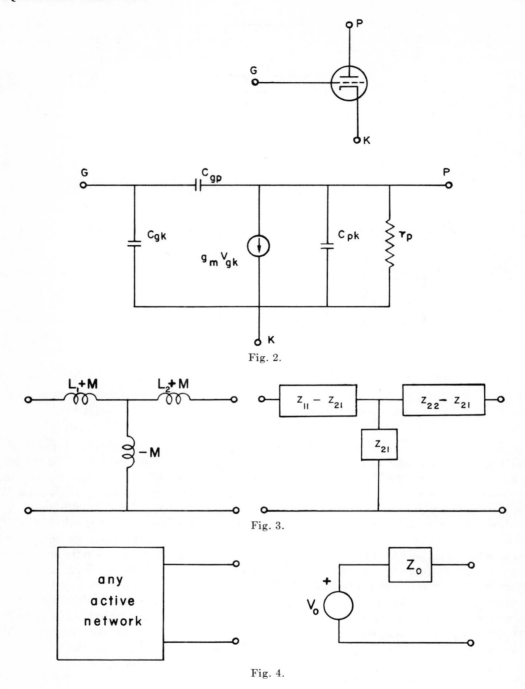

Fig. 2.

Fig. 3.

Fig. 4.

physical circuit. Replacing all or part of this network by an equivalent may lead to more practical element values.

What should be clear in this respect is that a *realizable* equivalent is required, one that contains positive elements. On the other hand, in problems of analysis, where a mathematical analysis is to be carried out rather than a physical circuit built, an equivalent circuit need not be realizable. As an example, the *tee circuit* shown in Fig. 3(a) is equivalent to an ordinary two-winding transformer; the mathematical equivalence holds even though the circuit contains a negative inductance. Figure 3(a) is a specific example of the general two-port equivalent shown in Fig. 3(b). The tee circuit having the branch impedances shown is equivalent to any linear passive, bilateral two-port whose open circuit impedance parameters are z_{11}, z_{21}, and z_{22}.

A very useful equivalent of an arbitrary two terminal active circuit is the *Thévenin equivalent* shown in Fig. 4. The equivalent consists of a voltage source in series with an impedance. V_0 is the transform voltage appearing across the terminals of the original circuit under open circuit, and Z_0 is the impedance looking into the circuit from these terminals when all *independent* (but not *dependent*) sources are removed-voltage sources short-circuited and current sources open-circuited. A circuit consisting of the parallel connection of a current source $I_0 = V_0/Z_0$ and the impedance Z_0 is also equivalent to the Thévenin circuit; it is called the *Norton equivalent*. I_0 is the short circuit transform current at the terminals of the original circuit.

NORMAN BALABANIAN
RAJENDRA NANAVATI

Cross-references: *Coupled Circuits, Network Analysis, Network Synthesis*

ERRORS IN MEASUREMENTS

Measurements are required in every branch of science. Although the methods, equipment, personnel, type of product, etc., differ for these measurements, the end result is the same—a number multiplied by a dimensional unit. There is definitely a need to know how closely a measurement approaches the true value. The true value for any measurement is unknown owing to factors that cause errors. Errors can be classified as follows:

A. *Errors from Known Causes*

1. *Test Conditions.* Environmental con-

ditions (e.g., temperature and humidity) and external influences (such as magnetic fields and rf fields) can affect the operation of certain types of measurement equipment, changing results. Recognition of this source permits establishing suitable correction factors.

2. *Measurement Equipment Errors.* All measurement equipments have calibration errors. During manufacture they are checked against standard equipment whose calibration is traceable to the Bureau of Standards. This agency provides the basic primary standards upon which all scientific measurements are based.

3. *Mistakes.* Mistakes can occur for any number of reasons and their effect on the end result is usually large so that careful recheck of the measurement should isolate the cause. Mistakes are often found in computations owing to an incorrect number of significant figures. The end result cannot have any more significant figures than the original data, which in turn depend upon the sensitivity and capability of the measurement equipment. There are established rules (see, for instance, F. K. Harris, *Electrical Measurements* Wiley, 1952) governing the number of significant figures obtained from the various arithmetic computations.

4. *Systematic Errors.* Systematic errors are caused by some phenomenon in either the test procedure, equipment, or test specimen itself that influences the end result in a consistent fashion. These errors are quite difficult to isolate, especially when only a few observations are recorded.

5. *Visual Errors.* Visual errors are introduced into measurements during reading of displays by observers and are primarily traceable to individual differences between people, fatigue, lighting, and personal bias. A good deal of investigation has been conducted for developing criteria to design displays to reduce visual error. These investigations have covered the areas of antiparallax viewing means, numbering of scales, size of graduations and numerals, spacing between graduations, and reading interpolations.

B. *Errors from Unknown Causes*

These errors are random in nature and no exact reason for them has been determined although there is some belief that the cause is related to transient changes in environmental conditions or in the behavior pattern of the observer. In most practical instances these errors are found to be subject to the laws of probability (*q.v.*) permitting mathematical analysis for predicting limits and they are characterized by the following general traits:

1. Small-error magnitudes are much more frequent than large-error magnitudes.

2. Very-large-error magnitudes are quite infrequent; when they occur, an assignable cause is usually found.

3. Both positive and negative errors appear equally frequently in the data.

Error Analysis. It is necessary in any planned experiments to try to eliminate all errors that arise from known causes; this goal can be accomplished by exercising suitable precautions. Since errors that originate from unknown causes cannot be eliminated, it is necessary to make a series of measurements to determine both the best value and a measure of the probable limit of error variation, designated as the precision index. The final result can then be expressed as $V \pm P$ where V is the best value and P is the precision index. The definition for V, known as the Arithmetic Mean, follows: The *Arithmetic Mean* is the algebraic summation of all the observations divided by the number of readings and can be expressed as

$$V = \frac{1}{n} \sum_{i=1}^{n} V_1$$

where n is the number of observations. The reliability of the Arithmetic Mean increases as the square root of the number of observations.

Several Precision Indices have been developed for use in data analysis; however, the selection of which one to use is unimportant because they are interrelated. The definitions for the terms are predicated on a Gaussian or normal probability distribution of the observations, which is usually shown in graphical form by plotting the deviation of each observation from the Arithmetic Mean along the abscissa and the frequency of occurrence along the ordinate. The definitions for the individual precision indices follow:

The *Standard Deviation* is the root mean square of the summation of the difference between each individual reading and the Arithmetic Mean and can be expressed as

$$P_1 = \left[\frac{1}{n} \sum_{i=1}^{n} (V - V_i)^2 \right]^{1/2}$$

where n is the number of observations.

The *Average Deviation* is the numerical summation of all the deviations from the Arithmetic Mean divided by the number of observations:

$$P_2 = \frac{1}{n} \sum_{i=1}^{n} (V - V_i)^2$$

where n is the number of observations.

The *Probable Error P_3* of a single observation is defined as that deviation from the Arithmetic Mean of the observed data for which the probability that it will be exceeded is equal to the probability that it will not be exceeded. The three precision indices are interrelated as follows:

	P_1	P_3	P_2
P_1	1.0000	1.4826	1.2533
P_3	0.6745	1.0000	0.8453
P_2	0.7979	1.1829	1.0000

The precision index is expressed either in terms of absolute units or of percentages. Percentages are generally more useful because a comparison can be readily made with the required tolerance for the measurement to determine acceptance.

G. STOLAR

Cross-references: *Indicating Instruments, Integrating Instruments, Probability, Standards*

EXPANSION: see COMPRESSION AND EXPANSION

EXTRATERRESTRIAL RADIO SOURCES

Since Jansky's discovery in 1931 of radio emission from the galaxy, more and more astronomical radio sources have been discerned. Radio techniques have thus been added to the methods of astronomers in many branches of the subject, and in general, the new techniques contribute data complementary to what is deducible from optical observations. Often, indeed, the radio emission takes place in regions that are invisible.

The Moon. Microwaves are emitted by the subsurface layers of the moon, in accordance with the blackbody radiation laws. The Rayleigh-Jeans approximation to Planck's formula tells us that the radio brightness b of a black body, at temperature T and wavelength λ, is given by

$$b = \frac{2kT}{\lambda^2} \text{ wm}^{-2}(\text{cps})^{-1}\text{sterad}^{-1}$$

where k is Boltzmann's constant (1.38 $\times$ 10^{-23} joules deg^{-1}). The moon's *surface* temperature rises and falls, during the month, between about 200 and 400°K, reaching a maximum when the sun is overhead.

The moon's radio emission has been observed from wavelengths of a few millimeters to nearly a meter, with the following results. At the shortest wavelengths there is a monthly variation that is sinusoidal, has a range of about 100°K, and reaches its maximum three or four days after full moon. These phenomena are explicable if the radiation escapes from some depth below the surface. Then the sinusoidal fundamental component of the temperature variation predominates and suffers the attenuation and phase lag appropriate to the depth. At wavelengths longer than about 10 cm, no variation is discernible, presumably because the emission is from depths that the temperature wave does not reach.

The observations narrow the range of possible thermal and electromagnetic constants of the moon's surface, and have been interpreted as indicating that the moon is fully covered by a thermally insulating blanket such as dust in vacuo. As antennas of greater resolving power are brought to bear on the moon, more detailed contributions about the physical properties of lunar surface features can be expected.

The Sun. At millimeter wavelengths the sun behaves like a black sphere at a steady temperature little above the optical value of about 6000°K.

In the decade from 3 to 30 cm, several distinct types of variability set in on top of the *quiet sun*. First there is a *slowly varying component* that, in the course of months, causes changes of about three to one, and reveals a 27-day recurrence tendency. Then there are *microwave* bursts of emission, having durations of a few minutes, that are often small but occasionally double the total emission of the sun. The burst may be followed by a weaker, but longer lived, *postburst increase*.

The source of the microwave emission of the quiet sun lies in the chromosphere and lower corona, several tens of thousands of kilometers above the visible surface, and is distributed in height in accordance with the microwave attenuation constant of the solar plasma. In general the average height of emission increases with wavelength, and since the temperature of the medium also increases with height, the sun's apparent temperature increases with wavelength. For example, at 10 cm the radio brightness b of the quiet sun at the center of the disk corresponds to a temperature of about 40,000°K. This quantity, which is known as the brightness temperature T_b, is defined in terms of b by

$$b = \frac{2kT_b}{\lambda^2}$$

and is used for convenience whether the emission is by a thermal mechanism or not. The brightness temperature falls off towards the poles, but appears to increase towards the equatorial limbs.

The source of the slowly varying component has been localized in a vertical column of extra dense plasma exuded from, or con-

TABLE I. SOLAR RADIO EMISSION

Source of emission	Source characteristics		Radiation				Characteristics		Associated phenomena	Remarks
	Duration	Diameter	Name	Maximum brightness temp. °K	Variability	Spectrum	Polarization	Origin		
Quiet sun	11-year cycle (?)	>32′, increases with λ; cm and dm limb brightening; polar limb darkening	Quiet sun radiation	$<10^6$ increases with λ	Stable	cm, dm, m noise	Unpolarized	Thermal	Free-free radiation of ionized hydrogen and helium	
Radio condensations	Several rotations	1 to 10′, like faculae	Slowly varying component	$<2\times10^6$	Stable	cm, dm, m (?)	Unpolarized	Thermal (?)	Coronal condensations, optical centers of activity, faculae	May be of the same nature
	Days or months	~1′		$<5\times10^5$	Stable	cm, dm (?)	Partial circular	Thermal (?)	+ magnetic field above spots	
Microcondensations	Minutes to hours	~½′	Gradual rise and fall	$<5\times10^5$	Stable	cm, dm	Partial circular	Thermal (?)		
R centers	Hours to days	<1′ to ~10′	Noise storm	10^9	Continuum + amounts of type I	m	Circular	Non-thermal (?)	Vague association with the optical centers of activity	Source susceptible to slow movements in the corona
Type I	Tenths of seconds	?	Type I	?	Simple	m, some Mc	Circular	Non-thermal (?)	?	Originate in R centers
Type III	Seconds	up to 10′, increases with λ	Type III, U bursts, inverted bursts, fast bursts, isolated bursts	$>10^{11}$	Simple or in harmonic groups	m, dm, 10-Mc drift rate $\pm$ 100 Mc	Variable	Synchrotron (?) Plasma oscillations (?)	Often with first phase of flare	Drift rate corresponds to speeds of a fraction of the velocity of light (high energy particles? waves?)
Type II	Minutes	?	Type II, outbursts or slow bursts	$>10^{10}$	Very complex, harmonics, splitting	m, dm, cm (?) drift rate -1 Mc	Usually little polarization	Plasma oscillations (?) Synchrotron (??)	First phase of flare	Rising disturbance $V \sim 100 - 300$ kMc (short waves). Cause of magnetic storms (?)
Type IV	Minutes to hours	up to 10′, increases with λ	Type IV, late (storm phase) burst	$>10^{11}$	Very stable	cm, dm, m several octaves	Often circular	Synchrotron (?)	After large flares, sometimes 10 or 20^m	Possibly associated with production of solar cosmic rays; the source first moves with type II speeds, then stabilizes
Centimeter bursts	Minute	~2′	Centimeter bursts	$>10^9$	Simple + postbursts	cm, dm	Variable	Synchrotron (??)	Close connection with flares	

densed above, the principal sunspot groups. At any given wavelength a slice of this column is the source. Its angular diameter is from one to several minutes of arc. There are commonly half a dozen such sources on the whole sun at any one time, and as the solar rotation carries them around the limbs, the characteristic 27-day recurrence is generated. During the many months of life of a source of slowly varying component, sunspot groups below it may come and go several times replenishing or reactivating it.

As an index of solar activity, the strength of the slowly varying component has had much success. Its region of origin is apparently also a source of ionizing radiation that maintains the terrestrial ionosphere, and consequently there is a close correlation with ionospheric critical frequencies, and usable frequencies for long-distance radio communication. A close agreement between the slowly varying component and an irregular component of friction on earth satellites has also been demonstrated. Radiation from the columnar condensation heats the earth's upper atmosphere causing it to rise and thus increase in density at the height of the satellite.

The conditions of electron density and temperature appear to be favorable for the generation of ultraviolet and soft X-rays, and this prediction has been confirmed by rocket observations.

Microwave bursts have their origin in, or very close to, the columnar condensations, and occur at the same time as a solar flare. Consequently, they are connected with the wide range of phenomena caused by flares—magnetic storms, short-wave fadeouts, cosmic ray increases, X-ray bursts, etc.—and may be expected to contribute to the understanding of the fundamental nature of sporadic solar activity.

At the time of occurrence of a solar flare, monochromatic optical observation reveals that quantities of matter are catapulted forth from the vicinity of the flare, often to fall back later under the influence of gravity. Some ejections escape from the sun, however, for the terrestrial magnetic storms of the type known as "sudden commencements" are known to be caused by the arrival in the earth's atmosphere of corpuscles ejected by flares. As the streams of particles rise through the solar corona, the medium is provoked into secondary emission of radio waves at frequencies closely connected to the local plasma frequency. The emission extends from microwaves to some low frequency limit that descends right through the radio spectrum in a matter of about 20 min. This phenomenon is known as a solar radio outburst, and is particularly intense, often exhibiting brightness temperatures of the order of 10^{10} °K. The study of outbursts should extend our knowledge of the phenomena accompanying the passage of particle streams through plasmas, especially the mechanisms of energy conversion (q.v.). A clue to the processes involved is provided by the appearance of a strong second harmonic, which has often been noted.

Following an outburst, a rather stable source of continuum emission may develop at an altitude of some solar radii, and remain for some hours. It is surmised, from the circular polarization and spectrum, that a swarm of high-energy electrons has established itself within a magnetic bottle, and radiates by the synchrotron mechanism (magnetobremsstrahlung). It may well be that further observation will reveal such swarms of particles breaking away from the sun. A phenomenon of this type is required to explain the fact that solar cosmic rays may take 20 min or more to reach the earth; and also the fact that the auroral particles take several days, but arrive with much greater penetrating power than their slow speed would suggest.

Several other types of burst are known, as well as the long-lived noise storm, which are shown in the table. In addition, the quiet sun sets a lower limit at all times, with a brightness temperature approaching 10^6 °K in the meter and decameter range.

Jupiter. A very intense source in the 15- to 35-Mc band, Jupiter is the strongest source of nonmanmade interference. The emission is sporadic, sometimes absent, polarized and very strong, with peak outputs up to 100,000 megawatts/Mc. Since the rotation period of 9 hr 55 min 30 sec is clearly apparent in the intensity variation, the source must be unevenly distributed in longitude. In fact, it completely avoids one quadrant, whose longitude can be determined with precision. In addition to this unexpected phenomenon there is a less intense but equally unexpected type of emission on decimeter wavelengths. Observations at 3 and 10 cm had confirmed that Jupiter emits thermally at the expected temperature of about 145°K, but apparent disk temperatures of 2000°K have been reported at 21 cm and 8000°K at 31 cm. This radiation comes from the space surrounding Jupiter, possibly from relativistic electrons such as occupy the earth's Van Allen belt. Phenomena such as this have not been observed in connection with the other planets, but thermal emission has been recorded from Venus, Mars, and Saturn.

Cosmic Radio Waves. Although attempts were made around the turn of the century to receive the radio waves that the sun must emit, nevertheless the first extraterrestrial radio waves observed originated far beyond the solar system. These cosmic radio waves may be divided into two classes according as to whether their source is within our galaxy or is extragalactic. First we consider the galactic emission.

As viewed with an antenna of low resolving power, the cosmic radio emission is concentrated towards the plane of the Milky Way. Furthermore, within this galactic belt there is a further concentration towards the center of the galaxy. These facts indicate that radio emissivity is a property that is generally distributed throughout the galaxy. The emission does not, however, take place from the stars, but comes from the matter in the space between the stars; in fact only a single star, other than the sun, has been identified as a radio source. Such stars promise interest for the future.

When an antenna of better angular resolu-

tion is used, discrete sources are also apparent, but the breakdown into discrete sources and distributed background is different at different frequencies. For example the microwave sky is quite different from the meter-wave sky, and the decameter sky has further differences.

The microwave sky exhibits principally discrete sources, about 60 of which are known. Distributed background is present but has a brightness temperature less than 3°K even in the direction of the galactic center. The discrete sources, however, lie along the galactic equator, with a handful of exceptions to which we shall return later. The radiation is emitted thermally by gaseous nebulae, or H II regions, that are kept ionized by hot stars. A typical H II region has a thickness of 10^{20} cm, an electron temperature of 10,000°K, and an electron density of 10 cm^{-3}. Calculating from the attenuation constant of radio waves in such a plasma, we can show that such a region would be opaque at frequencies less than about 20 Mc; consequently at these frequencies the region would exhibit a brightness temperature of 10,000°K. At higher frequencies, as the region becomes partially transparent, the brightness temperature falls off as f^{-2}.

It is customary to measure the strength of a discrete source by its flux density S which is defined by

$$S = \frac{2kT_b}{\lambda^2} \Omega \quad \text{watts m}^{-2}(\text{cps})^{-1}$$

where Ω is the solid angle subtended by the source. Evidently if T_b is varying as f^{-2}, then the flux density S has settled down to a constant value. The microwave sources in the galactic plane obey this law, and Table 2 gives a list of microwave flux densities in units of 10^{-26} watts m^{-2}(cps)$^{-1}$.

Three conspicuous microwave sources (Cassiopeia A, Taurus A and Cygnus A) reveal by their spectrum that they are not thermal. Their flux densities vary roughly as f^{-1} (less steeply in the case of Taurus A) as contrasted with variation as f^2 (low frequencies) or $f^°$ (high frequencies) for a thermal source. It will be clear that, in the meter wavelength range, the thermal sources will have faded away, whereas the nonthermal sources will be even stronger. Many thousands of meter wave sources have now been catalogued.

Meter wave sources have proved in large proportion to be extragalactic objects and as such are taken up later. Cassiopeia A and Taurus A, however, lie within the galaxy, and there are about 30 others. It is now considered that these sources are supernova remnants. Taurus A lies in the direction of the Crab nebula, an expanding cloud of matter liberated by a type I supernova explosion in 1054 A.D. It is at a distance of 1000 parsecs. Cassiopeia A is (probably) a type II supernova remnant, larger, more distant, and caused by an explosion 250 years ago. About a dozen sources have been associated with visible nebulosities which, from their circular outline and high expansion velocities, are thought to be supernova remnants.

It is generally considered that the galactic supernovae of the past may suffice to explain the bulk of the other radio sources, which, from their small angular diameter, or closeness to the galactic plane, apparently represent the supernovae in the remote parts of the galaxy that cannot be reached optically.

Ancient supernovae, which have now spread beyond recognition as discrete sources, may also play an important role in the radio emission of the galaxy.

The synchrotron emission mechanism. For some time it was not clear how the Crab nebula could radiate about 10^{26} watts in the radiofrequency spectrum without at the same time emitting much more light. It now appears that kinetic energy of the expanding shell is converted rather efficiently to electromagnetic form by the emission of relativistic electrons accelerating in a magnetic field. This so-called synchrotron emission has a hump in the radio-frequency spectrum, but also extends right into the visible. For many years a mystery, the visible continuum of the Crab nebula has been accepted as synchrotron emission since proving to be linearly polarized, as predicted.

The galactic corona. From the background surveys it is clear that the relative intensities in the directions of the galactic center and galactic pole are not those to be expected from a disk-like source distribution, but rather indicate a large spherical volume of emission. At one time it seemed reasonable to ascribe much of this to isotropic extragalactic sources. Meanwhile, however, observations have shown the Andromeda nebula to be imbedded in a roughly spherical radio source 10° in diameter, and it is now not doubted that our own galaxy is similar.

Since there was no prior indication from optical observation of the existence of a material corona surrounding the galaxy, only an extremely tenuous medium could be invoked as the source. It has successfully been demonstrated that as few as 10^{-4} relativistic electrons per cubic centimeter, emitting by the synchrotron process in a field of 10^{-5} gauss, can explain the observations. This development is of great significance for astrophysics inasmuch as cosmic rays now receive an explanation as the positive-ion component of the galactic corona. Future observations of the radio emission of the galactic corona may shed light on the structure of the galactic magnetic field which apparently plays a key role in the as yet not understood evolution of a spiral galaxy.

The galactic disk. Both continuum and line radiation are received from the galactic disk. The line emission at a wavelength of 21 cm,

TABLE 2. MICROWAVE SOURCES IN THE GALACTIC PLANE

NGC number	Name	Flux density 10^{-26} wm^{-2}(cps)$^{-1}$	Right ascension (1950) hr	min	Declination (1950)	
6618	Omega	700	18	18	−16°	14′
1976	Orion	450	5	33	−5	27
6357		400	17	22	−34	9
6334		250	17	17	−36	0
6523	Lagoon	200	18	1	−24	23

TABLE 3. SOME OF THE STRONGER GALACTIC AND
EXTRAGALACTIC SOURCES

NGC number	Name	Flux density 10^{-26} w m^{-2}(cps)$^{-1}$		Right ascension (1950)		Declination (1950)	
		100 Mc	1000 Mc	hr	min		
1952	Taurus A*	2,000	1000	05	31	21°	59′
—	Cassiopeia A*	20,000	3000	23	21	58	32
224	Andromeda†	100	25	00	40	41	00
—	Cygnus A‡	13,000	2000	19	58	40	36
5128	Centaurus A‡	9,000	1800	13	22	−42	46
4486	Virgo A‡	1,000	300	12	28	12	40
1316	Fornax A‡	600	150	03	21	−37	24

* Galactic.
† Normal external galaxy.
‡ Peculiar external galaxy.

which has proved to be a powerful tool in revealing the spiral structure of the galaxy, takes place from neutral hydrogen in the ground state when the spin of the nucleus reverses. The precise frequency, measured in the laboratory, is 1420.4058 Mc. Because of the Doppler shift associated with galactic rotational velocities, it is possible to separate sources distributed in the same line of sight, and to make maps of the distribution of the neutral hydrogen. It proves to occupy a complex spiral domain, and to lie within a disk 250 parsecs thick to half density. This type of structure was expected from earlier optical studies of external galaxies, but an unexpected feature is a radial outflow of hydrogen, at a velocity of the order of 50 km/sec, in the inner part of the galaxy.

Continuum radiation from the galactic disk appears as though its source is distributed in space in the same way as the neutral hydrogen, even the spiral structure appearing to be preserved. In all respects but its spatial distribution, the continuum radiation is similar to that from the galactic corona.

External sources. Since our own galaxy is a strong radio source, it is to be expected that similar galaxies nearby would be detectable, as indeed has proved to be the case. In addition, however, there are vastly more powerful radio galaxies which are in some way peculiar; e.g., Virgo A has a jet protruding from its nucleus, which emits polarized light. Cygnus A is a galactic collision, or fission, taking place at a distance of 90 megaparsecs and involving an energy of 10^{59} ergs.

Table 3 gives the strength and position of some of the stronger galactic and extragalactic sources.

R. N. BRACEWELL

Cross-references: *Bremsstrahlung, Interference, Ionization, Propagation, Radar Astronomy, Radiation (Terrestrial)*

F

FACSIMILE

Facsimile is a form of communication that reproduces graphic copy at a remote point by electronic means. A facsimile system systematically converts a picture or other fixed graphic copy into electrical signals which are transmitted by wire or radio to a receiving point where these are converted back into a replica of the original.

In a simple system, the copy to be sent is wrapped around the drum. The surface of the drum is brightly illuminated and an image of the copy is formed in a manner similar to that in a camera, but on a metal plate instead of on film. The metal plate has a very small hole in its center. The size of the hole is the same as the smallest detail to be resolved and limits resolution in a manner similar to the grain size of film. Behind this hole is located a phototube, which sees a very small spot on the copy and controls the amplitude of an ac signal in proportion to brightness. If the signal is in the audio frequency spectrum, it can be sent over a voice-type circuit to the receiving point. At the receiving point, the signal controls the brightness of a recording lamp, which is focused onto a small spot on film mounted on the receiving drum.

The speeds of the two drums must be almost exactly the same and are usually controlled by a frequency standard at each end. Before each transmission the two drums are phased to center the recorded image on the film.

The rotating drum is used in many systems. It is possible to have the drum itself move in front of the scanning and recording points or have the drum only rotate while the optical systems move across in front of the drum.

Several systems are used to generate a moving spot across the surface of a flat piece of copy to be scanned or recorded.

In one such system, an image of the copy being scanned is formed on the surface of a slit. The width of the slit is the same as the elemental area and the length of the slit is the same as the copy image width. Beneath this slit and very close to it is a drum, which has a helical slit making one turn around the drum. The width of this slit intersecting with the width of the straight slit determine the elemental area size. Light from the image passing through this aperture is picked up by a phototube. As the drum makes one revolution, the point of intersection traverses across the copy image. For the next revolution of the drum, the spot again traverses the copy image, but this image is slowly moving across the slit so that the second line is scanned adjacent and parallel to the first.

A second system forms an image in the same manner on a slit across the copy width. Behind the straight slit is a disk with a single turn spiral slit. The intersection between the spiral slit and the straight slit determines the elemental area size. A variation of this system uses two spirals: a multiturn spiral and a single-turn one. The multiturn spiral rotates N times the speed of the single turn spiral if N represents the number of complete spirals on the multiturn one. The advantage of using a multiturn spiral is that a more rectangular spot is obtained between the intersection of the slits and the variations of linearity owing to speed instabilities in the system is minimized.

An oscillating mirror is used for a third type of mechanical flying spot scanner, or recorder. An optical system forms an image of the copy being scanned on an aperture plate and the phototube sees the light passing through the aperture. The optical system uses two separate lenses mounted at right angles to each other with a mirror between them to change the direction of the light beam. The angle of the mirror controls the position of the image on the aperture plate. If the mirror is tilted at a uniform rate, the phototube sees a succession of spots in a straight line across the copy. The copy is advanced past the scanning line position at a uniform rate. The movement of the mirror is obtained by using a cam that has a linear rate of angular movement across the scanning line and a fast return. The return signal is blanked out. Another method of obtaining the mirror movement uses the surface of a multifaced prism which is rotated at a constant angular velocity. Both systems are used for transmitting and receiving equipments.

A fourth scanning system also uses an oscillating mirror. The mirror surface in this case is spherical instead of being flat. An incandescent tungsten ball about 0.01 in. in diameter in a special lamp is focused by the spherical mirror onto the surface of the copy being scanned. As the mirror is tilted the spot formed moves across the copy width in a straight line. A phototube placed near the copy surface picks up light reflected from the copy.

In a fifth system using a mechanically generated flying spot, the copy is formed into the shape of a half cylinder. An optical system of the type used on the rotating drum equipment is mounted to rotate on the center of the cylinder. Two optical heads are used 180° out of phase. The same principles are also used with 120° sector of a cylinder being used for the copy and three scanning heads.

In a nonmechanical system of flying-spot scanning (*q.v.*) or recording, the spot is formed on the surface of a cathode-ray tube. An image of this spot is formed on the copy to be scanned or on film to be recorded. As the spot is swept in a linear fashion from one side to the other, the copy to be scanned or the film being exposed is advanced past the scanning line, or the recording line. Since the edge of the spot is not sharply defined, the resolution is less for a given scanning spot size than systems using aperture plates. One

type of equipment using a CRT flying spot does not have the usual phospor on the surface of the tube. Instead, the phospor is on a rotating drum located inside the tube. This system makes it possible to use a much higher brightness of spot since the heat produced by it is dissipated over a large surface.

Another method, which is used for both scanning and recording, uses an electron beam on the surface of a cathode ray tube to generate a raster similar to that used in television pictures. The light from the spot is focused onto the surface of the copy to be scanned or the recording medium. No physical movement of the copy is required.

In addition to the methods mentioned above which may be used for either scanning or recording, there are other techniques which are suitable for recording only. These recording systems do not employ photographic recording techniques used by the systems just described, but produce a visible image as recorded (direct recording).

One recording system consists of a helix and blade with recording paper passing between them. A wire is wrapped in a single helical turn around a drum intersecting with a flat blade parallel to the axis of the drum. An electrolytic recording paper is used and the passage of current between the blade and the helix wire causes a marking on the paper at this point.

A second system also employs a helix and blade with the paper between them as before. In this case, however, the recording is by pressure sensitive techniques.

In a third direct recording system, three or more recording heads are mounted on a continuous belt that runs between two pulleys. Recording paper supplied from a roll passes by the edge of the belt as it traverses between the pulleys. These heads are tungsten stylus wires which touch the surface of dry electrosensitive recording paper. As current passes from the stylus wire into the paper, the top surface is burned off leaving the dark undercoating exposed to produce a permanent black mark. The band moves at a uniform rate such that when the first stylus records a line and passes the right edge of the paper, the second stylus starts recording on the left edge. A variation of this system uses magnetic recording heads on the band. Inside each recording head is a magnetic plunger with a small metal ball. Signal current through the electromagnet presses the ball onto the paper surface producing a mark on pressure sensitive paper.

A fifth type recorder uses a large number of stylus needles placed in a row with the spacing equivalent to the width of a recording line. For recording on paper with an 8-in. recording line and 100 recording lines/in., 800 styli are needed. A commutator connects to each of the stylus needles so that each of the recording styli is energized in turn as the facsimile transmitter scans across one line. An individual amplifier is usually used for each recording stylus and the input to the amplifiers is commutated. These stylus needles may mark either electrolytic or dry electrosensitive recording paper.

A sixth recording system uses a single recording head which transfers ink to the face of a moving endless belt. As the belt moves into position across the recording paper, it is snapped against the paper to transfer one complete ink line at a time. The recording head is meanwhile inking the next recording line onto the belt face.

Transmission. Facsimile signals are a form of real-time data signals and the recorded copy is distorted by anything which distorts the time of arrival of the signals at the recording point. Most of the facsimile systems operate over voice type wire lines since they are readily available and are suitable for the transmission speeds usually required. These circuits are usually suitable for sending about 2400 elemental areas per second although higher rates are being used on special circuits or where some degradation of quality is acceptable. If these elemental areas are black or white only, the rate of sending is 2400 bits/sec. For photographic transmission, a continuous-tone gray scale is required and each elemental area may represent 32 or more different levels

depending upon the quality of reproduction required. If 32 levels are represented by an elemental area, each elemental area then represents 5 bits of information. This type of signal may still be transmitted at the rate of 2400 elemental areas per second giving an information transmission rate of 12,000 bits/sec over a voice type circuit. Since a 12,000-bits/sec circuit would be required for digital transmission of copy at the same rate, an analog transmission circuit is preferred for transmission of pictures.

Wire lines and radio-relay circuits usually have the same general characteristics as far as terminal equipments are concerned. Speed of transmission is limited mainly by envelope delay distortion due to nonlinearities in the phase-frequency characteristic caused either by loading coils on wire-line circuits or by channel-deriving filters used on carrier and radio-relay circuits. For high-quality photographic transmission, the amount of envelope-delay distortion that can be tolerated over the frequency band required to send the signals is plus or minus the amount of time taken for $\frac{1}{2}$ an elemental area. For message transmission, double this limit is usually acceptable.

Amplitude modulation is generally used for wire line transmission. For voice frequency circuits, a carrier frequency of 2400 cps is acceptable for vestigial sideband transmission using the lower sideband. The vestigial-sideband techniques are similar to those used in television (q.v.). The carrier amplitude is attenuated 6 db and the summation of the upper and lower sideband frequencies in the vicinity of the carrier is a constant amplitude. Double-sideband transmission using a carrier frequency between 1800 and 2000 cps is also common.

Television channels are sometimes used for high speed facsimile transmission. These channels have envelope delay distortion equalization and are suitable for high-speed facsimile transmission. Facsimile use differs from TV transmission in that a carrier frequency is used rather than sending the video rate as a base band signal. Other channel bandwidths between the voice circuit and the video circuit have been used. One of these is a group circuit which has a nominal bandwidth of 48 kc. In order to make effective use of this bandwidth, it is necessary to use envelope-delay distortion-equalization networks. A super-group bandwidth of a nominal 240 kc is also usable for facsimile transmission. This type of channel does not require much envelope delay distortion equalization in order to be used effectively. Neither the group nor super-group circuits are generally available from the telephone companies but can be made available in certain cases by special arrangements.

High-frequency radio transmission of facsimile signals employs frequency-shift modulation techniques. This type of modulation is required in order to limit the signal at the receiving station and eliminate the effects of fading, as far as signal amplitude is concerned. The main distortion introduced by this type of circuit is that due to multipath distortion produced by signals arriving at the receiving point over several different paths. Frequently, the strongest signals switch from one path length to another. Variations of more than a millisecond are common and cause a corresponding displacement in the recorded spot causing jitter of a line which is perpendicular to the recording line. Atmospheric noise and interference from other stations also degrade copy quality. Under good conditions, it is possible, however, to get quality very comparable to that obtained on high quality wire line. The speed of transmission is limited to that of a voice-type wire line circuit or sometimes even less for high-quality copy.

Systems. *Telegram Collection and Distribution.* Over 40,000 facsimile transceivers are used in offices to send and receive telegrams between the office and the telegraph company. This is a very simple machine which uses power line synchronization to keep the drums of the transmitter and receiver in step. Either the copy to be sent or a recording blank is placed on a drum for written communications to the telegraph

company. Recording is done by single-stylus wire riding on the surface of dry electrosensitive paper.

News Photo Transmission. The Associated Press and the United Press International are the two large U. S. news photo systems that employ extensive networks for facsimile transmission. These circuits are operated throughout the United States on more than 20,000 miles of telephone lines specially treated for delay distortion equalization. Pictures from overseas are received at certain main points by radio and placed on these networks. The Atlantic cable is used for pictures between Britain and Canada but not to the United States. Photographic recording is used for obtaining sharpness and the best fidelity of the picture gray scale. Direct recording is used where some loss of picture quality is acceptable or for monitoring of pictures being received.

Weather Map Distribution Systems. The WAN analysis center at Suitland, Md., collects weather information for the Northern Hemisphere and plots many different types of charts on a regular schedule. These charts are distributed to more than 500 stations over approximately 30,000 miles of telephone lines. Charts are received and used by the U. S. Air Force, Navy, Signal Corps, and Weather Bureau, and by commercial airlines, private meteorologists, and others to make available through the country consistent and expert weather analyses. The size of the chart on this network is 18×12 in. Some of the other weather facsimile networks use the same width of chart and a longer length. The WAN circuit now has a capacity of over 120 charts per day. Many other weather circuits using phone lines are in use for specialized maps are not handled on the WAN circuit. Weather charts are also broadcast by radio on more than 100 different frequencies. In addition to the standard types of weather charts, sea conditions charts are transmitted that allow ships to avoid heavy sea swells and to reduce the crossing time.

Interoffice Communications. Several types

of equipment are used for rapid transmission of letter-size messages between fixed points. Direct recording systems which require no processing are generally used with electrolytic, dry electrosensitive, or pressure-sensitive recording. Electrostatic-printing (*q.v.*) techniques are also sometimes used. A resolution of about 100 lines/in. is required for message communications to give adequate sharpness for elite or pica type. Transmission time of an $8\frac{1}{2} \times 11$-in. copy over a voice-frequency circuit is about 6 min for a full page or a correspondingly shorter time for shorter messages. A public service for sending letter-size messages is available between certain major U. S. cities.

High-Speed Transmission of Newspaper and Magazine Proof Pages. Systems are in use that have been specially designed to handle a full-page proof of either newspaper or magazine copy. These systems are used where the printing plant is far removed from the editorial offices. A typical copy size is 16×24 in. and the number of scanning lines used varies from 300 to 1,000 lines/in. The higher-resolution systems are used to scan originals which contain half-tone screened pictures. In order to obtain good fidelity of reproduction, it is necessary to reproduce faithfully a dot which is about 10 per cent of the area of a full-size dot used in the screen. Group circuits or video circuits are generally used for transmission of this type of facsimile copy. The received film is used directly for printing the newspaper or magazine using letterpress or offset methods.

Other Facsimile Systems. X-ray films require transmission of densities running to 2.8 or higher, resulting in an extremely long dynamic range and a signal that it is impractical to send directly over a communication circuit. The signal range is compressed in a linear manner such that the ratio between the maximum and minimum signal level is compatible with the transmission circuit and the recording techniques (30 db maximum), and yet the small density variations in either the light portions or the dark portions of the film are preserved. A resolution of 50 lines/in. on a 14×17-in. original film is adequate for most cases. One hundred lines/in. may be required where sharp line fractures are involved.

The transmission of pictures from satellites such as Tiros have been used for sending cloud cover information over large areas of the earth. The methods used are similar to standard TV transmissions with each frame of the received image photographed on 35-mm film directly from a cathode-ray tube.

A system being used by the Signal Corps sends $3\frac{1}{4} \times 4\frac{1}{4}$-in. pictures or 70-mm film by dropping the copy to be sent into a slot and pushing a button. The copy is recorded on photographic paper or film from a roll inside the facsimile set. Processing is accomplished by lifting a button and pulling out a tab. About 1 min is required before the finished print or film can be removed.

Brand and Trade Names

Alfax
  Alden
Brokerfax
  Western Union
Deskfax
  Western Union
Electronic Messenger
  Electronics Communications
Faximile
  Hogan Laboratories
Faxpaper
  Hogan Laboratories
Hellfax
  Dr. Ing. Rudolph Hell

Hellschreiber
  Dr. Ing. Rudolph Hell
Intrafax
  Western Union
Klischograph
  Dr. Ing. Rudolph Hell
Letterfax
  Western Union
Mufax
  Muirhead Instruments
Messagefax
  Westrex
Pressfax
  Westrex

Photofax
  Associated Press
Photoscan
  Columbia Broadcasting
Sound Photo
  United Press International
Teledeltos
  Western Union
Telegnosis
  Westrex
Telephoto
  Westrex
Ticketfax
  Western Union

Timefax
  Westrex
Timemark
  Westrex
Videograph
  A. B. Dick
Weatherfax
  Westrex
Wirephoto
  Associated Press
Zetfax
  Dr. Ing. Rudolph Hell

K. R. McConnell

Cross-references: *Electrostatic Printing, Modulation and Demodulation*

FADING: see PROPAGATION

FARADAY EFFECT

This effect was the first demonstration of a connection between magnetism and light. Faraday found in 1845 that when plane polarized light was transmitted through glass in a direction parallel to an applied magnetic field the plane of polarization was rotated. Since Faraday's original discovery the phenomenon has been observed in many solids, liquids, and gases. It is important in the interaction of electromagnetic radiation with the ionosphere and in the study of charge carrier behavior in the laboratory. These effects may all be regarded as acting on the electric field associated with the wave. There is a second class of Faraday rotation phenomena in which the effect acts on the magnetic-field component of the wave. These effects are very large in ferromagnetic insulators and have made possible the development of a class of nonreciprocal microwave devices, which are described briefly in the concluding paragraph. Cgs units are used throughout this article.

Electric-field Effects

Optical Rotation from Spectral Transitions. In the region of the spectrum close to an absorption line, the dielectric proper-

ties of the medium are dominated by the absorption and its associated dispersion. In those cases of interest the absorption line is broadened or split by an applied magnetic field. One can show by quite general arguments that for every spectral component displaced linearly in the applied field there must be a second component that is displaced in the opposite direction. The simplest case is one in which the original spectral line splits into two lines with frequencies

$$\omega^- = \omega_0 - \omega_L \qquad \omega^+ = \omega_0 + \omega_L$$

where $\omega_L = geH/4mc$ is the Larmor frequency and g is called the spectroscopic splitting factor. One can again show by general arguments that in an isotropic medium a positively circularly polarized wave will be absorbed only at ω^+ and similarly a negative wave only at ω^-. With this theoretical background we may now consider the mechanism of rotation. Let us imagine that a linearly polarized wave at frequency ω is directed into the medium along the magnetic field. We can expect that if we decompose the incident wave into two waves of opposite circular polarization, the waves propagate independently. Each wave is characterized by its own dielectric constant and therefore its own phase velocity. If the dielectric constant of the positive component is larger than that of the negative component at frequency ω, then the positive component has the lower phase velocity and is rotated through a larger angle on passing through the medium. If we recombine the waves after a path length l we will find the plane of polarization to be rotated through an angle

$$\theta = \pi l (n^- - n^+)/\lambda_0$$

where λ_0 is the free-space wavelength and n^+ and n^- are the refractive indices for the two polarization directions. It is occasionally inconvenient to decompose the incident field into circular components. One can alternatively characterize the medium by a dielectric tensor. The off-diagonal elements of the tensor are given by

$$\mathcal{E}_{xy} = -\mathcal{E}_{yx} = (\mathcal{E}^+ - \mathcal{E}^-)/2j$$

By comparison with the earlier expression the rotation angle may be written approximately as

$$\theta = -j\pi\mathcal{E}_{xy}l/n\lambda_0$$

For the particular case considered here we have

$$\mathcal{E}_{xy} = 2j\omega\omega_p{}^2\omega_L/(\omega_0{}^2 - \omega^2)^2$$

where $\omega_p = (4\pi Ne^2/m)^{1/2}$ is the plasma frequency. One of the important advantages of Faraday rotation as a technique for studying optical spectra is that it permits a determination of the Larmor frequency under circumstances where it may not be possible to resolve the splitting directly. This technique is also of very considerable importance in the determination of internal magnetic fields in ferromagnetic materials.

Carrier Rotation. One can apply an analysis similar to the above in the case of free charge carriers. It is convenient to discuss the rotation by charge carriers in two limits. At frequencies low compared with the collision frequency of the carriers and to first order in the magnetic field we obtain

$$\mathcal{E}_{xy} = 4\pi\sigma_0\mu H/j\omega_c$$

where $\mu = e\tau/m$ is the carrier mobility and σ_0 is the low-frequency conductivity. The low-frequency Faraday effect and the Hall effect ($q.v.$) are closely related. At high frequencies the rotation is proportional to

$$\mathcal{E}_{xy} = j\omega_c\omega_p{}^2/\omega^3$$

where $\omega_c = eH/mc$ is the cyclotron fre-

quency. The Faraday effect is particularly important in the study of semiconductivity, where carriers move with an effective mass that may be considerably different from their free mass.

Magnetic-field Effects

In addition to the high-frequency Faraday effect, which is usually associated with electric dipole transitions, there are a number of low frequency rotation phenomena, which are associated with magnetic dipole transitions. Here the rotation is associated with the tensor properties of the magnetic permeability. The rotation angle is given by

$$\theta = -j\pi\mu_{xy}l/n\lambda_0$$

Paramagnetic Rotation. In a paramagnetic material the rotation is associated with the paramagnetic resonance absorption in much the same way that optical rotation is associated with optical absorption. For a paramagnetic material the rotation is proportional to

$$\mu_{xy} = -4j\pi\chi_0\gamma H/\omega$$

where γ is the magneto-mechanical ratio.

Ferromagnetic Rotation. In a ferromagnetic material very large rotations may be achieved because of the very large effective susceptibility $\chi_0 = M/H$. For magnetically saturated material we obtain

$$\mu_{xy} = -4j\pi\gamma M/\omega$$

Antiferromagnetic Rotation. Antiferromagnetic materials are characterized by resonance absorption even in the absence of a field. Applying the magnetic field along the symmetry axis we obtain

$$\mu_{xy} = -8j\pi\chi_\perp\omega\gamma H\omega_0{}^2/(\omega_0{}^2 - \omega^2)^2$$

where ω_0 is the zero-field resonance frequency and $\chi_\perp$ is the susceptibility perpendicular to the axis.

Applications

The principal application of the Faraday effect to electronics has been in the development of nonreciprocal microwave devices. Because of the nonsymmetric character of the permeability tensor in a magnetic field it is possible to fabricate devices that permit the nearly unattenuated passage of microwaves in one direction but will effectively block microwave transmission in the reverse direction. These devices, which make use of ferromagnetic insulators like ferrite or garnet, are of reduced effectiveness at high frequencies because of their inverse dependence on ω. Attention is being given to antiferromagnetic materials for use at high frequencies because of their increased transverse permeability in this range.

A. M. Portis

Cross-references: *Attenuators and Isolators, Characteristic Frequencies, Ferrites, Ferromagnetism, Hall Effect, Semiconductors*

FARMING (ELECTRONIC)

Electronic farming is a term applied to agricultural processes which employ electronic means to improve their effectiveness. In the tilling and grading of land, gyro compasses, electronic servomechanisms, and level sensors have been applied to the power steering of tractors to keep them on a straight course. Beacons and photoelectric sensors have been employed to guide tractors or grading equipment along a specific course. Deeply buried cables have also been proposed for electronic guidance of farm vehicles (as for cars on highways).

Until recently agricultural machinery made little use of closed-loop automotive control mechanisms, employing instead open systems controlled almost wholly by an operator. Competition has forced American agriculture to a greater mechanization and to a greater use of sophisticated closed-loop mechanisms and systems. Central to any closed system is the means of measuring and evaluating the desired quantities and qualities. Where in the past human judgment determined factors such as condition of the soil, maturity of crops, moisture level in hay, and animal marketability, these functions can now be determined in electronically controlled systems by special sensing mechanisms.

The following are a few areas where electronic techniques are employed in farming.

Eggs are being graded electronically and any color imperfections or blood spots are spotted automatically.

The difference in gamma ray radiation from lean and fat meat tissue is utilized in a technique for measuring the proportion of lean to fat tissue in livestock and poultry. The method can be modified for use on live poultry and livestock.

Recording photometers are in use for determining automatically the spectral reflection characteristics of vegetables for grading purposes, and for determining hollow spots in potatoes, etc.

Electronic control has been applied to the use of the anesthesia gas used in the humane slaughtering of hogs.

Ultrasonic techniques, which utilize the difference in sound velocity in fat and lean meat, are being used to obtain information or the proportion of lean to fat in hogs and other livestock.

Electronically controlled sorting and grading mechanisms are employed for fruits and vegetables.

Automatic soil-conditioning equipments, which employ special humidity and acidity probes in conjunction with electronic controls, are in use.

Small truck farms apply water, liquid fertilizers, sprays, and hormones automatically whenever required.

Electro mechanical systems using pneumatic tubes are used in poultry farms for distributing the correct amount of feed to each poultry house.

Electronic automation systems now under consideration include (1) automatic branders and readers of brand markings for automated breedings and recording of breeding; (2) fully automatic control of all poultry house functions; (3) fully automatic reapers, threshers, and harvesters; and (4) continuous feed testers for controlling silage mixtures.

Winston E. Kock

Cross-references: *Automobile Traffic Control, Mobile Communications, Servo Components*

FEEDBACK SYSTEMS

A feedback system is a collection of devices that measure a set of output signals, compare them with an appropriate set of reference input signals, and generate a set of error signals. The error signals (or functions thereof) are used in order to control the output variables in accordance with predescribed performance criteria.

There are many examples of feedback systems. The wall thermostat, the airplane automatic pilot (*q.v.*), missile guidance (*q.v.*), etc. are examples of such systems. One of the earliest, and most useful, systems was the flyball governor of James Watt (1736–1819) constructed in 1788. All of the feedback systems are characterized by one or more channels of information about the system response, so that the response may be compared with the desired one and, if there is any difference, corrective action may be employed.

The usefulness of the feedback systems lies in the fact that they correct inherent disturbances due to noise or equipment variations, which are not, in general, predictable. A system without feedback can be designed to accomplish a predetermined task accurately. However, the lack of feedback will cause the system to respond in an unacceptable fashion in the presence of noise. In addition, feedback systems are faster and have more uniform bandwidth characteristics.

Feedback systems (or closed-loop systems) may be divided into *continuous* and *sampleddata systems*. Continuous systems are char-

acterized by signals that are available at all times. Sampled-data systems (*q.v.*) are characterized by signals which are known only at discrete instants of time.

Feedback systems may be also divided into *linear* and *nonlinear*. Linear systems (*q.v.*) are described by a set of linear differential equations. Linear systems may be *stationary*, if the coefficients of the differential equations are constants, or *time-varying* (*q.v.*), if the coefficients of the differential equations are functions of time. Nonlinear systems (*q.v.*) are described by a set of nonlinear algebraic or differential equations. Nonlinear systems may also be classified as stationary or time-varying.

Certain feedback systems are also called *servomechanisms* (slave mechanisms). A servomechanism is a feedback system in which a function of the error signal is used in order to control the magnitude and/or the power direction of the output.

Linear Time-Invariant Feedback Systems

The Laplace transform (*q.v.*) and the concept of the transfer function are used almost universally for the analysis and design of stationary linear control systems. The basic configuration of a negative-feedback control system is illustrated in Fig. 1, where $r(t)$, with its Laplace transform $r(s)$, is the *reference (input, command) signal*, which describes, in general, the desired response of the system; $c(t)$, with its Laplace transform $c(s)$, is the *controlled (output, response) signal*, which describes the actual behavior

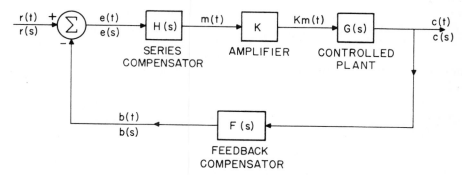

Fig. 1. General feedback-system configuration.

of the system; $e(t)$, with its Laplace transform $e(s)$, is the *error signal*—since the system of Fig. 1 is a negative-feedback system, $e(t) = r(t) - b(t)$; $H(s)$ is the transfer function of a series compensator and is included in the system because its purpose is to improve the system response; $m(t)$ is the response of the compensator $H(s)$ and is called the *manipulated variable*; K represents the amplitude and/or power amplifying device in the loop; $G(s)$ is the transfer function of the controlled plant (usually an unalterable component, as for example the antenna and associated motors and gears in a tracking system); and $F(s)$ is called the feedback compensator, used to improve the response of the system.

The transfer function of the over-all closed-loop system of Fig. 1 is given by the equation

$$\frac{c(s)}{r(s)} = \frac{KH(s)G(s)}{1 + KF(s)H(s)G(s)} \quad (1)$$

Equation (1) may be obtained from the set of the obvious equations

$$c(s) = KH(s)G(s)e(s)$$

$$e(s) = r(s) - b(s) \quad (2)$$

$$b(s) = F(s)c(s)$$

In servomechanisms, also called servos, the output $c(t)$ is directly subtracted from the input $r(t)$. Thus in servos, $F(s) = 1$.

Not all feedback systems utilize negative feedback. If in Fig. 1 the error signal $e(t)$ is the sum of $r(t)$ and $b(t)$, instead of the difference, then the system is a positive-feedback system. With positive feedback the transfer function of the closed-loop system becomes

$$\frac{c(s)}{r(s)} = \frac{KH(s)G(s)}{1 - KF(s)H(s)G(s)} \quad (3)$$

Types of Feedback Systems. Consider the unity-feedback system shown in Fig. 2.

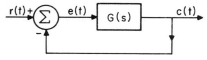

Fig. 2. Unity negative-feedback system.

In general the transfer function has the form

$$G(s) = K_n \frac{(sT_1 + 1)(sT_2 + 1)\cdots(sT_m + 1)}{s^n(sQ_1 + 1)(sQ_2 + 1)\cdots(sQ_p + 1)}$$

$$n = 0, 1, 2, \cdots \quad (4)$$

Accordingly, feedback systems are classified as follows:

Type 0 ($n = 0$): The output signal for these systems, due to a step input, tends to a constant. There exists a steady state error inversely proportional to K_0.

Type 1 ($n = 1$): The output signal, due to a step input, tends to increase linearly with time, i.e., the derivative of the output tends to a constant. There does not exist a steady-state error due to step inputs; however, there exists a steady-state error if the input is a ramp function, i.e., $r(t) = t$. The amount of such steady-state error is inversely proportional to K_1.

Type 2 ($n = 2$): A step input causes the second derivative of the output signal to tend to a constant. Such systems have no steady-state error for step and ramp inputs, but they have a steady-state error for parabolic inputs, i.e., $r(t) = t^2$.

One may continue such a classification to higher values of n.

Performance Criteria. The most difficult part of the design of a feedback system is the determination of the closed-loop transfer function of the over-all system. The choice of the transfer function must not only satisfy the specifications imposed on the performance, but in addition, it must require a cheap, simple, and reliable system. It is highly unlikely that there will ever exist a criterion for design satisfying all these requirements. It is often necessary to try different educated trial-and-error designs. However, one needs to be able to compare each one of these designs against the other. This comparison requires the establishment of a set of performance criteria, which, in conjunction with the physical constraints, can be used in the design of control systems. The most common of the criteria are listed below:

$$\text{Integral of error} = (\text{IE}) = \int_0^\infty e(t)\, dt \quad (5)$$

Integral of absolute value of error = (IAE)

$$= \int_0^\infty |e(t)| \, dt \quad (6)$$

Integral of the square of the error

$$= (ISE) = \int_0^\infty e^2(t) \, dt \quad (7)$$

Integral of time multiplied by absolute error

$$= (ITAE) = \int_0^\infty t |e(t)| \, dt \quad (8)$$

Moment of error squared = (MES)

$$= \int_0^\infty te^2(t) \, dt \quad (9)$$

and the most general criterion

$$G = \int_0^\infty f[e(t), t] \, dt \quad (10)$$

Each of the above criteria has its advantages and disadvantages. Most of them are not trivially computable and the direct synthesis of a control system that leads to the absolute minimum of any of the above criteria is a very complicated process, especially if the system is of high order.

The ISE criterion has been used to advantage in the design of statistical systems; however, the integral is finite only if the feedback system has no steady-state error. From the mathematical point of view the criterion is quite convenient but in physical processes it almost always results in high values of gain in the loop and in responses that are too oscillatory impractical for many applications. Furthermore, it lacks selectivity, i.e., the minimum is not sharply defined.

The ITAE criterion punishes late errors more severely than early ones. It has in general better selectivity than the ISE and leads to acceptable designs in many control-systems applications.

The various performance criteria given are not universal. Engineers must use a careful balance of the information available to them by the specifications, the weight and cost limitations, and other considerations in order to determine the criteria best suited for a particular problem. Some other criteria, not mathematically elegant, that are used are:

The *rise time* (t_r) defined as the time required for the output, due to a step input, to go from 10 to 90 per cent of its final value.

The *setting time* (t_s) defined as the time required for the error to reach and remain within a fixed percentage value, usually 5 or 2 per cent of its initial magnitude.

The *peak-overshoot-ratio* (P.O.R.) in %

$$= \frac{\text{value of error at first overshoot}}{\text{initial magnitude of error}} \times 100\%$$

To recapitulate, for a given problem a system performance criterion must be selected, in the basis of *à priori* information. Then alternate designs may be compared with each other and the particular design that is close to the minimum of the performance criterion must be selected.

Terminology Used in Feedback Systems. Many complicated feedback systems can be examined, in a first approximation, by the position of their dominant poles. A dominant pole or poles are those which are closest to the origin of the s-plane and which are not cancelled by zeroes. The dominant poles control to a large extent the system response, and as such they deserve some attention.

Consider the pair of complex poles shown in the s-plane by Fig. 3. The position of the poles is denoted by X. The poles are located at $s = -\alpha_n \pm j\omega_n$. The angle ψ, measured

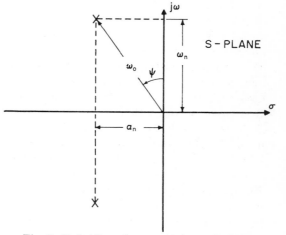

Fig. 3. Definitions for a complex pole pair.

in radians counterclockwise from the $j\omega$ axis, is called the *stability margin*. The smaller the angle ψ the more oscillatory is the system output. The radial distance ω_0 from the origin of the s-plane to the pole is called the underdamped frequency of oscillation. The distance ω_0 is measured in radians per second. The larger ω_0 the larger the bandwidth of the system. The vertical coordinate of the pole ω_n, measured in radians per second, is called the natural (damped) frequency of oscillation. The horizontal coordinate of the pole α_n, in radians per second is called the envelope damping factor. The dimensionless quantity ζ_n defined by

$$\zeta_n = \frac{\alpha_n}{\omega_n} = \tan \psi \qquad (11)$$

is called the damping factor. The smaller the ζ_n the more oscillatory the system output.

The system with the s-plane configuration of Fig. 3 has the transfer function

$$G(s) = \frac{K}{(s^2/\omega_0{}^2) + (s^{2\alpha_n}/s\omega_0) + 1} \qquad (12)$$

and its response to a step input of unit amplitude is

$$c(t) = K - \frac{K}{\cos \psi} e^{-\zeta_n \omega_n t} \cos (\omega_n t - \psi) \qquad (13)$$

Stability of Linear Feedback Systems. Although all the components of a system may be stable by themselves, their interconnection in the feedback configuration may lead to an unstable over-all system. An unstable system produces unbounded output signals even if the inputs are bounded. The output of unstable systems increases in magnitude in an exponential manner, thus becoming impractical in servo applications. In many cases other than servomechanisms, such as in oscillators, the system is made unstable deliberately in order to cause oscillations that are constant in amplitude owing to the saturation of the amplifying element. However, saturation of amplifiers in feedback systems is undesirable since the large oscillations may harm the electromechanical components of the system.

The stability of a system may be predicted simply by the examination of the poles of the closed-loop system. From Eq. (1), the poles of the closed-loop system are the zeros (roots) of the polynomial

$$1 + KF(s)H(s)G(s) = 0 \qquad (14)$$

Therefore, the roots of the equation are the values of s such that the magnitude condition

$$|F(s)H(s)G(s)| = 1/K \qquad (15)$$

and the angle condition

$$< F(s)H(s)G(s) = (1 + 2m)\pi m = 0, \pm 1, \pm 2 \qquad (16)$$

are satisfied simultaneously.

If any one of the values of s determined from (15) and (16) has a positive real part, then the closed loop system is unstable. If all of the roots determined have a negative real part, then the feedback system is stable.

The Root-Locus Method. A useful technique in the analysis and design of feedback systems is the root-locus method developed by Evans in 1948. Through the use of the root-locus plot one gains insight into the operation and stability of the feedback system using the open loop transfer function.

The root locus is a plot of the roots of the characteristic equation of the closed-loop system, given by (14), as a function of the gain K. The above definition implies that the root locus is the collection of all points in the s-plane such that the angle relationship (16) is satisfied.

As an example, consider

$$KF(s)H(s)G(s) = \frac{K}{s\left(s + \dfrac{1}{T_1}\right)\left(s + \dfrac{1}{T_2}\right)} \qquad (17)$$

The root loci are shown in Fig. 4 by the heavy lines. The step-by-step construction of the root loci is as follows:

(1) Plot the poles and zeroes of the function $F(s)H(s)G(s)$ in the s-plane. In Fig. 4 the poles are indicated by X. Note that (17) has no zeroes.

(2) Using a spirule, or any other angle-measuring instrument, determine all points

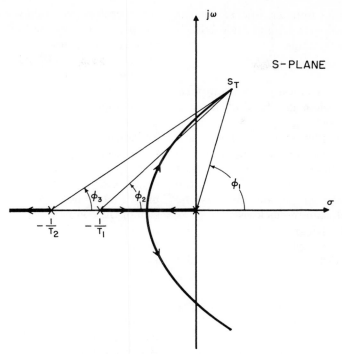

Fig. 4. Root locus for system given by Eq. (17).

in the s-plane such that the sum of the angles from the zeroes to the test point minus the sum of the angles from the poles to the test point is $(1 + 2m)\pi$, $m = 0$, ± 1, ± 2, $\cdots$. In Fig. 4, since there are no zeroes, for the test point s_T, $\phi_1 + \phi_2 + \phi_3 = -180°$, hence s_T is on the root locus.

The position of the closed-loop poles is determined by (15) and (16). The points on the root loci were determined by (16). Hence, for a fixed value of K Eq. (15) may be used to determine the particular points on the root loci which are the poles of the closed-loop system for that value of the gain K.

In Fig. 4 the arrows indicate the "motion" of the poles as the value of K is increased. It is seen that the root loci extend to the right half of the s-plane. Hence, if the value of K is large enough the closed-loop poles will be in the right half s-plane; hence they will have positive real parts, resulting in an unstable feedback system.

The simplicity of the root locus offers the designer, in addition to stability considerations, the freedom to adjust the gain K in order to have a closed loop system with a particular ζ_n. The specification of ζ_n fixes the position of the dominant closed-loop poles and the gain K necessary is easily determined. Then the position of the other closed loop poles may also be found.

Frequency Response. In many practical systems one does not know the transfer function of the components á priori. The usual method of evaluating the transfer function is to test the components with a sinusoidal input and observe the steady-state magnitude and phase shift at different test frequencies. To illustrate this technique consider the transfer function

$$G(s) = \frac{(s + z_1)(s + z_2)\cdots(s + z_m)}{(s + p_1)(s + p_2)\cdots(s + p_n)} \quad (18)$$

where, z_1, $\cdots$, z_m are the zeroes of $G(s)$, p_1, $\cdots$, p_n are the poles of $G(s)$, and for physical systems $m \leq n$. Now set $s = j\omega$, where ω is the frequency of the applied sinusoid. Thus,

$$G(j\omega) = \frac{(z_1 + j\omega)\cdots(z_m + j\omega)}{(p_1 + j\omega)\cdots(p_n + j\omega)} \quad (19)$$

$G(j\omega)$ is a complex number, and as such it may be described by its magnitude $|G(\omega)|$ and its phase $\phi(\omega)$. Thus,

$$G(j\omega) = |G(\omega)| \, e^{j\phi(\omega)} \tag{20}$$

The magnitude and phase relationship may be exhibited in various graphical forms. The most common are:

(1) The Polar Plot (Nyquist Diagram). The polar plot is a complex plane on which the complex number $G(j\omega)$ is plotted as a function of the frequency ω. $|G(\omega)|$ is the distance from the origin and $\phi(\omega)$ is the angle, measured counterclockwise.

(2) The Bode Diagram. The Bode diagram consists of two plots: (a) The plot of $20 \log_{10} |G(\omega)|$ vs $\log_{10} \omega$, and (b) The plot of $\phi(\omega)$ vs $\log_{10} \omega$. The units of $20 \log_{10} |G(\omega)|$ are decibels.

(3) The L-plane (Nichol's Chart). The L-plane is a conformal mapping of the s-plane. In the L-plane $20 \log_{10} |G(\pi)|$ is plotted vs $-\phi(\omega)$. The scale divisions are such that 6 db is equal to $39.6°$.

All three of the above plots are used extensively in control-system analysis and synthesis. The Bode diagram may be used in order to determine the transfer function of a system from the experimental data using straight line asymptote techniques. The L-plane may be used in order to determine the position of the dominant complex-pole pair of the closed loop system using the experimental open loop data. In addition, the stability of the closed loop system may be predicted from the open-loop plots of all of the above diagrams.

Linear Compensation. Given an unalterable component $G(s)$, as in Fig. 1, and given that the performance of the closed-loop systems with $H(s) = F(s) = 1$ is unsatisfactory, one may improve the performance of the closed-loop system through the use of compensating devices or networks. If the compensator is introduced in the forward loop, as $H(s)$ in Fig. 1, then it is called a series (cascade) compensator. If the compensator is introduced in the feedback path, as $F(s)$ in Fig. 1, then it is called a feedback compensator. As a rule the design of a series compensator is easier than the design of a feedback compensator using either the root-locus or frequency-response plots. However, the use of a feedback compensator minimizes the effects of noise at the output and makes the system performance insensitive to inaccuracies or changes in the elements of the forward loop, such as slight nonlinearities in the amplifiers.

If the transfer function of all the components is known, then the root locus techniques offer the easiest approach to the design of the compensator. First, the root locus of the uncompensated system is drawn. Depending on the shape of the root loci the experienced designer can immediately decide the kind of compensator required, i.e., lead network, lag network, lead-lag, bridged-T, etc. After the choice of the compensator is completed, the designer draws a series of root loci as a function of one or more parameters that were unspecified. The root locus most satisfactory is chosen, and then the gain can be adjusted in order to place the closed loop poles at their most optimum configuration.

If the transfer functions of the components are not known beforehand and if the only available information is experimental, one may design series compensators by plotting the experimental data in the L-plane or in the Bode diagram. One then easily designs compensators by prespecifying the approximate resonant frequency and the maximum resonant rise of the closed-loop system.

Feedback compensators are easiest to design by means of the Bode diagram. Of course, in a complex problem one may use many series compensators and, in addition, feedback compensators. The feedback compensators are used around the elements that are most likely to change their characteristics or those which contain nonlinearities.

Linear Time-Varying Systems

If the differential equations describing the system have coefficients which are functions of time then the techniques described for the stationary systems cannot be applied directly. In some problems one may still use Laplace transforms; however, the general problem is handled by using classical mathematical methods. The reader is referred to the section on Systems (Time-Varying).

Nonlinear Systems

In every physical problem there are one or more components that are nonlinear. The linear theory may be used only when the signals in the system are small enough so that the nonlinear effects are not dominant. Examples of nonlinearities in feedback systems are:

(1) The saturation of every amplifying element.

(2) The mechanical stops that might exist in a mechanical transducer.

(3) The stiction that occurs in moving mechanical elements.

(4) The backlash found in gear trains.

(5) Hysteresis which exists in magnetic amplifiers (*q.v.*).

(6) Relays with hysteresis and/or dead zone.

One of the popular methods of analysis of nonlinear feedback systems has been the *describing-function* approach. This method is used to predict the steady-state response of the system. Using the describing function one may determine whether the system will oscillate at the steady state, the amplitude and frequency of the sustained oscillations, and the relative stability of each oscillation. (The techniques are described in more detail in the section on relay systems.) The describing function for a nonlinear element is a function with a magnitude and phase, independent of frequency, but dependent on the amplitude of the sine wave applied at the input to the nonlinearity. In order for the results obtained by the describing function to be valid it is necessary for the controlled plant to be a low-pass filter that passes only the fundamental component of a complex waveform generated by the nonlinearity.

There are many control systems for which the deliberate introduction of a nonlinearity improves the response of the feedback system. The most celebrated example of these designs is the deliberate introduction of a relay in the control loop, acting as the power amplifier, which leads to the bang-bang (maximum-effort) control system, which may be used to reduce the error to zero in minimum time. The methods used are the analysis of the system response through its trajectories in phase space.

It is generally believed that for a given task a nonlinear system is superior to a linear one. However, at present, the systematic theory for nonlinear systems is incomplete.

MICHAEL ATHANASSIADES

Cross-references: *Laplace and Fourier Transforms, Randomly Varying Systems, Sampled-Data Systems, Servo Components, Systems (Linear), Systems (Nonlinear), Systems (Time-Varying)*

FERRIMAGNETISM

Ferrimagnetism is a term first suggested by Néel to describe the magnetic properties characteristic of certain classes of materials, notably the ferrites. As the name implies these ferrimagnetic materials are closely related to the usual ferromagnetic materials but differ in certain important respects. Ferrimagnetism is exhibited by crystalline materials within whose lattice structure two or more types of lattice sites, or sublattices, are occupied by magnetic ions. The interaction between ions residing in the two or more different types of sites is such that the magnetic moments of ions on different sublattices normally tend to align themselves antiparallel.

As a result of this antiparallel alignment of magnetic moments on different sublattices ferrimagnetics are characterized by a saturation magnetization that is much smaller at absolute zero than that which would obtain if all moments were aligned parallel. Above the Curie temperature the thermal variation of the inverse of the susceptibility χ is hyperbolic, and a plot of $1/\chi$ vs T is concave downwards obeying the relation: $1/\chi$ =

$[(T - \theta)/c] - [\zeta/(T - \theta')]$ where c, θ, θ', and ζ are constants of the material. In ferromagnetic materials the reciprocal susceptibility is a linear function of temperature of the form $1/\chi = (T - \theta)/c$, where θ and c are constants of the material. The thermal variation of spontaneous magnetization of a ferrimagnet may differ drastically from the Brillouin function characteristic of ferromagnets. While the individual sublattices obey the Brillouin formulation, the total net magnetization, being the difference between various sublattice magnetizations, can exhibit a thermal variation that may assume a wide variety of shapes; Néel points out six possible forms. In some cases ferrimagnets exhibit compensation points at temperatures where the sublattice magnetizations are so balanced as to yield a total net magnetization equal to zero. Such compensation points may occur far below the Curie temperature, and above these compensation points the magnetization rises with increasing temperature to a maximum before decreasing again as the Curie temperature is approached.

In most respects the behavior of ferrimagnets is identical to that of ferromagnets, and they can for most purposes be considered as ferromagnets with a magnetization equal to the resultant magnetization of the sublattices. The sublattice structure is, however, manifested in certain other respects.

The over-all magnetocrystalline anisotropy is now believed to be the resultant of the magnetocrystalline anisotropy of each sublattice, and that for each sublattice is believed to arise from the interaction between electron spins and the crystalline electric field. This anisotropy of individual sublattices may be either positive or negative so that the resultant total anisotropy may be either the sum or the difference of sublattice anisotropies. The thermal variation of the total anisotropy constant may therefore be fairly unconventional—possibly exhibiting compensation points where the net anisotropy vanishes in changing from a negative to a positive value and vice versa.

Although not commonly observed in microwave resonance studies certain differences exist between ferromagnetic resonance and ferrimagnetic resonance. In all ferrimagnetic materials the g-factor, or spectroscopic splitting factor, is in reality an effective g-factor and, as pointed out by Wangsness for a two sublattice system, can be expressed in terms of the g-factors of the individual sublattices as:

$$g_{eff} = \frac{M_{total}}{M_1/g_1 - M_2/g_2},$$

where M_{total} represents the total resultant magnetization of the material, and $M_{1,2}$ and $g_{1,2}$ represent the magnetizations and g-factors of the individual sublattices. In the vicinity of a magnetic compensation point the effective g-factor then exhibits a dispersion as has been observed in various rare earth-iron garnet materials.

Also in the immediate vicinity of a magnetic compensation point a second resonant mode, the "exchange" resonance, occurs in a frequency range observable in the laboratory. Still another property of resonance in a ferrimagnet near a magnetic compensation point is a tremendous broadening of the resonance absorption line as the effective anisotropy field (inversely proportional to the net magnetization) becomes large and dipolar narrowing forces (directly proportional to the net magnetization) become vanishingly small.

The sublattice arrangement of lattice sites within a crystal is normally found in oxides, and the anti-parallel alignment of nearest neighbors on different sublattices is generally attributed to an indirect negative interaction between magnetic ions through an intermediate anion in an excited state, i.e., superexchange as postulated by Kramers.

The most important ferrimagnetic materials in use today are the ferrites including those with spinel, garnet, and hexagonal crystal structures.

G. P. RODRIGUE

Cross-references: *Ferrites, Ferromagnetism*

FERRITES

The term ferrites has come to be used to refer to practically all magnetic oxides containing iron as a major component, and is even used at times to refer to mixtures of such magnetic oxides and certain nonmagnetic oxides. In chemistry the word ferrite refers to nearly pure αFe, containing about 0.06 per cent of carbon in interstitial solid solution. It is the former definition that is of interest here. The three most common groups of ferrites are those characterized as spinels, garnets, and hexagonal ferrites, the classifications being dictated by crystal structure.

Spinels. The ferrites having the spinel (the mineral spinel is $MgAl_2O_4$) crystal structure generally have the chemical formula $MeFe_2O_4$, the iron being trivalent, and Me being a divalent metal ion with ionic radius approximately between 0.6 and 1 Å. For most ferrites, Me is one of the transition elements Mn, Fe, Co, Ni, Cu, and Zn, or Mg and Cd. One then speaks, for example, of nickel ferrite ($NiFe_2O_4$). Most spinels are soluble in one another, and it is possible to form mixed crystals of two or more ferrites, generally without limit on either constituent. Thus one might form a nickel-cobalt ferrite of composition $Ni_{1-\alpha}Co_\alpha Fe_2O_4$, where α can lie between zero and unity. Similarly, it is possible to replace all or part of the trivalent iron by trivalent Al, Ga, In, or Cr, since these ions produce spinel structures also. Thus one obtains mixed crystals of, say, nickel ferrite ($NiFe_2O_4$) and nickel aluminate ($NiAl_2O_4$) of the form $NiFe_{2-t}Al_tO_4$, with t lying between zero and two. Such compounds are commonly called ferrites, although they are more accurately characterized as ferrite-aluminates, for example. These compounds are normally ferrimagnetic at room temperature if the concentration of nonmagnetic ions (Al, Ga, etc.) is not too high. This process of forming mixed crystals can be extended to include a large number of constituents, as mentioned; in fact most useful ferrites contain several constituents, for example the nickel-copper-cobalt-manganese ferrite-aluminate of composition $Ni_{.875}Cu_{.1}Co_{.025}Mn_{.02}Fe_{1.6}Al_{.3}O_{4\pm}$. This last formula illustrates the point that ferrites are often not mixed stoichiometrically. In this case, the amount of oxygen per formula unit necessary to produce a valence balance is not exactly equal to four; and since the exact distribution of metallic ions in the various valence states would have to be known to determine the amount of oxygen, a plus-or-minus sign is often used in the physics literature to indicate the uncertainty involved.

The symbol Me can represent a combination of ions having an average valence of two; thus lithium ferrite $LiFe_5O_8$ can be written $[Li_{0.5}^+Fe_{0.5}^{+++}]Fe_2O_4$ to put it in the standard form. Also other combinations of valences in the general formula XY_2O_4 can occur in spinel structures. Thus the ferric ions can be partially replaced by tetravalent Ti or Ge, with the valency of an equal part of the ferric ions being lowered by one. Obviously then, a large variety of spinel ferrites is possible.

There are eight formula units or "molecules" of $MeFe_2O_4$ in a unit cell of the spinel structure; thus there are 32 oxygen ions, 16 ferric ions, and 8 Me ions in one unit cell. The large oxygen ions form a cubic close-packed structure in which occur two types of interstitial sites which metallic ions can occupy. These are the 64 tetrahedral or A sites (surrounded by 4 equidistant oxygen ions) and the 32 octahedral or B sites (surrounded by 6 equidistant oxygen ions). In each cubic unit cell, 8 of the A sites and 16 of the B sites are occupied by metal ions. In some cases the 8 divalent ions are in the A sites, with the 16 trivalent ions in the B sites; these are *normal* spinels ($ZnFe_2O_4$ is an example). If, however, the 8 divalent ions lie on the B sites, and the 16 trivalent ions are distributed evenly between the A and B sites, then the result is an *inverse* spinel ($NiFe_2O_4$ is an example). Most ferrites are predominately inverse, although a given ferrite is seldom completely inverse or completely normal.

These ferrites are ferrimagnetic, and generally (though not always) the ions on the A sites form one magnetic sublattice with parallel magnetic moments, while the ions on the B sites form another magnetic sublattice with parallel moments, but antiparallel to the moments on the A sites. Hence, if the ionic distribution is known, the magnetic moment or saturation magnetization of the material can be calculated.

Garnets. Ferrites having the garnet (the mineral garnet has the formula Mn_3Al_2-Si_3O_{12}) crystal structure are usually called, simply, garnets, and have the general formula $3Me_2O_3 \cdot 5Fe_2O_3$. Here Me is either Yttrium (Y) or one of the rare earths Sm, Gd, Tb, Dy, Ho, Er, Tm, Yb, or Lu. One then has, for example, yttrium-iron garnet (YIG), $3Y_2O_3 \cdot 5Fe_2O_3$. It is also possible to prepare yttrium-aluminum garnet, $3Y_2O_3 \cdot 5Al_2O_3$ for example. As in the case of the spinels, mixed crystals of the garnets can be made in infinite variety. For example, one can prepare $3Y_2O_3 \cdot (5 - x)Fe_2O_3 \cdot xAl_2O_3$ with x varying from zero to 5. Similarly, the Me ion can represent combinations of the appropriate ions listed above; such a garnet is the yttrium-gadolinium-iron garnet $(3 - x)Y_2O_3 \cdot xGd_2O_3 \cdot 5Fe_2O_3$. Since the properties are varied in a variety of ways by such mixtures, many of the technically useful garnets are mixtures; however, the yttrium-iron garnet is probably the single most used magnetic garnet.

The garnet formula is sometimes written as $Me_3Fe_5O_{12}$; however, the form used here, $3Me_2O_3 \cdot 5Fe_2O_3$, is perhaps more common, and is referred to as a "formula-unit." The cubic unit cell contains four such formula-units, i.e., 96 O ions, 40 Fe ions, and 24 Me ions. All the metallic ions are trivalent. Twenty-four of the small Fe ions occupy tetrahedral sites, and 16 occupy octahedral sites. The 24 Me ions occupy sites surrounded somewhat irregularly by eight oxygen ions.

The iron ions on the tetrahedral and octahedral sites form magnetic sublattices, respectively, which are antiparallel to one another, the resultant moment of the iron ions being thus due to the eight extra ions on the tetrahedral sites. The Me ions which have magnetic moment are coupled antiferromagnetically to the net moment of the iron ions; hence the Me moments lie parallel to the iron ions on the octahedral sites. This coupling is much weaker than that between the iron ions, and thus the magnetization of the rare earth ions falls rapidly with increasing temperature. Most of the rare earths have a large magnetic moment, and it predominates at low temperatures; but since it decreases rapidly with temperature, the moment of the iron ions predominates at high temperatures, and thus there is a compensation point of the magnetization at some intermediate temperature.

The iron sublattices discussed above are common to all the garnets listed, and the antiferromagnetic coupling between these lattices is much stronger than the coupling to the rare earth ions. Hence the coupling between iron ions determines the Curie point, which is thus about the same for all the iron garnets, namely about 273°C.

Hexagonal Ferrites. The ferrites having hexagonal crystal structures actually comprise several families of materials, each family being characterized by a particular crystal structure, but with variable chemical composition. Less is known about such materials, by and large, than about the spinels, for example; also the materials have certain similar characteristics arising from the hexagonal form of their structures, so that all these materials are commonly lumped together under the term "hexagonal ferrites."

The four most common such compounds are often designated by the letters M, W, Y, and Z, with chemical composition as follows:

M: $BaFe_{12}O_{19}$
W: $BaMe_2Fe_{16}O_{27}$
Y: $Ba_2Me_2Fe_{12}O_{22}$
Z: $Ba_3Me_2Fe_{24}O_{41}$

Here the divalent Me ion represents Mn, Ni, Fe, Co, Cu, Zn, or Mg, or combinations such as occur in the spinel structure, for instance Li^+ and Fe^{+++}. If Me is Ni, for example, one refers to Ni_2W, Ni_2Y or Ni_2Z, as a shorthand notation.

The crystal structures of the various classes above are all different, but all materials within one group have the same structure. Thus, as in the case for spinels, mixed crystals can be prepared. For example, one might form a Ni-Co W compound of composition $BaNi_{2-\alpha}Co_\alpha Fe_{16}O_{27}$ with α lying between zero and two. In other words, Me can represent combinations of the divalent ions listed. Also, in most cases the Ba ion can be partly or completely substituted by Sr, Pb, or Ca, and the trivalent iron ion by trivalent Al or Ga. Furthermore, the iron ion can be replaced by combinations of divalent and tetravalent ions; for example, one may thus form the compound $BaCo_\delta^{++} Ti_\delta^{++++}Fe_{12-2\delta}$-$O_{19}$. Obviously then, an innumerable number of compounds are possible within each crystal class listed, i.e., M, W, Y, and Z. And as before, the properties of such materials are strongly dependent on composition. Thus, many useful materials (consisting of such combinations) have been synthesized to emphasize one or more properties.

A most distinctive property of these hexagonal materials is that of their magneto-crystalline anisotropy. If the magnetization of the material likes to lie along the C-axis of the crystal (that is, the C-axis is an easy direction of magnetization), then the material is said to be uniaxial. In certain of the materials, however, the basal plane (perpendicular to the C-axis) is a perferred plane of magnetization, and such materials are called planar materials. The M material is uniaxial, and so are all the simple W and Z materials except Co_2W and Co_2Z. These are planar, as are all the simple Y materials. By mixing planar and uniaxial crystals with the same structure, say Co_2Z and Zn_2Z, materials can be prepared that range from uni-axial with high positive anisotropy (Zn_2Z) to planar with high negative anisotropy (Co_2Z).

Properties. Perhaps the most important things that can be said about ferrites are that they are magnetic and that they have a high resistivity ($10^6 - 10^{10}$ ohm-cm, usually). It is this high resistivity that distinguishes them most dramatically from magnetic metals, and makes their magnetic property useful in many applications where metallic magnetic materials would not be useful, particularly at higher frequencies.

All the ferrites discussed above have saturation moments ($4\pi M_s$) ranging from near zero to about 5000 gauss at room temperature. Curie temperatures for the more useful materials range from about 80°C to 600°C. The ferromagnetic resonance line width in polycrystalline ferrites varies greatly, depending on density, anisotropy field, magnetic moment, and other properties. Generally, however, it lies in the neighborhood of a few hundred oersteds for the more useful spinels, 30 to a few hundred oersteds for the most useful garnets, and several hundred to about 2000 oersteds for the most useful hexagonal materials. Ferrites have permeabilities ranging from slightly greater than unity to several thousand. Spinel and garnet type ferrites maintain this permeability up to frequencies in the range 1 to 100 Mc, with low loss. The maximum usable (low-loss) frequency depends on the material, but is in the aforementioned range, in general. This maximum usable frequency tends to go inversely as the permeability. Certain of the planar hexagonal ferrites are distinguished by the fact that the permeability remains constant, with low loss, to much higher frequencies than is the case for spinel ferrites. The maximum usable frequencies (determined by the amount of magnetic loss) for these materials lie between 100 and 1000 Mc, in general.

Ferrites have numerous low frequency applications (below about 100 Mc), such as in filter inductors, antenna cores, flyback transformers, TV deflection yokes, IF transformers, magnetic memories and switches in computers, and magnetic amplifiers. In the microwave and UHF range, ferrites are used extensively in isolators, circulators, duplexers, switches, variable attenuators, phase shifters, harmonic filters, limiters, and parametric amplifiers, as discussed below.

J. E. Pippin

Microwave Applications

Because of their magnetic properties, low conductivity, and minimum hysteresis loss, ferrites have found use at microwave frequencies. The permeability is made to vary by means of an externally applied magnetic field. The resulting devices may be classed as reciprocal, for which the effect of the applied magnetic field is the same for both directions of propagation of electromagnetic waves; and nonreciprocal, for which the anisotropic properties of the tensor permeability are used to cause unlike effects for the two directions. Reciprocal phase shifters and attenuators are used in antenna array structures so as to obtain electronic scanning of the radiation pattern. It is the nonreciprocal devices that are described below.

Faraday Rotation Isolators and Circulators. If a wave within a waveguide is propagating through a region containing an axially magnetized ferrite rod, the polarization of the emerging wave is rotated through an angle related to the length of the ferrite rod and the direction of the magnetic field. This

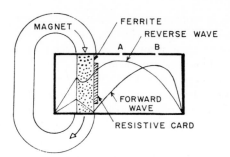

Fig. 2. Field-displacement isolator.

wave is indicated in Fig. 1a by the solid arrows. For the returning wave (shown by the dashed arrows) the sense of the polarization angle shift is the same. This *Faraday rotation* effect is applied to obtain isolation between the two directions of propagation. The returning wave is absorbed by the resistive vane, 3. Removing the resistive vanes and attaching the waveguide sections to the main circular waveguide at points 3 and 4 results in a *circulator*. A signal incident at 1 emerges at 2, whereas a signal incident at 2 emerges at 3, and so on. One use of this device is to circulate electromagnetic energy from the transmitter to the antenna and from the antenna to the receiver as shown in Fig. 1b.

Field Displacement Phase Shifter, Circulator, Isolator, and Directional Coupler. In the field displacement device illustrated in Fig. 2, if the resistive card is omitted, the forward propagating wave experiences phase shifts in traversing the waveguide section containing the ferrite. The reverse wave undergoes phase shifts of a different amount according to the value of magnetic field applied. A combination of several nonreciprocal phase shifters in a ring arrangement can be made to act as a *circulator*. If the resistive card is placed in the position indicated in Fig. 2, the forward wave encounters minimum attenuation whereas the reverse wave is heavily attenuated. Such a device may be used to *isolate* signal sources from variations in their load. In coaxial lines, the fields can be distorted by dielectric segments in such a way that ferrite segments affect the two directions of propagation much the same

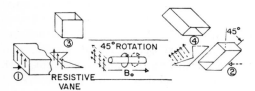

Fig. 1(a). Isolator.

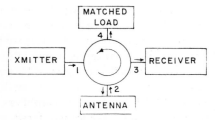

(b). Circulator application.

way as in a waveguide. An arrangement of this type is applicable to lower frequencies. With the same basic design as shown in Fig. 2, but removing the resistive card, it is possible to construct a *directional coupler*. The reverse wave has minimum coupling to a slot cut at A and considerable coupling to a slot at B. The forward wave couples to A but not to B. It is then possible to connect auxiliary waveguides to these slots to directional coupling. The practical coupler takes on many forms of which the one described is but one.

Resonance Isolator. With large enough transverse magnetic field applied, it is possible to have resonance absorption for one of the propagating directions only. Such an isolator has an appearance similar to that of Fig. 2. The ferrite slab is located about a quarter of the way across the waveguide and, of course, there is no need for the resistive card since the loss is assumed by the ferrite. A dielectric slab next to the ferrite can improve the performance. If instead of a single ferrite slab two are used and placed at the upper and lower walls, resonance isolation can still be obtained. The advantage of such a design is in heat dissipation due to contact with the walls. This is called the H-plane resonance isolator, whereas the other is called the E-plane type.

Other Applications. Ferrites have been used to tune klystrons and resonant cavities. They have been used to modify radiation patterns of slot antennas. They are being used in power dividers, amplitude modulators and switches. By varying the phase rapidly, frequency modulation can be obtained. Harmonic generation has been done with ferrites as well.

D. J. Angelakos

Cross-references: *Attenuators and Isolators, Circulators, Ferrimagnetism, Magnetic Cores, Magnetism*

FERROELECTRICITY

A crystal is called ferroelectric when it possesses a spontaneous polarization that can be reversed with an electric field. Hence, the relationship between polarization **P** (or dielectric displacement $\mathbf{D} = \epsilon_0 \mathbf{E} + \mathbf{P}$) and field **E** is not linear, as in normal dielectric materials, but is represented by a hysteresis curve just as in ferromagnetic crystals the relationship between magnetization **M** [or magnetic induction $\mathbf{B} = \mu_0(\mathbf{H} + \mathbf{M})$] and magnetic field **H** is represented by a ferromagnetic hysteresis loop. This formal analogy is the reason for the term ferroelectric, although other terminologies such as Rochelle or Seignette-electric are sometimes also used from the surname of the crystal that was first found to exhibit a reversible polarization. One difference between the magnetic and the electric phenomenon is that spontaneous magnetization, whenever it is found to occur, is always reversible, whereas spontaneous polarization frequently occurs without being reversible. (Crystals bearing a spontaneous polarization are called pyroelectric, owing to the fact that their polarization can be changed with temperature.)

The existence of a spontaneous polarization means that the unit cell of the crystal has a finite electric moment, i.e., that charges, ionic and electronic, are distributed in the lattice in such a way as to give rise to a unique (polar) axis of symmetry. The reversibility of the spontaneous polarization implies that the polarized state is a comparatively small distortion of a closely related nonpolarized state, as such a distortion can be made to change sign by means of an electric field applied externally. It is reasonable to expect that this lattice distortion is a function of temperature. Hence, with decreasing temperature, it may become so large as to be insensitive to external electric fields (freezing-in of the spontaneous polarization); with increasing temperature, it may become smaller and smaller until, if the crystal does not melt or decompose before, it finally disappears and the crystal structure becomes nonpolar. In this case, a phase transition occurs, i.e., a transition from a polarized to a nonpolarized state. The temperature at which this occurs is called a Curie point (T_c) by analogy with the ferromagnetic case.

Most ferroelectric crystals have a Curie point: the highest known to date is that of bismuth titanate ($Bi_4Ti_3O_{12}$) at 675°C, the lowest is that of lithium thallium tartrate monohydrate ($LiTlH_4C_4O_6 \cdot H_2O$) at −263°C. The Curie temperature of barium titanate ($BaTiO_3$) is 120°C; that of tri-glycine sulfate [($NH_2CH_2COOH)_3 \cdot H_2SO_4$], 49°C; that of potassium dihydrogen phosphate (KH_2PO_4), −150°C. Some ferroelectrics decompose before they leave the polarized state and hence have no Curie point, as lithium trihydrogen selenite [$LiH_3(SeO_3)_2$], guanidinium aluminum sulfate hexahydrate [$C(NH_2)_3Al(SO_4)_2 \cdot 6H_2O$], and tetramethyl-ammonium trichloro-mercuriate [$N(CH_3)_4 \cdot HgCl_3$]. Other crystals are ferroelectric only in a relatively narrow temperature range, e.g., Rochelle salt ($NaKC_4H_4O_6 \cdot 4H_2O$) between −18°C and +24°C, and ammonium bisulfate (NH_4HSO_4) between −3°C and −119°C.

Generally, the dielectric constant ϵ' measured along the polar axis exhibits an anomaly at the Curie temperature T_c. In some cases ($BaTiO_3$, KH_2PO_4, Rochelle salt, tri-glycine sulfate) this anomaly is quite pronounced and ϵ' reaches values of the order of 10^4–10^5 at the temperature T_c. Above this critical point, it decreases hyperbolically according to the Curie-Weiss law, $\epsilon' = C/(T - T_0)$, where C is called the Curie constant, T is the temperature, and T_0 is equal to, or little lower than, T_c. This dielectric anomaly gives rise to similar anomalies of the piezoelectric, elastic, electro-optic and other properties of the crystal. Hence, in a few cases certain piezoelectric moduli can reach values of the order of 2×10^{-4} cgs units, to be compared with the value 6×10^{-8} cgs units for d_{11} of quartz. Accordingly, the coefficient of electro-mechanical coupling k (a measure of the efficiency with which electrical energy can be converted into mechanical energy) is quite large in some ferroelectrics (k is of the order of 0.8

in Rochelle salt, 0.5 in $BaTiO_3$, and only about 0.1 in quartz).

The magnitude of the spontaneous polarization varies widely from one ferroelectric to another. In $BaTiO_3$, for example, the spontaneous polarization is 26×10^{-6} coulomb/cm²; in $LiH_3(SeO_3)_2$, 15×10^{-6}; in KH_2PO_4, 5×10^{-6}; in some methylammonium alums, about 1.0×10^{-6}; and in Rochelle salt, 0.25×10^{-6} coulomb/cm². It should be noted that in normal dielectrics such polarizations could only be achieved theoretically with electric fields of the order of 10^6–10^7 v/cm.

Such large electric polarizations could hardly be possible and uniform in big crystals, owing to the large depolarizing fields generated, were it not for the fact that the crystals split into small regions of uniform polarization that differ only in the direction and sense of such polarization. These regions are called ferroelectric domains and range in size from a few thousands Ångstroms to a few millimeters. All ferroelectrics exhibit domains that are polarized antiparallel to one another and are separated by so-called 180° walls. Within these walls, which are only a very few lattice spacings thick, the spontaneous polarization decreases in magnitude without changing its direction, goes through zero, and then increases in the opposite direction. Quite complicated domain configurations are possible in ferroelectrics in which the spontaneous polarization can occur along several axes that are equivalent in the nonpolarized state, as in the perovskite ferroelectrics ($BaTiO_3$, $KNbO_3$, etc.). The process of polarization reversal, then, occurs by way of domain wall motions, as domains oriented in the direction of the applied field grow at the expense of those oriented oppositely to it. The speed with which these domain walls move is field dependent so that the speed with which a ferroelectric crystal switches its polarization depends upon the strength of the electric field applied. For large fields (of the order of 10^4 v/cm) most ferroelectrics reverse their polarizations in times of the order of a fraction of a microsecond. For small fields, the switching times become larger and larger, and there is no critical field below which the crystal cannot reverse its polarization, if it is given sufficient time for it.

The latter property represents a serious obstacle to the obvious application of ferroelectric materials as storage elements in the field of digital computers and telephone switching systems. There are also other problems of electrical stability and fatigue effects to be eliminated before ferroelectrics can be put to practical use in this field. Other applications of ferroelectric crystals, however, have been realized. One, and probably the most important, is the use of these materials as electro-mechanical transducers (accelerometers, microphone and record player pickups, etc.). Not only is the electro-mechanical coupling coefficient highly favorable but it is also possible to prepare poly-crystalline (ceramic) bodies that exhibit piezoelectric properties and can be formed in a wide variety of shapes. Another practical application is that of (ceramic) condensers of small size and large capacitance, an obvious utilization of the high dielectric constant exhibited by some ferroelectrics in the vicinity of the Curie temperature. Other potential applications aim at the exploitation of the nonlinearity of the dielectric constant in devices such as dielectric amplifiers and microwave modulators, and the use of the large electro-optical effects for the modulation of light beams.

F. Jona

Cross-references: *Capacitors, Ferroelectrics, Ferromagnetism, Piezoelectricity and Pyroelectricity, Transducers*

FERROELECTRICS

The class of materials known as ferroelectrics exhibits the following general characteristics:

(1) They are spontaneously polarized over some range of temperatures.

(2) They exhibit a hysteresis in polariz-

ability as the applied electric field strength is varied.

(3) They have at least one Curie point, above which the material is no longer ferroelectric, but paraelectric.

(4) They have dielectric constants which are dependent on the applied electric field strength.

(5) They have dielectric constants whose real part, ϵ'/ϵ_0, ranges from a few hundred to tens of thousands.

(6) They are piezoelectric.

There are two major classes of ferroelectric materials: the perovskites, of which barium titanate is a commonly studied member, and a group of hydrogen-bonded isomorphous substances, of which Rochelle salt and potassium dihydrogen phosphate are examples. All ferroelectric materials possess a pseudo-symmetric crystal structure which places them in the polar class. Further, all ferroelectric materials are piezoelectric, though the converse is not true.

Most perovskite forms are obtainable as single crystals or as ceramics. They have the molecular form ABO_3, where A is a divalent positive ion and B is a quadrivalent positive ion. In the ferroelectric phase the perovskite is tetragonal, and the B ion is displaced toward one of the face-centered oxygen ions. In the region above the Curie point, the phase is cubic, and no spontaneous polarization is observed. In analogy to ferromagnetic materials, the material is said to be paraelectric in this region; and the dielectric constant obeys a Curie-Weiss law as a function of temperature,

$$\epsilon' - 1 = \frac{C}{T - T_c}$$

where T_c is a temperature close to the Curie point and C is a constant.

Solid solutions among perovskites alter the lattice constants of the materials and thus have a pronounced effect on their electrical properties. For example, the partial substitution of strontium for barium in $BaTiO_3$ lowers the Curie point markedly (from 123°C to less than −150°C for pure $SrTiO_3$).

Domain structure in ferroelectric crystals may be observed by transmitted polarized light. External electric fields tend to produce new domains rather than to cause existing domains to grow. Hence the direction of the polar axis may be altered by application of external electric fields.

Much current interest in ferroelectrics derives from their characteristic decrease in dielectric constant under the influence of applied electric fields. The greatest drawback to application of ferroelectrics has been the high loss factor associated with most materials, especially in the high-frequency and microwave regions.

A. L. STANFORD

Cross-references: *Ferroelectricity*

FERROMAGNETIC CRYSTALS

The existence of a spontaneous magnetization requires a regular arrangement of atoms within a crystal lattice. All ferromagnetic bodies are, therefore, ferromagnetic crystals, but the term crystal is usually applied to denote single crystals as differentiated from polycrystalline ferromagnets.

Single crystals of ferromagnetic materials exhibit the same properties as do polycrystalline samples, though there may be quantitative differences in the values of various parameters. Moreover, most physical properties depend to a greater or lesser extent on on the direction of measurement with respect to crystal axes. This directional dependence is observable only on single crystals. The study of single crystals permits the determination of additional physical properties, e.g., magnetocrystalline anisotropy and magnetostriction, that are completely masked by the random orientation of crystallites in the polycrystalline state.

As an example, magnetocrystalline anisotropy which expresses the preference of the magnetization within a unit cell to align itself along certain crystallographic axes is measurable only on single crystals. Many other magnetic properties of polycrystalline material, such as initial permeability and ferromagnetic resonance linewidth are

strong functions of this anistropy. Hence, the determination of this anistropy constant is of real and important value.

The granular nature of polycrystalline samples, on the other hand, introduces effects that are not representative of the intrinsic nature of the material. Nonmagnetic inclusions between grains or crystals cause a broadening of the resonance absorption line over that characteristic of the intrinsic material. Grain boundaries tend to snag domain walls, thus affecting their motion and the initial permeability as measured on a polycrystal. For these reasons many properties measured on polycrystals depend not only on the true chemical composition and lattice structure of the material but also on the method of preparation, density, etc. Properties measured on single crystal materials are thus more nearly intrinsic properties.

Single-crystal ferromagnetic materials have thus far found little practical application. One of the chief reasons has been the lack of single-crystal material of sufficient size for such applications. For many years, however, crystals have been prepared and investigated in order to determine those intrinsic properties that effect the usefulness of polycrystalline materials in various applications. No method has yet been developed to grow large, perfect ferromagnetic single crystals. Various techniques are available that produce small single crystals with varying degrees of perfection. Nickel, iron, cobalt, and various alloys have been prepared in crystalline form by slow cooling from above the melting point. The oxidic ferrites have been prepared most successfully by slow cooling of a solution containing one or more fluxes. Single-crystal ferrites have also been prepared by the Vernueil method and by zone melting techniques similar to those used in the preparation of semiconductor crystals. In the current state of development the last-named group of techniques does not yield crystals with as high a degree of perfection as do flux techniques.

One of the most interesting of the single crystal ferromagnetic materials is the yttrium-iron garnet. Most extensive effort in developing crystal-growth techniques has been expended on this material. Chief interest in this compound arises from the fact that it exhibits the narrowest ferromagnetic resonance linewidth yet observed. Linewidths of less than an oersted are commonly measured on single crystals of this material. This extremely narrow linewidth makes possible many microwave devices that are not feasible with materials having broader responses. Polycrystalline samples of yttrium-iron garnet have linewidths of the order of 30 to 50 oersteds and, therefore, cannot be used as a substitute for single crystals in the most advanced devices with stringent requirements on the material. The narrow linewidth of single crystal yttrium-iron garnet also facilitates the investigation of various basic physical phenomena and has led to a more thorough understanding of fundamental solid-state processes. In particular, the study of this material has enabled scientists to understand and control more completely the rather complicated effects which set in when relatively high levels of microwave power are applied to a material.

There is also extensive interest in obtaining single-crystal ferromagnetic material which is at the same time ferroelectric and ferromagnetic. No such materials have thus far been prepared or identified. However, single-crystals of the chemical formula, $Ga_{2-x}Fe_xO_3$, have been prepared and found to be simultaneously piezoelectric and ferromagnetic. Such materials offer the rather interesting possibility of controlling the magnetic properties of a solid state material through the application of an electric field.

G. P. RODRIGUE

Cross-references: *Ferrites, Ferroelectricity, Ferromagnetism, Magnetostriction, Piezoelectricity and Pyroelectricity, Semiconductor Manufacture*

FERROMAGNETISM

When any material is placed in a uniform magnetic field of intensity H it exhibits a magnetic polarity, and is said to be magnetized. The *intensity of magnetization M*

of the material is defined as the average magnetic moment per unit volume of the material, and is found, for most materials, to be proportional to the magnetizing force, i.e., $M = \chi_m H$, where χ_m is called the *susceptibility* of the material. The total flux density B in the material is now

$$B = \mu_0(H + M) = \mu_0(H + \chi_m H) = \mu_0(1 + \chi_m)H$$

where μ_0 is the permeability of free space $(4\pi \times 10^{-7}$ henry/m). The dimensionless quantity $1 + \chi_m$ is called the *permeability* of the material, and is denoted by μ'. Hence B is also proportional to H; the ratio is usually represented by the greek letter μ (mu), or $\mu = \mu'\mu_0 = B/H$.

Materials are commonly divided into classes depending upon the value of the susceptibility: (1) a *diamagnetic* material is one whose susceptibility is negative or whose permeability is less than unity; (2) a *paramagnetic* material is one whose susceptibility is positive but small. For most paramagnetic substances the permeability is less than 1 per cent greater than unity; (3) *ferromagnetic* materials are those that are so highly paramagnetic that they are classed by themselves. Nickel and cobalt, with permeabilities at 100°C as high as 40 and 55, are usually classed as ferromagnetic, but the permeability of iron and some of its alloys may be many thousand. These metals are all of crystal structure and many of them are characterized by very large values of B/H.

W. E. Weber (1804–1891) is responsible for the theory that each atom of a magnetic substance is itself a permanent magnet. Under ordinary conditions the atomic magnets are supposed to lie at random or, in small groups, form elementary magnetic circuits that give no magnetic field outside themselves. As the magnetizing force is gradually increased, Weber assumed that the atoms turn in the direction of the magnetizing field until, at saturation, they all lie with their N poles in the same direction. The relation between H and B follows the curve OA of the figure, except that this curve is not smooth but is made up of a

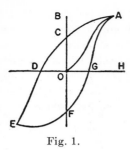

Fig. 1.

large number of minute steps. H. Bark-hausen (1881–1956) placed a coil of wire, connected to a telephone, around the sample of iron being magnetized. As the magnetizing field was slowly increased successive clicks were heard in the telephone. These indicated small discrete increments in the flux through the iron.

The value of $\mu = B/H$ is practically constant in diamagnetic and paramagnetic substances. In this case the B-H curves in the figure would be one straight line. In ferromagnetic substances the value of B/H is by no means constant, but depends upon the intensity of the magnetizing field and upon the magnetic history of the specimen. For a given magnetic cycle, B has two values for each value of H, one as H increases and another as H decreases. Starting at point A in the figure, the B-H relation follows the curve $ACDE$ as H decreases and the curve $EFGA$ as H increases, enclosing a definite area. It can be shown that the loss of energy while the iron is being carried through a complete cycle is proportional to this enclosed area. This lost energy appears as heat in the iron.

This phenomenon, resulting from the tendency of a magnetized substance to persist in its state of magnetization, is known as *hysteresis*, and the B-H curve is called the hysteresis loop. The phenomenon of hysteresis is analogous to mechanical inertia, and the energy losses due to hysteresis are analogous to those due to friction.

Theories of magnetism are still based upon the belief that individual atoms are elementary magnets. Each atom is believed to consist of a positively charged nucleus

with negatively charged electrons revolving in orbits around the nucleus. An electron revolving in such an orbit gives the magnetic effect of an electric current flowing in a circular wire loop. The electron may contribute further to the magnetic moment of the atom by spinning on its axis. In fact, measurements of the magnetic moments of the atoms of ferromagnetic substances indicate that these moments are largely due to uncompensated spins, not orbital motions, of so-called *internal electrons*, i.e., electrons closely associated with the nuclei of the atoms even in a crystal structure. Other electrons, not so closely associated with the nuclei, appear to be shared by neighboring nuclei in the crystal lattice and are responsible for the forces which hold the nuclei in their positions in the lattice structure. These *exchange forces* appear to favor the alignment of all the unbalanced electron spins in the same direction within microscopic *crystal domains*, so that they behave like tiny magnets.

The iron crystal is cubic in form and experiments upon a single large crystal show that a relatively small magnetizing force produces saturation when applied, in either direction, perpendicular to a pair of faces. A larger magnetizing force is required to produce saturation in other directions, particularly along the face or body diagonals. Thus we have, in the crystal, directions of *easy magnetization*. An ordinary specimen of iron is composed of a large number of microscopic crystals. If a gradually increasing magnetizing force is applied to such a specimen, the curve $EFGA$ of the hysteresis loop in the figure will indicate the process of magnetization. With small fields the domains lying in positions of easy magnetization become saturated. Then the curve becomes steeper as other domains, with axes inclined to the field, become magnetized and snap into alignment, causing the clicks heard in the Barkhausen experiment. Damped oscillations accompanying these shifts dissipate their energy in heat and may account for the hysteresis loss. Finally the curve levels off as the last of the domains come into alignment and the specimen becomes saturated.

While the theory of revolving and spinning electrons accounts for many of the phenomena of magnetism, it does not account for others, and some of the assumptions underlying the theory are unorthodox.

NORMAN E. GILBERT

Cross-references: *Diamagnetism, Electromagnetic Theory, Ferromagnetic Crystals, Magnetism, Paramagnetism, Permanent Magnets*

FIELD EMISSION

Electrons are emitted by cold conductors subjected to strong electric fields. This process, called "field emission," was first reported in 1897 by R. W. Wood. Early technological difficulties have now been largely overcome, and field emission has become a controlled process of growing practical interest.

Basic Processes

Theory. Fowler and Nordheim derived in 1928 a quantitative theory which ante-

dated reliable experimental data by 10 years and became one of the early successes of quantum mechanics.

The Fowler-Nordheim theory of field emission from a cold metal into vacuum is based on the energy diagram of Fig. 1. Emission occurs when a sufficiently large electric field is applied to thin the surface energy barrier to the extent where electrons with Fermi energy have an appreciable probability of tunneling through the barrier and into vacuum. Use of Fermi-Dirac statistics and the W.K.B. approximation yields:

$$J \cong AF^2 \exp\left(-\frac{B\phi^{3/2}}{F}\right) \qquad (1)$$

where J is the field-emitted current density in amp/cm^2, F is the field in v/cm, and ϕ is the thermionic work function (*q.v.*) in ev; $A = 3.5 \times 10^{-5}$ and $B = 6.12 \times 10^8$ for tungsten ($\phi \cong 4.5$ ev).

The theory has been extended to the more complex cases of emission from metals into dielectrics or semiconductors, and from semiconductors into vacuum.

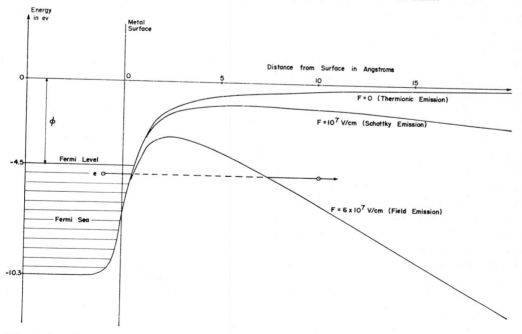

Fig. 1. One-dimensional energy diagram used in the theory of field emission, showing the form of the potential energy surface barrier for several types of emission. Electron energy levels correspond to tungsten.

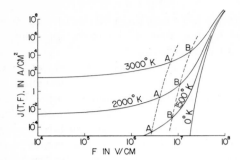

Fig. 2. Theoretical dependence on temperature T and field F of the emitted current density J, for a work function of 4.5 ev (e.g., tungsten). The region to the left of dotted line AA corresponds to thermionic and Schottky emission, that to the right of dotted line BB corresponds to T-F and field emission.

Thermionic and field emission represent two extremes in a continuous range of emission processes. Schottky and T-F emission are intermediate processes in which both temperature and field combine to produce emission. "T-F emission" is defined as emission from a heated conductor subjected to a field large enough so that most electrons are emitted through rather than above the surface energy barrier. T-F emission is of practical interest because it obviates the high-vacuum requirements associated with long-term stability of field-emission cathodes, and thus provides a high-density emission process compatible with present commercial vacuum conditions.

Figure 2 shows the theoretical relationship between J, T, and F, for $\phi = 4.5$ ev; field emission is included as a special case ($T = 0$). To the left of points A (thermionic and Schottky range), tunneling accounts for less than 10 per cent of the total emission; J is sensitive to T but relatively insensitive to F. To the right of points B (T-F and field emission range) emission occurs primarily or solely by tunneling; J increases rapidly with F, becoming both very large and relatively insensitive to T.

Experiment. Fairly extensive experimental verifications of the field and T-F emission theories have been made, particularly by Dyke. Good agreement was found, up to the highest emission densities tested ($\cong 2 \times 10^8$

amp/cm^2), when space-charge effects were taken into account. These effects, which come in gradually above $J \cong 10^5$ amp/cm^2, do not preclude higher emission densities, but must be overcome by an appropriate increase in applied voltage. In theory, emission densities above 10^{10} amp/cm^2 could be reached; in practice, J is limited either by resistive heating of the cathode or by power-dissipation considerations. Measurement of the energy distribution of the emitted electrons provides an excellent test of the theory. Recent careful measurements by Young and Müller confirm the predicted total energy distribution, which is exponential with a mean value proportional to applied field and about 0.25 ev in practice.

Cathodes

Geometry. Very sharp needle-shaped cathodes, formed by electrolytic or chemical etch, are used to reconcile the high field required with reasonable grid voltages and cathode-grid spacings. Conditioning for operation, by vacuum heating or field desorption, cleans and rounds the cathode to a preselected tip radius (typically in the range 0.1 to 1 micron). Controlled, useful emission has been obtained, by appropriate choice of tip radius, at grid voltages ranging from 250 v to 500 kv.

Materials. Field emission has been studied experimentally for most refractory metals, semiconductors such as germanium and silicon, and refractory compounds such as zirconium carbide and lanthanum hexaboride. The latter appear promising, but further data are yet required to assess their practical usefulness.

Tungsten is at present used for practical applications. Single-needle cathodes have yielded low-perveance beams with peak currents above 1 amp. Close-spaced multiple-needle cathodes have yielded higher beam currents (30 amp) and perveances (8 μa/v$^{3/2}$). Rapid further progress is expected.

Life and Stability. With very high vacuum (10^{-12} mm of Hg), cold tungsten cathodes have exhibited stable field emission over several thousand hours at power levels above 100 w. With intermediate vacuum (e.g., 10^{-9} mm of Hg), contamination and sputtering cause gradual instability; however, brief heating of the cathode restores the initial characteristics. With this reconditioning process, which may be repeated as often as desired, individual cathodes have accumulated operating times above 15,000 hr, and no life terminating mechanism has yet been found. In a "commercial" vacuum (10^{-6} to 10^{-8} mm of Hg at present) high contamination and sputtering rates preclude cold cathode operation, but T-F cathodes exhibit stable emission. T-F cathodes are limited to pulsed operation and their life is statistical (with a present average of 500 hr), terminating abruptly by vacuum arc. T-F cathodes made of very pure materials, expected to exhibit much longer average life, are currently under test.

Applications. Field emission combines three advantages: (a) energy need not be supplied to the cold cathode; (b) very high emission densities have been demonstrated; (c) despite the very high emission density, the emitted electrons have a relatively narrow initial energy spread (favorable from the standpoint of beam noise and beam focusing).

On the other hand, field emission requires high fields and high vacuum. Only recently have techniques and basic knowledge progressed enough to justify work on devices. While present development is on a modest scale and concentrated on selected experimental devices, future prospects appear to be good.

In present experimental field-emission microwave devices, the cathode is incorporated in an input cavity similar to that of a klystron (q.v.) and its emission is modulated by the input gap voltage. With the use of compact multiple-needle cathodes, useful power levels may be retained well above 10 kMc. Emission bunching removes the need for long transit times and beam focusing, yielding a compact tube with high phase stability. The strong nonlinearity of the emission allows strong bunching and amplification with high electronic efficiency; it also allows the device to be redesigned for efficient operation as a microwave mixer, rectifier, or harmonic generator at relatively high peak power levels, offering promise for millimeter-wave generation (q.v.).

High-resolution storage and display devices require finely focused beams. The figure of merit for such beams is the electron optical brightness (beam current per unit area per unit solid angle at the focus). As shown by Langmuir, the maximum attainable brightness is limited by the electron source, being proportional to the ratio of emission density to energy spread of the emitted electrons. The field cathode, for which this ratio can be 10^6 times that of thermionic cathodes, appears ideally suited to high-resolution electron-optical devices. In preliminary confirmation, a resolution of 2000 lines/in. was measured in an experimental cathode-ray tube using a field cathode.

Other devices under investigation include high-voltage rectifiers, hard-vacuum high-voltage regulators whose response is very fast and insensitive to environment, and high-peak-power switch tubes. Hard vacuum T-R tubes (q.v.) with negligibly short response and recovery time are another interesting possibility.

The T-F cathode is used successfully in high-intensity flash X-ray tubes ("Fexitrons"), which find several applications; one is the photography of hypervelocity events. Controlled T-F emission yields a rectangular current pulse and a beam dense enough (1000 amp/cm^2) to heat the target to 3000°K within the 0.2-μsec pulse, thus maximizing X-ray source intensity. Peak powers above 10^9 w (2400 amp at 600 kv) have been achieved. Current development is toward still higher voltages and shorter pulses, to increase penetration and time resolution. "Fexitrons" are used in radiobiological experiments requiring extremely high dose rates ($\geq 10^8$ roentgens/sec). Finally, use of a lower voltage "Fexitron" led to the recent development of a lightweight (85 lb) battery-powered medical X-ray unit.

Microscopy

The field-emission microscope ("FEM"), first developed by Müller, is a powerful tool for the detailed and quantitative study of surface phenomena. It is a spherical projection microscope in which electrons from a sharp field emission tip strike a phosphor screen, yielding a highly magnified electrical image of the tip. The magnification is approximately the ratio of screen to tip radius, typically 10^5 to 10^6 X; the resolution, limited by the energy spread of the emitted electrons, is typically 30 Å. Pattern detail arises from local variations in field and work-function, and the pattern is characteristic of the crystal structure for a clean smooth tip. Most contaminants can be detected through their effect on local work-function. FEM uses include:

(a) measurement of emission parameters such as work-function; (b) study of crystal structure and its defects; (c) study of phase transformations in metals and alloys; (d) study of the adsorption, migration, and desorption of contaminants on various substrates, their dependence on temperature and field, and corresponding activation energy measurements; (e) study of the effect of very high fields on chemical reactions; and (f) study of sputtering.

Dyke and co-workers have used a low-duty-cycle pulsed viewing field to extend the versatility of the FEM. This technique minimizes the perturbing effect of the field on the event under study, and allows use of a higher field which makes visible certain surface lattice steps only 2.2 Å high. They used the method to study transport phenomena in heated single crystals of refractory metals, measuring the activation energy for surface migration, the effect of electrostatic stresses on migration rates, and the surface tension in the solid phase.

Field Ion Microscopy

The field ion microscope, developed mostly by Müller, has outstanding resolution (1.5 Å, sufficient to resolve adjacent surface atoms). The geometry is identical to that of the FEM, but the voltage polarity is reversed and the image is produced by ions instead of electrons. For this purpose, low-pressure helium is introduced and the voltage is raised until helium atoms near the tip are field-ionized, the electron tunneling into the tip and the ion being driven to the screen. With the tip at liquid hydrogen temperature and the voltage properly adjusted, incoming helium atoms are first cooled to tip temperature (thus losing most of their random thermal velocity) then ionized preferentially in front of protruding surface atoms (where the field is locally enhanced), which explains the high resolution achieved and the image formation process. Applications are more limited than in the case of the FEM, but when applicable the field ion microscope yields more detailed information.

Field Ionization Mass Spectrometer

The field ionization process discussed above can be used in mass spectrometers, with the advantage (over the conventional hot cathode and electron collision approach) that the ionization process is less likely to cause chemical alteration of the substances under study. Several field ionization mass spectrometers are currently being developed.

REFERENCE

R. Gomer, "Field Emission and Field Ionization," Harvard Univ. Press, 1961.

F. M. Charbonnier

Cross-references: *Electron Microscopes, Photoelectric Emission, Secondary Emission, Statistical Mechanics, Thermionic Emission*

FILTERS

Filters, often called wave filters, are frequency selective networks designed to "pass" sinusoidal waves in one or more continuous frequency bands and to "stop" or reject sinusoidal waves in the complementary bands. Single pass band filters are classified as *low-pass*, *high-pass* and *band-pass* depending on the bands of frequencies which are passed. They are also classified as *image-parameter* filters or *insertion-loss* filters according to the theory by which they are designed.

Image Parameter Filter. An image parameter filter consists of a cascade of two-port *sections* whose image impedances are *matched* at their junctions. If the filter were matched at the terminals also, the image attenuation would be zero in the pass band. However, since the image impedance is frequency dependent and the terminations are usually resistive, the filter is not matched at its terminals at all frequencies.

Figure 1 shows an *m-derived pi half-section* which forms one component of a filter. Its dual is an *m*-derived tee half-section. The values of C and L are $L = R/\omega_c$ and $C = 1/R\omega_c$, where R is the load resistance and ω_c the cut-off frequency. The parameter m lies in the range from 0 to 1 and determines a frequency in the stop band at which the attenuation becomes infinite according to the relation $\omega_\infty^2 = \omega_c^2/(1 - m^2)$. The value $m = 1$ corresponds to the prototype section. A cascade of several such sections each with a different value of m provides for any desired behavior of the attenuation in the stop band. The image impedances at the two ends are

$$Z_{01} = R/\sqrt{s^2 + \omega_c^2}$$

and

$$Z_{02} = R \sqrt{s^2 + \omega_c^2}/(s^2 + \omega_\infty^2)$$

The second of these, having more parameters, can be adjusted to give a better match to a resistive load at the terminals. Hence, the *terminating sections* should have a number 2 end facing the outside of the filter. If a better match at the terminals is required, image impedances with more adjustable parameters can be used.[1, 2, 3]

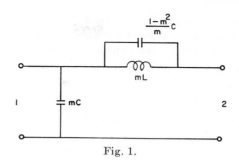

Fig. 1.

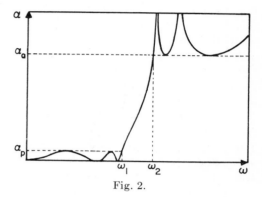

Fig. 2.

Insertion Loss Filter. An alternative method of filter design is based on the insertion loss. Figure 2 shows a typical requirement for a low-pass filter. The insertion loss is required to remain below a certain pass band maximum α_p, in the range of frequency from zero to ω_1, and to remain above a certain stop band minimum α_a, for frequencies higher than ω_2. The width of the interval $\omega_2 - \omega_1$ is a measure of the required selectivity.

An efficient design is the equal-ripple pass band and stop band loss shown in Fig. 2, originally described by Darlington. The structure of the resulting filter often is the same as a cascade of *m*-derived sections but the element values are different. For the same number of sections, the Darlington design gives a better filter performance than the image parameter design, but it has the disadvantage of requiring much greater computational effort.[4, 5]

The incidental dissipation in the filter components causes the actual loss curve to depart from the theoretical to a considerable extent, especially near the edge of the band and in the vicinity of the infinite loss points. It is possible to compensate for this loss by a *predistortion* technique which, however, introduces a flat loss in the pass band.[4]

High pass and band pass designs can be obtained from the low pass by appropriate frequency transformations.

At very low frequencies the physical size of coil demanded by the design may become prohibitively large in some applications. In this case a filter using only R's and C's can be used. The image parameter design procedure is not applicable here but the insertion loss procedure can be adapted. Of course the disadvantage is that the filter will have loss even in the pass band.

Active Filters. The filters described so far consist of passive electrical elements. Filters utilizing active devices can often achieve comparable or superior performance. *Active filters* can include amplification to supply the flat loss introduced by predistortion. Furthermore, by permitting the use of feedback, active filters can increase selectivity and reduce sensitivity to changes in element values. Figure 3 shows an example of an active filter using feedback through a twin-tee circuit.

Electromechanical filters include mechanical components which utilize either the piezo-electric effect, the magnetostrictive effect, or the electrostrictive effect. Of these

the piezoelectric crystal filters are the most widely used. The equivalent circuit of a quartz crystal properly cut is basically a series tuned circuit shunted by a capacitor. The advantages of using the crystal instead of electrical components are the high Q's achievable ($Q = 30,000$ being a typical value) and the high degree of stability of the element values.

Crystal filters find application in *comb filters*, which have many narrow pass bands separated by narrow stop bands. The sharply resonant feature of the crystal makes its use in this application desirable.

REFERENCES

1. ALEX J. GROSSMAN, "Electrical Engineer's Handbook," 3rd ed., Vol. 2, John Wiley & Sons, pp. 6–33 to 6–61; 1936.
2. S. SESHU AND N. BALABANIAN, "Linear Network Analysis," John Wiley & Sons, pp. 453–504; 1959.
3. A. T. STARR, "Electric Circuits and Wave Filters," Pitman, London; 1946.
4. S. DARLINGTON, "Synthesis of reactance 4-poles," *J. Math. and Phys.* 18: 257–353, 1939.
5. N. BALABANIAN, "Network Synthesis," Prentice-Hall, Ch. 6 and 9; 1958.
6. A. J. GROSSMAN, "Synthesis of Tchebycheff parameter symmetrical filters," *Proc. IRE*, 45: 454–473, 1957.

NORMAN BALABANIAN
RAJENDRA NANAVATI

Cross-references: *Network Synthesis, Network Theory*

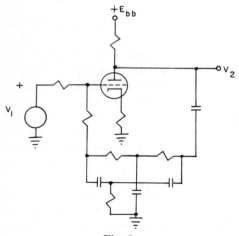

Fig. 3.

FISSION

The term "fission" was first used by Meitner and Frisch (1939) to describe the process of the disintegration of a heavy nucleus into two lighter nuclei of roughly equal size. The conclusion that this unusual nuclear reaction occurs was the culmination of a truly dramatic episode, and set in motion an extremely intense and productive period of investigation. After the discovery of the neutron by Chadwick in 1932, Fermi undertook an extensive investigation of the nuclear reactions produced by the bombardment of various elements with this uncharged projectile. He observed (1934) that at least four different radioactive species resulted from the bombardment of uranium with slow neutrons. These new radioactivities emitted beta particles and were thought to be isotopes of unstable "transuranium elements" of atomic numbers 93, 94 and perhaps higher. There was, of course, intense interest in examining the properties of these new elements and many radiochemists participated in the studies. The results of these investigations, however, were extremely perplexing and the confusion persisted until Hahn and Strassmann (1939), following a clue supplied by I. Curie and Savitch (1938), proved definitely that the so-called "transuranic elements" were, in fact, radioisotopes of barium, lanthanum and other elements in the middle of the Periodic Table.

Armed with the unequivocal results of Hahn and Strassmann, Meitner and Frisch invoked a new liquid-drop model of the nucleus (Bohr, 1936; Bohr and Kalckar, 1937) to give a qualitative theoretical interpretation of the fission process, and called attention to the large energy release that should accompany it. There was almost immediate confirmation of this reaction in dozens of laboratories throughout the world. These experiments confirmed the formation of extremely energetic heavy particles and extended the chemical identification of the products.

Most of the energy of fission is released in the form of kinetic energy of the fission fragments. The initial velocities of the separating particles are of the order of 10^9 cm/sec, and since this velocity is greater than the orbital velocities of the outermost electrons, the latter are stripped from the fragments by interaction with the medium, leaving a positive charge of about 20 units. In passing through matter, the fission fragments cause intense initial ionization. As the fragment is slowed down, outer electrons are captured, decreasing the positive charge, and the ionization intensity decreases. The energy loss at low velocities is due mainly to elastic collisions with the nuclei of the medium. Ranges of from 2 to 3 cm of air are observed for the fission fragments. The ionization produced by fission fragments is many times greater than that due to the most energetic alpha particles, and hence they are readily observed in ionization chambers, cloud chambers, and photographic plates. The recoil of the fragments is sufficient to eject them from the surface of the fissioning material and they can be collected on "catcher foils" or on a water surface in close proximity and identified by their radioactivity and chemical properties. These methods have all been used in confirming and studying the fission process.

The chemical evidence that was so vital in leading Hahn and Strassmann to the discovery of nuclear fission was obtained by the application of the "carrier" and "tracer" techniques. Since invisible amounts of the radioactive species were formed, their chemical identity had to be deduced from the manner in which they followed known "carrier" elements, present in macroscopic quantity, through various chemical operations. Known radioactive species were also added as "tracers" and their behavior compared with that of the unknown species to aid in the identification of the latter. The wide range of radioactivities produced in fission makes this reaction a rich source of tracers for chemical, biological and industrial use.

Although the early experiments involved the fission of normal uranium with slow neutrons, it was rapidly established that the rare isotope, U^{235}, was responsible for this phenomenon. The more abundant isotope, U^{238}, could be made to undergo fission only by fast neutrons with energy greater than 1 Mev. The nuclei of other heavy elements, such as thorium and protactinium, were also shown to be fissionable with fast neutrons, and other particles (such as fast protons, deuterons and alphas, as well as γ-rays) proved to be effective in inducing the reaction. Bismuth, lead, thallium, mercury, gold, platinum, tantalum, and even medium-weight elements such as copper, bromine, silver, tin and barium have been made to undergo fission by excitation with high-energy projectiles (of the order of 100 Mev or more). Some other nuclides that do not occur in nature but have been produced by transmutation reactions also undergo fission. Among these, U^{233} and Pu^{239} are fissionable with slow neutrons; Np^{237} requires fast neutrons.

The very interesting and rare occurrence of spontaneous fission in uranium was first observed in 1940. In this reaction, the nucleus undergoes fission in its ground state, without excitation from external sources. Although the half life for this process in uranium is about 10^{16} years, some of the isotopes of the new "transplutonium elements" exhibit half lives for spontaneous fission of the order of a thousand years, and it is very likely that eventually a nuclide will be discovered in which this process will represent the principal mode of decay.

The outstanding feature of nuclear fission is the tremendous energy release that accompanies it. A chemical reaction such as the explosion of TNT releases about 1.5×10^{11} ergs per gram; nuclear fission releases approximately 8×10^{17} ergs per gram. Fundamentally, the source of this energy lies in the fact that the total mass of the final products of fission is appreciably less than that of the reactants. This loss in mass appears as energy in an amount given by the famous Einstein relation, $E = mc^2$, one atomic mass unit being equivalent to 931 Mev.

The nature of the fission process may perhaps be best understood through a consideration of the structure and stability of nuclear matter. Nuclei are composed of neutrons and protons, the total number of them being equal to the mass number. The actual weight of the nucleus is always less than the sum of the weights of the free nucleons, the difference being the mass equivalent of the energy of formation of the nucleus from its constituents. This difference is known as the "mass defect" and is a measure of the total binding energy of the nucleus.

The neutrons and protons of which nuclei are composed are bound by a short-range attractive force that acts only between nearest neighbors. As long as the total number of protons is small, the long-range electrostatic repulsion between them is insufficient to overcome the cohesive forces between all nucleons. As the number of nucleons increases, the fraction of them near the surface (and hence with fewer neighbors) decreases, and the average binding energy per nucleon increases. At about mass number 55, this trend reaches a maximum, and a further increase in the number of nucleons decreases the average binding energy per nucleon due to the repulsive coulomb force between protons. In fact, in order to maintain stability, the number of protons must be diluted with an excess of neutrons as the mass number increases. Since a decrease in binding energy per nucleon means a decrease in the mass defect or an increase in the average mass per bound nucleon, uranium (with a greater mass per nucleon than that for nuclei of elements of medium atomic weight) is energetically unstable with respect to fission. Qualitatively, at least, the fission process is thus seen to be a consequence of the coulomb repulsion between protons.

Coulomb repulsion between protons causes heavy nuclei to have rather high neutron-to-proton ratios (of the order of 1.5) and when such a nucleus undergoes fission, the primary fragments formed will possess a similar ratio. For nuclei in the mass region of these products, however, such a ratio is higher than is consistent with stability. A ratio corresponding to stability is attained by the evaporation of neutrons from the highly excited primary fragments (within about 10^{-14} sec of the fission event), and by conversion of neutrons to protons through the beta decay process.

The average number of neutrons emitted per fission in U^{235} fission is 2.5, and hence a chain reaction becomes possible, the excess neutrons causing fission in other U^{235} nuclei which, in turn, contribute more neutrons. A vast energy source is thus made available for utilization in a controlled form (nuclear reactor or "pile") or in an explosion (atomic bomb).

A typical fission event in U^{235}, for example, may be described by the following equation:

$$92 \, U^{235} + {}_0n^1 \rightarrow (92 \, U^{236}) \rightarrow$$

$$_{38}Sr^{95} + {}_{54}Xe^{139} + 2{}_0n^1 + \gamma + Q$$

A slow neutron is absorbed by a U^{235} nucleus forming the excited compound nucleus, U^{236}, which then splits into two fission fragments, Sr^{95} and Xe^{139}, and two neutrons. The subscript at the left of the chemical symbol indicates the atomic number (nuclear charge) and the superscript to the right indicates the mass number. The fission fragments possess about 20 Mev of excitation energy that is emitted in the decay process they undergo in reaching the stable members of their respective "decay chains," $_{42}Mo^{95}$ and $_{57}La^{139}$. In addition, about 5 Mev of gamma radiation, represented by γ, is released at the instant of fission. (Some energetic alpha particles have also been observed in the fission act, but they are rather rare.) Q represents the kinetic energies of the fission fragments and neutrons and is approximately 170 Mev. Thus, the total energy of a fission event is close to 200 Mev. Both nuclear charge and mass number must be conserved in the fission process. Other combinations of primary fragments and number of neutrons are possible, but they are not all formed with equal probability. For example, the formation of the complementary fragments of masses 95 and 139 is about 600 times as probable as the formation of two mass 117 fragments and almost 10^6 times as probable as the formation of masses 72 and 162.

The probability distribution of masses in fission is an important feature of the process. The percentage of fissions that leads to a given mass is referred to as the "fission yield" of that mass. A fission yield curve is obtained by plotting the yields against mass number. Such curves have been obtained by radio-chemical investigations for fission of many nuclides at low and high energy of excitation. Ionization-chamber and velocity measurements indicate a spread in the kinetic energy of the fragments for a given mass split, associated mainly with a variation in the number of neutrons per fission. In general, fission induced by low-energy particles (generally referred to for convenience as "low-energy fission") is characterized by an asymmetric splitting into two main groups of mass numbers (the "light" and "heavy" groups) the most probable mass ratio of light to heavy product being about 2/3. As the mass number of the fissioning nucleus increases, the light group distribution shifts towards heavier masses whereas the heavy group remains relatively stationary. As the energy of excitation increases, the probability of symmetric fission increases, and at very high energies it becomes the most probable mode. The fission yield curves are not entirely smooth functions of mass, and regions of fine-structure have been observed. These are attributed to an enhanced probability for the formation of particularly stable nuclei having "closed shells" of 50 and 82 neutrons.

In addition to a distribution in mass, a distribution in nuclear charge for a particular mass split also occurs. The present data on charge distribution in slow-neutron induced fission indicate that the most probable primary charge of complementary fragments is that for which both fragments are equally displaced from the most stable charge for their respective mass numbers. Each primary fragment undergoes, on the average, about three beta disintegrations before achieving stability, each beta disintegration increasing the nuclear charge by one, but leaving the mass number unchanged. Since the primary fragments are highly excited, the decay energy of the first few members of a decay chain may be quite large. For some nuclides near closed-shells this decay energy may exceed the binding energy of a neutron, and the latter may be emitted in preference to a beta particle. Since these neutrons follow beta-emitting precursors in the decay chain, they are referred to as "delayed neutrons," thus distinguishing them from the "prompt neutrons" which are coincident with the fission event. Although delayed neutrons account for less than 1 per cent of all fission neutrons, they are an extremely important factor in the control of nuclear reactors.

ELLIS P. STEINBERG

Cross-references: *Atoms, Energy, Gamma Rays, Isotopes, Radioactivity, Reactors*

FLEMING, SIR JOHN AMBROSE (1849–1945)

J. A. Fleming was born at Lancaster in England on November 29, 1849, the son of a Congregational minister. His family moved to London in 1853 and he attended University College School and University College, where he received the B.Sc. in 1870. After a period of alternate science teaching and additional study, he entered Cambridge University in 1877 to work under James Clerk Maxwell in the new Cavendish Laboratory, where he helped to repeat the century-old electrical experiments of Henry Cavendish (1731–1810), whose notes on them had recently come to light. Fleming was made Demonstrator in 1880, and in the following year he became Professor of Physics and Mathematics in the newly constituted University College at Nottingham. He

Sir J. Ambrose Fleming

resigned after a year to become a consultant to the Edison Electric Light Co. in London; in 1885 he was appointed Professor of Electrical Technology at University College, a post he held for 41 years. He made many contributions to the design of transformers, the understanding of the properties of materials at liquid-air temperatures, to photometry, and to electrical measurements in general. He was an outstanding teacher: the right-hand rule (a mnemonic aid relating direction of magnetic field, conductor motion, and the induced electromotive force) is attributed to him. He was also an outstanding popular scientific lecturer and frequently spoke at the Royal Institution.

At University College he experimented widely with electric telegraphy and gave special courses on the subject. He was aware of Edison's observation of the "Edison effect" (he had visited the U.S.A. and met Edison in 1884) of unilateral flow of particles from negative to positive electrode and repeated some of the experiments, both with dc and ac, beginning in 1889. During the following years, he cooperated with Marconi in many of his experiments, and helped to design the transmitter employed by Marconi in spanning the Atlantic in 1901. Thus it was not until 1904 that he returned to his experiments on the Edison effect, managing to produce a rectifier that soon replaced the detectors then used in radiotelegraphy. He named the resulting device a "thermionic valve," for which he obtained a patent in 1904. This was the first electron tube.

Fleming led an incredibly active scientific life. He read the first paper ever presented to the Physical Society on its foundation in 1874, and read his last paper to the same body 65 years later, in 1939. He published over a hundred important papers. He was an active president of the Television Society from 1930 to his death and received many other honors, including the Hughes Medal in 1910 from the Royal Society (he was made an F.R.S. in 1892); the Faraday Medal of the AIEE (1928); the Gold Medal of the IRE (1933); and many others. He was knighted in 1929. He became Professor Emeritus after his retirement in 1926, but continued to be scientifically active nearly until his death at the age of 95 at Sidmouth, on April 18, 1945.

CHARLES SUSSKIND

Cross-references: *Historical Background of Electronics*

FLIP-FLOP CIRCUITS: see OSCILLATORS

FLUORESCENCE

Fluorescence is a process in which an atom or molecule emits radiation in the course of a transition from a higher to a lower electronic state. A more restricted definition, applicable particularly to atomic processes, excludes the special case, known as *resonance radiation*, in which the wavelength of the emitted radiation is the same as that of the exciting radiation. The term "fluorescence" is further restricted to phenomena in which the time interval between the acts of excitation and emission is small, of the order of 10^{-8}–10^{-3} sec. This distinguishes fluorescence from *phosphorescence*, where the time interval between absorption and emission may extend from 10^{-3} sec to several hours.

Fluorescence is exhibited both by free atoms and by molecules; it can occur in the gaseous, liquid, and solid states, although not necessarily in all three phases of the same substance. It is observed in its simplest form in the classical experiment of Lord Rayleigh, in which sodium vapor, confined in a quartz vessel at low pressure, is exposed to the ultraviolet radiation from a spark between zinc electrodes. This radiation causes the sodium vapor to glow with a yellow fluorescence corresponding in wavelength to the D-line transition of sodium atoms falling from the first electronically excited state to the ground state. The absorption of the ultraviolet radiation excites the sodium atoms to high electronic energy levels. Part of this excitation energy is dissipated by collision with other sodium atoms, or the walls of the vessel, reducing the atom to its lowest electronically excited state, from which it subsequently drops to the ground state with the emission of the D-line radiation. In such atomic processes the wavelength of the fluorescent radiation is always longer than that of the exciting radiation— a generalization known as Stokes' law. Fluorescence can occur also in molecules, but the process is more complex, since the electronic excitation and de-excitation processes may be accompanied by secondary changes in the vibrational and rotational energy of the molecule.

The relationship between the molecular structure and the fluorescence of organic compounds is less well understood than the factors determining the initial absorption process. It is important for fluorescence that the molecule should not only contain a chromophoric system to absorb the exciting radiation, but also that the excited electronic system should be shielded adequately from internal and external influences that would permit a too rapid dissipation of the excitation energy into vibrational motion before the fluorescence re-radiation act can occur. At present it is not possible to define the type of molecular structure required to induce strong fluorescing power, but certain substituent groups, notably the $-NO_2$ group, are commonly associated with a strong quenching effect on the fluorescence of any molecule to which they are attached as part of a conjugated system. Among organic compounds brilliant fluorescence is particularly associated with phthalein structures, and also with aromatic structures such as anthracene and naphthacene, which contain condensed systems of several benzene rings. Few inorganic compounds fluoresce strongly in the liquid state or in solution, but in the solid state the fluorescence of certain uranyl salts and platinocyanides is outstanding.

In solids, fluorescence is often greatly modified by the presence of trace impurities and a considerable literature exist on the nature of such phenomena, which are commonly associated with irregularities in the crystal lattice (F-centers). As examples we may note that the blue fluorescence of pure solid anthracene changes on the addition of 10^{-4} mole of naphthacene, and the resulting green fluorescence is characteristic of the naphthacene and not the anthracene molecule. Similar effects are noted in solid inorganic systems, particularly zinc sulfide, the blue fluorescence of which is greatly intensified by the addition of one part in ten thousand of cupric chloride. The application of such effects to the analysis of trace amounts of the activating substances will be apparent.

Fluorescence can be induced by other excitation mechanisms as well as ultraviolet irradiation. The excitation of fluorescence by electron bombardment constitutes the basic process in the illumination of cathode-ray-tube screens and the excitation of fluorescence by α-, β-, and γ-rays is employed in scintillation counters for the monitoring of radioactivity.

R. NORMAN JONES

Cross-references: *Atoms, Cathodoluminescence, Electroluminescence, Fluorescent Lights, Molecules*

FLUORESCENT LAMPS

When a material upon being irradiated with electromagnetic or corpuscular radiation emits electromagnetic radiation, the phenomenon is known as luminescence. If the emission ceases at once when the radiation is removed we speak of fluorescence, otherwise of phosphorescence. A clearer differentiation can be made by determining if the emission can be "frozen in," which is the case for phosphorescence but not for fluorescence. ("Frozen in" implies that by

lowering the temperature the emission ceases, but begins again when the temperature rises again sufficiently.) Examples of luminescence include illumination of an X-ray screen (irradiation with X-rays) the cathode-ray-tube screen (irradiation with electrons), and the fluorescent lamp (irradiation with ultraviolet).

The wavelength of the radiation emitted is usually longer than that of the exciting radiation. In the case of gases both radiations can be of the same wavelength. With solids the emission covers a more or less broad spectral band, independent of the wavelength of the exciting radiation. The intensity of the band, however, depends on the wavelength of the latter and is proportional to the irradiation intensity. In the fluorescent lamp, the radiation produced by the discharge is converted by a fluorescent phosphor into radiation of longer wavelengths. In the usual constructions, the resonance radiation of mercury vapor (1850 Å and 2537 Å) is used for the excitation. The fluorescent powder coating on the inner wall of the glass tube is usually a mixture of various phosphors, whereby the desired spectral distribution of the emission can be achieved. Figure 1 shows a fluorescent lamp L with fluorescent powder layer F and electrodes E, which usually consist of tungsten coils (double or triple coils) coated with an electron-emitting substance. The tube is filled with a rare gas (usually argon) at a pressure of a few millimeters of mercury, together with a small drop of mercury. The lamp is usually operated on ac in series with a choke C. To ignite the lamp a sufficiently high voltage can be employed such that the lamp immediately strikes. Usually, however, the electrodes are preheated to such a temperature that the ignition is assisted by thermal emission. This pre-heating can be carried out with a heater transformer or by using a starter (ST). (Special starting circuits can also be employed.)

The starter is usually a glow switch which works as follows. On applying the mains or transformer voltage a glow-discharge com-

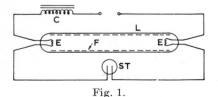

Fig. 1.

mences between the poles of the starter, at least one of which is made of bimetal. The heating effect of this discharge warms the bimetal and causes it to bend over into contact with the other pole. The "short-circuit" current through the choke then heats up the lamp electrodes. Through the short-circuit in the starter the glow discharge ceases and the bimetal cools down and breaks contact. The voltage surge produced by the choke due to the sudden interruption of the short-circuit current (dependent on the height on the moment of interruption) is thus applied over the discharge path in the lamp, which then ignites. If this does not happen at once, the cycle is repeated. Once the lamp ignites, the voltage across the lamp (about half the open-voltage) is insufficient to operate the glow-starter.

Lamps are manufactured in wattages up to ca 200 w and in lengths to 8 ft. There are standard colors (warm-white, cool-white and daylight) with a high efficiency (70–80 lumens/w) and the so-called "de luxe" colors with lower efficiencies (45–55 lumens/w) but with much improved color rendition. For dye-line printing (photochemical) and for medical purposes phosphors are used with peak emission at ca 4000 Å and 3000 Å, respectively.

W. ELENBAAS

Cross-references: *Electroluminescence, Fluorescence, Strobes*

FLYING-SPOT SCANNING

Flying-spot scanning is a system of television pickup which utilizes a moving spot of light from the screen of a flat-faced cathode-ray tube as the source of illumination. Within the cathode-ray tube, an electron-gun structure provides a beam of electrons which is sharply focused on the luminescent screen to produce a small spot of light. A magnetic deflection system causes the beam to scan the face of the tube at the standard television rate to produce a raster of uniform luminance and proper aspect ratio. The flat raster image is then focused on a transparency or film by a lens system. The transmission of light through the film is modulated by the film density at each particular point, and the modulated light beam is picked up and amplified by a multiplier phototube.

The basic requirements of a flying-spot tube are rather stringent: a phosphor screen with extremely short persistence and little or no phosphorescence, a high-resolution scanning beam, a flat faceplate, uniform focus, and high energy output. The phosphors used for the screen of the cathode-ray tube must have extremely short persistence because light from the tube face should ideally come only from the spot immediately under the electron beam. Otherwise, light from the previously scanned portion is focused on the film and amplified by the phototube to produce an unwanted signal. Practical phosphors are P16 (which is used most widely in black-and-white systems) and P24 (which is utilized in color systems because its spectral energy distribution extends over the entire visible spectrum).

The lens system must be of high quality and designed to produce a flat image when focused on a flat object, and should have a low f number for maximum light collection.

The phototubes should be of the head-on type for maximum sensitivity and collection. For the color system the light image is split into three color images and picked up in three different phototubes. The spectral sensitivity of a phototube should match the light reaching it.

The flying-spot system can be used in place of a monoscope (*q.v.*) for still-pattern pickup, and can also be used with changing patterns. The system is capable of good resolution and detail, but has the disadvantage of requiring an image that is small in area and close to the light source.

The flying-spot system has been used experimentally for simultaneous live color and black-and-white pickup. Several large-area multiplier phototubes are used to pick up the light reflected from a scene illuminated by a flying-spot tube. No light can be used during active scanning time other than that from the tube, whose raster is projected by means of a lens onto the scene being televised. Illumination for the studio personnel to read scripts and the like is provided by synchronized lamps which are turned on only during the vertical blanking interval.

G. A. Robinson

Cross-references: *Cathode-Ray Tubes (Display), Iconoscope, Image Orthicon, Monoscope, Photomultiplier, Television*

FOOD STERILIZATION: see RADIATION (IONIZING

FOUR-LAYER SEMICONDUCTOR DEVICES

The four-layer device is a two- or three-terminal element in which use is made of the current multiplication properties of the outermost two junctions to switch between a high-impedance state (≈ 10 megohm) and a low impedance state (≈ 1 ohm). The operation of such a device can be described in terms of the *pnpn switch* in Fig. 1.

The ratio of hole current to electron current in the two outer junctions is specified by the doping, lifetime, and dimensions of the semiconductor on both sides of the junction—i.e., by the injection efficiency associated with each of the junctions. The collector current when the device is in the high-impedance state can be written:

$$I_C = \frac{M\beta_P\gamma_P I_B + MI_{COP} + (M-1)I_{CON}}{1 - \gamma_n - M\beta_P\gamma_P - (M-1)\beta_N\gamma_N I_C}$$

where M is the avalanche multiplication factor at the reverse biased collector junction (assumed to be the same for holes and electrons), β_P and β_N are the minority-carrier transport efficiencies in the two base regions, γ_P and γ_N are the minority-carrier injection efficiencies for the two emitter junctions, and I_{COP} and I_{CON} are the collector saturation currents from each side of the junction. Regenerative breakdown is possible since the denominator in this expression can go to zero. The basic idea in the design of four-layer switching devices is to arrange for this denominator to be greater than zero for small collector currents and to go to zero for a specified value of collector current.

The static characteristic for a typical

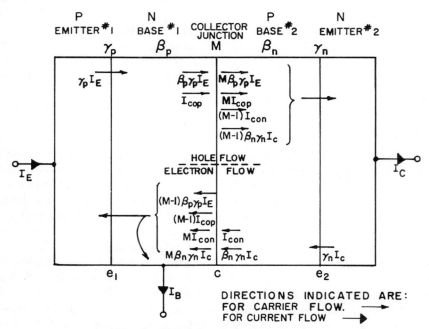

Fig. 1. Carrier flow in a pnpn switch.

three-terminal four-layer device is shown in Fig. 2 (pnpn diode characteristic is identical to that for $I_b = 0$). When voltage is applied in a direction to reverse bias the center junction and $I_b = 0$, the saturation current flows. For large values of collector-junction voltage, avalanche multiplication at the collector junction increases the device current to the level where the denominator goes to zero, at which point regenerative switching to the "on state" occurs. In the on state, all three junctions are forward biased and the total voltage drop across the device is very small (of the order of 1 v).

Various four-layer structures can be classified on the basis of the mechanism used to control the current level at which regeneration occurs. In the silicon *pnpn switch* it is the low injection efficiencies due to generation and recombination in the space-charge region that are used to keep the denominator positive for small values of current. In the *thyristor* and *trinistor* a metal-to-semiconductor contact for which the minority-carrier injection efficiency is a marked function of the majority-carrier current density is used at emitter 2. Proposals have also been made to use the variation of the current-transport efficiency across one or both of the base regions, to use a resistivity by-passed emitter junction, and to use a tunnelling junction. The choice of mechanism or the combination of mechanisms to be used depends on the degree of control achievable over the switching current.

The properties of the four-layer device that are of importance are the forward and reverse break-over voltages ($\approx$400 v), the current level at which regeneration sets in (the break-over current, $\approx$10 ma), the voltage across the device in the "on state" ($\approx$1 v), the speed of switching ($\approx$1 μsec), and, for some applications, the turnoff properties of the device. Present applications of the four-layer semiconductor device are largely in industrial power control where the small power dissipation associated with each of the two stable states and the large forward and reverse break-over voltages are the

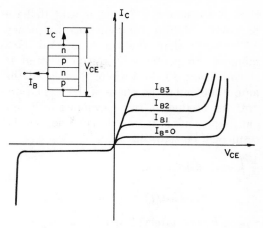

Fig. 2. Static characteristic for a four-layer switch.

crucial parameters. Application of this device for high-speed switching in computers is still on a small scale. The drawbacks for such applications are the long recovery time and the lack of appreciable current gain in turning off the device. Some applications of four-layer diodes in cross-point switching for telephone networks are also being considered.

JACK HILIBRAND

Cross-references: *Diodes (Semiconductor), Semiconductors, Switches, Transistors, Tunnel Diode*

FOURIER ANALYSIS

Fourier analysis was invented by J. B. J. Fourier (1768–1830) in his book *La théorie du chaleur*. The Fourier analysis of a given periodic function represents it as a sum of a number, usually infinite, of simply harmonic components. Because the response of a linear dynamic system to a simply harmonic input is usually easy to obtain, the response to an arbitrary periodic input can be obtained from its Fourier analysis.

A function $f(t)$ such that $f(t + T) = f(t)$ is said to be periodic with period T. Examples of such periodic functions are the functions $\cos (2n\pi t/T)$ and $\sin (2n\pi t/T)$ where n is any integer, positive, negative, or zero. Each of these functions represents an oscillation of frequency n/T and is said to be a harmonic of the fundamental frequency $1/T$. Note that the most general harmonic of frequency n/T can be written as $A \cos [(2n\pi t/T) + \alpha]$ where A is called the amplitude and α the phase of the oscillation.

If the product of two harmonics of different frequencies is averaged over a period, the result will be zero, that is,

$$\frac{1}{T} \int_P \cos [(2n\pi t/T) + \alpha]$$

$$\cdot \cos [(2m\pi t/T) + \beta] \, dt = 0, \qquad m \neq n \tag{1}$$

where P, the interval of integration, is any interval of length T e.g., $0 \le t \le T$ or $-\frac{1}{2}T \le t \le \frac{1}{2}T$. Because of (1), harmonics of different frequencies are said to be orthogonal. If the harmonics have the same frequency, that is, if $m = n$, then (1) becomes

$$\frac{1}{T} \int_P \cos [(2n\pi t/T) + \alpha]$$

$$\cdot \cos [(2n\pi t/T) + \beta] \, dt = \frac{1}{2} \cos (\alpha - \beta) \tag{2}$$

If a harmonic input is applied to an L-C circuit, the response is given by the solution of

$$L \frac{d^2I}{dt^2} + C^{-1}I = A \cos [(2n\pi t/T) + \alpha]$$

namely

$$I = A[C^{-1} - (4n^2\pi^2L/T^2)]^{-1} \cos [(2n\pi t/T) + \alpha]$$

Since the L-C circuit is linear, the response to a sum of harmonic inputs is the sum of the responses to the individual harmonics; consequently, the response to an arbitrary input $f(t)$ of period T is obtained if $f(t)$ can be represented as a sum of harmonics of frequency $1/T$. We assume

$$f(t) = \frac{1}{2} a_0$$

$$+ \sum_1^\infty [a_n \cos (2n\pi t/T) + b_n \sin (2n\pi t/T)] \tag{3}$$

where the unknown amplitudes a_n and b_n are determined by multiplying $f(t)$ by

$\cos (2n\pi t/T)$ and $\sin (2n\pi t/T)$, respectively, and averaging the product over an interval of length T. The resulting series (3) is called the Fourier series for $f(t)$.

Using (1) and (2), we find that

$$a_n = \frac{2}{T} \int_P f(t) \cos (2n\pi t/T) \, dt, \, n = 0, 1, 2, \cdots$$

$$b_n = \frac{2}{T} \int_P f(t) \sin (2n\pi t/T) \, dt, \, n = 1, 2, \cdots$$

(4)

If $f(t)$ is piecewise continuous and has a piecewise continuous derivative, the series (3) converges to $f(t)$ for all values of t at which $f(t)$ is continuous. At a point t_0 at which $f(t)$ is discontinuous, jumping from a value $f(t_0 - 0)$ to a value $f(t_0 + 0)$, the series (3) converges to

$$\frac{1}{2} [f(t_0 - 0) + f(t_0 + 0)]$$

The Fourier series in (3) may be defined for more general functions $f(t)$ but the question of convergence for such functions is a difficult mathematical one. For further details see a standard book such as Hardy and Rogisinski's "Fourier Series."

A useful alternative form for the Fourier series is the following complex form:

$$f(t) = \sum_{-\infty}^\infty c_n \exp (2\pi jnt/T) \tag{5}$$

where

$$c_n = \frac{1}{T} \int_P f(t) \exp (2\pi jnt/T) \, dt$$

Note that in (5) the sum is to be understood in the following sense:

$$\lim_{N \to \infty} \sum_{-N}^N c_n \exp (2\pi jnt/T)$$

If $f(t)$ is an even or an odd function of t, the formulas (4) may be simplified by integrating over half the interval $-\frac{1}{2}T \le t \le \frac{1}{2}T$. For $f(t)$ even, we find

$$f(t) = \frac{1}{2} a_0 + \sum_1^\infty a_n \cos (2n\pi t/T)$$

where

$$a_n = \frac{4}{T} \int_0^{T/2} f(t) \cos (2n\pi t/T) \, dt, \; n = 0, 1, 2, \cdots$$

Similarly, if $f(t)$ is odd,

$$f(t) = \sum_1^\infty b_n \sin (2n\pi t/T)$$

where

$$b_n = \frac{4}{T} \int_0^{T/2} f(t) \sin (2n\pi t/T) \, dt$$

The functions

$$1, \sqrt{2} \cos \frac{2\pi t}{T}, \sqrt{2} \sin \frac{2\pi t}{T}, \tag{6}$$

$$\sqrt{2} \cos \frac{4\pi t}{T}, \sqrt{2} \sin \frac{4\pi t}{T}, \cdots$$

are a typical example of an orthonormal set of functions, that is, a set of functions that are orthogonal in the sense defined previously and normalized because the average over a period of the square of any function is one. Consider the problem of approximating in the mean square to a function $f(t)$ by means of a sum of N terms from (6). This problem is equivalent to finding coefficients a_n', b_n' such that the integral

$$\frac{1}{T} \int_P [f(t) - s_N(t)]^2 \, dt \tag{7}$$

is as small as possible, where

$$s_N(t) = \sum_0^N [a_n' \cos (2n\pi t/T) + b_n' \sin (2n\pi t/T)]$$

By straightforward calculation with the use of (1) and (2) we find that (7) equals

$$\frac{1}{T} \int_P f(t)^2 \, dt - \sum_0^N (a_n a_n' + b_n b_n')$$

$$+ \frac{1}{2} \sum_0^N (a_n'^2 + b_n'^2)$$

$$= \frac{1}{T} \int_P f(t)^2 \, dt - \frac{1}{2} \sum_0^N (a_n^2 + b_n^2) \tag{8}$$

$$+ \frac{1}{2} \sum_0^N [(a_n - a_n')^2 + (b_n - b_n')^2]$$

It is clear that the minimum of this expression is attained when $a_n = a_n'$ and $b_n = b_n'$. Thus

$$s_N(t) = \sum_0^N [a_n \cos (2n\pi/T) + b_n \sin(2n\pi t/T)]$$

which is the Nth partial sum of the Fourier series of $f(t)$, is the best mean-square approximation to $f(t)$. It can be proved that as N goes to infinity, (8) approaches zero, thus giving *Parseval's theorem:*

$$\frac{1}{T} \int_P f(t)^2 \, dt = \frac{1}{2} \sum_0^\infty (a_n^2 + b_n^2)$$

BERNARD FRIEDMAN

Cross-references: *Fourier Integrals and Their Applications, Laplace and Fourier Transforms*

FOURIER INTEGRALS AND THEIR APPLICATIONS

Fourier and Laplace Integrals. The Fourier integral of $f(x)$

$$\mathfrak{F}[f(x)] = \int_{-\infty}^\infty e^{iux} f(x) \, dx \tag{1}$$

originally developed by Fourier for the analysis of heat flow, is generally used in the solution of differential equations of physics and in the statistical theory of distributions. The Laplace integral

$$\mathfrak{L}[f(t)] = \int_0^\infty e^{-st} f(t) \, dt \tag{2}$$

however, is better suited for the solution of the differential equations of circuits, with the Fourier integral, in the form of

$$\int_{-\infty}^\infty e^{i\omega t} f(t) \, dt$$

being reserved for steady state solutions, for pulse shapes that do not obey a differential equation, and for communication theory.

Fourier Integrals and Diffraction. The three-dimensional Fourier integral

$$G(u,v,w) = \iiint F(x,y,z) e^{i\phi} \, dx \, dy \, dz \tag{3}$$

is widely used to approximate the far field in the diffraction of scalar acoustic waves and transverse electromagnetic x-rays, optics, and microwaves. The scalar function F represents the distribution of coherent isotropic radiating points, whereas G is the equivalent single source which, if placed at the origin, would radiate the same plane wave in the far field in the direction $\mathbf{n} = (\ell i + m j + z k)$. If $\mathbf{r} = (x i + y j + z k)$ is the position vector of the radiating point, then the phase

$$\phi = k \, \mathbf{r} \cdot \mathbf{n} = k(\ell x + my + nz)$$
$$= (ux + vy + wz) \tag{4}$$

where $k = 2\pi/\lambda$. When all plane waves are reversed by reversing ϕ, they converge to reconstitute the source F, so that

$$F(x,y,z) = \iiint G(u,v,w)e^{-j\phi} \, du \, dv \, dw . \tag{5}$$

Certain normalization constants have been omitted from (3) and (5) which constitute a pair of Fourier transforms, indicated symbolically by the double arrow

$$F(x,y,z) \rightleftarrows G(u,v,w) \tag{6}$$

In the case of broadside arrays, $z = 0$, yielding the two-dimensional transformation $F(x,y) \rightleftarrows G(u,v)$; and for the one-dimensional line source, $f(x) \rightleftarrows g(u)$.

According to the Parseval theorem, the total power radiated in the F-space and G-space is equal. Thus,

$$\iiint FF^* \, dx \, dy \, dz = \iiint GG^* \, du \, dv \, dw \tag{7}$$

The asterisk indicates the complex conjugate. [Actually, directions for which

$$(\ell^2 + m^2 + n^2) > 1$$

are imaginary, resulting in evanescent waves that do not radiate in the far field.] One result of (7) is that orthogonal functions in F-space transform to orthogonal functions in G-space. For example, for the line source of normalized width $2a$, $e^{jn\pi x} \rightleftarrows g_0(\phi - n\pi)$, with $g_0(\phi) = (\sin \phi)/\phi$. Here, $\phi = (2\pi/\lambda)a \sin \theta$ is the maximum phase difference be-

tween the edge of the aperture and the center, when observed in a direction θ from the normal.

Integration by Parts. If $f(x)$ is continuous with continuous derivatives except at points x_k, then one may integrate the Fourier integral by parts:

$$g(u) = \sum_{k=1} \int_{x_k}^{x_{k+1}} f(x)e^{jux} \, dx$$
$$= \sum_{k=1} \frac{e^{jux}}{ju} \Delta\left[-1 + \frac{D}{ju} - \left(\frac{D}{ju}\right)^2 + \cdots\right]f(x) \tag{8}$$

where Δ is the finite difference in f or $D^n f$ at x_k. Thus, the far-out side lobes are dominated by the lowest-order discontinuities.

Derivatives of Fourier Integrals. On taking successive derivatives of G with respect to u, v, and w under the integral sign of (3),

$$D_u{}^a D_v{}^b D_w{}^c G \rightleftarrows j^{a+b+c} x^a y^b z^c F \tag{9}$$

For one dimension, $D^n g(u) \rightleftarrows (jx)^n f(x)$. Similarly, from (5) we derive

$$D^n f(x) \rightleftarrows (-ju)^n g(u)$$

These relations effectively indicate two different transformations of operators,

$$x^n \rightleftarrows (-jD_u)^n$$

and $D_x{}^n \rightleftarrows (-ju)^n$. They enable us in certain cases to obtain the differential equation (D.E.) of a function from the D. E. of its transform. A unique example is

$$(D_x{}^2 - x^2 + 1)f$$

the D. E. of the Gauss error function, $\exp(-x^2/2)$. Since $(D_x{}^2 - x^2)f \rightleftarrows (D_u{}^2 - u^2)g$ is an identical Fourier transform pair, it follows that the error function must be its own Fourier transform in any number of dimensions. This is fundamental in statistics.

Another application of derivatives is to the diffraction pattern $g_0(\phi) = (\sin \phi)/\phi$ of a plane wave passing through a slit of normalized width 2. Here, $f(x) = 1$, $-1 \leq x \leq 1$, so that $x^n \rightleftarrows (-jD)^n g_0(\phi)$. This leads to a solution for the pattern when $f(x)$ is a power series. For example, the Legendre polynomials $P_n(x)$ transform into the spherical Bessel functions $j_n(\phi)$.

Series Expansion—The Moment Problem. An efficient method of evaluation over the main lobe of G is to expand $e^{j\phi}$ in a power series in ϕ and then integrate term by term. If F is phased so as to reinforce in the z direction, then $\phi = ux + vy + (w - k)z$. For a line source, $g(u)$ reduces to

$$\sum j^n \mu_n u^n / n!$$

where

$$\mu_n = \int x^n f(x) dx$$

is the nth moment of $f(x)$. If the origin of $f(x)$ is at its center of gravity, $\mu = 0$ and the power P of the diffraction pattern is

$$\frac{P(u)}{P(0)} = 1 - \frac{\mu_2}{\mu_0} u^2 + \frac{1}{4} \left[\left(\frac{\mu_2}{\mu_0} \right)^2 + \frac{\mu_4}{3\mu_0} \right] u^4 - \cdots \quad (10)$$

On taking the natural logarithm, the drop from the peak in nepers is

$$N = \frac{\mu_2}{\mu_0} u^2 + \frac{1}{4} \left[\left(\frac{\mu_2}{\mu_0} \right)^2 - \frac{\mu_4}{3\mu_0} \right] u^4 + \cdots \quad (11)$$

Arrays of Arrays—The Convolution Theorem. An effective method of synthesizing new patterns is to let each point of one array F_1 spread out into a second array F_2. The resulting F is the *convolution* of F_1 and F_2, indicated by a star between them. In the one-dimensional case

$$f(x) = f_1(x) * f_2(x) = \int f_1(x - \alpha) f(\alpha) d\alpha$$

The corresponding Fourier integral G is the *product* of G_1 and G_2, indicated by a dot. This convolution theorem, corresponding to the multiplication theorem of frequency spectra in circuit theory, holds for any number of factors, in any order, and for any number of dimensions. Symbolically,

$$F_1 * F_2 * \cdots F_n \rightleftarrows G_1 \cdot G_2 \cdots G_n \quad (12)$$

One concludes that the nulls in each factor in G persist in the final pattern with directions unchanged.

Due to the symmetry of Fourier pairs, the convolution theorem can also be applied to problems with star and dot interchanged. This has application to the sampling theorem, and to the calculation of diffraction patterns of arrays of elements, including x-ray crystal diffraction.

Optics and Communication Theory. Wiener's general approach to the optimization of filters with due regard to the frequency spectra of the input functions and the noise has been applied to some extent in the design of optical instruments and antennas. Thus, from the standpoint of communication theory, a distant coherent point source is imaged as $G(u,v)$ the Fourier transform of $F(x,y)$ which is the amplitude over the aperture. An extended object $H(u,v)$ consisting of *coherent* point sources will be imaged as the *convolution* $H * G$. The frequency spectrum of the image is then the *product* of F and the Fourier transform of H. Thus, F acts like a band limited *angular* or *space frequency* filter which cuts off at $\pm a/\lambda$ cycles per radian, where $2a$ is the aperture diameter. Thus, if an aperture contains n wavelengths the cut-off is $n/2$ cycles per radian.

On the other hand, if H consists of *incoherent* points, the image is $H * P$ where $P = GG^*$. The equivalent filter spectrum is then the transform of P which, by the convolution theorem, is the autocorrelation of the aperture

$$A(x,y) = \iint F(\alpha,\beta) F[(\alpha + x)(\beta + y)] \, d\alpha d\beta$$

In this case, the width of the pass band is doubled, but the transmission tapers uniformly to zero near the edges of the angular frequency band at $\pm n = \pm d/\lambda$. For example, a row of trees with angular separation of $5.7°$ ($=0.1$ radians) would be at the cut-off frequency of a radar with a 10-wavelength diameter antenna.

Various criteria have been proposed for optimizing the aperture function F for application to detection; resolution; and faithful rendition of random detail. Also, studies have been made as to the effect on $A(x,y)$ of phase errors, aperture blocking and absorbing coating.

ROY C. SPENCER

Cross-references: *Antennas, Distribution Functions, Fourier Analysis, Laplace and Fourier Transforms*

FOURIER TRANSFORM: see LAPLACE AND FOURIER TRANSFORMS

FREQUENCY ALLOCATION

Frequency allocation is one aspect of radio spectrum management. It means designating various bands of radio frequencies for different categories of radio usage. It is ordinarily a function of government. Categories of usage usually are termed *radio services*, e.g., the Maritime Mobile Radio Service and the Police Radio Service. Frequency *allocation* should be distinguished from frequency *assignment*, the latter customarily being used to mean designation of a particular radio frequency for use by a particular radio station. For example, the frequency band 535 to 1605 kc is allocated in the Americas to the radio broadcasting service, and particular frequencies within the band 535–1605 kc are assigned to local broadcasting stations in each country and community.

The portion of the electromagnetic spectrum useful for radio purposes lies between the approximate limits of 10^4 and 3×10^{11} cps. For identification purposes, the radio

TABLE OF RADIO FREQUENCY ALLOCATIONS
(effective May 1, 1961)

Band Number	Frequency Range (lower limit exclusive, upper limit inclusive)	Corresponding Metric Subdivision	Abbreviations for adjectival band designations	Service Allocation
4	3 to 30 kc	Myriametric waves	VLF	Fixed, mobile, radiolocation, radionavigation, standard frequency.
5	30 to 300 kc	Kilometric waves	LF	Fixed, mobile radiolocation, radionavigation.
6	300 to 3000 kc	Hectometric waves	MF	Amateur, broadcasting, fixed, mobile, radiolocation, radionavigation, standard frequency.
7	3 to 30 Mc	Decametric waves	HF	Amateur, broadcasting, fixed, meteorological aids, mobile, standard frequency.
8	30 to 300 Mc	Metric waves	VHF	Amateur, broadcasting, earth-space, fixed, mobile, radiolocation, radionavigation, space.
9	300 to 3000 Mc	Decimetric waves	UHF	Amateur, broadcasting, earth-space, fixed, meteorological aids, mobile, radioastronomy, radiolocation, radionavigation, space.
10	3 to 30 kMc	Centimetric waves	SHF	Amateur, broadcasting, earth-space, fixed, mobile, radiolocation, radionavigation, space.
11	30 to 300 kMc	Millimetric waves	EHF	Earth-space, fixed, mobile, radiolocation, radionavigation, space. (Not allocated above 40,000 Mc.)
12	300 to 3000 kMc 3 Tc	Decimillimetric waves	—	—

spectrum is subdivided into bands such that adjacent ones differ from each other by a factor of 10. Each of these bands may be described in three ways; Band number; an adjective description of the frequency range; and an adjective description of the order of wavelength. The descriptive terms are internationally agreed. The relationship between wavelength in meters (λ) and frequency in cycles per second (f) is expressed by $c = \lambda f$, where c is the velocity of propagation of radio (and light) waves in space, approximately 3×10^8 m/sec.

The above table is a table of frequency allocations only in the broadest sense, since it does not describe precise band limits or conditions of sharing for each particular radio service.

Frequency allocation is the art of matching available spectrum space against operational requirements, with due regard for prior users and current technology. A complicating factor is that some radio user categories have several different operational requirements, in consequence of which several frequency allocations in different parts of the radio spectrum are required. Still another variant is the situation when a single high-priority operational requirement, which has been recognized for a period of many years, will at different times be satisfied in different parts of the radio spectrum owing to advances in technology—but generally retaining the old allocations also. This is a challenge to frequency-management specialists.

Some frequency bands are allocated exclusively to a single radio service, whereas other bands are allocated on a shared basis to two or more services. Sharing may be co-equal, with each station of one service having as much right to use a frequency band as stations of the other service(s). Alternatively, one service may be designated as primary, and the other secondary, so that prior use of a frequency by a radio station in a secondary service must give way to subsequent use of the frequency by a station in the primary service, if the secondary user causes harmful interference to the new primary user.

Geographic sharing is another device employed to obtain maximum usage of the radio spectrum with minimum harmful interference between stations. One finds a group of users that, on the average, are geographically separated from another group of users by a sufficient distance so that they do not cause harmful interference to one another in the frequency band in question. Example: Maritime mobile service operations in the vhf part of the radio spectrum (30–300 Mc), which has approximately line-of-sight propagation characteristics, can share frequencies with vehicular radio operations sufficiently remote from water areas where the maritime operations occur.

An important question is whether particular radio stations require protection from harmful interference within their normal service areas from other stations of the same or other radio services. If a particular user, as for example the operator of a small taxicab fleet, does not need to transmit continuously, it is possible, in the interest of spectrum economy, for him to share his frequency with one or more other taxicab fleet operators in the same city—even though the first operator would much prefer to have his own exclusive clear channel assignment. Conversely, a broadcasting station transmits its programs on a continuous basis and two such stations cannot use the same frequency in the same city. Only geographical sharing is feasible. Whether or not cochannel sharing in the same area is feasible is an important factor in deciding how much spectrum space needs to be allocated for a particular purpose.

In general, safety services and services that must radiate a continuous signal in order to carry out their purpose are the ones which are given exclusive allocations. The objective, nationally and internationally, is to have as much sharing as possible in order to obtain maximum use from a scarce commodity—the radio spectrum. Wherever sharing is feasible, it is made mandatory by governmental authorities, even though some inconvenience to individual station operators may result.

The hf portion of the radio spectrum deserves special mention. It lies between 3 and 30 mc. This is the portion of the spectrum most useful for long-distance intercontinental radiocommunication, pending the development of operational space satellite relay systems, which are expected to employ frequencies in the general range 1 to 15 kMc. In the hf region, six services have been recognized internationally. They are: Broadcasting (exclusively international in the United States, but also domestic in many other countries); maritime mobile; aeronautical mobile; fixed (point-to-point); and amateur and standard frequency broadcast. A few frequencies in this range also are used for space research and for meteorological purposes. Propagation of signals occurs in the hf region by reason of systematic reflection of radio waves from the several ionospheric layers of the earth's atmosphere. The characteristics of frequencies in the hf region are highly variable and have long been the subject of much research and scientific investigation. Because relatively small amounts of power can be used to communicate over great distances when the proper frequency is employed at the proper time, the hf portion of the spectrum is perhaps the most congested of all, on a world-wide basis. The use of obsolete or obsolescent equipment and unscientific choice of operating frequency contribute to this world-wide problem. Different frequencies within the hf band propagate over different distances at a particular time, and a particular frequency has different range capability at different times of the day and night (diurnal variation), the year (seasonal variation), and at different phases of the solar radiation cycles(s). Typically, therefore, a "family" of three or four frequencies in the hf range is required to maintain communication between any two points at all times of day, night, season, and year. Ideally, from the propagation viewpoint, many more frequencies could be employed in the family.

The special congestion problem in the hf portion of the radio spectrum has been recognized both in this country and abroad. In the United States, steps have been taken in two areas: (1) Drastic restrictions on domestic usage, including prohibition of broadcasts intended for domestic reception and severe limitations on establishment and/or operation of domestic point-to-point circuits; and (2) adoption (on both a voluntary and mandatory basis) of technical standards designed to result in the transmission of maximum intelligence in a minimum of bandwidth. In this latter category are use of directional antenna systems, more efficient (albeit sometimes more costly) modulation techniques, time-sharing arrangements, and use of alternate communication methods such as submarine cables, international air mail and uhf/shf relay-station chains.

Since radio waves do not respect political boundaries, frequency allocation problems are both national and international in scope. The specialized agency of the United Nations for telecommunications matters, including frequency allocations, is the International Telecommunications Union (ITU), with headquarters in Geneva in Switzerland. The ITU consists of those Administrations which accept the International Telecommunication Convention. There are approximately 100 member countries. Frequency allocations are set forth in the Radio Regulations annexed to the Convention. Technical problems are studied by the ITU's International Consultative Radio Committee (CCIR). Frequency-management matters are centered in the ITU's International Frequency Registration Board. The ITU also receives advice from other international organizations having specialized areas of interest, as, for example, the International Civil Aviation Organization (ICAO), the Inter-Governmental Maritime Consultative Organization (IMCO), and the World Meteorological Organization (WMO). The international Radio Regulations divide the world into three Regions for frequency allocation purposes. The Americas comprise one of these three Regions. There are a number of differences between the allocation pattern in each of the Regions, but there are more similarities than differences. The Regulations provide for negotiation of bilateral, multilateral, and Regional agreements on radio matters, as supplements to the basic international pattern. Countries signatory to the Radio Regulations agree that their national allocations and assignments will be in accordance with the international Regulations, or, if departures are made, that stations operating in derogation of the Regulations will function on the basis of causing no harmful interference to stations of other Administrations which do conform.

Within the United States, the responsibility for frequency management is divided between the President, who controls assignments to stations of federal Departments and Agencies, and the Federal Communications Commission (FCC), which controls assignments to all nonfederal users. The President ordinarily exercises his authority through an inter-Agency body known as the Interdepartment Radio Advisory Committee (IRAC), which has existed continuously since 1922. With two groups each having plenary authority to make assignments anywhere in the spectrum, chaos would result quickly if there were not the closest cooperation between them. The joint effort of the two groups has, over a period of years, resulted in establishment of a national Table of Frequency Allocations and many joint or parallel telecommunications policies. Some frequency bands are allocated exclusively to nonfederal users, some exlusively to federal users, and some bands are allocated for joint use, particularly in the field of navigation aids.

W. H. WATKINS

Cross-references: *Interference, Propagation, Radio Links, Satellite Communications*

FREQUENCY CONVERSION AND SERRODYNE

A frequency converter is an electronic circuit which, given an input signal of a certain frequency, produces an output signal whose frequency is shifted by some desired amount from that of the input. A frequency converter may also increase or decrease the power level of the signal.

If the input signal is a modulated carrier, then the output signal has a shifted carrier whose instantaneous frequency deviation and amplitude modulation are the same as those of the input. Similarly, each component in the input spectrum is shifted a constant amount, and the spectrum remains unchanged in relative amplitude and phase. (Variations of these properties are possible also and will be discussed below.)

It is to be noted that frequency multipliers (*q.v.*) and dividers are not frequency converters and do not conform to the above defining statements.

Synonyms for the term frequency converter include: frequency translator, frequency shifter, and single-sideband modulator.

Frequency converters are used in superheterodyne receivers, microwave relay stations, coherent radars, Doppler simulators, homodyne transmission measurement equipments, and in other systems and measurement applications. In some cases the power level of the signal is extremely low; in others, relatively high. Some applications need only a small percentage frequency shift; others, like the superheterodyne receiver, require a shift of the same order as the signal frequency.

A frequency converter generally consists of a mixer, a local oscillator, and a filter. The mixer is a nonlinear device whose purpose is to combine the input signal with the local-oscillator signal to produce intermodulation frequencies. These new frequencies are equal to sums and differences of the signal and local-oscillator frequencies or of their harmonics; one of the new frequencies is the desired output frequency. Usually, but not always, a passive filter is required to suppress all but the desired output frequency.

Analysis of the mixing process is usually performed either by (1) using a nonlinear equation with constant coefficients to describe the nonlinear mixing element, or (2) representing the mixing element and local oscillator action by an equation with a time-varying parameter. In the latter method, the variation with time of the parameter is determined by the nonlinear mixer characteristic and by the local-oscillator waveform. It is then correct to think of the mixer as a modulator and of the local-oscillator signal as the modulating wave.

Devices useful as mixers include: (1) Non-linear resistors (varistors), such as junction, point-contact, and vacuum diodes. (2) Non-linear reactors (varactors), including saturable inductors and semiconductor variable capacitors based on barrier-layer capacitance, diffusion capacitance, or drift of carriers in an electric field. (3) Modulable amplifiers or other two-port devices. Examples include modulation of transconductance in vacuum tubes and transistors (hybrid-pi circuit model), and modulation of phase or transit time in traveling-wave tubes, klystron amplifiers, and variable delay lines. Modulable amplifiers are often operated in a self-excited way. In that case the amplifier itself oscillates, and no external local oscillator is needed. (4) Mechanical devices, such as moving paddle wheels, which are sometimes used for doppler simulation. (5) Nonlinear negative-resistance devices like tunnel diodes, also useful in self-excited frequency converters.

The performance of a frequency converter may be specified by any or all of the following measures: (1) conversion gain or loss, (2) bandwidth, (3) distortion, (4) relative power levels of spurious output frequencies, (5) noise output, (6) sensitivity to adjustment, and (7) input and output impedances.

The power sources applied to a mixer are: (1) the input signal of frequency f_{in}, (2) the local-oscillator signal of frequency f_{local}, and (3) for some devices, a dc power supply. The local-oscillator power is normally made much larger than the input signal power. This inequality in power levels is usually necessary to prevent distortion of the amplitude-modulation content of the signal. (Sometimes the local-oscillator power is

purposely made much smaller than the input signal power, to achieve an amplitude-limiting action. With such an adjustment the output amplitude is relatively independent of input amplitude. Frequency modulation is still passed without distortion. The output spectrum then bears no simple relationship to the input spectrum.)

The intermodulation frequencies f_{out} at which power may be extracted from the mixer include all the frequencies given by

$$f_{out} = m f_{in} + n f_{local}$$

where m and n are positive or negative integers or zero, excluding those m,n pairs that would give a negative value for f_{out}. Other output frequencies not given by this equation, and not useful for frequency conversion, are produced by some varactor mixers (e.g., an oscillating parametric amplifier). The values of m and n specifying the desired output frequency are usually chosen to be either plus or minus one. If m is taken greater than unity in magnitude, then the circuit is said to produce *frequency multiplication* as well as frequency conversion. If the magnitude chosen for n exceeds unity, then the resulting action is called *harmonic mixing*. Notice that for $m = -1$, the frequency deviation of the output is the negative of that of the input. In that case the components of the input spectrum are shifted varying amounts, such that the output spectrum is inverted with respect to the input spectrum.

The *conversion gain* of a frequency converter is defined as the ratio of the power available at the desired output frequency to that available from the input signal source. If dc power is supplied to the mixer, then gain is possible through conversion of the dc power to ac output signal power. Mixer devices falling in this category include (1) modulable amplifiers, such as vacuum tubes, transistors, traveling-wave tubes, and klystrons, a parameter of which is modulated by the local-oscillator signal; and (2) nonlinear negative-resistance devices such as tunnel diodes.

If the mixer is passive and is not an

energy-storage element (i.e., is a varistor), then the conversion gain is less than unity, or actually a loss. A typical value of conversion loss for a microwave crystal mixer is 5 db. Energy is not stored in tubes and transistors used conventionally as mixers. Hence, even though these devices usually produce an absolute conversion gain greater than unity, the gain relative to that of the same device used as an amplifier is less than unity.

For mixers which store energy (varactors), conversion gain is possible even though no dc power is supplied. The local oscillator is then often called a *pump* and is the source of the power which is converted to output signal. Mixers operated in this way are used in magnetic amplifiers, dielectric amplifiers, and parametric amplifiers.

The input and output impedances of varactor mixers may have a negative real part. As a result, such devices are often relatively sensitive to changes in adjustment.

The waveform of the local-oscillator signal has an important influence on the conversion gain and on the spurious signal levels. Square-wave amplitude modulation of transconductance is conventionally employed with vacuum-tube and transistor mixers used in superheterodyne receivers. The theoretical gain is then 10 db less than for the same device operated as an amplifier. Phase-reversal modulation (square-wave phase modulation) has been used in certain mixer arrangements. The resulting gain is 4 db less than for operation as an amplifier.

The *serrodyne* frequency translation method theoretically produces perfect frequency conversion. Phase modulation by a sawtooth wave having nearly zero flyback time and a peak-to-peak deviation of 2π radians is employed. Traveling-wave tubes and klystrons are suitable devices for use as mixers. Their modulable time delay provides a good approximation to modulable phase. The gain obtained in practice is negligibly different from that of the same tube used as an amplifier. Perhaps even more important is the fact that spurious outputs are typically at least 40 db weaker than the desired output frequency, without the use of output filter-

ing. Frequency shifts of as much as 60 Mc have been achieved with serrodyne operation of traveling-wave tubes.

Another method besides filtering that is sometimes employed to suppress spurious output frequencies uses a pair of balanced modulators. The input, local-oscillator, and output connections to the balanced modulators are so phased as to cancel undesired output frequencies. This arrangement is usually called a single-sideband modulator. Four mixer elements are employed, two in each balanced modulator. Matching of these elements may become a problem, especially if wide bandwidth and dynamic range are required.

The random noise at the output of a frequency converter is important in receiving applications where a preamplifier is not used. For microwave varistor mixers the noise figure is somewhat greater in magnitude (of the order of 2 db greater) than the conversion loss. Varactor mixers by virtue of their dissipationless operation can give good low-noise performance when converting upward in frequency; a typical microwave value of noise figure is 2 db. Nonlinear negative-resistance mixers can have low noise even when converting downward in frequency; noise figures of less than 3 db have been achieved with tunnel-diode down converters. The noise figure of modulated-amplifier mixers like vacuum tubes, transistors, and traveling-wave tubes is usually, but not always, worse than the noise figure of the same device operated as an amplifier. This is a consequence of the fact that the conversion gain of such mixers is usually less than the ordinary-amplifier gain.

R. C. CUMMING

Cross-references: *Magnetic Amplifiers, Modulation and Demodulation, Parametric Amplifiers*

FREQUENCY MEASUREMENT

Frequency, the number of cycles per unit time, is of primary concern in many measurements and is a quantity that can be determined with accuracy and precision to as high an order as any other constant of nature. A large variety of devices and methods are available for its measurement, with accuracies from several percent to parts in 10^{11}, and with costs from a few dollars to the tens of thousands of dollars.

Wavemeters. A wavemeter is a frequency-sensitive structure composed of a combination of an inductor and a capacitor, or a section of transmission line, or a tunable cavity. These devices can be calibrated for resonant frequency in terms of their physical dimensions, or from known sources of standard frequency. Changes in dimensions or characteristics of materials owing to temperature or other environmental changes alter the calibration. The sensitivity of the device depends on the means employed to make a change in the system and on the sensitivity of the detector, and is inversely proportional to the Q of the resonant device, with lumped inductors and capacitors yielding a Q between 50 and 500, coaxial transmission lines slightly higher, and cavities approaching Q's of 5×10^5. In order to take advantage of the high resonant Q of a wavemeter, it must be loosely coupled to the source. In microwave measurements, the wavemeter may be connected to a branch circuit in such a manner that its tuning will affect the transmission in the main branch by a measureable amount, this reaction being the indicator of tuning.

Rate Meters. A class of frequency meters accurate to 0.1 per cent for frequencies below 1 Mc have found quite wide application as continuous-reading indicating devices and are known generally as rate meters. A frequency-independent impulse is generated and applied at the unknown frequency rate to a circuit that generates an output in proportion to the time average of the number of impulses. The response to frequency may be exponential or linear and the averaging time may be adjustable.

Grid-Dip Meters. Class C oscillators with calibrated tuning and a metering of oscillation amplitude indicate equivalence of frequency when the external source sup-plies enough energy to change the amplitude of oscillation and the beat between the two is reduced to zero. Grid-dip meters lack precision because of the tendency to lock on the external frequency. Such meters are also useful in determining the natural resonant frequency of a circuit portion to which it is coupled loosely, loading of the oscillator being a maximum at the resonant frequencies. Many grid-dip meters can be operated as passive wavemeters. Accuracies up to about 0.1 per cent can be obtained.

Counting-Type Frequency Meters. Electronic counters using a 10-state device which delivers one pulse for every 10 input pulses have been used for frequency measurement. Commercial counting units are being produced that count at frequencies above 10 Mc. A counting type of frequency meter is composed of at least these elements: a precision local oscillator, frequency division means to scale the local oscillator down to a low frequency to control the gate, an input amplifier and trigger circuit to generate a uniformly shaped pulse for counting, a gate circuit to control the application of the unknown frequency to the counting register, the counting register where the counts having a one-to-one correspondence with a particular point of the input wave are stored, and the gate control and reset circuitry. The counting register and the control circuitry are reset to the initial conditions of zero stored in the register and the control circuit ready to accept the start counting pulse from the timebase. The next pulse from the timebase causes the gate to open and pulses at the unknown frequency are applied to the counting register until a second timebase pulse closes the gate after the desired time interval leaving the number of times that the particular input condition existed in the interval between the two timebase pulses stored in the counting register. If the timebase interval were 1 sec, then the number stored would represent the average number of cycles per second. Commercial instruments of this class generally have several timebases available in the range from

10 sec by powers of 10 to 10^{-6} sec. The reference oscillators are usually crystal controlled and the stability of the oscillator is usually equal to or better than that required to yield a significant number in the counting register. External signals from other sources can also be employed as drive for the timebase.

The counting-type frequency meter usually counts when the voltage changes from a value on one side of some voltage to a voltage on the other side, with some minimum difference between the two voltage values. This type of instrument is not capable of distinguishing between a signal and noise when the peak-to-peak value of the input noise is in excess of the minimum input voltage required to count. Accuracies range from a part in 10^4 to parts in 10^8.

Heterodyne Frequency Meters. When several frequencies are impressed on a nonlinear mixer, the current contains components of the known and unknown frequencies applied, the sums and the differences of all the applied frequencies, and their harmonics. If the known frequency is adjusted until the difference between it and the unknown is zero, then there is a zero-frequency output current from the mixer, this component being termed a "zero beat." Zero beats are also obtained when a higher-order harmonic of the known is equal to the fundamental or a different-order harmonic of the unknown. The strength of the zero beat is in proportion to the relative magnitudes of the currents of the two signals combining to form the zero beat. Such measurements can be carried out to high precision when the frequency of the known oscillator has been determined to a high accuracy and where the isolation of the two signals is sufficient to prevent locking of the two signal sources. Commercial equipment in this class may have an accuracy rating of 0.005 per cent or higher and usually employs a quartz crystal oscillator as a calibration checking means, with isolation between the local oscillator and the unknown.

With a local reference frequency of 1 Mc

and integral multiples and submultiples of this reference, chains of mixers and bandpass filters can be established to subtract successively known frequencies less than the unknown from the unknown until the difference is small enough to measure by direct comparison to a precision low-frequency oscillator or by counting for an accurately known period of time. The unknown equals the sum of the final counted difference frequency and each of the multiples of the reference frequency used. The accuracy of this measurement method approaches the accuracy of the local reference oscillator and the measurement of the low-frequency difference. In commercial equipment measuring frequencies between 10 and 1000 Mc with the counter-type of low-frequency measuring equipment it is usual to obtain a 9-digit answer, some digits not significant because of the expected variation in the reference oscillator.

Transfer Oscillator Methods. The transfer oscillator measurements combine hetrodyne and frequency counting techniques to measure frequencies higher than can be counted. A stable, tunable oscillator in a frequency band covered by a counter drives a tunable multiplier supplying energy to a mixer assembly. The counting frequency meter measures the variable oscillator. Zero beats are found by adjustment of the variable oscillator. A typical measurement procedure is to find a first zero beat, where $F_x = (n + 1) F_1 k$, F_x the unknown frequency, n the harmonic of the multiplier output, k the multiplier factor, and F_1 the first frequency. The variable oscillator is then increased to F_2, the next zero beat, where $F_x = n F_2 k$. Solving these two equations gives $F_x = k F_1 F_2 / (F_2 - F_1)$.

A problem in instrumenting this method is to obtain a tunable oscillator with the requisite short-term stability and precision of tuning. The beat between the known and the unknown should be reduced to less than the fractional accuracy required; thus the mechanism of the oscillator tuning should allow a setting with ease to less than 1 part in 10^8. If the drift during the measurement time (several seconds) is more than this fractional part then the accuracy suffers proportionally. Commercial equipment is available for this measurement, and an added convenience in one instrument is a computing device for determining the factor n and a variable timebase on the counter set to this factor so that the number registered by the counter is the unknown frequency.

JOHN L. CORL

Cross-references: *Errors in Measurement, Frequency Conversion and Serrodyne, Frequency Multipliers, Frequency Standards, Modulation and Demodulation, Piezoelectricity and Pyroelectricity, Standards*

FREQUENCY MODULATION: see MODULATION AND DEMODULATION

FREQUENCY MULTIPLIERS

Frequency multipliers find use in many frequency measurement and generation schemes, and are based on the fact that a repeating nonsinusoidal waveform can be described as the sum of the sine wave with the frequency of the function, and other sine waves at frequencies that are integral multiples of this fundamental frequency and the zero frequency component. The magnitude of each component and its phase relation to the fundamental depends on the waveform of the nonsinusoid. One method is to use a device that generates a current pulse when the input wave changes direction and to apply this current pulse to a resonant circuit tuned to the desired harmonic frequency. Another method is to generate a current pulse having a shape like the peak of the wave and to apply this pulse to a tuned circuit. A Class C amplifier or a biased diode can be used to accomplish this last means, and a voltage-sensitive trigger circuit or a saturated magnetic element might be used to accomplish the former. Design characteristics that require attention are hum modulation, sidebands from insufficient

filtering, phase instabilities from lack of shielding, microphonic instability, and temperature sensitivity.

Modulating signals that alter the operating conditions within a multiplier stage have an effect on the phase of the output with respect to the input and within a time less than the period of the modulating signal this change in phase appears as a change in frequency; thus, slow variations of the phase shift in the multiplier are apt to be the more important in precision measurements where an appreciable averaging time is involved.

Temperature effects on the tuning of the selective circuits can cause phase instabilities. Where a single tuned circuit is used the Q of the circuit usually must be very high to remove unwanted sideband signal components, and the high Q gives rise to a higher rate of phase shift with frequency in the region of resonance than is obtained with a critically coupled double-tuned circuit with the same rejection at the sideband frequencies. The circuit Q's in the double-tuned case can be lower and the change in phase by temperature is less. Changes in the gain of the amplifier elements can also introduce phase changes since the input susceptance of a stage is a function of the gain of the stage and the impedances that are common to the input and output circuits of the stage. These impedances may not vary with any changes on the conditions of operation but their reflected effects depend on the gain.

JOHN L. CORL

Cross-references: *Frequency Measurement*

FREQUENCY STANDARDS

Frequency because of its singleness of dimension, t^{-1}, is of primary concern in physical measurements, and much effort has been exerted to establish as precise a standard as possible. There are three classes of devices that satisfy particular needs as standards of time or frequency. In decending order of precision they are the atomic standards, the primary crystal oscillator standard, and the secondary crystal oscillator standard.

The atomic standards are based on the theory that the energy of the photon is $E = h\nu$ where h is Plancks' constant and ν is the characteristic frequency, and that a process can be established that involves the change from a particular high-energy state to a particular lower-energy state with the emission of certain amount of energy as a photon with its characteristic frequency. The ammonia maser and the cesium beam resonator are members of this class with stabilities and reproducibility from unit to unit in the order of parts in 10^{10}. A low-frequency quartz crystal oscillator is often an integral part of the atomic frequency standard, the low frequency being multiplied to the frequency involved in the atomic process. A comparison between the atomic process frequency and the multiplied frequency yields a signal that is used to exercise vernier control on the low-frequency oscillator so that the difference approaches zero.

Primary standards of frequency are usually precision crystal oscillators or crystal stabilized oscillators provided with frequency-dividing means, so that a clock can be driven. Provision is made to compare the recorded time and time signals broadcast from a national standards laboratory and correct errors in the oscillator frequency. Since 9 October 1957 the second has been defined by a set of atomic standards compared with other standards with an agreement between each other of 5 parts in 10^{10} or better.

A secondary standard of frequency is like the primary standard except that provisions to compare time are not provided and the resultant uncertainties of measurement are greater. Quartz crystal oscillators are being supplied for routine measurement within a part in 10^6 of the desired frequency after shipping and a short period of operation for temperature stabilization; this accuracy is sufficient for many routine measurements. The manufacture of quartz resonators and oscillator circuits has been improved to the point that short term instabilities have been reduced to parts in 10^{11}, and drifts in a week to parts in 10^{10}.

The National Bureau of Standards distributes the United States Frequency Standard by broadcasts from WWV, WWVH, WWVB and various Naval Radio Stations are also stabilized to within a part in 10^{10}.

JOHN L. CORL

Cross-references: *Atomic Clocks, Frequency Measurement, Masers, Molecular-Beam Devices, Piezoelectricity and Pyroelectricity, Standards*

FUNCTION GENERATOR: see ANALOG COMPUTERS

FUSES

A fuse is an intentionally weakened part of an electric circuit that opens it if subjected to a dangerous overload. Its function is that of an electrical safety valve. One of the earliest references to fuses is in a patent granted to Edison in 1880. Continuous design improvements, combined with the efforts of the National Board of Fire Underwriters and their Underwriters' Laboratories, resulted in standardization of fuses for homes and industry by about 1904. Fuses used in the electronics industry today had their origin in "automotive glass" fuses about 1910, which today is abbreviated to Types 1-AG to 9-AG inclusive. These numbers were assigned by various manufacturers over a period of some 25 years and bear no relation to the accepted physical size they indicate. The size generally used by the electronics industry are 1-AG, 3-AG, 4-AG, 5-AB (ceramic enclosed), and 5-AG. A small transistor-size "Microfuse" is also now on the market.

Fuse Ratings and Other Characteristics

Rated voltage is the maximum a fuse will open without sustained arcing from a power supply of specified ampere rating. Most Underwriters' Laboratories tests are from a 10,000-amp power supply.

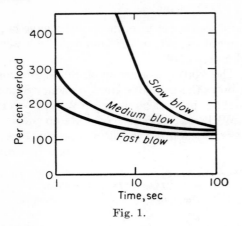

Fig. 1.

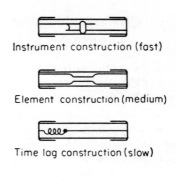

Instrument construction (fast)

Element construction (medium)

Time lag construction (slow)

Fig. 2.

Underwriters' Laboratories and most military specifications call for most fuses to carry 110 per cent of *rated current* indefinitely. Most specifications set up "blowing" limits at 135 and also 200 per cent of rating.

By far the most important fuse characteristic is its time-vs-current function. This relationship defines the time required for the fuse to open a circuit under a given degree of overload. Modern electronic circuits require roughly three ranges of time—current characteristics which might be defined roughly as fast, medium and delayed-action fuses. These time ranges can be defined as follows at 200 per cent of rated current overload applied to the fuses.

Fast: 2 μsec to $\frac{1}{2}$ sec. Used to protect semiconductors, meters, and hot-wire devices.

Medium: $\frac{1}{2}$ to 5 sec. Inexpensive. Used to protect transformer-type power supplies, wiring, and circuits generally with low switching surges.

Delayed ("Slo-Blo"): 5 to 25 sec. High surge circuits; i.e., motor starting circuits and those having solenoids, magnets, and capacitors. Also vibrator and chopper type circuits. Time current relationships and the types of fuse elements required to produce them are shown in Fig. 1.

Many specifications define the limits of heat rise, vibration resistance, shock resistance, cyclic fatigue, physical dimensions, and short-circuit test conditions. Most complete in this respect is MIL-F-15160.

The following table may serve as a guide to medium-lag, fuse rating selection for two types of applications:

Insulated Wire Protection	Fuse Ampere Rating
Wire size #16	10
14	15
12	20–30
10	40
8	50

Power Supply Rating, 115 v (w)	Fuse Ampere Rating
40–65	1
65–100	1½
100–150	2
150–250	3
250–350	5
350–450	6

In general the best results are obtained by using the maximum-rating fuse that affords protection. This avoids nuisance outages. Generally the normal current should not exceed 65 per cent of the fuse rating for fast and medium-lag fuses, and up to 80 per cent for time-lag fuses.

Every fuse must have a means of connection into the circuit allowing easy replacement. In the past 20 years panel-type holders permitting access to the use by means of an extracting knob in front of the panel have become popular.

E. V. SUNDT

Cross-references: *Circuit Breakers, Relays, Switches*

FUSION

Nuclear fusion is the process of joining two nuclei together to form a third one, which in turn may disintegrate into products. The mass of the products is nearly but not quite equal to the mass of the constituents. This slight difference in mass (times c^2) represents the energy difference between constituents and products and must be either externally supplied or is available as useful energy. In this broader sense all nuclear transformations involve fusion as a fundamental step, so that the original observation of Ernest Rutherford (1871–1937) of the transformation of the nitrogen nucleus by helium nucleii was fusion, but in more recent years fusion has been associated with the exothermic nuclear reactions among the lightest elements, hydrogen, helium, and possibly lithium. The fusion of hydrogen leading to the synthesis of helium (and ultimately of all elements) is the most important to man: first, because it is the primary source of energy of our sun and the stars, and second, because it is the basis of controlled thermonuclear power and the uncontrolled thermonuclear fusion of the H-bomb.

The nuclear synthesis of helium from hydrogen was first proposed by Hans Bethe as the source of energy of the stars on the basis of a complicated series of nuclear reactions involving the carbon nucleus in the equivalent role of a chemical catalyst. These series of reactions, called the carbon cycle, take place because of the *thermal* energies of the reacting nucleii; the thermal reacting energy must be high (high temperature) to enable the charged nucleii to overcome by their kinetic energy the repulsion of their electrostatic charge, and so approach one another sufficiently close to provide a sufficiently high quantum-mechanical probability of a nuclear reaction taking place. Of course this is a statistical problem, but even to achieve reactions on the vast time scale of stellar evolution, temperatures of a few million degrees and high densities are necessary. The higher the temperature and density, the more rapidly the reaction proceeds, in a completely analogous manner to chemical reactions. The basic constituent of stars, the single-mass isotope of hydrogen (the proton, *q.v.*), is an exceedingly nonreactive nuclear fuel, so that the time scale of stellar evolution is fortunately long. The reason for this nonreactivity is the requirement for the emission of a positron (*q.v.*) and neutrino (*q.v.*) in the direct fusion of two protons, and these light particles have an extremely small probability for creation. Even though this probability is so exceedingly small it has been shown in recent years by Salpeter that the direct fusion of protons may be responsible for the majority of the hydrogen synthesis in the stars.

Vastly more rapid reactions occur whenever the mass of the reacting nucleii are greater and the electrostatic charge is small. Consequently, in order to achieve thermonuclear fusion on earth (where neither the time nor the internal pressure of a star is available), man looks to the heavier isotopes of the lowest-charge elements. The most important fusion reactions with their products and exothermic energy (in Mev) are given in the following table.

Fusion Reactions

1. $D + D = He^3 + n + 3.25$ Mev
2. $D + D = T + p + 4$ Mev
3. $T + D = He^4 + n + 17.6$ Mev
4. $He^3 + D = He^4 + p + 18.3$ Mev
5. $Li^6 + D = 2He^4 + 22.4$ Mev
6. $Li^7 + p = 2He^4 + 17.3$ Mev

The fundamental concept of thermonuclear fusion demands that the rate of energy release from reactions must be capable of maintaining the required temperature for the period of reaction. In an H-bomb this is the period of dynamical expansion—small fractions of a microsecond; on the other hand *controlled* fusion (see, for instance, *Rev. Mod. Phys.* **28**: 338, 1956) must be achieved at static pressures, resulting in containment times of seconds. Since the required temperatures are hundreds of millions of degrees, the thermal insulation required to prevent the reaction from cooling before completion must indeed be perfect. No ordinary insulation could work, but fortunately at these high temperatures all matter is ionized and interacts strongly with a magnetic field. It is by means of this interaction that it is hoped that the high-temperature reactants— a plasma—can be isolated from the walls and contained. Controlled thermonuclear research concerns itself primarily with this problem of isolation and containment.

STIRLING A. COLGATE

Cross-references: *Fission, Magnetohydrodynamics (MHD), Plasma, Radiation (Ionizing)*

G

GAMMA RAYS

Gamma rays are one of the three types of naturally occurring radioactivity the others being alpha and beta emission. Gamma radiation is fundamentally the same as light and radio waves but falls in the high-frequency portion of the electromagnetic spectrum. The frequency range of gamma radiation in natural and artificial radioactive substances is from about 10^{19} to over 10^{22} cps. Gamma rays travel with the velocity of light in free space, which is 3×10^8 m/sec.

The origin of gamma rays is in the very rapid transition from one nuclear energy level to another or in the disintegration of elementary particles. Thus gamma rays consist of electromagnetic waves with their energy concentrated in very short wave trains. The wavelength of lower-frequency gamma rays can be measured by reflection from the atomic lattices in regular crystals and the application of Bragg's law. Gamma rays may be thought of as electromagnetic quanta or photons whose energy is given by $E = h\nu$ where ν is the frequency of the gamma radiation and h is Planck's constant, equal to 6.63×10^{-34} joule-sec. Photons may be thought of as stable elementary particles with zero charge and zero rest mass but having an intrinsic angular momentum, or spin, of $h/2\pi$.

X-rays (q.v.) are electromagnetic quanta produced by bombarding a target with high-energy electrons. X-rays have precisely the same fundamental nature as gamma rays and differ only in their means of production. Thus a 10-Mev gamma ray and a 10-Mev X-ray show no differences when interacting with matter.

A beam of gamma rays is highly penetrating in matter. Energetic photons have no definite range in water but instead are absorbed or scattered out of the beam according to an expotential law. Electromagnetic quanta interact with matter in three ways. A photon undergoes *photoelectric absorption* when it gives its entire energy to a bound atomic electron. The electron then emerges from the atom with the energy of the photon less its atomic binding energy. *Pair production* is the process in which a photon interacts with the intense electric field surrounding atomic nuclei and converts into two electrons, one positively charged, the other negatively charged. Since each electron has a rest mass equal to $m_e = 9.1 \times 10^{-31}$ kg, the minimum energy the photon must have to create an electron pair is $2\ m_e c^2$ which is slightly more than 1 Mev. In the *Compton Process* the photon is scattered by an electron or other particle and changes both its energy and direction. The cross sections for all these processes depend on the photon energy and the atomic number of the absorber.

Electron accelerating devices, such as high-voltage vacuum tubes, betatrons, synchrotrons, and linear accelerators may be used to generate high fluxes of photons with energies to 100 Mev and higher. At these energies the interesting phenomenon of cascade showers may occur in which a single photon incident on matter may produce a great number of lower-energy photons and electrons.

KINSEY A. ANDERSON

Cross-references: *Accelerators, Alpha Particles, Radioactivity, Radiation (Ionizing)*

GASES

The principal gases used in electronic devices are the rare gases helium, neon, argon, krypton, and xenon, and mercury vapor, hydrogen, and water vapor.

Table 1 gives the physical properties, critical potentials, and important spectral lines of these gases.

Electron Collisions in the Various Gases. Experimental data on electron collisions are usually expressed as a "probability" of collision, which is defined as the number of collisions an electron makes in travelling one centimeter in the gas at a pressure of 1.0 mm of Hg at a temperature of 0°C. The probability of collision is therefore the reciprocal of the electron mean free path at 0°C 1.0 mm of Hg pressure. Figure 1 shows elastic collision probability vs the square root of electron energy in volts. Figure 2 shows the collision probability for exciting lowest energy state, and Fig. 3 shows the probability of ionization as functions of electron energy.

Ion Mobilities. At low electric field strengths the drift velocity of ions is proportional to the electric field. The constant of proportionality is called the "mobility."

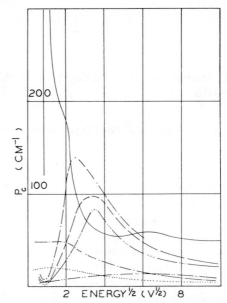

Fig. 1. Probability P_c of elastic collision at 1 mm of Hg vs square root of electron energy in volts.
———— Hg, ... He, —·—·— H₂ , —··— Ne, —···— A, — — — Kr, — —·— Xe.

Table 2 gives the mobilities at 760 mm of Hg, 0°C of various ions in various gases.

Ionization and Breakdown. Of particular importance for gaseous dielectric break-

TABLE 1

	He	Ne	A	Kr	Xe	Hg	H₂	H₂O
Boiling pt. (°C)	−268.9	−245.9	−185.7	−152.9	−107.1	356.9	−252.8	100
Vapor Pressure (mm of Hg)								
0°C						1.85×10^{-4}		4.58
20°C						1.20×10^{-2}		17.54
50°C						1.27×10^{-2}		92.51
Density at 1.0 atmo 0°C, (g/ liter)	0.178	0.900	1.78	3.71	5.85	3.88 (357°C)	0.0899	0.596 (100°C)
Specific Heat at Constant Pressure (1.0 atmo) (cal/g)	1.25 (−180°C)	0.25*	0.125	0.060*	0.038*	0.0249 (357°C)	3.39	0.482 (100°C)
Viscosity at 1.0 atmo 0°C (dyne sec/cm² × 10⁻⁶)	186.0	311.1	209.6	232.7	210.0	620.0 (357°C)	83.5	127.0 (100°C)
Heat Conductivity 0°C (cal/ cm sec deg × 10²)	0.344	0.110	0.039	0.0211†	0.0121†	0.0232† (357°C)	0.416	0.055 (100°C)
Lowest Excitation Potential‡	19.80 M	16.62 M	11.55 M	9.91 M	8.32 M	4.67 M	10.20 (atomic)	
Ionization Potential	24.58	21.56	15.76	14.00	12.13	10.43	13.60	
Persistent Spectral Lines (to nearest Ångstrom)	3889 5876	5401 6402	4201 4300	5570 5871	4624 4671	4358 5461	4861 6563	

* Calculated from 5 $k/2$ per atom-degree, assuming a perfect gas.

† Calculated from viscosity, assuming a perfect gas.

‡ M signifies metastable state.

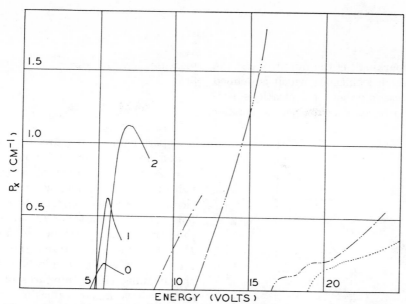

Fig. 2. Probability P_x of excitation, 1 mm of Hg, vs electron energy in volts.
—— 0, 1, 2, Hg $^3P_0$, $^3P_1$, $^3P_2$ states, $\times \frac{1}{10}$, ... He, —.— H$_2$, —..— Ne, —...— A.

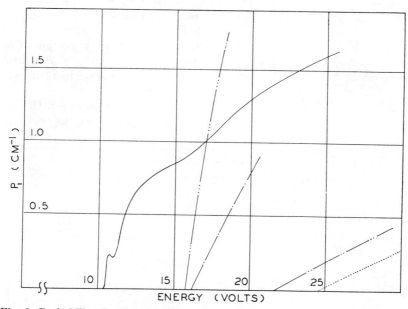

Fig. 3. Probability P_i of ionization at 1 mm of Hg vs electron energy in volts.
—— Hg $\times\frac{1}{10}$, ... He, —.— H$_2$, —..— Ne, —...— A.

TABLE 2

	Gas												
	He			Ne			A			Kr		Xe	
	Ion												
	He$^+$	He$_2^+$	Hg$^+$	Ne$^+$	Ne$_2^+$	Hg$^+$	A$^+$	A$_2^+$	Hg$^+$	Kr$^+$	Kr$_2^+$	Xe$^+$	Xe$_2^+$
Mobility (cm²/v sec)	10.5	20.5	19.6	4.1	6.6	5.9	1.6	2.6	1.85	0.98	1.2	0.58	0.8

down or "sparking" is the quantity α_i, the first Townsend coefficient, which is defined as the *average* number of ionizations produced per *average* electron per centimeter measured in the direction of the electric field:

$$\alpha_i = \frac{1}{n}\frac{dn}{dx}$$

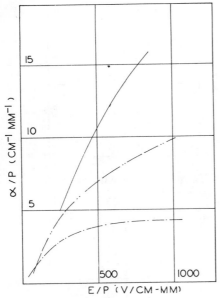

Fig. 4. α/P vs electric field ÷ pressure, in volts/ cm per mm of Hg.
———— Hg, —.— H_2, — —..— H_2O.

Experimental data are frequently presented in terms of the related quantity $\eta = \alpha_i/E$, the number of ionizations per volt of potential difference traversed by the electrons. For a given gas, η is a function only of E/p, the ratio of electric field to gas pressure. Figure 4 shows α_i vs E/p for H_2O, H_2, and Hg. Figure 5 shows η vs E/p for the rare gases. In addition, because of the Penning effect, mixtures of gases frequently have higher values of η than either one separately; Fig. 6 shows η vs E/p for Neon-Argon mixtures.

Secondary Electron Emission Due to Ion Bombardment. Neutralization of an ion at a surface results, in a fraction γ_i of the events, in the liberation of an electron. Table 3 below gives γ_i for singly charged ions of the rare gases incident on atomically clean tungsten:

Further information on the properties of the gases described, as well as of many

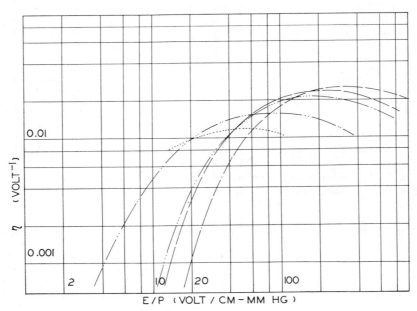

Fig. 5. η vs E/P in volts/cm per mm of Hg.
..... He, —..— Ne, —...— A, — — Kr, — —.— — Xe.

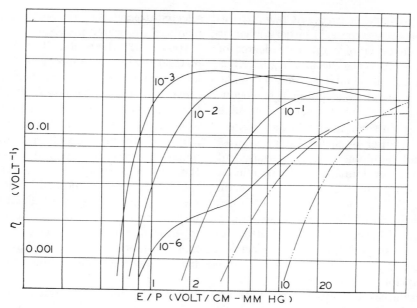

Fig. 6. η vs E/P in volts/cm per mm of Hg for Ne-Argon mixtures.
—..— Ne, —...— A, ——— Ne + A; figure beside each curve gives fractional concentration of argon in mixture.

TABLE 3

Ion	He⁺	Ne⁺	A⁺	Kr⁺	Xe⁺
γ_i	0.295	0.21	0.092	0.048	0.017

others, is to be found in S. C. Brown's "Basic Data of Plasma Physics," Wiley, New York, 1959.

JOHN F. WAYMOUTH

Cross-references: *Electric Discharge, Fluorescent Lights, Magnetron, Materials Used in Tube Technology, Plasma, Secondary Emission*

GEOPHYSICAL PROSPECTING

The physical methods employed in the search for ores and petroleum, and in geological aspects of civil engineering, each depend upon the measurement of a physical property contrast between the target sought and the adjacent rock or soil. In each instance the physical property distribution within the earth is obtained by quantitative and qualitative interpretation of numerous force field measurements made on some remote surface (e.g., on the earth's surface, from an aircraft, down a well bore, or in an underground opening). An attempt is made to separate a significant force field anomaly, presumed to be due to the target sought, from an extraneous background "noise." The noise may be either larger or smaller than the anomaly anticipated and is attributed to such factors as (1) geological noise or a background of anomalies due to physical property contrasts of no importance to the problem at hand; (2) quasi-anomalies caused by topography; (3) instrument noise; and (4) natural or artificial fields and other causes. By analogy with the circuit problem, intelligent use of geophysical methods centers about attaining the desired signal-to-noise ratio so that logical inference may be made about the constitution of the subsurface.

It is of fundamental importance to note that geophysical methods do not establish uniquely the existence of oil or ore, but merely indicate physical property configurations favorable to their presence.

The concepts of the theory of filters

(*q.v.*) are particularly pertinent here, as the undesirable noise often is of either higher or lower frequency or of a different degree of randomness than the desired signal. The above analogy is valid provided we make space in the geophysical problem analogous with time in the circuit problem. Continuing this analogy, in some instances the data are obtained at discrete space intervals with "broadband" equipment, .e.g., measurement of the earth's gravitational field at numerous points on the surface of the earth; whereas in other instances it is obtained continuously with "narrow-band" equipment, e.g., airborne inductive electromagnetic devices for locating natural electrical conductors. "Narrow band" in this instance infers that force field horizontal gradients lying outside certain preselected limits are automatically discarded by taking advantage of suitable time constants in the detecting equipment installed in the aircraft. Filtering by digital techniques may be employed with data taken at discrete intervals to effect the improvement of signal-to-noise ratio.

Most ground geophysical surveys involve recordings at intervals dictated by statistical considerations of the minimum density of observations required to detect (or in most instances to delineate clearly) anomalies due to hidden objects of assumed sizes and shapes. The closer the spacing of observation points, the higher is the upper space-frequency cutoff. Frequently the density of observations resulting is such that random variations due to instrument noise or operator error are recognizable.

Surveys from aircraft are, with one exception, based on continuous recording of a force field function. The speed and heights of the aircraft, coupled with the time constant of the instrument, determine the upper space-frequency cutoff; differentiating circuits may be employed to establish the lower space-frequency cutoff. The spacing of the parallel aircraft traverse lines and to a lesser extent the height of the aircraft are selected to satisfy the statistical requirements of the search problem.

Bases of Methods. The *gravitational* method involves measurement of variations in the earth's gravitational field (a natural force field) caused by lateral density variations in the rocks and ores of the crust. Measurement of the earth's main magnetic field, as influenced by lateral variations in magnetic susceptibility and remanence of the subsurface rocks and ores, is the basis of the *magnetometric* method. The *electrical resistivity* method is an artificial force-field method employed to detect the presence of layering of the soil and rock and to detect masses of ore contained within closed surfaces. The electrical conductivity of soils, rocks, and ores may be ionic or metallic. Where the mode of conduction changes, polarization potentials are established upon application of current to the ground. The decay of these potentials once the artificial current source is removed is governed by the time-constants of the electrochemical circuits. Detection of an existing potential after current is interrupted is the basis of the *induced polarization* method. Measurements of induced polarization may be made in the time domain (observation of the decay of an applied square pulse) or in the frequency domain (observation of the frequency dependence of the impedance of the ground). The *self-potential* or *spontaneous polarization* method depends upon the existence of natural unidirectional potentials in the earth. These potentials may be of physical or chemical origin and their mere existence is employed as a means of deciphering certain geologic occurrences. The *inductive electromagnetic method* is based upon the measurement of changes in the mutual impedance of a pair of coils as this impedance is affected by the presence of natural conductors or ferrites. Considerable rejection of extraneous features may be achieved by appropriate choice of operating frequency, and coil configuration. Natural *radioactivity* contrasts between rocks, soils, and ores as recorded by Geiger counters and scintillometers in aircraft, on the ground, or in boreholes are used to deduce the nature of the subsurface. The thickness of layers of sedimentary rocks to any desired depth may be measured with the *seismic-reflection* method provided an acoustic impedance mismatch occurs between adjacent layers. For depths to about 5000 ft, the *seismic-refraction* method yields sonic velocities and layer thicknesses provided sonic velocity increases continuously with depth. With both seismic methods a charge is detonated at or near the surface and the times of travel of compressional waves (occasionally shear waves) are recorded at transducers suitably disposed on the surface. Both velocities and depths to reflecting or refracting horizons may be interpreted from plots of times of shock events versus detector-shot point distances.

Equipment. *Gravity.* Measurement of variations in the force of gravity as small as 1 part in 10^8 are required in mineral exploration. Such precision is obtained only by mechanical-optical magnification of the extension of a spring with a mass on it. No electronic devices are used to measure gravity. An airborne gravity meter for geodetic purposes possesses a relative accuracy of 1 part in 10^5.

Magnetics. Magnetic-field measuring devices employed in geophysical prospecting are of two types (a) mechanical (e.g., compass, dip needle, needle magnetometer, and the torsion magnetometer) and (b) electronic (fluxgate and nuclear precession). The latter four instruments will record magnetic field variations as small as 10^{-5} oersted, i.e., 0.5 γ of a nominal 50,000-γ earth's field. The rubidium-vapor, helium, and Hall-effect (*q.v.*) magnetometers theoretically may detect total field variations as small as 10^{-8} oersteds and hence possess sufficient sensitivity to be used as gradient measuring devices. Both the fluxgate and nuclear precession instruments are used to record *total* field intensity continuously while mounted in, or trailed from, an aircraft. In most ground magnetic surveys, only the vertical component of the earth's field is recorded.

Resistivity. Either alternating or direct current is applied to the ground through one pair of electrodes and the voltage appearing at another pair of electrodes is measured. One of the numerous possible electrode arrays is selected and the electrodes are moved across the surface of the earth so as to permit the maximum of useful information about the subsurface to be obtained for each individual problem. The "apparent" resistivity ρ_A of the earth is calculated according to the formula

$$\rho_A = \frac{1}{2\pi} \frac{V}{I} \left[\frac{1}{\dfrac{1}{r_1} - \dfrac{1}{r_2} - \dfrac{1}{r_3} + \dfrac{1}{r_4}} \right]$$

and compared with apparent-resistivity distributions for theoretical models; r_1 and r_2 are measured from the potential electrodes to one current electrode, r_3 and r_4 are measured to the other current electrode. An ac generator of 25, 50, or 60 cps is frequently used as a source, in conjunction with a VTVM as a detector. Alternatively, the use of direct current usually involves voltage measurement by means of a battery-operated chopper potentiometer. For greatest simplicity when propecting to shallow depths, a "Megger" earth tester may be used.

Induced Polarization. The expression $\mu = (\rho_{f1} - \rho_{f2})/\rho_{f1}\rho_{f2}$ (metal factor) is used to calculate the polarization when measurements are made in the frequency domain. Differences in $\rho_{f1} - \rho_{f2}$ of the order of 1 per cent for $f_1/f_2 \approx 5$ to 10 must be measured with portable apparatus. (Usually 0.25 per cent is the limit of detectability of the best equipment.) This requirement places a great demand on frequency and voltage stabilities. Inductive coupling between the current and potential circuits necessitates use of frequencies no higher than 10 cps and as low as 0.001 cps. Pulse techniques used in time-domain measurements pose similar problems. Most commonly the frequency-domain measurements involve use of a 400-cps generator whose output is modulated by heavy-duty transistorized square-wave generators operating at the low frequencies required. This energy is fed to the ground through current electrodes and potential is measured by means of a detector and an infrasonic voltmeter at another pair of electrodes.

Electromagnetics. The signal generated in a circular air-core coil by an alternating magnetic field $He^{-j\omega t}$ has the magnitude $|e_s| = (WR)^{1/2}(\delta\rho)^{-1/2} \mu_0 rfH$ volts, where W, R, δ, and ρ are the total weight, total resistance, density, and resistivity, respectively, of the material of the wire; μ_0 is the permeability of free space, r is the radius of the coil, and f is the frequency. These are the variables the engineer has available with which to achieve the desired signal level. The magnetic intensity is $H = NAI/2\pi a^3$ amp-turns/m for maximum coupling between the transmitting coil of turns N, area A square meters carrying current I amperes, and a detector at a distance a. Correct design demands that tube noise and thermal agitation noise in the detecting coil, and input grid resistance, should be small relative to noise induced in the detecting coil by natural alternating magnetic fields of the operating frequency. Narrow-band detecting equipment is employed so that the noise level may be written

$$e_{mn} = (WR)^{1/2}(\delta\rho)^{-1/2}\mu_0 rh_m(\Delta f)^{1/2}f$$

where h_m is the magnetic noise intensity for a 1-cps bandwidth. The signal-to-noise ratio then is

$$\frac{e_s}{e_{mn}} = \frac{NAI}{2\pi(\Delta f)^{1/2}h_m a^3}$$

for maximum coupling. The bandwidth must be sufficiently broad so that frequency drift in the transmitter is unimportant; e.g., a Q of 25–30 is typically employed in a receiving-coil circuit. In ground equipment, the transmitter and receiver may be separated by as much as 2000 ft and as little as 200 ft; the power supplied is varied accordingly. In some instances angular measurements of resultant field directions are made so that no physical connection between transmitter and receiver is necessary to measure the change in coupling. Otherwise, a reference voltage is led from the transmitter by a cable and compared (both phase and amplitude), in a bridge, to the voltage induced in the receiving coil. In airborne systems this latter technique, employed exclusively, suffers from three additional sources of noise; random mechanical rotation of one coil relative to the other, mechanical oscillation of the receiving coil in the earth's main magnetic field, and ignition noise. In those systems in which the receiver is towed 500 ft behind the aircraft-mounted transmitter, proper aerodynamical and acoustical design is essential to minimize the former two additional noise sources. If the two coils are mounted on a rigid structure (e.g., fore and aft on frame mounted beneath a helicopter), a very demanding rigidity complicates the acoustical design. Mechanical resonances must lie well away from the chosen electrical resonances. Simultaneous transmission and detection of two low audio frequencies differing by a factor of five is commonplace. Iron-cored coils are used frequently in receivers and less frequently in transmitters; they should possess a large length-to-diameter ratio and the magnetostriction noise sources must be controlled.

Radioactivity. One special requirement of airborne scintillation equipment is a fast counting rate so that a good statistical recording of radioactivity is obtained at each point in space. Gamma-ray spectrometers often lead to specific identification of radioactive minerals. Pulse height analyzers permit detection of only those gamma rays of energies within prescribed band widths.

Reflection and Refraction Seismic. A damped electromagnetic transducer (geophone) converts vertical earth movements as small as 10^{-8} in. to voltages. These voltages constitute the input, in older systems, to high-gain, high-dynamic-range amplifiers that drive galvanometers recording photographically. The frequency response of the geophones may range from 5 to 150 cps; the response characteristics of the amplifiers is governed by high- and low-pass filters designed to encroach upon the geophone range. More recently, wide-band, 5- to 300-cps equipment has been used throughout and the output of the amplifiers used to frequency-modulate a carrier recorded on magnetic tape, drum, or disk. With this latter system, filtering is performed at will, upon playback, to effect the best signal-to-noise ratio. Up to 48 geophones and associated amplification and tape channels are used simultaneously. Timing marks precise to 1 msec or less are obtained from crystal (or tuning-fork) controlled oscillators and placed on the records. The shot-moment is transferred to the recorder from the blasting circuit by radio.

Playback can be so sophisticated that apparent lithologic sections are plotted directly by the "variable-density," "variable-area," and "clipped-trace" techniques described in the literature. Great variability in design is evident in available equipment.

For ready solution of depth-of-soil problems arising in civil engineering, "hammer seismic" instrumentation is available. A pulse circuit is triggered at the moment of impact of a sledgehammer blow on the earth; a counter continues until arrival of a signal from a geophone. The time elapsed between shock and first detected signal is displayed digitally on a lighted panel.

Continuous sonic depth sounding with spark-gap or electro-mechanical transducers is commonplace in the marine environment.

Miscellaneous. Natural alternating electric and magnetic fields are employed in a few prospecting methods. For example, audiofrequency natural noise fluctuations may be used to detect subsurface conductors. Instrumentation for such equipment is highly specialized but really amounts to an ultrasensitive electromagnetic detector; nat-

ural signals of 10^{-11} oersted producing input voltages of $\frac{1}{10}$ μv are detectable.

Every oil well drilled, productive or otherwise, is logged by several continuously recording instruments. Included in the methods are sonic velocity, self-potential, resistivity, neutron, gamma, nuclear magnetic resonance, thermal, and induction electromagnetic. Well logging applied to mining and civil engineering problems is much less developed.

Bombardment of beryllium, in any chemical environment, by gamma rays having an energy higher than 1.66 Mev, results in emission of neutrons. Detection of these secondary neutrons is a means of locating beryllium-bearing minerals.

S. H. WARD

Cross-references: *Magnetometer, Radioactivity, Scintillation Counters*

GLASS

Glass has a unique combination of properties which render it extremely valuable to electronics. These properties include high dielectric strength, high stability (mechanical, thermal, electrical, and chemical), nonpermeability to gases and moisture, controlled transparency to visible and other radiation, and the ability to be hermetically sealed to metals, ceramics, and other glasses. This combination of properties, together with the versatility of glass and its adaptability to low-cost mass manufacture, are largely responsible for the wide range of glass materials utilized in electronics.

Glass for Device Enclosures. The principal application for glass in electronics is as a structural material, particularly for hermetically sealed enclosures for devices such as receiving, transmitting and power, cathode-ray, X-ray, and rectifier tubes, and particle accelerators. Electric lamps and phototubes require glass envelopes with excellent transmission in the spectral region where output is desired, often with partial or total absorption in other parts of the spectrum. Solid-state devices and electronic components are often hermetically enclosed in glass.

Metallized Glass. Metallized glass is used for hermetic and moisture-impervious seals in applications where a high temperature sealing process is not feasible. Glass can be metallized by firing into it glass-bonded silver, followed by metal plating and tinning. The metallized glass can then be soldered to metal or to another piece of metallized glass at conventional soldering temperatures. Structural parts made of metallized glass include enclosure tubes for electronic components, bushings for high-voltage terminals, and hermetically sealed instrument and meter windows.

Metallized glass is also utilized to make stable metallized electronic components, most important of which are inductances and trimmer capacitors. The inductances comprise a metallized spiral on a glass tube and are used for high-frequency tuning applica-

tions requiring temperature stability, ruggedness, and low loss. The trimmer capacitors, also used for high-stability requirements, are made of a glass tube with a metallized band on the outside and an adjustable metal slug in the bore.

Sintered Glass. Small structural parts can be made of glass by a sintering technique closely resembling powder metallurgy. Pulverized glass is molded and sintered to form a vacuum-tight product whose physical and electrical characteristics are approximately those of the parent glass. Sintered-glass parts can be mass-produced in shapes, patterns, and tolerances not readily attainable by conventional glass-working processes. Applications for sintered glass include television gun mounts, tube bases, headers, and sealing beads.

High-Temperature Glasses. A number of glasses are now available for high-temperature applications, the choice of glass depending on the specific requirements.

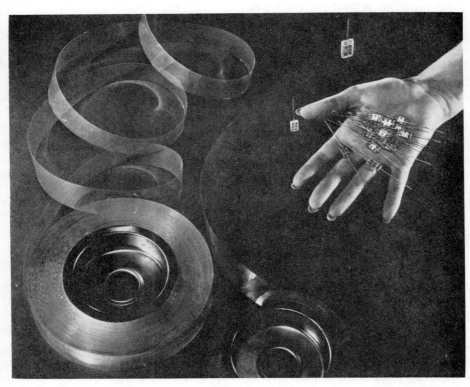

Fig. 1

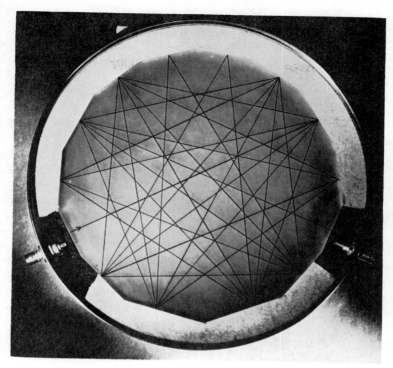

Fig. 2

Fused silica and 96-percent silica glass have softening points of 1585°C and 1500°C, respectively, and very great resistance to thermal shock because of their low thermal-expansion coefficients. A new calcium alumino-silicate glass can be outgassed and used at temperatures several hundred degrees above the capability of conventional glasses for electron-tube enclosures. This new high-temperature glass has excellent electrical properties: its resistivity is much greater even than that of fused silica itself.

Fused Silica. Fused silica of extreme purity and homogeneity is used as the delay medium in ultrasonic delay lines. Long delays are achieved by means of a "folded" path, in which the energy is reflected from facet to facet of a precision-ground polygon of fused silica. For long delay times transmission of the energy through the ultrasonic medium with minimum loss and scattering is essential. High purity fused silica with low ultrasonic loss is employed in these lines.

Other applications for fused silica include ultraviolet transmitting windows, camera windows for high-speed aircraft and missiles, crucibles for semiconductor material fabrication, and applications where optical clarity is required in heavy radiation fields.

Photosensitive Glass. Four types of photosensitive glasses have been developed to date, in which an image is produced in the body of the glass by exposure to ultraviolet light and then developed by subsequent heat treatment.

The first is a color-transparency glass, for an actual color transparency is produced in the body of clear glass. Second is a photosensitive opal glass in which an opalescent image is formed in the exposed areas.

A third type makes possible the production of extremely accurate electrical and mechanical parts (tolerances down to ±0.001 in.). In this glass the opalescent image is of a chemical composition that can be etched away, leaving behind the portions of the glass that had not been exposed to ultraviolet light. This chemical machining

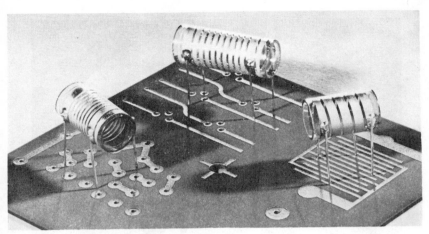

Fig. 3

produces precise patterns hitherto impossible in glass, thereby opening the way to many new applications such as fine mesh screens for electronic storage tubes and solid-state image storage devices.

The fourth type is a highly crystalline material resembling a ceramic. Made from a photosensitive glass by proper exposure and heat treatment, it has good electrical properties and high strength—about three times that of conventional glass. It is available in chemically machined form. This type of ceramic is used for electronic circuit boards, substrates for microcircuitry (*q.v.*), and for other applications requiring precision patterns and dimensional stability.

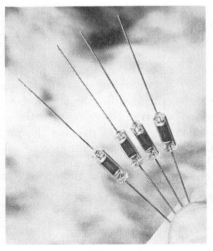

Fig. 4.

The chemically machinable glass materials described above are being utilized for pneumatic and hydraulic servo and computer elements employing newly developed principles of fluid amplification.

Ribbon Glass. Glass can be drawn continuously in the form of thin ribbon down to about 0.001-in. thickness, sufficiently flexible to be coiled around a 1-in. radius. This ribbon glass is homogeneous and is entirely free of holes, cracks, and other imperfections. A lead silicate glass manufactured in ribbon form is used as the dielectric in high-stability precision-type glass capacitors. The ribbon glass and alternate layers of metal foil are sealed together at high temperature to form integral rugged monolithic units. The resulting glass capacitors find widespread use in applications calling for high stability, high Q, low and reproducible temperature coefficient of capacitance, and small size.

Electrically Conductive Glass. Many methods are available for rendering glass electrically conductive, but the major share of commercially available conductive glass comprises metallic oxides fired onto the surface of the glass at elevated temperature. Although these coatings are less than 0.0001 in. thick, they are rugged, highly stable, durable, and inert. They can be produced in the resistance range from 10 ohms to 1 megohm/ square, but the properties required for most electronic applications are obtained in the range from 10 to 1,000 ohms/square.

The largest application of conductive glass is for high-stability resistors. Glass resistors are now mass produced for all types of resistor applications including general purpose, power, high frequency, and precision. They are utilized as standard components in entertainment, industrial, and military equipment.

A number of applications for conductive glass arise from the combination of visual transparency and electrical conductivity, as in electroluminescent lighting panels, non-fogging electrically heated windows, and instrument windows with electrostatic shielding and static charge dissipation.

Gamma-Ray Sensitive Glasses. Special glasses are used to detect and measure gamma radiation. These glasses, after irradiation by gamma rays, fluoresce when they are exposed to ultraviolet light. The intensity of the induced light emission is proportional to the total gamma-ray dose received. Reading instruments translate the emission into the gamma-ray dose. These glasses together with the reading instruments are used as dosimeters.

Radiation Resistant Glass. Because of its inorganic nature and its random network, glass has a high degree of resistance to nuclear radiation. A number of glasses are available that can withstand very high levels of X- and gamma radiation. Glasses that match or improve the absorbing properties of concrete and steel are now available. These glasses are employed in lenses and prisms in radiation fields and for radiation shielding windows. Massive shielding windows up to 8.5 ft thick and 18,000 lb weight are now in use.

Glass-Ceramics. A new family of materials, crystalline glass-ceramics, is finding highly useful applications in electronics.

These materials are crystalline ceramics that have been converted from a glassy state by the use of heat treatment. Certain nucleating agents are added to the glass batch, which is then melted, formed, and cooled. When the glass is reheated at temperatures which permit crystallization, billions of invisible crystallites are formed throughout the glass body. Each crystallite acts as a center for crystal growth as the heating continues. Composition of the glass and heat treatment determine the type of crystallization. The resultant material is an opaque ceramic article. It is stronger and harder than the parent glass, has greater scratch, impact, and abrasion resistance, and is characterized by improved thermal shock, high temperature and electrical properties.

One of the new materials has excellent dielectric properties at microwave frequencies and at elevated temperature. It is used for radomes (*q.v.*) for supersonic missiles. Similar materials in powdered form are utilized as thermal setting cements to seal glass to glass, metal to metal, ceramic to ceramic, or combinations thereof. Depending on type, these cements fire at temperatures from 425° to 750°C and withstand subsequent processing temperatures up to 700°C. This property permits the high bakeout temperatures advantageous for many power, microwave, and cathode-ray tubes.

JAMES K. DAVIS

Cross-references: *Ceramic Materials, Resistors*

GONIOMETER: see NAVIGATION

GROUND-CONTROLLED APPROACH: see NAVIGATION

GUIDANCE: see INERTIAL GUIDANCE; MISSILE GUIDANCE

GYROSCOPE: see INERTIAL GUIDANCE AND GYROSCOPE

H

HALL EFFECT

In 1879 E. H. Hall (1855–1938) discovered that when a conductor was placed in a magnetic field perpendicular to the direction of current flow, a voltage was developed across the conductor. This voltage was perpendicular to both the plane of the current and the magnetic field. This effect has since become known as the Hall effect, and the voltage developed is known as the Hall voltage.

The voltage is developed because the moving charges that make up the current are forced to one side of the conductor by the magnetic field, and they accumulate on an edge of the conductor until the force associated with the accumulated charge is equal to the force exerted by the magnetic field,

$$eE_y = ev_x H_z = J_x H_z/n$$

where e is the electronic charge in coulombs, E_y is the electric field developed in the y direction (when the charge carriers move with a velocity v_x in the x direction in the presence of a magnetic field H_z in the z direction), and J_x is the current density. As a result of the charge accumulation on the edge of the conductor and the associated electric field, the equipotential lines, which normally are at right angles to the current, are skewed, and a potential difference exists between points directly opposite to each other on the conductor. The angle between the current and the resultant electric field is the Hall angle and is defined as

$$\text{Hall angle } \theta = \tan^{-1} E_y/E_x$$

where E_x is the field that generates the current in the x direction.
The ratio

$$E_y/J_x H_z = 1/ne = R_H$$

is defined as the Hall coefficient, where n is the number of electrons per cubic centimeter.

The Hall coefficient is determined from the Hall voltage, V_H (volts)

$$R_H = V_H t \times 10^8/I_x H_z$$

where I_x is the current (amp) and t (cm) the thickness of the conductor; R_H then is measured in cm³/coulomb. Other common units for R are volts-cm/amp-gauss and emu.

The Hall coefficient is an important tool in understanding the conductivity processes in metals and semiconductors because from it the number of conduction electrons can be obtained. In cm³/coulomb the Hall coefficient for most metals is of the magnitude 10^{-3}.

In a mutually perpendicular system with the current in the positive x direction and the magnetic field in the positive z direction, the electric field would be in the negative y direction; the Hall coefficient then is said to be positive. This occurs in iron, zinc, cadmium, or cobalt. In lithium, gold, silver, copper, sodium, or bismuth, the electric field is in the opposite direction and the effect is said to be negative. The sign of the effect in iron, zinc, cadmium, etc. suggests that the conductivity is effectively carried by positive charges; this is explained by the band theory of solids as conductivity by positive holes. A hole is the vacancy of an electron in the lattice structure. These vacancies behave like particles with a positive charge equal to the electronic charge.

The Hall effect is much more pronounced in semiconductors, where the conduction process is due to impurities occupying lattice sites in the crystal structure. It has been seen that the Hall coefficient is inversely proportional to the number of carriers per cubic centimer, so that by controlling the impurity density the Hall coefficient is in effect controlled. Generally, the reverse is true—the Hall coefficient is used as a tool to determine the impurity content. With both types of carriers present (intrinsic conduction) the interpretation of Hall measurements is more difficult; the Hall coefficient in this case is defined as

$$R_H = \frac{3\pi}{8e} (n\mu_n{}^2 - p\mu_p{}^2)/(n\mu_n + p\mu_p)^2$$

where μ_n is the mobility of the electrons, μ_p is the mobility of the holes, and n and p represent the density of electron and holes, respectively. Mobility is usually expressed in cm²/volt-second.

Mobility is determined two ways by the Hall effect: first, from the Hall angle θ:

$$\theta = \tan^{-1} E_y/E_x = \mu_H H_z \times 10^{-8}$$

and, second, by the Hall coefficient:

$$\mu_H = R_H/\rho_0$$

where μ_H denotes the Hall mobility and ρ_0 is the zero magnetic field resistivity (ρ varies with magnetic field). The Hall mobility is the mobility of the electrons or holes in a semiconductor as determined by the Hall effect. The Hall mobility differs slightly from the drift mobility.

CHARLES A. SIMMONS

Cross-references: *Magnetism*

HANSEN, WILLIAM WEBSTER (1909–1949)

W. W. Hansen was born in Fresno, California, on May 27, 1909 and showed great precocity in his understanding of electricity and mathematics. He entered Stanford University at sixteen, studying first electrical engineering and then physics, and obtaining the Ph.D. in 1933. After a year and a half as a National Research Fellow at Massachusetts Institute of Technology, he returned to Stanford in 1934 as an assistant professor of physics. Through an earlier interest in X-rays, his attention was turned to the problem of accelerating electrons for purposes of experimentation in nuclear physics and he was inspired by the work of D. H. Sloan at the University of California in Berkeley to concentrate on techniques

employing electromagnetic resonators. His first accelerator cavity was constructed during 1936–37, but never saw employment as a linear accelerator (*q.v.*).

In the same year, the brothers R. H. and S. F. Varian devised a method of velocity modulation (*q.v.*) of electrons, and employed resonating cavities similar to those devised by Hansen to devise the first klystron (*q.v.*). During the ensuing years Hansen developed many novel techniques of microwave measurements and (with J. R. Woodyard) discovered a new principle of the design of antenna arrays by proper phasing of the elements.

In 1941 Hansen and his collaborators moved to the Sperry Gyroscope Co. plant in Garden City, Long Island, to work on the klystron. He stayed there until the end of World War II, making frequent trips to the Radiation Laboratory at M.I.T. In addition to his work on the klystron, which became an important component of radar sets, he also worked on Doppler radar, gun-laying radar, and blind-landing microwave systems. Owing to his great versatility, he was also able to contribute toward such diverse problems

W. W. Hansen

as the design of aircraft superchargers and the harnessing of atomic energy.

He returned to Stanford in 1945 and resumed his work on the linear electron accelerator, to be powered by giant klystrons. The various accelerators built there, including the multi-Bev machine now under development, are all based on Hansen's original design. He also participated in the development of nuclear magnetic resonance (NMR, q.v.) by his colleague Felix Bloch, who later received the Nobel Prize (in 1952).

Hansen's weak constitution was severely affected by the hard work of the war years and he died on May 23, 1949, at the age of 39, a few weeks after his election to the National Academy of Sciences. He may be considered to be the founder of the field of microwave electronics.

CHARLES SUSSKIND

Cross-references: *Historical Background of Electronics*

HEARING AIDS

The electronic hearing aid is essentially a miniature public-address system composed of microphone, amplifier, and speaker (receiver or earphone). In almost all cases, the microphone is housed with the amplifier section. In conventional body-worn hearing aids and in some of the instruments worn on the head, the receiver is separate but connected by a cord with the amplifier. For a small percentage of users, acoustic energy is fed through bone pathways to the inner hearing mechanism by an oscillator ("bone conduction receiver" held in place against the mastoid by a headband). In most of the head-worn models the receiver is housed with the amplifier, its output fed through a clear plastic tubing held in place at the ear by the earmold.

The microphone in transistorized hearing aids is usually of the variable reluctance balanced-armature type. The diaphragm is connected by a drive-pin with a thin metal reed centered in a coil of fine wire and positioned between two magnets. When displaced from dead center position under the drive of the microphone diaphragm, this reed conducts the magnetic flux which induces alternating currents in the coil. These currents are amplified in the amplifier section.

The amplifier is built around junction-type transistors (q.v.), usually pnp type. Associated resistors, condensers, switches, contacts, etc., are extremely miniaturized. Response modifications are effected in some by tone control systems; in others, gain and power limits or "automatic-gain-control" circuitry provide loudness limiting.

The external receiver (or earphone) connected with the amplifier by a cord is usually of the magnetic type, in which one or two high-permeability pole pieces are centered in a coil or coils of fine wire. Alternating signal currents fed to the coils from the amplifier exert magnetic influences on the diaphragm of the receiver, and the resulting diaphragm movements generate acoustic waves of the same pattern received by the microphone. In head-worn models, the receiver incorporated in the amplifier housing is usually of the variable-reluctance type, similar in construction to the magnetic microphone. The coil energized by alternating signal currents drives the reed, which generates the acoustic energy to which the ear responds. The acoustic output of the receiver is presented to the ear through a length of clear plastic tubing and into an earmold, a clear plastic device made from an "impression" of the ear by techniques somewhat like those employed in making dental plates.

Most of the sounds important to the understanding of speech fall in a range of frequencies from 300 to 3000 cps, and it is over approximately this band of frequencies that the average hearing aid provides useful amplification, although research is tending toward expansion of this range with more uniform amplification. Extended range performance should provide advantages to many hearing-handicapped, especially those (such as very young children) who must learn language through amplifier systems.

Wearable hearing aids are divided into body-worn types, in which the amplifier and microphone in one case are worn in the clothing, connected with the receiver or oscillator at the ear by a cord; and on-the-head types which include those in eyeglass temples (Fig. 1) and models worn behind the ear (Fig. 2), either with receiver enclosed with the amplifier or connected with it through a short cord. Amplification and power designed into head-worn instruments are limited by the tendency of such systems to "feed back" under high levels of output. Body types, however, may be of moderate

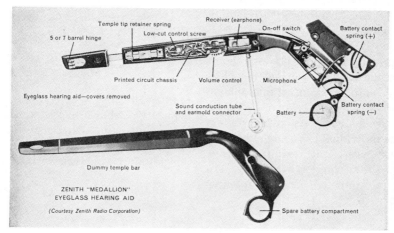

Temple tip retainer spring

Receiver (earphone)

5 or 7 barrel hinge   Low-cut control screw   On-off switch   Battery contact spring (+)

Printed circuit chassis   Volume control   Microphone

Eyeglass hearing aid—covers removed

Sound conduction tube and earmold connector   Battery   Battery contact spring (−)

Dummy temple bar

ZENITH "MEDALLION"
EYEGLASS HEARING AID

(Courtesy Zenith Radio Corporation)

Spare battery compartment

Fig. 1.

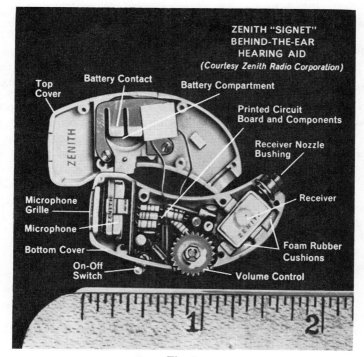

ZENITH "SIGNET"
BEHIND-THE-EAR
HEARING AID

(Courtesy Zenith Radio Corporation)

Top Cover   Battery Contact   Battery Compartment

Printed Circuit Board and Components

Receiver Nozzle Bushing

Microphone Grille

Microphone

Receiver

Bottom Cover

On-Off Switch

Foam Rubber Cushions

Volume Control

Fig. 2.

gain and power output for mild to moderate hearing losses; or of high gain and output for severe losses.

A useful feature in some hearing aids is an induction-coil pickup for telephone use. Such a coil switched into the circuit in place of the microphone picks up radiations from the telephone voice coil when held close to the telephone receiver, providing satisfactory hearing together with rejection of airborne sounds.

Less frequently encountered hearing aid devices are group hearing aids used in schools or classes for the hard of hearing. For class use, these aids employ a central microphone and amplifier with up to 50 sets of clamp-on headphones, each with its own volume control. Some individual desk-model hearing aids, equipped with either clamp-on headphone or small hearing aid receiver, are used by severely impaired persons in learning situations.

RALPH L. WAGNER

Cross-references: *Earphones, Electroacoustics, Loudspeakers and Microphones*

HEATING (ELECTRONIC)

There are two basic types of electronic heating, induction and dielectric, both utilizing the loss factor characteristic of the material to be heated.

Induction Heating

Induction heating can be analyzed in a straightforward way by the application of transformer theory, where the coupling or work coil is considered as the transformer primary, and the work or load as the transformer secondary. The current flow in the primary induces a current flow into the load which is a function of the coupling coefficient and the equivalent turns ratio. This induced secondary current does not penetrate deeply into the work owing to the skin effect (*q.v.*). The induced current density is thus quite high and the resulting power loss causes a

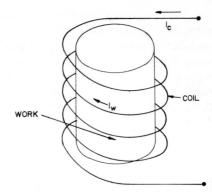

Fig. 1. Induction-heating coil-work configuration.

temperature rise. The coil and the work are typically as shown in Fig. 1. Since the work is the short-circuited transformer secondary, the depth-of-penetration relation gives the power induced into the work as

$$P = 2\pi^2 I_c^2 N^2 \sqrt{\rho\mu'f}\, \frac{d}{l} \times 10^{-9} \text{ (kw)} \qquad (1)$$

where

I_c = coil current (amp)
ρ = resistivity (microhm-cm)
l = work length (cm)
f = frequency (cps)
N = number of coil turns
d = diameter of work (cm)
μ' = relative permeability

The coil current required to produce a given power can now be calculated from this equation by solving for current or ampere turns as a function of P and the material constants. The total power required to produce a given temperature rise in a load is given by

$$P = 0.0176 SW\Delta TA \qquad \text{(kw)} \quad (1)$$

where

S = specific heat (BTU/lb-°F)
ΔT = temperature rise required (°F)
W = weight of material (lb/min)
A = rule-of-thumb loss factor

This power, in addition to that lost in the coupling coil and connecting leads, is required to produce the temperature rise. The

factor A of Eq. (2) is the loss factor accounting for loss of heat from the work owing to
conduction, radiation, and convection. A
rule-of-thumb value for A is in the range of
1.5 to 2.

The transformer interpretation provides
only an approximate solution, under certain
restricted conditions, and is sufficiently accurate only when the skin depth is small
compared to the work dimension. Solutions
have been derived from basic field theory
and these are much more exact. (See, for
instance, F. W. Curtis, *High-Frequency Induction Heating*, McGraw-Hill, 1950.) The
field theory solutions can be utilized for any
configuration and have been solved for both
solid and hollow cylinders, and for rectangular and flat-plate conditions.

Power requirements for induction heating
can be generated in a variety of ways. Normally the power-level requirements and the
frequency determine the type of power generating equipment to be used. Motor-generator sets are employed in the range between 1 and 10 kc. Spark-gap converters
have application in the range of 20 to 80
kc, with occasional uses as high as 400 kc.
Vacuum-tube oscillators are normally utilized in the range between 200 and 500 kc,
but are finding greater application at frequencies up to several megacycles for surface heating and plating operations. Applications of induction heating include metal
joining techniques such as soldering and
brazing, reflow of tin plate, heat treating,
hardening, annealing, heating for forging or
extrusions, and melting. A recent use has
also been in the generation of heat for germanium and silicon crystal growing in semiconductor manufacture (*q.v.*).

Dielectric Heating

Dielectric heating utilizes the flow of rf
currents through the dielectric medium to be
heated. The rf current flows through the dielectric material, where the material is the
dielectric of a capacitor and the electrodes
are the capacitor plates. The basic arrangement is shown in Fig. 2.

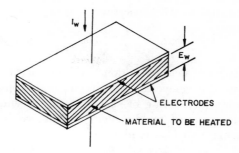

Fig. 2. Dielectric-heating electrode-work configuration.

The power required for a given temperature rise of the material can be determined
from its mass, its specific heat, and the temperature difference as shown in Eq. (2). The
heat-loss factor can be utilized in the same
way since conduction, radiation, and convection losses are present. The power dissipated in the material in a given configuration
can be determined from the following equation, which is derived from the parallel-
plate capacitance formula and the loss factor of the material:

$$P = 1.41\, f E_w^2 \epsilon' \delta\, \frac{A}{d} \times 10^{-12} \text{(w)} \qquad (3)$$

where

f = frequency (cps)
A = electrode area (in.²)
ϵ' = dielectric constant
E_w = rms voltage across material
d = material thickness
δ = loss factor

For a given power requirement the required
work voltage can be determined, and the rms
voltage is found from Eq. (3). The peak
value, or 1.4 E_w , must be less than the dielectric strength of the material, preferably
with a safety factor of 2. In a given system
the frequency may be chosen to insure that
this condition is being met.

The electrode voltage must appear across
an equivalent circuit consisting of a capacitance of

$$C = 0.224 \epsilon'\, \frac{A}{d}\ (\mu\mu\text{f}) \qquad (4)$$

in parallel with a resistance

$$R_s = \frac{1}{2\pi f C \delta} \text{ (ohms)} \quad (5)$$

Dielectric heating is done at frequencies of several megacycles, and up, and finds application in bonding of sheet plastics, drying, preheating of mold pellets, baking, rubber curing, and plastic film sealing.

H. E. GRUEN

Cross-references: *Cooking (Electronic), Radiation Hazards (Nonionizing Radiation), Welding (Electronic), Zone Melting*

HEAVISIDE, OLIVER (1850–1925)

Oliver Heaviside was born on May 18, 1850 in London, the son of an artist. His mother was the sister-in-law of Sir Charles Wheatstone (1802–1875). He was self-taught in the application of higher mathematics to electrodynamics, and except for a brief period of work as a telegrapher (1870–1874), he pursued his work privately. At the age of 23 he made proposals for making duplex telegraphy practical and during 1885 to 1887 he published a remarkable series of papers in *The Electrician* that established his reputation, although few could comprehend his ideas. His many contributions to the development of electromagnetic theory proved to be of lasting importance to practical applications. He recognized the importance of operational calculus to the investigation of transients, anticipating the general employment of Laplace and Fourier transforms (*q.v.*) in electrical engineering. He was the first to formulate the *telegraphers' equation*

$$\frac{1}{C} \frac{\partial^2 V}{\partial x^2} = L \frac{\partial^2 V}{\partial t^2} + R \frac{\partial V}{\partial t}$$

and predicted that inductive loading of telegraph cables would improve their design. His discovery that the values of resistance, inductance, capacitance, and conductance in a cable could be optimized to produce a distortionless mode of propagation proved to have wide application in general dynamics.

(He was the first to use the term *impedance*, in 1886, which originally referred to circuits containing resistance and inductance only.) He also suggested a new unit system (*q.v.*) similar to the Giorgi (MKS) system now in general use. In 1902 he predicted the existence of a region of ionized air above the earth that would affect propagation (*q.v.*); the existence of such a region was later confirmed and it is known as the Kennelly-Heaviside layer, in recognition of a similar prediction made by A. E. Kennelly (1861–1939), a professor at Harvard (and later MIT) who independently made the same observation in the same year.

Heaviside was elected a Fellow of the Royal Society in 1891, and received the Faraday Medal of the AIEE. Throughout his life, he generously gave of his time in response to requests for his help in the solution of intricate mathematical problems from scientists in the universities and from others. From 1889 on he lived in Devon in modest circumstances, receiving a small government pension toward the end; he died in Torquay on February 3, 1925.

CHARLES SUSSKIND

Cross-references: *Historical Background of Electronics*

HELITRON

The helitron is an electrostatically focused backward-wave oscillator, as shown schematically in Fig. 1. The frequency of oscillation is determined by the voltage between the four-segment circuit and the cathode in the electron gun. Typically, the frequency can be tuned over a range for which the ratio of the highest to the lowest frequency is more than 2:1 for a voltage variation of 3:1. Power output is of the order of tens of milliwatts and helitrons have been made to oscillate in frequencies ranging from 200 to 4,000 Mc.

The principal advantage of the helitron over the straight-beam backward-wave oscillator is that no magnet is required for

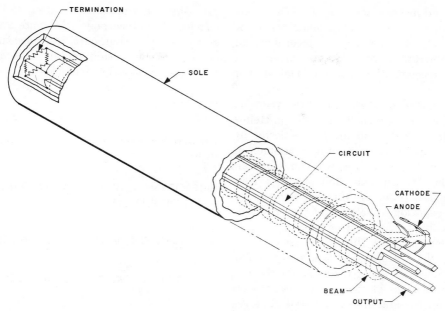

Fig. 1. Schematic representation of the helitron. Because of a balance between radial electric and centrifugal force, the electrons are focused along the spiral path.

focusing, thus reducing the over-all weight of the device to about 1 lb.

The name is derived from the fact that the electrons follow a helical path. An electron beam is launched at one end at a slight angle to the axis of the circuit The circuit is maintained positive with respect to the cathode and the outer cylindrical electrode, labeled *sole*, is maintained at a potential near that of the cathode so that there is an inward radial electric force on the electrons. This force is balanced by an outward centrifugal force resulting from the motion along the helical path. Stable beam focusing results. The electron beam thus focused excites a TEM wave traveling from the left toward the gun by inducing an rf voltage across the gaps between the four sections of the circuit. The circuit sections are excited by an rf wave with a polarity which is plus-minus-plus-minus at a frequency equal to the reciprocal of the time it takes an electron to pass from one gap to the gap diametrically opposite. The circuit sections are tied together in pairs at the output (gun) end and then connected to a balanced output line.

The end of the circuit opposite to the output is terminated by a resistive load matching the characteristic impedance of the circuit. This match prevents the rereflection of reflected power from the load and the consequent interference with the oscillation process.

D. A. WATKINS

Cross-references: *Backward-Wave Tubes, Traveling-Wave Tubes*

HERTZ, HEINRICH RUDOLF (1857–1894)

Heinrich Hertz was born on February 22, 1857, in Hamburg, the son of an attorney (and later judge and senator). He received a classical secondary education there but also attended a vocational school (on Sundays), where he demonstrated a special talent for drawing and mechanical tools. He began to study civil engineering in Dresden, but interrupted his studies after one semester for the obligatory one year of military service as a cadet. He determined to continue the course at Munich, but soon switched to physics and mathematics and in 1878 moved to Berlin, where he quickly made his mark with a prize-winning paper concerning the kinetic energy of an electric current. In 1880 he received the doctorate *magna cum laude*.

He remained in Berlin for three years as an assistant to the great Hermann von Helmholtz (1821–1894) and after a semester at Kiel was appointed professor of experimental physics at the Institute of Technology in Karlsruhe. It was there that he devised an experimental proof of Maxwell's theory of the propagation of electromagnetic waves by attaching long wires to a small spark gap and observing that the discharge was accompanied by a spark in a second, similar arrangement at some distance. Hertz observed the nodes of the standing waves on this primitive antenna and noted that reception was improved when transmitter and receiver were "tuned" to each other; from the lack of sharpness of the nodes he concluded that his oscillations were strongly damped. All of these conclusions were subsequently confirmed. He next investigated the effects of interposing various isolators and, by the employment of an ingenious reflecting arrangement, demonstrated the existence of standing waves in space, calculating the wavelength to be 8 m. This result led him to employ a mirror antenna with the transmitter at its focus, with a similar arrangement at the receiver, with which he demonstrared that his waves (now reduced to a wavelength of 0.5 m) followed all the laws of geometrical optics, including refraction and polarization. These discoveries, in addition to demonstrating Maxwell's theory that light and electromagnetic waves were one and the same, laid the basis for the development of radiotelegraphy.

Following upon the publication of his results, the Royal Society invited Hertz to London, and he also visited America. In 1889 he became professor at the university in Bonn. Here he devoted himself principally to theoretical work, with the exception of an experiment on the transmission of cathode rays through thin metal plates (1892). He concluded that cathode rays were made up of waves rather than particles, since the electrons penetrated thin metal films and he could not believe that particles could do so.

He died prematurely on January 1, 1894, in Bonn, at the age of 37.

CHARLES SUSSKIND

Cross-references: *Historical Background of Electronics*

HETERODYNE ACTION: see MODULATION AND DEMODULATION

HIGH-FIELD EMISSION: see FIELD EMISSION

HISTORICAL BACKGROUND OF ELECTRONICS

Electronics as a technological discipline grew out of two developments in the history of science: the understanding of the nature of electromagnetic wave propagation through space, and the discovery of the electron.

The principles of electromagnetic wave propagation were first enunciated by James Clerk Maxwell (1831–1879). In formulating the famous "Maxwell's equations," he cast aside the action-at-a-distance concept that had dominated theories of electricity and magnetism throughout the classical era, as exemplified by the work of Charles Augustin Coulomb (1736–1806), Hans Christian Oersted (1777–1851), André Marie Ampère (1775–1836), and Michael Faraday (1791–1867). This era came to an end with the work of Faraday, who first thought of electromagnetism in terms of field theory; but his ideas, although brilliant, were not formulated mathematically. Such a formulation was first provided by Carl Friedrich Gauss (1777–1855), by means of his famous theorem which relates a flux of force lines out of a region to the total charge within the region. But not until Maxwell were the electric and magnetic fields considered as the fundamental quantities, to be related by means of differential equations. Although an impressive background of mathematical theory of fields and potentials was available (based on the results obtained by many distinguished mathematicians with regard to gravitational fields), Maxwell extended this theory considerably, notably by introducing the idea of displacement current, and provided a fitting framework for the intuitive concepts of Faraday.

Once he had arrived at his equations, Maxwell predicted that a perturbation of an electromagnetic field would not be instantaneously perceived at another point in space; rather, the change would propagate as a wave, and that with the speed of light. Maxwell's achievement may be thus considered perhaps the greatest in all of 19th Century physics: he replaced the action-at-a-distance theory by a field theory, and he showed that optics is a branch of electromagnetism.

Like many great advances, Maxwell's theories were not immediately accepted, but his results were put entirely beyond doubt when Heinrich Hertz (*q.v.*) showed that electromagnetic waves actually existed, in his famous experiment. The utilization of such waves for radio communications followed very quickly.

The other great advance, the discovery of the electron, might have likewise come on the basis of a discovery of Faraday: the laws of electrolysis. Since the same amount of electric charge is always associated with an equivalent weight of a chemical element in the electrolytic process, and since this equivalent weight can be related to the atomic weight of the substance, Faraday might have readily concluded that a definite quantum of electricity is associated with every atom. He did not come to this conclusion, perhaps because he was preoccupied with the above-mentioned concept of the lines of force.

Instead, the discovery of the electron came about through the study of gas discharges. Several investigators had noted the existence of cathode rays in the course of this investigation, and learned that they could

James Clerk Maxwell

be deflected by electrostatic or magnetic fields. C. F. Varley (1828–1883) finally concluded that cathode rays consist of negatively charged particles, but he met with much skepticism; among those opposing this view was Heinrich Hertz (*q.v.*) who had not been able to repeat Varley's experiments, largely owing to technical difficulties. Hertz believed that cathode rays were electromagnetic waves, a belief that was reinforced when he noted that they could pass through thin metal films. However, Hertz proposed that if they were particles, it should be possible to determine the ratio of their charge to their mass by combined electrostatic and magnetic deflection. He did not attempt such an experiment himself, but others did and in 1897 J. J. Thomson (*q.v.*) obtained the astonishing result that the particles were much lighter, by three orders of magnitude, than hydrogen atoms. This discovery led to a proper understanding of many phenomena that had been observed before, such as the Edison effect, and formed the point of departure for modern electronics as a branch of technology.

Elsewhere in this volume short biographies of two dozen of the scientists who were among the most prominent in developing electronics technology appear under the following headings:

Armstrong, Edwin Howard (1890–1954)
Baird, John Logie (1888–1946)
Barkhausen, Heinrich (1881–1956)
Braun, Karl Ferdinand (1850–1918)
Crookes, Sir William (1832–1919)
De Forest, Lee (1873–1961)
Edison, Thomas Alva (1847–1931)
Fleming, Sir John Ambrose (1849–1945)
Hansen, William Webster (1909–1949)
Heaviside, Oliver (1850–1925)
Hertz, Heinrich Rudolf (1857–1894)
Langmuir, Irving (1881–1957)
Lodge, Sir Oliver Joseph (1851–1940)
Lorentz, Hendrik Antoon (1853–1928)
Marconi, Marchese Guglielmo (1874–1937)
Meissner, Alexander (1883–1958)
Popov, Aleksandr Stepanovich (1859–1905)
Poulsen, Valdemar (1869–1942)
Pupin, Michael Idvorsky (1858–1935)
Steinmetz, Charles Proteus (1865–1923)
Tesla, Nikola (1856–1943)
Thomson, Sir John Joseph (1856–1940)
Watson-Watt, Sir Robert (b. 1892)
Zworykin, Vladimir Kosma (b. 1889)

CHARLES SUSSKIND

HORNS: see ANTENNAS; LOUDSPEAKERS

HUMAN ENGINEERING

Human engineering is the engineering of machines and equipment for human use. By taking into account the capabilities and limitations of the human operators, the performance characteristics of machine components, and the operational requirements for the man-machine system, human engineering seeks to make the most efficient use of the human in terms of over-all system performance.

Historical antecedents to human engineering may be identified in the work of F. W. Taylor (1856–1915), F. B. Gilbreth (1868–1924) and L. E. Gilbreth (b. 1878), and others in engineering, and various ex-

perimental and applied psychologists prominent in the early history of scientific psychology. However, the significant beginnings of human engineering occurred during World War II. Prior to this time, machines were designed and developed primarily by engineers whose principal concern was to insure the efficiency of machines from the mechanical-design point of view. Efforts to match human operator performance to machine characteristics and operational requirements consisted, for the most part, of selection and training of human operators by industrial and personnel psychologists.

Several factors contributed to the development of a new approach to machine design procedures during World War II: (1) machines became more complex, (2) large numbers of machines, and consequently large numbers of human operators, were required, and (3) psychologists, with a background of training in a scientific approach to the study of human behavior, became interested in the practical problems of man's interaction with mechanical features of his environment.

As machines became more complex and, in many cases, were endowed with higher performance capabilities, they made greater demands upon the human operators in terms of requirements for speed and accuracy of responses, both for decision making and continuous control. Selection and training procedures for human operators were no longer adequate to supply the number and caliber of operators required.

Early work in human engineering was directed primarily at the design of displays and controls by which the operator interacted with the machine. Much of the pioneer work in this field consisted of efforts to redesign controls and displays for already existing machines in order to permit more efficient operation by humans. Almost immediately, however, it became apparent that a more fundamental problem for human engineering was to determine and insure the proper assignment of functions to the human and to the automatic devices in order to maximize over-all system performance.

Ideally, human engineering on a system begins with the earliest stages of preliminary design. With knowledge about the mission and system requirements, the operating characteristics of potential system components, and the behavioral capabilities and limitations of humans, the human engineer assists in conducting trade-off studies of alternative methods for accomplishing system functions. In most cases, the system design problems are not concerned primarily with making decisions between the alternatives of human or automatic performance of functions. More often, the decisions must be made between alternatives that consist of a combination of automatic and manual participation in the performance of a required system function.

After making the preliminary assignment of system functions to be performed by the human operator, the human engineer determines the specific information that must be displayed to the operator, and the manual controls and control system dynamics that are required for the operator to perform his assigned functions. These must then be reconciled with the potentially feasible methods for the sensing, processing, and coding of information for display and for the implementing of control modes. At this stage it may be necessary to reallocate certain system functions.

When the information and control requirements have been established for the system functions finally assigned to the human operator, the detailed design configurations for displays and controls are developed. At this stage, as in all preceding stages, human sensory and motor capabilities and limitations are accorded primary consideration. In this case, they not only set design limits, but also determine optimum design configurations.

The field of human engineering encompasses two recognizably different but closely related kinds of activity. One is concerned with the scientific study of human behavior as the human interacts with machines. The other is concerned with the application of results of scientific studies to the design of man-machine systems. This division is the result of both practical necessity and individual predilection.

From a utilitarian viewpoint human engineering must include research activities. Scientifically determined information about human behavior in relation to a complex machine environment is not the typical result of basic research in either the behavioral or physical sciences. Applied research in the area of man-machine systems is necessary to provide the basis for sound human-engineering practice.

Equally important from a historical point of view is the polarization of interests of the individuals engaged in human engineering. Initially, the majority of personnel in this field differed in terms of their formal education and professional training and experience. In general, a background in engineering predisposed one to an engineering application approach, whereas a background in psychology predisposed one to research activities. As the field of human engineering has developed the kinds of activities in which an individual participates have become less dependent upon his background of training and experience. Many engineers conduct research and many psychologists perform systems analyses and engineering studies.

Formal courses of training in human engineering are now offered both in engineering departments and in psychology departments of universities. These programs produce engineers and psychologists that not only recognize the necessity for both research and engineering activities but also have the necessary training to effectively participate in either as may be required.

CHARLES OWEN HOPKINS

Cross-references: *Automation, Integrated Instrumentation, Medical Electronics, Operations Research, Systems*

HYPERBOLIC SYSTEMS: see NAVIGATION

HYSTERESIS: see MAGNETISM

I

ICONOSCOPE

The iconoscope, one of the first camera-pickup tube types, is a photoelectric storage device, limited to slide and motion-picture film reproduction because of its low sensitivity.

The light-sensitive storage surface consists of a thin sheet of mica on which discrete particles of photoemissive silver are deposited to produce a mosaic. Because the elements of the conductive photoemissive material are electrically free, the tube can store a charge image corresponding to the picture being televised. The mica sheet serves as the dielectric of a storage element capacitor; the mosaic elements on one side of the mica act as one plate, and a continuous-conducting signal electrode on the other side of the mica acts as the other plate.

As the picture is focused on the mosaic within the bulb, illuminated elements liberate electrons which leave a positive charge pattern on the elements. This charge pattern is stored until the scanning beam passes over and neutralizes the element. The liberated electrons are collected by a positive-voltage electrode which determines the maximum voltage to which an element may charge.

The scanning beam supplied by an electron gun neutralizes stored image charges by depositing electrons on the positively charged elements. The change of charge which is deposited as the beam scans from element to element is capacitively coupled to the signal electrode producing the video signal.

The high velocity of the scanning beam complicates the action because the secondary emission from the scanned surface is rather high and causes unwanted shading effects. These effects can be minimized to generate a more accurate picture by edge-lighting the mosaic mounting strips to provide photoelectrons which even out the background potential, and by back-lighting the mosaic and bulb walls to help stabilize the mosaic potential as a whole.

The sensitivity of the iconoscope is quite low in comparison to that of other storage camera tubes because of the inherent low sensitivity of the photosurface, the loss of useful area owing to the voids between mosaic elements, and the low storage ability. When the exposure is continuous, as with slides, the storage ability is low because re-distributed secondary and photoelectrons tend to neutralize the stored information between scans.

The illumination required for slide pickup is about 5 ft-candles on the mosaic. For film use the light must be pulsed on only during vertical retrace interval, otherwise the initial surge of electrons from the mosaic produced by the sudden application of light would cause a surge of current to flow out of the signal plate. This surge constitutes an objectionable spurious video signal. The peak illumination required for film use is between 500 and 1000 ft-candles on the mosaic.

G. A. ROBINSON

Cross-references: *Cathode-Ray Tubes (Display), Flying-Spot Scanning, Image Orthicon, Photo-electric Emission, Storage Tubes, Television*

IFF: see COUNTERMEASURES

IGNITRON

The ignitron is a mercury-pool gas tube with characteristics similar to a thyratron. It has an anode, a mercury-pool cathode, a starting device called an ignitor, and may have one or more grids. The mercury-pool cathode has practically unlimited electron emission. Currents of over 50,000 amp have been conducted for short periods of time.

The ignitor is a short length of material of comparatively high resistivity, one end of which is submerged in the mercury-pool cathode. A connection is made to the upper portion of the ignitor, which leads through the envelope by means of an insulating seal to an external terminal. The ignitor acts as a trigger that starts an arc discharge of which the negative arc spot is on the mercury surface. Current is collected by the anode when positive. By using a thyratron to control the ignitor, the very small grid currents characteristic of the thyratron can be used to control the large currents characteristic of the ignitron.

Electron flow is from cathode to anode. When the anode is made negative by the external circuit current, flow stops. Like most gas tubes, neither the ignitor nor a grid can stop the current flow.

The forward tube drop is from 12 to 20 v when the tube is operated on industrial circuits at 60 cps.

In pulse-type circuits where capacitors are discharged, the ignitor can be made to start the discharge in less than 1 μsec, with less than 0.1 μsec jitter, the anode voltage falling from the hold off value of 20 kv to less than 100 v in less than 0.5 μsec. The above values are for operating tube temperatures above 30°C, and with high-current ignitor circuits. In industrial ignitor circuits lower currents are used, the firing time being of the order of 100 μsec.

Tubes designed for industrial circuits operate at about 1000 v inverse. On ac circuits problems of deionization between conducting periods are encountered that limit the operating voltage. On single-pulse operation or repeated pulses at relatively long intervals, deionization is not so important and much higher voltages are possible. Where high-voltage operation is required in spite of deionization difficulties, recourse is usually had to internal baffles or grids to promote local deionization in the vicinity of the anodes.

A major application for the smaller ignitrons is for control of the large currents used

in resistance welding. Several types of circuitry are used for this purpose. Most common is single-phase control, where two ignitrons are used as a single-pole switch. They are connected in reverse parallel, the ignitors are controlled by thyratrons connected from the anode to the ignitor terminal of each tube. The combination can be used as an on and off control and in addition by control of the thyratron grids the average circuit current can be controlled. Thus the welder can be supplied with a predetermined intermittent current of integral numbers of sine waves, with the starting point of each half wave determined by the relative phase of the ignitor pulses.

Ignitrons for resistance welding service are industry rated as follows:

Size	Maximum Current (amp)		Maximum Averaging Time (sec)	Supply Voltage (v, rms)
	Average	Peak		
A	22.4	850	11.0	440
B	56.0	1700	9.0	440
C	140.0	3400	7.1	440
D	355.0	6800	5.6	440

The ignitors used in welder control ignitrons are designed for reliable intermittent operation.

For rectification, tubes similar to those used for resistance welding are supplied with ignitors designed for continuous service. Internal baffles between anodes and cathodes are provided to promote deionization and consequently improve the operating voltage rating. These tubes are provided with two ignitors of which one can be used as a spare to increase the life of permanently sealed types. Two industry standardized sizes are available rated at 100 and 200 amp dc per tube. Six of these tubes in a double-three-phase rectifier circuit deliver respectively 150 or 300 kw dc. Many of these units have been applied for dc power in coal mines.

Ignitrons in larger sizes are made both permanently sealed and continuously pumped. Many of the latter have been applied to the generation of dc power in the aluminum industry. The large sealed types have been used to furnish dc power to drive railroad locomotives.

Ignitrons containing grids are commercially available. These tubes are rated at 20 kv inverse. One size is rated at 150 amp average anode current and a smaller size is rated at 50 amp. Three grids are used. Two serve as deionizing electrodes and the third can be used to control starting phase. It is possible to fire the ignitor but to prevent complete ionization by use of the control grid for a short period. Where very accurate starting phase is required, the grid may be used. Applications for these tubes have been as high-voltage rectifiers, large frequency-changer systems, and as "crow bars."

This last application consists of use of the tube as a short-circuiting device to prevent damage to a more delicate tube such as a high-vacuum radio oscillator on overload or voltage flashover. The ignitron is connected in parallel with the device to be protected. The ignitor firing circuit is triggered by a device sensitive to momentary voltage reduction across the protected tube. It fires rapidly, reducing the voltage across the protected tube in a matter of microseconds. The resulting power short circuit is rapidly cleared by the power supply circuit breaker before damage can occur to the ignitron.

Small ignitrons have recently been used by various universities and government agencies in connection with experimental work on atomic fusion (*q.v.*). Tubes 2 in. in diameter have been used to discharge capacitors charged to 20 kv. Discharge currents of 35,000 amp per tube have been measured. Duration of the discharge varied from 50 to 1500 μsec. In this service the tube loses its rectification properties after the discharge has occurred and conducts in both directions until the current falls low enough for the deionization to be effective.

D. E. MARSHALL

Cross-references: *Rectifier Tubes, Switches, Thyratrons*

IMAGE INTENSIFIERS

An image intensifier is a device, usually an electronic tube, which converts a faint, sometimes invisible, image to a bright visible one.

Most image intensifiers employ a photoemissive coating on which the faint image is focused and a phosphor screen on which the intensified image is observed. Electrons emitted under the influence of light from the photoemissive surface are caused to travel through the tube, and by one of the methods described below, to produce a highly intensified image on the phosphor screen.

Demagnified Image Intensifier. In this tube (Fig. 1) the image is demagnified electron-optically. Since the electron density in the image increases inversely as the square of the magnification, an image reduction of one sixth gives an electron density and a resultant brightness gain of thirty-six times. Using accelerating potentials as high as 40 kv, images over a thousand times brighter than the original scene are formed. By introducing an X-ray fluorescent screen into the tube in front of the photosurface, this tube serves as an X-ray intensifier for fluoroscopy.

Cascade Image Intensifier. A second type of image intensifier tube is the cascade image tube (Fig. 2) in which two or more image converter tubes are constructed in tandem such that the phosphor screen of the first is separated from the photocathode of the second only by a transparent glass mem-

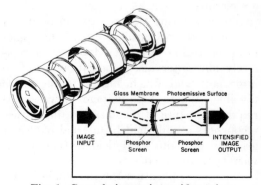

Fig. 1. Cascade image intensifier tube.

brane. In this way the first tube serves as a light preamplifier for the second. Two- and three-stage cascade tubes are available that produce brightness gains of over 50,000.

Transmission Secondary Emission Intensifier. This tube (Fig. 3) uses thin membranes of aluminum oxide coated with a secondary emitting material as electron image multipliers.

The electron image from the photoemissive surface is focused successively on each membrane. When one electron impinges on the front side of the membrane, four to eight electrons are emitted from the rear. Brightness gains of over 60,000 have been achieved in these tubes using five secondary emitting membranes.

Image Orthicon Intensifier. A somewhat different type of image intensifier employs the principles of television (*q.v.*). The system is operated as a closed circuit and uses a modified image orthicon (*q.v.*) camera tube. This tube serves as an intensifier by virtue of the signal integration which takes place on its target between scans. A special magnesium oxide target is used to provide greater low light level sensitivity.

Image Intensifier Orthicon. By incorporating the image converter tube as a light preamplifier to the image orthicon tube, the gain of this system can be further increased. The image intensifier orthicon is shown in Fig. 4.

Solid-State Image Intensifier. In this device an electroluminescent phosphor layer and a photoconductive coating are sandwiched between transparent conducting

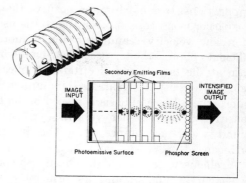

Fig. 3. Transmission secondary-imission intensifier tube.

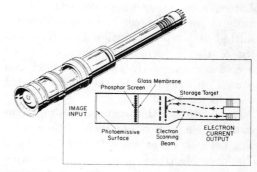

Fig. 4. Image intensifier orthicon tube.

coatings on parallel glass plates. If an image is focused on the photoconductive layer, it becomes conductive, permitting the electric field to appear across the phosphor with a resulting emission of a brighter image.

MYRON W. KLEIN

Cross-references: *Image Orthicon, Solid-State Displays, Vidicon*

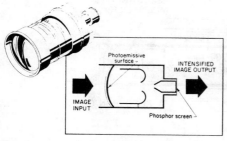

Fig. 2. Demagnified image intensifier tube.

IMAGE ORTHICON

The image orthicon is a television camera tube used to convert an optical image into a time-varying electrical signal. Owing to its fast response, high resolution capability, and ability to handle a wide range of light levels, it has become one of the most widely used camera tubes in television broadcasting and has also found educational and scientific applications. It is much more sensitive than the earlier iconoscope (*q.v.*) owing to the use of a low velocity scanning beam, a more efficient photocathode, secondary-emission gain at the target, and electron-multiplication of the output signal. In some applications, where less emphasis is placed on high sensitivity, the simpler vidicon (*q.v.*) has found wider acceptance than the image orthicon.

A schematic diagram of the image orthicon is shown in Fig. 1, and its principles of operation are as follows: Light from the scene to be televised is imaged onto the photocathode, a photoemissive surface on the inside of the tube face. The photoelectrons, emitted at a rate proportional to the intensity of the incident light, are accelerated toward the target by an electric field and focused on the target by the magnetic field of the focusing coil.

The target is a thin semiconducting membrane, which in most commercial tubes consists of a sheet of glass 0.0002 in. thick. The photoelectrons strike the target with sufficient energy (about 400 ev) to eject several secondary electrons for each incident electron. These secondaries are collected by a fine-mesh metal screen mounted close to the target and at slightly higher potential. On the target, therefore, a pattern of positive charges results which is a replica of the optical image projected onto the photocathode. Owing to secondary-emission gain, the total charge stored on the target is greater than that released from the photocathode.

While this charge pattern accumulates on one side of the target, a finely focused electron beam periodically scans the opposite side. The target is sufficiently conductive for these charges to neutralize each other in the time between successive scans, which in U. S. commercial television is $\frac{1}{30}$ sec. Its lateral resistance is high enough so that the definition of the stored charge image does not deteriorate between scans.

The scanning-beam electrons are emitted by the cathode of the electron gun at zero potential and are accelerated to about 200 v. After leaving the defining aperture of the gun, the electrons travel through a magnetic field. This is the resultant of the focusing field and of the time-varying horizontal and vertical transverse fields produced by the deflection yoke which cause the beam to scan the target.

As the beam electrons approach the target, they are decelerated to cathode potential. Electrons are able to land on each point of the target until the positive charge accumulated there has been neutralized. The remaining beam electrons are reflected and, following the magnetic field, return toward the gun where they enter a five-stage secondary-emission multiplier. Since the return beam contains the original electrons less those deposited on the target, it is amplitude-modulated (with inverted polarity) in accordance with the charge pattern which it has just erased.

The multiplier yields a gain of several hundred without adding appreciable noise to the signal. This process is important even

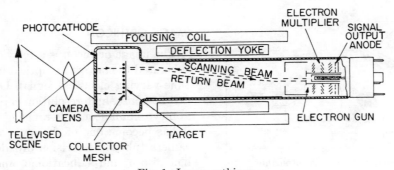

Fig. 1. Image orthicon.

at high light intensities, but it is indispensable for low-light operation at which the signal level of the return beam is below the noise level of the camera amplifier.

With increasing illumination, the amount of charge stored on the target at first increases linearly, but eventually saturates when the high-light areas reach collector-mesh potential. However, good picture contrast is maintained even under very high illumination, owing to scattering of secondary electrons from areas corresponding to the brighter portions of the scene to neighboring areas which correspond to less bright regions. Consequently, the image orthicon can handle a very wide range of light levels.

Image orthicons are capable of resolution better than 1000 television lines at high lights and can also give images of useful quality with photocathode illuminations down to 10^{-4} ft-candles or less.

Semitransparent photocathodes with quantum efficiencies up to 30 per cent in the blue spectral region and good efficiencies over the entire visible light range are commonly made.

The orthicon differs from the image orthicon shown in Fig. 1 by not having a photocathode-to-target image section nor an electron multiplier and therefore the orthicon is less sensitive. Its target consists of a thin insulating element with a transparent conducting signal plate on the lens side and a closely-spaced fine dot pattern of photoemissive elements on the scanning beam side. The collector mesh lies next to this mosaic and operates at a few volts positive with respect to the gun cathode. It serves to collect the photoelectrons emitted by the light image formed upon the target mosaic and to limit the potential to which the mosaic can charge. The scanning beam successively discharges the mosaic elements and thus produces a modulated current in the signal-plate lead.

The image-intensifier orthicon used for ultra-low light levels consists of an image orthicon to which a one- or more-stage image brightness intensifier has been added before the photocathode, all within a single envelope.

STEFAN A. OCHS AND JOHN E. RUEDY

Cross-references: *Cathode-Ray Tubes (Display), Iconoscope, Image Intensifiers, Photoelectric Emission, Photomultiplier, Secondary Emission, Television*

IMPEDANCE MEASUREMENTS

Impedance is the ratio of voltage to current. In general, it is a ratio between algebraic expressions, such as Laplace transforms, which are applicable to both periodic and transient waveforms. Impedance measurement with transient signals is possible, but the interpretation of results is likely to be difficult, and actual resistors, capacitors, and inductors may not behave as their ideal counterparts over the frequency range included in the signal. Therefore it is usual to measure impedance with sinusoidal signals, one frequency at a time.

A sinusoidal voltage or current is commonly visualized as the projection of a rotating vector on a fixed axis. The ratio between voltage and current is then a stationary vector whose magnitude, or length, is the ratio of voltage magnitude to current magnitude, and whose angle, or direction, is the difference between the phase angles of the voltage and current vectors.

The impedance at a particular frequency is often described in terms of its equivalent series or parallel combination of resistance and reactance (inductance or capacitance). Either the series or parallel equivalent circuit is equally useful at the specified frequency; neither is necessarily valid at any other frequency. Impedance Z, resistance R, and reactance X, can be replaced by their reciprocals—admittance Y, conductance G, and susceptance B. An impedance can also be described by one of the two elements in the series or parallel equivalent circuit together with the value of dissipation factor D, or storage factor Q; D is the cotangent of the impedance angle,

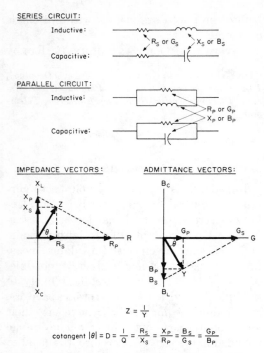

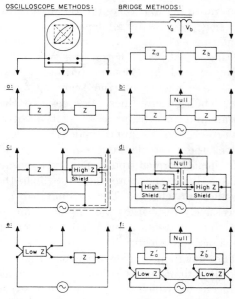

Fig. 1. Equivalent series and parallel circuits.

and Q is its tangent. Therefore D is always equal to $1/Q$. The relationships between these quantities are shown in Fig. 1.

The measurement of an unknown impedance is usually accomplished by connecting it in series with a known impedance, or standard. The vector voltage ratio is then equal to the vector impedance ratio. Where high accuracy is not required, the voltages can be compared by an elliptical pattern on an oscilloscope (Fig. 2a). For more accurate measurements, a bridge circuit is used, in which the pair of impedances is connected in parallel with a pair of known impedances or a tapped transformer winding, and adjusted for a null (Fig. 2b). When there is no voltage at the null indicator, the two voltage ratios are precisely equal, allowing accurate calculation of the unknown impedance.

Stray capacitance or leakage resistance in parallel with a high impedance may need to be controlled, as can be done by "three-terminal" construction, in which the high-impedance element is built into a metal

case or shield, from which both of its terminals are insulated. External stray impedance between the two high-impedance terminals can then be eliminated by shielding one terminal and lead from the other. Care must be taken to minimize the effect of the capacitance and leakage from each terminal to the shield. If the other impedance in series has a much lower value than the three-terminal impedance, the effect of impedance to the shield can be greatly reduced by the shield connection in Fig. 2c. In the bridge method, two three-terminal impedances can be compared (Fig. 2d) if the other two bridge arms have a much lower impedance, or if a transformer ratio is used.

The resistance of the terminals and leads in series with a low impedance may be too large to ignore. Low-impedance elements are therefore often constructed with four terminals—one pair for current input and the other pair for voltage measurement, so that the ratio of voltage to current will not be affected by external series resistances. If the other impedance in series has a much higher value than the four-terminal impedance, the effect of terminal and lead resistances will be greatly reduced by the circuit of

Fig. 2. Impedance measurement circuits.

Fig. 2e. If both the standard and the unknown are low-value four-terminal impedances, they can be connected in series and their voltages compared in a Kelvin bridge circuit (Fig. 2f) or by means of isolation transformers.

The concept of impedance as a fixed parameter applies only to a linear circuit element—that is, one in which a voltage change is accompanied by an exactly proportional change in current. Many practical devices, such as iron-core inductors and electrolytic capacitors, are not truly linear. In this case an impedance measurement must be accompanied by a specification of the voltage or current at which it is measured. A nonlinear element also generates harmonics of the applied frequency. If the voltage is sinusoidal, the current contains harmonics; if the current is sinusoidal, the voltage waveform is distorted. The impedance is then defined as the ratio between the fundamental frequency components of the voltage and current.

Merle L. Morgan

Cross-references: *Bridges, Coils, Condensers, Microwave Measurements, Resistors, Standards, Standing-Wave Ratio*

INDICATING INSTRUMENTS

Most indicating instruments measure an electrical current and the indication is observed by noting the position of a pointer in relation to a calibrated scale. Movement of the pointer is obtained by forces acting upon conductors carrying current in a magnetic field in the moving-coil permanent-magnet type of dc instrument and the electrodynamometer ac and dc instrument. A common type of ac instrument, called the moving iron vane, depends upon the action of a movable iron vane with a magnetic field for the motion of the pointer.

The *Moving-Coil Permanent-Magnet Instrument* (Fig. 1) measures small direct currents. It can be supplied with various components, converters, and transducers to enable it to indicate many electrical and mechanical quantities. The magnetic field is produced by a permanent magnet and the conductors are many turns of wire wound on a moving coil suspended in the air gap of the magnet by pivots and jewels. Torque developed in the moving coil is

$$T = \frac{B2RLIN}{10} = \frac{BAIN}{10}$$

where T = torque (dyne-cm)
   B = flux density (lines/cm²) in air gap
   A = coil area (cm²)
   I = moving-coil current (amp)
   N = turns of wire in moving coil.

Direct current supplied to the moving coil produces a torque that turns the moving coil. The deflection of the moving coil is opposed by spiral springs and a position of equilibrium is reached. The pointer, attached to the moving coil, assumes a definite position with respect to the scale, which can be calibrated in terms of the moving-coil current. Deflection of the pointer or indication is proportional to the average value of the direct current.

Response time and damping of the moving system is controlled by the torque, inertia, flux, moving-coil circuit resistance, and conducting frame on which the moving coil is wound.

Shunting the moving coil with a low resistance (shunt) makes it possible to measure higher currents. Voltage is meas-

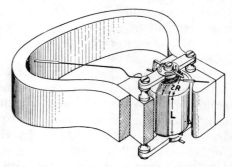

Fig. 1. Permanent magnet moving-coil mechanism. (Courtesy Daystrom Inc., Weston Instruments Division.)

ured by connecting resistance in series with the moving coil so as to produce full-scale current with full-scale voltage applied to the instrument.

Measurement of alternating voltages and currents is made by converting or rectifying them to direct current to be measured by the dc instrument. Alternating current is passed through a wire to which a thermocouple is attached making thermal contact. The current heats the wire and the thermocouple develops a dc voltage causing a moving coil to deflect. The indication is proportional to the square of the ac input and thus indicates the rms value of the alternating current. Frequency errors are usually a function of thermocouple construction and resistors if used. By proper design it is possible to use thermocouples to measure in the megacycle range.

Copper oxide, germanium and silicon rectifiers are also used to convert to a direct current. The instrument responds to the average value of the rectified current but is usually calibrated in terms of the rms value of a sine wave and is accurate only when measuring sinusoidal sine wave currents and voltages. The frequency range is limited by capacity effects and the switching time of the rectifier. Rectifier instruments are usually not designed for accurate use beyond the rf range.

Direct-current instruments are connected to many other transducers to measure other quantities. Among a few are thermocouples and resistance bulbs to measure temperature; photocells to measure light; generators to measure revolutions per minute; networks to measure frequency; and Hall elements to measure current and power.

The *Electrodynamic Instrument* has a moving element as above, with the magnet structure replaced by one or two fixed coils usually without an iron circuit (air-core field circuit). Torque is produced by the action between the flux in the moving and field coils and is proportional to the instantaneous product of the current in each coil.

All coils are connected in series to measure current. Currents above 500 ma usually require a shunt across the moving coil. Voltages are measured by winding the coils with many turns of fine wire and connecting them in series with a fixed resistor. In all cases the response is proportional to the current squared and thus indicates the rms value.

The instrument measures watts in a load when the field-coil circuit is connected in series with a load and the moving coil circuit is across the load. Deflection is proportional to $EI \cos \theta$ where E and I are load voltage and current and θ is the angle between them.

Two moving coils on a common staff and two field-coil systems are used to make a two-element wattmeter to measure polyphase power with one instrument. Two moving coils at right angles operating in one field-coil system are used to measure the ratio of currents in each moving coil. With the proper circuit arrangement this instrument can be made to measure power factor.

Damping is usually provided by a vane on the moving element. The vane can be confined in a chamber to provide air damping or be placed between the poles of a permanent magnet to provide magnetic damping.

This instrument is usually designed for dc and 25–125 cps. It is used as a basic transfer instrument between dc and ac. Frequency compensation to higher frequencies such 2500 cps is usually possible. These instruments require a great deal more power to operate than the dc instrument. The coils may consume up to 1 w with several watts in the series resistor or shunt.

The *Moving Iron Vane Instrument* consists of a magnetic vane free to rotate in an electromagnetic field produced by a fixed coil. Torque spring, pointer, and pivots complete the moving element. The electrical torque opposed by the spring is produced by the reaction between the moving iron vane and the electromagnetic field or by repulsion between the moving iron vane and a fixed iron vane placed in the field. Air or magnetic damping is provided as in the electrodynamic instrument.

A field coil of few turns carries the full current for ammeters, whereas many turns and series resistance are used for the voltmeter. Torque is proportional to current squared and the rms value of the current is measured and indicated.

Frequency range is usually 25–125 cps with frequency compensation possible to approximately 2500 cps. Some special designs can also be used on direct current.

Ammeters usually require up to 1 w in the field coil to produce full-scale deflection. Voltmeters require several more watts in the series resistance.

Indicating instruments are affected by external influences such as position, temperature, waveform, magnetic fields, overload, vibration, shock and other factors.

R. F. Estoppey

Cross-references: *Integrating Instruments*

INDICATOR TUBES

In the design of electronic equipment, there has been a trend toward the incorporation of visual indicating devices that can display alphabetical or numerical characters. The indicating devices employed have taken several forms including cathode-ray tubes, incandescent lamps, electroluminescent displays and neon glow tubes.

Cathode-ray tube applications have been limited to rather specialized computer readout displays in which alphanumeric information is incorporated as part of a larger display requirement.

Incandescent lamps and neon glow tubes are most often utilized as simple "on-off" indicators. However, in some electronic equipment such as counting instruments, a vertical array of ten such devices is used to provide a decimal readout corresponding to the pulse information that the instrument accumulates. In addition, incandescent lamps and neon glow tubes can be positioned in matrix array to provide a representation of numerals, letters, or other characters by selective excitation.

Electroluminescent displays also operate on the matrix principle. Here, a layer of phosphor material is sandwiched between a pair of conductive plates, one of which is transparent. The phosphor emits light and can be viewed when an alternating potential is applied between the conductive plates. By segmenting the phosphor layer or the conductive plates, individual areas can be illuminated to form alphabetical or numerical characters.

Most of the devices mentioned require somewhat complex decoding circuitry or must be interpreted with regard to position by the observer. One device which eliminates these considerations is a cold-cathode glow tube known as the NIXIE® tube. Figure 1 shows the appearance of tubes of this type. These devices operate directly from decimal logic and provide an in-line presentation of numerals and alphabetical characters.

In the NIXIE indicator tube design, metallic cathode electrodes are mounted within a transparent glass envelope. Each of the cathodes is formed in the shape of numerals or other characters, depending upon the readout requirements. The stack of cathode electrodes is partially enclosed by a common anode electrode which is in the shape of a cup. Electrical connections to the cathodes and anode are made by means

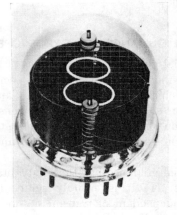

Fig. 1.

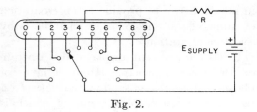

Fig. 2.

of leads attached to pins which are sealed in the base of the tube.

The entire tube envelope is filled with an inert ionizable gas of a type capable of providing cathode glow such as neon, argon, or combinations thereof. When the required potential is connected between the anode and the selected cathode, a sheath of gas close to and surrounding the cathode glows in the shape of the corresponding character.

A simple representation of the driver circuitry is shown in Fig. 2. Here, a switch is used to select the desired character and a current limiting resistor in the common anode controls the ionization within the tube.

R. J. BRADY AND R. A. GREEN

Cross-references: *Cathode-Ray Tubes (Display), Cold-Cathode Tubes, Computer Printout and Reading, Electrostatic Printing, Fluorescent Lights, Solid-State Displays*

INDUCTANCE: see COILS

INDUCTION HEATING: see HEATING (ELECTRONIC)

INERTIAL GUIDANCE AND GYROSCOPE

Inertial guidance is the process of directing the movements of a craft, a rocket, or other vehicle, from one point to another, with the aid of apparatus that senses acceleration of the craft and integrates acceleration to determine velocity and distance.

Inertial guidance has these advantageous features: (1) it is entirely self-contained, being independent of transmission or reception of any form of radiant energy; (2) it is generally applicable with no inherent limitations as to speed, maneuvers, or flight path of the vehicle being guided; and (3) potential accuracy is limited ultimately only by the quality of the instrumentation, since the laws on which the operation is based (Newton's laws of motion) are exact.

The inertial method of guidance had its first practical application, in a rudimentary form, in the German V2 (A4) rocket missiles near the end of World War II. Since that time large-scale development has been carried on in the United States and elsewhere, resulting not only in greatly improved forms of rocket-guidance systems but also in systems applicable to ships, aircraft, and land vehicles.

In Fig. 1 are indicated the elements of a representative inertial-guidance apparatus. A set of three gyros (more properly, *gyroscopes*) and a set of three accelerometers are provided, in fixed relation to each other to form a stable element. The stable element is supported in gimbals, servo-controlled from the gyros, so that the stable element defines a space-fixed framework of reference, independent from any vehicle maneuvers. The complex is called a stable platform. Each accelerometer has associated with it a pair of integrators, and a computer is provided. (The y channel, which is substantially identical to the x channel, is omitted for clarity.)

Application of the system to ballistic-missile guidance is outlined below, together with the modifications required for navigation of aircraft and ships. For simplicity the earth is assumed to be truly spherical and nonrotating. The actual state of affairs necessitates various corrections but does not affect the principles of operation.

Ballistic Missile Guidance

The guidance system has two functions. One is to steer the missile and control its attitude in the manner of an autopilot—to suppress rolling, yawing and pitching. The other function is to determine the instantaneous velocity of the missile, so that the computer can compute the miss distance if the actual trajectory were to be followed, and adjust the cutoff time to make the miss distance zero.

The gyros aid in both functions. First, the means of missile-attitude control (swiveling rocket engines, movable control vanes, etc.) are controlled from the platform gimbal pickoffs. A clockdriven mechanism rotates the pitch gimbal pickoff according to the prescribed schedule. Second, the gyros serve to establish a definite spatial orientation for the acceleration-sensing operations.

If we consider only the accelerometers in the x–z plane (guidance plane), and neglect gravity, the first time integrals of sensed acceleration components are $\dot{x}$, $\dot{z}$, which are utilized by the computer as described.

However, gravity can by no means be neglected. Acceleration (change of velocity) of the missile relative to the earth cannot be distinguished by the accelerometers from the acceleration of gravity g. Thus, the z-axis accelerometer would indicate a spuri-

ous upward $\ddot{z}$ equal to g, unless compensation were made. Similarly, upon movement of the missile laterally from the launching-pad vertical, a component of g appears at the x-axis accelerometer, and a spurious velocity signal would result.

The components of g appearing at the accelerometers are functions of the distances x, z of the stable platform, laterally and vertically, from the takeoff point. These distances are determined by double integration of accelerations along the x and z axes as described, and biases proportional to the computed components are applied to the accelerometers, so as to "blind" them, in effect, to the g components.

In the case of the lateral g-compensation channels, a condition of negative feedback exists, such that error owing to faulty acceleration sensing or computation results in bounded, rather than accumulative, errors in the computed lateral velocity and distance values. Errors in these channels are propagated in sinusoidal form, the period of oscil-

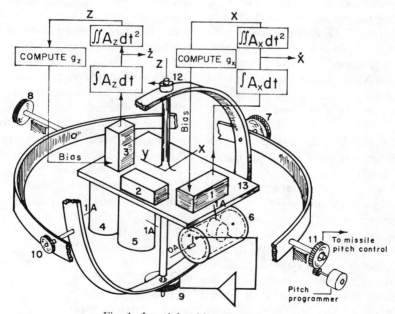

Fig. 1. Inertial guidance apparatus.

1, 2, 3	Accelerometers sensing along x,y,z axes
4, 5, 6	Gyros stabilizing about x,y,z axes
7, 8, 9	Gimbal servo motors, controlled from gyros
10, 11, 12	Gimbal angle pickoffs
13	Stable element

lation being $T = 2\pi \ (R/g)^{1/2}$ where R is earth radius. The value of T at the earth's surface is about 84 min.

In the case of the vertical channel a condition of positive feedback exists, and the g-compensation is subject to divergent error. In the present state of the art, double integration of vertical acceleration to find height is practicable only as a short-term process—long enough to guide a rocket but not long enough to provide an "inertial altimeter" for aircraft. But double integration of *lateral* acceleration yields a practical long-term method of determining distance or position, because of the non-accumulative nature of the error buildup, so far as spurious accelerations are concerned. It must be noted, however, that gyro error (drift) can result in accumulative errors that cannot be bounded without reference to sources of information exterior to the inertial system.

Navigation of Ships and Aircraft

In navigation, guidance, like propulsion, is a continuing process, from start to finish, rather than a process of setting initial conditions. The desired output from the navigation system is position, rather than velocity, and for convenience position should be read out in a spherical (e.g., latitude-longitude ϕ, λ) rather than a Cartesian coordinate system.

Accordingly, an inertial navigator computer includes means for dividing the lateral velocity components $\dot{x}$, $\dot{y}$, by R, and $R \cos \phi$, to determine components of angular velocities about the center of the earth. These terms are processed as latitude and longitude rates, $\dot{\phi}$, $\dot{\lambda}$, and integrated to yield ϕ, λ.

In many aircraft and marine inertial navigators, control torques are applied to the gyros (from the computer) so as to keep the stable element level at all times, instead of allowing the stable element to preserve the spatial orientation it had at the takeoff point. In such case, and with the platform disposed with the outer gimbal axis along the longitudinal axis of the craft,

steering signals can be taken from the z-axis gimbal pickoff. The z-axis accelerometer-integrator channel can be omitted in such level-platform systems.

Gyroscopes ("Gyros")

A gyro is a device which makes use of the property of a suitably supported, rapidly spinning inertial rotor, of resisting change from any predetermined direction in space, under the influence of inevitable disturbing torques. Gyros for inertial guidance are classified as single-axis and double-axis types.

In Fig. 1 single-axis gyros are shown; more particularly gyros of the damped or so-called "rate integrating" type. Referring to the gyro 6, the rotor is mounted in a (cylindrical) gimbal for one degree of freedom about a so-called output axis (OA). The gimbal is damped by being submerged in viscous liquid in a closely-surrounding case. Deflection of the support about the input or stabilizing axis 1A (the z axis, for this particular gyro) results in a proportional OA deflection of the gimbal. An OA pickoff detects such deflection and, through a servo controller, causes servo motor 9 to drive the platform gimbal in a sense to nullify the OA deflection and hence the 1A deflection. The other gyros similarly control motors 7 and 8.

One kind of two-axis gyro includes a spherical rotor universally supported as by a gas-lubricated or electrostatically supported bearing, and driven as an eddy-current induction motor. A pickoff system detects angular deflection of the gyro case (attached to the stable element) relative to the rotor spin axis, about two quadrature axes, and controls the platform gimbal servo motors to nullify the deflection. A three-axis platform requires only two such gyros.

Accelerometers

Accelerometers for use in inertial guidance systems, especially those utilizing a digital computer, are highly specialized devices. One reason lies in the extreme accuracy requirements; another in the practical necessity for the accelerometer to produce a signal in the form of a frequency or pulse train, so that integration can be effected by algebraically summing cycles or pulses. Many varieties of so-called integrating accelerometers or "velocity meters" exist. One form makes use of a miniature single-axis gyro, mounted for input-axis freedom relative to the stable element and unbalanced along the spin axis. Acceleration in the direction of the input axis results in a proportional output-axis precession torque and hence a proportional input-axis precession rate. A pulse generator on the input axis then gives N pulses per second, per unit of acceleration, as is desired.

J. M. SLATER

Cross-references: *Missile Guidance, Navigation and Navigational Systems, Transducers*

INFORMATION THEORY

A very considerable amount of science and technology was developed relative to the transmission and processing of messages before it became clear how to measure information content, how to define the limits of capacity of a communication channel, and what were the basic laws of a quantitative science of information.

This science, information theory, is based largely on the work of C. E. Shannon, whose papers published in 1948 form the principal classical reference to the subject. Fundamental to this work is the application of probability theory to communication concepts and especially the results based on the concept of entropy measure of information.

Considered abstractly, information is stored or communicated in terms of a representation (such as written symbols, sounds, electrical waveforms, etc.), and the operation of a communication system requires transformations from one representation to another (and usually back again).

A transformation is information-lossless if it is reversible; i.e., if an inverse transformation exists that exactly restores the original representation. Otherwise there is a loss of information in the transformation. The types of transformation of most interest in information theory are called codes.

Thus a theoretical model of a communication system is assumed to consist of a series arrangement of subsystems called respectively message source, transmitter or encoder, channel, receiver or decoder, message destination.

The capacity of a system to store or communicate information depends essentially upon the number of distinguishable states that can be used to represent distinguishable messages. For a system having n distinguishable states, the information capacity was defined by R. V. L. Hartley as $\log n$. Similarly, for a discrete noiseless communication channel which can transmit sequences of symbols of different durations, the channel capacity was defined by C. E. Shannon as

$$C = \lim_{T \to \infty} \log n(T)/T$$

where $n(T)$ denotes the number of permissible sequences of duration T.

The source is assumed to consist of a stationary stochastic process which generates symbols in some representation. Any sequence S of N symbols has a probability $p(S)$, and we define the entropy measure for S by

$$H_N = -\sum_S p(S) \log_2 p(S)$$

The entropy per symbol is then defined by

$$H = \lim_{N \to \infty} \frac{H_N}{N}$$

The properties of the entropy function can be presented as a part of probability theory without the context of a message source. In probability theory a complete system of events $A_1, A_2, \cdots A_n$ means a set of events such that one and only one of them must occur at each trial. We postulate probability numbers $p(i)$ each between 0 and 1 such that

$$\sum_{i=1}^{n} p(i) = 1$$

Then the entropy of this probability distribution is measured by the quantity

$$H(A) = -\sum_{i=1}^{n} p(i) \log_2 p(i)$$

The entropy is a maximum in case

$$p(i) = \frac{1}{n}, \quad \text{for all } i$$

Further, we may have two systems of events A and B and we may measure the entropy in the joint occurrence of pairs of events $A_i B_j$ with probabilities $p(ij)$. Then

$$H(AB) = -\sum_{ij} p(ij) \log_2 p(ij)$$

By use of the expression for conditional probability

$$p_i(j) = \frac{p(ij)}{p(i)}$$

we can write

$$-H(AB) = \sum_{ij} p(i)p_i(j)[\log p(i) + \log p_i(j)]$$

$$= \sum_i p(i) \log p(i) \sum_j p_i(j)$$

$$+ \sum_i p(i) \sum_j p_i(j) \log p_i(j)$$

$$= -H(A) - \sum_i p(i)H_i(B)$$

where $H_i(B)$ denotes the conditional entropy of B given that a particular A_i has occurred.

By defining the quantity

$$H_A(B) = \sum_i p(i)H_i(B)$$

we can write

$$H(AB) = H(A) + H_A(B)$$

Similarly $H(AB) = H(B) + H_B(A)$.

The entropy measure satisfies certain uniqueness properties that enhance its basic significance. Thus it has been proved that, if a function $H(p_1, p_2, \cdots p_n)$ is defined for all non-negative values of p_k, where

$$\sum_{k=1}^{n} p_k = 1$$

and if for any n this function is continuous with respect to all its arguments, and if it has the properties 1, 2, and 3, below, then it is necessarily of the form

$$H(p_1, p_2, \cdots p_n) = -\lambda \sum_{k=1}^{n} p_k \log p_k$$

where λ is a positive constant. The choice of λ amounts to a choice of a logarithmic base and the base 2 is conventionally chosen. The three properties referred to are:

(1) For given n and for $\sum_{i=1}^{n} p_i = 1$, the function $H(p_1, \cdots p_n)$ takes its largest value for $p_i = 1/n$, $(i = 1, 2, \cdots n)$.

(2) $H(AB) = H(A) + H_A(B)$

(3) Formally including messages of zero probability does not affect the value of entropy; i.e., if $p_{n+1} = 0$, then

$$H(p_1, p_2, \cdots p_n, 0) = H(p_1, p_2, \cdots p_n)$$

When the entropy is less than its maximum value, it is often convenient to refer to the redundancy, defined by the expression

$$1 - \frac{H}{H_{max}}$$

Shannon has proved that, with sufficiently large storage capacity in an encoding device, it is possible to encode the messages so as to transmit as near the average rate C/H symbols per unit time as we please, but it is not possible to transmit at a greater rate.

An example of a way to approach the maximum rate is given by the following method of coding. Consider the possible sequences of N symbols from the source and arrange the probabilities p_i in decreasing order

$$p_1 \; p_2 \; p_3 \; \cdots \; p_s$$

Let

$$P_i = \sum_{j=1}^{i} p_j$$

The ith message is encoded by expanding P_i as a binary fraction and using only as many significant places as are required to distinguish each message from other messages. Thus P_{i-1} differs from P_i by p_i and a difference shows in one or more of the first t_i places if

$$t_i \geq \log_2 1/p_i$$

Further it is sufficient to have

$$t_i < 1 + \log_2 1/p_i$$

The average length of the encoded message is

$$E(t) = \sum_i p_i t_i$$

Hence

$$\sum_i p_i \log_2 1/p_i \leq E(t) < 1 + \sum_i p_i \log_2 1/p_i$$

This will approach the maximum rate per symbol as $N \to \infty$.

When there is noise in the channel, the transmitted signal sequence x and the received signal sequence y must be distinguished in the analysis. Let the joint probability of x and y be $p(x,y)$ and the conditional probability of x given y be $p_y(x)$. Then, from the relation

$$\log p(x,y) = \log p(y) + \log p_y(x)$$

joint and conditional entropy measures are defined by

$$J(x,y) = -\sum_{x,y} p(x,y) \log p(x,y)$$

$$= -\sum p(x,y) \log p(y) - \sum p(x,y) \log p_y(x)$$

$$= J(y) + J_y(x)$$

and in the limit of infinitely long sequences

$$H(x,y) = H(y) + H_y(x)$$

The conditional entropy $H_y(x)$ is called the equivocation and measures the information lost through the noise effect.

The actual rate of transmission of information in the noisy channel is thus defined as

$$R = H(x) - H_y(x)$$

and the channel capacity is the maximum value of R for all possible message sources.

Continuous Signal Processes

In the case of continuous signal processes in the presence of noise the information content remains finite and the information (entropy) measure J of a set of continuous variables is defined by

$$J = -\int f(x) \log f(x) \, dx$$

where $f(x)$ is the probability density function. The value of J changes with change of coordinates affecting the density function. However, the transmission rate R is invariant to a change of coordinates:

$$R = H(x) - H_y(x)$$

$$= \lim_{T \to \infty} \frac{1}{T} \left\{ -\int f(x) \log f(x) \, dx \right.$$

$$\left. + \iint f(x,y) \log \frac{f(x,y)}{f(y)} \, dx dy \right\}$$

$$= \lim_{T \to \infty} \frac{1}{T} \iint f(x,y) \log \left[\frac{f(x,y)}{f(x)f(y)} \right] dx dy$$

The entropy measure of a discrete source is a maximum if all symbols are equally probable. However, the continuous distribution with maximum entropy for a given standard deviation is the normal distribution. For if

$$H = -\int f(x) \log f(x) \, dx$$

is maximized subject to

$$\int f(x) \, dx = 1$$

$$\int x f(x) \, dx = 0$$

$$\int x^2 f(x) \, dx = \sigma^2$$

The result is

$$f(x) = \frac{1}{\sqrt{2\pi\sigma^2}}\, e^{-x^2/2\sigma^2}$$

and

$$H = \log_2 \sqrt{2\pi e\sigma^2}$$

Expressions for channel capacity have been derived for certain cases of a noisy channel. In the case of a channel limited to bandwidth W, with a signal source limited by a maximum average power S, and with band-limited white noise of power N, the channel capacity is

$$C = W \log_2 \left(1 + \frac{S}{N}\right)$$

ROBERT P. COLEMAN

Cross-references: *Character Recognition, Congestion and Waiting Systems, Decision and Game Theory, Linear Programming, Markov Processes, Monte Carlo Method, Probability, Random Processes, Sampling Theorem, Signal Detection, Statistical Communication Theory, Transmission Reliability*

INFRARED

The infrared region is that portion of the electromagnetic spectrum between the long-wavelength sensitivity limit of the human eye and the short-wavelength limit of the microwave region. Thus the infrared occupies the wavelength band between approximately $0.8\,\mu$ ($1\,\mu = 10^{-4}$ cm) and about 1 mm.

The utility of the infrared spectral region stems from two major physical phenomena. First, the energy levels that result from the molecular structure of matter coincide with the photon energy in the infrared region of the spectrum, resulting in strong interactions between the two. Thus the transmission, emission, and scattering of infrared radiation can serve as a probe of the structure, composition and identity of physical, chemical, and biological matter. Second, every physical object emits thermal radiation as a consequence of the electronic structure of matter, the radiation intensity being a rapidly increasing function of the object's temperature. Even for source temperatures as high as 5000°K the predominant wavelength region for this thermal emission is in the infrared portion of the electromagnetic spectrum, and at temperatures below 1000°K more than 90 per cent of this energy resides there.

The design of infrared detection systems spans the technologies of optics, solid state physics, mechanics, and electronics. In addition, military and space applications often involve a host of other factors related to other disciplines such as geophysics, aerodynamics, and propulsion.

Sources. Objects are observed at a distance either by their self emission or by scattered radiation from a celestial, atmospheric, or local source. Because of the temperature-thermal radiation relationship many more objects can be observed passively (viz., by self emission) in the infrared than in the visible. The concept of a black body or perfect absorber is very useful in discussing thermal radiation. The spectral energy distribution of blackbody radiation is given by Planck's Law, the derivation of which is fundamental to modern quantum theory:

$$W_\lambda = \frac{3.740 \times 10^4}{\lambda^5 \left[\exp\left(\frac{1.4385}{\lambda T}\right) - 1 \right]}\ \text{w cm}^{-2}\ \text{micron}^{-1}$$

where W_λ is the spectral radiant emittance of the blackbody radiated into a hemisphere, λ is expressed in microns, and T in deg K.

The emissivity of a physical material is defined as the ratio of its radiant emittance to that of a blackbody at a specific wavelength.

Figure 1 exhibits the emissivity (or equivalently, by Kirchoff's law, the absorptivity) of typical materials as a function of wavelength and temperature.

Pure metallic surfaces exhibit a decrease in emissivity with wavelength. Many semiconductors show reversals of this behavior. Gases exhibit a rapid variation of emissivity with wavelength characteristic of their molecular vibration-rotation constants.

Laboratory infrared sources consist principally of high-temperature lamps or arcs. Temperature-variable cavity type blackbody sources are also widely available for sources up to 1000°K.

For low-temperature objects detected by scattered light, the reflectivity determines the observed spectrum. For all materials the sum of reflectivity, absorptivity, and transmissivity is unity. For metals of any appreciable thickness, the transmissivity vanishes, so that reflectivity is equal to one minus the absorptivity (emissivity). For gases, the reflectivity is negligible so that the absorptivity is one minus the transmissivity. In the infrared, out to at least 10 μ, the sun appears as a 5700°K blackbody source. Non-selective reflectors such as clouds, earth, moon, etc., mirror this spectrum (the average reflectivity is then designated the albedo and is approximately 50–80 per cent, 35 per cent and 7 per cent for these bodies, respectively) in the near infrared (less than 5 μ) but have superimposed on their spectrum the blackbody radiation from their much lower temperature thermal emission.

For objects at very high temperature or in the case of convectively isolated bodies, such as satellites or space vehicles, radiation exchange is the dominant factor in determining thermal equilibrium. In this case the spectral emissivity is a crucial parameter and surface coatings can be utilized to modify the equilibrium temperature radically.

In the case of infrared detection problems the object of interest, or target, is normally immersed in an ambient background flux. Improvement in target to background ratios (viz., contrast) can be made by taking advantage of spectral and spatial differences between the two. The former is achieved by filters or multiple detectors and colorimetric classification. The latter is achieved by space filtering, the two-dimensional analog of electronic filtering. This is accomplished by introducing an aperture function which discriminates against the background flux (usually containing low space gradients) in

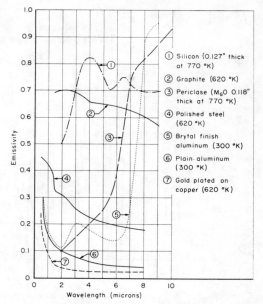

Fig. 1. Emissivity as a function of wavelength for various materials.

favor of the target (usually containing very high space gradients such as a point source).

Transmission of Atmosphere and Optical Media. The infrared flux emanating from a "target" and its surroundings is modified by the intervening atmospheric path to the detector. In addition, optical elements used to collect and focus the radiation on the detector further modify these signals.

By virtue of the constituent gases and aerosol particles present in the "clear" atmosphere the atmosphere attenuates infrared radiation by absorption and scattering. Clouds, fog, and precipitation introduce considerably more obscuration, and infrared detection techniques, much like visual techniques, consequently suffer from not being "all-weather."

The three major gaseous constituents of the clear atmosphere whose infrared absorption properties dominate over gases with much greater abundance are water vapor, carbon dioxide and ozone. In addition the infrared spectrum of some minor constituents is of interest principally in studies of atmospheric chemistry utilizing infrared

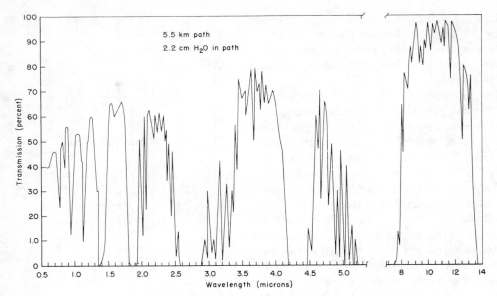

Fig. 2. Atmospheric transmission.

techniques as a probe (viz., nitrous oxide, carbon monoxide, methane, etc.). The infrared absorption properties of the earth's atmosphere are of profound significance in determining the heat budget of the earth; that is, the relative radiation transfer involved in the fundamental solar-terrestrial heat exchange via the intervening atmosphere.

Figure 2 exhibits the infrared transmission of the atmosphere for a 5.5-km horizontal path at sea level. The water vapor content of the path was 2.2 precipitable centimeters (the equivalent thickness of path if all the water vapor was liquified at 1 atm pressure). The spectral regions of relatively high transmission are known as "windows" and infrared detection over long paths is limited to their exploitation. Such cases, as for example when a lead sulfide detection element is filtered by germanium to reduce sunlit backgrounds and exploit the 1.9 to 2.7 micron window, can be treated by phenomenological formulas that exhibit a logarithmic dependence of the window transmission upon the precipitable water content. Attenuation at the peaks within the windows is due to aerosol scattering; the equivalent phenomenon in the "visible window" is referred to as

the visibility. The variation in the aerosol scattering coefficient with wavelength is very complex in the infrared owing to the comparable size in wavelength and particle size as well as the absorption occurring in the liquid water component of the aerosol particles.

In the design of infrared instrumentation for laboratory and, especially, for field equipment, one important requirement pertains to the choice of satisfactory optical materials. In contrast to the visible region, which covers a comparatively narrow spectral range, the infrared spectrum includes a very broad wavelength range over which the optical properties of any material can be expected to vary widely. Materials are thus usually limited in their utility to the specific range of applicability—1–3 μ (near infrared), 3–6 μ (intermediate infrared), 8–13 μ (far infrared), 15 μ and beyond (the very far infrared). To avoid transmittance problems and chromatic aberrations, reflective optical systems have been used preferentially. More recently, the availability of large optical material elements of sapphire, silicon, germanium and arsenic trisulfide glass, as well as optical engineering techniques for successfully fabricating such materials in aspheric lenses, have focused attention on the exploitation of fast refractive systems.

Detection. Radiation detectors are normally classified according to the parameters of "sensitivity" and "speed of response." In the near-infrared low-noise photomultipliers are preferred. Where image-forming light is to be observed, or when the integration of long time exposure can be utilized, infrared sensitive photographic film is used. However, these techniques are limited to applications in the very near infrared. For the remainder of the near infrared, and more especially the intermediate infrared, and most recently even the far infrared, the internal photoelectric effect or photoconductivity (*q.v.*) process provides the most useful radiation detectors. For a long period film photodetectors of the lead salts, lead sulfide, lead telluride, and lead selenide have been preferred. Recent advances in semiconductor technology have provided improved crystalline materials exhibiting both intrinsic and impurity-type photoconductivity. Indium antimonide is among the most useful of the former materials, which include other intermetallic semiconductors such as indium arsenide, indium phosphide, mercury telluride, gallium arsenide, etc. The doping process of injection of small quantities of impurities permits almost a hand-tailoring process to peak the wavelength response of a detector. Germanium doped with zinc, copper, or antimony offers some of the fastest ($\tau < 10^{-8}$ secs) and most sensitive detectors available for the intermediate and far-infrared. In order to take full advantage of the sensitivity of these latter detectors, cryogenic equipment to maintain the detectors at liquid air temperature or even liquid helium temperature must be used. Various miniature cooling devices of either the Joule-Thomson or liquid refrigerant storage type are available for field use, however.

For many applications in which very high speed of response is not a primary requirement, the thermal sensors that respond to temperature changes, rather than absorbing photons, are most useful. These spectrally flat radiation detectors include the thermocouple or multielement thermopile, metal type and super-cooled bolometers, as well as the very popular and rugged thermistor (*q.v.*) bolometer.

Figure 3 contains plots of the detectivity (the signal-to-internal noise output when irradiated with 1 w of monochromatic radiation) for the most common infrared detectors, as a function of signal wavelength. (Unit electronic bandwidth and unit area of the detector surface are assumed.) Also shown on Fig. 3 is the fundamental detectivity limit set by the radiation noise or photon fluctuations in the ambient background flux which the detector "sees." This limit can be ameliorated by cooling various optical elements and field stops over a portion of the total angle of view of the detector or inherently in space or very-high-altitude environments when the ambient flux is characteristic of a much reduced temperature.

Signal Processing and Presentation. As a measurement and analysis tool infrared techniques yield information on the identity, intensity and spectral quality of a source.

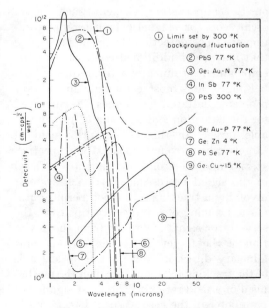

Fig. 3. Detector performance.

This is useful as a probe of laboratory matter such as in infrared spectroscopy, or indeed on atmospheric matter such as in meteorological satellites, and studies of planetary atmospheres. In these applications sensitivity in the required spectral region, fidelity of output to input, and adaptability to the measurement environment are the design objectives.

Infrared image-forming devices are utilized to paint a scene in all the many emission and reflection hues of the physical pallet. Such information is useful in radiation transfer analyses, exploration and mapping reconnaissance, and battlefield-surveillance applications. Although design objectives would invite utilization of frame time integration, as in the case of visible-TV pick-up tubes, such devices are not yet available beyond the very near infrared, owing to several technological difficulties such as the unavailability of a sufficiently high-resistivity photoconductive long-wavelength signal-storage retina. Hence the image is usually formed by the sequential scanning of single or mosaic elemental detectors. Some kind of object-space scanning device employing electro-mechanical elements is therefore employed and the image is reconstructed on a semipersistent element such as an oscilloscope or magnetic tape for presentation after postdetection electronic processing that may yield additional contrast with the employment of multicolor techniques.

Finally, and most commonly in military problems, infrared techniques are employed for the detection and tracking of an identifiable target. In this case improvement of target-to-background contrast by spectral, spatial and electronic filtering are utilized in the signal processing. Feedback systems involving a tracking servo loop permit automatic tracking of a target. In this case, the servo error signal is derived from the deviation of the target line of sight from some fiduciary direction such as the optical axis of the tracking telescope, through the mechanism of a field reticule. The most significant parameter in the case of such detection and

tracking systems is the maximum detection range. The problem can be treated as in the analogous radar range equation with the important exception that the infrared system is usually passive, and therefore there is a second-power dependence of signal level with distance to target rather than a fourth power as in the active radar case. For a high single-look probability of detection a signal-to-noise level of at least 5 is desirable. Cumulative probability of detection can be computed from the frame time and geometry. As mentioned above, infrared detection range is limited within the atmosphere by scattering and absorption processes and this factor is usually taken into account in range determination by an iterative numerical computation.

Sidney Passman

Cross-references: *Cryogenics, Photomultipliers, Pyrometers, Radar, Semiconductors, Spectroscopy (Light and Infrared)*

INTEGRATED CIRCUITS AND DEVICES

A conventional circuit is built of separate components; an integrated circuit, or device, is a small piece of solid into which several active and/or passive components have been "integrated" so that the piece performs the function of a circuit. Most integrated circuits utilize a semiconductor such as germanium or silicon, part of which performs as an active device (e.g., transistor, tunnel diode, etc.) and part of which performs as a passive device (semiconductor resistor, junction capacitance, diode, etc.). The principal advantages of integrated circuits are extremely small size, potentially low cost and potentially high reliability. The last two claims have not yet been demonstrated in practice, however, as integrated circuits, evolving mainly since 1958, are still mostly in the laboratory stage.

Two different approaches have been followed in terms of the fabrication techniques employed, one centering on active-device techniques used for building transistors, the other centering on passive-device techniques used in fabrication of resistors and capacitors. The application of these techniques to the integration of a simple circuit is shown in Fig. 1. The circuit is a flip-flop circuit commonly used in computer and pulse equipment. At the top is shown a conventional circuit diagram encompassing two transistors, six resistors, and two capacitors. Next is shown the same circuit in integrated form using transistor techniques. The integrated circuit consists of two interconnected identical sticks of silicon, each encompassing one transistor, three resistances and one capacitance. The circuit diagram is such that the three resistances may be joined end to end forming one bar with suitable connection

points. The capacitance is obtained by evaporating an insulator such as silicon monoxide over one of the resistors and subsequently covering it with a second coat of evaporated metal. The two sticks may be interconnected with printed-circuit wiring supported on a thin ceramic wafer which at the same time may be part of the encapsulation necessary to keep moisture and various gases away from the semiconductor. At the bottom of Fig. 1 is shown the same circuit integrated with a different method using mainly passive-component techniques. On the substrate of glass or ceramic are laid down by vacuum evaporation thin layers of metal in patterns constituting resistor elements and

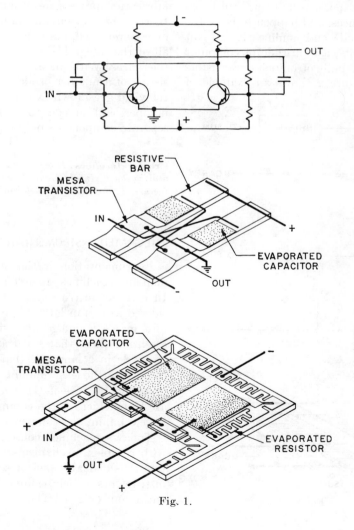

Fig. 1.

also their interconnections. In the same manner capacitor elements are laid down through successive deposition of metal, insulator, and metal. Finally active elements, in this case the two transistors, are incorporated into the circuit either in encapsulated form, or else the entire circuit is encapsulated.

In this manner most of the circuits in pulse and continuous signal applications may be constructed in an integrated form.

Another approach to integrated circuits is offered by the use of unipolar transistors (q.v.). A unipolar transistor constitutes a voltage-controlled relay and may therefore be used to build conventional relay logic circuits. Furthermore, as unipolar transistors are also resistances, and happen to be of the correct magnitude and nonlinearity to suit switching circuits, a multitude of computer circuits may be built of unipolar transistors exclusively. Figure 2 shows an example of

such a circuit, in this case a halfadder which is shown at the top in block diagram, then with separate unipolar transistors and resistors, and finally in complete integrated form.

The packing density possible with circuits of this form, without shrinking the transistor element from the size it has in conventional transistors, is approximately 10^8 components /ft³ $(5 \cdot 10^4$ components/in.³) compared to approximately 10^5 for circuits built of miniaturized but separate components, and less than 10^2 for most television, radio, and computer sets.

The main difficulty with integrated circuits is their sensitivity to errors in the fabrication process, resulting in poor yield. In conventional circuits faulty components may be replaced, but in an integrated circuit all of the integral elements must be within tolerances. With an integrated circuit consisting of a number of identical components the yield goes down exponentially with that number, but in conventional circuits with separate components only linearly.

J. T. WALLMARK

Cross-references: *Diodes (Semiconductor), Miniaturization, Printed Circuits, Semiconductor Manufacture, Transistors, Tunnel Diode*

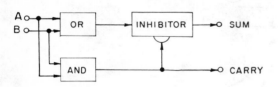

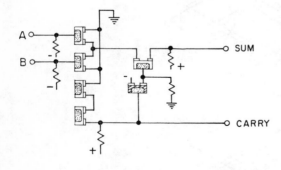

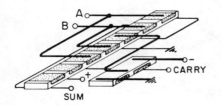

Fig. 2.

INTEGRATED INSTRUMENTATION

Instrumentation is the means by which man and machines are able to communicate. In a sense, instrumentation might be considered as a translator of machine language into man's language and vice versa. It is essential, then, that the translation should be made in a language that can be understood with the least amount of further interpretation because if the man and machine are to be efficient, the communication must have a minimum of impedance.

Today's machines confront the operator with complex mechanisms for instrumentation. His display panel presents an array of instruments which cannot be read as an entire unit (Fig. 1). The operator must scan, choose, and interpret numerous bits of information before he can initiate the appropriate control responses in the performance of his task, causing undue interpretation and integration by the operator and resulting often in errors, disorientation, accidents, aborted missions, and deterioration of morale.

Attempts have been made to align instruments to reduce the scan pattern or to combine instruments, but these efforts have led to clutter rather than a more readable display.

If we are to develop an efficient system, the instrument display must be designed to require a minimum of mental interpretation, translation, and integration. The presentation must give the operator direct responses to the questions he needs answered.

In order to comprehend the problem of instrumentation we must examine the total man-machine system since the term instrumentation implies not only the display and

the medium for display, but the means for producing the display.

In examining the man-machine system (Fig. 2), the operator is concerned with those tasks he performs most efficiently. To this end, man must have available to him certain basic information, and his immediate surroundings must conform with the physiological requirements of his body.

One of the building blocks of the generalized system is that of the sensors, or data-gathering elements. Constituted into such fundamental groups as electromagnetic, temperature, force, physical quantity, geometry, and chemical, the sensors send information to a central computer, which would select information necessary for operator displays and control. The computer transmits information into display generating equipment which drives the operator's display to present data fulfilling the information requirements, thus enabling the operator to take appropriate action through the

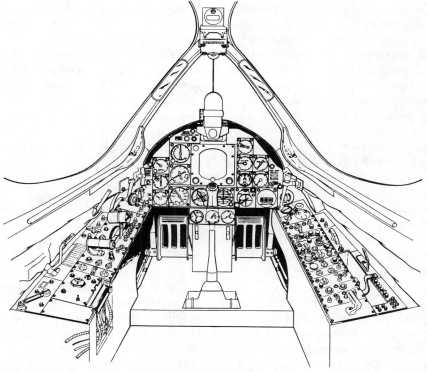

Fig. 1. Today's cockpit.

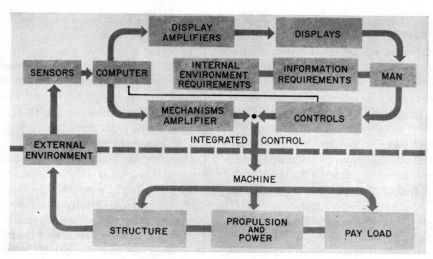

Fig. 2. Man-machine system.

controls. Simultaneously the computer provides information to satisfy the requirements of the automatic portion of the over-all system. The combined control signals are amplified and fed into the vehicle. The resulting action is then transmitted back to the sensors through the external environment, thus closing the loop.

With the man-machine system in mind we start with the information requirements that must be determined for the system for which instrumentation is desired. To uncover the fundamental information requirements, it is necessary to interrogate operators of similar systems to determine "why" specific information is necessary. Such a technique distinguishes the fundamental requirements from those based upon unsubstantiated opinion.

Information requirements fall into three basic categories. Orientation information, or "Where am I and what am I doing?" Director information, or "What should I do and when?" Quantitative information, or "How am I doing?"

Displays required to meet these information requirements must be integrated if the operator is to assimilate the information with maximum efficiency because man is essentially a differentiator rather than an integrator. One of the major problems experi-

enced with present-day instruments is that of training operators to integrate mentally the bits and pieces of information in order to create a mental picture of the existing situation.

Since man evolved in a visual world his sensory systems and central nervous system are programmed to function by observing integrated displays. In order to create displays analogous to those to which man is most accustomed it is necessary to utilize the basic cues that are apparent in the real world and integrate these as they appear in their natural form. This does not mean that the real world must be duplicated but rather that the basic cues should be synthesized as a function of the information requirements. Displays for aircraft can be integrated to synthesize real world cues. The real world does not, in general, contain command or director information; however, director information can be achieved in a manner compatible with the cues for basic orientation by reproducing pathways.

The means for displaying integrated information can best be achieved by the employment of cathode-ray tubes, because they permit the reproduction of many variables simultaneously.

Sensors, computers, and display generators are required to provide the necessary data processing. Coverage of these items is not possible within the scope of this discussion but it must be understood that these components must be designed to meet the display and control requirements.

In summary it can be stated that since all things are created by, for, or against man, any system must be designed to meet man's requirements. It must also be remembered that man is an excellent differentiator but a very poor integrator. Integration then, is the real purpose and function of instrumentation.

G. W. Hoover

Cross-references: *Human Engineering, Indicating Instruments, Integrating Instruments, Radar Displays*

INTEGRATING INSTRUMENTS

An integrating instrument, by means of its component elements, makes a continuing addition of the magnitudes of a quantity, definable by physical concepts, between two limits of time or between two selected points on a mathematically expressed or experimentally derived curve.

A watch is an integrating instrument, though not thought of as such, adding successive small time intervals to give a continuous addition of elapsed time.

The record on a strip chart wattmeter showing power variations in a supply line to a welder, for example, may be traced around with a planimeter to determine the area under the curve. The area divided by the length of the base zero line gives an average value of the ordinate, the watts. The measured area itself is proportional to watthours, a measure of energy. The planimeter is the integrating instrument, and its use has converted the recorded readings to an integrated value.

A dc indicating instrument such as used in electric power measurements has a permanent-magnet stator pole piece construction and a rotor held from continuous rotation by current carrying spiral control springs which are deflected till their counter-torque balances the driving torque set up by the quantity being measured. The pointer attached to the rotor traverses the scale plate calibration markings.[1]

With elimination of the control springs and their substitution by current-carrying brushes bearing upon a commutator continuous rotation results with a tendency to "run away." The required damping torque is provided by a "U" shaped permanent magnet having its tines embracing with little clearance the peripheral area of a disk, generally of aluminum. The effect of the eddy currents induced in the disk is to provide a damping force proportional to the speed of rotation and the magnitude of the quantity being measured. Thus the element of time is introduced and the meter is an integrating meter, in this case a coulomb or ampere-hour meter.

The motor revolutions are integrated on a register train of several decade dials in series or (rarely, because of higher variable friction losses) on a direct reading cyclometer.

By interposing a precise and necessary speed-reduction gear between the rotor and the first register dial, the integration is direct in ampere hours.

If the line supply voltage is sufficiently constant, the meter with suitable register ratios is an energy meter integrating watthours. Further, by replacing the permanent magnet by a field winding excited from the voltage supply line, any variations in that supply voltage are of no consequence; the meter then integrates true watthours.

For ac operation, at power frequencies, use of the same motor with ac excitation of both its rotor and stator field is conceivable but practical considerations preclude its use; the induction-type of meter is superior in every respect and is cheaper to build and maintain.

The utilization of the phenomenon of in-

---

[1] The terms "indicating instrument" and "meter" are synonymous; however, it is preferable to regard an indicating instrument as indicating only. A meter may indicate, too, but may also have a recording chart, a totalizing register, or both.

duction in ac circuits permits indicating instruments and integrating meters to be designed in rugged, simple forms without current-carrying control springs. When supplied from the secondaries of current transformers, CTs, and potential transformers, PTs, a small 5-amp 120-v meter can furnish the metering of large blocks of power by using an installation multiplier equal to the product of the PT and CT ratios.

Induction instruments do not operate on dc; any attempt to do so will probably ruin them.

The induction principle is used on ammeters, voltmeters, and wattmeters, but the number of applications is greatest in the field of integrating meters. Such meters have been built in the tens of millions in the U.S.A. The best of the modern forms operate with excellent compensation of all inherent errors over wide departures from their normal rating in voltage, current, temperature, and power factor. They function with acceptable accuracy from 1 per cent normal current rating to continuous operation at over 600 per cent. Maximum nominal current rating is 50 amp; CTs provide for higher ratings. Complex polyphase forms are required for metering modern power needs.

The outstanding feature of induction type indicating instruments is a rotating vane, disk, or cup of aluminum; exceedingly rarely is the aluminum replaced by copper. Flux passes through the disk from an electromagnet excited by the current to be measured. Eddy currents are generated in the disk by induction. These currents react with an out-of-phase flux produced by the equivalent of a short circuited copper loop, a "shading" loop, embracing a fraction of the electromagnet pole face. This reaction produces rotation of the disk in the same manner that a current carrying wire positioned in a magnetic field has a force exerted upon it at right angles to that magnetic field.

The integrating induction meter in the simplest form is the ac single-phase watthour meter. It has a circular disk, approximately 4 in. in diameter and $1/16$ in. in thickness,

rotating in a horizontal plane about its central axial shaft. This shaft is supported by a lower jewelled thrust bearing and guided in an upper ring jewel.[2] The peripheral area of the disk is embraced between the lines of a "U" shaped permanent magnet, thus providing for a retarding torque proportional to rate of rotation.

One "U" shaped electromagnet with a core of silicon steel laminations carries the load current or a known fraction of it from the secondary of a CT. It is placed on one side of the disk with the two pole faces parallel to and clearing the disk by approximately $1/20$ in. The plane of the centerline of the core is parallel to a tangent to the disk circle. On the other side of the disk is an electromagnet excited from the voltage supply or from a PT.[3]

The torque to rotate the disk is derived from the interaction of the flux from the current coil and the flux from the potential coil; both fluxes cross through the disk.

At unity power factor the line voltage and line current are in phase. The flux in the current coil is in phase with its current. Since an emf is generated in a loop and is lagging 90° behind the flux producing it, an emf is generated in the disk that causes eddy currents to flow in the disk, and since the disk is resistive, the eddy currents are in phase with the emf and thus lag 90° behind the line current.

The potential flux in phase with the potential current lags the line voltage by approximately 90°, giving the result that on a unity-power-factor load the potential flux

[2] All watthour meter manufacturers in U.S.A. now can furnish magnetically suspended disks, thus no longer needing lower thrust bearings but only upper and lower guides. This suspension is more rugged than the earlier, though still much used, jewel and pivot.

[3] This potential electromagnet has a three-leg core, "E" shaped with the three pole faces parallel to the disk surface and clearing the disk by approximately $1/20$ in. The plane of the centerline of the core is the same plane as is occupied by the centerline of the current electromagnet core on the other side of the disk. The potential winding is on the center leg.

is approximately in phase with the eddy currents in the disk.

At other power factors the line current and line voltage are separated by the angle whose cosine is the power factor. Accordingly, the potential flux across the disk is out of phase with the eddy currents in the disk by the same angle and the true torque is the torque at unity power factor multiplied by the cosine of the power factor angle.[4]

The name "rotating standard" is given to a very carefully built portable single-phase watthour meter. It is used for testing the general run of watthour meters, either in factory production tests, meter shop tests or field tests of other installed watthour meters. The best of our modern watthour meters leave little to be desired in improved accuracy; all inherent errors are compensated by built-in adjustments so that rotating standards can have little improvement in accuracy over that of the general watthour meter. Their main advantage is their portability with convenient terminal arrangements and multi-ranges for 120, 240, and (with a separate series impedance) 480 v; also for 1, 5, 12.5, 25, and 50 amp. Their extremely high price, in comparison with a single-phase watthour meter, is due to the addition of a resetting dial pointer mechanism, the advantage of multiranges and the fact that relatively few are manufactured.

Integrating vs Indicating Instruments. Disagreements may arise between interested groups on the relative merits of integrating meters—rotating standards— versus indicating instruments for use on important tests such as those made to determine over-all efficiency of ac generators. These tests are run under A.S.M.E. rulings and may last for more than a week.

When using indicating instruments there is an ammeter, voltmeter, and wattmeter in each phase. With the aid of magnifiers, one reading of each instrument is taken per minute, needing three observers and possibly a supervising engineer. Each run can continue for 1–2 hr. On light loads, the deflections may be low on the ammeter and wattmeter scales. All these readings must be averaged and corrected for scale calibrations and instrument transformer errors before computing the power output. When using rotating standards, one is connected in each phase along with a voltmeter and ammeter which are only in circuit to check load conditions and to choose the optimum range on the rotating standard so that rate of rotation may be as close as possible to that at full load speed, which is generally 1000 rpm.[5] The register repeats itself after 100 revolutions so tally must be kept of the number of cyclings, noting that it would be impossible to slip up one hundred count and not know it very soon. One observer can start and stop the standards simultaneously noting at the end of the test run the total revolutions and reading the elapsed time from a high-precision quartz crystal or tuning fork operated timer. Corrections for the rotating standards are applied along with those for the instrument transformer errors and the total output is computed.

Having conducted many tests using rotating standards, and having observed other engineers using indicating instruments, the writer favors the use of integrating meters for such measurements. The laboratory work of making the calibrations is slow and exacting but the final tests at the power plant are readily made.

N. M. ALBERT

Cross-references: *Errors in Measurement, Indicating Instruments, Standards*

[5] Special rotating standards may have four current ranges with the maximum a value of 5 amp.

[4] As the disk material, aluminum, has a large temperature coefficient of resistance, the torque on the disk varies accordingly. Temperature compensation is achieved by shunting more or less of a small portion of the damping magnet flux through a temperature-sensitive magnetic alloy.

INTERFERENCE

The term Radio Frequency Interference, often abbreviated RFI, is used in modern electronic parlance to distinguish it from purely mechanical interference or other non-electronic forms of interference. RFI can be defined as any induced, radiated, or conducted electrical disturbance or transient that causes undesirable responses or malfunctioning in any electrical or electronic equipment, device, or system.

RFI is divided into two major classes.

Narrowband interference is generated by modulated and unmodulated cw signals, AM, FM, or SSB. In general it is any interfering signal with a much narrower bandwidth than that of conventional communications receivers. This type of interference falls under the jurisdiction of the FCC, which regulates frequency allocation (*q.v.*).

Broadband interference is all other rf energy not included in the narrowband definition. It includes impulse and random noise and other types of nonsinusoidal energies having a frequency distribution considerably wider than the bandwidth of conventional communications receivers.

Causes of Broadband RFI. Broadband RFI is generated by a rapidly varying field, current, voltage, or impedance. It is classified as either impulsive noise or random noise. The pulses of electrical energy in impulsive noise have a regular repetition rate. The rate may vary somewhat but does not approach the true random unrelated conditions that characterize random noise. The pulses do not overlap each other. Impulse noise is generated by rotating machinery such as motors, generators, electric shavers, and by vibrators, ignition systems, switches, relays, and electronic circuits. A simple example is a switch used to connect and disconnect a current-carrying circuit. When a switch turns a circuit on, the currents and voltages in the circuit must make a rapid readjustment from zero to full value. Since all circuits contain capacity and inductance, the change in current and voltage values cannot occur instantly. During the short interval in which the current and voltage is changing to the new value, rf transients are produced. The spectral distribution of the RFI is dependent upon the magnitude of the current, voltage, and impedance of the circuit. Impulsive RFI covers a wide frequency spectrum. The shape and duration of the individual pulses as determined by the current, voltage, and impedance of the circuit gives the characteristic "spectrum signature" to the RFI. Roughly, the width of the frequency band covered by an individual pulse is inversely proportional to the duration of the pulse. A pulse of very short duration, such as found in ignition systems, covers a very wide spectrum. The longer the duration of a single pulse, the more of its electrical energy will be found at the low-frequency end of the spectrum. The faster a pulse rises to its peak magnitude, the higher the frequencies generated.

In addition to the transients caused by the changing values in the circuit, another source of broadband RFI is the sparking or arcing of the contacts of switches, relays, and commutators of various kinds. A magnetic flux is generated by the arc in accordance with Lenz's law. Mechanical conditions which cause and sustain the arc are contributing factors to the interference. For example, in a relay the contact spring tension, contact chatter, armature impact, and the air gap in the magnetic circuit all contribute to the magnitude and duration of the arc at the relay contacts. A simple switching circuit is not generally a very serious source of interference because a switch is operated only infrequently. A dc motor comprises a series of switches in the commutation necessary for operation and is therefore a prolific source of interference. The ionization of gases as in a thyratron or a fluorescent lamp also constitutes a varying circuit condition which is a source of RFI.

Atmospheric noise is a special form of random noise caused by fluctuations in the electrical charges existing in the atmosphere. It becomes important as interference only when its magnitude is large with respect to the signal being received by a receiver.

Measurement of RFI. The field intensity of radiated RFI is measured in much the same way that a broadcast signal is measured, with one important difference. In the measurement of broadband RFI, it is necessary to include the bandwidth of the receiving equipment in the statement of measurement. It is customary to relate the measurement to 1 kc or 1 Mc of bandwidth. Therefore, the intensity of radiated RFI is measured in terms of "microvolts-per-meter-per-kilocycle" (or per-megacycle) of receiver bandwidth. In many military specifications it is deemed more convenient to state the measured magnitude in "db-above-one-microvolt-per-megacycle." This term is often abbreviated, dbmc. Especially designed receiving equipments are used in measuring broadband RFI, owing to the great dynamic range necessary to respond to impulse signals with a rapid rise time. They are calibrated in a known cw field intensity using basic antennas (with mathematically known characteristics). The bandwidth of the receiver is accurately measured so that the final corrected calibration can be in terms of dbmc. An alternative method is to compare the receiver output on an unknown signal with its output on a signal from a calibrated broadband signal source. The calibrated source is a special form of impulse generator, the output of which is calculated accurately in terms of dbmc. In the alternative method, it is not necessary to know the bandwidth of the receiver accurately since its response to the unknown is the same as to the calibrated signal source which includes bandwidth in its calibration.

Conducted RFI existing on any line is measured with respect to ground on each side of the line. Since the impedance of the line affects the magnitude of the conducted RFI at any point on the line, it is customary to measure the RFI across a known value of line impedance. The artificial line impedance is called a Line Impedance Stabilization Network, or L.I.S.N. If all conducted RFI measurements are made using the L.I.S.N., a correlation can be made between any two interference-generating devices since the RFI output of each is imposed upon a common impedance value. An alternative

method just being introduced is that of measuring the impedance of the line under actual operating conditions and record it with the interference magnitude. Until recently this method has suffered from the difficulty of measuring the impedance on a line that is actively carrying large power-line currents and voltages. The latest technique utilizes two toroidal current transformers around the line being measured. A signal from a standard signal generator is injected into the line using one current transformer and the resultant signal across the line impedance is picked up by the other current transformer. The received signal is measured with a frequency selective rf voltmeter and the line impedance is calculated from the relation of the input signal to the output signal. The relation is given by the formula:

$$Z = [Z_{add}]\left[\frac{V_{in}}{V_{out}} - 1\right]$$

where

Z = unknown line impedance

Z_{add} = impedance added to primary conductor by the current transformer

V_{in} = voltage into one current transformer

V_{out} = voltage out of second current transformer

Effects of RFI. The effect of broadband RFI on any electrical or electronic equipment or system is a function of the magnitude of the RFI, as well as of the susceptibility of the equipment or system being interfered with. With the advent of the transmission of electromagnetic energy in space to and from satellites and eventually space ships and other planets, the "nuisance value" of RFI is becoming far more significant. Communications receivers at all frequencies are designed to receive weak communications signals and to be immune to locally generated RFI or deliberate jamming. Communications receivers are more sophisticated so that they have built-in "noise-immunity" circuits and reduced susceptibility to signals falling on the image frequencies, intermediate frequencies, and spurious frequencies. Ordnance devices widely used in various military applications are designed so that the presence of large magnitude RFI signals on the various control wires does not detonate the devices. Defense systems such as ballistic missiles, space vehicles, and command systems are all made immune to the baneful effects of RFI.

Intermodulation. In a nonlinear system, the various components of a complex wave interact and modulate each other. This effect is known as intermodulation. It is sometimes the result of adjacent channel signals acting upon nonlinear elements in the early stages of a receiver. One frequency appears to amplitude-modulate another signal. Also, a series of sum and difference frequencies is generated in the nonlinear device. Receiver responses of this nature are considered interference effects.

Intermodulation effects are sometimes generated by external nonlinear devices such as ground straps, conduits, or wiring loops which insert poor contacts in a conductor. These spurious signals may be conducted or radiated into a receiving system and therefore constitute a source of interference ("crosstalk").

Interference due to close frequency spacing of two or more signals is usually classed as intermodulation. However, an extremely strong signal can overload the first stage of a receiver and therefore cause it to be nonlinear and result in intermodulation effects. At weaker signal levels, such adjacent-channel interference is not likely to occur.

RFI Control. Ideally, the control of RFI must be achieved in the initial design stages of an equipment or system. The true status of RFI control is a design function which must be considered at the same time that components are selected for an equipment or system design. The control of RFI centers in two basic areas, (1) Suppression at the source, (2) Reducing susceptibility to RFI in equipments and systems.

The use of *shielding* to prevent undesired signals from bypassing selective circuits or entire amplifier stages is recommended. The use of Faraday shields and the proper design of input selective circuits to minimize mutual capacity coupling reduces the possibility of signal feedthrough.

In *RFI filter design*, the input connections to the filter must be well shielded from the output leads. The use of feedthrough-type capacitors is essential in designing RFI filters for power lines, control wires and other nonsignal carrying wires. Ferrite cores in toroidal coils provide increased rf losses for RFI filter applications.

In receivers, intermodulation and adjacent channel interference can be minimized by placing selective circuits ahead of amplification so that only the desired signals are presented to the amplifier. The use of narrow-band directive antennas to discriminate against signals coming from an undesired direction reduces interference. Improved selectivity and the use of traps at spurious and image frequencies and at the IF reduce the *susceptibility* of the receiver.

Determining the actual source of RFI is the first step in *suppression*. The source may be inductive surges, thyratron hash, cold-cathode ionization, bearings in motors and gear trains, relay contact action, or rf contact discontinuity. Inductive surges due to dc solenoids or relay coils cause low-frequency RFI, which may be suppressed by connecting a small semiconductor diode across the coil with such polarity that it does not conduct in the forward direction but conducts during the reverse current surge caused by opening the circuit to the coil. However, the switching action of the diode itself is often a disturbing cause of RFI, especially at the higher frequencies. A series capacitor and resistor connected across relay contacts generally serves to both suppress the arc and reduce the RFI. Filters used to suppress RFI are low-pass types, which must be designed for maximum rf loss in the frequency range of interest. Shielding between sections of the filter prevents section-to-section coupling of RFI which renders the filter ineffectual. RFI caused by poor contact in motor bearings or in gear trains can be eliminated by a good wiping contact shunting the offending point.

A. T. PARKER

Cross-references: *Extraterrestrial Radio Sources, Modulation and Demodulation, Noise, Proximity Fuzes, Pulse Generation, Radiation (Terrestrial)*

INTERFEROMETER METHOD (OPTICAL)

The interferometer method is a powerful tool used in a wide variety of length measurements. It is based on the interference of light waves giving rise to a pattern of bright and dark interference fringes. Measurements on fringe separations and fringe shifts yield length measurements to a fraction of a millionth of an inch. Such high accuracy is rendered possible because the measurements are related to the wavelength of light which, for green light, is 5000 Å or 0.00005 cm.

Light interference often takes place between two waves reflected from slightly separated or slightly inclined surfaces. Only *stationary* interference effects are visible; they are produced by *coherent* waves, that is, waves originating from one point of a single source.

For example, interference fringes can be formed in the following manner. A narrow slit is placed parallel to the refracting edge of a symmetrical prism of which the base angles are small, say $\frac{1}{3}$°. Monochromatic light, diverging through the slit, is refracted by the two halves of the prism forming two virtual images. These act as coherent sources and produce a series of parallel fringes on a screen placed at some distance behind the prism. They are alternately bright and dark, corresponding, respectively, to the superposition of crest and crest, or crest and trough, of the light wave.

The biprism method described above is one example of fringe formation through division of wavefront. Other methods are the double-mirror method and the split-lens method.

Interference effects arise also from division of amplitude. Thus reflected light beams from the first and second faces of a thin film are coherent and can produce interference fringes. A small-angle air wedge can yield a series of interference fringes whose spacing depends on the wedge angle. Newton's rings are an example of this phenomenon and are produced when the convex surface of a lens is placed against a flat glass plate. The fringes formed in these cases are fringes of equal thickness. Fringes of equal inclination arise from parallel surfaces when an extended source is used.

Interferometry with *multiple* beams, as opposed to *two* beams, leads to increased sharpness in the fringes. In producing Newton's rings, for example, if the lens and the plate are both coated with a reflecting silver layer, the ring system becomes much sharper. Much more accurate measurements can be made in this manner.

Interferometers

The Rayleigh interferometer is used for measuring the refractive indices of gases. Two beams, originating from the same source, pass through two tubes, one beam through each. They are then brought to a focus by a lens and the fringes are viewed here. If one tube is evacuated, and the given gas is admitted into the other, a shift in fringes takes place which is a measure of the refractive index of the gas.

Newton's rings are used for measuring small linear displacements, for example, the thermal expansion of a crystal. The expansion reduces the gap between the polished, plane face of the crystal and the lens surface resulting in a fringe displacement.

In the original form of the Michelson interferometer, a half-silvered mirror divides a beam into a reflected and a transmitted part of equal intensity. These then meet mirrors at practically normal incidence, return to the beam-splitter and recombine. Fringes are formed in this manner. On moving one of the mirrors the fringe system shifts and thus small distances can be measured.

The interference microscope is a valuable modification of Michelson's interferometer. The surface to be studied takes the place of one of the mirrors while the other mirror is a reference flat. The fringe system formed is a contour pattern of the given surface. Surface irregularities corresponding to a fraction of a wavelength of light, and their location, are studied in this manner.

The most versatile of all interferometers is the Fabry-Perot instrument. Here the fringes are formed by two parallel, reflecting films of silver, the distance between which can be varied continuously. The multiple reflections give a sharp ring system consisting of very narrow bright fringes as seen by transmitted light. The instrument is used for absolute wavelength measurements, evaluation of the meter, resolution of spectral lines, determination of refractive indices of gases, measurement of small displacements, etc.

Several improved forms of the main types of interferometer described above are currently being used for precision measurements.

The thickness of thin films can be measured by using multiple-beam methods. The film is deposited on flat surface and provided with a sharp edge. Over this a thin silver layer, extending beyond the film edge, is deposited. Monochromatic light gives rise to wedge-fringes showing a step which is a measure of the film thickness.

Multiple-beam methods have also been used for the study of surface microtopography. The faces of diamonds and other crystals, cleavages in mica, bismuth, topaz, etc., indentations on metals and single crystals, diamond wear and abrasion resistance and the effects of impacts on metals have been studied using this powerful technique.

Among other types of measurements using the interferometer method are the determination of stellar diameters and the angular separation of double stars, the study of the oscillations of quartz crystals, and several applications in metallurgy and crystallography.

T. K. Lakshmanan

Cross-references: *Microwave Measurements, Optics*

ION PROPULSION

The production of thrust through the electrostatic expulsion of ions (charged atoms) is termed ion propulsion. It has been evident for many years that, in principle, thrust could be obtained in reaction to the ejection of ions which have been electrostatically accelerated. However, the ion engine has not been considered to be a practical device until recent advancements in light-weight power systems, such as nuclear-turbogeneration and thermionic direct energy conversion, which indicated that they would be applicable to space flight. The significant features of these newer power systems is that they may eventually be capable of at least a year's continuous operation and weigh as little as 10 lb/kw of electrical power.

The most outstanding advantage of the ion engine system over the more conventional chemical rocket devices lies in the attainability of a very high exhaust velocity or specific impulse I_s (the exhaust velocity divided by the acceleration of gravity at sea level g_0, or the thrust divided by the propellant flow rate). Chemically propelled rockets are generally limited to a value of I_s of not much more than 400 sec. Nuclear propulsion may boost this figure to 1000 sec. Electrostatic propulsion, on the other hand, is capable of specific impulse values in the tens of thousands of seconds. In most instances, though, the highest I_s is not necessarily desired. The advantage of a high specific impulse can be seen from the definition, in that lower propellant flow rates and hence a lower total propellant weight is required which, in turn, allows more weight for useful equipment or payload. However, in counterdistinction a more powerful and therefore heavier power plant is required as I_s increases, since the beam power P is proportional to the product of thrust F and I_s ($P = \frac{1}{2} F I_s\ g_0$). It follows that for any given space mission there exists an optimum I_s where the sum of the powerplant and propellant weight is a minimum. Typical values of I_s would lie around 9000 sec for a flight to Mars and 5000 sec for a flight to the moon.

This engine is characteristically a low thrust device (from tenths of a pound to a few pounds as compared to the millions of pounds produced by booster rockets). It attains the large impulse Ft required for space missions by virtue of its long operating time. As a consequence, the vehicle's orbit is a spiral expanding slowly outward from the attracting gravitational center in contrast to the rapid transfers from one elliptical orbit to another by high-thrust rockets. One advantage of this mode of flight is the possibility of gradual corrective guidance throughout the entire trajectory.

It is important to consider the requirements for the expellant for use in the engine. The choice of a charged particle depends upon several factors, among others the ease of ionization, production of a single charged species, and the resulting engine size. It has been found that the use of alkali metals affords the efficient production of a singly charged ion and that cesium, the heaviest nonradioactive alkali, allows the minimum engine size. The ionization of cesium is best accomplished by passing the vapor phase over a heated, high work function substance such as tungsten. This method of ionization is known as surface-contact ionization. The arc source has also been proposed and may prove to be applicable. However, the contact ion source does have an advantage in that it affords a well-defined surface for ion optical design of the accelerator structure. The greatest disadvantage is that the heated tungsten surface radiates a significant amount of power, which results in a serious

loss of thermal efficiency at low values of specific impulse. For the present time, however, the cesium contact source offers the most efficient and simplest method of producing ions for electrostatic propulsion.

The ion engine itself is an adaptation of the electron gun (q.v.) to the acceleration of cesium ions. It operates in the following fashion. Cesium vapor is fed from storage to the back side of a porous tungsten ionizer with pores on the order of 1μ in diameter. The pressure is kept in the millimeters of mercury range because the required flow rates are very small, from tens of micrograms to tens of milligrams per second. Upon diffusing through the pores to the front surface, the atoms are ionized. The ionizer temperature (around 1000°C) and propellant flow rate are critical, in that a few percent surface coverage of cesium must be maintained to produce a high ratio of ions to neutral atoms evaporated from the surface. The ions are then accelerated through a region bounded by the ionizer surface, the focusing electrode, and the accelerator electrode. Two factors are of concern in the accelerator region: (1) the interception of the high-energy ions (in the kilovolt range) can cause the sputtering away of electrode surfaces and the consequent degradation of the ion beam optics, and (2) charge exchange scattering of the ions by the accumulation of neutral cesium can also result in electrode impingement by both ions and atoms.

Immediately after the ions pass through the aperture of the accelerating electrode they are usually decelerated to the desired final exit velocity. This sequence (accel-decel system) serves two purposes: (1) with the higher accelerator voltage an increase in the ion beam current density and beam power density is gained over that which would be obtained with the lower exhaust potential, thereby improving the over-all power efficiency of the engine, and (2) the accel-decel produces an axial potential distribution which presents a potential barrier to the neutralization electrons which are next injected into the beam, preventing them from flowing back to the ion emitter.

Finally, the electrons or perhaps negative ions in later developed models, are injected into the beam to neutralize the ion space charge. Neutralization must satisfy two conditions: (1) zero current must flow from the whole system to maintain charge neutrality of the space vehicle and (2) the beam space-charge density must be zero on the average to prevent excessive build-up of potential in the beam as it leaves the engine. Potential build-up is especially difficult to avoid if the ion beam is formed with a near limiting value of perveance (beam current divided by the exhaust potential to the three-halves power). In this region of perveance the ion beam is decelerated appreciably and a virtual anode may also form which would greatly reduce the beam current. This condition must be avoided in any practical engine design.

The ion engine described here is one of the simplest and best-developed devices included in the more general classification of electrical propulsion. The competitive devices depend for their operation upon the electrostatic acceleration of molecular ions and colloidal particles, the ejection of a plasma (plasmajet), and the acceleration of a plasma by electromagnetic fields. All these devices are being developed to meet the high-specific-impulse requirement of space flight.

S. L. EILENBERG

Cross-references: *Ionization, Plasma Propulsion*

ION SCATTERING

The elastic scattering, or deflection, of charged particles from a high-energy beam of ions by the strong electric fields near nuclei can be used for quantitative analysis of surface films. This technique takes advantage of the limited range of an ion beam in solid matter to restrict the analysis to a few microns of depth into the sample. Very

high sensitivity, of the order of millimicrograms of an element per square centimeter of surface, can be obtained by the detection of scattered ions.

A collimated beam of protons, deuterons, or alpha particles (or even heavier ions) is produced by a suitable apparatus (such as a Van de Graaff, *q.v.*) at an energy of the order of 1 Mev, with a spread in energy of 0.1 per cent or less. The beam is focused on the sample in a very small area, and the momentum distribution of the particles backscattered at some specific angle to the incident beam is measured by a high-resolution momentum analyzer. The momentum analyzer can be a suitable type of focusing magnet, or an electrostatic analyzer, or a time-of-flight measurement apparatus.

The momentum of the scattered ions is less than their initial momentum by a ratio that depends on the nuclear mass of the scattering elements in the sample. The ratio of the final velocity V_s to the initial velocity V_0 of a particle of mass M_1, elastically scattered at an angle θ by a particle of mass M_0 initially at rest, is given by

$$V_s/V_0 =$$
$$[M_1 \cos \theta + (M_0{}^2 - M_1{}^2 \sin^2 \theta)^{1/2}]/(M_0 + M_1)$$

For $M_0 \gg M_1$, the fractional change in velocity Δ is given approximately by

$$\frac{V_0 - V_s}{V_0} = \Delta \cong \frac{M_1}{M_0 + M_1} (1 - \cos \theta).$$

Each isotope is identified by a characteristic value of Δ, which decreases with increasing nuclear mass. However, the change in Δ becomes very small for adjacent heavy elements, so that the resolving power of the analyzer and the homogeneity of the incident beam must be very great to resolve the heavy elements. A momentum resolving power of 2000 is necessary for the resolution of adjacent isotopes (1 unit different in mass) of mass near 60, by proton scattering.

For the analysis of heavy elements, it is preferable to use heavier incident particles, such as alpha particles, since the resolving power for nuclear masses is proportional to the mass of the scattered particle. Although the scattering yield from deuterons or alphas is less than that with protons by factors of 2 and 4, respectively, at a given bombarding energy, the high yield from the heavy elements makes this loss unimportant.

The incident particles, in penetrating the sample, also lose energy continuously by ionization, approximately in proportion to their depth of penetration. Therefore, an element in a thick film, or homogeneously distributed in the sample, produces a step in the momentum distribution, the high-velocity edge of the step being located at the theoretical value of Δ for that element. This property makes it possible to measure the variation of concentration with depth, with a depth resolution of the order of 0.01 micron.

The yield of scattered particles from a thick sample depends on the concentration of scattering nuclei, the particle energy, the scattering cross section of the element for the incident particles, the stopping power (a measure of the energy loss by ionization) of the sample, and geometrical factors of detector resolution and solid angle.

In a sample material containing various elements a_i, in the relative atomic proportions n_i, the following formula gives the number of particles Yj scattered from a given element a_j and counted in a given momentum interval by a momentum spectrometer:

$$Y_j = 1.2 \times 10^{13} \left(\frac{d\sigma}{d\Omega} \right)_j \frac{q\Omega E_1 n_j}{R_s}$$

$$\left[\Sigma_i n_i \left(\epsilon_{i1} + \frac{\epsilon_{i2} \cos \theta_1}{K_j \cos \theta_2} \right) \right]^{-1}$$

where $d\sigma/d\Omega$ is the differential scattering cross section (in center of mass coord.), R_s is the spectrometer resolving power (particle momentum divided by momentum band accepted), E_1 is the incident particle energy, q is the incident charge (in microcoulombs for singly ionized particles), Ω is the spectrometer solid angle (in center of mass coord.), ϵ is the atomic stopping cross section

of each atomic species with subscript 1 referring to the particle before scattering, subscript 2 after scattering (in same energy units as E_1), K is the ratio of the particle energy after scattering to the energy before scattering, $K = (V_s/V_0)^2$, and θ_1 and θ_2 are the angles between the normal of the surface of the sample and the direction of the incident (1) and scattered (2) beams.

The calculation of concentration by means of the yield formula above is rather cumbersome, particularly in the case of multi-component samples. A more convenient (and usually more accurate) procedure for measurement of concentrations is by comparison with the yield from reference samples of known concentrations of each of the elements of interest. However, since the reference samples may not have the same stopping power as the unknowns, it may be necessary to make corrections for the different value of the bracket term in the yield formula.

Because of the low penetrating power of ions, the incident and scattered ion beams must be contained in a vacuum system, in which the samples are placed for analysis. This restricts the analyzable materials to those which will not decompose or volatilize too rapidly at the temperatures produced by the ion bombardment.

The beam current can be very small, 10^{-2} μa or less, which will dissipate 10^{-2} w in the sample at 1-Mev energy. Generally, poor heat conductors with a low decomposition temperature cannot withstand even this small power focused on a very small area. Metal or refractory materials are bombarded without difficulty.

This technique is particularly useful for the detection and analysis of surface contaminants; changes in surface composition as a result of some treatment; and measurements of film thickness or of penetration depth. The precision of measurement of the concentration of a given element depends on the concentration and on the background due to scattering by the heavier elements in the sample. The maximum sensitivity is obtained with surface elements of greater atomic weight than the elements composing the bulk of the sample.

SYLVAN RUBIN

Cross-references: *Electron Diffraction and Scattering, Neutron Diffraction*

IONIZATION

The process by which a neutral or an uncharged atom or molecule acquires a charge, thus becoming an ion, is known as *ionization*. This process usually occurs by various mechanisms in liquid, gaseous, or solid media, acting on atoms or molecules constituting the medium, or dissolved in it. When a substance dissolved in a liquid, or a liquid itself, undergoes ionization, oppositely charged ions are formed, which may still interact with each other or the un-ionized solvent. When a substance in the gaseous state is ionized, usually by a collision process or by absorption of radiation, ions of positive charge only may be formed as a result of loss of an electron, and the electron is free as a result of the process. In all cases the ions formed are subject to motion or deflection in electric fields, and under suitable conditions, may recombine to form neutral atoms or molecules. Their motion in an electric field constitutes an electric current and, outside of metallic conductors, this is the mechanism of electrical conduction in most systems.

The atoms of a neutral molecule are held together by a number of molecular forces, among them the electrostatic attraction between charged portions of the molecule, which may be ions. If interionic attraction is the major force binding a molecule together, any significant reduction of this attraction will dissociate the molecule into two or more charged particles, each of which behaves as a more or less independent kinetic entity. This is the mechanism in the case of ionization of electrolytes in solution, where the solvent dielectric properties reduce the electrostatic forces between the

ions and cause the molecule to dissociate. In a solvent such as water, some of the solvent molecules themselves are ionized, though to a very limited extent.

Ionization of gases differs from ionization of solutes in a solvent both in the mechanism by which it occurs and the products formed. The atoms or molecules of gas lose an electron by collision with another electron, producing a positively charged ion and a free electron, rather than two oppositely charged ions. The ionization of gases occurs when an electric discharge is maintained in the gas at low pressure, as in a glass tube nearly evacuated of the gas in question. The electrons traveling from cathode to anode in the gas may, if their energy is sufficient, ionize the gas by detaching an electron from it. A particular voltage is required to do this, differing for each gas and known as the *ionization potential* of the gas. When the electrons emitted by the electrodes of the discharge tube strike an atom of the gas, the collision may result in excitation or ionization of the atom, depending on the magnitude of the voltage, or the energy of the electron. Excitation results when an electron of the atom is knocked to a higher energy level, without being ejected from the atom completely, whereas ionization results if the voltage is sufficient to cause the electron to be ejected completely. The highest frequency of radiation the normal atom is capable of radiating can be used to calculate an energy of ionization, which should and actually does agree with experimentally observed values using the electric discharge method. The positive ions produced in the manner described above can be subjected to electric and magnetic fields to determine their mass and charge, which is the operating principle of the mass spectrograph.

Ionization of gases, liquids, or solids may also occur by the action of radiation on the atoms or molecules. The energy of the radiation, which may be particle or energy radiation, may be absorbed by the atoms encountered to knock an electron from them, forming an ion. α, β, and γ as well as cosmic rays (*q.v.*) may ionize a substance under suitable conditions, and the latter are considered responsible for the low level of ionization always present in the atmosphere. Conditions of extreme temperature may also ionize the gases existing at these temperatures.

ROBERT KUNIN AND ALVIN WINGER

Cross-references: *Ions, Electric Discharge, Ionization Counters, Electrochemistry, Plasma, Radiation (Ionizing)*

IONIZATION COUNTERS

The passage of nuclear radiations through a gas causes ionization of some atoms of the gas. An electric field applied to the gas space separates the positive and negative charge carriers, thereby causing a current to flow across the gas space. If the ionizing events occur frequently, a mean current results across the gas space; if the events are infrequent, a current pulse coincident with each ionizing event occurs. This is the basis of *gaseous-radiation detectors* used extensively in nuclear research. Nuclear radiation can be detected and measured by amplifying and measuring either the current pulses or the mean current flowing across the gas space between collecting electrodes. Detectors of this simple type are often called *counters* (pulse operation) or *ion chambers* (mean-current operation). The gas employed in the detector is usually one which exhibits high electron and positive-ion mobilities to insure fast charge collection, thereby reducing recombination of the charge carriers.

The wide variety of types of nuclear radiation results in several variants in the basic ionization detector. Generally speaking, heavy highly charged particle radiations (e.g., alpha particles, *q.v.*, fission fragments) produce dense ionization tracks and the quantity of charge released by these events is adequate for the simple detector to give a signal large enough for measurement purposes. At the other extreme, uncharged particles such as neutrons produce no ionization by direct processes. To detect these particles, an intermediate nuclear reaction is used. Slow neutrons may be detected by filling the detector with boron trifluoride. The following reaction occurs:

$$B^{10} + n = Li^7 + \alpha$$

This results in an alpha particle for each neutron captured by a B^{10} nucleus. The alpha particle is then detected by its ionization. Some neutrons pass through the counter producing no reaction; thus the counter has a counting efficiency less than unity which depends upon the neutron energy and other factors. Inclusion of a hydrogeneous material in the gas or the walls of the detector allows detection of fast neutrons by virtue of the knock-on protons produced by neutron collisions with hydrogen nuclei.

Light charged particles (e.g., beta particles) produce less dense ionization than heavier slow-moving particles, which results in much smaller signals with consequent detection difficulties. Electromagnetic radiations (gamma rays, *q.v.*) interact with atoms in the detector wall materials[*] and in the gas to produce energetic electrons by a photoelectric mechanism, Compton scattering, or by pair production. A gamma-ray detector operates by virtue of the ionization produced by these energetic secondary electrons. Therefore, the remarks regarding beta-particle detectors apply also to gamma-ray detectors. If beta particles or gamma rays occur frequently, the average current flowing in the detector may be used as a measure of the radiation field. However, since the small signals are masked by electrical noise, individual beta particles or gamma rays are not generally detected by simple ionization

---

[*] In the small volume used for detector purposes, most of the gamma-ray interactions occur in the walls of the detector. Thus, if the ionization produced in a gamma-ray field is to be the same as would be produced if the detector were immersed in an infinite volume of air (i.e., no walls), the wall materials must have the same average atomic number as air. Such a wall is said to be air-equivalent and is essential if the chamber is to be used for radiation dosimetry.

detectors. To overcome this difficulty gas multiplication, as described in the following paragraphs, is used to increase the detector signals.

Proportional and Geiger Counters

In these types of counters the electric field in part of the gas space is increased to the point where electrons produced by the original ionizing event gain sufficient velocity between collisions with gas atoms to cause further ionization. Each event thereby initiates a Townsend avalanche in the high-field region of the counter. Various electrode configurations may be employed. Co-axial cylindrical electrodes are common, the outer cylinder being the cathode and the center cylinder being a fine-wire anode. The high-field region near the wire is responsible for the charge multiplication.

Low voltages applied to the counter collect the primary ionization and slowly increasing the voltage produces no effect on the current until the field near the central wire reaches a critical value where gas amplification begins. The amplification increases rapidly with further increase in applied voltage, but over a limited voltage range the charge flow across the counter is proportional to the primary ionization. Proportional counters are operated in this voltage region. As the applied voltage is further increased, a new critical voltage is reached at which photo-electrons released from the cathode by the action of the ultra-violet produced in the discharge cause a sudden large increase in the ionization. Above this voltage, all pulses produced by the detector have the same size, which is independent of the amount of primary ionization. This is known as the Geiger region, and detectors operated in this mode are called Geiger counters. In these counters each ionizing event triggers the counter into a self-sustaining breakdown. The discharge may be quenched by electrical means (reducing the applied voltage temporarily) or by including a quenching vapor or gas in the counter. The latter type of counter is said to be self-quenched and is the most common type. Quenching agents commonly used include various organic vapors and halogen gases. The quenching action depends upon dissociation of the molecules of the quenching agent to absorb ultraviolet radiation produced in the gas discharge. Organic molecules, once dissociated, do not re-associate. Thus the vapor is slowly exhausted and the life of this type of counter is limited. However, halogen quenched-counters appear to exhibit almost infinite life.

Associated Electronic Circuits

(a) *Mean Current Detectors.* Currents produced by these detectors are minute, ranging from 10^{-16} to about 10^{-5} amp. Amplification of these small currents demands very sensitive dc amplifiers. In the range 10^{-12} to 10^{-5} amp an electrometer tube is usually used as the input device. Amplifiers for less than 10^{-12} amp use a vibrating-reed capacitor to convert the dc input current to an ac signal which can then be amplified. This scheme reduces drift problems in dc amplifiers and also produces a very high input impedance.

(b) *Pulse Detectors.* The pulses produced by ionization detectors using no gas amplification are very small and require considerable amplification before they can be used to operate electrical counters. If the energy absorbed from the ionizing particle is small or if the energy is to be measured accurately by determining the pulse amplitude, the electrical noise produced by the pulse amplifier must be extremely small. Counters using gas amplification impose less stringent conditions on the amplifier; the pulses produced by Geiger counters require almost no amplification. However, these types of detector cannot be used for accurate particle energy measurements since the signals they produce are not exactly linearly related to the primary ionization produced by the particle.

F. S. GOULDING

Cross-references: *Ionization, Radiation (Ionizing)*

IONOSPHERE: see PROPAGATION

IONS

Atoms, or groups of atoms, which have either taken up or surrendered one or more electrons from their outer electronic shells are known as *ions*. These ions consequently bear positive or negative charges that are integral multiples of the elementary charge of the electron, 4.77×10^{-10} electrostatic unit. Positively charged ions are called *cations* and negatively charged ones are known as *anions*.

The charge carried by "simple" ions, i.e., those consisting of a single charged atom, is numerically equal to the valence of the elemental atom; or the number of electrons the neutral atom must gain or surrender in order to acquire a stable electronic configuration. Thus, the neutral sodium atom has one electron in its outer orbit and can acquire a stable configuration by losing that one to an atom lacking a single electron in its outer orbit, such as a halide atom. The resultant sodium ion has a positive unit charge and the halide ion a negative unit charge. Doubly charged ions such as the positive calcium ion may combine with a singly charged negative ion to form a singly charged complex ion—a class of ions that is very important in most natural geological and biological systems.

The charge carried by the ions is largely responsible for their unique properties in or out of solution, which differ markedly from the properties of the neutral atoms or groups of atoms. In solution the ions interact with the solvent to produce a kinetic entity, or solvated ion, whose properties are modified to a considerable degree by the solvent molecules attached in varying degrees to the ion. Out of solution, ions may exist in the solid crystalline state, as in the sodium chloride lattice; or in the gaseous state, where they are produced by the action of high-energy radiation on neutral atoms or molecules.

A fundamental property of ions is the electrostatic attractice force between ions of opposite charge and the repulsive force between those of like charge. The former is largely responsible for the formation and stability of many crystalline and other type "ionic" compounds; taken together these polar forces are responsible for the formation of the "ionic atmosphere" around each ion in solution, important in the Debye-Hückel theory of electrolytic solutions. In crystalline "ionic" compounds, the ions acquire their charge by a transfer of an outer orbital electron from one atom to the other, each atom thus acquiring a stable electronic configuration similar to that of the inert gases. The ions so formed are held together in a crystalline formation by the powerful electrostatic forces between them.

When an external electric field is applied across an electrolytic solution by means of suitable electrodes, the cations are electrostatically attracted to the negative electrode, or cathode, and the anions are attracted toward the positive electrode, or anode. If a chemical reaction occurs at both electrodes that transfers electrons from electrode to ion, or vice versa, the ions in the solution will move toward the electrode attracting them; and this movement constitutes the electric current in the solution. The electrical conductivity of solutions depends, then, on the concentration and mobility of the ions in the solutions. The mobility of an ion is defined as the velocity (cm/sec) attained by that ion under a potential gradient of 1 v/cm. Although the motion of a charged particle in a field is, in general, accelerated according to Newton's law that force equals mass times acceleration, ions are almost instantaneously accelerated to a limiting velocity determined by the viscous drag of the solvent, and thus move at a constant velocity under given conditions, which for ordinary fields is directly proportional to the applied field. Ohm's law is for this reason valid for electrolytes subjected to ordinary fields.

The mobility of an ion in a given solvent depends on the size of the solvated ion, in other words, upon the ion-solvent interaction. Measurement of the mobility of an ion combined with Stokes' law of motion of spherical particles in a continuous medium provides a means for calculating a radius of the solvated ion, usually referred to as the "Stokes-law" radius. Since electric current in solutions results from the motion in opposite directions of oppositely charged ions, each ion species can be considered to carry a certain proportion of the current. The fraction of the total current carried by a particular ion species is known as the transport (or transference) number of that ion. Evidently, it is proportional to the relative concentration of that ion in the solution, as well as to the magnitude of the charge on the ion and its absolute mobility under the given conditions.

The importance of ions in all natural processes can be understood by the realization that electrical conduction in all aqueous and other nonmetallic systems is almost entirely carried on by the movement of ions, and that most inorganic reactions involved in geological and biological systems are ionic in nature. The energy released in ionic reactions may take the form of electrical energy, as in storage and "dry" batteries, and the flow of ions in living systems owing to concentration gradients gives rise to electrical potentials and impulses of great physiological significance, accounting in part for the great importance of ion concentration, particularly the hydrogen ion concentration, in living tissue.

ROBERT KUNIN AND ALVIN WINGER

Cross-references: *Atoms, Electrochemistry, Ionization, Plasma, Radiation (Ionizing)*

IRASER: see LASER; MASER

ISOLATORS: see ATTENUATORS AND ISOLATORS

ISOTOPES

An isotope is one of two or more atoms having the same number of protons in the nucleus (i.e., a member of same chemical species and therefore exhibiting the same chemical behavior) but having different atomic weights and sometimes exhibiting different radioactive behavior. Isotopes are either radioactive, in which case they dissipate energy through the emission of radiation, or stable, i.e., nonradioactive.

The name was proposed by F. Soddy, the British physicist, in 1913, after he, A. S. Russell (A British chemist), and K. Fajans (a German physicist) had developed a generalization to explain the approximately forty radioactive species then known to exist for the last twelve places in the periodic table. During the preceding two years much effort had been spent trying to identify and explain the relations of the decay products of uranium, actinium and thorium.

As early as 1910, strong evidence had been developed to show the chemical identity of (1) ionium, thorium and radiothorium, (2) radium and mesothorium, and (3) lead and radium D. Earlier in 1907, H. N. McCoy and W. H. Ross, Americans, were unable to achieve any measurable separation of radiothorium even through almost 200 precipitations involving ammonia, chromate, hydrogen peroxide, oxalic acid or thiosulphate. This was apparently the first demonstration to show that two different radioelements might be chemically identical.

In 1911, Soddy, using then known evidence, particularly on the chemistry of radium and thorium plus the emanations of inert gases which were always present, suggested that the expulsion of alpha particles causes a radioelement to adopt properties equivalent to a change in its position in the periodic table into the next but one group in the direction of diminishing group number. However, the impact of beta disintegrations upon the elements was not appreciated. In 1912 and 1913, after a very painstaking study of the radioelement, A. Fleck, a British chemist, showed that radium B, radium D, thorium B, and actinium B were identical chemically with lead and, therefore, behaved as lead. Further, he showed that the elements arising from the loss of a beta particle (radium C, radium E, thorium C and actinium C, respectively) were identical chemically with Bismuth. This evidence led to Soddy's group displacement law which satisfactorily explained the relations of the radioelements and their position in the periodic table.

Concurrently with the establishing of the group displacement law and the evidence that the radium, actinium and thorium series decayed to the single element lead, it became apparent to Soddy that lead should exist in forms having an atomic weight of 206 and 208 as compared with ordinary lead's atomic weight of 207.2. This was a startling conclusion as it had been believed that all elements had definite atomic weights. Study of lead from uranium and thorium minerals, principally during 1913 and 1914, established the atomic weight of uranium lead to be in the range of 206.01 to 206.08 and that of thorium lead as 207.8 or 207.9. This confirmed conclusively the existence of species chemically identical but having different atomic weights. Variation of radioactive characteristics, of course, had been recognized earlier.

In 1912, using a positive-ray deflection apparatus containing neon gas, J. J. Thomson (*q.v.*) produced photographic plates which showed two parabolic streaks at the approximate position where one should have been found for neon gas having atoms of single atomic weight. Thomson, however, at first suspected that the less dense streak was produced by a CO_2 ion having a double charge. This possibility was eliminated by passing the gas charged into the apparatus through tubes immersed in liquid air. Plates produced from this gas showed a complete disappearance of the streak resulting from a CO_2 ion impurity (mass weight 44) but still contained an undiminished streak at the 22 atomic weight position. This result led an assistant of Thomson, F. W. Aston, to attempt a separation of neon into two fractions.

After failing to produce any detectable separation by distilling neon adsorbed on charcoal cooled in liquid air, Aston tried separation by diffusing through a pipe-clay tube. After rediffusing 100 cc of ordinary neon many times, he obtained 2 fractions that proved to have atomic weights of 20.15 and 20.28 as compared with 20.18 for ordinary neon. Positive-ray photographs produced from these samples showed an appreciable difference in the relative brightness of the streaks. Although this evidence strongly suggested the existence of two isotopes of neon, Thomson was still concerned lest a type of neon-hydrogen compound (such as NeH_2) might be present.

World War I interrupted this research, but immediately after the war Aston returned to the problem. By redesigning the positive-ray deflection apparatus he was able to focus the rays arising from particles of equal mass into thin lines (rather than a parabola) on the photographic plates and thus increase the accuracy of the instrument.

In 1919, utilizing the redesigned positive-ray deflection apparatus (i.e., the mass spectrograph), Aston proved conclusively the existence of neon with atomic weights of 20 and 22 and chlorine (atomic weight 35.457) with atomic weights of 35 and 37. By the end of 1920 he had found that 9 out of 19 elements examined had two or more isotopes. It was interesting to note that he failed to find isotopes in elements (such as helium, carbon, nitrogen, oxygen, fluorine, and phosphorus) whose atomic weights were close to whole numbers. This result led to the formulation of the whole number rule: All atomic weights are very close to integers and variations noted from chemical determinations result from mixtures of two or more isotopes having an approximate integral atomic weight.

Later and more exacting work showed that small amounts of isotopes exist in helium, carbon, nitrogen and oxygen. At present helium (at. wt. 4.003) is known to exist as helium 3 ($1.3 \times 10^{-4}\%$) and helium 4 (99.9999%); carbon (at. wt. 12.010) as carbon 12 (98.9%) and carbon 13 (1.1%);

nitrogen (at. wt. 14.008) as nitrogen 14 (99.62%) and nitrogen 15 (0.38%); and oxygen (at. wt. 16.000) as oxygen 16 (99.757%), oxygen 17 (0.039%) and oxygen 18 (0.204%). Only two isotopes of chlorine have been found—chlorine 35 (75.4%) and 37 (24.6%); however, a third isotope of neon (neon 21) with a natural abundance of only 0.28% has been discovered. Tin, for example, exists in 9 stable isotopes. However, some elements contain natural atoms with only one atomic weight; examples are beryllium (at. wt. 9.02), fluorine (at. wt. 19.0000), sodium (at. wt. 22.997), aluminum (at. wt. 26.97), phosphorus (at. wt. 30.98) and 15 other elements.

After successful separation of isotopes for purposes of detection and atomic-weight measurement, it then became of interest to separate them in a manner permitting isolation of the different species. Aston's partial separation of neon isotopes and Harkins' enrichment of chlorine isotopes by diffusion techniques were early instances. The pressing need for Uranium 235 during World War II provided the impetus for the development of large-scale isotope separation methods. In the case of Uranium 235-Urandium 238, the gaseous-diffusion method proved to be most practical. Although the ratio of the molecular weights of these isotopes in the gaseous hexachloride form is only 349 to 352, the slightly greater velocity of the lighter material over the heavier at constant temperature is sufficient to yield a practical difference in their diffusion rate through a porous barrier. In each diffusion stage, the proportion of Uranium 235 in the isotopic mixture is raised by a factor of about 1.0014; hence, to increase the abundance of Uranium 235 from its natural 0.7% to 99% would require approximately 4000 diffusion stages, or cascades. That an enrichment of this magnitude could be accomplished was demonstrated by the successful operation of the gaseous-diffusion plant at Oak Ridge, Tennessee.

Two other separation methods were investigated at the same time. The first of these, the electromagnetic method, derives from the mass spectrograph. Here again, despite the small difference in the masses of the Uranium 235 and Uranium 238 ions, the paths they describe in an appropriately oriented electromagnetic field result in semicircles of different radii. The individual species are collected by placement of collection pots in the path of the two ion beams.

The thermal-diffusion process is dependent upon both thermal diffusion and thermal convection. The lighter atoms or molecules in an isotopic gaseous or liquid mixture tend to congregate in hot areas, whereas the heavier ones tend to congregate in cool areas. At the same time, the thermally hot atoms or molecules tend to rise and the cool ones tend to sink. Advantage of this characteristic may be taken to separate Uranium 235-Uranium 238 by placing the isotopic mixture in a vertical tube, the walls of which are cooled and the center of which is heated (by means of an electric wire). The Uranium 235 tends to concentrate near the hot center wire and at the same time rise to the top of the tube. The Uranium 238, on the other hand, collects near the cooler walls and tends to sink to the bottom of the tube. Through the use of a number of such tubes in series, practical separations can be effected.

Despite the wartime genesis of techniques for the large-scale production of stable and radioactive isotopes, these materials now find their greatest value in basic and applied research and development, industrial applications, agricultural studies, and medical research, diagnosis, and therapy.

J. E. MACHUREK

Cross-references: *Atoms, Chemical Elements, Mass Spectrometry*

K

KERR EFFECT

The *Kerr effect* is the occurrence of double refraction in a substance, when it is placed in an electric field. More exactly called the *Kerr Electro-optic effect*. It was first discovered for a solid (glass, in 1875) but it exists for liquids and gases also. Liquids exhibit large effects, and behave like uniaxial crystals with the optic axis parallel to the electric field direction.

The difference in indices of refraction, for electromagnetic radiation with its electric vector parallel or perpendicular to the optic axis, is proportional to the square of the electric field strength.

The effect is caused either by natural or induced anisotropy of the individual molecules, and a lining up of the molecules by the applied electric field.

The *Kerr Magneto-optic effect* is the change in polarization of light reflected from a polished metal pole of a magnet. Linearly polarized light, incident normally, is reflected as elliptically polarized light.

S. P. DAVIS

Cross-references: *Faraday Effect, Hall Effect, Optics*

KLYSTRON

The klystron is a vacuum tube using velocity modulation (*q.v.*) of an electron beam to amplify rf signals. It is distinguished by the use of resonant cavities as circuit elements to couple energy into and out of the beam. Figure 1 illustrates the operation of a klystron amplifier.

The electrons move axially in a cylindrical beam originating from a thermionic cathode, typically concave. They are drawn toward an anode shaped to create a radial electric field, converging to form a beam smaller in diameter than the cathode. Surrounding the cathode is a focus electrode, at cathode potential, to shape the electric field properly. For modulation of the dc beam current (for switching or AM output) the diode electron gun may be converted to a triode by the addition of a control grid. In the center of the anode is a hole through which the beam passes, entering a region free from electrostatic fields except for the space-charge repulsion between electrons.

The power klystron uses a magnetic field to keep the beam focused in a cylinder. In the focusing scheme illustrated, the beam enters (at the point of minimum diameter) the axial magnetic field through a hole in an iron polepiece. The electrons acquire rotational velocity as they enter the field. After that, the rotational velocity cuts the axial flux lines to produce an inward force that prevents the beam from expanding. The rf signal is applied to the beam as it traverses a gap in the input cavity. Across the gap appears the maximum cavity rf voltage generated by a drive signal coupled from the input transmission line. The rf voltage alternately speeds up and slows down the electrons. Since the energy transferred to accelerated electrons from the circuit is replaced by energy absorbed from the decelerated ones, the rf power required is low.

As the beam proceeds down the field-free "drift tube" beyond the input cavity, the fast electrons catch up with the slow ones to form bunches. Thus an ac component of beam current grows. Where the ac is maximum, the beam crosses the gap of the output cavity. Since the lines of force from the electronic charges must end on induced charges on the drift-tube walls, the induced charge transfers from one side of the gap to the other as the electrons cross, constituting a driving current in the cavity. The cavity is

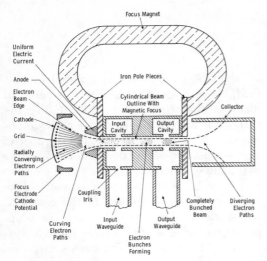

Fig. 1. Schematic cross section of a 2-cavity klystron power amplifier.

coupled to the useful load by an output transmission line, the coupling being adjusted so that the resonant impedance of the cavity matches the source impedance of the electron beam for optimum energy transfer.

After traversing the output cavity, the spent electron beam emerges from the focusing magnetic field and is spread by space charge repulsion. It then strikes the inside of a hollow "collector," where the remaining kinetic energy is dissipated.

In low-power klystrons (10 w at 10 kMc, for instance), a focus magnet is not necessary. The beam diverges slowly enough under electrostatic repulsion so that it can get through the cavities before it is too wide. However, the drift-tube must be of large diameter; for good coupling to the beam, grids are used across the drift-tube tips. This scheme concentrates the electric field in a short axial distance in the gap so that the electrons can interact with it in a transit time that is short compared with an rf cycle. In gridded tubes a convex grid is frequently placed across the anode hole to supply uniform accelerating field across the cathode.

The two-cavity klystron described above has a typical gain of 10 db. For more gain,

intermediate cavities are inserted between the input and output forming a "cascade" amplifier. An intermediate cavity has no external circuit connection. It is excited by the rf beam current, producing rf voltage that remodulates the beam at an amplified signal level. Each intermediate cavity adds about 20 db gain. Stable gains of 90 db have been achieved and 50 db is common. The intermediate cavities may be stagger-tuned to produce a bandpass characteristic.

The klystron amplifier is linear for small signals. With increasing drive it saturates smoothly at 40 to 50 per cent electronic efficiency. Thus AM signals may be amplified by use of the linear region with a peak efficiency of about 30 per cent and an average efficiency lower than this by the average-to-peak ratio of the signal. FM signals are amplified to full saturation output and efficiency.

Present-day klystron amplifiers have power outputs ranging from 1 w to 30 Mw peak and 75 kw average. They are useful at frequencies from 200 Mc to 30 kMc. At any microwave frequency, the klystron amplifier can produce higher power than other known devices—largely because the rf circuit (whose size is dictated by the wavelength) does not intercept electrons.

The klystron becomes an oscillator when feedback is added. Two-cavity oscillators typically have internal feedback by an iris between the cavities. They are used for powers in the 1- to 100-w range.

A single-cavity oscillator is formed by making the electron beam traverse the same cavity twice. In this "reflex klystron," just beyond the cavity there is a "repeller" electrode which is negative with respect to the cathode. The beam becomes bunched in the retarding-field region and is reflected back through the cavity, which acts as both buncher and output circuit. The reflex klystron, with one resonant circuit, is easily tuned mechanically. Electronic tuning, or frequency pushing, is accomplished by varying the dc bias on the repeller electrode, which changes the phase angle of the reflected beam current. The repeller draws no current, so that a high-impedance modulating voltage may be used.

Reflex klystrons give powers from 10 mw to 1 w with a typical efficiency of 2 per cent. They are widely used at frequencies from 3 to 35 kMc.

R. B. NELSON

Cross-references: *Applegate Diagram, Bunching, Millimeter-Wave Generation*

L

LAND COLOR THEORY: see TELEVISION (COLOR)

LANGMUIR, IRVING (1881–1957)

Irving Langmuir was born in Brooklyn, N. Y., on January 31, 1881. After completing his elementary education in public schools in Brooklyn, he traveled with his parents to Paris, where he studied for three years. He then returned to the United States, studied for a year at Chestnut Hill Academy in Philadelphia, and then at the Pratt Institute in Brooklyn and at the School of Mines at Columbia University, from which he graduated in 1903 with a degree in metallurgical engineering. He returned to Europe to study at the University of Göttingen and received the doctorate there in 1906. He taught chemistry for three years at Stephens Institute of Technology, and in 1909 became associated with the General Electric Research Laboratory in Schenectady, N. Y., remaining there until his retirement in 1950. He made important contributions to pure scientific knowledge in many fields, including electron emission, gaseous discharges, the study of surface chemistry, and the study of proteins. He also participated in the development of many important technological devices, including the gas-filled incandescent lamp, the high-vacuum power tube, atomic hydrogen welding, and the condensation-mercury pump for producing very high vacuums. He also discovered a method by which precipitation may be induced from certain types of clouds, leading to artificial climate control. He received many honors, including the Nichols Medal of the American Chemical Society (twice, in 1915 and 1920), the Hughes Medal of the Royal Society (1918), and the Rumford Medal. In 1932 Langmuir became the first American industrial scientist to win the Nobel Prize, granted for his researches in the field of surface chemistry. In 1944 he became the fourth American to receive the coveted Faraday Medal of the Institution of Electrical Engineers in London. He died at Falmouth, Mass., on August 16, 1957. His contributions to electronics alone, notably in the fields of electron emission and space-charge phenomena, would have sufficed to assure his lasting fame even if he had not made his many important contributions to chemistry.

CHARLES SUSSKIND

Cross-references: *Historical Background of Electronics*

Irving Langmuir

LAPLACE AND FOURIER TRANSFORMS

Laplace and Fourier transforms are members of a general class of integral transforms of considerable importance in mathematical analysis. They are used extensively in the physical sciences for the analysis and synthesis of systems which can be described by linear integrodifferential equations with constant coefficients.

The Fourier transform of a function $f(t)$ is defined by

$$F(\omega) = \int_{-\infty}^{\infty} f(t)e^{-i\omega t}\, dt \tag{1}$$

when the integral on the right exists. It can be shown that the integral exists when $f(t)$ satisfies the requirement

$$\int_{-\infty}^{\infty} |f(t)|\, dt < \infty \tag{2}$$

In other words, for each function $f(t)$ that satisfies (2) there exists an $F(\omega)$ defined by (1). The inverse operation exists and is given by

$$f(t) = \frac{1}{2\pi} \int_{-\infty}^{\infty} F(\omega) e^{j\omega t}\, d\omega \tag{3}$$

Hence, given the Fourier transform $F(\omega)$ of a function $f(t)$, it is possible to find the original function $f(t)$ using (3). The function $f(t)$ and its associated $F(\omega)$ are known as a Fourier transform pair.

The function $F(\omega)$ is in general a complex function of ω. The magnitude of $F(\omega)$ for a particular value of ω gives the relative content of frequency ω in $f(t)$. Consequently, $F(\omega)$ is often called the *spectrum function* of $f(t)$.

It should be noted, however, that many important functions do not possess a Fourier transform, i.e., they do not satisfy the requirement (2). Examples are $f(t) = 1$ and $f(t) = \sin t$. In each of these cases the integral in (1) does not exist for real values of ω.

The Laplace transform of a function $f(t)$ is defined by

$$F(s) = \int_{0}^{\infty} f(t) e^{-st}\, dt \tag{4}$$

where s is a complex variable, $s = \alpha + j\omega$. The integral on the right of (4) exists for certain values of s if $f(t)$ satisfies the requirement

$$\int_{0}^{\infty} |f(t)|\, e^{-\sigma t} dt < \infty \tag{5}$$

for some real number σ. In this case the integral of (4) exists for all values of $s = \alpha + j\omega$ such that $\alpha > \sigma$. The number σ is called the *abscissa of absolute convergence*, and $F(s)$ is an analytic function of s for all values of s such that $\alpha > \sigma$.

The inversion formula for the Laplace transform is

$$f(t) = \frac{1}{2\pi j} \int_{c-j\infty}^{c+j\infty} F(s) e^{st}\, ds \tag{6}$$

where $c > \sigma$. The functions $f(t)$ and $F(s)$ form a Laplace transform pair. A list of Laplace transform pairs can be found in many mathematical tables.

It should be noted that the Laplace transform exists for many functions that have no Fourier transform. For example, the functions $f(t) = 1$ and $f(t) = \sin t$ both satisfy condition (5). Most functions used to describe physical quantities satisfy condition (5) and hence, possess a Laplace transform.

Several important properties of the Laplace and Fourier transforms can be derived from the defining integrals (1) and (4). Let $\mathcal{L}\{f(t)\}$ denote the Laplace transform of $f(t)$. The Laplace transform of the derivative of $f(t)$ is

$$\mathcal{L}\{f'(t)\} = \int_{0}^{\infty} f'(t) e^{-st} dt \tag{7}$$

When integrated by parts, (7) becomes

$$\mathcal{L}\{f'(t)\} = e^{-st} f(t) \Big|_{0}^{\infty} + s \int_{0}^{\infty} f(t) e^{-st} dt \tag{8}$$

If $f(t)$ satisfies condition (5) and α, the real part of s, is greater than σ, (8) becomes

$$\mathcal{L}\{f'(t)\} = -f(0) + s \int_{0}^{\infty} f(t) e^{-st} dt \tag{9}$$

By definition the second term on the right of (9) is just $F(s)$, the Laplace transform of $f(t)$. Hence,

$$\mathcal{L}\{f'(t)\} = sF(s) - f(0). \tag{10}$$

The above procedure can be repeated for higher derivatives to yield the general expression

$$\mathcal{L}\left\{\frac{d^n f(t)}{dt^n}\right\} = s^n F(s) - s^{n-1} f(0)$$
$$- s^{n-2} f'(0) - \cdots - f^{(n-1)}(0) \tag{11}$$

Integration by parts can also be used to find the Laplace transform of

$$\int_0^t f(t) \, dt$$

which is

$$\mathcal{L}\left\{\int_0^t f(t) \, dt\right\} = \frac{1}{s} F(s) \qquad (12)$$

Equation (12) can be easily extended for higher order integrals.

Properties of the Fourier transform similar to those given above for the Laplace transform can be derived from (3) using integration by parts.

The transform method will be demonstrated using the Laplace transform to find the solution of the linear integro-differential equation (13) for $y(0) = 0$ and

$$\frac{dy(t)}{dt} + 6\int_0^t y(t) \, dt + 5y(t) = e(t) \qquad (13)$$

where $e(t) = 3$ for $t \geq 0$, $e(t) = 0$ for $t < 0$.

The Laplace transform can be applied to all terms in (13) to give

$$sY(s) - y(0) + \frac{6}{s} Y(s) + 5Y(s) = E(s) \qquad (14)$$

where

$$Y(s) = \mathcal{L}\{y(t)\} \quad \text{and} \quad E(s) = \mathcal{L}\{e(t)\}$$

Because of the properties (11) and (12) of the Laplace transform, the original integro-differential equation is reduced to an algebraic equation involving the unknown $Y(s)$:

$$Y(s) = \frac{s}{s^2 + 5s + 6} E(s) \qquad (15)$$

Since $e(t)$ is known, $E(s)$ can be found from (4) or standard tables to be $E(s) = 3/s$. Hence,

$$Y(s) = \frac{3}{s^2 + 5s + 6} \qquad (16)$$

The solution $y(t)$ can now be found from standard tables or the inversion formula (6) to be

$$y(t) = 3e^{-2t} - 3e^{-3t} \qquad (17)$$

The solution of (13) for any other $e(t)$ can be found by simply repeating the last two steps above with the new $E(s)$.

W. H. WATTENBURG

Cross-references: *Fourier Analysis, Fourier Integrals and Their Applications*

LARMOR FREQUENCY: see CHARACTERISTIC FREQUENCIES

LARYNX (ELECTRONIC)

The electronic larynx is an artificial substitute for the normal voice, actuated electronically, that enables a person who has lost the use of his vocal cords (usually by surgical removal or from paralysis) to regain his ability to speak. Several types have been in use for nearly a century, but the recent application of electronic techniques to the problem has resulted in devices with notable improvements in speech quality, compactness, cleanliness, and reduction of required operating power.

Features common to all types are (1) a means for producing at will a sound having a usable frequency spectrum, and (2) a method of introducing the sound into the vocal tract. In the electronic larynx, the sound is produced by using an electronic pulse generator to drive a transducer that converts the electrical pulses into sound vibrations. The sound is then conducted into the vocal tract either (1) through a flexible tube inserted in the mouth, or (2) by holding the vibrating diaphragm of the transducer firmly against the side of the throat, the vibrations passing through the tissues into the pharynx. The latter method is used in the electronic larynx developed by the Bell Telephone Laboratories. Once in the vocal tract the sound vibrations are formed into words and sentences by movements of the throat, jaws, tongue, and lips in the same manner in which one normally talks when using the vocal cords.

It is desirable, of course, that the speech produced in this artificial way should sound as natural as possible. The periodic tone produced naturally by the vocal cords is variable in frequency and rich in harmonics, with amplitudes falling off with increasing frequency at about 9 db per octave. The resonant cavities of the vocal tract modulate the harmonics into groups, each vowel sound having its own characteristic set. To approximate in the electronic larynx such a source of sound the pulses that drive the transducer are made sharp and narrow, since pulses of this shape have many harmonics. The frequency range required is from about 100 cps to several thousand.

The electronic circuit that generates the pulses is preferably one using transistors. A design that also provides a variable pitch control is described below in some detail. A relaxation oscillator with two transistors is used, followed by a power transistor. The pulse frequency is controlled by an RC combination, and may be varied by the user with a thumb-operated rheostat. The duration of each pulse is determined by a second RC combination. Since pulse duration directly affects the loudness and quality of the speech output as well as the useful life of the batteries, it was chosen by careful testing. A value of 0.5 msec proved to be optimum. The circuit is powered by two 5-v mercury batteries, and the average current drain is about 0.025 amp. Battery life varies greatly with the talking habits of the user, and in field tests ranged from two weeks to four months.

The transducer actuated by the pulses is a modified telephone receiver. Since it is pressed against the throat, the loading on the diaphragm is very different from the value when working into air, since the characteristic mechanical impedance of flesh is about 4000 times that of air. This heavy loading requires several modifications in the receiver, including adjustments of magnet strength, coil impedance, and diaphragm thickness and position.

The components described above are all combined into a hand-held unit weighing about 8 oz. In use the transducer diaphragm is pressed against the throat and the sound turned on and off by the thumb control, which on further pressing also raises the pitch. This pitch control brings to the user the advantages to be gained from inflection of the voice for questions, emphasis, sentence endings, etc., thus contributing much to make the voice sound more natural.

It is found that a person requires a little practice in finding the proper place and pressure on the throat before good speech output volume can be achieved. After a short period of experimentation one can attain a normal conversational level.

Comparisons by means of visible-speech spectrograms of natural speech and speech using this unit show surprisingly little difference. The results also indicate that the frequency spectrum after transmission into the throat has approximately the right high-frequency components. Listening tests with isolated single words have been also made. These show that with a moderate amount of practice, about 59 per cent of the words can be understood correctly, which is found to correspond to 95-percent sentence intelligibility.

F. E. HAWORTH

Cross-references: *Earphones, Electroacoustics, Hearing Aids, Loudspeakers and Microphones, Visible Speech, Vocoder*

LASER

An acronym for *l*ight *a*mplification by *s*timulated *e*mission of *r*adiation; similar in operating principle to the maser, therefore also referred to as an optical maser. The laser is a device capable of amplifying or generating coherent light. Highly monochromatic optical radiation is emitted in the form of a nearly plane wave with a beam angle divergence theoretically limited only by diffraction effects. Principal applications include space communications and very high resolution radar. The nearly parallel beam can be, in principle, focused to a spot a few ten millionths of an inch in diameter, thereby producing enormous localized flux densities. Medical, chemical, and biological applications might use this property. Applications utilizing the high degree of coherence are meteorology and other interferometric techniques.

The laser utilizes the interaction of electromagnetic radiation with a material having an appropriate set of discrete energy levels. Consider a pair of such levels with energies E_1 and E_2 ($E_2 > E_1$). An oscillatory field of frequency $\nu_{21} = (E_2 - E_1)/h$ (h is Planck's constant) stimulates both absorption and emission. Atoms in the lower level make transitions to the upper level, each absorbing energy $\epsilon = h\nu_{21}$. Similarly, upper-level atoms are stimulated downward, but each of these gives up energy to the field by radiating a quantum of energy ϵ. The net effect of the radiation field interacting with the system (absorption or emission) is proportional to the absorption coefficient $\alpha =$ const. $(N_1 - N_2)$, where N_1 and N_2 are the number of atoms in these two levels. Since in thermal equilibrium $N_1 > N_2$, a wave propagating through a length l of the material is *attenuated* by the factor $e^{\alpha l}$.

In a substance with a third energy level $E_3(E_3 > E_2 > E_1)$, energy can be supplied to the system by radiation of frequency $\nu_{31} = (E_3 - E_1)/h$. If other parameters (relaxation times) in the material are suitably related, an inverted population ($N_2 > N_1$) is produced. Here the net interaction with a field of frequency ν_{21} is emission (α is a negative quantity) and a propagating wave is *amplified* by the factor $e^{|\alpha|l}$. Oscillation can be produced by providing a feedback mechanism.

Visible light covers the electromagnetic spectrum from 4×10^{14} cps (red) to 7.5×10^{14} cps (violet). A substance as described above with energy levels such that ν_{21} lies in this frequency range could therefore amplify or generate visible light; ruby (Al_2O_3 doped with Cr_2O_3) has been successfully employed.

A cylindrical ruby rod with a reflecting coating at each end is coaxially placed in a helical flash lamp. Green light from the lamp (ν_{31}) is absorbed by the ruby and red light (ν_{21}) is generated and coupled out of the system through a hole in the reflecting coating at one end of the rod. Regeneration results from waves traveling back and forth through the rod many times. The highest-Q modes of the rod resonator correspond to waves traveling nearly parallel to the rod axis and account for the parallel output beam. Similarly, regeneration selects only frequencies very close to the transition ν_{21} and accounts for the narrow output spectrum.

T. H. MAIMAN

Cross-references: *Interferometer Method (Optical), Masers, Optics*

LIGHTHOUSE TUBE

A lighthouse tube is an electron tube designed in a form particularly suitable for the attachment of external tuning cavities, named for its characteristic lighthouse-shaped profile.

Many undesirable features in tubes of conventional construction are the result of the fact that the tube and tuning system are separate units. These features include the effects of lead inductance, lead capacitance, and radiation. However, in many cases, compelling reasons may exist to favor separate units. An extended tuning range and the ability to change or discard one unit without the other are two reasons. The lighthouse tube is one form of a so-called disk-seal design that has many of the advantages and few of the disadvantages of separate units.

The active portions of the tube structure are in the form of planes or disks. Connections to the external resonators or cavities are made by means of metal rings attached to the disk electrodes. The cavity electromagnetic fields are coupled to the interaction space within the tube through glass portions of the tube and the interaction space is essentially an integral portion of the cavity.

Lighthouse tubes may be used as amplifiers or as oscillators and are usually operated in a configuration known as a grid-separation circuit. This description refers to the fact that the input cavity is connected between the cathode and the grid, whereas the output cavity is connected between the plate and the grid of the lighthouse tube.

Although lighthouse tubes have been used at frequencies as high as several thousand megacycles, the greatest utility in competition with tubes of other types is in the frequency range of a few hundred to the order of a thousand megacycles.

J. G. SKALNIK

Cross-references: *Klystrons, Magnetrons*

LINEAR ACCELERATORS

Linear accelerators were developed because very high voltage cannot be applied to electrodes in an insulating vacuum tube without breakdown. Several million volts equally distributed along a hundred insulated sections in series avoids breakdown. Higher voltages were desired. A moderate rf voltage was applied between alternate drift tubes having lengths increasing with the velocity of ions to be accelerated through them. The time to travel from one gap between tubes to the next gap was half a cycle of the rf voltage. Alternate drift tubes were connected to one end of an oscillator LC tank circuit. A beam of ions was obtained from the plasma of an arc generally, but ions of potassium came from hot tungsten struck by a beam of neutral atoms. Near the beginning end of a long sequence of aligned drift tubes, the lengths were so short that a few were replaced by disks, with suitable correction for the smaller energy receive in traveling through changing fields. Less time was spent in the diverging field at the exit than was spent in the converging field at the entrance of an accelerating region, when the velocity was small and increasing appreciably. This focusing disappeared as the percentage velocity change

per gap became less, and was then replaced by another due to delaying the time of passage across gaps until the fields were decreasing so that outward component of field at the exit was weaker than the inward component at the time of entering the gap. Axial defocusing or debunching then occurred, slow ions receiving least energy and becoming slower.

This lack of phase stability is inherent in linear accelerators for particles with changing velocity. It does not occur with relativistic velocity particles which merely become heavier and overswing across the axis less and less. Nor does it occur in cyclotrons, where slower particles travel shorter paths and remain in phase.

After being fairly well focused in the initial few gaps, a change of spacing permitted the ions to enter the remainder of the system too late and with too much velocity for synchronism. Focusing improved as the particles advanced into synchronism and bunching improved as they moved ahead further in phase without seriously defocussing radially. It is not known how often this strong-focusing sequence could be repeated.

Use of grids across entrances of cylinders to reduce outward forces was examined but not used. In later cavity enclosed systems it was found to be very useful.

Strong accelerating fields within cavities evolved by enclosing a million volt tank coil with distributed capacitance within a metal tank, later replacing the coil by a coax line inner conductor, and shortening this inner conductor. A simultaneous development (fields reflected within a metal enclosure) by W. W. Hansen led even more directly to cavity resonators (*q.v.*).

A linear sequence of such cavities variously connected, led first to drift tubes within a long cavity, and then to disk-loaded waveguides that have less loss when particle velocity approaches that of light because drift tubes become very long and carry enormous current. Disk-loaded waveguides built prior to 1940 were intended for long pulse operation, with many reflections from end to end, thus having backward and forward waves. This operation required half-wavelength spacing between disks. Post World War II loaded guides dissipate the energy without reflections, allowing arbitrary spacing as long as phase and particle velocities are equal. Progressively changing spacing and diameter prevents excitation of other modes.

Postwar magnetrons (*q.v.*) and klystrons (*q.v.*) have been used as driving power sources, but prewar beam tetrodes called resnatrons (*q.v.*) were developed for this purpose also. Very recently, a magnetron has been built in a drift tube, capable of supplying power to a cavity containing many drift tubes.

D. H. SLOAN

Hansen Linear Electron Accelerator

The term "linear accelerator" (often abbreviated to *linac*) implies acceleration of particles in a straight line. Thus, in the strictest sense, this nomenclature would include electrostatic machines such as the Van de Graaff accelerator (*q.v.*). However, common usage reserves this terminology for those machines employing time varying fields to achieve straight-line acceleration.

In another type of accelerator, the ion linear accelerator (see below), the particles are shielded by means of drift tubes from the fields during alternate (decelerating) half cycles. This method is especially suited to acceleration of heavy particles such as protons, deuterons, and ions which can achieve appreciable kinetic energies at velocities low compared to c, the velocity of light. At a fixed operating frequency, this technique becomes less efficient as the particle velocity approaches c because of the increasing length of the drift tubes.

Since the mass of the electron is quite small, compared to that of the proton, its velocity approaches c at comparatively low kinetic energies. For example, a 2-Mev proton has a velocity of only $0.065c$, but an electron of the same kinetic energy has a velocity of $0.979c$. This feature makes the use of an electron accelerating structure possible which is uniform in dimensions over most of its length.

A type of structure commonly used in electron linacs is shown in Fig. 1. It is based upon the cavity resonator developed by W. W. Hansen (*q.v.*) in 1937. For analytical purposes this structure may be considered either as a series of coupled cavities or as a cylindrical waveguide in which periodic metallic *loading* disks are introduced to establish the desired in-phase relationship between the electrons and the wave along the entire length of the structure.

The accelerator structure is supplied with rf power from an external source such as a magnetron or klystron (*q.v.*). Power entering the structure sets up an electric field configuration having a strong axial component as indicated in Fig. 1. The structure may

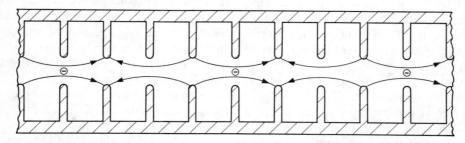

Fig. 1. Disk-loaded structure used as electron linac. Rf power fed into this structure sets up electric fields having a strong axial component as illustrated schematically. The dimensions of the structure are adjusted so that the phase velocity of the useful component of the electromagnetic wave equals the electron velocity. The electrons *ride* along on the traveling wave gaining energy as they pass through the accelerator.

be designed to operate either as a *standing-wave* or as a *traveling-wave* device. In the former case, the loading disks are located at half-wavelength intervals; because of reinforcement of reflections there are both forward and backward waves of equal amplitude which *beat* together to set up the standing wave. In the traveling-wave accelerator the disks are spaced more closely (usually at intervals between one-third and one-quarter wavelength) and only the forward wave exists. The traveling-wave structure is usually preferred over the standing-wave structure because no power is consumed in setting up a backward wave that does not contribute to the accelerating process, and because it is easier to supply the traveling-wave structure with power since it presents a constant impedance during the build-up time; whereas the standing-wave structure presents a variable impedance starting with short-circuited conditions when power is first turned on.

The *phase* velocity of the useful wave in the disk-loaded structure may be made equal to the electron velocity by proper choice of the dimensions and spacing of the loading disks and the inside diameter of the waveguide. The *group* velocity in such a structure is characteristically small compared to c. This is the basis for the strong electric fields and also for the typically long filling time of the structure; in a traveling-wave structure this time is equal to the length divided by the group velocity.

The energy of particles produced by a linac is given by

$$V = k(PL)^{1/2}f^{1/4} \qquad (1)$$

where P is the rf input power, L is the accelerator length, f is the operating frequency, and k is a constant depending upon the dimensions and shape of the accelerator cavities. This equation indicates that for maximum energy with a given length and input power, the frequency should be as high as possible. Since the transverse dimensions of the structure vary inversely with frequency,

a practical upper limit on frequency is determined by the minimum aperture required for the passage of the electron beam. Another limitation is the reduced outputs available from power sources at the higher frequencies. All existing electron linacs operate at frequencies between 1 and 10 kMc. Since electron energy varies as the square root of the input power, most linacs are operated under pulsed conditions to obtain high energies without excessive consumption of average power.

The electron energy given in Eq. (1) is called the *no-load* energy; it is the energy obtained with negligible beam current. As the beam current is increased and an increasing fraction of the rf power is converted to beam power, the electron energy decreases linearly with current; this phenomenon is called *beam loading*.

The electron linac cannot have simultaneous phase and radial stability without the use of external focusing devices. Electrons in the focusing region behind the wave crest experience de-bunching forces; those in the phase-stable region ahead of the crest experience de-focusing forces. However, long linacs are feasible since, because of relativistic effects, the radial forces vanish and the electrons become more massive as the electron velocity approaches c.

A structure consisting of a number of cavities as shown in Fig. 1 is called an accelerator *section*. A typical linac includes one or more sections, each independently fed from an individual amplifier-type rf *power source*, a single low-power oscillator called the *driver* that supplies rf power to the sources, an electron *gun* that supplies electrons at the low-energy end of the accelerator, a *buncher* that groups the electrons into packets of small phase spread before they are injected into the accelerator, and a *target area* at the output or high-energy end.

The electron linac has been used for many purposes. Among the most important applications are: physics research, radiation therapy, radiation processing of materials (*q.v.*)

such as plastics and chemicals, and injection into large circular accelerators.

RICHARD B. NEAL

Ion Linear Accelerator

A linear ion accelerator consists of a large evacuated cylindrical cavity resonator excited in the TM_{010} mode. The chief electric field is along the axis of the cylinder and is in the same phase at all points. Doughnut-shaped electrodes, called *drift tubes*, are placed along the axis of the cavity as shown in Fig. 2. Ions injected along the axis are accelerated by the electric field in the gaps between drift tubes when the electric field is in the same direction as the ion velocity. During the reverse part of the rf cycle the ions are shielded from the field by the drift tubes. Since the ions pass from one gap to the next in one rf cycle, the lengths of both gaps and drift tubes increase with ion velocity.

In practice there are deviations from the ideal in field strength, in ion velocity, and in phase at which the ions cross the gaps. These deviations do not cause the ions to get out of synchronism with the rf field if the ions cross the gaps when the accelerating field is increasing. Ions that cross a gap late gain more velocity and catch up with ions that cross at the ideal or *synchronous* phase.

Similarly ions that cross early or that have the wrong velocity tend toward the synchronous values, and the motion is *phase stable*.

The radial component of the accelerating fields shown in Fig. 2 point inward on the low-energy side of the accelerating gap and outward on the high-energy side. Since for phase stability the ions must cross the gaps while the electric field is increasing, the defocusing field (on the high-energy side) is stronger than the focusing field. The defocusing component of the field can be eliminated by grids across the input apertures of the drift tubes, but in a linac with many drift tubes such grids intercept a large part of the beam. Alternatively, focusing magnets can be placed inside the drift tubes —either solenoidal magnets producing an axial magnetic field or quadrupole magnets producing a transverse field. The polarity of quadrupole magnets must be alternated to produce *alternating-gradient focusing* or *strong focusing*.

Ions are usually injected with a velocity of about $0.03c$ by a 500-kv Cockcroft-Walton accelerator (*q.v.*). The rf frequencies are from 50 to 200 Mc. Above 200 Mc the drift tubes at the input end are impractically small; below 50 Mc the size of the cavity and the rf power consumption become too

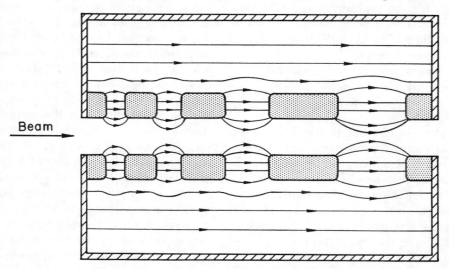

Fig. 2. Cross section of linac cavity showing electric field lines.

large to be attractive. The several million watts of rf power required is supplied by several triodes. Operation is usually pulsed to reduce the average rf power consumption. Proton linacs are from 20 to 110 ft long, and their output energy is from 3.7 to 68 Mev.

Acceleration of heavy ions such as nitrogen or neon is inefficient unless they are highly ionized. Beams from ion sources, however, contain few highly ionized ions. Therefore in some linacs built for heavy ions the beam is accelerated to a moderate energy, then passed through a thin layer of matter to strip more electrons off the ions before they are accelerated further. These accelerators, called *hilacs*, produce beams with 10 Mev for each nucleon in the nucleus (e.g., 140 Mev for nitrogen, 400 Mev for argon).

The beam is more easily extracted from linear accelerators than from circular machines, and intense external beams of monoenergetic well-focused ions can be obtained. A linac with a special injection system has produced an external beam of 200 ma. The properties of the external beam make linacs useful as injectors for proton synchrotrons as well as for nuclear research.

EDWARD L. HUBBARD

Cross-references: *Accelerators, Alternating-Gradient Focusing, Undulator*

LINEAR PROGRAMMING

Linear programming is the name applied to a class of optimization problems in which one seeks to minimize (or maximize) a linear form of variables subject to linear constraints on the variables. In a typical problem, the "diet problem," one is to minimize the cost of the total food for, say, one week, given the cost per pound for each foodstuff and the content of each constituent that must be included. For example, suppose that one is to purchase x_i pounds of the ith foodstuff, at a cost of a_i dollars per pound, and that each pound contains b_{ij} units of the jth constituent. Then the linear pro-

gramming problem is to choose values of the x_i that minimize $c = \Sigma a_i x_i$, subject to constraint equations, $\Sigma b_{ij} x_i \geq d_j$, one for each constituent j. It is always assumed that the "cost function" is to be minimized, and that all variables are nonnegative; obvious changes are made in the model if this is not already the case.

To put the problem in "standard form," an additional nonnegative "slack variable" is added to each inequality to convert it into an equality. There result n equations in m variables where, of course, $m > n$; of these variables, $m - n$ may be chosen at will.

The solution of this problem is based on a theorem of Dantzig that states that the vector which minimizes the linear form has at most n of the variables nonzero. One chooses any feasible basis (a set of values for n of the variables that satisfies the constraint equations when the remaining variables are set equal to zero) and then may proceed by standard matrix-manipulation methods to find different bases that successively reduce the cost. The algorithm for choosing these successive bases is called the "Simplex method," and includes a criterion for knowing when the minimum cost has been achieved.

In some cases it is not immediately clear how to form a first feasible solution. In this case, additional "artificial variables" are added in order to obtain a feasible solution in "canonical form," and then the sum of these artificial variables is minimized by the Simplex algorithm. It is possible in a small number of steps to find a canonical form in which the sum of these artificial variables is zero (in which case, since they are nonnegative, they are all zero and may be dropped) if and only if a feasible solution exists to the original problem.

There are two and only two cases where no feasible solution exists for the linear programming problem. In the first case, in terms of the diet problem, one foodstuff may have negative cost, in which case the minimum cost is associated with an infinite amount of that foodstuff. The second case involves, say, poisons in some of the foodstuffs, with associated constraints on the maximum amounts of these foodstuffs that may be incompatible with the minimum amounts.

Every feasible linear programming problem is mathematically equivalent to a two-person zero-sum game. It follows that every linear program has a dual (one being a maximization and the other a minimization) with the same solution.

In the geometric interpretation of linear programming, each constraint is a hyperplane in m-space, as is the cost function. The intersection of the constraints is a convex polyhedron, and the solution is the intersection of this polyhedron with the lowest plane parallel to the cost function. Because of the linearity, this intersection must be on a vertex (or in degenerate cases a line, plane, etc.) of the polyhedron, which is equivalent to the theorem of Dantzig mentioned above; each such vertex corresponds to a basis in the simplex algorithm. Because of the convexity, it is possible to go to successively lower adjacent vertices and be certain of reaching the solution.

Linear programming has become of considerable importance since its introduction in about 1950, because of the large number of practical problems to which this model is appropriate, because of the straightforward algorithmic solution method available, and because routines are available for this algorithm at almost every computing center.

ROBERT E. MACHOL

Cross-references: *Computer Programming, Operations Research*

LODGE, SIR OLIVER JOSEPH (1851–1940)

Oliver Lodge was born in Penkhull in Staffordshire on June 12, 1851, the son of a prosperous merchant and a brother of (Sir) Richard Lodge (1855–1936), the historian. He was educated privately until he was 14 and then entered the family business, not resuming his education until the age of 22,

at the Royal College of Science. He received the D.Sc. in 1877 and was appointed a Demonstrator at University College in London. He became a professor at University College, Liverpool, in 1881. He came close to discovering electromagnetic radiation but was anticipated by Heinrich Hertz. He named the *coherer* and made important contributions to the design of wireless transmitters, performing experiments that foreshadowed ultra-short-wave propagation. He also performed a fundamental experiment to show that the "ether" in the neighborhood of bodies moving through it does not move with them—a result that is said to have ushered in a new era in electromagnetic theory, the era that culminated in the discovery of the theory of relativity.

Lodge became Principal of the newly established University of Birmingham in 1900, having been made a Fellow of the Royal Society in 1887 and awarded its Rumford Medal in 1898. He was knighted in 1902 and served at various times as president of the Physical Society, of the British Association, and of the Society for Psychical Research, an interest that dominated his life after his young son Raymond was killed early in World War I. He resigned his post at Birmingham in 1919 and retired to Lake near Salisbury, where he lived until his death on August 22, 1940.

CHARLES SUSSKIND

Cross-references: *Historical Background of Electronics*

LOGIC CIRCUITS

Logic circuits are the decision-making gates of the digital computer, extensively employed in the arithmetic and control sections but used also in other portions of the computer. There are two basic forms of logical organization in use—*Boolean logic*, and *majority* (or *linear input*) *logic*. The Boolean logic, first described by George Boole (1815–1864) in 1854, is mechanized with AND and OR circuits. These circuits have been the predominant logic elements for the computer industry, and the majority of present day machines are so mechanized. Majority logic, first discussed as a theoretical mathematical model of neurons in living organisms by McCollock and Pitt in 1943, uses both of these circuits as well as a majority (or *voting*) circuit. These basic circuits are defined by their output characteristics, as follows:

AND—the output is true only if *all* of the inputs are true

OR—the output is true if *any* of the inputs are true

Majority—the output is true if the *majority* of the inputs are true (whence the term "voting")

Basic logic circuits are aided by other circuits, which perform such functions as signal amplification, speed buffering, signal delay, and local high-speed storage. These support circuits are often formed from the basic elements of the logic circuits themselves.

The first large-scale arithmetic machine was mechanized with relays performing the logic function. A set of relay contacts in series performed the AND function; the OR function was performed by the junction of the AND circuits.

There was also a brief period during the initial rapid growth of computer technology when vacuum tubes were used as logic elements. For example, the pentode was utilized as a two-input AND gate; in this configuration, the pentode produced a high output voltage at all times except when high input voltages were applied to both the control grid and the suppressor grid.

The semiconductor diode has found favor as the basic element in the mechanization of the AND/OR circuit. Many variations on the method of utilizing the diode have evolved with the advance of the computer art. The diode is found in systems described as current-mode logic, voltage-mode logic, and in hybrid combination with the transistor (*q.v.*), where the base-to-emitter diode of the transistor is used logically as the diode decision element.

Either of the diode gates shown (Figs. 1a

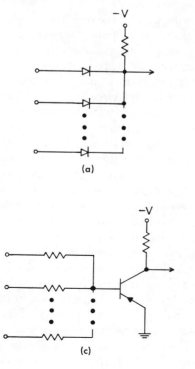

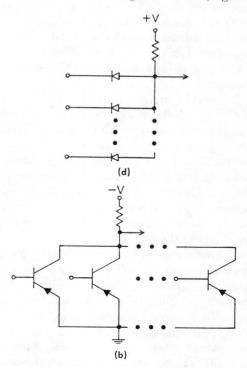

Fig. 1.

and b) can be used for the AND or the OR function, depending upon whether the most positive or most negative excursion of the signal voltage is used in the machine design as the true condition for the data. The output of Fig. 1a assumes the voltage of the most positive input; and the circuit is thus a positive OR element. Only when all of the inputs are negative is the output negative; for this type of true signal, the circuit becomes an AND gate. These functions are inversely true for the gate arrangement of Fig. 1b.

The transistor has found broad use in all areas of computer design, and continues to be the basic active circuit component in developmental systems. A logic circuit frequently employed is the resistor, or *NOR gate*, circuit, which is used in conjunction with a transistor as shown in Fig. 1c. The same basic configuration may be used throughout the system as either the AND function or the OR function. The output of Fig. 1c is positive (OR function) if any of the inputs is negative, and is only negative (AND function) if all the inputs are positive. The true condition for a signal is thus inverted as it is transmitted through the circuit, and the logic flow must be arranged such that an AND gate is followed by an OR gate and vice versa.

In hybrid transistor-diode logic, the base-to-emitter diode of the transistor is used logically as the diode decision element. There are many variations on the transistor gate, the earliest of which is direct-coupled transistor logic (Fig. 1d). The logical function of the gate is similar to that of the NOR gate configuration in which the signal is inverted, and in which the same gate serves as either the AND or the OR.

Magnetic-core techniques, slightly older than transistor techniques, were used extensively in the early days of computer development, and continue to be used in specialized applications requiring extraordinary reliability. Magnetic-core logic offers many subtleties of its own, but is basically similar to AND/OR techniques.

Magnetic thin-film logic shows considerable promise as a potential replacement for transistor or diode logic.

The majority decision principle permits a complex logical function to be performed in one level of logic. Logical elements based upon this principle have been receiving increased attention. Activity in this area has been spurred by the invention of the *tunnel diode* (*q.v.*), an element that has a threshold sufficiently abrupt to encourage the design of a majority gate. Many test vehicles have been built throughout the industry using the tunnel diode, but since the emphasis in these vehicles has been on speed, the engineering difficulties thus imposed upon the system by attempting so to employ a two-terminal active device have penalized the network for this application.

It is also feasible to use the bistable magnetic core or thin film as a basic majority logic element. Engineering difficulties in maintaining tolerances limit the number of inputs to a gate to such a small number that the future of the device for this purpose remains questionable.

The Japanese have constructed computers that utilize a simplified version of the majority logic with parametron circuits. The parametron (*q.v.*) is a subharmonic oscillator employing a magnetic core and a capacitor in each circuit element. The Japanese machines are relatively slow and appear to have limited application. Investigations are, however, under way in this country to determine the value of the technique for high-reliability applications, inasmuch as complete parametron circuits can be constructed without semiconductors or resistors.

The two most restrictive hardware limitations in digital computers are the speed of operation (delay per logical level) and the packing density of the decision elements.

The delay due to the transmission of a signal through a logical gate is a function of many parameters, including the fan-in and fan-out requirements, the packaging concept, and the power requirements of the system. If all of these considerations are optimized, it is possible to achieve a delay per logical level of approximately 1 ns for a system of moderate size. This delay increases as a prime function of the size of the system, and depends essentially on packaging (*q.v.*). Until recently, the physical size of a computing system had little effect on operating speed, but some systems already constructed, and many now in development, have approached or passed the design threshold in which proper timing among subsystems becomes dependent upon the physical length of transmission lines.

Components are becoming available that are so small as to make essentially no contribution to total equipment volume; the volume is dictated by the interconnections between components and by the heat exchanger hardware which is essential in a tightly packaged system. A small advantage may be achieved with the use of molecular circuits containing 10 to 20 components, but digital computer packaging density will remain interconnection-limited until complex logical nets containing perhaps 1000 elements can be economically fabricated as an integral molecular mass.

JOHN T. LYNCH

Cross-references: *Coding and Coding Circuits, Digital Computers, Nonlinear Circuits*

LORAN: see NAVIGATION

LORENTZ, HENDRIK ANTOON (1853–1928)

Hendrik A. Lorentz (not to be confused with Ludwig V. Lorenz, 1829–1891) was born in Arnhem in the Netherlands in 1853 and received his secondary education there. He entered the University of Leiden in 1870 and received the doctorate *summa cum laude* in 1875. After a brief activity as a teacher he was appointed professor of theoretical physics at Leiden at the age of 25. Together with Heinrich Hertz and Oliver Heaviside he became one of the main elaborators of Maxwell's theories, notably with regard to the forces resulting from the motion

of charged particles through a magnetic field. This force (the **B** × **v** force) is generally known as the *Lorentz force*.

He collaborated with Pieter Zeeman in the discovery of the Zeeman effect (*q.v.*) and shared the Nobel Prize for physics with him in 1902. He also contributed to the development of optics, molecular physics, thermodynamics, radiation, and the development of modern physics generally, notably by proposing the transformations named after him, which played an important part in the development of the relativity theory (*q.v.*).

His most significant work from the viewpoint of modern electronics was his electron theory of matter, which has had a profound influence on the understanding of semiconductors (*q.v.*). His calculation of the waves emitted from a harmonically oscillating electron is strikingly similar to the theory of Hertz for an oscillating dipole; together, the two theories form the basis for the understanding of antenna radiation. Moreover, his electron theory has a bearing on the modern theory of the ionosphere and of the atmosphere of the earth. In 1892, Lorentz introduced "retarded potentials" in electromagnetic theory to account for the finite velocity with which electromagnetic waves propagate. He also anticipated the reciprocity theorem for linear systems and generalized Heaviside's theorem (according to which a condenser can be charged from a dc source with an efficiency no greater than 50 per cent) to distributed-constant networks.

Although the bulk of his work was in theoretical physics he showed that he could turn his hand to a practical problem with good effect when he became chairman of a committee charged with supervising the enclosure of the Zuiderzee, a large tidal basin in north Holland. His calculations of the harmonic oscillations caused by tides greatly simplified the planning of the project and placed an entire section of hydraulic engineering on a firm scientific foundation. The bulk of this work was done after he had retired from the university in 1923, at the age of 70. He visited the United States repeatedly, the last time in 1927. He died in Haar-lem on February 4, 1928. A Chair in Physics for visiting professors at the University of Leiden was created by the Netherlands government on the occasion of the centenary of his birth, in 1953.

CHARLES SUSSKIND

Cross-references: *Historical Background of Electronics*

LOUDSPEAKERS AND MICROPHONES

Loudspeakers

A loudspeaker is an electroacoustic transducer that converts electric energy into sound energy.

Two basic loudspeaker types are in common use today: the direct radiating type and the horn type. The horn loudspeaker is used where the generation of large amounts of sound is required and efficiency of conversion is important, e.g., in public-address applications. The direct-radiating type is used in a variety of applications ranging from small table radios to large high-fidelity systems, and is used because of its wide frequency response and relatively small size.

Direct Radiating Loudspeaker. The basic generator used in the direct radiating loudspeaker is electromagnetic; a coil, mounted in a magnetic field, provides the driving force (Fig. 1). Displacement of the cone by this driving force results in the radiation of sound energy. This radiation must be possible throughout a bandwidth of frequencies and is described primarily by the axial frequency response of the loudspeaker: the axial sound pressure at a fixed distance

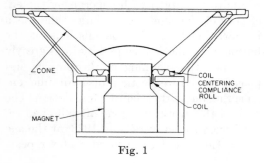

Fig. 1

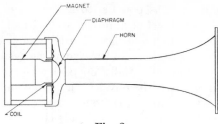

Fig. 2

from the loudspeaker measured as a function of frequency with a constant electrical power input.

Frequency response is controlled by the magnitude of the cone displacement, by the radiating characteristics of the cone, and by the type of enclosure used with the loudspeaker. At low frequencies the mechanical resonance of the system, combined with the air load on the cone and the size and type of enclosure, determine the sound output. In general, large cone areas and large cone displacements are required for effective radiation of sound at low frequencies. At higher frequencies the cone ceases to move as a piston and 'breaks up' into numerous modes of vibration. There is a tendency towards peaks and dips in the frequency response caused by this 'breakup' of the cone. Radiation at the higher frequencies also becomes directional, thus tending to maintain a constant sound output on the loudspeaker axis throughout the frequency range in which the mass of the mechanical system causes a declining total sound energy output.

In addition to axial frequency response, such factors as efficiency, polar response, and distortion are important measures of performance.

Horn Type Loudspeaker. Typical construction of a horn-type loudspeaker is shown in Fig. 2. The driver unit is electromagnetic, as in the direct radiating type, the magnet, steel structure, coil, and diaphragm forming the basic generating unit. The diaphragm is coupled acoustically to the throat of a horn.

Efficiency of conversion, measured by the sound output level for a specified electrical power input, is an important measure of performance. The horn-type loudspeaker is superior in this respect to the direct-radiating type because of the improved coupling of the driver to the air resulting from the use of a horn. Efficient conversion also dictates the use of large, oriented magnets of Alnico V or ceramic material and a well-designed steel structure.

The second important measure of performance of this type of loudspeaker is axial frequency response. The mass of the coil, the compliance of the diaphragm, and the acoustical characteristics of the horn in a large measure determine frequency response. The size of the horn mouth and the rate of horn taper are of particular importance since they, in effect, determine the low-frequency limit of the frequency response.

A third important characteristic of the horn type is polar response. In the ordinary unit in which a straight, round horn is used the polar response becomes increasingly narrow with increasing frequency. Multicellular, diffraction, and compound horns are modifications that reduce this variation in polar response with frequency.

Microphones

A microphone is a transducer that converts sound energy into electric energy. This conversion is used for the accurate reproduction of music and speech, as in the radio, television, and movie industry, for the reproduction of intelligible speech in communication applications, and for instrumentation. Basically a microphone consists of a generating element coupled to a sound field, and the use of different types of generating elements and different methods of coupling results in many different microphone types.

Three fundamentally different microphone types result from different methods of coupling the generating element to the sound field: pressure, pressure gradient, and wave interference.

Pressure Microphones. A pressure microphone is coupled to only one point in the sound field. For this reason, microphones of this type are nondirectional and respond to sound fields from all directions with equal intensity. Within the same physical limitations pressure microphones are more sensitive than gradient microphones. Unlike gradient types, pressure-microphone output is independent of the distance from the microphone to sound source.

Pressure-Gradient Microphones. A pressure gradient microphone is coupled to two points in the sound field and responds to the difference in pressure at these two points. The distinguishing feature of a pressure gradient microphone is that it is directional. Most pressure-gradient microphones are designed to reject sounds from certain directions when operated in a plane-wave sound field. This directional feature is useful in applications where sound in the form of noise or reverberation must be excluded. This type of microphone is widely used with recording and reproducing equipment. Close-talking microphones are a special type of pressure-gradient microphone. Sensitivity is normal for near sound sources and low for distant sound sources. The close-talking microphone is used for voice communication in high-noise sound fields.

Wave-Interference Microphones. Wave-interference microphones are coupled to the sound field over an area and respond to the sum of the pressures over this area. This type of microphone can be made very directional. Two inherent disadvantages limit their usefulness: polar response variation with frequency and large size. The line microphone and microphones using parabolic reflectors are examples of wave-interference microphones.

Generating Elements. Pressure, pressure-gradient, and wave interference type microphones can be designed using a variety of generating elements. Principal among these element types are the dynamic, ribbon, magnetic, condenser, carbon, ceramic, and crystal. These generating elements utilize several different physical principles. In the dynamic, ribbon, and magnetic microphone types conversion is by electromagnetic induction. In the condenser microphone conversion is electrostatic involving the displacement of one plate of a capacitor. The ceramic and crystal microphones utilize the piezoelectric effect (*q.v.*); and in the carbon microphone conversion is achieved by the mechanical variation of electrical resistance.

The choice of generating element is a complex decision involving cost and requirements dictated by the end function of the microphone. For example, the manner in which a lavalier microphone is used dictates that it should be small in size and that long cables should be employed. Furthermore, the use of this microphone type determines the necessary frequency response bandwidth and commercially available input equipment determines the necessary sensitivity. Several different generating elements could fulfill these requirements, but the element of cost in this example favors the dynamic microphone.

In a like manner, in other applications the end use of the microphones determine the required specifications. The most important parameters specified are frequency response, sensitivity, and impedance.

Frequency Response. Two general specifications are used: wide-range response, with accuracy of reproduction a prime requisite; and voice-range response, where intelligibility is the first requirement.

Microphones used in radio, television, movie, public address, and instrumentation applications require wide-range frequency response. Generally this range is from 30 to 100 cps on the bass end to 6000 to 20,000 cps on the high end. This general frequency response requirement can be achieved with dynamic, ribbon, condenser, crystal, and ceramic microphones. The use of carbon and magnetic microphones is limited to applications where voice range frequency response is required.

In applications requiring primarily communication of intelligible information, response is limited to 200 to 300 cps on the bass end to 2,000 to 5,000 cps on the high end. Although any of the mentioned types fulfill these requirements other considerations normally limit microphones used in this application to dynamic, carbon, and magnetic microphones.

Sensitivity. The sensitivity of crystal and ceramic microphones is usually given in voltage output referenced to 1 v for 1 dyne/cm^2 of sound pressure. Voltage output for crystal microphones is usually between -50 db and -55 db re 1 v/1 dyne/cm^2; voltage output for ceramic microphones is usually between -55 db and -60 db re 1 v/1 dyne/cm^2.

The sensitivity of dynamic, magnetic, condenser, and carbon microphones is given in both voltage output referenced to 1 v/1 dyne/cm^2 and power output referenced to 1 mw/10 dynes/cm^2.

Dynamic microphones usually have sensitivities between -50 db to -63 db re 1 mw/10 dynes/cm^2. Magnetic microphones generally have sensitivities -50 db and -55 db re 1 mw/10 dynes/cm^2. Carbon microphones output is between -45 db to -50 db re 1 v/dyne/cm^2, when operated into a 150-ohm load. Condenser microphone sensitivity is usually close to -33 db re 1 mw/10 dynes/cm^2.

Impedance. The impedance of dynamic, ribbon, carbon, and magnetic microphones is nearly always less than 40,000 ohms and is essentially resistive. The use of transformers internally or at the equipment input is a common practice with dynamic, and ribbon microphones. The low impedances necessary for use with long cables have been standardized at 50, 150, 250 ohms.

The impedance of crystal, ceramic, and condenser microphones is that of a capacitor. The very low capacitance of the condenser transducer makes the use of a cathode follower mandatory with the condenser microphones. Ceramic and crystal microphones are used without cathode followers, but cable length must be restricted since the capacitance of the cable loads the microphone.

Other specifications of importance include size, dynamic range, distortion (for high level sound fields), and shielding.

ROBERT C. RAMSEY

Cross-references: *Acoustics, Earphones, Electroacoustics, Hearing Aids, Sound Recording*

M

MACHINING (ELECTRONIC)

Electron-beam drilling and milling is a relatively new machining process. It draws on the principles embodied in the development of the cathode-ray tube, the vacuum tube, the X-ray tube, and the electron microscope.

Method of Operation. In an electric field between cathode and anode, electrons attain a kinetic energy $mv^2/2 = eV$. They can be concentrated by means of electric or magnetic focusing into small bounded regions. The effective diameter of the electron beam may be as small as 10^{-7} cm. The energy densities attained at the impact point may be as high as 10^9 w/cm^2. The incident electron beam transfers over 99 per cent of its kinetic energy to the target (the "work"). The energy transformation is not restricted to the surface. Above a certain energy density the transfer of energy takes place along a groove of a certain depth. In the impact region, the material is heated and spontaneously evaporated.

Part of the incident energy is passed on by thermal conduction to the vicinity of the impact point. This part may be kept small and undesired heating may be avoided. The electron beam must be effective during a sufficiently short period, for instance in pulses. The heat absorbed is conducted away during the interval between pulses.

Technology. The basic design of such an instrument is shown in Fig. 1. The electron gun consists of a tungsten wire heated to approximately 2600°C, the beam-forming control electrode, and the anode. The cathode and the control electrode are held at a high negative potential (up to 150 kv) with respect to the grounded anode. The control electrode is at a variable negative potential with respect to the cathode and serves to control the intensity of the beam current and to preform the electron beam. The elec-

tron beam passes through the anode aperture and is directed, by means of adjusting coils comprising mutually perpendicular pairs of coils capable of adjustment in two planes, into the electron-optical center of the focusing lens, which is usually magnetic. The beam also passes through a stigmatic control that corrects the initially elliptical cross section of the beam (by means of a magnetic or electric field adjustable in magnitude and direction) in such a way that a circular beam spot results in the focal plane of the focusing lens. The focal length of the magnetic lens, and thus the diameter of the focal point, may be varied by adjustments in the lens current.

Cathode emission is cut off by a sufficiently high negative potential on the control electrode. This electrode is pulsed positive by pulses from a pulse generator, via a pulse transformer, gating on the electron beam. The period of its effectiveness can be varied from continuous beam to 1 μsec/pulse. The pulse repetition frequency may be adjusted at will.

This process makes it possible to produce bore holes with diameters as small as a few microns and a diameter-to-depth ratio of 1:40.

To produce a complicated configuration over a larger surface, a profile-control device is used. Between the lens and the work the electron beam passes through a deflection system that consists of several staggered magnetic fields, which deflect the electron beam from the axis. Direction and magnitude of the resulting magnetic field, and thus of the deflection, are regulated by the profile control. This profile control may comprise, depending on the proposed application, any desired additive combination of simple basic motions (straight lines, circles), punched-tape or magnetic-tape control, or even the direct transformation of the contents of a model drawing or photograph. The control

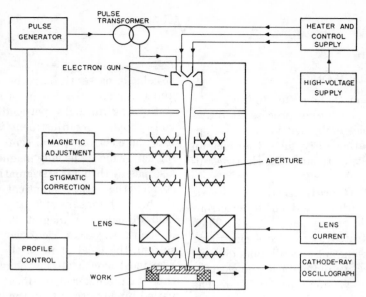

Fig. 1. Schematic diagram of an electron-beam drilling and milling apparatus.

connection to the pulse generator makes it possible to gate on the electron beam only in such a manner as to be compatible with the deflection.

The depth and duration of the machining process may be exactly controlled. One can obtain drilling or milling operations to a prescribed depth (Fig. 2), starting at about 0.01 mm; or right through the material (Fig. 3).

To prevent gas discharges in the acceleration region and to attain a sufficiently long free path for the electrons, the entire process is carried out in vacuum below 10^{-3} mm of Hg. This pressure is readily obtained and maintained with an oil diffusion pump and a rotating forepump. The size of the pumps is determined by the time available for evacuation and by the size of the work space, which in turn depends on the size of the work, its motion, and possibly its storage.

The electron gun and the auxiliary electron-optical components (adjustment, stigmatic control, focusing lens, and beam de-

Fig. 2. Machining of a resistive layer on a ceramic base 8 × 8 mm; slit width, 0.01 mm.

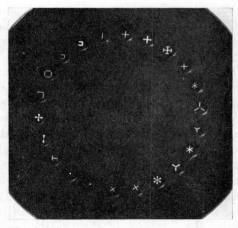

Fig. 3. Section of spinneret plate with milled profiles (stainless steel, 0.5 mm thick). Smallest slit width, 0.05 mm; length, 0.5–1 mm.

flectors) are attached to the work enclosure as a unit, so that control, cleaning, and cathode replacement can be readily carried out.

Since the spot to be machined is small, variations of lens current or accelerating voltage (and hence of focal length and deflection angle) strongly influence the accuracy and reproducibility of the result. The electronic controls limit such variations to 10^{-3}–10^{-4} of the desired value.

Applications. The process has found the following applications to date:

(1) Milling and drilling in hard metals (tungsten carbide), ceramic materials, quartz, and glass.

(2) Profile milling for spinnerets and for injection nozzles.

(3) Microscopic spot welds on metallic and nonmetallic materials, as well as the joining of different materials.

(4) Development and manufacture of electron components of miniature size.

(5) Application in the production of components in semiconductor technology.

K. H. STEIGERWALD

Cross-references: *Cathode-Ray Tubes (Display), Electroforming, Electron Microscopes, Electron Optics, Microcircuitry, Printed Circuits, Semiconductor Manufacture, Welding (Electronic)*

MAGIC T: see WAVEGUIDES

MAGNETIC AMPLIFIERS

The term magnetic amplifier may be applied to any circuit that exploits the nonlinear properties of ferromagnetic or ferrimagnetic materials in order to obtain power amplification. The output circuit of the amplifier is characterized by the series or parallel connection of an ac power supply, a load impedance, and the power winding of a nonlinear magnetic core. Power flow from the source to the load is controlled by the state of the nonlinear magnetic core. The state of the magnetic core is determined by the joint action of the power supply and a control signal. The control signal may assume the form of a dc or ac voltage or current and may be injected into the power circuit or into a separate control winding. A wide variety of practical circuit configurations are possible.

The relatively recent development of magnetic materials with almost equal residual and saturation flux densities and almost constant magnetic field intensity requirements in the unsaturated region, the rectangular BH loop materials, has resulted in high performance magnetic amplifiers. The term magnetic amplifier is normally associated with the circuits that incorporate magnetic cores of these materials. These materials normally have saturation flux densities in range of 0.2 to 2.0 webers/m² and static coercive forces in the range of 0.5 to 50 amp-turns/m. The ratio of residual to saturation flux density is normally greater than 0.85. The following descriptions pertain to magnetic amplifiers which use these rectangular-loop materials.

The circuit diagram of one of the most important types of magnetic amplifiers is shown in Fig. 1. The two cores function as first open and then closed switches on alternate half-cycles of the alternating supply voltage e_s. The output in the load resistance R_L consists of pulses whose width is determined by the time during the half-cycle at which the active or gating core saturates. This firing time in turn is determined by the preset flux level that exists at the beginning of the half-cycle. For instance, on the positive half-cycle of e_s, the lower core is initially approaching saturation from the preset flux level with $e_s \cong N_G d\phi/dt$. The upper core is being reset by the combined action of e_c and $N_c e_s/N_G$. After the bottom core saturates

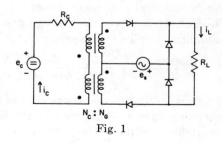

Fig. 1

$i_L = e_s/R_0$, in which R_0 is the total series resistance, and e_c continues the reset action alone until the end of the half-cycle. On the next half-cycle the roles of the upper and lower cores are interchanged.

The normal control range corresponds to negative values of the control voltage of the polarity assumed in the figure. The average control current $i_c = e_c/R_c$. Maximum output occurs when $i_c \geq -I_{c0}$, the threshold magnetizing current of the core, and in the absence of control signal the amplifier is self-saturating. Minimum output occurs when $i_c = -I_{cd}$, the average magnetizing current corresponding to a flux reset sufficient to prevent saturation of the core on the gating half-cycle. Intermediate values of output correspond to intermediate values of control current and consequently control voltage. Normal excitation of the magnetic amplifier is defined by the relation $E_s = 4fN_GA_cB_s$, in which E_s is the half-cycle average of e_s, f is the supply frequency, A_c is the core area, and B_s is the saturation flux density.

The values of I_{cd} and I_{c0} are approximately associated with the widths of the static and dynamic BH loops of the material. However, because of the highly complex nonlinear behavior of ferromagnetic materials, the accurate determination of the appropriate values to use in a given circuit from independent tests is very difficult. The currents I_{cd}, I_{c0}, and the intermediate values of current corresponding to a given reset flux are a function of the waveforms of e_s and e_c, the relative size of R_c, and the minor loop behavior of the core material. Several commercial tests are available that give approximate results for many circuit configurations and parameter values.

The linearized or average voltage gain of the amplifier may be expressed as

$$K_v = \frac{R_L}{R_0} \frac{E_s}{(I_{cd} - I_{c0})R_c} = \frac{R_L}{R_0} \frac{4fN_GA_cB_s}{(H_{cd} - H_{c0})l_c} \frac{N_c}{R_c}$$

with normal excitation and the neglect of the magnetizing current that flows in the load at minimum output. The length of the

magnetic circuit is l_c and H_{cd} and H_{c0} are the field intensities corresponding to I_{cd} and I_{c0}. The incremental field intensity increases with dB/dt and consequently with frequency. If this increase were linear, e.g., predominately due to linear eddy-current losses, then the gain would be independent of frequency. However, nonlinear incremental losses are usually present to some degree. Normal voltage gains for amplifiers of this type are in the order of 20 to 200. The power gain in terms of average values may be determined as $K_v^2R_c/R_L$ and the current gain as K_vR_c/R_L. Normal power gains for these amplifiers are in the order of 10^3 to 10^5. Normal input and output impedances range from a fraction of an ohm to several thousand ohms.

The time response of the magnetic amplifier is not determined by the control-circuit inductance within the usual definition of this term. The delay in the output change when a step voltage change in the input occurs is caused by the fact that the preset flux level of the gating core is partially determined by the output in the previous half-cycle. This dynamic behavior has the nature of a positive feedback around a half-cycle delay. If this feedback from the gating core to the reset core is interrupted either by a very large R_c or by the control-circuit configuration shown in Fig. 2, then the result is half-cycle response. The basic transfer function of the magnetic amplifier is then of the form

$$G_v(s) = \frac{N_G}{N_c} \frac{R_L}{R_0} \frac{Ke^{-Ts}}{1 - Ke^{-Ts}} \quad \text{with } T = \frac{1}{2f}$$

in Laplace transform notation. The term e^{-Ts} represents the half-cycle delay, which is inherent since the reset flux level cannot affect the output until the next gating half-cycle. The factor K is associated with the efficiency with which voltages in the control circuit effect a flux change. The approximate value of K may be obtained from the fact that $G_v(s)_{s\to0} = K_v = N_GR_LK/N_cR_0(1 - K)$ and from the previous expression for voltage gain.

If the response time of the magnetic amplifier is long compared to T ($0.9 \gtrsim K \gtrsim 1$) and signal frequencies small compared to the supply frequency, then an approximate continuous transfer function may be obtained by $e^{-Ts} \cong 1 - Ts$. The result is $G_v(s) \cong K_v/(1 + \tau s)$ with $\tau \cong T/(1 - K) \cong K_{v0}/2f$, in which K_{v0} is defined from $K_v = N_G R_L K_{v0}/N_c R_0$ as the normalized gross voltage gain.

In Fig. 2 is shown a typical fast-response magnetic amplifier. The operation of the gate circuit is identical with the circuit previously described. However, the voltage of the gating core is decoupled from the resetting core by the control rectifiers. The reset flux is determined only by $N_c e_s/N_G$ and e_c and the amplifier responds in one half-cycle to a change in e_c. The voltage gain, however, is limited to $N_G R_L/N_c R_0$ for small values of control-circuit resistance.

For high-power applications three-phase versions of the magnetic amplifier offer the advantages of less harmonic output, better utilization of the cores and rectifiers, and balanced loading of the power lines. One of many possible configurations is shown in Fig. 3. This circuit has steady-state and dynamic characteristics similar to those of the circuit of Fig. 1, although the coupling within the gate circuit and between the gate circuit and control circuit is somewhat more complicated.

The rectifiers in series with the windings, from which the self-saturating feature is derived, are usually solid-state selenium, germanium, or silicon rectifiers. If the reverse leakage current of these self-saturating rectifiers is comparable to the core magnetizing current, then the gate voltage can contribute directly to core reset through the rectifiers. A reduction in gain results. This effect is seldom appreciable with silicon or germanium but may occur with selenium.

Feedback from the output current or voltage to the magnetic-amplifier input in order to modify the steady-state and dynamic behavior of the device is often used. The feedback signal may be connected in shunt or series into the main control circuit (electric feedback) or may be connected to a

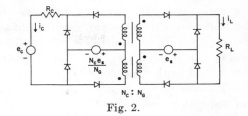

Fig. 2.

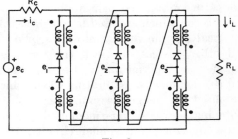

Fig. 3.

separate control winding (magnetic feedback). The results of feedback are similar to those of standard feedback amplifier theory. Negative feedback increases linearity and stability. Sufficient positive feedback results in bistable operation. Practical magnetic amplifiers usually have several control windings for use as feedback windings, bias windings, and for the magnetic mixing of several control signals.

The magnetic amplifiers described illustrate typical configurations. Other configurations accept phase-reversible alternating signals or polarity-reversible direct signals and deliver phase-reversible alternating or polarity-reversible direct outputs in any combination. Some circuits, which have no self-saturating feature, are used in certain special applications. Low-level amplifiers with pulse power supplies are practical with inputs less than 10^{-6} w. High-power amplifiers are practical with ratings greater than 500 kw.

H. C. BOURNE, JR.

Cross-references: *Amplifiers, Ferrimagnetism, Ferromagnetism, Magnetic Core, Magnetism*

MAGNETIC CORE

In the broad class of electrical and electromechanical devices which operate by the interaction of electric currents and magnetic fields, it is usually of advantage to confine the magnetic field and increase its effectiveness by the use of a core. The core is generally linked with the electrical conductors and is made of a material that provides a low reluctance magnetic path.

Magnetic cores may be divided into two groups according to their application: (a) linear cores, which are used in most rotating electrical equipment, transformers, chokes, and other devices in which the terms inductance and permeability are important; and (b) nonlinear or saturating cores, which are used in magnetic amplifiers, static switching devices, bit memory systems, static invertors, and similar circuits. Here inductance and permeability become artificial or meaningless terms and cores are classed and specified in terms of other parameters of the core flux-mmf characteristics. The practical dividing lines between the classes is often hazy, but the division simplifies the discussion of the important core properties.

For the general class of linear cores, the most important characteristics are permeability and losses. These are both basic properties of the magnetic material in the core. Permeability, denoted by the symbol μ, is the factor of proportionality between the magnetic flux density B and the magnetic intensity H. Thus, $\mu = B/H$ is a measure of the effectiveness of the core in providing a magnetic path of low reluctance.

Energy losses take place in the material because of the circulation of electrical currents within the core which are induced by changes in the magnetic field. Additional losses are caused by imperfections in the atomic structure of the material which impede the change of magnetization. The first of these is usually called eddy-current loss. The second is termed hysteresis loss. In practical cores, hysteresis losses are controlled by the proper choice of magnetic material, whereas eddy currents are reduced by increasing the resistance of the electrical paths in the core material through which

they might flow. Thus, the core material may be laminated or powdered, or it may be chosen for high resistivity.

Nonlinear or saturating cores have a more or less rectangular B-H characteristic. They are generally classified and measured in terms of the saturation flux density B_m, the residual flux density B_r, and the coercive force H_c of the core material. The slope and shape of the sides of the B-H loop are also of interest as are the hysteresis and eddy-current loss properties.

For studies of basic core material properties and correlation with metallurgical work, measurements are frequently made by classical ballistic galvanometer fluxmeter methods. This technique is less useful for production testing of cores since it is slow and gives no indication of dynamic core losses. The fluxmeter method provides data for a complete B-H characteristic and is useful for either linear or saturating cores. Since an indication of eddy-current losses under ac excitation is usually needed in practical applications, dynamic test methods are widely used. Core losses are usually measured by the voltmeter-ammeter-wattmeter method for cores with substantial losses. Examples of these might be laminated cores for power transformers or rotor-stator laminations for a motor.

Cores used in applications requiring low losses are frequently measured by bridge techniques using a Maxwell or Hay bridge. Losses are measured in terms of an equivalent ac resistance appearing at the terminals of the core winding.

More recently, special dynamic measuring techniques for the saturating cores have been developed. Those in most common use fall into three categories: (a) voltage-current loop displays in which the voltage induced in a core winding is plotted against the magnetizing current; (b) circuits in which voltages and currents are applied to core windings in a manner simulating the operation in a magnetic amplifier; and (c) pulse circuits in which cores intended for computer or pulse transformer applications are tested under simulated operating conditions.

Specifications for many of the core testing methods are to be found in the standards of the electrical professional societies and industry associations.

Materials and Fabrication. Practical core materials in common use fall into two general categories, ferromagnetic alloys and ferrites. The ferromagnetic alloys make use of one or more of the ferromagnetic elements Fe, Ni, Co and may incorporate other additions to improve any of the desired properties such as resistivity, temperature coefficient, or workability.

Among the alloys, a few of the many possible combinations have become widely accepted and are commercially available. Since almost all cores are used under dynamic excitation conditions, the bulk of the magnetic alloys are produced in the form of thin flat strip or in the form of powders so that, in the process of core fabrication, the eddy-current losses can be easily controlled. Some of the more important alloys have the following nominal compositions:

(a) $3\% \text{Si}—97\% \text{Fe}$
(b) $50\% \text{Ni}—50\% \text{Fe}$
(c) $79\% \text{Ni}—4\% \text{Mo}—17\% \text{Fe}$
(d) $50\% \text{Co}—50\% \text{Fe}$

Many other alloys are also used. Each alloy and each technique of alloy production can result in a magnetic material with widely differing properties and costs.

The steps in the fabrication of ferromagnetic cores vary according to the materials used and the end application. Materials with high permeabilities or very rectangular *B-H* loops do not exhibit these optimum characteristics if used in a core configuration having a substantial air gap. These materials are usually used in strip form wound spirally into a toroid or punched into rings.

Lower permeability materials are frequently punched from strip into a variety of shapes that may be stacked or interleaved into a core. Such stacks are economical to fabricate, but always have somewhat poorer magnetic properties because of the air gaps in the magnetic path.

For cores intended for operation at high frequencies, magnetic alloy powders are often used, molded into toroids, slugs, and a variety of other shapes. Ferrites are also fabricated by a molding process. These are magnetic oxides of iron and other elements and are advantageous at high frequencies because the high resistivity of the oxides minimizes the flow of eddy-current.

C. B. WAKEMAN

Cross-references: *Bridges, Coils, Ferrites, Magnetic Amplifiers, Magnetism*

MAGNETIC TAPE

Magnetic tape in its most common variety—iron oxide particles thinly coated on a plastic base forming a ribbon of permanent magnet material—has largely supplanted wire and metallic recording media. Tape, which can be played back immediately after recording without processing, is used with a ring-type record playback head which has a soft iron core with an air gap of less than 0.0005 in. over which the tape passes. The same head can be used for both recording and playback; a similar head with a wider gap is used for erasing.

In audio recording, sound waves are picked up by a microphone which turns them into electrical waves or signals. These signals are amplified and fed to the recording head. Actually an electromagnet, the head magnetizes the oxide-coated side of the tape in magnetic patterns corresponding to the original sounds. On playback the procedure is reversed. Magnetic patterns on the tape cause the head to react, setting up electrical waves. These signals are amplified from approximately 1 mv at the playback head and fed to a loudspeaker. Since all frequencies are not reproduced with equal sensitivity, equalizer circuits are needed to assure faithful reproduction.

As 1000 to 4000 cycles of information can be recorded per inch, tape speeds of 3.75 to 15 ips are commonly used for sound frequencies. Tape has a coercive force of about 250 oersteds which provides permanency in storage and use; however, it can be erased an indefinite number of times by application of a high-intensity alternating field above 1000 oersteds and new recordings made without deterioration. An entire reel can be erased at once on a "bulk" eraser, which is in reality a large ac electromagnet.

Base material of most tapes is cellulose acetate, polyethylene teraphthalate, or un-plasticized polyvinyl chloride 0.001 to 0.0015 in. thick. Special tapes having thicker or thinner bases also are manufactured for applications with unusual mechanical requirements. The plastic is coated with acicular iron oxide particles approximately 1 micron in length. In pigment form, the oxide (gamma Fe_2O_3) is mixed with a binder, a complex blend of resins and plasticizers compounded to provide maximum adherence of coating to backing and to resist wear and abrasion of the tape surface as it passes over the heads. After the coating process, tape is dried in ovens that cause solvents in the binder to evaporate leaving the oxide particles permanently bonded in place in a uniform coating only 0.0005 in. thick.

Resolution and noise level depend upon the smoothness of the tape surface. Output voltage depends upon the thickness of coating and the magnetic density of coating, which is measured by the remanent induction (usually in the range 700 to 1200 gauss for oxide-coated tapes). Decreasing the thickness of coating increases the voltage output but increases the resolution of the tape. Therefore the best thickness is a compromise between these two factors; a number of different coating thicknesses are commercially available to meet varying requirements.

Tapes for recording sound are usually $\frac{1}{4}$ in. wide and have a capacity of from 1 to 4 recorded tracks. Computing and instrumentation systems require tapes $\frac{1}{2}$ to 4 in. wide, having a recording capacity of from 7 to over 50 tracks.

Because of its high information storage density, speed of recording and reproduction, erase and immediate playback features, magnetic tape is a widely used recording medium in such fields as broadcasting, education, television, computer, telemetry, machine tool control, geophysics (oil prospecting), and music duplication, in addition to the common home-type recording applications.

R. A. VON BEHREN

Cross-references: *Sound Recording, Storage, Video Recording*

MAGNETISM

The distinctions among *diamagnetism, ferromagnetism*, and *paramagnetism* can be best established by reference to the articles under those headings. Because of the technical importance of ferromagnetism, various aspects of it are described in the present article, including general considerations, eddy currents, generation of very large fields, shielding, and thin films. Cross references to various applications are given at the end of the article.

Ferromagnetism is a property of a group of substances including iron, nickel, and cobalt as well as various compounds, all of which exhibit strong magnetic effects such as strong attraction or repulsion when magnetized, high permeability, and magnetic hysteresis effects. The ultimate source of the magnetic properties of matter is the orbital motion of the electrons around the nucleus and the spin of the electron about its own axis, both of which produce a magnetic dipole moment. However, it is primarily the electron-spin magnetic moment that is responsible for ferromagnetism, with the orbital motion playing only a minor role.

In those atoms in which the electrons form complete shells around the nucleus, the electronic arrangement is symmetrical so that the magnetic contributions of the individual spins or individual orbital motions neutralize one another and result in diamagnetic atoms. In iron, nickel, and cobalt, however, there is an inner third shell (3d sub-shell) which is incomplete and the electrons are so arranged as to leave a net number of uncompensated spins and thus a net magnetic moment. The magnetic dipolar interaction of these magnetic moments is much too small to explain the parallel alignment of the neighboring spins under the influence of small applied fields when this alignment is opposed by thermal energy tending to disorient the spins. In 1907, Pierre Weiss (1865–1940) was therefore led to postulate the existence of a large internal magnetic field that tends to overcome the disordering effect of thermal agitation. This Weiss internal field is now identified with the quantum-mechanical forces of exchange which are electrostatic in origin and which, in ferromagnetic materials, cause the parallel alignment of neighboring spins to the extent possible in the face of thermal agitation. The vector sum of the individual magnetic moments per unit volume is called the magnetization M. This magnetization decreases with increasing temperature until the *Curie temperature* is reached, at which the net alignment of the atomic moments by the exchange field is eliminated because the thermal energy exceeds the exchange energy. For iron the Curie temperature is 1040°K, which indicates that the exchange field is equivalent to 4×10^8 amp-turns/m.

Domain Theory. In order to explain the possibility of zero net magnetization in zero applied field despite the huge internal exchange field, Weiss postulated the domain theory. According to this theory, which has been extensively verified, magnetic materials are composed of many small regions or domains each of which has a net saturation magnetization. However, these domains can orient themselves in such a way as to cancel their moments thus leaving the sample as a whole with no resultant magnetization as shown in Figure 1a. When an external field is applied, the domains become rearranged so as to result in a net magnetization along the applied field as shown in Figures 1b and 1c.

Domains are formed in a magnetic material so as to minimize the total potential energy. Thus, if a crystal were uniformly magnetized as a single domain, the free poles at the ends of the sample would give rise to a large magnetostatic energy. By subdividing the material into many domains, and by forming domains of closure, (Fig. 1a) it is possible to minimize the magnetostatic energy. One cannot continue to subdivide the material into smaller and smaller domains because of the domain walls that are created in this process. These domain walls extend over a large number of atoms whose spins change gradually in direction. These walls add exchange energy because neighbor-

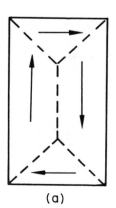

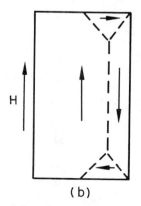

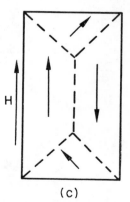

(a)   (b)   (c)

Fig. 1. Schematic representation of domains:
a) Unmagnetized state; the triangular prism domains are termed "domain of closure" and minimize the magnetostatic energy; b) Magnetization by domain wall movement; c) Magnetization by domain rotation.

ing spins are no longer parallel in the wall. Furthermore, magnetic materials exhibit magnetocrystalline anisotropy which causes them to require more energy to be magnetized along a hard direction (body diagonal for iron) than along an easy direction (cube edge for iron). This anisotropy arises from the combined effect of spin-orbit coupling and the electric field of neighboring charged ions. Since the spins within the domain wall mostly point away from the easy directions of magnetization, anisotropy energy is associated with every domain wall. Finally, the domain configuration must also minimize the magnetostrictive energy which is associated with a change in dimension due to a change in magnetization. The above domain theory has been verified in detail particularly by means of the Bitter technique in which a colloidal suspension of iron oxide is placed on a polished magnetic surface to reveal the details of the domain configuration.

Magnetization Curve and Hysteresis Loop

In ferromagnetic materials, B and H are related as follows:

$$B = \mu_r \mu_0 H = \mu_0(H + M) = \mu_0(1 + \chi)H$$

where, in rationalized MKS units
H = field intensity (amp turns/meter)
B = flux density (webers/meter^2)
μ_0 = permeability of vacuum = 4×10^{-7} (henry/meter)
μ_r = relative permeability
χ = susceptibility
M = magnetic moment/unit volume (amp/meter)

A representative magnetization curve and hysteresis loop is shown in Fig. 2. The magnetization curve can be divided into three parts. In the initial portion, OA, of the curve, the magnetization increases by means of reversible domain wall displacements which result in the growth of the favorably oriented domains as shown in Figure 1b. The steep portion, AB, of the curve results

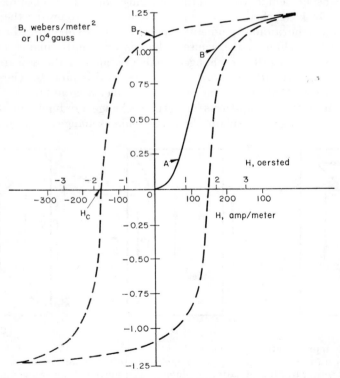

Fig. 2. Magnetization curve (full line) and hysteresis loop (broken line) for iron.

from the sudden irreversible movement of a domain wall from one stable position to another, with these points of stability being determined by the location of crystal imperfections and inclusions. Therefore, the magnetization in this steep part proceeds discontinuously as was first discovered by Barkhausen in 1919. Finally, in strong fields the magnetization usually changes by rotation of the magnetization of whole domains, as shown in Fig. 1c, until saturation is reached.

If the magnetic field, H, is reduced from its saturation value, the flux density, B, follows the hysteresis curve shown dashed in Fig. 2 and always lags behind the change in applied H. With H reduced to zero, the flux density is still near its saturation value and is equal to B_r, the *residual flux density* or *remanence*. In order to reduce B to zero, the negative field, H_c, called the *coercive force*, must be applied. The area enclosed by a hysteresis loop is proportional to the energy lost as heat during the traversal of the loop. For transformers and electromagnetic machinery, therefore, one must use soft magnetic materials which have narrow hysteresis loops and high permeability. To obtain magnetically soft materials, the domain walls must be able to move easily and reversibly so that the material must be free of imperfections and impurities. For permanent magnets one uses hard magnetic materials with high coercive force. In these materials domain wall motion is made difficult by non-magnetic inclusions and imperfections produced by heating and sudden quenching. Permanent magnets can also be made from very fine particles which are so small that they form a single domain. Magnetization and demagnetization can therefore only be accomplished by rotation of the magnetization in each particle which requires a higher field than domain wall motion.

When conducting magnetic materials are used in alternating fields, *eddy currents* are set up due to the electromotive force generated by the changing magnetic flux. The power loss associated with the eddy currents

is proportional to the square of the frequency at low frequencies, and to $f^{3/2}$ at high frequencies. In addition to the power loss, eddy currents do not allow the alternating field to penetrate into the interior of the material, thus reducing the effective permeability. To minimize the effects of eddy currents, magnetic cores of transformers are often laminated or powdered and placed in an insulating binder. Ferrites have a very high resistivity and therefore have negligible eddy currents.

M. T. Weiss

Eddy Currents

Eddy currents are set up in a conducting medium as a consequence of an applied changing magnetic field. In general, eddy currents depend on the permeability, resistivity, and configuration of the medium. They are accompanied by heating losses and, in addition, cause a diminution in the magnetic flux density in the interior of the medium. In ferromagnetic materials, the eddy-current loss is in addition to the hysteresis loss. Lenz's law states that the electromotive force induced in the medium in accordance with Faraday's law of electromagnetic induction is always such as to oppose the change in field. Faraday's law states that if the magnetic induction **B** in a conductor is changing, an electric field **E** is produced which is given by the vector relation

$$\nabla \times \mathbf{E} = -\partial \mathbf{B}/\partial t$$

Because the current in a conductor flows in accordance with Ohm's law, we may replace **E** by $\sigma \mathbf{J}$ where σ is the resistivity of the medium and **J** is the current density. The current flowing in a conductor of uniform permeability μ produces a magnetic field given by

$$\nabla \times \mathbf{B} = \mu \mathbf{J}$$

Eliminating **B** from the equations gives the general eddy-current relation,

$$\nabla^2 \mathbf{J} = \frac{\mu}{\sigma} \frac{\partial \mathbf{J}}{\partial t}$$

This equation (which neglects displacement current) is the same as that used in the theory of heat. The equation also holds when **J** is replaced by **B**. The general solution of the eddy-current equation includes the skin effect (q.v.), which may be described as a crowding of the flux and current toward the surface of the medium. An exact mathematical calculation cannot be made for media in which the relation between B and H is nonlinear. However, an approximate solution may be obtained by assuming the permeability to be constant. An analysis of eddy-currents that ignores skin effect is sufficiently accurate for devices using laminated cores at power frequencies.

A restricted solution illustrating the main aspects of eddy-currents is readily obtained by considering a semi-infinite medium of permeability μ and resistivity σ whose boundary is the x-y plane. The real part of the solution for current density in the medium in response to a changing magnetic field at the surface is

$$\mathbf{J}_x = \mathbf{J}_s \exp\left(-\sqrt{\omega\mu/2\sigma}z\right) \cos\left[\omega t - \left(\frac{\omega\mu}{2\sigma}\right)^{1/2} z\right]$$

The amplitude decreases exponentially and the phase angle changes uniformly as the medium is penetrated. The power p absorbed per unit surface area is given by

$$p = \frac{I_e^2 \sigma}{\delta}$$

where I_e is the effective value of the current and δ is the skin depth given by $\sqrt{\omega\mu/2\sigma}$. The ac resistance is higher than the dc resistance and the inductance of a wire due to the internal flux is decreased as the current is crowded toward the outer layer of the conductor. Under the condition of complete flux penetration (at power frequencies) the power loss P in laminations when subjected to sinusoidally varying fields is given by

$$P = k_e B_m^2 f^2 l^2$$

where k_e may be determined theoretically but more accurately determined from measurement, B_m is the flux in webers/m^2, f is the frequency of excitation, and t is the thickness of the lamination in meters. At high frequencies the power loss is proportional to $f^{3/2}$. The flux carrying capacity of laminations varies with frequency and is expressed in terms of an effective permeability $\bar{\mu}$ defined as the ratio of B averaged over a lamination to the applied H field. For high frequencies $\bar{\mu}$ is inversely proportional to $f^{1/2}$.

Louis R. Hirschel

Generation of Very High Fields

The energy density $B^2/8\pi$ of a magnetic field B amounts to 4000 joules/cm^3 when B is 10^6 gauss. High magnetic fields are most easily generated by pulsing the required magnetic energy E_m into an air-core coil from a capacitor bank or motor-generator. If the pulse time is kept short compared with the decay time τ_d of the current in the coil (L/R time), then the energy loss due to the coil resistance can be kept negligible. The pulsed-field technique was first used by P. Kapitza in Cambridge in England in the 1920's. Kapitza reached 320 kilogauss over a few cubic centimeters of useful volume, with pulse lengths in the millisecond range.

The maximum field achieved to date in dc operation is the 100 kilogauss produced in a coil of 25 cm^3 useful volume by F. Bitter at M.I.T. in 1939. The power requirement P of Bitter's magnet is 1.5 Mw. A general scaling law for P can be derived by noting that

$$P \propto E_m/\tau_d$$

and

$$\tau_d \propto l^2/\eta$$

where η is the mean resistivity of the coil material and l is a linear dimension. Thus one obtains

$$P \propto \eta B^2 l$$

A number of dc magnets at the 100-kilogauss level make use of low-temperature coolant to reduce the resistivity and thus the input power, but the advantage is usually offset by the refrigeration costs. For very large systems, liquid-helium-cooled sodium or aluminum coils are expected to be practical. Very recently, superconductors with critical magnetic fields above 90 kilogauss have been developed at Bell Telephone Laboratories that hold out even greater promise for large high-field dc installations.

The energy density associated with high magnetic fields implies a magnetic pressure $B^2/8\pi$ that amounts to 5.6×10^5 psi when B is 10^6 gauss. Accordingly the mechanical stress in Kapitza's wire-wound coils, rather than the energy requirement, proved a limitation to the attainment of very high fields. On the basis of the tensile strengths of metals, one expects to be able to withstand about 800 kilogauss in a solid (single-turn) coil of hardened steel, and somewhat less in solid bronze coils. These figures have actually been reached experimentally at the Cambridge Air Force Research Laboratories and elsewhere. In practice, single-turn coils are often inconvenient, because of their low impedance, and massive helical coils have been found to give almost equally good performance.

Mechanical forces in coils can be ideally reduced to very low values by making the coil volume large compared with the useful volume, but arrangements of this kind tend to be wasteful of coil materials as well as of stored magnetic energy and dissipated power. The most efficient approach to the elimination of mechanical forces is to wind coils so that the current flows along, instead of across, magnetic field. Such "force-free" coils consist essentially of nested toroidal winding surfaces with helical windings of varying pitch.

Magnetic fields in the 1–2×10^6 gauss range have been generated for microsecond times, by relying on the inertia rather than on the tensile strength of coil materials. High explosives have also been used to implode copper tubes containing magnetic flux, thus magnifying the initial field by compression. Fields as high as 14×10^6 gauss have been reached in this way for

several microseconds at Los Alamos Scientific Laboratory.

In pulsed, wire-wound coils the thermal problem is somewhat secondary to the mechanical one. In solid metal coils, where skin effect confines the coil current to the surface, the heat density deposited during a pulse is comparable to the energy density of the magnetic field. As a result, mechanical failure and melting tend to occur at comparable field strengths. In dc magnets operating at normal temperature the heat-removal problem imposes the prime limitation, as can be seen from the largeness of the input power requirement. Low-temperature or superconducting dc magnets are, of course, free from this limitation.

HAROLD P. FURTH

Permanent Magnetism

A permanent magnet is a device which, without consuming energy, produces or maintains a magnetic field of considerable strength and constancy in some region of space. In contrast to the electromagnet, which supplies a magnetic field during the time when it is energized, the permanent magnet is energized (magnetized) prior to its use and supplies a magnetic field after the energy source has been removed.

Uses. Permanent magnets, whose only practical application up to the 19th century was in compass needles, are now widely used for:

(1) Transformation of mechanical to electrical energy, as in generators, magnetos, dynamic and velocity microphones.

(2) Transformation of electrical to mechanical energy, as in electric motors, meters, galvanometers, and loudspeakers. Permanent magnets are also used in the deflection of electron paths, as in magnetrons, traveling-wave tubes, cloud chambers; and for isotope separation in mass spectroscopes.

(3) Tractive effort, as in magnetic chucks, separators, conveyors and latches, limit switches in thermostats and pressure controls, holding and lifting devices, toys and novelties.

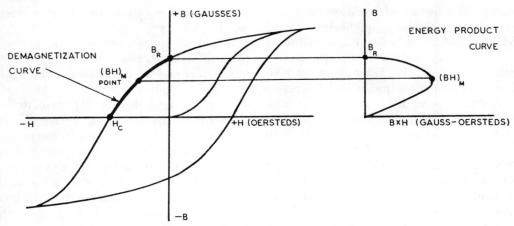

Fig. 3. General form of hysteresis loop.

Permanent-Magnet Materials. Permanent-magnet materials (also called "hard" magnetic materials) are a special class within the general category of ferromagnetic materials.

Each ferromagnetic material (including the ferrimagnetic) has a hysteresis loop, the general form of which is shown in Fig. 3. A permanent-magnet material differs from others in that its coercive force is very high, ranging from 50 to 5,000 oersteds. Furthermore, its usefulness for magnet applications increases with flux density (magnetic induction) for a given configuration. Since an air gap is an inherent part of a permanent-magnet device, the material always operates at a flux density lower than its residual or remanent value owing to self demagnetization produced by the air gap. The self demagnetizing field caused by the air gap is equivalent to a negative magnetic field applied to a material sample without an air gap. Hence, the material operates on that portion of the hysteresis loop between B_r (residual flux density) and H_c (coercive force). This portion of the loop is called the *demagnetization curve* and is used for design purposes. The smaller the air-gap length relative to the magnet length, the closer is the flux density to B_r. The product BH for any point on the demagnetization curve is proportional to the magnetic energy per unit volume of material and also propor-

tional to the energy per unit volume of air gap; BH is therefore called the *energy product*. Its maximum value $(BH)_{max}$ occurs somewhere between B_r and H_c. *The highest magnetic field in a given gap volume is produced when a given volume of material is operating at its maximum energy product $(BH)_{max}$.* Hence, three important criteria for judging the quality of permanent-magnet materials are coercive force (H_c), residual (or remanent) flux density (B_r), and maximum energy product $(BH)_{max}$.

Historically, the first permanent magnet, the natural lodestone (containing magnetite, Fe_3O_4), was used in crude compasses over 4,000 years ago. Later, alloys of iron hardened with carbon, tungsten, chromium, and cobalt were developed. Present-day materials have coercive force values ranging from 40 to over 4,000 oersteds and energy products from 200,000 to 10,000,000 gauss-oersteds. The choice of a material depends upon technical and economic requirements of the application. In addition to magnetic requirements for a given space, resistivity, density, strength, and workability must also be considered in many applications. Stability, i.e., insensitivity of the magnetic properties to metallurgical aging, shock, vibration, high and low temperatures, nuclear radiation, external magnetic fields, or contact with other magnetic materials is another important consideration.

TABLE 1. PERMANENT MAGNET MATERIALS

Material	Coercive Force, H_c (oersteds)	Max. Energy Product, $(BH)_{max}$ (10^6 gauss-oersteds)
Magnet steels (carbon, tungsten, chrome, cobalt steels)	40–250	0.20–0.98
Aluminum-nickel-cobalt alloys	40–1,000	0.40–8.6
Alnico V	580–725	5.0–6.5
Fine particle cobalt-iron (Lodex)	650–1400	3.6–1.6
Barium ferrites	1,600–2,200	0.8–3.5
Fine-particle MnBi (Bismanol)	3,700	5.3
Platinum-cobalt	4,300	9.5

Table 1 illustrates the range of materials available today.

DANIEL I. GORDON

Shielding

Well-engineered circuits are often affected by extraneous magnetic fields, which can be eliminated to some degree by properly orienting the components on the chassis. Where the field is generated within a transformer-core structure certain design considerations can be adopted to minimize this condition. Some relief can be obtained by placing the lamination air-gaps inside the electrical coil by use of E-E or similar type punchings. Another method is to use a humbucking type of construction in which some of the extraneous fields are bucked out by splitting the windings on the magnetic core structure. If the spurious field cannot be eliminated at its source, it must be prevented from reaching the equipment under consideration, by containment of the unit in a magnetic shield.

The magnetic shield is a low-reluctance path in which the field is concentrated or "trapped." For this reason magnetic shields are generally made of a high-permeability nickel-iron alloy such as Mumetal, Permalloy 80, or Armco 48 Alloy. The first two materials provide maximum shielding at low flux densities; the last is best at higher flux densities. These materials are used almost exclusively because of weight and space considerations. Cast iron and materials of relatively low permeability have been used but their low permeabilities must be offset by using heavier thicknesses.

Design formulas for determining the proper thickness of a shield are given in the literature. These formulas generally pertain to ideal shapes which are seldom encountered in practice. For example, most nickel-iron shields used for shielding transformers, cathode-ray and photomultiplier tubes, etc., are generally produced in thicknesses of 0.025–0.035 in. In some instances 0.014 in. has been used successfully; other designs have required as much as 0.060 in. In addition to the thickness required for adequate shielding one must also allow sufficient section for rigidity, particularly when shielding large tubes.

Nesting of Shields. There are many low-level applications in which a single shield does not reduce the field to a low enough value and a nest of shields is necessary. Additional shields are placed over the first one to achieve the degree of isolation required. The shields should be completely separated from each other to insure maximum permeability of the group and a high-reluctance gap between them, which is often accomplished by using 0.010-in.-thick Kraft paper as a separator.

In some cases telescoping sets of nickel-iron and copper shields are used alternately without the paper spacers. The copper cans provide a path of high electrical conductivity. As a result the flux which passes through the first nickel shield sets up eddy currents in the copper shield, in turn generating a counter field that bucks out some of this flux.

Fabrication Techniques. Structurally, magnetic shields fall into two broad classes: those produced by deep drawing from flat blanks and those which are formed and welded. Owing to the difficulties involved in deep drawing the nickel-iron alloys, the drawn shields are usually confined to the smaller sizes, as used in small input transformers, recording heads, relays, etc. The drawn shields are usually cylindrical in shape although some tape-recorder-head shields have a more rectangular form.

Because the nickel-iron alloys work harden very rapidly in drawing, generous radii must be provided to prevent tearing. In drawing Mumetal cans one must be careful to eliminate the strains developed as quickly as possible. The shields should be normalized at a temperature between 1450° and 1600°F within 3 hr after drawing. Failure to relieve these strains often result in intercrystalline fractures that do not show up until the final heat treatment at 2050°F. At this temperature the shields so affected split wide open.

Shields for transformers, cathode-ray tubes, photomultiplier tubes, etc., are fabricated from flat, unannealed sheets. The material is bent on brakes or rolls and the joints are overlapped and spot welded. All holes and slots are pierced prior to the forming operation. After fabrication the shields are given the final heat treatment in pure, dry hydrogen at 2050°F to develop the required permeabilities. Before this final treatment, the permeability is only about 5 per cent of the ultimate developed in the above annealing process. For the most critical applications, any deviation from this treatment results in an inferior unit with nonuniform magnetic characteristics and lower permeability.

It has been found that a ⅜-in. overlap of material is sufficient to prevent any penetration by the extraneous field. Likewise, spot welding at intervals of ½ in. or so is adequate. Solid-seam welding of Mumetal is difficult, expensive, and unnecessary.

Placement of the joints in the shield surface has an interesting effect upon shield efficiency. In a cathode-ray-tube shield, for example, joints in the axial direction have little effect but joints normal to the axis reduce the effectiveness of the shielding. Some shields are designed so that they closely follow the shape of the tube; this procedure usually results in excessive costs.

It is very arduous to make quantitative measurements of shielding efficiency since low-level, uniform magnetic fields are difficult to establish. Results of such measurements indicate that well-designed shields should provide insulation from 45 to 80 db. This attenuation should adequately eliminate the effect of the extraneous fields in most instances.

W. S. SPRING

Thin Films

A physical concept of the thin-film solid state is an ordered arrangement of atomic strata ranging in thickness from two or three strata to nearly 3000 Å. In general, however, specific crystallographic textures are known to exist for this geometrically specialized solid state. Thin-film magnetic materials—e.g., iron, nickel, cobalt, bismuth, and alloys of these materials and others—display unusual and emphatic magnetic properties, because of the third-dimension restriction and the crystallographic textures.

Thin films are prepared by any one of the following fabrication processes: vacuum evaporation, ionic sputtering, electroplating, and chemical vapor deposition. They are supported, usually, by a substrate of rigid and thicker materials. Thickness is controllable by deposition time, and crystallographic structure is determined by both the substrate and the physical mechanisms present during the atomic transportation process.

The structure of magnetic thin films, and consequently their magnetic properties, are conveniently described by considering physical results that are currently representative. Specific illustrations will be concerned with vacuum evaporated nickel-iron thin films.

Structure. High-melting-point metals and their alloys, when vacuum-evaporated into the thin-film state, have a micro- and polycrystalline structure. In Fig. 4, two transmission electron micrographs demonstrate this concept by the appearance of the dark and light areas due to electron diffrac-

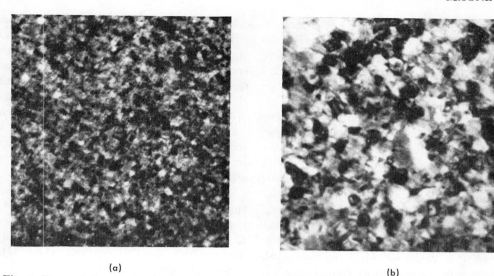

(a)   (b)

Fig. 4. Transmission electron micrographs of nickel-iron, vacuum-evaporated, magnetic thin films about 750 Å thick, deposited upon a thin layer (about 50 Å) of carbon and magnified 120,000 times. (a) Substrate at room temperature; (b) Substrate at 320° C.

tion by Ni-Fe thin films that have been deposited and then stripped from an amorphous glass substrate. The effect of substrate temperature is also demonstrated by the increase in crystallite size with an increase in substrate temperature. X-ray diffraction experiments also indicate a small cubic crystallite texture that is generally randomly oriented. In the thicker films, and for films deposited on single-crystal substrates, both at the higher substrate temperatures, a preferred orientation of these crystallites begins to occur. Because of the fabrication environment, it is generally believed that many gaseous elements are present in measurable quantities in the film, having been trapped during the deposition process; hence, the crystallites of Fig. 4 are not clear-cut, idealized atom arrangements.

Magnetic Properties. Since crystallographic orientation of magnetic thin films is, in general, random, their macroscopic magnetic properties are similar to those of polycrystalline bulk materials except as modified by the specialization of the inherent geometry. Randomly oriented nickel-iron films, near 82.3% nickel with a 100-Å particle size, display an unusually strong magnetic anisotropy, as shown in Fig. 5, which

is a 60-cps hysteresis loop of such a film for two directions of magnetization at 90° to each other. The square loop is observed in the same direction as a magnetic field present during the evaporation of the film. This preferred direction of magnetization for the small particle domains has been induced magnetostrictively during the fabrication of the film. The inherent stress mechanism is thought to be assisted further by the preferential presence of impurities within the crystallite lattice sites. The magnetic anisotropy can be increased in films, if a

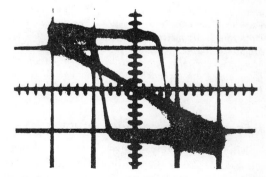

Fig. 5. 60-cps hysteresis loop traces of a 2000-Å nickel-iron magnetic thin film with the applied field parallel (square loop) and perpendicular to the direction of the magnetic field that was applied during fabrication by vacuum evaporation.

specific amount of crystallite orientation is achieved, since for this case magnetocrystalline anisotropy no longer becomes averaged out of the physical picture. This phenomenon has been observed in the case of iron and other nickel-iron alloy thin films.

In a direction perpendicular to the plane of the film, the demagnetization field is one thousand times that in the other two degrees of freedom; hence, when the magnetic moment of the crystallites changes direction, it is energetically favorable to change in the plane of the film. This type of dynamical behavior demonstrates a purely rotational remagnetization mechanism and is readily observable in magnetic thin films in general. In the case of the nickel-iron thin films, small particles that are single domains remagnetize superparamagnetically; hence, the magnetic flux changes in a rotational manner rather than by the movement of a domain wall, unless the small paramagnets align to form domain walls.

A final specialized magnetic property has been observed in magnetic thin films as the thickness is decreased. The absolute magnetic moment of the material begins to decrease in the neighborhood of 50 Å. A physical reason for this event is the decrease in the nearest neighbor atomic exchange interaction as the number of atoms decreases.

J. D. Blades

Cross-references: *Antiferromagnetism, Diamagnetism Electromagnetic Theory, Electron Paramagnetic Resonance, Faraday Effect, Ferrimagnetism, Ferrites, Ferromagnetic Crystals, Ferromagnetism, Hall Effect, Magnetic Amplifiers, Magnetic Cores, Magnetic Tapes, Magnetohydrodynamics (MHD), Magnetometer, Magnetostriction, Nuclear Magnetic Resonance, Paramagnetism, Permanent Magnets, Relays, Transformers*

MAGNETOHYDRODYNAMICS (MHD)

Magnetohydrodynamics (hereafter abbreviated MHD) is the study of the interaction between electrically conducting fluids and electric and magnetic fields. The fluid may be either an ionized gas or a conducting liquid. The motion of the fluid across a magnetic field induces electric currents in the fluid. These currents have several effects, among which are the modification of the original field, and the production of a Lorentz body force on the fluid. Any external electric fields imposed upon the fluid also produce currents with the above effects. Thus electromagnetic fields may be used to control fluid motion, and conversely, electromagnetic energy may be generated from a fluid flow.

Areas of Application. The existence of this interaction was recognized by the early researchers in electromagnetism; e.g., Faraday published an account of an MHD flow meter in 1832 and Ritchie disclosed an MHD pump. However, neither of these devices, nor any of those suggested over the next hundred years, were practical in their time, except for the "magnetic blow-out" circuit breaker (*q.v.*). Many of these devices were impractical because of the low conductivity of the proposed fluid. High conductivities in gases imply high temperatures and the technology to produce them.

The modern era of MHD may be dated from Alfvén's theoretical discovery (1942) of a low frequency wave mode which travels along magnetic field lines in a conducting fluid with a speed $V_A = B(4\pi\rho)^{-1/2}$ (where B is the field intensity and ρ the fluid density). He used these waves to explain certain astrophysical phenomena; these theories in turn stimulated the astrophysical community to consider very seriously the interaction of astronomical matter and magnetic fields and led to the first *systematic* study of MHD. The understanding gained, along with various technological developments, and advances in fluid mechanics and ionization phenomena, has restimulated interest in engineering MHD.

Practical MHD liquid metal pumps and associated flow meters are now available for atomic-reactor coolants. The addition of easily ionized "seed" materials to gases heated by combustion yields conductivities sufficiently high that efficient MHD generators for conversion of chemical to electrical energy may now be designed. The use of magnetic forces to accelerate plasmas promises propulsion units for space flight of higher exhaust velocities than can be achieved with systems that only heat the propellant. MHD forces might be used advantageously in high-speed, high-altitude flights, the conducting fluid being the atmosphere ionized by the strong shock waves associated with such flight. The possibility of controlled nuclear fusion has stimulated much effort to contain and manipulate high-temperature plasmas with magnetic fields.

Similitude Parameters. MHD studies fluids under widely different conditions; the physical mechanisms that are important under one set of circumstances need not be the same as those under some others. The relative importance of two different mechanisms can be determined by forming the ratio of some characteristic property of the two mechanisms. Indeed, a set of such ratios involving all possible mechanisms provides a complete description of the system. Ordinary fluid mechanics gives rise to a set of such numbers, all of which may also apply to MHD; in the following paragraphs are discussed some of the important parameters that are peculiar to MHD.

Magnetic Reynolds Number. A change in the magnetic field at the boundary of a conductor has effect only within a "skin depth" δ where

$$\delta = c \sqrt{\frac{t}{4\pi\sigma}}$$

with t the time available for the field to diffuse and σ the conductivity of the material. If the fluid is flowing with a speed V, it travels a distance $L = Vt$ in time t. The square of the ratio of these lengths is called the magnetic Reynolds number:

$$R_m = L^2/\delta^2 = 4\pi\sigma LV/c^2$$

Thus when $R_m \gg 1$, $R_m^{-1/2}$ is the fraction of the volume of the flow that can be penetrated by magnetic fields. An external magnetic field does not diffuse into such a fluid; any fields already in the fluid must remain "frozen" to that part of the fluid in which they find themselves. Conversely, if R_m is small, field lines may diffuse easily through the fluid; in this case R_m may be interpreted as the ratio of the magnetic field due to currents induced in the fluid to the magnetic field due to external sources.

Magnetic Pressure: β. The terms in Maxwell's stress tensor are of the order of magnitude $B^2/8\pi$. The ratio of the ordinary fluid pressure to $B^2/8\pi$ is usually denoted by β. Along with R_m, β measures the relative importance of magnetic forces and fluid pressure in determining the flow pattern. When R_m is large all of the magnetic pressure may act upon the fluid, and hence β itself determines whether the field controls the flow (β small), or the fluid motion dominates the field (β large). However, when R_m is small, the fluid may slip across the field and only the fraction R_m of the magnetic pressure is effective on the fluid; hence, the quotient R_m/β measures the relative importance of the field in determining the flow pattern.

Mach Number Based on Alfvén Speed. Alfvén's work on MHD waves has been extended by others, and it is now known that his waves are a special case of a complex system of waves that can propagate in any direction and over a wide band of frequencies. The typical speed for these waves is the Alfvén speed V_A. The waves are the mechanism by which the fluid adjusts to a localized disturbance. The nature of a flow depends critically upon the fluid's ability to adjust to a disturbance before the arrival of the source of that disturbance. Hence, the ratio V/V_A is an important parameter (Mach number based on Alfvén speed).

Continuum Behavior and Conductivity. A charged particle moving in crossed electric and magnetic fields gyrates about the magnetic fields with its center of gyration drifting perpendicular to both fields. After collision with another particle it resumes such motion, but displaced about one radius of gyration in the electric-field direction. Thus, the ratio of the average time the particle has to spiral freely to the time for the particle to rotate through one radian significantly influences its behavior, including the direction relative to the electric field in which it drifts. This ratio is denoted by $\omega\tau$.

In an MHD medium there are at least two kinds of charged particles, electrons and positive ions, and hence two different $\omega\tau$'s. Because of their lower mass, the electrons have the larger $\omega\tau$. Then three distinct situations may arise. If $(\omega\tau)_{\text{electrons}} \ll 1$, the net electric current is in the direction of the electric field and a scalar conductivity may be defined. The motion of all species is essentially controlled by collisions and the fluid is maintained in local equilibrium. The fluid may be described by the usual equations of continuum flow, the Navier-Stokes equations, including terms to describe the electromagnetic body forces and the electrical Joule dissipation.

If $(\omega\tau)_{\text{ions}} \ll 1 \sim (\omega\tau)_{\text{electrons}}$, the heavy species, and hence, the mass motion of the fluid, is still collision dominated and the Navier-Stokes equations apply. However, the current is no longer parallel to the electric field so that the conductivity becomes a tensor.

If $(\omega\tau)_{\text{ions}} > 1$, collisions lose their dominating role. The flow may not be adequately described by the Navier-Stokes equations. At present writing, the correct equations for such a fluid are not known, but it is believed that attention should center on disordered ("turbulent") macroscopic motions. At very low densities there may be no mechanism for continuum behavior, in which case the system is best described in terms of individual particle orbits.

FRANK J. FISHMAN

Cross-references: *Energy Conversion, Ion Propulsion, Plasma, Plasma Propulsion, Reactors*

MAGNETOMETERS

The magnetometer is an instrument for measuring weak magnetic-field intensity; the upper limit is generally considered to be the maximum intensity of the earth's field. Several types exist: (1) Mechanical magnetic balances compare the magnetic intensity with a known force (gravity, torsion, etc.); (2) component systems measure the effect of the magnetic field intensity, or changes in magnetic intensity, along one axis of the sensor (coils, Hall effect, electron beam); (3) spin-precession detectors monitor the interaction of the total magnetic field and atomic particles (proton free precession, optical pumping and monitoring).

Categories (2) and (3) may be considered to be electronic. All known component methods measure a vector component of the ambient field and are therefore orientation dependent. They provide a measure of relative intensity, as an amplitude variation, since they depend upon accurate calibration for absolute accuracy. Magnetic-field values taken with the spin-precession methods are orientation independent and give an absolute measure of the total magnetic intensity. The output of spin-precession detectors is a frequency proportional to the ambient field, and the accuracy of the device is primarily limited by the knowledge of the atomic constants. Although the component methods are inherently suited for vector measurements, three orthogonal sensing elements can be combined to measure the total field. Conversely, the spin-precession sensing element may be suitably biased to obtain component measurements.

Absolute accuracies of the order of 8 parts per million are possible with the 1960 knowledge of the proton frequency-to-field (gyromagnetic) ratio. Greater sensitivities (short-term relative changes), on the order of a few parts in 10^8, are possible with optically pumped and monitored systems.

Component Methods. The sensing devices utilized in some component systems are fixed relative to the field vector component to be observed, as in the fluxgate or search-coil types. A *fluxgate* consists of a high-permeability core in which the ambient field induces a magnetization. When a winding is provided to stimulate the core by an alternating current, the iron reaches saturation. Secondary windings measure the asymmetry of the magnetization, as a result of the superimposed ambient field, which appears as a second harmonic of the sweep frequency. A variety of core and coil configurations are used, but the output is normally a voltage or current proportional to the vector field strength. *Search coils* are used to measure the variations (greater than 0.1 cps) of the ambient field; these result in an induced voltage in the winding proportional to $d\phi/dt$. Since the response falls off to zero at extremely low frequency, they may be considered as variometers only.

In an *earth inductor* a coil is rotated at a constant rate about an axis not parallel to the ambient field, and the rms voltage induced is a measure of magnetic intensity. Helmholtz coils may be used in a system of this type to balance the field being measured. The current required to null the field is then a measure of the ambient field.

The *Hall effect* is used as a measure of field value using a semiconductor as the sensing element. In materials that exhibit this effect, a difference in electric potential is measured normal to the direction of magnetic field desired as a known electric current is carried in the remaining orthogonal direction.

An *electron beam* is deflected by a magnetic field. A bias field is used to return to the beam to a neutral position, and the current required for the bias is a measure of the magnetic field.

Spin Precession Methods. The *proion free precession* method of measuring the earth's magnetic field was developed with the concepts of nuclear magnetic resonance. A fluid containing an abundance of protons (commonly water or a hydrocarbon) is polarized, in a direction not parallel to the ambient field, by passing a strong current through a surrounding solenoid. The nuclei spin axes are aligned along this field, and the current is abruptly cut off. The same solenoid is then connected as a pickup coil to measure the weak alternating voltage generated by the protons as they precess about the ambient field axis. Precession re-

sults from a force couple between the earth's magnetic field acting upon the nuclear magnetic moment and the angular momentum of the proton. The frequency of precession (f in kc) is a linear function of the field strength (H in gauss): $f = 4.25760\ H$.

Optical pumping and monitoring resonance systems rely on the effect of the magnetic field upon the structure of the narrow spectral lines of some gases (alkali vapors, helium). The normal energy state of the gas is split into several magnetic-field dependent sublevels by an ambient magnetic field (the Zeeman effect). A polarized light passed through a gas-filled cell results in an enhancement of the population of one Zeeman level. If the gas cell is excited by an rf field, at a frequency corresponding to the Larmor frequency of the gas, the over-populated Zeeman level is depopulated. A light and photodetector aligned normal to the pumping light and the rf coil can monitor this phenomenon by measuring the changing light intensity. (During pumping, transmitted light is absorbed; while the atoms are trapped at a Zeeman level, the transmitted light passes freely.) In a self-oscillating magnetometer, the frequency observed at the photodetector is amplified and transmitted to the rf coil surrounding the gas cell. The frequency of the "light shutter" is then a measure of the frequency difference between the Zeeman levels and is a function of the total magnetic field intensity.

Magnetometer Uses. The magnetic field is measured for scientific, commercial, and military purposes. Standard observatories exist in most countries to record this fundamental natural force. Absolute data are recorded to define and to predict the magnetic field. Relative records are made at a variety of variation rates to assist in correlating natural phenomena and predict radio transmission interferences. Space vehicles carry fluxgates, coil systems, and spin-precession systems to measure the terrestrial and interplanetary fields for future study as supporting data for theoretical ideas about space.

Oceanographic magnetic surveys cover extensive areas of the earth and assist in defining major structural trends and important local features. Millions of miles of aerial surveys have been flown to locate anomalies on the earth's field that might be important in defining geology in the search for petroleum and mineral wealth. Ground parties have used magnetometers for centuries to assist in geologic problems; in this capacity, it was probably the first geophysical exploration tool.

The development of the airborne fluxgate magnetometer during World War II was a major advance in anti-submarine warfare. This requirement has made the magnetometer an important weapon in modern warfare.

LEE LANGAN

Cross-references: *Characteristic Frequencies, Geophysical Prospecting, Hall Effect, Magnetism, Nuclear Magnetic Resonance (NMR), Zeeman Effect*

MAGNETOSTATICS: see ELECTROMAGNETIC THEORY

MAGNETOSTRICTION

Magnetostriction is defined as the change in dimensions of a body when subjected to a magnetic field. The changes in length, measured parallel and perpendicular to the field, are known respectively as the *longitudinal* and *transverse Joule effects*. These effects have been observed in most ferromagnetic materials (both in nonmetals such as the ferrites and in metals and alloys) and have also been detected in strongly diamagnetic substances such as bismuth.

In various ferromagnetic materials, the longitudinal and transverse Joule effects are either positive or negative, corresponding to extensions or contractions. Generally, at any given field, the transverse effect is opposite in sign to the longitudinal effect and about half in magnitude. Hence the net volume strain, known as the *volume magnetostriction*, is usually much smaller than any of the linear strains. In most ferromagnets, the variation of the linear magnetostrictive strains with

the applied magnetic field is monotonic; for example, in polycrystalline nickel, the longitudinal effect becomes increasingly more negative and the transverse effect increasingly more positive with increasing field. A notable exception is polycrystalline iron, whose longitudinal magnetostriction is positive at low fields, then gradually decreases, and becomes negative at higher fields. At sufficiently high fields for magnetic saturation, the linear magnetostrictive strains in all ferromagnets level off at essentially constant values, the only further changes being those associated with the volume magnetostriction.

When a magnetic field is applied along the length of a ferromagnetic wire carrying an electric current, a twisting of the wire is observed. This phenomenon, called the *Wiedemann effect*, may be regarded as the Joule magnetostrictive effect resulting from the combined action of the longitudinal field and the circular field produced by the current.

For each magnetostrictive effect in which a variation of the applied magnetic field causes an elastic strain in the material, there is a thermodynamically related phenomenon involving a change in the magnetic moment (and, hence, in the magnetic flux density) with an applied stress. The equation

$$l^{-1}\Delta l/\Delta H = D \, \Delta\sigma/\Delta S \qquad (1)$$

is the simple isothermal relationship between the linear strain $l^{-1}\Delta l$ produced by a magnetic field change ΔH, and the variation in magnetic moment per unit mass $\Delta\sigma$ produced by a change in applied stress ΔS; D is the density of the material. In this equation, a positive ΔS corresponds to an increase in tensile stress (or a decrease in compressive stress). Moreover, Δl and $\Delta\sigma$ can be either parallel or perpendicular to ΔH and ΔS, respectively. Hence, the left-hand side of Eq. (1) represents the longitudinal or transverse Joule effects; correspondingly, the right-hand side represents what are known as the *longitudinal* or *transverse Villari effects*. According to this equation, a material with a positive linear magnetostriction should show an increase in magnetic moment with increasing tensile stress. This, in fact, is found to be the case for polycrystalline iron at low fields. At higher fields where the linear magnetostriction of iron is negative, its magnetic moment is observed to decrease with increasing tension. This change in the sign of $\Delta\sigma/\Delta S$ is called the *Villari reversal*.

An expression closely analogous to Eq. (1) relates the volume magnetostriction to a *variation of the magnetic moment with hydrostatic pressure*. There is also an *inverse Wiedemann effect* which is the change in magnetic moment measured along the length of a current carrying wire when it is twisted. Moreover, a phenomenon arising from the Joule and Villari effects in a ferromagnet is the change of Young's modulus with magnetic field, often called the ΔE *effect*. Like all other magnetostrictive effects, the ΔE effect vanishes at the Curie temperature, above which the material is no longer ferromagnetic.

The theoretical basis for magnetostriction in a ferromagnet is the strain dependence of its magnetocrystalline anisotropy. Most ferromagnetic crystals can lower their anisotropy energy by distorting elastically about their axis of magnetization. When a single crystal of a cubic material, such as iron or nickel, is magnetized to saturation in any given direction, its departure from perfect cubicity may be represented as a linear strain along different directions as follows:

$$l^{-1}\Delta l = \tfrac{3}{2}\,\lambda_{100}\,(\alpha_1{}^2\beta_1{}^2 + \alpha_2{}^2\beta_2{}^2 + \alpha_3{}^2\beta_3{}^2 - \tfrac{1}{3})$$
$$+\, 3\lambda_{111}\,(\alpha_1\alpha_2\beta_1\beta_2 + \alpha_2\alpha_3\beta_2\beta_3 + \alpha_3\alpha_1\beta_3\beta_1) \qquad (2)$$

where λ_{100} and λ_{111} are the saturation values of the longitudinal magnetostriction in the $\langle 100 \rangle$ and $\langle 111 \rangle$ crystal directions, respectively; the α's and β's are the direction cosines (with respect to the $\langle 100 \rangle$ axes) of the magnetic moment and the measured strain, respectively. This equation is often used in analyzing the results of magnetostriction measurements along particular directions in a cubic ferromagnetic crystal rotated in a saturating field. For an initially demagnetized (or partially magnetized) crystal, Eq. (2) must be applied to the different regions of

uniform magnetization, or *domains*, into which the crystal is subdivided; the result for $l^{-1}\Delta l$, subtracted from the result obtained for the final state, gives the net magnetostrictive strain.

When Eq. (2) is summed over all the crystals of a randomly oriented polycrystalline ferromagnet, the saturation value of the longitudinal magnetostriction (relative to the demagnetized state) is found to be $(2\lambda_{100} + 3\lambda_{111})/5$. Room-temperature measurement on a nickel crystal give $\lambda_{100} = -46 \times 10^{-6}$ and $\lambda_{111} = -25 \times 10^{-6}$, whereas for an iron crystal, $\lambda_{100} = +19 \times 10^{-6}$ and $\lambda_{111} = -19 \times 10^{-6}$. Thus, the computed longitudinal magnetostriction for a polycrystal is -33×10^{-6} for nickel and -4×10^{-6} for iron, in good agreement with experimental values for magnetically saturated polycrystalline specimens.

For a partially magnetized polycrystalline material, the linear magnetostriction involves the effect of field on the magnetic moment direction in each magnetic domain in the material. When it is assumed that the magnetic moments are turned into the magnetic field direction against only the opposing forces of magnetocrystalline anisotropy, the field dependence of the longitudinal magnetostriction may be expressed as

$$l^{-1}\Delta l/\Delta H = \lambda_S \sigma_S F(\sigma/\sigma_S)/K \qquad (3)$$

where λ_S and σ_S are the saturation values of the longitudinal magnetostriction and the magnetic moment, respectively, and K is the anisotropy coefficient. The function F depends only on the ratio of the magnetic moment at a given field to its value at saturation, and is maximum when this ratio is approximately 0.6. For a particular material, this condition for maximum F defines the field at which $l^{-1}\Delta l/\Delta H$ and also $\Delta\sigma/\Delta S$ [by virtue of Eq. (1)] have their maximum values, and therefore gives the optimum operating point for the material used in a *magnetostrictive transducer*, which converts electromagnetic energy to mechanical energy and vice versa. Furthermore, according to Eq. (3), a good material for transducer application is one in which σ_S as well as λ_S are high and the anisotropy (or whatever else is restricting the magnetic permeability of the material) is low.

A large field dependence of magnetostrictive strain is also desirable in a ferromagnetic rod used as the resonant component of a *magnetostriction oscillator*. The resonant frequency of such an oscillator depends critically on the Young's modulus of the rod. Hence, fluctuations in the biasing field and temperature of the rod, which would vary its Young's modulus, must be minimized for good frequency stability.

J. S. KOUVEL

Cross-references: *Ferromagnetism, Magnetism, Piezoelectricity and Pyroelectricity, Transducers*

MAGNETRON

A magnetron is a thermionic vacuum tube which generates microwave power. It is used in both military and commercial types of microwave equipment. Some examples are radars, microwave ovens, and diathermy units.

The magnetron was initially investigated by A. W. Hull in 1921. The first high-power microwave magnetron was built by J. T. Randall and H. A. H. Boot in 1940.

Magnetrons can be operated under either cw or pulsed conditions. Some tubes are small enough to be held in the palm of the hand. These tubes generate only a few watts of average power. Others are too heavy to lift without mechanical means. Such tubes generate megawatts of peak power. Magnetrons are capable of operating at efficiencies well over 50 per cent, although efficiency is often sacrificed for other desirable operating characteristics. Tubes have been built with operating wavelengths in the region between tens of centimeters and several millimeters. Input voltages range from a few hundred volts for a very-low-power tube to many tens of thousands of volts for a very-high-power tube.

A magnetron has two concentric cylindrical electrodes. The inner one is the cathode and the outer one is the anode. The anode is divided into segments, which are equally spaced around the circumference. There are usually between eight and forty of these segments. They extend radially outward to form the walls of resonant cavities.

The electron cloud in the interaction space generates rf voltages between the anode segments and the cathode. These rf voltages excite the resonant cavities. Since all the cavities are coupled together, the anode structure can oscillate in a number of modes equal to the number of resonant cavities. These modes are characterized by the phase difference between the voltages on adjacent anode segments. Usually the coupling is designed to favor operation in the π-mode, in which the phase difference between adjacent segments is 180°. Since the resonant cavities are coupled to each other, all the rf power output can be extracted from only one of the cavities. A slot or a loop in the back of this cavity feeds into either a waveguide or a coaxial output line. Magnetrons are designed to give optimum performance when the impedance of the load is equal to the characteristic impedance of the output line.

There are many types of anode structure. Figure 1 shows two of them. In the strapped structure, alternate segments are connected together by a parallel-plane transmission line which closes on itself to form concentric rings. In the rising-sun structure, the alternate small and large sizes of the cavities favor operation in the desired mode. The coupling between cavities is provided by the rf electric fields which extend from the segments into the anode-cathode space. Another example of an anode structure is the interdigital structure (not shown). Here the anode segments form one wall of a single toroidal cavity which resonates at the oscillation frequency.

Magnetrons are usually constructed with a permanent magnet forming an integral part of the tube. Since the anode forms a part of the vacuum envelope, it is not insulated from the frame of the tube. For this

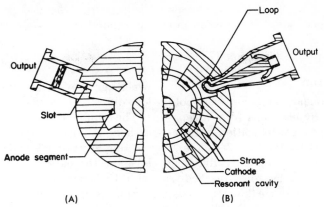

Fig. 1. (A) Rising-sun magnetron with waveguide output. (B) Strapped magnetron with coaxial output.

reason, the anode is commonly operated at ground potential. Input power is supplied to the tube by applying a negative voltage to the cathode.

Operating data for magnetrons are specified by:

1. *The performance chart,* in which contours of constant magnetic field, constant rf power, and constant efficiency are plotted in the anode-current anode-voltage plane. The output line is terminated by its characteristic impedance.

2. *The Rieke diagram (q.v.),* in which contours of constant power and constant frequency are plotted on a Smith chart (*q.v.*) as functions of the real and imaginary parts of the load impedance. The magnetic field and anode current are constant.

3. *The pushing factor,* or the rate of change of frequency with anode current for a matched output line and constant magnetic field.

4. *The pulling factor,* or the frequency excursion that occurs when a load of 1.5 VSWR is varied through all phase positions. The magnetic field and anode current are constant.

Most magnetrons can be tuned. A frequency range of 1.3 to 1 is typical for mechanical tuning. One type of mechanical tuner consists of axially moving plungers which insert metallic fingers into the resonant cavities. If these fingers enter regions

where the rf magnetic field is strong, the tuning is inductive and the frequency increases. If the fingers enter regions where the rf electric field is strong, the tuning is capacitive and the frequency decreases. A voltage-tunable magnetron can be tuned over a range of about 2:1. The operation of this tube is significantly different from the conventional magnetron. It has an anode structure of very low Q and a system of electron injection which replaces the cylindrical cathode. The frequency is varied by changing the anode voltage.

The space-charge cloud of a magnetron has the appearance of a rotating wheel. A hub of electrons surrounds the anode and a number of spokes extends outward from the hub to the anode. For π-mode operation the number of spokes is equal to one-half the number of segments. The spokes rotate and induce an rf voltage wave on the anode. This rf voltage wave generates power by causing rf currents to flow in the resonant cavities.

The electronic mechanism of power generation is characterized by the conversion of potential energy to microwave energy. A consideration of this energy conversion leads to an expression for the Hartree voltage. The Hartree voltage approximates the anode voltage. It can be determined from values of the anode and the cathode radii, the magnetic field, the number of segments, and the frequency.

Dimensional analysis is often used to scale a tube design to new values of power output and frequency.

CARLTON G. LEHR

Plasma Magnetron

Magnetron secondary emission from cold cathodes, started by electrons from a separate filament, or from gas ionization, was obtained prior to 1944 by Blewett. Jepson and Mueller found that in randomly diffusing across B flux lines, electrons reached a smooth anode with average kinetic energy corresponding to about half of V_a, the anode potential. A much larger number diffuse in the opposite direction with the other half of the energy, transferred to them by slipping-stream or diocotron oscillations. The ratio of secondary to primary electrons, δ, may exceed unity when primaries fall through voltage greater than V_s. If $V_a > 200 \, V_s$ the electrons may strike the cathode hard enough so that $\delta_{av} > 1$. These circuitless, random-frequency oscillations give anode volt-ampere characteristics similar to rf magnetron oscillations, and perhaps in competition with each other.

An electron travels cycloidally with a radius $r = mV_a/eB^2d$ about a center whose drift velocity is $v = E/B$, without space charge, in electric (E) and magnetic (B) crossed fields, between parallel electrodes. Their separation d is conveniently measured in units of length r.

It is assumed that diocotron or other plasma ocsillations cause electrons to be randomly displaced to new equipotentials, in steps of r, which add in a given direction to a distance $rN^{1/2}$. The N steps occur at rates proportional to B since the oscillation recurs at a rate proportional to the radian cyclotron frequency $\omega_c = Be/m$. The electron density n in a layer of thickness r near the cold cathode is assumed great enough to make the radian plasma frequency $\omega_p = e(n/m\epsilon_0)^{1/2}$ be as great as ω_c. This condition certainly exists near a hot cathode if the drift velocity there is laminar. It will be found that the density varies inversely with distance from the cold cathode. C. W. Hartman found the anode current

$$I \sim \frac{1}{d^2}\left(\frac{V_a}{Bd}\right)^3$$

which agrees with measured values of turbulent diffusion to a smooth anode.

The number of steps required to cross from cathode to anode varies as $1/r^2$, the speed of crossing as r^2 or V^2, and the number in the layer at the cathode ready to start varies with V; hence $I \sim V^3$.

Since step size varies inversely with B^2, the speed of crossing varies inversely with B^4, the number starting is unchanged, but the speed of a single step varies with B; hence $I \sim 1/B^3$.

Since increased d requires more of the original steps, but these steps also become smaller, the distance measured in step lengths appears to increase with d^2, and speed of diffusion across varies as $1/d^4$. The number available to start decreases with increased d, hence $I \sim 1/d^5$, indicating the importance of uniform distance.

The random waves have an upper frequency limit ω_c, but have maximum intensity for bunch wavelengths near $2d$. Waves start a beam with minimum pressure if the drift velocity is chosen so that its electrons have the maximum ionizing collision cross section. For copper, $\delta_{max} = 1.3$ and secondary emission is less important than electrons from gas. Oxidized aluminum has $\delta_{max} > 2$ and gaseous electrons are useful chiefly for starting; 20-Mw beams have been obtained. Molybdenum and tungsten have intermediate values of δ_{max} and both secondary and gas electrons are useful. If the smooth anode is replaced by a slow-wave structure with periodicity near $2d$, fewer electrons are needed. If the structure is synchronously driven by rf power, a single electron may start the beam. The largest current can be drawn from the cathode with the largest δ_{max}, which requires the least Bd to hold back a reservoir of electrons for back bombardment, to produce sufficient secondaries to sustain the reservoir. If V is increased at this maximum current, the reservoir is emptied and secondary emission ceases. This *maximum-current boundary* increases linearly with B and exponentially with δ_{max}. Strong fields permit current densities greater than 100 amp/cm². The most versatile secondary emission is obtained from hot oxide cathodes with large δ_{max}. Where cathode heating is a problem, plasma may be used for any of three purposes: (1) to provide initial heat; (2) to start secondary emission from a cathode that remains cold; or (3) to provide emission in a system with inadequate δ.

At 150 Mc, 50 kw of cw power has been obtained from aluminum, oxidized ($\delta_{max} > 2$) by air at 10^{-6} to 10^{-3} mm of Hg pressure. Using molybdenum at 10^{-1} mm of Hg pressure of hydrogen, 200-kw pulses at 8 mm wavelength were obtained by J. R. M. Vaughan.

DAVID H. SLOAN

Cross-references: *Amplitron, Backward-Wave Tubes, Crossed-Field Interactions, Millimeter-Wave Generation*

MAGNETS: see PERMANENT MAGNETS

MARCONI, MARCHESE GUGLIELMO (1874–1937)

Guglielmo Marconi was born on April 25, 1874 in Bologna of an Italian father and an Irish mother. He was educated privately and showed an early interest in the work of Hertz, adapting his apparatus to the transmission of messages by the Morse code. He was the first to use grounded antennas and made many other improvements, as in the design of coherers and receiver relays. By 1896 he was sending signals over a distance of 1¾ miles and went to London to demonstrate his system to William Preece and other engineers of the General Post Office. The demonstrations were successful, as were subsequent tests before Army and Navy officers, during which a distance of 8 miles

Marchese Guglielmo Marconi

was achieved. He also successfully demonstrated transmission over water in Bristol Channel. In 1897 he returned to Italy to erect a station at Spezzia for communication with warships, and in 1899 he established radio communication between France and England across the Channel. In the same year radio messages were used on two occasions to save lives in marine disasters. In 1901 radio spanned the Atlantic for the first time from Poldhu in Cornwall to St. John's in Newfoundland. He was then 27 years old.

In 1902 Marconi discovered diurnal variations in radio transmission. By the following year regular transatlantic communication was established, even though the circuits and antennas were not tuned. He introduced tuned circuits later and also invented a method of cw transmission, replacing the spark-gap transmitter generally used until then. In 1904 a radiogram service between Britain and ships at sea was opened to the public. Commander Peary took a transmitter with him on his journey of exploration to the North Pole in 1909 and the first news of his success reached the United States via radio. This event led to a movement to make radio compulsory on all ships, resulting in the saving of lives in many marine disasters, notably that of the *Titanic*, which sank in 1912 after colliding with an iceberg.

Marconi received many honors throughout his illustrious career, including the Italian knighthood in 1897, the Nobel prize in physics in 1909 (jointly with Ferdinand Braun, *q.v.*) and many decorations and honorary degrees. He was created a marquis by the Italian government in 1929. Toward the end of his life, he was much interested in microwaves and in diathermy. He died in Rome, on July 20, 1937.

CHARLES SUSSKIND

Cross-references: *Historical Background of Electronics*

MARINE NAVIGATION: see NAVIGATION

MARKOV PROCESSES

In classical physics, a basic role is played by the fundamental principle of scientific determinism: from the state of a physical system at the time t_0, one may deduce its state at a later instant t. As a consequence of this principle one obtains a basic method of analyzing physical systems: the state of a physical system at a given time t_2 may be deduced from a knowledge of its state at any earlier time t_1 and does not depend on the history of the system before time t_1.

For physical systems which obey probabilistic laws rather than deterministic laws, one may enunciate an analogous principle: the probability that the physical system will be in a given state at a given time t_2 may be deduced from a knowledge of its state at any earlier time t_1, and does not depend on the history of the system before time t_1. Stochastic processes that represent observations on physical systems satisfying this condition are called Markov processes (or processes without "after effects").

A discrete-parameter stochastic process $\{X_n, n = 0, 1, 2, \cdots\}$ or a continuous-parameter stochastic process $\{X(t), t \geq 0\}$ is said to be a Markov process if for any set of n time points $t_1 < t_2 < \cdots < t_n$ in the index set of the process, the conditional distribution of $X(t_n)$, for given values of $X(t_1)$, $\cdots$, $X(t_{n-1})$, depends only on $X(t_{n-1})$, the most recent known value; more precisely, for any real numbers $x_1, \cdots, x_n$

$$P[X(t_n) \leq x_n \mid X(t_1) = x_1, \cdots, X(t_{n-1}) = x_{n-1}]$$
$$= P[X(t_n) \leq x_n \mid X(t_{n-1}) = x_{n-1}]$$

Intuitively one interprets this equation to mean that the "future" of the process depends only on its "present" and is independent of its "past."

Markov processes are classified according to (i) the nature of the index set of the process (whether discrete parameter or continuous parameter) and (ii) the nature of the *state space* of the process. A real number x is said to be a possible value of a stochastic process $\{X(t), t \in T\}$ if there exists a time t in T such that the probability $P[x - h < X(t) < x + h]$ is possible for every $h > 0$. The set of possible values of a stochastic process is called its state space. The state space is called discrete if it contains a finite or countably infinite number of states. A state space which is not discrete is called continuous. A Markov process whose state space is discrete is called a *Markov chain*.

A Markov process is described by the *transition probability function* $P(x, t_0 ; E, t)$ which represents the conditional probability that the state of the system will at time t belong to the set E, given that at time $t_0(<t)$ the system is in state x. The Markov process is said to have stationary transition probabilities, or to be constant or homogeneous in time, if $P(x, t_0 ; E, t)$ depends on t and t_0 only through the difference $(t - t_0)$.

The theory of Markov processes is concerned with two main problems: (i) the "transient" behavior of the process: to find the transition probability function by finding and solving differential and integral equations which it satisfies; and (ii) the "steady-state" behavior of the process: to determine conditions under which there exists a probability measure $\pi(E)$ such that the limit

$$\lim_{t \to \infty} P(x, t_0; \ E, t) = \pi(E)$$

exists independently of x and t_0 .

EMANUEL PARZEN

Cross-references: *Information Theory, Probability, Random Processes, Statistical Communication Theory*

MASERS

The "maser" is an amplifier or oscillator which operates by induced emission. The principles were established by many 20th century physicists in the development of quantum theory. To obtain actual amplification, considerable detailed knowledge of specific materials and techniques were needed. These were not understood until a few years ago when maser devices first appeared. The fundamentals are briefly discussed below.

Atoms and molecules exist in certain energy levels or states. For an isolated atom to alter its state it must absorb a photon from an electromagnetic wave or it may emit a photon. This situation results from the principles of conservation of energy and momentum. Suppose, first, that the atom is in an upper energy level. When it "sees" an electromagnetic wave of the proper frequency and in the appropriate direction, it is induced or stimulated to emit a photon and drop to an available lower energy level. The wave does not lose energy by virtue of the stimulation, and it gains the energy of the emitted photon. This process occurs all around us since light waves are forever interacting with matter. At the same time, matter also gains energy; atoms absorb photons and become excited. Consequently, there is no net amplification process for the photons in nature.

In a quantum mechanical amplifier, the absorption process must be eliminated or reduced relative to the emission process. One may accomplish such a reduction with a collection of molecules which are mainly in the upper energy level. This distribution is not easy to obtain; much effort has been expended in developing means of inverting the normal population distribution.

It is important to note that light and rf-waves are identical except in frequency. Light waves are the order of a hundred thousand times higher in frequency than microwaves. As a result, the rules of induced emission and absorption apply equally to both types of waves. Thus it is the induced emission principle (using either light or microwaves) that results in amplification.

The first operating maser system was due to Gordon, Zeiger, and Townes (1954, 1955) who coined the term "maser" to stand for "microwave amplification by stimulated emission of radiation." The material utilized was an ammonia gas beam which had its upper state molecules separated from the lower state ones by an electrostatic field. The excited molecules passed through a microwave cavity of the appropriate frequency (about 24 kMc or 1.25 cm wavelength) and amplification or oscillation at this frequency could then be accomplished. Since the operating frequency is established by the nature of the ammonia molecule, there is no provision for tuning. Therefore the major application of the ammonia beam maser is as a "clock" or frequency standard. In this respect it is one of the most precise standards in existence. Although the power output is only of the order of a millimicrowatt, this value is sufficient for a frequency standard.

The ammonia maser is schematically shown in Fig. 1. The atoms with thermal translational energy of $3kT$ (k is Boltzmann's constant, and T is the Kelvin temperature) pass through collimating tubes to become a beam. A quadrupole electric field focuses on those ammonia atoms in the higher internal (vibrational and rotational) energy states into the central part of the field. The atoms entering the microwave cavity are almost entirely in upper energy states. In the Columbia University and most other ammonia maser systems, only the 6 per cent of the atoms in the 3,3 state are of interest. Owing to thermal radiation, a small number of these atoms spontaneously emit radiation of 23,870.140 Mc when inside the cavity. The waves are reflected from the cavity walls and act upon the other atoms to induce further emission. This emission is also reflected and the intensity of the radiation in the cavity builds up until the maximum power output of $\frac{1}{2}Nh\nu/t$ is achieved, where N/t is the number of ammonia atoms entering the cavity per second. From this elementary analysis, it may be observed that the limitation on power output is the number of available excited atoms per second.

As the possibilities of microwave amplifiers by masers became better understood, other schemes were proposed and tried. One of the most important and successful of these is the solid-state maser using a paramagnetic crystal for the active element. Paramagnetic atoms are analogous to miniature spinning magnets. At very low temperatures, which may be obtained by immersion in liquid helium, the magnetic atoms are relatively isolated from thermal vibration. The effect of this isolation is to extend the time during

which an atom may remain in a given energy state. The necessity for low temperatures is a consequence of the nature of crystalline structure.

When a paramagnetic crystal is placed in a magnetic field, the magnetic atoms assume only certain allowed energy states. Under ordinary equilibrium conditions, more atoms are in the lower energy levels than the upper. To obtain maser action, this situation must be reversed. Five means of level population inversion have been proposed. These are the three-level methods due to Bloembergen, the adiabatic fast passage of Bloch, an 180° pulse inversion discovered by Hahn, the sudden field reversal of Pound and Purcell, and cross-relaxation methods discovered by Bloembergen and Gorter. Of these, the three-level scheme appears the most practicable for microwave use and it has been widely employed.

A schematic form of the microwave circuit of a Bloembergen type of three-level maser is shown in Fig. 2. The crystal consists of some dilute paramagnetic salt often cooled

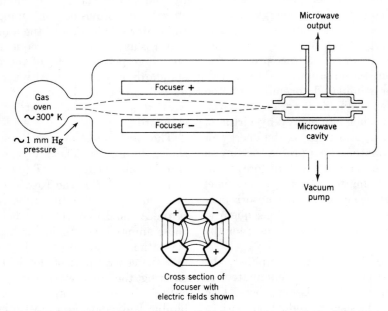

Fig. 1. A schematic of the ammonia maser. The field focuses the fraction of the atoms in the upper energy states. The cavity is tuned to the frequency of the molecular transition. (Reproduced from *Masers* by J. R. Singer, by permission of the publishers, John Wiley and Sons, New York, 1959.)

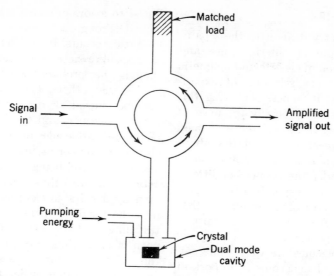

Fig. 2. A reflection-cavity three-level maser in schematic form. (Reproduced from *Masers* by J. R. Singer, by permission of the publishers, John Wiley and Sons, New York, 1959.)

to liquid helium temperature (4.2°K). A microwave pump provides energy to saturate two widely spaced paramagnetic energy levels which leads to a population inversion between two less widely spaced (lower-frequency) levels.

Once inverted population levels are available, amplification or oscillation may occur at a frequency determined by the magnitude of the magnetic field and the resonant frequency of the tuned circuit surrounding the crystal. The upper limitation on frequency is based mainly upon the difficulty in obtaining microwave structures in the submillimeter wave region with sufficiently high Q values. There is no doubt that the maser will play an important part in extending the usable radio spectrum.

Solid-state masers have been constructed that operate in both the two-level and three-level mode. They have been used at frequencies from 300 to 24,000 Mc, and these frequencies will be extended. Gains of 1000 (30 db) have been achieved with bandwidths of tens of megacycles. The noise temperature of these amplifiers has been experimentally found to be of the order of 2°K.

Maser studies show that there exists no upper frequency limitation in visible light frequencies in contrast to the situation for the more conventional generators such as klystrons (*q.v.*) and magnetrons (*q.v.*). Much effort, therefore, has been and is being expended in increasing the frequency of operation. No standardization of terms has occurred, and "maser" is often used to refer to optical and infrared amplifiers and oscillators operating by induced emission. However, some people have preferred the term "iraser" for infrared quantum mechanical amplifiers and "laser" for light amplifiers. The generation of coherent light has been discussed by Schawlow and Townes (*Physical Review*, 1959) and provides a new field of investigation. Present work has provided moderately coherent sources, and experimental studies will no doubt accomplish much more in the future. Both solid-state and gas optical masers have been experimentally successful, and much may be expected from further efforts.

J. R. SINGER

Cross-references: *Atomic Clocks, Laser, Millimeter-Wave Generation, Molecular-Beam Devices, Parametric Amplifiers*

MASS SPECTROMETRY

Mass spectrometry deals with the separation of gaseous ions of differing mass and charge by the action of electric and magnetic fields. By the proper selection of experimental conditions, it is possible, using this technique, to measure precisely the mass of various ions, to prove the existence of mass isotopes, and to measure the relative abundance of ions in a mixture. Organic molecules produce, under the proper conditions, a spectrum of ions corresponding to the parent molecule and most of the fragments that can be produced from it by bond rupture. Since the mass spectra of even closely related organic molecules are quite different, mass spectrometry has become an important tool for the analysis of organic mixtures.

The mass spectrometer and the mass spectrograph, though based on the same principle, are quite different. The spectrograph is employed for the precise measurement of mass, whereas the spectrometer is designed to measure precisely the relative abundance of ions. Both instruments are based on the observation of "positive rays" by Sir J. J. Thomson in 1912. The first spectrometer was built by Dempster in 1918; the first spectrograph was built by Aston a year later. In the following 25 years, the instruments were developed slowly and their application was confined primarily to university laboratories. Early in the Second World War, the need for precise, rapid analyses of complex mixtures of hydrocarbon compounds prompted the development of several spectrometers suited for this specialized application. Since 1945, these commercially available instruments have been developed into versatile tools for the analysis of a wide range of organic and inorganic compounds. This widespread application has, in turn, prompted an extensive search for other means of mass discrimination and for simplified instruments suitable for process-control applications.

In a mass spectrometer, the sample to be studied is first introduced into a vacuum bench, and, by suitable manipulations, reduced to a low pressure. The vapor is then passed through a beam of electrons, where ionization occurs. In the ionization chamber, all possible reactions can and do occur, although the probability of some is much greater than others. The molecule as a whole may be ionized, or it may fragment in any possible manner, and the fragments in turn be ionized. Molecules or fragments can both add or lose one or more electrons, the loss of a single electron being the most common reaction. The ions thus produced are accelerated by a suitable electric field and passed into the magnetic field. A charged particle traveling at high speeds follows a curved path whose radius depends on the speed of the particle and its mass-to-charge ratio (m/e). By varying either the speed of the particles (by changing the accelerating voltage) or by changing the magnetic field strength, ions of various m/e ratios can be focused on a collector plate and thus grounded. The current flowing as a result is amplified and recorded by a suitable electrometer circuit. The resulting plot of mass versus ion intensity is known as a mass spectrum. It is reduced to a mass pattern by dividing each of the peak intensities by the intensity of the largest (or base) peak.

No two molecules behave exactly the same on electron bombardment. Even closely related molecules or isomers show some differences in the manner in which the various bonds react. Thus, mass spectra can be used for qualitative analysis. The problem of identification of pure compounds and some mixtures is simplified by the fact that most molecules give rise to some ions of the same mass as the parent molecule, and thus the absolute molecular weight can be established directly. In mixtures, it is not always possible to identify these 'parent mass peaks,' and other methods must be used. From the study of many mass spectra, an experienced spectrographer can form generalities in behavior that aid him in predicting the probable components in the sample. The final identification, as in most types of qualitative analysis, requires direct comparison of the spectra of the known and unknown.

In quantitative analysis, the problem is somewhat different. First of all, the qualitative analysis of the sample must be known or determined. The mass spectrum of a mixture is then simply the sum of the spectra of the components in the ratio of their partial pressures in the sample. The method of establishing the ratio of components depends upon the components in the sample. In the simplest case, each component gives rise to a characteristic ion not formed by any other component, and a direct breakdown of the mixture is possible. In the other extreme, each component gives rise to some of each of the observed mass peaks, and linear simultaneous equations are needed to make the analysis. Consider the simple example of a mixture of n- and iso-butane. Here, both molecules have a 58 peak due to the parent molecule and a 43 peak due to the fragment remaining after the loss of a methyl group. Then

$$M_{58} = a_{58}x + b_{58}y$$

$$M_{43} = a_{43}x + b_{43}y$$

where M is the peak intensity, a and b the pattern coefficients measured for the pure components, and x and y the concentrations of n- and isobutane, respectively. Solution of these equations leads to the analysis of the mixture. There is no limit, in theory, to the number of components which can be handled in this manner. In practice, it becomes difficult to find a mixture of more than 8 or 10 compounds that can be effectively handled. Electrical computers for the solution of 12 linear simultaneous equations are available to help in this work.

The analysis of most mixtures is done by combining these two approaches. Some compounds in the mixture give rise to characteristic peaks, and their contributions can be subtracted directly. Linear equations may then be set up to handle the remaining components. By suitable combinations of technics, as many as 20 or more components can be determined in a single mixture.

Mass spectrometric analyses are relatively rapid, an hour or two generally being sufficient for the analysis of a moderately complicated mixture. Where a sufficient number of samples of a given type are being analyzed, specialized computational facilities may be used to reduce this time considerably. In the extreme case, the signal from the electrometer circuit is fed directly into an electrical computer (rather than a recorder) and the calculation made directly. In this case, the answer is available almost as soon as the spectral scan has been completed. The precision and accuracy of the instrument likewise depend upon the type of sample being examined. In general, ± 1 mole percent can be achieved.

R. E. Kitson

Cross-references: *Ionization, Isotopes*

MATERIALS USED IN TUBE TECHNOLOGY

Despite the enormous growth of the transistor industry, the manufacture of electron tubes of all kinds is also still a growing activity. We are here concerned with the production of conventional receiving tubes, transmitting tubes, cathode-ray tubes, picture tubes, phototubes, electron multipliers, image tubes, counter tubes, X-ray tubes, switch tubes, and the large group of microwave tubes, such as traveling-wave tubes, magnetrons, klystrons, amplitrons, carcinotrons etc. Electron microscopes and particle accelerators of various types are electron tubes, in the general meaning of the term, as are gas-discharge devices and plasmatrons.

The many tubes enumerated perform a variety of tasks, as partly indicated by their names (see separate entries); they differ widely in physical size; they may be sealed off or continuously pumped; but they have one aspect in common: they must be designed and initially fabricated as high-vacuum devices, even if some of them are later filled with a gas, or vapor, or both.

The need for a high vacuum is readily understood in the case of an electron tube which functions by virtue of electric or magnetic controls exerted on the flight of free electrons on their way from a cathode to an anode or collector. If an excessive number of gas molecules were present in the tube, electrons would collide with them, be scattered, and deviate from their assigned paths. In a gas-filled tube, such as a thyratron or a voltage-regulator tube, the performance characteristic is adversely affected by gas impurities. For this reason, air and foreign gases must be eliminated before the desired gas of high purity is admitted to the tube and sealed into the envelope.

In selecting materials for the construction of electron tubes, first attention is thus given to the vacuum properties of the materials, i.e., their vapor pressure; at any temperature encountered during processing on the pump, and during operation later on, this pressure must not exceed the pressure that can be attained with modern pumping systems ($<10^{-9}$ Torr).* This requirement must be fulfilled by the materials used for the tube envelope, the internal components that make up the electrode structure, and those used for joining the various elements, if the joint is contained within the tube, or if it can "see" the inside of the tube.

A metal such as nickel, for example, is an acceptable material as long as it is not contaminated by impurities either in the form of surface films or as occlusions in its body in the form of gases or solids. To insure this state of cleanliness and purity is one of the main concerns of the materials engineer. Vacuum firing, hydrogen firing, and chemical cleaning are thus important operations in any tube plant or laboratory. Assembly operations are carried out more and more in so-called clean rooms (q.v.) where the air is filtered, special lint-free clothing and finger cots are worn by the operators, and accumulation of dust is minimized by avoiding ledges and corners on walls and fixtures. A tiny thread of lint, if it were to find its way

* Torr is the unit adopted for the pressure exerted by a column of mercury 1 mm high.

into a tube, could make it inoperative by causing a short circuit between critical electrodes after it was transformed into a thread of carbon during heat treatment. Similarly, a fingerprint on a metal or insulator would present a copious source of gas and could poison an oxide-coated cathode beyond any chance of recovery.

The degree to which insistence on clean materials can be carried in practice is a question of cost. Tubes that are expected to have a very long service life, such as submarine cable tubes or tubes to be used in satellites, warrant the utmost effort, but other tubes, where replacement after failure is not such a critical matter, can be made under less stringent conditions to permit sale at a reasonable price.

The environment in which the tube is expected to exist is a determining factor for the choice of materials in another sense also, rather than just accessibility for replacement. If the tube will be exposed to extreme temperatures, to extreme shock and vibration, or to nuclear radiation, special restrictions are placed on the choice of materials and the methods of construction. If the tube is to survive in such a "critical environment," "reliable tubes" (or "trustworthy valves") are made with this purpose in mind.

To drive occluded and adsorbed gases from the materials that constitute a tube, the latter is baked on the pump at as high a temperature as feasible, and the internal elements are subsequently heated to a red heat by eddy-current heating, or high-frequency induction heating (q.v.), which is another name for the same process. During this treatment, the materials must maintain their physical shape and they must not begin to vaporize and produce objectionable deposits within the tube. At the same time, it is desirable to perform baking at as high a temperature as possible to minimize release of gases later during the operational life of the tube. The material from which the tube envelope is made thus has a decisive effect on the life expectancy of the tube because the maximum permissible bake-out tempera-

SELECTED PHYSICAL CHARACTERISTICS OF SOME ELECTRON TUBE MATERIALS

(A) *Metals and Alloys*

Material	Specific Gravity g/cc	Melting Point °C	Temperature for $p = 10^{-6}$ torr °C	Magnetic at 20°C yes/no	Thermal Exp. Coeff. cm/cm°C × 10⁷		Electr. Cond. ohm⁻¹ cm⁻¹ × 10⁻⁶	Yield Strength 0.2% offset psi
OFHC[1] Copper	9.0	1083	862	no	186	(0–600)	0.5907	6,000
"A" Nickel sheet (annealed)[2]	8.9	1440	1260	yes	155	(25–600)	0.146	15,000–30,000
Cupronickel 20%	8.94	1175	—	no	164	(20–300)	0.037	15,000
Monel "403"[2]	8.9	1325	—	no	161	(20–600)	0.0048	32,000
Inconel[2]	8.6	1417	—	no	165	(20–600)	0.0098	30,000
"Kovar,"[3] "Rodar,"[4] "Therlo,"[5] "Nicoseal"[6]	8.2	1450	—	yes	50	(30–400)	0.020	50,000
304 Stainless Steel	7.9	1400	—	no	187	(0–650)	0.0139	33,000
Molybdenum	10.2	2620	1837	no	60	(0–700)	0.179	50,000
Tungsten	19.3	3395	2367	no	46	(20–600)	0.182	—
Tantalum	16.6	2996	2237	no	66	(0–500)	0.065	39,000
Titanium	4.5	1660	1227	no	97	(30–600)	0.0018	60,000

1) Registered Trademark, American Climax, Inc.
2) Registered Trademark, The International Nickel Company, Inc.
3) Registered Trademark, Westinghouse Electric Company (distributed by The Carborundum Company, Refractories Division, Latrobe, Pa.)
4) Registered Trademark, Wilber B. Driver Company
5) Registered Trademark, Driver Harris Company
6) Registered Trademark, The Carpenter Steel Company

(B) *Insulators*

Material	Designation	Specific Gravity g/cc	Max. Oper Temp. °C	Thermal Exp. Coeff. cm/cm°C × 10⁷		Dielectr. Const. (1 Mc)	Loss Tangent (1 Mc) × 10⁴	Compr. Strength (20°C) psi × 10⁻³
Soft glass	Corning 0012	3.05	380	89	(0–300)	6.7	12	⎫
Hard glass	Corning 7720	2.35	460	36	(0–300)	4.7	27	⎬ 70–180
Extra hard glass	Corning 1723	2.63	650	48	(0–300)	6.4	15	⎭
Fused silica	Corning 7940	2.20	1,100	5.6	(0–300)	3.8	0.1	(195–245)
Steatite	Alsimag 665	2.7	950	69	(25–300)	6.3	8	80
Mullite	Coors SI-1	2.8	1,700	45	(25–200)	7.0	(14)	75–80
Forsterite	Alsimag 243	2.8	1,000	100	(25–300)	6.2	4	85
Alumina								
(85%)	Coors AD-85	3.40	1,400	56.8	(25–200)	8.16	9	>240
(96%)	Coors AD-96	3.72	1,700	67	(25–200)	8.95	0.84	>300
(99%)	Coors AD-99	3.90	1,725	67	(25–200)	9.35	0.3	>300
Zircon	Coors ZI-4	2.83	1,400	33.6	(25–200)	6.30	22	70
Beryllia	BeO	2.7	2,000	80	(25–300)	7.5	3	115

ture depends on the physical characteristics of the envelope.

Soft glass has been the common envelope material for lamps and tubes for decades and is still being used for radio receiving tubes, picture tubes, and cathode-ray tubes in mass production. Soft glass, i.e., soda-lime glass, is cheap, readily worked in the flame, transparent to radiation, and sufficiently strong for ordinary handling; but it cannot be baked safely above 350°C. Hard glass, i.e., borosilicate glass, has a higher softening point and can be baked at 480°C. Many special-purpose tubes, transmitting tubes, microwave tubes, and others are made from such hard glasses. Extra-hard glasses, such as aluminosilicates, have a still higher softening point and can be baked at 750°C. Even fused silica is used for "quartz" lamps to contain a mercury vapor discharge. Transmitting tubes have also been made from this material.

Ceramics are refractory crystalline materials (in contrast to glasses, which are non-crystalline). The softening ranges of special ceramics are so high that bakeout at 1000°C is feasible but is generally restricted to about 650°C for other reasons.

In all tubes, it is necessary to provide leads through the envelope to make electrical connection to the internal elements. These leads take the form of wires in conventional tubes and often become disks or cylinders in high-frequency tubes so that glass-to-metal seals or ceramic-to-metal seals are necessary. The members so joined must have, in general, closely matching thermal expansion coefficients to avoid mechanical stresses on heating and cooling.

Very few metals are available for sealing to any given envelope material. In glass-to-metal seals, the bond is formed by the metal oxide; in ceramic-to-metal seals, the ceramic surface is metallized and the metal is brazed to it by suitably chosen filler metals such as nickel-gold alloys. During bakeout, these seals must of course also remain vacuum-tight, and special techniques are required when 650°C is to be exceeded. In addition, the metals themselves become leaky at high temperatures, so that an auxiliary vacuum jacket must be provided around the tube during the bakeout.

In choosing materials for the internal components of a tube, a number of additional requirements must be met that are dictated by the expected performance. Metallic electrodes are assembled to form suitable structures; they must be electrically insulated from one another, and the assembly must be rigid enough to withstand shock and vibration without change of the critical dimensions. The metals must not warp during heating. The metals should generally have high values of electrical and thermal conductivity; sometimes certain members must have low thermal conductivity to avoid unwanted heat drain, from a cathode, for instance. The magnetic properties are important, as are tendencies toward emitting primary and secondary electrons, especially when thin films of alkali metals are formed on the surfaces near an oxide-coated cathode.

The cathode of a tube, no matter of what type, generally is a most sensitive surface which is adversely affected by impurities and foreign gases or ion bombardment. The insistance on the best possible vacuum thus has two reasons: first, to insure copious emission of electrons, and second, to maintain these electrons in flight along prescribed paths, as mentioned earlier.

It is nearly impossible to prevent the release of some gases from the various tube elements, especially when they are bombarded by electrons. Such gases can be trapped by the use of *getters*. Their sorptive properties are specific for different gases and vary with temperature. Barium films on the inside of the tube envelope are most commonly used but other types exist. Such getters essentially act as auxiliary pumps during the life of the tube. Primary getter pumps have been developed in recent years to take the place of conventional oil or mercury diffusion pumps and find increasing use in the industry. The following table lists the properties of a number of materials commonly employed in vacuum-tube construction. For more information on this subject, see the book by W. H. Kohl, *Materials and Techniques for Electron Tubes*, Reinhold, 1960.

WALTER H. KOHL

Cross-references: *Ceramics, Environmental Testing, Gases, Glass, Manufacture of Electron Tubes, Radiation (Ionizing), Vacuum Techniques*

MATRIX ALGEBRA

A matrix is a system of *mn* quantities, called elements, arranged in a rectangular array of m rows and n columns. This array is usually written in the form

$$[A] = \begin{bmatrix} a_{11} & a_{12} & \cdots & a_{1n} \\ a_{21} & a_{22} & \cdots & a_{2n} \\ \multicolumn{4}{c}{\cdots\cdots\cdots\cdots} \\ a_{m1} & a_{m2} & \cdots & a_{mn} \end{bmatrix} = [a_{ij}]$$

If $m = n$, then $[A]$ is said to be a square matrix of order n. Two matrices are equal if they have the same number of rows and of columns, and corresponding elements are equal. A matrix that has n rows and m columns is said to be of order (m,n). If the rows of a given matrix $[A]$ are changed to columns so that the first row becomes the first column, etc., of a new matrix then the new matrix is called the transposed matrix of $[A]$ and is denoted by $[A]'$.

Basic Types of Matrices. (a) *Symmetric Matrices*. If a matrix is equal to its transposed matrix so that $[A] = [A]'$ then $[A]$ is a symmetric matrix.

(b) *Skew-Symmetric Matrices*. If the elements of a matrix are such that $[a_{ij}] = -[a_{ji}]$ the matrix $[a_{ij}]$ is said to be skew-symmetric. The diagonal elements of a skew-symmetric matrix must be zero.

(c) *The Zero or Null Matrix*. If all the elements of a matrix $[a_{ij}]$ are zero, it is a zero or null matrix.

(d) *Diagonal Matrix*. If all the elements not on the principal diagonal are zero in a square matrix, the matrix is said to be a diagonal matrix. If all the elements of a diagonal matrix are equal, the matrix is said to be a scalar matrix. A diagonal matrix whose elements are all equal to unity is called a unit matrix, and denoted by I.

(e) *Singular Matrix*. If the determinant formed from the elements of a square matrix vanishes, the square matrix is said to be a singular matrix. If the determinant does not vanish it is said to be a nonsingular matrix.

Fundamental Matrix Operations. (a) *Addition and Subtraction of Matrices*. The sum and difference of two matrices of the same order, $[a_{ij}] \pm [b_{ij}] = [a_{ij} \pm b_{ij}]$.

(b) *Scalar Multiplication*. The product of a scalar k and a matrix $[a_{ij}]$ is the matrix $[ka_{ij}]$.

(c) *Matrix Multiplication*. The definition of matrix multiplication is such that two matrices can be multiplied by each other only when the number of *columns* of the first matrix equals the number of *rows* of the second. That is, in order for the matrix product $[a][b]$ to be defined it is necessary that the order of $[a]$ be (m,p) and the order of $[b]$ be (p,n). Matrices that satisfy this condition are said to be *conformable* matrices.

If $[a]$ is a matrix of order (m,p) and $[b]$ a matrix of order (p,n), then by definition, the product is the matrix $[c]$ given by, $[a][b] = [c]$, where

$$c_{ij} = \sum_{k=1}^{p} a_{ik} b_{kj}$$

The product matrix $[c]$ is seen to be of order (m,n). As an example of the general definition, let

$$[a] = \begin{bmatrix} a_{11} & a_{12} & a_{13} \\ a_{21} & a_{22} & a_{23} \\ a_{31} & a_{32} & a_{33} \end{bmatrix}, \quad [b] = \begin{bmatrix} b_{11} & b_{12} \\ b_{21} & b_{22} \\ b_{31} & b_{32} \end{bmatrix}$$

Then the product matrix is given by

$[a][b] =$

$$\begin{bmatrix} a_{11}b_{11} + a_{12}b_{21} + a_{13}b_{31} & a_{11}b_{12} + a_{12}b_{22} + a_{13}b_{32} \\ a_{21}b_{11} + a_{22}b_{21} + a_{23}b_{31} & a_{21}b_{12} + a_{22}b_{22} + a_{23}b_{32} \\ a_{31}b_{11} + a_{32}b_{21} + a_{33}b_{31} & a_{31}b_{12} + a_{32}b_{22} + a_{33}b_{32} \end{bmatrix}$$

It can be seen that as a consequence of the general definition of matrix multiplication, $[a][b]$ is not in general equal to $[b][a]$ so that matrix multiplication is not commutative. Therefore it is necessary to distinguish between *premultiplication*, as when $[b]$ is premultiplied by $[a]$ to yield the product $[a][b]$, and *postmultiplication*, as when $[b]$ is postmultiplied by $[a]$ to yield the product $[b][a]$. The unit matrix I, it may be noted, commutes with any square matrix of the same order. That is, $I[a] = [a]I = [a]$.

Except for the noncommutative law of multiplication, the associative law of multiplication of continued products is valid; we therefore have $([a][b][c]) = [a]([b][c])$ provided the matrices are conformable. The distributive law of multiplication also holds for matrix algebra. If the product of two matrices is zero, it does not follow that one of the matrices is zero. For example,

$$\begin{bmatrix} a & 0 \\ b & 0 \end{bmatrix}\begin{bmatrix} 0 & 0 \\ c & d \end{bmatrix} = \begin{bmatrix} 0 & 0 \\ 0 & 0 \end{bmatrix}$$

(d) *Matrix Inversion.* The operation of division is not defined in matrix algebra. However, the operation of matrix inversion plays a role that is analogous to division in ordinary algebra. If $[a]$ is a square matrix whose determinant does not vanish so that $[a]$ is nonsingular, then $[a]$ possesses a reciprocal, or inverse, matrix $[R]$ defined by

$$[a][R] = I = [R][a]$$

where I is the unit matrix of the same order as the matrix $[a]$. If this equation is expanded, the elements of $[R]$ may be determined; and the matrix $[R]$ may be expressed in the following form:

$$[R] = [A_{ji}]/\det[a] = [a]^{-1}$$

the elements of the matrix $[A_{ji}]$ are the cofactors of the elements of the transposed matrix of $[a]$, and $\det[a]$ is the determinant formed from the elements of the square matrix $[a]$. The notation $[a]^{-1}$ is used to denote the inverse or reciprocal matrix $[R]$.

It can be shown that $([a][b][c])^{-1} = [c]^{-1}[b]^{-1}[a]^{-1}$. This is the reversal law of reciprocated products. Another useful relation is $([a][b][c])' = [c]'[b]'[a]'$.

A very important matrix that arises frequently in the application of matrices to physical problems. This matrix has the property that $[a]^{-1} = [a]'$ or $[a][a]' = I$, the unit matrix. A matrix that has this property is called an *orthogonal matrix.*

The Characteristic Equation and the Eigenvalues of a Matrix. If μ is a scalar parameter, and $[M]$ is a square matrix of order n, the matrix $[K] = [\mu I - M]$ where I is the nth order unit matrix is called the *characteristic matrix* of the matrix $[M]$. The determinant of the characteristic matrix, $\det[K]$, is called the characteristic polynomial $p(\mu)$ of the matrix $[M]$. The equation $p(\mu) = \det[K] = 0$ is the *characteristic equation* of the matrix $[M]$. In general if $[M]$ is a square matrix of the nth order, its characteristic equation is an equation of the nth degree in μ. The n roots of this equation are the characteristic roots or *eigenvalues* of the matrix $[M]$.

L. A. PIPES

REFERENCES

A. D. MICHAL, Matrix and Tensor Calculus, Wiley, New York, 1947.
L. A. PIPES, Applied Mathematics for Engineers and Physicists, McGraw-Hill, New York, 1958.

Cross-references: *Stress Tensor, Vector Algebra*

MAXIMUM-EFFORT SYSTEMS: see SYSTEMS (NONLINEAR)

MEDICAL ELECTRONICS

The period from 1945 to 1955 saw a steady increase in the application of electronic principles and techniques to problems in biology and medicine. The interest focused more frequently on clinical instrumentation than on fundamental studies, and by 1955 the cream had been well skimmed from the instrumentation field. It then became necessary to undertake a serious examination of medical electronic activity to see what should be done if progress were to continue.

The communication problem between engineers and physicians continued to be one of major importance, and it seemed that the best solution might be to educate a new type of engineer—a medical electronic engineer, or a biomedical engineer. This engineer would be concerned with the application of engineering science theory and techniques to problems in biology and medicine; for example, the application of engineering concepts to research on the structure and function of biological systems, and to the development of practical results from such work. Fortunately, there are now a number of graduate level programs leading to the M.A. degree and the Ph.D. in medical electronics and biomedical engineering. It may seem unusual to discuss education in a review article, but in this case such attention is justified because these education programs have opened a channel by which the engineering scientist can learn directly about problems in biology and medicine where his skill is badly needed. Also, as a result of this training he will be able to contribute more readily to biomedical research in universities, industry, and government agencies.

In a field as diverse as medical electronics, it is difficult for an engineer or a medical researcher to locate the pertinent literature. He should know that the Institute of Radio Engineers periodically publishes a Bibliography on Medical Electronics, devotes entire issues of its *Proceedings* to the subject, and publishes quarterly *Transactions on Bio-Medical Electronics*.

The present article contains material from three broad subject areas: (1) electrical properties of tissue; (2) microelectrodes and transducers; and (3) the use of electronic computers in medicine. The author has also published previous reviews dealing with clinical instrumentation (*New England J. Med.* 252:580, 1955) and with research (in "Medical Physics," vol. 3, Year Book Publishers, Chicago, 1960).

Electrical Properties of Tissue

In order to understand the body surface potentials which reflect the electrical activity of the heart (the electrocardiogram) we need to have information about the electrical activity of the heart itself, and about the electrical characteristics of the tissue media surrounding the heart. Studies on the electrical properties of tissue have brought us to the point where it is possible to investigate the relationship of the fine structure of the electrocardiogram to the heart activity.

Valuable information has been obtained by careful examination of the electrical properties of biological material over the range of frequencies from 1 cps to 100 kMc. It has been pointed out that the mechanism predominantly responsible for the observed data changes with frequency. These data include such effects as time-dependent interface polarization, accumulation of charges owing to inhomogeneous structure, and the orientation of polar molecules. From a consideration of the electrical properties of water and electrolytes, protein suspension, etc., it is possible to make a synthesis of the experimentally observed dielectric parameters of tissues. Biological membranes are a particularly interesting type of tissue because (1) they surround the interior of biological cells and confine its content and (2) they regulate the exchange of matter between the inside and the outside of the cells. By using techniques of ac spectroscopy Schwan has been able to show that from a determination of the frequency dependence of a suspension of cells (e.g., red blood cells) it is possible to obtain the capacity of the cell membrane; the dielectric constant and conductivity of the cell interior; and the dielectric constant and conductivity of the cell exterior.

These studies of cell properties and cell suspensions have provided basic biologic information, and on the basis of this knowledge a clinical instrument, an electronic hematocrit meter, has been designed. Okada and Schwan have shown that the electrical conductivity of whole blood k_B is a very accurate index of the hematocrit. In the range from 0 to 15.1 $\times$ 10^6 erythrocytes/mm^3 the relationship of k_B and the erythrocyte count is linear. The electronic hematocrit meter uses a 10-kc oscillator and bridge circuit, one arm of which contains the whole blood sample (0.02 cc). Unbalance of the bridge is a measure of the volume concentration of erythrocytes in whole blood. The entire circuit is transistorized and requires no warm-up. Because the meter is small and portable, it is easily carried to the patient's bedside. A variety of such small, rugged, and reliable instruments would be helpful in laboratory and clinical medicine.

Two related problem areas of applied interest should be mentioned: (1) diathermy and (2) injury from microwave radiation exposure.

Diathermy is the use of artificially induced local heat for therapeutic purposes. High-frequency currents of 27 Mc or microwave radiation of 2450 Mc is usually applied. It is important to know how deep in the tissues the induced heat penetrates and how much heat is generated in any particular part of the body. For the scientific application of diathermy more knowledge of the capacitive and resistive properties of body tissue needs to be accumulated.

Man's ability to generate microwave power has been increasing at the rate of about 15 db per decade. With the possible development by 1965 of high-power devices capable of generating 1000 kw of average power, it is obvious that injury from microwave radiation exposure must be considered and safety measures adopted. A flux level of 10 mw/cm^2 absorbed energy has been suggested for tolerance purposes. Such an opinion was the result of work on tissue properties in the radar frequency range. There is still much to be learned about the scattering characteristics of man in relation to the amount of absorbed energy.

Microelectrodes and Transducers

It may be true that physiological amplifiers offer no exotic problems, but most investigators would agree that there is a great deal of work to be done on the design of microelectrodes and transducers. With microelectrodes we are interested in the nature of the coupling to tissues at the cellular level. With "transducers" we are interested in the coupling to the body in order to record physiologic phenomena such as blood pressure, respiration, heart sounds, etc.

Existing microelectrodes are of two types: (1) low-pass electrolyte-filled pipettes and (2) high-pass metal-filled pipettes. There is no universal electrode. The metal probe is useful under conditions where one is interested in propagated signals only as signals, whereas the fluid-filled probe is better for studying membrane processes. The two probes are actually complementary since the fluid pipette is good for intracellular records and other slow changes of potential, and the metal tip is good for extracellular records and rapid changes.

The investigator who tries to find a transducer which is "just right" for his problem will sympathize with the statement of one worker that "all who set out to measure and record physiological phenomena using electrical techniques have been impressed by the fact that there are few commercially available transducers to convert physiological events to electrical signals. The few that do exist come from two sources; either they are derived from industry, or they have an origin in a particular area of physiology and medicine. In either case they are usually integrated into specialized instruments designed to measure a single quantity." A third source should be perhaps added, and that is the government and industry laboratories doing work on physiologic monitoring for space travel. The problem here is to find a method for making the information available to medical investigators. Actually, this comment applies in general to the biomedical engineering field. Many electronic techniques that have been developed for military purposes doubtless have immediate application to biological and medical problems. How can we make these techniques available to medical investigators? This question is one of the most pressing in the field of medical electronics. Several solutions have been suggested. Since there are many electronic companies working on military contracts, a possible solution would be for each of these companies to have a small group of individuals who were familiar with both the company projects and with medical problems. These individuals would be looking constantly for the biological and medical uses of the latest electronic developments.

If the investigator wishes to design transducers, he should take great care to construct all components of the system to provide faithful reproduction of the physiologic event, maximum efficiency, and extreme standardization. The transducer should not cause undue stress to the subject, and in general transducers should be located near the patient.

Use of Electronic Computers in Medicine

In the biomedical sciences investigators are just beginning to use computers. Perhaps one of the greatest application of computers eventually will be in the biomedical field. As computers are applied to a field of activity outside the fields that primarily employ mathematics and logic in their theories, that field undergoes greater formalization. There is already evidence that useful standardization of terminology is being fostered by the current efforts to apply computers to medical data processing.

Work toward attaining "artificial intelligence," self-organizing systems, etc., is drawing on information from varied fields such as biology, psychology, neurology, and electronics. Fortunately, the information exchange flows freely in both directions— from electronics to biology and vice versa. The interest in bionics, which may be defined as the application of biological principles to engineering problems, is one example of the biological contribution to electronics.

The concept of man-computer symbiosis is one of particular importance to the future of biomedical computing. The computer must be considered in the context of the environment in which it operates. Computers that have been developed for business applications or the physical sciences are not well suited for many problems in biology and medicine. A great deal of thought and experiment needs to be given to the specifications for biomedical computing equipment. The best attitude at present probably is one of extreme flexibility in which computers of different designs and different sizes will be tried by investigators in an attempt to deter-

mine what type of machine gives the most help in solving which classes of problems.

The range of biomedical computer applications is very broad. One must consider (1) the "on-line" requirements of the psychophysiologist and neurologist; (2) the automation of hospital procedures such as the chemical analysis laboratory and the medical records; (3) the problems of medical literature retrieval; and (4) computer aids to medical diagnosis. One of the questions concerning equipment development is whether it is necessary to develop special-purpose computers such as the average response computer for measuring statistics of neuroelectric activity or the SVEC for vector cardiography. Is it probable that new programming systems and the large general-purpose machines now being developed will be able to do a better job on biomedical problems? At the present time not enough information is available to answer these questions with any degree of certainty.

Some examples of work in progress have been selected which illustrate the use of analog and digital computers.

The Analog Computer as System Simulator. Until analog computers were available it was very difficult to make a realistic model with which to test theories of how chemical reactions proceeded in the body or how organ systems functioned.

MacNichol (*Proc. IRE* **47**: 1869, 1959) set out to construct an analog computer to simulate, as nearly as possible, the flux of material in systems of coupled bimolecular reactions. It is important to understand such reactions because in the living organism metabolic processes proceed by steps that are coupled to one another. The true reaction sequence of such coupled reactions can be studied in terms of the concentration of a product in the reaction and in terms of how this concentration changes with time. Equations for such reactions require solution of simultaneous equations, a very laborious project when a large number of reaction steps are present. MacNichol has demonstrated very well that a simple analog machine can help to decide between various reaction schemes so that the most likely system can be subjected to more accurate analysis on a digital computer.

MacNichol's computer originally constructed in the period 1951–1953 was made to study biochemical reactions such as this:

$$\text{source} \rightarrow A + B \underset{\beta_1}{\overset{\alpha_1}{\rightleftharpoons}} \overset{\overset{\textstyle D}{+}}{C} \underset{\beta_2}{\overset{\alpha_2}{\rightleftharpoons}} E \rightarrow Z \rightarrow \text{sink}$$

In the model the material fluxes in the chemical system are represented by the flow of electric charges into and out of capacitors in electronic integrators. The concentration of each substance is then represented by a voltage across a capacitor in the corresponding integrator. One of the interesting features of the model is the system of "pumps" that produce a flow of charge from capacitors, representing products. This charge-flow rate is determined by the triple product of two concentrations and a rate constant, which are represented in the computer by the voltage across capacitors and a fixed potential. The charge pump consists of two units; an actuator, which is controlled by a voltage proportional to the rate constant and to the concentration of the reactants and a pump unit, which transfers charge in response to pulses from the actuator. The pump actuator uses an interesting and somewhat unusual multiplying circuit to produce triangular pulses of an amplitude proportional to the product of two variables, and a frequency proportional to a third. The pump units are diode step counters which transfer a pulse of charge proportional to the amplitude of each actuating pulse and thus permit a current to flow which is proportional to the input quantities.

With a system of integrators it is possible to make a very satisfactory simulation of a number of coupled bimolecular reaction systems for study.

The Analog Computer for Analysis of Control Mechanisms in the Body. The work of Warner is an excellent example of how the analog computer has been used to study regulation of the circulatory system. The human heart and blood vessels form a closed-loop system whose self-regulatory properties have not been satisfactorily analyzed. In Warner's experiment the computer was programmed to represent the carotid sinus, a part of the mechanism that controls arterial blood pressure. The following description is quoted from Warner (*Proc. IRE* **47:** 1913, 1959): "The organ being simulated by the computer is the carotid sinus, a small organ made up of stretch-sensitive nerve endings in the wall of a large artery in the neck. The variable controlled by this organ is arterial pressure.

"From work done by others using an isolated carotid sinus preparation it is known that the frequency with which action potentials move along the carotid sinus nerve from the carotid sinus toward the brain is directly related to the pressure in the carotid artery (as long as the pressure exceeds a certain minimum value) and is also a direct function of the rate of change of arterial pressure. In the present study the transfer function used to represent the carotid sinus is

$$\frac{n}{p - p_0} = k_1 s + k_2$$

where n is the frequency of impulses on the carotid sinus nerve, p is the pressure in the carotid artery, p_0 is the minimum static pressure capable of eliciting impulses on the carotid sinus nerve, s is the Laplace operator, and k_1 and k_2 are constants."

In the computer experiment the computer input voltage comes from a transducer which senses the arterial pressure. The computer output voltage rises as the arterial pressure rises according to the transfer function and then this output voltage varies the frequency rate of a stimulator which is connected to the carotid sinus nerve. The increased frequency of impulses on the carotid sinus nerve produces relaxation of the smooth muscles of small arteries and a fall in blood pressure results which tends to bring the pressure back to the normal level.

This experiment shows how an analog computer can act as an analysis and a control device. Continued development of transducers and research on control systems of the body will add to our understanding of how these controls act and we hope they will hasten the practical application of compact, efficient artificial internal organs.

The Computer as an Aid in Medical Diagnosis. In previous articles Ledley and Lusted have discussed some of the potential advantages of computer aids to medical diagnosis and medical data processing (*Science* **130**: 9 and 1225, 1959). It was proposed that the logical analysis part of medical diagnosis could be formalized in terms of the propositional calculus and conditional probability. From a large amount of reliable medical data in memory, the computer then could (1) produce a list of possible diagnoses consistent with medical knowledge from a given set of signs and symptoms presented by the patient and (2) indicate further diagnostic tests which best differentiate among the remaining diagnostic possibilities.

In pursuing this subject the progress has been very slow because of the many problems in collecting accurate and complete medical data. This emphasizes the point which was made earlier about the formalization of a field not previously concerned with mathematics and logic. Encouraging recent results lead the writer to believe that computer calculations using Bayes' formula will give a reliable listing of disease possibilities for a given patient.

Biomedical research and clinical medicine will be increasingly concerned in the future with getting computers to take over a large portion of the problem-solving tasks. We must pay particular attention to the development of appropriate input-output devices for the biomedical investigator. Then with the help of large time-sharing computing systems we should have a powerful "thinking-aid" for biomedical research.

LEE B. LUSTED

Cross-references: *Bionics, Computer Applications, Neuristor, Neuron, Radiation (Ionizing), Radiation Hazards (Nonionizing Radiation)*

MEISSNER, ALEXANDER (1883–1958)

Alexander Meissner was born in Vienna on September 14, 1883 and began his professional activity with Telefunken in 1907. He was the first to use a self-excited vacuum-tube signal generator involving feedback, which had a decisive influence on the progress of radio engineering, especially in Europe; until then, undamped high-frequency oscillations had been obtainable only by means of alternators coupled with frequency multipliers, or by the use of the arc discharge as a type of negative resistance. Not until the employment of the feedback vacuum-tube transmitter did it become possible to exceed the narrow confines of the older methods, a development in which Meissner played a decisive part. He also made a number of contributions to the understanding and improvement of the electrical properties of materials, notably with regard to increasing the efficiency of isolating materials by improving their thermal conductivities.

He received many honors in Germany and abroad during his long career: he served as a vice-president of the IRE in 1929, and in

Alexander Meissner

1957 he was decorated by the German Federal Republic and named an honorary senator of the Technical University in Berlin. He died in Berlin on January 4, 1958.

CHARLES SUSSKIND

Cross-references: *Historical Background of Electronics*

MESONS

In 1935, Yukawa proposed that the strong short-range nuclear forces between nucleons (neutrons and protons) may be transmitted through a meson field strongly coupled with the nucleons, just as Coulomb forces arise from the interaction of charge with the Maxwell field. The known properties of nuclear forces required that this meson field must have neutral and charged massive quanta, of charges $+e$ and $-e$ (e, the electron charge) and of mass about 300 m_e (electron masses).

These general requirements of Yukawa's theory are satisfied by the π-mesons, which were first identified in cosmic rays (1947). Since 1948, charged and neutral π-mesons have been copiously produced in the laboratory by bombardment of nuclei with high-energy nucleons (threshold $\sim$170 Mev), or with bremsstrahlung (*q.v.*) photons from high-energy electrons (threshold $\sim$150 Mev). The mass of the $\pi^\pm$ mesons is 273.0 ($\pm$0.5) m_e, the π_0 meson being 8.8($\pm$0.6)m_e lighter. Studies of the reactions occurring between π^+, π^- mesons and deuterium nuclei have shown that the π-meson is *pseudoscalar*, i.e., that the π-meson has odd intrinsic parity and zero spin.

An outstanding property of the π-meson nuclear interaction is its "charge independence," best expressed through the concept of isotopic spin. The π-mesons form a charge triplet of isotopic spin $T = 1(2T + 1 = 3$ charge states), the neutron-proton doublet having isotopic spin $T = \frac{1}{2}$. The nuclear interaction between a π-meson and a nucleon then depends only on their total isotopic spin ($T = \frac{1}{2}$, or $T = \frac{3}{2}$), not on their charges. Further, this interaction is particularly strong when the meson and nucleon are in a relative p-state of total angular momentum $\frac{3}{2}\hbar$ and have total isotopic spin $\frac{3}{2}$, a very broad but marked resonance being observed at about 195 Mev in the scattering of π-mesons by protons. This resonance appears very strongly in meson production from protons by photons, and its effects may also be traced in many other π-meson processes.

Recent work has established that the π-nucleon interaction also becomes resonant for a number of higher π-meson energies. $T = \frac{1}{2}$ resonances occur at 680 Mev and 950 Mev in π^--proton (but not π^+-proton) collisions; a further $T = \frac{3}{2}$ resonance occurs at 1300 MeV in π^--proton and π^+-proton collisions; and there is evidence for still further resonant energies. The detailed properties of these resonance states are being intensively investigated.

In the free state, the π-mesons are unstable. The π_0-meson decays to two photons with mean life about 2×10^{-16} sec. The $\pi^\pm$ mesons decay to a neutrino and $\mu^\pm$ meson with mean life 2.55($\pm$0.1) $\times$ 10^{-8} sec. The $\mu^\pm$ mesons (mass 207.0($\pm$1.0)m_e), known since 1937, occur copiously in cosmic rays at sea level as a product of $\pi^\pm$ meson decay and their nuclear interactions are extremely weak. Their mean life is 2.1($\pm$0.05) $\times$ 10^{-6} sec for decay to an electron (or positron) and two neutrinos.

With the pseudoscalar meson theory, a reasonable semiquantitative explanation may be found for the resonance phenomena mentioned above, the appropriate coupling strength for the meson-nucleon interaction being given by a dimensionless coupling parameter $g^2/\hbar c$ of about 15. Besides the general features of nuclear forces, the theory also accounts directly for the strong tensor component of nuclear forces, the strength predicted for $g^2/\hbar c \sim 15$ being about that necessary to account for the observed quadrupole moment of the deuteron. The theory indicates that, owing to their meson field, the nucleons must have a finite structure, and measurements on the magnetic moments of the nucleons and on the extent of their charge cloud are in rough accord with the expectations of this theory. However, the coupling parameter is rather large and no adequate methods have yet been devised for reliable calculations of the content of the theory, so that no detailed quantitative agreement with experiment can be claimed for the theory at the present stage.

Furthermore, the existence of many other unstable particles has become known, first from cosmic ray studies and more recently from laboratory experiments using high-energy (multi-Bev) proton accelerators. Two K-meson doublets are well-established, comprising two neutral K-mesons (both of mass 974 m_e, and with lifetimes 1.0×10^{-10} sec and 6×10^{-8} sec) and two charged ($K^{\pm}$) mesons (of mass 966.5 m_e). In addition there are a number of supernucleonic particles (known as the *hyperons*), a Λ^0 singlet particle (mass 2183 m_e) which decays to a proton and a π^- meson, a Σ^-, Σ^0, Σ^+ triplet (mean mass 2333 m_e) the charged members of which also decay to a nucleon and a II meson, the neutral member transforming rapidly (lifetime of order of 10^{-19} sec) to a Λ^0 particle and a photon, and a Ξ^-, Ξ^0 doublet (mass 2580 m_e) whose decays lead to a Λ^0 particle and a π meson. These supernucleons (excepting Σ^0) all have life-times of the order of 10^{-10} sec. The collision processes in which these new particles (referred to collectively as *strange particles*) are produced, and their interactions with nuclear matter, have been studied intensively in recent years. Current experiments suggest there exist yet further particles that are much less stable than these strange particles. All of these particles have strong interactions with nucleons and a complete meson theory must give some account of them and their mutual interactions. At the present time, the nature of the strange particles and their role in mesonic and nuclear phenomena are not at all understood.

RICHARD H. DALITZ

Cross-references: *Cosmic Rays, Neutrinos, Nucleonics, Radiation (Ionizing)*

METEORS: see PROPAGATION

MICROCIRCUITRY

The terms microcircuitry or microelectronics are used to describe any electronic circuit, subsystem, or system whose parts density exceeds, by an order of magnitude or more, that attainable utilizing conventional components. These phrases do not delineate the many approaches to miniaturization. Any method or technique that produces a reduction in size described above is included within the above definition.

The most satisfactory classification distinguishes among techniques with respect to the extent of the integration of the electronic function. In this kind of a classification, three major groupings can be discerned. They are (1) interconnected miniaturized components, (2) integrated circuits, and (3) molecular electronics.

Collections of Interconnected Discrete Miniaturized Components. Microelectronics systems in this category represent primarily packaging techniques. Miniaturized components take on form factors (round, flat, square, rectangular, tubular) that best suit the realization of a required packing density. One example in this area is the "Micromodule." Ceramic wafers 0.310 in. square each hold a separate discrete circuit element. They are stacked one upon the other to make up a circuit with peripheral vertical wires interconnecting the wafers both electrically and mechanically. There may be a multiplicity of a given type of circuit element on a single wafer, but each wafer contains only one type of circuit element. Circuit modules can then be interconnected to form fully operating systems. Another approach in this area utilizes ceramic vacuum-tube elements whose wafers are round instead of square. Triodes and diodes using single wafers for grids, cathodes, and plates with separate wafers for the passive elements are built up.

Many companies have done work on the pre-packaging of miniature passive and active components into small holes in a board sandwiched between two printed wiring boards for interconnection. This approach has been dubbed the "Swiss cheese" approach. Another similar method, whose name aptly describes the technique, is the "cordwood" approach. These techniques employ components and devices known today and make use of unique and special interconnecting methods in order to gain weight and size reductions. These methods have advantages in terms of component availability and in the fact that components can be tested and evaluated prior to insertion in the circuit. They have disadvantages in that the number of interconnections and components for a given system are not reduced, so that the gain in size and weight reductions are limited.

Integrated Circuits. The integrated circuit is one in which a multiplicity of types of circuit elements are brought together on a single substrate. This category of microelectronics is conveniently further broken down into two groups; that in which the substrate does not form a part of the circuit and that in which the substrate is utilized for the active elements in the circuit. In the first case the passive elements of the circuit (resistors, capacitors, and all interconnections) can be prepared from composition materials such as resin-carbon compositions for resistive inks, noble metal-glass compositions for conductive areas, and dispersed dielectric materials for the capacitor, or they can be deposited by vacuum processes (evaporation or sputtering). In certain instances, ceramics are used as both the substrate and the capacitor dielectric.

Where vacuum processes are used, metals such as Al, Ag, Pd, Au, Ni, Cr, Pt, or alloys of these, can be used for the conductive system. Resistive elements are usually prepared from Ni, Cr, or Ni-Cr alloys. More recently, mixtures of metals and dielectrics (e.g., Cr-SiO) have been used as resistive elements. Dielectrics for capacitors are obtained by the evaporation of SiO, MgF_2, or CsF. Oxides of elements such as tantalum, titanium,

or bismuth may also be utilized as dielectrics, deposited by a reactive sputtering technique or by evaporation and subsequent oxidation. In this approach, once the passive elements are deposited, the active elements are added by soldering or bonding of these elements to the deposited circuitry. The second approach to integrated circuits uses the single-crystal semiconductor as the substrate. Both the active and the passive elements can be fabricated directly onto the substrate by such processes as diffusion, alloying, etching, and evaporation. The advantages of the integrated circuitry are (1) a major decrease in the number of soldered or mechanical interconnections, (2) a major gain in size and weight reduction, (3) a reduction in the total number of processing steps necessary to form a circuit.

The disadvantage in this method is that a complex device may have to be discarded because of the failure of one circuit element within the device. There are also manufacturing problems with respect to the yield of a multicircuit element piece made as a single component.

Molecular Electronics. In the molecular-electronics approach, materials (primarily in the semiconductor class) are modified in such a way as to perform a given over-all electronic function. In the most advanced consideration of this method the concept of discrete circuit elements is discarded. The techniques and phenomenon used to gain the end product may be film deposition, diffusion, cryogenics (*q.v.*), junction formation, or geometry. Interconnections within the "functional block" are absent.

The semiconductor-substrate integrated circuit approaches this concept very closely, but in practice still prepares specific areas or volumes to perform the function of R and C. In the "molectronic" approach the performing of these functions is not independently carried out but rather the end result is an equivalent circuit obtained in a fully integrated sense. In the ultimate this approach would have the advantage of eliminating all interconnections with the exception of the inputs and the outputs to the "circuit" and presumably could simplify the problem of system design. However, much research remains to be done in the areas of materials and techniques for energy conversion, system function, and network synthesis and analysis before this approach can be considered available and practical.

JOHN J. BOHRER
SIDNEY J. STEIN

Cross-references: *Integrated Circuits and Devices, Miniaturization, Modular Construction, Packaging, Printed Circuits, Semiconductor Manufacture*

MICROSWITCHES: see SWITCHES

MICROTRON

The microtron (electron cyclotron) is a relativistic charged particle accelerator which is similar in one sense to a cyclotron, since it operates with a fixed magnetic field, but differs in that the energy increments per turn are closely limited to amounts bearing a simple relation to the rest mass of the particle accelerated. It is one of two conceptions published by Veksler in 1944 and was independently proposed by others. First brought to actual operation by Henderson, LeCaine, and Montalbetti in 1948, the microtron has since been built, or proposed in various forms, for accelerating electrons and protons to design energies of 30 Mev and several Bev respectively, with rf power sources ranging from 2.8 to 24 kMc.

Figure 1 illustrates its operation. A cavity resonator driven by a pulsed high-power microwave source emits field emission electrons that circle in the magnetic field in cotangential orbits in such a way that the orbital period is increased on each resonator passage by some simple multiple of the cavity period T_0. This action may occur since each orbital period is $T_n = (2\pi/Hec)E_n$ where E_n is the *total* energy of the particle ($m_0c^2 + \Sigma_n \Delta E_n$) and ΔE_n is the energy gain

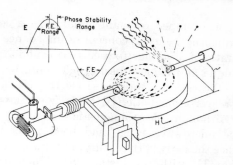

Fig. 1.

at the nth resonator passage. Fixed increments of T are obtained for fixed values of ΔE that bear a simple ratio to or a multiple of m_0c^2. A microtron can operate in a considerable number of "modes" obtainable by choice of compatible values of wavelength $\lambda = c/T_0$ and magnetic field H. In actual operation a particle cannot maintain exact phase in the resonator field, but, as in Veksler's second conception, the synchrotron, the deviations in particle mass from "synchronous" mass produce compensatory changes in the orbital periods and phase stability exists over a part of the rf cycle.

Electrons are easily extracted using magnetic shield tubes, due to the considerable spacing in orbits ($\sim\lambda/\pi$). The electrons are bunched by cavity action and the application of these bunched beams in rf power generation in undulator devices has been proposed. Development of the microtron for such special uses or for attainment of high particle energy has been the subject of several papers.

Cross-references: *Accelerators, Betatron and Cyclotron, Bunching, Synchrotron and Bevatron, Undulator*

H. F. KAISER

MICROWAVE MEASUREMENTS

The microwave spectrum covers the wavelength range from several decimeters to a few millimeters. In this range of wavelengths, waveguides replace conventional transmission lines and cavity-type resonators replace lumped resonant circuits. As a consequence, the usual concept of impedance as a ratio of a voltage to a current is no longer unique and a more useful definition, based on the ratio of transverse electric (E) and transverse magnetic (H) fields, is employed.

Although electromagnetic radiation in the microwave range had been generated since the early 20th century, not until World War II, with the historic development of radar, did the microwave art come to its full stature. By 1945, the basic tools for microwave measurements were more or less fully developed; the main effort since then has been in the direction of greater precision, flexibility, reliability, and speed. This trend is continuing with the development of electronically swept oscillators, broadband components, and with the use of nonreciprocal components such as isolators. The basic inventions that have made this development possible are traveling-wave tubes (q.v.), backward-wave tubes (q.v.), and the carcinotron, as well as the discovery of interaction of microwave energy with new materials, especially of the solid-state type, resulting in novel devices such as masers (q.v.), the ferrite harmonic multiplier, and parametric amplifiers (q.v.). The present wavelength limit of these devices lies somewhere near the 1-mm range where mechanical tolerances of both tubes and components become prohibitively small and the basic interaction efficiency becomes low. It is not probable that harmonic techniques will be the best way to generate submillimeter waves; judging by success in related areas, such as the production of coherent light, a breakthrough in the area of generation of submillimeter waves by a completely new process may not be far off.

Microwaves in Research and Applications

The evolution of reliable microwave sources and components combined with newly evolved techniques has had a deep impact on all fields of science. Since the performance of microwave devices is char-

acterized by operation over a percentage bandwidth, a fixed bandwidth becomes more easily available at higher frequencies. In communications, this circumstance has led to the high interest in waveguide propagation in a specific mode (TE_{01}), whose loss decreases with frequency. The required repeater amplifiers (traveling-wave tubes) and waveguide components in the millimeter range have been developed for this application. High-power cw devices such as the klystron (q.v.) have made tropospheric communication possible. Pulsed megawatt devices in the X-band region and below, as well as new types of low-noise amplifiers such as the maser and parametric amplifier, have made satellite communications (q.v.) a reality. Broadband devices operating at high pulsed powers, such as the multicavity klystron, the disk-loaded waveguide, and the crossed-field amplifier are making long-range radars more flexible and jam-free. More compact devices, by the use of novel beam focusing principles, such as periodic magnetic and electrostatic focusing, have been shown to exhibit characteristics equal to those of conventionally focused devices.

In the area of research, the impact has been equally impressive. Periodically loaded waveguides, together with the development of high-power pulsed klystrons, have made possible the development of linear accelerators (q.v.) producing peak energies in the 1-Bev range. The penetration of these high-energy, highly bunched electrons is sufficient to yield some data on the structure of the nucleus. At lower energies, typically 25 Mev, the linear accelerator is being used for the treatment of cancer and food sterilization. In the field of fusion physics, which may provide the next source of energy beyond nuclear energy, high-power broadband microwave devices are being used to compress plasmas (q.v.) in cavities in attempts to heat them by compression to fusion temperatures. Transmission of microwave energy through a plasma is providing one of the most effective techniques for measuring the electron density and hence the temperature of the plasma. As in the optical and infrared range, the characteristic absorption of microwave energy in gases, liquids, and solids is proving to be a powerful tool in the basic study of their structure. For example, the techniques of electron paramagnetic resonance (*q.v.*) provide a method of studying the influence of atomic and molecular structure on the magnetic states of the electron. Thus, it is possible by proper interpretation of the complex resonance curves to study a wide range of substances that possess an electronic magnetic moment. Stimulated emission of microwave energy, as a result of interaction with molecular beams, has proven useful in setting new frequency standards (*q.v.*).

The understanding of the band structure of semiconductors, particularly silicon and germanium, and the ability to grow extremely pure single crystals of these materials, have led to the evolution of new components such as transistors and tunnel diodes. The transit time of these devices is sufficiently small to allow them to be useful as oscillators or amplifiers in the microwave-frequency range and their full impact, especially in the area of miniaturization, is yet to be felt. The modulation of light at microwave frequencies, and microwave amplification using a plasma as a propagating medium, the generation of lattice vibrations (in quartz) at microwave frequencies, illustrate other developments which are bound in time to evolve into practical devices.

Basic Concepts

As at low frequencies, the basic properties of any microwave network are its impedance, its loss or gain characteristic, and its equivalent circuit. In order to determine these properties, the network is incorporated into a system consisting typically of a laboratory oscillator, miscellaneous sections of connecting transmission lines, and a number of components such as attenuators (resistive strips) phase shifters (dielectric strips), wavemeters (high-Q cavities), directional couplers (which sample a known amount of power through a coupling aperture into an auxiliary line), and detectors (crystal rectifiers or bolometers). The main development in the last decade has been to put these components into accurately calibrated units, sufficiently broadband so that no adjustment need be made typically over a 2:1 frequency range, making it possible to make routine measurements rapidly.

Laboratory Oscillators. The most commonly used laboratory oscillator, owing to its ease of modulation (both AM and FM), is the reflex klystron. Automatic reflector voltage tracking and mode switching has made possible the use of such signal generators over a 2:1 frequency range up to 30 kMc with several milliwatts of output, adequate for most measurements. With the advent of compact electronically tunable oscillators such as the backward-wave oscillator, the carcinotron, and the voltage-tuned magnetron, it is now possible to obtain the same frequency range by tuning electronically (by varying voltage) rather than mechanically (by varying cavity dimensions). The voltage-tuned magnetron is extremely compact and is currently useful as a source of several watts of cw power over a 2:1 frequency band. Advanced crossed-field (M-type) backward-wave oscillators are capable of over 100 w cw power up to X-band, typically with 25-percent tunability. If additional amplification is required, the oscillator can be used in conjuction with a broadband traveling-wave-tube amplifier. In the lower microwave-frequency range, typically up to 4 kMc, closely spaced triodes can also be advantageously used as laboratory oscillators. For the reflex klystron, good short-term frequency stability ($2:10^8$) can be obtained by impressing an external signal of similar frequency (so-called phase locking) and by the use of reaction from high-Q circuits. With a high-Q cavity-stabilized oscillator, a circulator, and a phase-locked oscillator, a power gain of 10 db is easily obtained with a frequency stability improvement by a factor of 20. Although transistors have been made to oscillate up to 100 kMc, they have not as yet been used as practical laboratory sources.

Waveguides. Electromagnetic waves can be propagated either as free waves, such as radiation from a dipole or a horn, or guided waves, such as low-frequency propagation along two-wire lines or microwave propagation along hollow single conductors (waveguides, *q.v.*). A solution of Maxwell's equations for the proper boundary conditions (such as rectangular, circular, or elliptical boundary) yields a behavior similar to a high-pass filter, with real-energy propagation above a fixed cutoff frequency. Sufficiently close to this cutoff only the principal mode propagates and the cross section of the waveguide is selected to assure this at the frequency of interest.

Impedance and Standing Waves. At high frequencies, where the voltage and current vary spatially according to a standing-wave pattern whose wavelength is comparable to circuit dimensions, the wave impedance based on the ratio of the transverse components of the electric (E) and magnetic field (H), is used. On this basis, the modes that can propagate in waveguides can be divided into two groups: the transverse electric (TE) and the transverse (TM) modes. If a network is connected to the transmission line, unless it is properly matched, standing waves result, which are typically detected by a crystal detector connected to a movable probe in a slotted line. From the ratio of the maximum to the minimum signal to the crystal, the reflection coefficient of the load can be obtained. For purposes of matching only the normalized impedance needs to be measured, so that for most purposes the absolute value of the wave impedance need not be known.

Resonators. The conventional LCR tank circuit composed of individual inductors, capacitors, and resistors coalesces at microwave frequencies to a cavity where the region of strong E field corresponds roughly to the capacity, the region of strong H field near the outer walls to the inductance, and

the loss due to penetration of microwave energy up to the skin depth of the wall material to the resistance. However, as in the low-frequency case, the cavity can be represented by a simple LCR equivalent circuit provided this impedance is referred to the proper position in the input terminal. For a few simple geometrical shapes such as cylindrical, rectangular, and spherical symmetry, the resonant frequencies of all modes can be calculated from first principles. The size of the coupling aperture determines whether the cavity is matched (critically coupled), overcoupled, or undercoupled for a given mode. The cavity is characterized by a Q factor defined as ($2\pi \times$ energy stored)/ energy loss per cycle.

One of the most powerful techniques for measuring an electromagnetic field in a cavity is by the so-called perturbation technique. If an obstacle is inserted into a cavity so that either the E or H field is displaced, the following change in frequency takes place:

$$\frac{d\lambda}{\lambda} = \frac{-df}{f} = \frac{\int (\epsilon E^2 - \mu H^2)\, d\tau}{\int (\epsilon E^2 + \mu H^2)\, dv}$$

where $d\tau$ is the element of volume displaced by the perturbation, and dv is the elemental cavity volume. An increase in the resonant frequency thus indicates an H field and a decrease indicates an E field. For example, if we wish to plot the variation of a field on the axis of a cavity or a slow-wave circuit, all we need to do is pull a small perturbation, say on a string, along the region of interest, and measure the resultant change in frequency. From a knowledge of the size of the bead and the Q of the cavity all the parameters of the resonator can be calculated. This measurement is useful in calculating the interaction impedance of various traveling-wave circuits.

Measurement Techniques

Wavelength and Frequency. Wavelength is basically a measurement of a length (in a transmission line) or of a dimension (in a cavity resonator). In a transmission line, the guide wavelength is obtained from the distance between two minima of the standing-wave pattern using a slotted line. In the coaxial line the guide wavelength is equal to the free-space wavelength λ_0, and in a waveguide, it is related to λ_0 through the waveguide dimensions. In a resonator, for some simple geometries, the wavelength can be calculated directly from its dimension; however, most wavemeters are resonators of shapes that do not lend themselves to calculation, calibrated against a standard. Typical accuracies in length measurement are $1:10^4$. The main considerations in design of a wavemeter are: sufficiently high Q, operation free from higher-order modes, and linearity of tuning range. A wide range of wavemeters, both coaxial and waveguide types, are in common use.

The measurement of frequency differs from the measurement of wavelength inasmuch as it relates to a standard of time rather than length. The primary standard of time is the astronomical observation of the period of rotation of the earth and until very recently the primary standards of frequency consisted of carefully controlled crystal oscillators calibrated against this standard. Present long-term accuracy of such devices is typically $\pm5:10^{10}$ and the Q of typical quartz crystals is in the region of 2×10^6. The narrow line widths of molecular absorption and emission lines as well as of some atomic transitions at microwave frequencies have resulted in the use of molecular-beam masers as primary frequency standards. Quartz clocks as frequency standards are being replaced in many countries by ammonia masers and more recently by cesium atomic beam clocks with accuracies of few parts in 10^{11}. Useful secondary standards are provided by sealed temperature-compensated cavity resonators calibrated against primary standards. Since the advent of commercially available counters with typical accuracies of $1:10^8$, heterodyne frequency meters for frequency comparison have become outdated.

The frequency is doubtless the most accurately measurable quantity in the laboratory, and combined with a wavelength measurement yields the phase velocity of electromagnetic radiation, or light.

Impedance. At a given frequency, the value of the impedance is important both for matching purposes and for the determination of the basic properties of materials at microwave frequencies. The normalized complex impedance is most conveniently represented graphically as a point on the Smith chart. Its numerical value at a fixed reference point in the transmission line is determined from the experimentally observed magnitude of the standing-wave ratio and the position of the minimum in the standing-wave pattern.

If a section of a uniform transmission line or cavity is filled with a liquid or solid material, the guide wavelength (for low loss material) gives a direct measure of the dielectric constant or the permeability of the material (or their product $\mu\epsilon$). From a measurement of the cavity Q and the change in frequency caused by the insertion of such a material, the complex dielectric constant and permeability can also be calculated. In matching, the low-frequency analogs of inductance and capacity can be simulated by inductive and capacitive windows or resonant posts, which by proper location (predictable from the Smith-chart presentation) can be used to match a given impedance. Multielement filter sections, with dimensions calculated from network synthesis, can be used successfully to obtain relatively broadband components such as couplers, crystal mounts, ceramic windows, etc. Electronically swept wideband oscillators have proved to be invaluable in designing such components and observing the effect of a given change simultaneously over a whole frequency band. Automatic impedance plotters giving both phase and amplitude are commercially available.

For measurement of extremely small reflections, the so-called nodal-shift technique is still widely used. By moving a short circuit plunger behind a discontinuity and observing the shift in the node in front of the discontinuity, it is possible to calculate the magnitude of the reflection directly. This technique can be used to control mechanical tolerances in any periodically loaded transmission line.

Another basic quantity of interest is the magnitude of the electric or magnetic field in a given region of a microwave network. Although these fields can be sampled selectively by loops or probes and detected by crystal rectifiers, a more useful method is the perturbation technique previously described, in which a displacement of either region of field by a properly shaped object results in a change of frequency. From this measurement both relative and absolute values of the field in a cavity, or in a short-circuited section of a periodic circuit such as a helix or filter-type circuit, can be obtained, leading to predictable values of the interaction impedance. In a cavity, say for klystron interaction, this leads to a dimensionless value of the parameter R/Q which, together with the Q of the cavity, leads to an absolute value of the shunt resistance. Selectively shaped perturbations, such as beads, needles, etc., can be used to detect a desired component of the field. Perturbation techniques have also been successfully applied to measurement of radiation fields, for example by the use of a rotating dipole, near the focus of a microwave lens.

Power. Power is one of the few absolute quantities that can be measured at microwave frequencies. Using static or circulating water loads, microwave power can be directly converted into heat and measured calorimetrically. Such water loads or dry load calorimeters are primarily useful for powers of the order of 10 w or more. For lower powers, thermal detectors (bolometers, *q.v.*), whose change of resistance in a microwave field is detected by an unbalance of a resistance bridge, are more useful. Microwave power is measured by direct substitution: an equivalent amount of low frequency power is injected into the bridge

to rebalance it. The bolometer element itself can be of two types: a barretter (a fine wire or thin resistive film with a positive resistance coefficient) or a thermistor (a semiconducting bead with a negative resistance coefficient). The time constant of typical barretters is about 100 μsec and the limiting power that can be detected is approximately 10^{-8} w. Thermistors (*q.v.*) have a slower response time but because of their compact size are more advantageous at high microwave frequencies. Microwave power can also be measured by the radiation pressure it exerts on an object such as a vane mounted inside a waveguide. Instruments which can detect 10 w or more with a 2-percent accuracy have been built on this principle. Although bolometers are very useful where the absolute knowledge of the response law is required, the most common detector of microwave power is the silicon and germanium crystal rectifier, which is considerably more sensitive. At sufficiently low levels, it can be assumed to have a square-law response and is commonly used for most impedance measurements. Recent years have seen the development of broadband bolometer and thermistor mounts, which together with automatic self-balancing bridges and broadband high-directivity directional couplers have made microwave power measurements almost routine.

New Techniques

Multiterminal Networks. Three terminal waveguide and coaxial devices are frequently used for power splitting, to connect two circuits in series or in parallel, or to insert a variable reactance element into the circuit for matching purposes. As such, the waveguide T and Y junctions, both of the series and shunt type, are frequently used. Their behavior is reasonably well understood from an equivalent-circuit point of view and proper matching, mostly empirical, has resulted in relatively wide-band operation. The magic T, which is an example of a four-arm junction that can be similarly analyzed, has symmetry properties that make it useful as an impedance bridge or a balanced power splitter. Considerable progress has been also made in another four-arm junction, the directional coupler. Both by use of network synthesis and empirically, multihole couplers with high directivity and accurate coupling (as low as 3 db) over the full waveguide range have been developed, thus extending the useful range of power measurements and providing accurate reflectometers and power splitting devices. One result of this has been the development of high-Q resonant-ring circuits, by means of which components may be tested at high power levels with a low-power source.

A number of nonreciprocal elements, using primarily ferrites (*q.v.*), have recently come into widespread use in the entire microwave range. These elements include variable phase-shifters that can be used to modulate the phase of a given signal, isolators, and circulators. They have been used to advantage in increasing the frequency stability of a given source and to provide isolation between parts of circuits. Peak powers in the hundreds of kilowatts and average powers in the hundreds of watts, with typical insertion loss of less than 1 db, have been achieved.

High-Speed Measurements and Pulse Techniques. The need for high speed impedance measurements has been met by the availability of broadband electronically swept oscillators, broadband reflectometers, and waveguide components. As a result, automatic Q-circle plotters, automatic impedance plotters, and electrically controlled elements such as attenuators and phase shifters have been developed. Evaluation of novel components such as electronically scanned antennas (with ferrite elements) or broadband transducers for new microwave devices, has been made relatively easy. For rapid switching, duplexers using arc discharges have been developed capable of withstanding peak powers in the megawatt range which can be closed in tenths of microseconds and opened in a few micro-

seconds. In the study of plasmas, the electron density may be varying rapidly over periods of 10^{-7} sec and techniques for making transmission measurements within 15 μsec are being evolved. With the advent of high speed oscilloscopes, the relaxation times of the order of 10^{-9} sec are becoming observable and the techniques of modulating microwave energy and producing pulses with millimicrosecond rise times are becoming increasingly important. Continued progress in the development of spectrum analyzers and microwave oscilloscopes as well as in electronically tunable narrow-band receivers can be expected.

Millimeter-Wave Technology. Owing to the interest in millimeter-wave generation, conventional waveguide components are becoming available up to 300 kMc, including novel standing-wave indicator designs (at 2 mm) which employ a fixed probe and an adjustable phase-shifter that sweeps the standing-wave pattern past the probe. Propagation of surface waves along dielectric lines is becoming important as a tool for measuring properties of such dielectrics and for the study of the transmission of high frequencies by such media. Hybrid methods of both optical and microwave technology are being used, for example in the direct measurement of wavelength of millimeter waves in free space. Using microwave horns and microwave reflectors as analogs of a classical Michelson interferometer, the wavelengths at millimeter waves can easily be determined from a change in the input impedance caused by a motion of the reflector. A microwave analog of a Fabry-Perrot interferometer is also being built to measure the velocity of light at millimeter wavelengths.

In conclusion, it may be said that the greatest revolution in microwave measurements during the last decade has been the practical realization of wide-band electronically swept oscillators and nonreciprocal components that have made basic measurements rapid and simple. We can look to increased use of solid state devices in the future and greater use of optical techniques in the millimeter wave range.

ERVIN J. NALOS

Cross-references: *Attenuators and Isolators, Bolometers, Bridges, Circulators, Coaxial Lines, Ferrites, Impedance Measurements, Interferometer Method (Optical), Resonators and Wavemeters, Smith Chart, Standing-Wave Ratio, Waveguides and Waveguide Components*

MICROWAVE RADIATION HAZARDS: see RADI-ATION HAZARDS (NONIONIZING RADIA-TION)

MICROWAVE SPECTROSCOPY

The portion of the electromagnetic spectrum extending approximately from 1 mm (300 kMc) to 30 cm (1 kMc) is designated the microwave region. This region lies between the far infrared and the conventional radio-frequency regions.

With some exceptions, absorptions of microwave energy represent changes of the absorbing molecules from one rotational energy level to another. The absorption spectrum is characteristic of the absorbing molecule as a whole, as contrasted for example with data characteristic of functional groupings in infrared absorption spectroscopy or of elements in ultraviolet emission spectroscopy. The specimen in microwave spectroscopy ordinarily must be in the gaseous state. In general, any molecule possessing a permanent dipole or magnetic moment absorbs characteristically in the microwave region.

As in any other type of absorption spectroscopy, the apparatus required in microwave spectroscopy consists essentially of a source of radiation, a sample cell, and a detector. The most common type of microwave source is the klystron (*q.v.*). The klystron output is monochromatic under any given set of conditions, so that no separate monochromator is required in microwave spectroscopy. The frequency of the output of any klystron may be varied somewhat by mechanical and/or electrical adjustment, and different types are available to cover various portions of the microwave spectrum. The sample cell usually consists of waveguide (*q.v.*) with rectangular cross section. Typical dimensions are 20 ft long and $1 \times \frac{1}{2}$ in. in cross section. The detector usually consists of a silicon crystal, although bolometers (*q.v.*) and other heat-type detectors are occasionally used.

In addition to these three basic components, a complete typical microwave spectrometer includes provision for modulation of the absorption spectrum, an ac amplifier for the detector output, a final indicator consisting either of a cathode-ray oscilloscope or a strip recorder, a sweep generator to vary synchronously the source frequency and one axis of the final indicator, a means of frequency measurement, a gas-sample handling system, and the necessary electronic power supplies. The modulation is necessary in order to obtain sufficient sensitivity in the measurements, and is commonly based upon the Stark effect. The ac amplifier must be tuned to the frequency of modulation. Methods of measuring frequencies in the microwave region can be accurate to within one part in several million.

A few fields of application of microwave spectroscopy may be listed to illustrate the scope. Structural information concerning bond lengths, bond angles and nuclear masses may be in many instances calculated from suitable measurements of absorption frequencies. Nuclear-spin and quadrupole-coupling information may be obtained from data on the fine structure of some absorption bands. Internal rotation, hindered and unhindered, of organic molecules may be studied. An atomic clock (*q.v.*) in which the frequency of a particular absorption line of ammonia gas serves as the standard provides true accuracy of one part in ten million, somewhat better than time standards based on the rotation of the earth. Some useful analytical applications have been developed, particularly isotopic analyses.

The microwave region of the electromagnetic spectrum has only recently been explored, only one paper having been published prior to 1946. However, this region has been found to be a very fruitful one in molecular spectroscopy, and the microwave region has rapidly taken its rightful place in the broad field of spectroscopy.

ROBERT B. FISCHER

Cross-references: *Electron Paramagnetic Resonance, Nuclear Magnetic Resonance, Spectroscopy Light and Infrared)*

MILLIMETER-WAVE GENERATION

Within the last five or six years there has been an increasing effort directed towards extending the frequency range of microwave tubes to shorter wavelengths. Several applications for millimeter waves are for plasma diagnostics, measurement of molecular absorption lines, pump sources for lower frequency low-noise amplifiers, for short-distance communication on earth, or for long-distance communication in outer space. The approaches to millimeter-wave generation can be roughly divided into three categories:

(1) Scaling conventional tubes
(2) Harmonic generation
(3) New approaches

Scaling Existing Devices. The most successful millimeter sources thus far developed have resulted from an extension of conventional microwave devices to shorter wavelengths. This includes klystrons, magnetrons, traveling-wave tubes, and backward-wave oscillators (see also under individual entries). The difficulties involved in constructing these tubes for short wavelengths have been:

1. Critical dimensions for these tubes are less than the free space wavelength.

2. Very high current densities become necessary for starting current as an oscillator or for appreciable gain as an amplifier, with an attendant beam interception problem.

3. The fact that surface resistivity increases as $\sqrt{f}$ causes a lower Q at high frequencies.

4. The heat dissipation problem becomes increasingly difficult as the device is scaled for shorter wavelengths.

Table I is a tabulation of commercially available oscillators for wavelengths of approximately 5 mm or less.

The reflex klystron is compact, simple to operate, provides a relatively low power cw output, and is mechanically tunable over a bandwidth of 10–15 per cent. The backward-wave oscillator is somewhat more difficult to fabricate, provides a voltage tunable output over about the same bandwidth, and it operates cw at rather low power levels. Magnetrons provide a high peak power, pulsed signal, and are mechanically tunable over about a bandwidth of about 10 per cent.

TABLE I

Manufacturer	Number	Type of Device	Center Frequency	Frequency Range	Peak Power Output	Duty Cycle	Beam Voltage	Cathode Current
			(kMc)	(kMc)			(kv)	(amp)
Amperex	DX151	Reflex klystron	70.0	67.0–73.0	0.1 w	cw	2.5	0.018
Amperex	DX164	Magnetron	73.7	73.2–74.2	11 kw	0.0002	13	10
Raytheon	QX295	Reflex klystron	55.0	50.0–60.0	0.005 w	cw	3.5	
Bomac	BL220	Magnetron	58.3	56.5–60.0				
Bomac	BL202	Magnetron	60.0	57.0–63.0				
E.M.I.	R9551	Magnetron	80.0	80.0	2.5 kw		12	8
Bendix	TE66	BWO	66.0	61.0–71.0	0.010 w	cw	3	0.005
Bendix	TE71	BWO	70.0	65.0–75.0	0.005 w	cw	3	0.01
Sylvania	PM1779	BWO	69.0	63.0–75.0	0.003 w	cw		

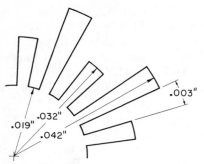

Fig. 1. The resonant circuit for a Columbia Radiation Laboratory magnetron for 107 kMc.

Typical dimensions encountered in milli-meter-wave oscillators are shown in Fig. 1, which shows the dimensions for an experimental magnetron developed at Columbia Radiation Laboratory for a wavelength of 3 mm with a 2.5-kw peak power output.

In addition to the tubes listed in Table I, there are a number of tubes under development in various laboratories. At Ohio State University, work is proceeding on retarding-field klystrons, in which the repeller is an integral part of the cavity in contrast to the usual reflex klystron where the repeller is outside the interaction gap. A typical tube covers a bandwidth from 57.6–69.8 kMc with an output of 1–5 mw. Elliott Brothers in England are developing a 4-mm source that extracts the second harmonic from an electron beam bunched at 8 mm by a float-ing-drift-tube klystron. This device uses an 8-mm floating-drift-tube klystron cavity to provide bunching, and then the beam passes through an output cavity resonant at 4 mm.

C.S.F., in France, has achieved impressive results building 0-type backward-wave os-cillators. Using a comb structure, they have achieved 4-w cw output at 70 kMc, with a 7-percent tuning range. This tube, the COE-40, has a beam area convergence of 100:1, with 150 amp/cm² passing through a 0.008-in. diameter hole. Higher-frequency versions of this device are a 2-mm oscillator with 7-percent bandwidth and output power up to 0.3 w, and a 250- to 294-kMc tube with up to 10 mw of cw power. Raytheon has developed the QKK 865–867 reflex

klystron series to cover the spectrum 60–100 kMc, with over 100 mw at the low-frequency end and up to 40 mw at the higher range.

Bell Telephone Laboratories have devel-oped forward-wave amplifiers and backward-wave oscillators for millimeter wavelengths. They have a cw forward-wave helix-type amplifier for the 5- to 6-mm wavelength region with an output power of about 0.5 w, and a gain of approximately 35 db. A backward-wave oscillator designed by Karp has gone as high as 200 kMc, producing somewhat less than 1 mw.

Harmonic Generation. Any medium or material that exhibits nonlinear character-istics can be used for harmonic generation. Considering only the medium itself and neglecting external loss mechanisms such as dissipation in the associated circuitry, a nonlinear reactance is theoretically capable of 100-percent energy conversion from the driving frequency to any harmonic fre-quency, and a nonlinear resistance has an nth harmonic output power which is $1/n^2$ times the input power. Harmonic generation has been achieved or suggested using the following nonlinear elements:

(1) Crystals
(2) Ferrites
(3) Electron beams
(4) Field emitters
(5) Plasmas

One of the first successful attempts to generate short millimeter and submillimeter coherent radiation was accomplished by crystal harmonic generation. Gordy, at Duke University, generated 0.5 mm wavelength giving a detectable signal on an oscilloscope using a silicon crystal and a 9-mm reflex klystron driver. The crystal harmonic gen-erator is a fairly straightforward technique for generating cw microwatt to milliwatt power levels at millimeter wavelengths.

A ferrite exhibits the characteristic that its magnetization along the direction of a dc magnetic field has a frequency component at twice the frequency of an applied RF sig-nal polarized in a plane normal to the dc magnetic field. This principle has been used as the basis for ferrite doublers. At Melabs, using a 4-mm pulsed magnetron, up to 50 w of peak power has been obtained at 2 mm, with an average power up to 2 w.

Harmonic generation from bunched electron beams has been intensively investigated by Coleman at Illinois. An electron beam accelerated to about 1 Mev was bunched at S-band by means of a two-cavity bunching device. The harmonic power was extracted by means of a cavity resonant at the harmonic frequency, or by passing the beam close to a dielectric surface. Thirtieth-harmonic power was obtained, corresponding to 3–4 mm wavelengths with tens of milliwatts of peak pulsed power, and a microsecond pulse duration. At Stanford University, using an X-band linear accelerator to bunch and accelerate the beam, approximately 3 mw of peak pulsed at 1 mm has been obtained, with a magnetic undulator as the device for extracting the harmonic energy. The use of relativistic electron beams for harmonic generation is quite inefficient, since the dc beam power is of the order of 100 kw.

Field emitters have a highly nonlinear relationship between the applied voltage and the emitted current. The high current densities involved, 10^7 amp/cm^2 near the emitter point, lead to predictions for millimeter pulsed peak levels as high as 20 kw. One of the difficulties is that it is not a simple matter to fabricate and to maintain emission.

Hanley, Uenohara, and Baird have obtained harmonic generation from a plasma. Typical results indicate that the second harmonic is down between 20 and 30 db from the fundamental, and succeeding harmonics decrease at the rate of about 5 db per harmonic. Using a 10-kw X-band pulsed magnetron as the driver, approximately 10 mw of power was produced at 4.3 mm.

A novel type of harmonic generator has been suggested by Jaynes. This is a quantum harmonic device that would release one photon of radiation at the natural resonant frequency of some molecule by absorption of three photons of applied radiation at one-third the resonant frequency. As yet, no experimental work has been performed along these lines.

Other Approaches. Many schemes have been suggested for constructing sources at millimeter wavelengths that are quite different from the conventional methods used at lower microwave frequencies.

1. *Fast Wave Tubes.* In the usual traveling-wave device, cumulative interaction occurs between an electron beam and a periodic circuit. It is possible to invert this situation, by having the electrons traverse a periodic trajectory and interact with a circuit propagating a wave with a phase velocity greater than the velocity of light. The periodic trajectory can be obtained by dc electric and/or magnetic fields. The primary advantage of this approach is that it allows the circuit to be large compared to a wavelength, and the primary disadvantage is that at millimeter wavelengths the dc electric or magnetic focusing fields become quite large. For example, a tube using magnetic focusing would require approximately 10^5 gauss for a wavelength of 1 mm. This value could be accomplished quite readily for pulsed operation, and typical operating characteristics for a 1-mm tube might be several watts of peak output for a pulse duration of 1 msec and a 10^{-3} duty cycle.

2. *Plasma Amplifier or Oscillator.* Several methods have been proposed for using plasmas as millimeter-wave amplifiers or oscillators. For example, growing waves occur on an electron beam passing through a plasma provided that the plasma frequency is close to the signal frequency. At 1 mm this requires high plasma densities, approximately 10^{15} electrons/cm^3. By using a magnetic mirror to obtain high plasma densities, Tchernov succeeded in obtaining amplification at about 8 mm. If a magnetic field is used in conjunction with a plasma, backward-wave modes exist that could be used for providing backward-wave oscillations.

3. *Masers and Parametric Amplifiers.* The

gas maser, which is a two-level maser, depends upon a static focusing system for population inversion and therefore has an advantage over most other masers and parametric amplifiers in that it does not require a higher-frequency pump field. The problems for millimeter wave generation are to find materials with the desired energy level spacing and to construct rather high-Q cavities. The gas maser could be a fixed-frequency cw source at power levels below 1 μw. Several methods have been suggested for other types of masers and parametric amplifiers that use a pump frequency lower than the frequency to be generated. For example, in a maser it might be possible to fabricate materials with sufficiently different relaxation times between energy levels so that inversion can occur with a lower frequency pump. Alternatively, it might be possible to use an optical-frequency pump source. For millimeter-wave parametric devices, the problem is to obtain materials with appreciable nonlinearity and low-loss properties. It has been suggested that ferrites might be useful as the nonlinear element for millimeter-wave parametric amplifiers or oscillators.

4. *Pulsed Ferrite*. It is possible to store energy in a resonant circuit and then suddenly to change the parameters of the circuit so as to increase the resonant frequency. The stored energy is then released at a higher frequency. As related to a ferrite, to generate 1 mm this would mean pulsing a magnetic field from several hundred gauss to 10^5 gauss in several millimicroseconds (ns). It is predicted that this approach might produce several watts of peak power at 1 mm over a time interval of about 10 ns. One difficulty with this idea is to prevent radiation of energy at frequencies lower than the desired output frequency during the rise time of the magnetic field.

5. *Moving Reflector*. A signal emitted by a moving source is shifted in frequency, and the amount of shift depends upon the velocity of the source and the phase velocity of the signal. This idea of Doppler shift has been suggested for millimeter-wave generation by means of a moving reflector such as a bunched electron beam. An electromagnetic wave with a phase velocity opposite to the velocity of the electrons can be totally reflected from the electron beam at a frequency that is higher than the frequency of the impinging signal.

6. *Swirling Electron Cloud*. Weibel has proposed a generator consisting of a rotating pencil beam of electrons in a magnetic field. The electrons are first trapped by time-varying electrode potentials, and then a magnetic field is pulsed on. For a 1-mm wavelength output, the magnetic field would have to be pulsed to 10^5 gauss, which is the requirement for electron cyclotron resonance. Weibel predicts peak power outputs in the order of kilowatts for microsecond time durations.

7. *Beam-Pattern Rotation*. As in an oscilloscope, an electron beam can trace a pattern in a plane such that the velocity of the pattern is greater than the velocity of light. The reason is quite simple, for at each point different electrons are producing the pattern. This method has been suggested for coupling energy to a circuit at a high harmonic of the frequency at which the beam is being swept.

R. H. PANTELL

Cross-references: *Backward-Wave Tubes, Ferrites, Field Emission, Klystron, Laser, Magnetron, Masers, Parametric Amplification, Plasma, Traveling-Wave Tubes, Undulator*

MINIATURIZATION

The demands of modern science, business prosperity, and military security have caused industry to turn its attention to the development of ever smaller components and finished products capable of maintaining or even of increasing efficiency, performance, and reliability. The successful large-scale development of such miniature components and finished products has resulted in the comparatively new and dynamic science of miniaturization.

The modern history of miniaturization dates back to 1948 with the development of the transistor (*q.v.*) which replaced for the first time the bulky, hot, fragile vacuum tube so important in electronic devices. However, a fascination with miniaturized craft and art work has gripped mankind for centuries. Both Oriental and Western sculptors have done work so minute that it could be seen in all detail only under magnification. Painters have done tiny portraits with brushes made of a single sable hair. Many people are familiar with the work of shipbuilder hobbyists who long ago learned how to mount an inch-long cannon that would load and fire. Watchmakers have been practicing what is essentially miniaturization since the 13th century; and in the mid-19th century, tiny ball bearings small enough to replace the jeweled workings in a watch ultimately became vital components in the successful development of the famous Norden bombsight during World War II.

Since 1948, however, the interest in miniaturization has become scientific rather than artistic. The growth of miniaturization during the past few years has been so rapid that even the term itself has been undergoing changes to keep up with developments. The terms subminiaturization, microminiaturization, and ultraminiaturization are all used, the meaning of each term varying from company to company within various industries. The general term "miniaturization," however, includes all degrees of shrinking implied by these newly coined words.

Miniaturization in Defense. Modern miniaturization has received its greatest impetus from national defense programs. It has been estimated that anywhere from 50 to 80 per cent of all U. S. miniaturization production today is designed either directly or indirectly for defense.

The complexity and multiplicity of modern weapons of warfare make miniaturization a matter of imperative necessity for survival. For instance, a standard radio pack used in World War II weighed 40 lb. Today the pack weighs 15 lb, and it is expected that within a few years the pack will be down to a mere 5 lb.

A 1930 destroyer carried about 350 electronic components. A new destroyer carries about 350,000 components. Room can be found for this additional equipment only by reducing and miniaturizing their size and weight.

As far as military application is concerned miniaturization receives its widest acceptance in the aircraft, missile, and space fields. By reducing the weight of airborne equipment the weight of the propellant or power plants may be substantially reduced. A weight reduction ratio of 1:100 for missile equipment and propellant is possible.

Miniaturization in Industry. The impetus given to miniaturization by national defense needs has pushed this new science into many peacetime applications. One of the significant areas in data processing (*q.v.*), for instance, is miniaturization of memory storage elements.

To match the ingenuity of tiny electronic components new ways of building circuits have been contrived. Bulky metal chassis, long leads, and solder globs have been practically eliminated. Conductors and resistors are now photographically printed onto an insulating background. There is also a vacuum-deposited method in which thin metallic films are evaporated onto insulating material. Recently, Bell Telephone Laboratories succeeded in "sputtering" an entire circuit by first laying a thin film of tantalum in an intricate pattern on a ceramic base to form the connectors. Further progress in microcircuitry and "molectronics" is being made every day.

In automation, to keep the controls from growing larger than the machines, miniaturization of components must be highly developed. The controlling devices would consist of both pneumatic and hydraulic equipment as well as electronic equipment.

Miniaturization for the Consumer. In the consumer field, miniaturization promises the opening up of vast new markets. So far, however, manufacturers have only begun to tap the great potential that exists. We see the appearance of hearing aids, portable transistor radios, high-fidelity units, and for a long time there has been the promise of truly portable TV.

To guarantee that all components will measure up to the rigorous demands of customers dealing in the field of miniaturization quality control becomes a focal point of the manufacturing process. This constant testing is costly. For instance, of every 100 transistors used by one manufacturer for its tiny new 9-lb missile and satellite TV, only seven to ten pass their tests; the rest must be discarded. In general, inspection and quality control costs average around 20 per cent of manufacturing costs, and in some cases run as high as 30 per cent.

In the production of parts of very high precision such as precision miniature ball bearings final assembly is typically carried out in a room sealed off from the rest of the plant. The air here is filtered to remove particles down to 2 μ. Employees dressed in special lint-free garments enter the room through a series of air locks each equipped with cleaning devices. A positive air pressure which is maintained in the room prevents any dust from entering when parts enter through a single small window. In this atmosphere, in a constant temperature of 68–70°F under 200-ft-candle soft light, finished miniature parts may be washed, assembled, washed again, gaged, tested for performance, washed, lubricated, and then packaged either in sealed vials or hermetically sealed plastic strips, like pills. No sunlight enters the room, lest the heat expand the parts. Components are handled with rubber gloves or special tweezers to prevent them from being corroded by perspiration from worker's hands. Most of the techniques employed in this operation, including the methods of testing, the equipment used, as well as the lubricating oils and the packaging vials and pouches used, are generally developed over a period of time and at con-

siderable expense by individual companies which set their own standards.

HORACE D. GILBERT

Cross-references: *Clean Rooms, Integrated Circuits and Devices, Machining (Electronic), Modular Construction, Printed Circuits*

MINIMAL-TIME PROBLEMS

Minimal-time problems constitute an important class of problems that are receiving increasing attention in the design of sophisticated control systems. The majority of servomechanism designs are based on the assumption that the system is linear; in the preliminary stages of the design it is also usually assumed that arbitrarily large forces or torques can be applied by the actuators to the remainder of the system. In minimal-time problems an additional constraint is introduced to the effect that these forces must remain within a prescribed finite range; the dynamics of the system may or may not be linear. It is this restriction on the forces that prevents the time required to perform a specific operation to become arbitrarily reduced. For example, the problem might be to design a servomechanism so that the reading head of a magnetic-memory disk moves from one reading position to another in the minimum time or that a missile changes its orientation (or its course) in minimum time. Space exploration has given a tremendous impetus to minimal-time problems because, in general, the control problems involved have far tighter requirements than the usual control problems and the equipment is so expensive that a considerable amount of research on the control problems is justified.

Minimal time problems can be classified as follows. (a) The regulator problem: given the initial state of the system find the control signals that will bring the system to equilibrium in minimum time. (b) The steering problem: given the initial state of the system generate the control signals that will bring the system to another specified state in the minimum time. (c) The pursuit problem: given the initial state of the system and the trajectory of the pursued object find the control signals that will cause a collision in the minimum time. In these three cases when the system's dynamics is linear and the applied forces are restricted to be smaller or equal to known values, the optimum control signals are of the "bang-bang" type, i.e., the control signals must be at all times equal to their maximum allowed value or to their minimum allowed value, with instantaneous switching between these two extremes.

Minimal-time problems may be generalized in three ways: first, by taking into account the fact that the state of a system is never known exactly because it is obtained by measurements and hence noise causes uncertainties; second, by allowing the dynamics to exhibit some of the nonlinearities usually encountered in physical systems; and third, by considering a different cost function: instead of minimizing time one may wish to minimize fuel expenditure or a combination of time and fuel expenditure.

C. A. DESOER

Cross-references: *Systems*

MISSILE GUIDANCE

Radio guidance differs from *inertial guidance* (*q.v.*) in that vehicle position and/or velocity are determined by the use of electromagnetic fields. In present practice, position determination and required trajectory computations are carried out on the ground and steering commands are sent via radio to the vehicle, often as special modulation on the position-determining radio signal.

Some advantages of this mode of operation are: (1) Light weight of vehicle-borne components. Weights of 10–15 lb of vehicle-borne equipment, including the command decoding function, have been achieved in some applications. Corollary advantages are: simplicity, ruggedness, reliability, uninvolved pre-launch checkout, and simple support logistics. (2) Accuracy. With relatively simple existing techniques it is possible to determine vehicle positions to within a fraction of a radio wavelength (i.e., within a few feet). Moreover, this accuracy is not subject to cumulative errors that arise in inertial systems owing to gyro drifts, accelerometer errors, gravity approximations, etc. (3) Flexibility. Essentially any desired trajectory can be steered, and mid-course or pre-impact corrections based on up-dated observations may be made. This feature is especially useful in experimental programs such as orbital or space shots, and the early phases of weapon-system developments.

The major elements of a radio guidance system are: (1) The position or velocity sensor, (2) the computer, and (3) the command link.

The function of the system is to steer the vehicle in such a manner that a desired trajectory is achieved.

The function of controlling the vehicle in roll, pitch, and yaw is performed by a vehicle-borne autopilot, into which are introduced the steering commands called out by the guidance system.

Position or Velocity Sensors. Position sensors in current use may be divided into two classes, angle-tracking radars and interferometers. These systems may appear in combination with each other and may be aided by velocity sensors.

Angle-Tracking Radars. Current guidance radars normally consist of a large two-axis antenna structure and the electronic equipment necessary to point the antenna at the vehicle and determine its range.

Data output is azimuth angle, elevation angle, and range as functions of time. Thus the vehicle position is determined in a system of spherical coordinates with the radar antenna as origin.

To obtain the desired angular accuracies some sort of beam-sharpening technique such as lobe comparison is usually employed; monopulse is very often chosen as the practical implementation.

Lobe-comparison schemes function as

follows. (Consider the azimuth plane only, as the elevation plane is similar.) The antenna and feed are arranged so that there are effectively two receiving patterns in the azimuth plane. These patterns are symmetrically disposed about the boresight axis of the antenna. If the signal source is on the boresight axis, the output signals from the two antenna lobes are equal; if the signal is off-boresight, the signal from one lobe is greater and from the other lobe, lesser. Thus a signal can be derived that is a function of off-boresight angle. The lobe comparison can be made sequentially by mechanical or electronic means, or simultaneously by electronic means (monopulse).

Active radar transponders are usually carried aboard the vehicle, for two main reasons: (1) accurate localization of the apparent echo point to the transponder antenna, rather than a less clearly defined skin echo, and (2) enhancement of range capability.

Interferometers. Interferometers consist of two or more legs made up of receiving antennas spaced several wavelengths apart. Phase comparisons are made between the signals from the two antennas of a leg. Determination of the phase difference defines a hyperboloidal surface that contains the vehicle. An observation from another leg then can be used to define a line of position for the vehicle, and a third leg or another type of measurement can be used to define the point in space occupied by the vehicle.

At distances large with respect to the leg dimension l, the hyperboloidal surfaces of position may be accurately approximated by conical surfaces of position defined by the relationship $\phi = (2\pi l/\lambda) \sin \theta$, where θ is the signal angle of arrival relative to the leg normal, ϕ is the measured phase difference in radians, λ is wavelength, and l and λ are in the same units.

Vehicle position is thus determined in a system of hyperboloidal (or conical) coordinates, sometimes in combination with a range or range-rate measurement.

A more general relationship for angle of arrival which shows a possible ambiguity is $l \sin \theta = [(\phi/2\pi) + n]\lambda$, $n = 0, 1, 2, 3, \cdots$; physically the ambiguity arises because the measuring equipment has no means of determining which wavefronts are to be used for the phase comparison. Any mechanization must therefore include some means of resolving this ambiguity. Antennas intermediate on the legs, low-frequency subcarriers, and pulse measurements are schemes which might be used for ambiguity resolution.

Ground receiving antennas may have some directivity but are not auto-tracking; rather, they are aimed at a fixed point in space.

Velocity Sensors. Velocity sensors are based on the relationship between Doppler frequency shift and radial velocity relative to the receiver. Coherent systems, which have been used in many past applications, consist of a cw ground transmitter, a vehicle-borne transponder that multiplies the received signal by a rational fraction (2, 3, $\frac{1}{2}$, etc.), and a ground receiver. A comparison of the received signal frequency with the known transmitted frequency permits the extraction of the two-way Doppler shift and deduction of vehicle velocity.

One-way Doppler information can also be obtained by comparing the signals from vehicle-borne and ground-based oscillators of identical frequencies and high stabilities.

The function of the *computer* is to accept data from the position sensor, make required coordinate transformations, compare observed trajectory with desired, and generate appropriate vehicle steering commands.

Digital computers are used almost universally because of their speed, accuracy, and flexibility in programming.

The *command link* conveys the steering commands issued by the computer to the appropriate vehicle systems. The commands are usually sent as some sort of modulation on the pulses of the radars or as modulation on the ground-to-vehicle link of an interferometer if such a link is used.

GEORGE HETLAND, JR.

Cross-references: *Antennas, Automatic Pilot, Doppler Navigation, Inertial Guidance and Gyroscope, Interferometer Method (Optical), Radar*

MOBILE (VEHICULAR) COMMUNICATIONS

Land mobile vehicular communications had their first application in the early 1920's. In the period from 1920 to the early 1930's one-way communication from base station to police vehicles was accomplished by conventional AM systems operating in the 1600- to 2000-kc region. These systems were extremely limited in range by summer static and suffered badly from nighttime co-channel interference. These factors, together with the extreme inefficiency of feasible-size mobile antennas at 2000 kc, resulted in two-way operation being applied only on an experimental basis.

The first practical two-way mobile communication occurred in the early 1930's, with AM systems in the 30- to 40-Mc region. At these frequencies the three major disadvantages of static, nighttime co-channel interference, and antenna size were substantially eliminated, and range was largely limited by ignition noise and other interference characteristic of AM reception.

In 1935 E. H. Armstrong (*q.v.*) demonstrated the new FM system, designed primarily with the static-free reception of broadcast program material in mind. It was not long before the mobile communications industry began to investigate its noise-reducing properties with a view towards improving systems range over AM. In 1938 tests were conducted in the Albany-Schenectady area using a variation of the Armstrong system that reduced the frequency deviation in direct proportion to the audio range ratio between that required for broadcast program material (75-kc swing for 15 kc audio) to that required for speech transmission (15-kc swing for 3 kc audio). These tests, conducted over a period of about a year, were witnessed by all the principal mobile radio users, including the military, and were culminated by an FM/AM compatibility demonstration to the Federal Communications Commission (FCC) and a request to allow the licensing of such FM systems in the then existing 30- to 40-Mc AM bands. The first large FM two-way system was placed in operation for the Connecticut State Police in 1940.

The successful performance of two-way FM systems in the early 1940's generated a tremendous growth in application. During World War II FM solved the long-standing problem of communication from the noisy environment of tanks and provided the means for secure multichannel communications across the European continent between headquarters and battle areas with the ANTRC equipments.

During the mid- and late 1950's, as military requirements tapered off, land mobile vehicular radio usage underwent a rapid expansion from its predominantly public safety applications to a host of commercial uses. Industry, in response to an FCC appeal, formed the Radio Technical Planning Board (RTPB), the recommendations of which were used as a basis for the creation by the FCC of a large number of new commercial frequency assignments.

The almost explosive growth of vehicular communication in the late 1940's and early 1950's created severe frequency congestion of the 30- to 40-Mc band with the result that it was expanded to 30–50 Mc and two new bands were opened, 150–174 Mc in the late 1940's, and 450–470 Mc in the early 1950's. Also, as channel loading increased in each of these bands they were successively "split" by halving the channel spacings originally used. The first experimental "split-channel narrow-band FM" operation in the 30- to 50-Mc region took place in Texas around 1948 when channel spacing was successfully reduced from 40 to 20 kc and the FM swing reduced from the original 15 to 5 kc.

During the period 1951–53 a cooperative systems study was undertaken by the mobile radio industry under an ad-hoc committee known as the Joint Technical Advisory Committee (JTAC). Largely as a result of their findings, the FCC, by the imposition of new rules and technical standards, was able to double, and in some cases, anticipate trebling, the channel capacity of the existing mobile communications frequency assignments. Since then the 150-Mc band has been "split" from the original 60-kc spacing to 30 and is proposed for splitting to 15 kc. The 450-Mc band has also been split from 100 to 50 kc and a further split to 25 kc is proposed.

During 1950–60, besides the commercial frequency assignments, the FCC also created a Citizens' Radio Service in the 30- and 460-Mc regions. This service provides for limited-power, limited-range communication allocations for any private citizen who can make a showing of need to the FCC.

The sophistication of equipments for use in the mobile communications bands has had to grow to match the problems created by the increased frequency of each new assigned band and to alleviate the effects of the ever increasing channel loading in each band. These latter systems considerations can be summarized in tabular form as follows:

puts far removed from the carrier and the low-pass audio filter restricts spurious outputs near the carrier owing to modulation.

In the receiver the tuned circuits in the rf amplifier and first mixer reduce susceptibility to intermodulation and help limit far off-spurious responses; the major adjacent channel selectivity is contained in the tuned circuits of the second IF amplifier. The receiver squelch circuits turn off the audio amplifier until signals of a predetermined signal-to-noise-ratio are received.

The techniques used in mobile communication equipment had their largest change of direction around 1957 when the first all-transistor receivers were built to cover the 30- and 150-Mc bands. The transistorization of transmitters has not been as extensive as that of receivers because of the frequency/power limitations at the output stage. Transistorized equipment offers definite advantages in reliability, size, weight, and power drain over equipment containing tubes but

Transmitter

1. Rf power output
   (a) 15–100 w output, mobile
   (b) 15–330 w output, station
2. Transmitter noise and modulation spectrum
   (a) Noise 60–90 db down at adjacent channel; depends on spacing
   (b) Modulation spectrum 40–100 db down at adjacent channel; depends on spacing
3. Transmitter intermodulation and required antenna spacing
   (a) Transmitter itself 10 db
   (b) Antenna spacing 20–90 db
4. Transmitter spurious frequency outputs
   (a) 40–85 db down; depends on power
5. Transmitter frequency stability
      0.002% 30–50 Mc
      0.0005% above 50 Mc
6. Transmitter frequency deviation
   (a) Wide-band ± 15 kc
   (b) Narrow-band ± 5 kc

Receiver

1. Sensitivity
   (a) 0.3–1.0 μv in 50 ohms for 20-db noise reduction
2. Selectivity
   (a) 40–90 db of rejection of undesired signal while receiving a desired signal

3. Receiver intermodulation due to multiple signals
   (a) 50–90 db; depends on channel spacing
4. Receiver spurious frequency responses
   (a) 60–100 db down from normal sensitivity
5. Receiver frequency stability
      0.002% 30–50 Mc
      0.0005% above 50 Mc
6. Receiver modulation acceptance
   (a) Wide-band ± 17 kc
   (b) Narrow-band ± 7 kc
      Width of receiver allows acceptance of modulation plus receiver and transmitter stability.

In the transmitter extensive use of tuned circuits between stages is required to reduce spurious outputs near the carrier frequency. The low-pass rf filter reduces spurious out-

at increased cost. As a result both types of equipment are in use as the economics of the situation dictates.

JARED SCOTT SMITH

Cross-references: *Frequency Allocation, Interference, Modulation and Demodulation, Radiotelephony*

MODULAR CONSTRUCTION

The construction of electronic equipment in modular form dates back to the desire to achieve the economics of subassembly production methods. The increased emphasis being given to new production techniques and modular packaging schemes arises from the complexities of modern electronic gear, the difficulties of designing tailor-made systems, and the still greater difficulties of maintenance by relatively unskilled personnel. Modules as standardized electronic functions can be looked upon as functional electronic building blocks, made in large and economic numbers, taken from stock for incorporation into equipments of widely diverse applications.

An example of advanced modularization techniques is shown in Fig. 1, a 1024-character, 8-bits-per-character sequential interlaced buffer manufactured by the General Ceramics Division of the Indiana General Corporation. The sliding drawer contains the more bulky power units and the plug-in board assemblies comprise the bit-forming functions. In manufacture, plug-in boards are easier to handle, inspect, and test. For maintenance, they offer quick accessibility for individual component test and replacement, and represent a considerable advance in packaging techniques over those of a few years ago.

Other factors, however, have recently begun to exert a powerful influence over the forms that modular techniques are exhibiting. Among these factors are reliability, maintenance, packaging density, weight, and resistance to extreme environmental factors such as heat, shock, and vibration. To meet these criteria, previously unheard-of techniques in the miniaturization of components have emerged from the electronics laboratories. Among the foremost is the deposition of resistors as printed paths on a ceramic substrate and the additional use of the sub-

Fig. 1

strate as a high-dielectric-constant material in the formation of capacitors. CR networks are often produced as single modular units.

Using the ceramic substrate in layer form produced the "Tinkertoy" module of the National Bureau of Standards following World War II. The U. S. Army Signal Corps and RCA have now evolved the ceramic-layer "Micro-Module," a 0.3-in. cube that performs a complete electronic function.

Many other companies are producing and beginning to use other modular forms embracing the more modern conventional components as a logical step between the older and bulkier components and the ultrasophisticated techniques of solid-state and molecular physics. In Fig. 2, a semiconductor network produced by Texas Instruments, has made possible the reduction in size shown between the printed circuit assembly and that shown to the right as a small layer block. The techniques used to fabricate these modules also eliminate many of the soldered interconnections previously necessary in interconnecting components to form a logic-circuit function.

Whatever form may be taken by these building-block modules, their objectives embrace the criteria previously noted. As a result they are almost universally hermetic-sealed or encapsulated in epoxy type resins.

The incorporation of modules into electronic systems still poses some problems, however, in that their packaging density has strained the means of interconnecting modular functions. Design, the economics of manufacture, logistic supply, and the necessary ease of maintenance also all point toward "disposal-at-failure" or "expendable" modules. A more sophisticated type of interconnecting circuitry is required, whether serial as in communications equipment, or parallel as used in the logic wiring of complex computers. AMP Inc. has introduced a concept for serial wiring in which the modular function blocks are interconnected by means of a shorting connector. Plug-in blocks, rather than soldered into a printed circuit, are easily removed for test and replacement. For parallel circuitry, such as that used in computers, interconnections between plug-in modular blocks are made by parallel-circuit runs as shown in Fig. 3, and between strings of modules by the base printed circuit. Another concept is that of the "modular module." This feature allows for a dimensional volume change in the module without destroying the integrity of a logical grid system, standardized connecting circuits, and contacts. In this case the change in volume with the size of the electronic function is accommodated by

FIG. 2

Fig. 3

changing the length of the module in even increments. The length-to-width ratio can also be adjusted to provide more or fewer input-output circuits. This is another step in the evolution of modular forms and interconnecting systems that are becoming commonplace throughout the electronic industry.

Modular techniques are creating new demands and fields of usefulness for electronic equipments because of the resulting increase in reliability, compactness of packaging, and the ease of maintenance.

ROBERT C. SWENGEL

Cross-references: *Epoxy Molding Compounds, Integrated Circuits and Devices, Miniaturization, Packaging, Printed Circuits*

MODULATION AND DEMODULATION

General

Sound waves, striking a microphone, cause variations in an electric current. This current, in turn, controls the frequency emitted by a radio transmitter. A distant receiver generates a current varying with the frequency variations of the transmitter, and a loundspeaker converts this current into sound waves similar to the original ones.

Each of the four processes described in this example constitutes a form of modulation. In general, modulation is a process that impresses information on a carrier. This carrier, which may be a form of energy totally different from the initial one, is often selected for its ability to convey the information via some medium which could not transmit it in its original form. In the example above, for instance, the rf carrier could easily transmit voice signals many miles without transmission lines, a difficult feat indeed for either audio-frequency currents or acoustic waves.

A process of recovering the original information, or some analog of it, from a modulated carrier has often been called demodulation, particularly with reference to rf signals. This type of process can also be considered as modulation, since it is also a transformation of information from one form to another by some predetermined function.

The carrier, whose presence is implied in any modulation process, may have zero amplitude without impairing the transmission of information; in fact, removal of the carrier may allow more power to be devoted to transmitting information, as in single-sideband transmission. To illustrate the principle of carrier suppression, consider the various types of microphones that could be employed in the example above. Some, such as the carbon type, require a dc "carrier," whereas others, such as dynamic types, do not; yet all perform the same function of generating voltages which are modulated in accordance with the incident sound waves.

In the following discussions, the carriers will usually be depicted as rf currents, but it should be noted that analogous processes and methods often apply to other disciplines, such as acoustics or mechanics.

Amplitude Modulation

Electrical transmission of information began with telegraph systems employing on-off keying of a direct current, a special case of amplitude modulation (AM). When radio transmission appeared, the same coded keying was applied to the transmitters, and survives today as cw (continuous-wave) modulation. With the advent of vacuum tubes, true AM became possible at rf. In this process, the amplitude of a rf transmission is made to vary continuously in accordance with the information to be transmitted.

For example, assume a sinusoidal carrier (in general, any waveform could be used) of the form $A_0 \cos \omega_0 t$, where A_0 is the carrier amplitude and ω_0 is its radian frequency. If this carrier is multiplied by $[1 + kV(t)]$, it is said to be linearly modulated by $V(t)$. The modulated wave is then

$$M(t) = A_0[1 + kV(t)] \cos \omega_0 t$$

The effect of this process is shown in Fig. 1. If the modulating function $[1 + kV(t)]$ falls instantaneously to zero, but is never negative, the carrier amplitude goes to zero and the carrier is said to be fully modulated. If the modulating function should become negative, the transmitted amplitude would remain at zero (in conventional AM) and the received waveform would be distorted (see

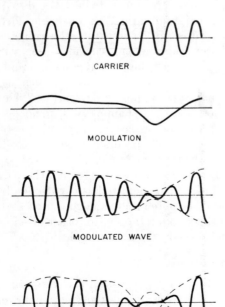

CARRIER

MODULATION

MODULATED WAVE

OVER-MODULATED WAVE

FIG. 1. Amplitude-modulation waveforms.

Fig. 1). This effect is called over-modulation and generally results in broadening of the transmitted frequency spectrum, which can create interference at other frequencies.

By reversing the carrier phase during the negative modulating function and transmitting an amplitude proportional to the magnitude of the modulating function, the frequency spreading is eliminated and the modulation can be received undistorted by using an exalted-carrier or synchronous detector instead of the conventional envelope detector at the receiver. This process is called reduced-carrier AM, and can be carried to the extreme of reducing the carrier to zero, called *suppressed-carrier* AM. In this case, the modulated wave becomes

$$M(t) = A_0 k V(t) \cos \omega_0 t$$

In the normal AM case, if the modulation is sinusoidal, such as $A_m \cos \omega_m t$, the modulated wave becomes

$$M(t) = A_0 [1 + A_m \cos \omega_m t] \cos \omega_0 t$$
$$= A_0 \left[\cos \omega_0 t + \frac{A_m}{2} \cos (\omega_0 - \omega_m)t \right.$$
$$\left. + \frac{A_m}{2} \cos (\omega_0 + \omega_m)t \right]$$

This function is the sum of three sinusoids: the original carrier, $A_0 \cos \omega_0 t$, and two "sidebands" displaced above and below the carrier by an amount equal to the modulating frequency ω_m and proportional to the amplitude of modulation A_m. These sidebands convey the information being transmitted, and each contains one-fourth as much power as the carrier during full sinusoidal modulation.

By Fourier-transform methods, any general modulation function can be shown to generate symmetrical sidebands which constitute the spectrum of the modulating functions (positive and negative frequencies) translated by the carrier frequency. The bandwidth occupied by the modulated carrier is therefore always twice the information bandwidth. In general, linear modulation of any frequency by any other frequency (true multiplication of the time functions) produces the sum and difference frequencies, as does the superposition of the two frequencies in a square-law device.

These principles are used to mix, or heterodyne, two frequencies to obtain a new frequency which is the sum or difference of the original ones. For example, the superheterodyne receiver operates by modulating the incoming rf signal on a strong local oscillator signal, and selectivity amplifying the difference frequency is an intermediate-frequency (IF) amplifier. Since the receiver is then sensitive to a frequency different from the local oscillator by a fixed amount, it can be tuned by tuning the local oscillator, but its selectivity is constant as determined by the IF amplifier.

Angle Modulation

Angular modulation arises when the signal intelligence function is used to change either the phase angle $\psi(t)$ or its time derivative. The amplitude of the carrier in either case is constant.

$$e(t) = A_0 \cos \psi(t)$$

In *phase modulation* the phase angle of the carrier frequency is made to vary according to the signal intelligence function $f(t)$ directly:

$$\psi(t) = \omega_0 t + \Delta\theta f(t)$$

where $\Delta\theta$ is a proportionality constant relating the amount of phase shift per unit change of the intelligence function.

For a sinusoidal intelligence function $[f(t) = \cos p\, t]$ the phase angle is

$$\psi(t) = \omega_0 t + \Delta\theta \cos pt$$

where $\Delta\theta$ represents the maximum phase excursion from the phase of the carrier. The sine function is a useful type for further analysis as most physically realizable functions can be expressed as a sum of sinusoids by a Fourier-series expansion.

In *frequency modulation* (FM) the instantaneous frequency is made to vary according to the intelligence function:

$$\omega(t) = \omega_0 + \Delta\omega f(t)$$

The instantaneous frequency is also the time derivative of the instantaneous phase. Hence the two modulation methods are directly related by

$$\omega(t) = \frac{d[\psi(t)]}{dt}$$

or

$$\psi(t) = \int \omega(t)\, dt = \omega_0 t + \omega \int f(t)\, dt$$

For the case of a sine wave intelligence function, $f(t) = \cos pt$

$$e(t) = A_0 \cos\left(\omega_0 + \frac{\Delta\omega}{p} \sin p\right) t$$

where $\Delta\omega$ is the maximum frequency excursion from the carrier frequency.

The ratio $\Delta\omega/p$, defined as $\Delta\theta$ here, is often referred to as the frequency-deviation ratio or modulation index and defined symbolically by m_f.

The FM waveform can be written in exponential form as

$$e(t) = A_0 \exp\left\{ -j\left[\omega_0 t + \Delta\omega \int f(t)\, dt \right] \right\}$$

If the modulating function $f(t)$ is periodic the waveform can also be expressed by means of a complex Fourier series expansion as

$$e(t) = \sum_{n=-\infty}^{\infty} A_n \exp j(\omega_0 + m\omega_a)t$$

where

$$A_n = \frac{\omega_a}{2\pi} \int_0^{2\pi/\omega_a} \exp j\left[\Delta\omega \int f(t)\, dt - n\omega_a t \right] dt$$

and ω_a is the fundamental modulating frequency.

For a sine-wave modulating function the coefficients turn out to be the well-known Bessel functions.

$$J_n(\Delta\theta) = \frac{p}{2\pi} \int_0^{2\pi/p} \exp j[\Delta\theta \sin pt - npt]\, dt$$

$$= \sum_{k=0}^{\infty} \frac{(-1)^k (\Delta\theta)^{n+2k}}{p!(k+n+2)!}$$

$\Delta\theta = 3.0$

$\Delta\theta = 16.0$

p →| |←

FIG. 2. Spectrum for angular modulated waveform with small and large deviation ratios.

One possible form of expressing the spectrum of the waveform is

$$e(t) = A_0\{J_0(\Delta\theta) \cos \omega_0 t$$
$$- J_1(\Delta\theta) [\sin (\omega_0 + p)t + \sin (\omega_0 - p)t]$$
$$- J_2(\Delta\theta) [\cos (\omega_0 + 2p)t + \cos (\omega_0 - 2p)t]$$
$$+ J_3(\Delta\theta) [\sin (\omega_0 + 3p)t + \sin (\omega_0 - 3p)t]$$
$$+ \cdots .\}$$

This equation shows that the waveform contains the carrier frequency and an infinite number of sidebands separated by multiples of the modulating frequency p. The amplitudes of the carrier and sidebands are determined by the order of the corresponding Bessel function. As a matter of fact, the carrier frequency can be made to disappear by a judicious choice of deviation ratio. For small deviation ratios the Bessel function argument decays rapidly and only the low-order sidebands are significant. For large deviations, however, more of the signal energy is in the higher order sidebands and less in the lower sidebands. A much wider bandwidth spectrum results, as shown in Fig. 2. The frequency-deviation-ratio parameter provides an effective means for adjusting the bandwidth of the FM signal.

Threshold effect. If the desired signal is larger than the noise or interfering signal, the noise or interfering signal is greatly suppressed, as can be seen with the aid of the phasor diagram of Fig. 3. If the desired sig-

nal is stronger than the undesired signal, the resultant phase never differs by more than 90° from the desired signal. However, the resultant amplitude can be greatly altered. A detector that responds only to phase or rate-of-phase changes then tends to follow the modulation of the strongest signal only. This property gives angular modulation a characteristic threshold effect such that the detector locks to the strongest signal and suppresses the weaker signal. The degree of suppression increases for higher deviation ratios; however, a higher threshold is also required.

In order to realize the noise rejection potential from angular modulation the detector must respond to phase or frequency changes and must be insensitive to amplitude changes. Often these functions can be combined in a single circuit such as a *ratio detector*. Otherwise the insensitivity to amplitude variations of the received signal can be obtained by first passing the signal through an amplitude limiter. The device that translates the phase or frequency variation to amplitude variations is called a discriminator. The linearity of the discriminator characteristic is very important in determining the distortion of the detected modulation.

Applications

In addition to direct analog transmission by amplitude or angle modulation, various systems are in use that have properties different from either, such as single sideband. All of these variations, however, can be obtained by a suitable combination of amplitude- and phase-modulated components. Some of the more common methods, which are generally called modulation systems even though they can be shown to consist of combinations of the two basic systems, are as follows:

A. *Single sideband*, in which only one of the two sidebands generated in amplitude

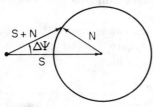

FIG. 3. Vector representation of resultant phase of signal plus noise with signal amplitude greater than the noise.

modulation is transmitted. Either sideband may be sent, and the carrier included, reduced, or suppressed. The bandwidth occupied is equal to the information bandwidth.

B. *Double sideband, suppressed carrier*, in which both sidebands are transmitted but the carrier is suppressed or reduced. The bandwidth occupied is twice the information bandwidth.

C. *Frequency-division multiplex*, in which many signals, each of which is a modulated transmission in a separate frequency band, are added to form the modulation function of another carrier.

D. *Pulse-type modulation*, in which periodic samples are taken of the intelligence waveform and the amplitude of the samples used to control some characteristic of a pulsed transmission of the carrier frequency. Two classes of pulse modulations can be listed:

(1) Pulse Time Modulation (PTM) in which the intelligence is imbedded in some function of the time of the pulse. Examples are:

(a) Pulse-position modulation (PPM), where the intelligence modulates the time position of the pulse in relation to a reference time.

(b) Pulse-interval modulation (PIM), where the intelligence modulates the time interval between pulses.

(c) Pulse-duration modulation (PDM) or pulse-width modulation (PWM), where the intelligence modulates the length of the pulse.

(d) Pulse-frequency modulation (PFM), where the intelligence modulates the frequency of the transmitted pulse.

(2) Pulse Amplitude Modulation (PAM) in which the intelligence is imbedded in the amplitude of the pulse only.

Pulse code modulation (PCM) is sometimes listed as a class of pulse modulation. Actually pulse code modulation involves quantizing and coding a sample of the intelligence waveform into a sequence of N-level pulses. These pulses are then used to modulate a train of the transmitted pulses in one or more of the ways described above.

L. H. RORDEN
B. M. SIFFORD

Cross-references: *Bandwidth Reduction, Fourier Analysis, Multiplexing, Pulse Code Modulation (PCM), Radiotelegraphy, Radiotelephony*

MOLECULAR-BEAM DEVICES

The precision study of atomic and molecular properties under conditions of minimum perturbations to the atoms or molecules involved is achieved through the use of beams. A beam or jet of neutral atoms or molecules is generated by thermal effusion through channels into an evacuated space. Measurements of the quantum states are made during flight while perturbations due to interactions with other molecules are essentially zero. Beams are sometimes referred to as the fourth state of matter.

Electric and Magnetic Resonance Methods

General Description. Measurements can be made on beams by deflecting them in electric or magnetic fields and by inducing electric or magnetic transitions between states using suitable exciting radiation. Since there is essentially a one-to-one correspondence in the technique for the electric and magnetic cases, only the magnetic case is discussed below. Also the early widespread use of nonresonance techniques, involving only beam deflections, has been almost completely superseded by the resonance methods involving radiation-induced transitions; discussion is accordingly limited largely to this method.

A typical schematic of a magnetic-resonance equipment is shown in Fig. 1, which also shows the basic arrangement for an atomic clock making use of the beam method. A neutral beam of atoms such as cesium is emitted by the oven into the evacuated chamber and collimated by means of slits. If no fields were present, the atoms

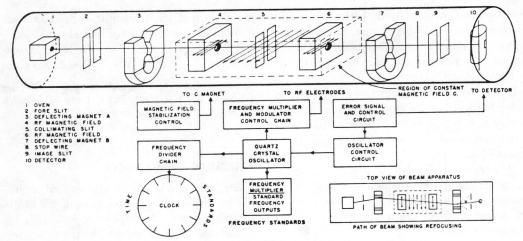

FIG. 1. Schematic of atomic beam clock and frequency standard.

would proceed in a straight line to the detector wire at the far end. However, two magnets *A* and *B*, usually called the deflecting and refocusing magnets, cause the path of the beam to be bent as shown, greatly exaggerated, in the lower right corner of the figure. Magnetic moments, either field-induced or permanent, cause the atoms to be deflected by the inhomogeneous fields of the magnets. The magnets and collimating slit serve to select only those atoms in certain desired states, these atoms being focused on the detector. A change of state is then induced by an oscillatory magnetic field in the *C* region between the magnets causing, in general, a change in the net magnetic moment. The detector current then drops, since the refocusing depends on the atom's net magnetic moment. In this way the entire line shape for the transition can be traced out by varying the input frequency. Transitions occur whenever the oscillator frequency equals one of the Bohr frequencies, $\nu_{ij} = (W_i - W_j)/h$, where $W_{i,j}$ are the energies of the two states and h is Planck's constant.

Experimental Techniques. *Excitation Methods.* Two general methods of applying the oscillatory excitation fields are in use at one or at two regions of the beam. The latter is more practicable at very high frequencies and gives sharper resonances.

Sources. The beam is usually generated by thermal effusion from an electrically heated oven containing the proper material. Sometimes a molecular beam must be dissociated, as for atomic hydrogen obtained from a Wood's tube.

Detectors. Four of the principal types of detectors in use are (1) surface-ionization detector, (2) electron-bombardment ionizer, (3) Pirani gage, and (4) radioactivity detector. Sometimes a mass spectrometer or electron-multiplier tube is used in addition.

Applications

Scattering, Surface and Chemical Measurements. Molecular beams obviously lend themselves to the study of scattering in gases and interactions with solid surfaces. Collisions in general can be studied, such as those which lead to chemical reactions. Such studies give information on intermolecular forces. Ideally, crossed beams can be used. However, collisions with a surface are easier to deal with; the molecules can be in well-defined states and the surfaces uncontaminated and in a vacuum. Diffraction from crystal surfaces has been measured, as well as reflection, absorption, surface migration, and other properties.

Nuclear, Atomic, and Molecular Properties. A beam of neutrons can be used instead of X-rays (*q. v.*) to study solids by diffraction techniques. Precision measurements of the neutron magnetic moment have also been made by beam resonance methods. The magnetic moments of both stable and radioactive nuclei, nuclear quadrupole moments, atomic and molecular magnetism, magnetic shielding, anomalous hyperfine structure, the anomalous electron moment, and Lamb shift are some of the important measurements precisely made by beam techniques.

Atomic Clocks and Frequency Standards. Perhaps the principal molecular beam devices to reach an advanced stage of engineering design and even commercial application are masers and magnetic-resonance-type atomic clocks. The first high-precision atomic clock and frequency standard used a beam of cesium atoms as shown in Fig. 1. The method of exciting the atoms at the resonance frequency is by means of waveguide cavities through which the beam passes. The exciting fields are derived from a very stable quartz crystal oscillator and frequency multiplier chain. The detected beam current is used to control the crystal oscillator frequency in a servo loop that contains discriminator circuits that generate an error signal when the oscillator drifts off the correct frequency. The quartz crystal drives a synchronous clock. Such a clock is now the standard of time used in both the United States and Britain. Accuracies of $\pm 1.7 \times 10^{-11}$ and precision of 2×10^{-12} have been achieved. The frequency of the cesium $F = 4 \rightarrow 3$ transition, in zero magnetic field, in terms of Ephemeris Time has been measured by the atomic clock beam method to be 9, 192, 631, 770 $\pm$ 20 cps.

HAROLD LYONS

Cross-references: *Atomic Clocks, Frequency Standards, Masers*

MOLECULAR CIRCUITS: see INTEGRATED CIRCUITS

MOLECULES

Molecules are chemical units composed of one or more atoms. The simplest molecules contain one atom each; for example, helium atoms (one atom per molecule) are identical with helium molecules. Oxygen molecules (O_2) are composed of two atoms, and ozone (O_3) of three. Molecules may contain several different sorts of atoms. Water (H_2O) contains two different kinds, hydrogen and oxygen, and dimethyl amine $[(CH_3)_2NH]$ has three kinds. Molecules of many common gases [hydrogen (H_2), oxygen (O_2), nitrogen (N_2), and chlorine (Cl_2)] consist of two atoms each.

Not all substances are molecular in structure. Some are atomic and many are ionic. Molecular substances are characterized by low boiling points and poor conductivity of electricity when dissolved or melted. Gases are generally molecular, and so are many liquids and some solids. All compounds of hydrogen and nonmetallic oxides are molecular. These compounds are considered to be bonded by a force called a covalent bond (or bonds) which consists of one or more shared electron pairs.

Gases. According to Avogadro's principle, equal volumes of gases, regardless of composition, contain the same number of molecules at the same temperature and pressure. As a consequence of this principle, the gram molecular weight of any gaseous substance occupies 22.4 liters at standard temperature (0°C) and pressure (760 mm of Hg). The number of molecules per gram mole has been calculated by different methods of increasing refinement through the years, and is now considered to be 6.023×10^{23} (atoms per gram atom, or molecules per gram mole), and it is accurate within 0.1 %. For example, one mole of ammonia gas (NH_3) weighs 17.037 grams, occupies a volume of 22.4 liters at standard temperature and pressure, and contains 6.023×10^{23} molecules.

The size of molecules, especially of the smaller ones, is so tiny that it is difficult to make a meaningful comparison. Let us assume that the water molecules in a cup of water are dyed so that they can be identified. If this cup had been thrown into the ocean 2000 years ago, these molecules would have become distributed evenly in all bodies of water on the earth. A cup of water, taken at random from your nearest supply, would yield at least one hundred of the original dyed molecules! The exceedingly large number of molecules of water in a cup of water is, of course, directly related to the fact that each molecule is exceedingly small.

Liquids. At the same temperature, molecules of a liquid move at the same rate as those in a gas. In a liquid, however, the extent of motion must be more restricted. Liquids flow as a stream and tend to form drops to a greater or smaller extent, thus giving evidence of the importance of the force of cohesion between the molecules in a liquid. When liquids are heated, as a rule they expand, an effect explained by the tendency of the molecules to occupy more space when they move at a faster rate. Also, increase in pressure has only a slight effect on the volume of a liquid. Liquids in general are but slightly compressible. From this evidence it is argued that molecules in a liquid are adjacent, close enough to flow in a continuous stream.

The molecules in a liquid, like those in a gas, are not all moving at the same velocity, but at the same average velocity at a given temperature. The molecules at the surface of a liquid, unlike those below the surface layer, have no force of attraction from molecules above. Some of the more rapidly moving molecules overcome the cohesive force of their neighbors and leave the surface. The tendency to leave the surface or to evaporate varies from liquid to liquid, and it increases when the temperature is raised. The pressure caused by the evaporation of molecules from a liquid, measured at equilibrium with the returning molecules at a given temperature, is called the vapor pressure. In general, vapor pressure increases when the temperature rises. With continued addition of heat, the vapor pressure rises still more until the vapor pressure reaches the vapor pressure of the atmosphere above the liquid. Then evaporation goes on throughout the liquid, and the liquid is boiling. Obviously the act

of boiling can be accomplished either by raising the temperature of the liquid or by reducing the pressure or the atmosphere above the liquid.

Solids. Since solids have their own shape rather than that of the container (as for liquids and gases) and generally do not flow, the extent of molecular motion in a solid is even more limited than that in a liquid. True solids are crystalline, bounded by plane surfaces that meet in a definite dihedral angle, and have a characteristic melting point. The molecules in a solid have the same kinetic energy as those of a liquid or a gas at the same temperature, and if they are molecules of the same substance, they are moving at the same average velocity. The motion of molecules in a solid must be confined, and probably it is a vibration or oscillation about a fixed point.

Crystals composed of molecules may evaporate in a manner similar to that of liquids. The phenomenon is called sublimation, and it may be noticed in solid carbon dioxide (dry ice), paradichlorobenzene, camphor, and many odorous solids. Nonmolecular solids show little tendency to sublime. The van der Waals force between the particles in molecular solids is apparently less in general than the coulomb forces between ions in nonmolecular solids. As with liquids, solids vary greatly in their tendency to sublime, and the rate of sublimation varies with the temperature and inversely with the pressure.

In some solids the crystal is composed of molecules in a pattern that repeats. Graphite, for example, consists of atoms that are bonded in a hexagonal pattern in one plane, and the hexagons tie in with one another as if they were floor tiles. The properties of graphite are associated directly with this planar structure of the carbon atoms with only weak forces to hold the planes together.

The structure of the carbon atoms in a diamond is a far different one from that in graphite. Each atom is supported in a diamond crystal by a pyramid of three other carbon atoms, the four atoms spaced as at the vertices of a regular tetrahedron. The pattern continues as it does for graphite, but in three dimensions. One layer of graphite or a single diamond crystal can be considered a giant molecule.

Cellulose from wood pulp contains as many as 1800 glucose units, and cellulose from cotton linters may have 3500 units. These units are linked in a long chain, giving the fibers characteristic of cellulose, a giant molecule. Latex from *Hevea brasiliensis*, another giant molecule, contains about 6000 isoprene units, and its molecular weight varies from 130,000 to 400,000. Protein molecules have weights extending into the millions.

ELBERT C. WEAVER

Cross-references: *Atoms, Chemical Elements, Polar Molecules*

MONOSCOPE

The monoscope is not a pickup tube, but it is a camera tube that generates a video signal from a fixed pattern inside the tube. It is useful in providing a source of video signal which is easily reproduced whenever desired without auxiliary lighting equipment or optical lenses. Because the same video signal can be obtained day after day, the monoscope is an important device for checking the performance of studio and transmitter equipment, amplifiers, receivers, and picture tubes. Comparisons of performance can also be made using the monoscope as a known fixed reference.

The tube consists of an electron gun, a signal plate, and a collector electrode enclosed in an evacuated envelope. The signal plate is generally made of aluminum foil that has been oxidized to provide a surface having a high secondary-emission ratio. The pattern to be reproduced is printed on the aluminum foil with a special ink developed specifically for printing on metal foil and has a relatively low secondary-emission ratio.

An electromagnetic deflection system causes the electron beam formed by the electron gun to scan over the surface of the signal plate. The electron beam is focused to a small spot where it strikes the signal plate to produce good resolution. As the signal plate is scanned by the electron beam, secondary electrons are emitted and collected by the collector electrode, which may be the wall coating on the inside of the bulb envelope. Because the aluminum oxide portions of the pattern have a higher secondary-emission ratio than the inked portions, variations in magnitude of secondary-emission current exist as the beam scans the signal plate. The change in current to the signal plate caused by the varying secondary-emission ratio constitutes a video signal.

Because video signal current varies directly with beam current the beam current is kept as high as possible consistent with good resolution. The strong output signal and lack of spurious signals permit an excellent picture with good contrast.

G. A. ROBINSON

Cross-references: *Cathode-Ray Tubes (Display), Storage Tubes, Television*

MONTE CARLO METHOD

A problem need not be very complicated before it gets too difficult for even a modern high-speed computer to do in a straightforward fashion. One powerful technique that often makes a seemingly intractable problem tractable, if not easy, and one that is particularly well suited to the electronic computer, is the so-called Monte Carlo method. This fashionable name has been given to the use of random sampling to estimate the answer to a precise mathematical problem. A game of chance is devised with the property that the average of the scores of a large number of plays of the game is the number being estimated. While the game may be played by using gambling devices such as a roulette wheel, dice, or coins, usually the simplest and most practical such device from the viewpoint of the computer is a table of random numbers. Such a table presents a strange appearance to the layman. It is nothing but a haphazard collection of the digits 0 to 9, but extreme care is taken to see that the collection is uniformly haphazard and random. By using this table it is possible to simulate the play of any mechanical gambling device. On electronic computers the random numbers can be generated by the computer by devising suitable pseudo-random mathematical processes.

The game of chance can be a direct analog of the problem being studied or it can be an artificial invention. The only property that it must possess is that its average score is the answer to the desired problem. It is not necessary to use the first game that comes to mind since it is often possible to render this estimation more efficient by making changes in the game that do not disturb its expected score. The new game may be more efficient because it is less erratic or perhaps because it is cheaper to play.

Therefore, when using the Monte Carlo technique to solve a problem, one directs attention to three main topics:

(1) choosing the probability process (picking the game of chance)

(2) generating sample values of the random variables on a given computing machine (playing the game)

(3) designing and using variance reducing techniques (modifying the game to be more efficient).

As an example of a very simple game that leads to the evaluation of the intergral

$$p = \int_0^1 g(x) \, dx, \qquad 0 \le g(x) \le 1,$$

consider the following:

(1) A play of the game consists in picking a point (x,y) at random with uniform probability over the unit square.

(2) If this point is underneath the curve $y = g(x)$, a success is scored. If the point is above the curve, i.e., between the curve $y = g(x)$ and the line $y = 1$, the play is called a failure.

(3) The above process is repeated many times and the proportion of successes is calculated.

It is clear that the experimentally estimated probability of winning this very simple game will give the area underneath the curve $y = g(x)$ since the probability of the randomly selected point (x,y) landing in that area is numerically equal to the area. It should also be clear that it would be very easy to generalize the above process to a multidimensional integral. Lastly it should be clear that the efficiency of the process does not depend at all upon the detailed microscopic character of the function $g(x)$ but only on a very gross characteristic—the total area, or in the case of a multidimensional integral, the total multidimensional volume.

In the general case one uses the computing machine to select n sample values $x_i(i = 1$ to $n)$ out of a probability distribution $g(x)$ and evaluates a function $g(x_i)$ n times. Under very general conditions the average value of $g(x_i)$ given by the formula

$$\frac{1}{n} \sum_{i=1}^{n} g(x_i)$$

is an estimate of

$$\int_0^\infty g(x) f(x) \, dx$$

with a variance given by

$$V = \int_0^1 g^2(x) f(x) \, dx - \left[\int g(x) f(x) \, dx \right]^2$$

For large enough n, the probability that the estimate will be in error by more than $\pm \lambda \sqrt{V/n}$ is given by the following table.

λ	Probability
0.68	0.50
1.00	0.32
2.00	0.05
3.00	0.003
4.00	0.0001

It can be seen from the above table that deviations greater than $\pm \lambda \sqrt{V}/\sqrt{n}$ will be frequent, deviations greater than $\pm 2\lambda \sqrt{V}/\sqrt{n}$ not uncommon, and deviations greater than $\pm 3\lambda \sqrt{V}/\sqrt{n}$ so uncommon that if the table applies the possibility that this last even may occur can usually be ignored.

The reason why sampling is useful in evaluating multiple integrals of a high order is that the error does not depend on the dimensionality of the integral. The number of points required to evaluate a multidimensional integral to a fixed level of accuracy depends only on V. By contrast, in almost all standard techniques the number of points required to evaluate an integral goes up in geometrical progression with its dimensionality.

In spite of its generality and flexibility, it must be admitted that in practice Monte Carlo has not shown up very well in competition with standard techniques, when the standard techniques were at all reasonable. It has been most useful where the standard numerical techniques are inadequate. In this sense it is a method of last resort.

HERMAN KAHN

Cross-references: *Decision and Game Theory, Information Theory, Probability, Random Processes, Sampling Theorem, Statistical Communication Theory*

MÖSSBAUER EFFECT

Mössbauer effect is the name given to the phenomenon of recoil-free gamma-ray resonance absorption. In the basic experiment, as shown, the gamma-ray absorption cross section of the absorber is measured by studying the percentage of gamma rays that pass through it into the counter. If the gamma rays from the source come from the decay of a nucleus from an excited state to the ground state, there is the possibility that a nucleus of the same type in the absorber will be raised to the excited state. If the gamma ray is of just the right energy to raise the absorbing nucleus to the excited state, the absorption is very strong; hence, "resonance absorption."

Under most conditions this process cannot be observed, because of the recoil energy loss.

For a free radioactive atom, the energy of the gamma ray emitted is $R = E_0{}^2/2Mc^2$ less than E_0 (E_0 is the energy of the nuclear transition, M is the mass of the atom, and c is the velocity of light) due to the recoil of the atom, which is necessary to conserve momentum. Correspondingly, the gamma-ray energy required to fulfill the resonance absorption condition is $E_0 + R$, since the absorbing atom recoils in a similar way. The $2R$ difference between the energy of the gamma ray emitted and energy required for resonant absorption is generally much greater than Γ, the natural width of the resonance, so that the resonant absorption cannot be observed.

In 1957, R. L. Mössbauer of Heidelberg (Nobel prize winner in physics in 1961), discovered that if the radioactive atom were firmly held in a crystal lattice, the recoil momentum of the gamma-ray emission could be taken up by the entire crystal rather than by the radioactive atom alone. This effect results in an increase of M in the above formula by a factor of 10^{10} to 10^{20} (the number of atoms in the crystal), and a corresponding decrease in the recoil energy loss. A similar phenomenon can occur in the absorbing atom. This makes R very much smaller than Γ, so that the gamma rays emitted from the source have just the right energy to be resonantly absorbed. The resonance is so sharp that even very small variations in source energy (frequency) can destroy it. For example, in Fe^{57}, the most commonly studied isotope, the gamma ray has an energy of 14.4 kev (frequency of 3.5×10^{18} cps), and the effective Q of the resonance is about 3×10^{12}.

If the source energy has been shifted slightly, the resonance can be restored by introducing an appropriate velocity between

SOURCE OF
GAMMA RAYS

GAMMA RAY
COUNTER

VELOCITY   ABSORBER

FIG. 1. Basic Mössbauer experiment.

source and absorber (generally less than 10 cm/sec); the resulting Doppler shift compensates for the change in source energy. By measuring the Doppler shift necessary to restore resonance, the source energy shift can be accurately determined. The measurements of very small energy shifts have been the primary use of the Mössbauer effect.

For example, the study of the gravitational effect on source energy at different heights ("red shift") resulted in strong experimental confirmation of the theory of relativity. The atomic hyperfine structure and hyperfine structure anomaly effects on the nuclear energy levels provide information on the electric and magnetic fields inside solids, and have been especially significant in adding to knowledge of the basic processes that occur in ferromagnetism. The energy shift of the gamma ray with externally applied fields gives the nuclear moments, and the width of the resonance can be used to measure the half life of the excited state. An experiment has been performed in which the source was moved at about 20 Mc by a quartz crystal to Doppler-frequency-modulate the gamma ray, and the complex sidebands produced were studied. Various other experiments have been done, all making use of the very high Q of the Mössbauer emission and absorption processes.

It is unfortunate that no method is known for dividing down the high frequencies that are required in the recoil-free process, since such a frequency standard would have a long- and short-term stability far surpassing even the atomic clocks (q.v.) and masers (q.v.).

RICHARD L. COHEN

Cross-references: *Frequency Standards, Gamma Rays*

MULTIPLEXING

Multiplexing is concerned with the simultaneous transmission of a number of independent channels of information through a single greater channel. In general, a multiplex system consists of a multiplexer which has several inputs and a single output and a demultiplexer which has one input and several outputs. The prime channel may be divided into subchannels in a number of ways. The basic dimensions that describe the channel are time, frequency, and amplitude. If the primary method of separating the subchannels is based on frequency the system is termed a frequency-division system. If the primary method of separating the subchannels is based on time intervals the system is termed a time-division system. The dynamic range of amplitude of the system is defined by the ratio of the maximum allowable level to the noise power level and defines the maximum amount of information that may be carried in a given time-frequency interval, as defined by Shannon's channel capacity theorem. Most multiplex systems are a combination of both frequency division and time division and very frequently complex systems are designed that are multiplex systems operating within subchannels of larger multiplex systems.

Multiplex systems using *frequency division* exclusively are used for the transmission of analog information, such as speech, voltage and current waveforms, and other continuous data. In such systems the several input signals are each modulated on to a subcarrier signal and then combined for transmission. The method of modulation may be amplitude, frequency, phase or single sideband. At the receiving end the combined signal is separated into its subchannels by selective filters, one tuned to the subcarrier frequency of each subchannel. The output of each filter is then demodulated and amplified to the desired output level. The frequency spacing of the subcarriers and subchannel filters, and the bandwidth of the subcarrier filters, depend on the bandwidth of the signals to be transmitted in the subchannel, the modulation technique employed, the allowable crosstalk interference between subchannels, and the transient response required in the subchannel. Frequency-division systems may only be used on channels that are essentially linear since the presence of several subcarriers on a nonlinear channel would result in the generation of spurious tone interference.

Time-division systems are used for the transmission of quantized data. These data may be inherently digital or may be sample values from continuous data. All time-division multiplexing systems must have some method of coding time in order to allow the separation of time intervals into the proper subchannel relationships at the receiving terminal. For this reason, all such systems have some degree of time synchronization. One extreme is termed a synchronous system and requires that both the sending and the receiving terminal operate in a continuous prearranged time correspondence. This method usually involves the transmission by the sender of a uniform set of time intervals with a high degree of precision. The sender may include a special signal carrying timing information for use by the receiving terminal in maintaining time correspondence. The synchronizing signal should have unique characteristics to allow the receiver to identify it among the data signals. Since the synchronizing signal uses channel capacity that could be used to transmit data it is only transmitted as often as required by the inherent stability of the receiving timing system. The synchronous type of system requires the added complexity of precise time standards but allows the channel capacity to be used more fully. In systems which place more emphasis on lower cost and complexity a form of semisynchronous operation is used. In such systems a synchronizing signal is transmitted for a group of pulses of prearranged length. The time interval between groups is variable and depends on the rate at which data signals arrive at the sending terminal. A restriction on this type of system is that the subchannel rates must be identical or the system must operate at the rate of the fastest channel with a buffer storage and dummy pulses for the slower subchannels.

An example of a common multiplexing system would be that used for transmitting data on flight characteristics of missiles to ground recording stations. Such a system may have a radio frequency carrier operating in the ultra high frequency spectrum near 200 Mc, frequency modulated with a maximum deviation of 150 kc. Subcarrier frequencies can range from 400 cps to 100 kc and may be amplitude or frequency modulated. One or more of these subchannels may carry a time division multiplex system. The simplest such system may consist of a mechanical commutator at the sending end and a similar decommutator at the receiving end. More recent systems use electronic commutation and employ various forms of pulse modulation such as pulse position modulation, pulse width modulation, pulse repetition frequency modulation or pulse code modulation.

D. F. Babcock

Cross-references: *Channel Capacity, Modulation and Demodulation, Radio Links, Radiotelegraphy, Radiotelephony, Telemetry*

MULTIVIBRATORS: see OSCILLATORS

MUSIC (ELECTRONIC)

Electronic music, properly so called, is music produced in the laboratory without benefit of musical instruments or performers.

So defined, the term excludes all music composed for, or performed on, electronic instruments of which the Theremin, the Ondes Martenot, the Trautonium, the Sphaerophone and the Hammond Organ are the best known examples. The Hammond Organ employs electromagnetic means; the other instruments named vary high-frequency oscillations of radio vacuum tubes, the control devices being different in each case. Whether such instruments try to imitate conventional ones or attempt to produce new tone colors, they all are meant to be played on; the composer still needs the performer to bring his music to life.

In electronic music proper, sound is generated and manipulated in the laboratory. Sound events are meaningfully combined, or composed. The final result, or composition, appears in form of a tape: the performer is completely eliminated.

Sound-generating and manipulating techniques vary from one studio to another; the equipment is not standardized.

The basic material is usually derived from sine oscillators (used singly or mounted in oscillator banks), from white-noise generators, and other waveform generators. The electronic music studio of the Cologne Broadcasting Station makes use of an Electronic Monochord (a specially designed Trautonium) and a Melochord. Pierre Schaeffer, the originator and protagonist of Musique Concrète in Paris, prefers natural—or "concrete"—sounds recorded by microphone. The sound material described can be manipulated and modulated as follows:

Using tape recorders, the composer can vary the speed, and with it the spectrum, the rhythm, and the dynamics of his original material. He can combine different events by mixing sound sources. Tapes can be cut and spliced in an acoustical montage reminiscent of film technique; they are easily reversed (a process markedly different from playing a piece backward on an instrument); tape loops produce canonic and ostinato effects without difficulty. At every stage the material can be filtered and reverberated in various ways (echo chamber, feedback). Ring modulators produce frequency transposition, i.e., displacement of frequency spectra to other frequency ranges while retaining the frequency intervals. Four-pole modulators produce four different frequency spectra of the sounds to be mixed.

Tape recorders (with two or four channels), filters, and reverberation devices are the basic apparatus for changing and shaping the sound material in the various ways just described. They are common to all studios. Some studios, however, enjoy unique facilities worth mentioning:

Pierre Schaeffer (Paris) uses a keyboard Phonogène of his own invention, which enables him to transpose his material to any tone of the tempered chromatic scale. He also uses a Morphophone to produce artificial reverberation. It is basically a tape recorder with ten play-back heads connected to pre-amplifiers whose gain and response curves are modified by filters. The New York studio in Columbia University has the benefit of the RCA Electronic Music Synthesizer, an apparatus capable of producing every conceivable variation in time, frequency, waveform, intensity, and interrelated effects. The tonal characteristics wanted by the composer must be clearly thought out, pre-set, coded and fed into the circuits.

Hugh LeCaine of the National Research Council in Ottawa developed the Multitrack Tape Recorder, with provisions for:

(1) Variation of pitch of the same timbre through a keyboard which allows for the direct production of melody.

(2) Possibility of combining up to twelve separate sound sources, and sounding these individually or in combination at constant and/or varying pitch.

(3) A mixing panel through which any number of sounds and/or musical events may be recorded simultaneously, consecutively or in selected combinations with constant or individually variable volume.

(4) Varying the duration and/or volume of individual tones directly and immediately through a touch sensitive keyboard control.

The above facilities are realized through an ingenious arrangement of amplifiers and rheostats which allow continuous tape loops to be sounded at will.

The electronic music studio of the University of Toronto uses, in addition to LeCaine's multitrack tape recorder, a Hamograph invented by Myron Schaeffer. The Hamograph provides the following means for producing and organizing sounds:

(1) Rhythmic organization of sound at-

tacks in melody and/or rhythmic motives with the tempo repeatable, constant, or variable.

(2) The shaping of individual tones through dynamic growth, decay, and duration with constant or variable speed.

(3) Means of producing melodic textures varying from widely separated to overlapping tones.

(4) Shaping of melodic phrases dynamically and with rubato.

(5) Variation in tempo without affecting a change in pitch.

(6) Means of repeating the same melodic contour or rhythmic pattern with different timbres.

(7) Means of performing complex and difficult rhythmic patterns which performers or orchestras could not accomplish.

The above facilities are realized through an arrangement of resistance chains, brushes, control bands, and conductive contours which allow for the pre-planning of rhythmic organization as well as the dynamic shaping of the individual tones.

At the University of Illinois Lejaren A. Hiller succeeded in programming a large digital computer to produce original compositions.

Electronic music as defined in this article developed in less than a decade. It is probably too early to evaluate its musical (as different from technical) achievements or to predict its future. It has been (and will be) eminently useful in providing sound effects and background patterns for radio, film, and television; ballet and opera are promising fields, as shown by Pierre Schaeffer's "Symphonie pour un homme seul" and Henk Bading's "Salto Mortale." Whether or not electronic music can have other than referential meanings is an unsolved problem. It cannot be solved by speculation (which abounds) nor by experimenting with traditional forms—only by invention and acceptance of structural elements and form-giving devices growing out of the medium itself.

Herbert Eimert maintains that electronic music appeared in a most opportune moment in history: due to the rationalization of musical elements which is no longer reducible to manual performance, the latest instrumental music has become unplayable; electronic music that needs no performer will breach the gap. Such determinism, however, is not too widely shared

A number of recordings of Musique Concrète (Paris), Electronic Music (Cologne), and Music for Tape (New York) are on the market. Pierre Schaeffer, Pierre Henry, Herbert Eimert, Karlheinz Stockhausen, Otto Luening, and Vladimir Ussachevsky head a long list of composers devoting their efforts to the development of the new and challenging medium.

ARNOLD WALTER

Cross-references: *Electroacoustics, Musical Instruments (Electric)*

MUSICAL INSTRUMENTS (ELECTRIC)

Electric musical instruments are devices capable of electrically producing complex tones in real time under the instantaneous control of a player. The tones frequently simulate those of other familiar instruments. Two categories exist: (1) standard musical instruments, e.g., basses, accordions, harps, and cellos, whose vibrations are electrically amplified; and (2) instruments in which tones are generated electrically, e.g., pianos and organs. Electric guitars, which are often used, frequently lack the usual body, use one or more electromagnetic or permanent-magnet pickups, and have one to four necks. Electric pianos consist of high-impedance electrostatic pickups located near reeds excited by piano hammers. In any of the amplification schemes, the frequency response or gain may deliberately be altered to create interesting special effects and to change the timbre. Electronic rhythm percussion devices generate tones by shock exciting phase shift oscillators. Keying and the selection of one of a variety of percussive sounds is manual or automatic.

Electric organs generate tones entirely electromechanically or electronically and have one to four keyboards and a pedalboard, the larger ones serving very well in place of pipe organs. Electromechanical types often consist of wheels which generate signals and rotate synchronously with the power-line frequency, so that they are always in tune. A ferromagnetic, serrated wheel may revolve in juxtaposition to a chisel tipped permanent magnet wound with a coil. The few millivolt, low impedance signal is applied to a L-C or R-C filter to create a good sine wave in spite of large mechanical tolerances. The outputs of several harmonically related generators may be simultaneously switched at each key and combined to synthesize complex waves. Complex electrostatic tone wheels are similarly used to create sine waves at high impedance. The polarizing potentials required may be keyed through R-C networks to provide elementary control of the attack and decay. Variable area or variable density sound tracks on disks may be used to modulate light beams complexly, which are then photodetected. These types of generators have proved to be very reliable. In another organ, the motions of an air-blown metal reed are detected by one or more electrostatic pickups. Again, tones may be recorded on a length of magnetic tape; the tape is brought up to speed by clamping it suddenly against a continually rotating cylinder by a key. Attack transients and steady states may be very accurately reproduced by starting the tape exactly at its beginning and by moving it against a spring, which quickly returns the length of tape to its initial position upon release of the associated key. The duration of each note is limited (≈ 8 sec). Standard rhythms and harmonies may be recorded for key-controlled, semiautomatic accompaniment of a melody.

In electronic organs both tube and transistor circuits generate signals; these signals are free of wow and flutter. Sine wave oscillators, stable over short times to 0.01 per cent and usually of the Hartley type, are almost always used. In some cases there is one or more at each nominal frequency, the beats producing an excellent impression of many instruments playing simultaneously. The B+ may be keyed through a R-C network to control the attack and decay in an elementary way. In other cases, a separate oscillator is used only for each of the top twelve notes of the organ, thereby greatly facilitating its tuning and maintenance. A chain of frequency dividers is connected to each oscillator. Each divider may be a bistable multivibrator, a blocking oscillator, a gas tube relaxation oscillator, or a biased phase-shift oscillator. Each relaxation or phase-shift oscillator is synchronized to half the trigger frequency and generates the trigger for the next stages. In all cases, active or more often passive high pass, band pass, or low pass R-L-C formant filters are used to control timbre. Sine waves are frequently distorted, often by limiters, to create waves rich in harmonics. Both the simple and complex waves at both the fundamental and harmonically related frequencies may be simultaneously keyed and applied to the filters. A square wave may be created by adding to a saw-tooth wave a second saw-tooth wave, inverted and of half amplitude, of twice the frequency, and in phase with respect to the first. Balanced modulators or gates, keyed through biased R-C networks, are exploited to provide elementary control of the amplitude of a signal. Varistors controllably biased, photoresistors controlled by light, variable condensers, and high-quality potentiometers are used to control volume noiselessly.

Vibrato can be achieved in several ways: (1) by use of a low-frequency oscillator, the phase shift type being common, to modulate the potentials applied to the oscillators or to control the effective capacity across a tank circuit; (2) by cyclically varying the parameters of a phase shifting bridge, the amplitudes of two quadrature signals being periodically altered; (3) by sweeping a pickup back and forth along an electrical delay line to which the unmodulated signal is applied; (4) by rotating the loudspeakers slowly. This latter method also creates a desirable uncertainty in the location of the sound source. Artificial reverberation can be generated in several ways: (1) The musical signal may be applied to a set of springs stretched between two electromechanical transducers. If the springs are sufficiently mismatched to the transducers, many reflections will take place simulating the multiple reflections in a room. (2) Active speakers may drive passive, spring-loaded speakers. The wave on the spring is reflected at the anchor and reradiated. (3) A resistor and condenser may be used to prevent the rapid decay of independent oscillators or the bias applied to gates after a key is released. (4) The musical signal may be recorded on an endless loop of tape and continually detected and erased. Part of the detected signal is recycled repeatedly.

Future musical instruments should be much more versatile and controllable, and should produce much more natural sounding tones. Multiple generators may be used to create a choral tone, the tone produced by a group of instruments playing in unison. Alternatively, a narrow ($\approx$1-percent), semicontinuous distribution of partials about each harmonic may be created by multiple, asynchronous modulation at infrasonic rates. Staggered attack can be generated by multiple detection of a signal multiply timedelayed. Multiplication of the output of one choral unit by another leads to very massive choruses with comparatively simple equipment. Separate sources for choral and solo tones are sometimes used. Progressive keying of suitably juxtaposed waveforms can be used to reproduce the actual changes of waveshape that take place during the course of a musical instrument tone and to make touch sensitive keying possible. Such keying may be accomplished by measuring the distance a mass moves against a force, by securing this mass in its extreme position to the key, and by using this mass to select the appropriate waveform. The speed of depression of the key regulates the initial intensity of the note; the subsequent motion of the key against Coulomb damping and nonlinear springs regulates the intensity at any later time. Intensity nuances are thus made possible. Some of the new monophonic instruments use formant filters tuned by individual keys, pressure-dependent keys that vary the resistance in an electric circuit, keys that can change the frequency continuously, timbre vibrato, and/or ring modulators for multiplicative mixing of two sounds. Environmental conditions may be altered by recreating the boundary conditions at the walls of the actual room as would exist in their absence and in the presence of the desired environment. Suitably delayed, attenuated, and reverberated signals are applied to loudspeakers appropriately placed around the walls of a room. The system may be used to control the apparent location of the sound source.

MELVILLE CLARK, JR.

Cross-references: Electroacoustics, Music (Electronic)

N

NAVIGATION AND NAVIGATIONAL SYSTEMS*

General

Navigation, derived from the Latin *navis*, or ship, has been defined by Webster as, "the science of navigating a ship, airplane, etc. (from one point to another) through the use of calculations as to position and direction." Avigation, derived from the Latin *avis*, or bird, has been defined as "the science and art of conducting aircraft in flight from one point to another," and is the more correct term when referring to air navigation. Although electronic aids to navigation are by definition devices that establish or help establish position and direction, the more sophisticated modern navigation systems not only actually avigate aircraft but also actually navigate ships and submarines (e.g., the inertial navigation of U.S.S. Nautilus under the polar icecap).

All navigation, including that accomplished by today's most sophisticated systems, is based on a knowledge of present position and the direction or heading. Position may be derived within the craft or may be determined on the ground with radar and/or direction-finder techniques and transmitted to the craft via radio communications. Knowing a vechicle's or craft's present and desired future position, the navigator, pilot, or ship's captain places the craft on a heading that will bring it toward its destination along the desired course of travel or route. Knowledge of past position, heading steered between past and present position fixes, winds, tides, currents, drift, etc. helps the navigator to select the heading for successive legs of this journey so as to return to or remain on or near the desired course he wishes to travel.

Early marine navigation was by reference

* The editor gratefully acknowledges the aid of E. A. Post who, in addition to contributing the first two subsections, helped to organize this entry

to landmarks or celestial position fixes. Early, and much of today's, avigation over land having readily identifiable landmarks is based on pilotage or reference to landmarks. Early long distance navigation over water relied almost entirely on celestial position fixes and this tool is still an important main or supplementary navigation aid in many long-distance operations today.

This background explains why radio communications was the first electronic aid to navigation by providing time signals; hence, more accurate celestial fixes. Although improved chronometers and shorter flight times have reduced long-distance aircraft requirements for time signals enroute, ships continue to rely heavily on time signals. Ships and aircraft also rely on communications for navigational warnings and for weather and operational information enroute. Communications was followed by direction-finding techniques on the ground and on the craft. These techniques were simpler to use than celestial navigation and provided bearings from known radio transmitters, i.e., position fixes, even when the skies were overcast.

Missile and space navigation and guidance are new fields calling for new electronic aids and techniques. Space navigation, a major subject by itself, is mentioned only briefly at this point. The accuracy demands of space navigation are such that they probably can be met only by the use of an automatic star tracker combined with an inertial navigation system and associated computer. Even the most accurate earth-based long-distance electronic systems would fall far short of providing the required accuracy except perhaps in the return-to-earth phase of the flight.

Air Navigation

The airplane was born in the same year in which the broadcast of time signals probably became the first application of electronics in marine navigation. Cw or code communications became the first application of electronics to avigation during World War I. The manual DF (Direction Finder), which found early use in marine navigation, saw only limited use in the air because of its initial size and the time required for its use. The avigation requirements of the pilot were met more satisfactorily by the development of the four-course A-N radio range which began to see service in the late twenties, when satisfactory ignition shielding made possible the first use of voice communications instead of cw and greatly extended the range of radio-range reception.

The mid-thirties ushered in the Left-Right Radio Compass, which was followed a few years later by the automatic (radio) direction finder (ADF). The 75-Mc marker-beacon system came into use at about the same time and experiments also were started aimed at improved navigation and communication through the use of static-free Very High Frequencies (VHF) in the 100- to 150-Mc band.

While the first electronic-assisted "blind" landing was actually made in a flying boat in 1921, and many systems were tried as the years rolled by, it was not until World War II that combined Signal Corps and Civil Aeronautics Authority work produced the SCS-51 Instrument Landing System (ILS), which has become the world's standard. Improvements in this system, coupled with the development of integrated instrumentation (q.v.), automatic pilot couplers, and improved approach and runway lighting, has greatly improved the all-weather reliability of aviation operations even though aircraft performance and size has increased markedly during this same period.

World War II greatly accelerated development of electronic avigation aids and produced equipment useful not only for military missions but also for routine air operations. Surveillance radar, which was relied on heavily for military avigation, has found a secondary application in this role in civil operations and a major role in avoiding severe weather. Radar altimeters found an

application in long-distance over-water avigation and made possible pressure-pattern flight procedures. While falling short of operational requirements, Consol and Loran (see below) have continued in use since then as the standard long-distance avigation aids. While other hyperbolic system developments promise to come much closer to meeting operational requirements, recent Doppler radar and computer developments (see below) look more promising as the future ultimate long-distance avigation system.

In short-distance avigation, the VAR (VHF Visual Aural Range, see below) came into limited use after World War II, providing static-free, visual avigational guidance plus straighter courses. It was superseded, however, by the more flexible VOR (VHF Omni-Directional Range, see below) which with the addition of DME (Distance Measuring Equipment, see below) has become the world's standard short-distance avigation aid.

World War II also saw great advances in the development of gyro stabilized magnetic-compass systems, automatic pilots, and avigation instrumentation. Electronics has made these improved systems possible, the development of which has been essential to meeting the higher performance requirements of post-war piston, turboprop and pure jet aircraft. Many of the other instrumentations and control systems of these modern aircraft have shifted from pneumatics and mechanics to electronics to meet the higher performance requirements, such as pressurization, air conditioning, fuel quantity and flow, etc.

Air Traffic Control (ATC), which began in 1936, has, over the years, turned increasingly to electronics for solutions to its problems. Surveillance radar has become an integral part of today's ATC for expediting traffic in the enroute as well as the terminal areas. Radar beacons have increased the utility of radar by providing easier identification of aircraft and the ability to see aircraft at greater distances and through precipitation and terrain clutter. Automatic Ground VHF Direction Finders have assisted the traffic controller and provided an invaluable aid to lost pilots. Digital computers are in use in a number of ATC centers relieving the human of detail computations and paper work. More sophisticated computers plus electronic displays are being tested and will initially further automate the routine and coordination functions of ATC and later provide the controller with conflict prediction and resolution assistance.

Aeronautical communication for some years has used voice instead of code even for long-distance purposes, and automatic communications via "data link" has been used by the military and is entering the planning and evaluation stage for routine communications functions such as ATC. Automation, which encompasses electronics, will play an ever-increasing role in avigation of the future as traffic increases and we enter the age of supersonic air and space travel.

E. A. Post

Marine Navigation

The application of electronics to navigation probably began with the broadcast of radio time signals in 1903. Navigational warnings were begun in 1907. The direct use of electronics for position finding started when the radio direction finder, then called a radio compass, was developed during World War I. Its navigational usefulness was enhanced with the installation of the first radio beacon in 1921. The first practical echo sounder was developed in 1922.

Despite these developments, electronics was little used in marine navigation prior to World War II. The development of radar provided a valuable new aid for entering and leaving port and coasting during periods of reduced visibility.

Various techniques for utilizing radar in navigation have been tried. In rivers and other relatively narrow waterways, the matching of the search-radar plan-position-indicator (PPI) image to a chart has been used successfully. The development of special charts, some with fluorescent ink, has contributed to this success. The development of an optical-chart comparison unit made possible direct matching of the PPI picture and a chart. Because of differences in antenna height, distance from shore, propagation, radar characteristics, etc., map matching in harbors and along the coasts has not enjoyed great popularity. A more common technique is the use of radar to measure bearing and distance from radar-conspicuous objects, both natural and man-made. Some such objects are indicated on charts, which have tended to give more attention to topographic detail since the development of radar. Marine radar beacons have not proved to be fully successful, but a number of buoys have been fitted with radar reflectors. Shore-based radar installations have made important contributions to safe navigation in a number of ports of the world, notably in Europe.

During the early years of World War II a different type of radio navigation aid was introduced. It utilizes transmitters operating in pairs at permanent sites at selected points ashore. Synchronized signals from these station pairs are received at the craft and utilized for determining the differential difference between the craft and the two transmitters. Each station pair provides a pattern of hyperbolic lines of position. The one that passes through the craft is identified by means of a special chart or table. Signals from two or more station pairs are needed to fix the position of the craft.

A number of hyperbolic systems have been developed.* Loran-A uses pulse modulated signals in the 1.75- to 2.00-Mc range. A direct time difference reading is obtained by matching of pulses at the receiver. A number of different pulse repetition rates are used so that the same frequency can be utilized in a number of adjacent station pairs.

The GEE system is somewhat similar to

* A more complete description (with application to avigation) appears in the subsection on Hyperbolic Systems below.

Loran-A, but operates in the 20- to 85-Mc range, and is thus limited to line-of-sight distances.

The Decca system utilizes cw in the 70- to 130-kc range, with 70- to 80-mile base lines between stations. Differential distance is determined by phase comparison. Ambiguities are resolved by a coarse measurement made automatically at short intervals. The accuracy of this system is high, but its useful range is limited to about 250 miles.

Loran-C, recently developed, operates in the 90- to 110-kc band. It combines pulse matching technique for coarse position determination with phase comparison (cycle matching) of individual waves within the pulses to improve accuracy, at useful distances up to 2000 miles or more.

The Omega system, under development, has a range of 5000 miles, with a potential half-mile accuracy. This is a cW system operating in the 10- to 14-kc frequency range, and utilizing skywaves. If the method proves successful, world coverage can be provided by six to eight suitably located stations.

With very short base lines, a hyperbolic system becomes essentially a radial system. This type system was developed in Europe, where it is called Consol. An American version is known as Consolan. Bearings are obtained by counting a series of dots and dashes during a short keying cycle and referring to a special chart or table. Although simple to use, the system suffers from sky-wave contamination and reduction of accuracy with divergence of the radial lines as distance from the stations increases.

All of the systems discussed above might be classed as piloting aids because they provide means for determining position relative to one's surroundings. The methods require a prior survey of the objects used as radar targets or the positions of transmitters used as navigational aids. A self-contained, dead-reckoning ship's inertial navigation system (SINS) determines position by measurement of direction and distance of travel over the bottom.

A radio sextant operating in the short

microwave region has successfully tracked the sun and moon to provide lines of position during overcast, thus introducing electronics to celestial navigation. Its extension to discrete radio sources (radio stars) is less promising, because of low flux density and high noise level.

Artificial earth satellites offer an additional source of radio transmissions that might be useful. Transit, the only system under active development, utilizes the frequency shift due to the Doppler effect during a pass of a satellite in a circular orbit at an optimum distance of 500 miles from the surface of the earth to establish a fix at the time of the nearest approach of the satellite. Operational feasibility has not yet been demonstrated.

At least two other possible techniques are promising. One would use primary or secondary radar for direct range measurement. Both the Doppler and range-measuring techniques are essentially piloting in nature. Satellites might also be used as celestial bodies in an angle-measuring system, using a modified form of radio sextant.

Ship's Inertial Navigation System (SINS). The basic techniques of inertial guidance (*q.v.*) used in long-range missiles have been adapted for use in ships. They are particularly useful in submarines because the system is completely self-contained, requiring no antenna or optical equipment above water. This system has been used by the U.S.S. Nautilus and other submarines while operating under the polar ice.

Several versions of the system have been developed. All use gyroscopes as sensitive accelerometers and as essential elements of a stable platform essential to success of the system. Primarily because of gyro imperfections, a slow drift causes increasing uncertainty of results with time.

Although inertial systems are adequate for relatively short flights of missiles, and even for somewhat longer flights of aircraft, ship's inertial navigation systems, which are dead reckoning in nature, require resetting from time to time, usually at intervals of several hours. Any positional information of greater accuracy than that provided by the inertial navigators can be used for this purpose. The principal advantage of an inertial system is that it provides continuous positional information when other sources may not be available.

With the development of better gyroscopes and other refinements, inertial navigators can be expected to perform more reliably over longer periods of time and to yield more accurate results, giving them less reliance on external sources of positional information for satisfactory results.

ALTON B MOODY

Direction-Finding Systems

In its broadest sense, a direction finder can be defined as a device that determines the direction of propagation of an electromagnetic wave. In this context, the term is often applied to such techniques as celestial observations (star tracking), detection of the source of nuclear explosions, human perception of light beacons such as rotating airport beacons in aviation, and lighthouses in marine service. The term is sometimes loosely applied in direction measurements using phenomena other than electromagnetic; these include such techniques as the magnetic compass, sonar and other devices utilizing sound waves, and gyroscopes used as references for changes in direction. The following discussion is limited to direction finders of the electromagnetic type, normally referred to as radio direction finders.

The direction finder determines a line-of-position only, and not a "fix" or location. In navigation usage, a line-of-position suffices if the vehicle is to "home" upon the station used as the source of signal. More commonly, a fix is desired and is obtained by triangulation from two or more stations.

Radio-direction-finder facilities are available in two forms: (1) on the vehicle (aircraft, ship, car, etc.) in which case it is

called a radio compass; or (2) at a known fixed location on the ground, as part of a direction-finding network. Any known source of radiation of the proper frequency may be used for a radio compass, such as broadcast stations. Other specially installed omnidirectional transmitters exist for navigation purposes and are referred to as "radiophares" or "beacons." Conversely, a network of stations on the ground may determine the position of the vehicle by utilizing any appropriate radio transmission generated by the vehicle. Again, a fix is obtained by triangulation from DF readings taken from two or more ground stations.

In aircraft, the output of the radio compass is often coupled to the automatic pilot, thereby permitting the automatic navigation of the aircraft to the radiophare. The radio compass provides the autopilot with deviations from the desired course (or line-of-position) and automatic corrections are applied by the automatic pilot in a closed-loop system involving the controls of the aircraft.

For requisite accuracy with simple antenna systems, such as may be installed aboard aircraft, direct spacewave reception is required. Accordingly, LF (30–300 kc) and VHF (30–300 Mc) frequencies are normally employed to avoid gross errors due to skywave propagation. Since ground DF installations may have receiving antennas of any required degree of complexity, there are no restrictions on frequency, and ground DF equipments have been developed for virtually every frequency band. High frequencies (2–30 Mc) may be utilized with skywave distances ranging in hundreds, or even thousands, of miles. Such distance ranges are particularly useful for transoceanic navigation. However, for overland operation, expediency has indicated the use of the direct spacewave with corresponding ranges of the order of 100 miles.

Although many techniques and equipments exist for radio direction finding, the most prominent are:

(1) Loop direction finders (radio compass)

(2) Adcock DF arrays

(3) Wullenweber DF arrays

(4) Commutated-antenna direction finders

(5) Doppler direction finders

(6) Directive antenna systems

These various techniques are briefly described below.

(1) *Loop Direction Finders.* The loop antenna forms the basis of all low-frequency aircraft direction finders or radio compasses. It consists, basically, of a coil of wire, and electrically can be considered as the secondary of a transformer subjected to the varying flux of the magnetic component of the electromagnetic radiation. This magnetic component, in a normally polarized wave, is at right angles to the direction of propagation. Accordingly, if the wave is traveling parallel to the plane of the loop, no voltage is induced. Conversely, if the plane of the loop is broadside to the direction of propagation, a maximum voltage is induced. If this voltage is plotted as a function of bearing angle, a figure-of-eight pattern results with two maxima and two nulls. The null is used, rather than the maxima, since the null has greater sensitivity with respect to azimuth and provides better accuracy.

In common usage, the output of the loop is combined with the output of an omnidirectional antenna to resolve ambiguity. In operation, the receiver is tuned to the desired frequency and the loop manually turned until the signal disappears. A line-of-direction or bearing is then obtained from an indicator which displays the position of the loop.

In airborne radio compass work, a shielded loop is used to improve the electrical properties and to serve as an ideal mechanical construction capable of withstanding aircraft service. The metallic cover is broken at one point and connected to ground. The circulating currents in the shield are negligible for all practical purposes, since the magnetic field penetrates the shield and acts on the conductors within. The automatic direction finder (ADF) operates in the same manner,

except that a null seeking circuit is added to position the loop automatically.

(2) *Adcock DF Arrays.* The basic operation of the Adcock array is based upon the figure-of-eight pattern which is formed when the spacing between two omnidirectional receiving elements is small compared with a wavelength. Practical Adcock arrays utilize two crossed Adcocks associated with an inductive-type mechanical goniometer, or its electrical counterpart, and form the equivalent of a rotatable single Adcock. Mechanically, this configuration corresponds to four receiving antennas located at the corners of a square. Each pair of diagonally placed antennas is connected to a fixed coil (or stator) in the goniometer. The two stators are mounted at right angles and couple to a single rotatable coil or rotor. The resulting flux in the rotor is the vector sum of the flux produced by each stator. Accordingly, if the rotor is adjusted until a null is obtained, an indication of the direction of propagation can be derived after proper calibration.

The electronic goniometer may take a variety of forms. In one form, two balanced modulators supply a two-phase modulating voltage to the Adcock system. In the common receiver, the signal voltages corresponding to the two antennas may be individually recovered by reference to the two phases of the special modulating signal. In a second form, the north-south antenna is fed to the receiver through a balanced modulator operating at one audio frequency, whereas the east-west antenna is similarly fed operating at a different audio frequency. The resulting sidebands are then separated through filters, and are used to represent the amplitude and phase of the voltages induced in the two Adcocks by the incoming wave.

With any system, sense of the bearing may be introduced by proper combination with the output of a nondirectional antenna.

(3) *Wullenweber DF Arrays.* This array consists of a multiplicity of receiving antennas located on the perimeter of a circle. Typical arrays in the 2- to 30-Mc range have

diameters of 500 to 600 ft and include as many as 120 elements. In its most elementary form, DF information is obtained by combining the outputs of the individual antennas, or groups of antennas, in appropriate phasing networks and goniometers. After proper amplitude and phase adjustment, the Wullenweber array can be imagined to be a broadside array extending across the diameter of the circle. By goniometric means, the array can be turned electrically so as to obtain a maximum signal from the intercepted wave. In effect, this simulates the rotation of a highly directive array, and DF information is derived from the "position" of the array when maximum signal is received.

(4) *Commutated-Antenna DF*. The CADF utilizes a multiplicity of receiving antennas arranged in a circle whose diameter may be of the order of 2 wavelengths. In operation, a commutator is used to sample the output of each antenna sequentially, and to look for a maximum phase difference between any two adjacent antennas. In theory, this maximum occurs at a point in the circle where the line of propagation is tangent to the array. Conversely, at 90° to this position, adjacent antennas intercept the wavefront simultaneously and therefore exhibit no phase difference. When properly instrumented, this polar "phase pattern" indicates the direction of propagation.

(5) *Doppler Direction Finders*. In its simplest form, the Doppler direction finder can be considered to be a single omnidirectional antenna rotated circularly in space in the horizontal plane. In considering the action of this antenna, the following phenomena occurs: During its segment of rotation *along* the direction of propagation and *towards* the source, the receiving frequency is momentarily increased. At the diametrically opposite point, the travel is *away* from the source and the frequency will be momentarily decreased. At right angles to these positions, the antenna travels *across* the direction of propagation and shows no shift in frequency. These shifts are, of course, recog-

nized as being a Doppler phenomenon. When properly instrumented, the direction of propagation can be determined from the position of the rotating antenna at the time the maximum Doppler shift occurs.

(6) *Directive Antenna Systems*. The most easily understood direction-finding systems are those utilizing highly directive antennas such as parabolas. Here, the direction of the intercepted signal, whether it be generated in the vehicle or reflected as in radar, is determined simply by rotating the antenna until a maximum signal is detected. Since the pattern is highly directive in bearing, in some cases fractions of a degree wide, great accuracy can be obtained. In common usage, this technique is applied in all forms of radar and in radio astronomy.

In summarizing the above techniques, it can be seen that all direction-finding methods can be classified as one of three major types; (a) null methods (loops or the interference patterns between two or more antennas), (b) the Doppler phenomena, or (c) highly directive antenna arrays.

ANTHONY CASABONA

Radio Beacons

Originally the word "beacon" as applied to radio was intended to mean the radio counterpart of the navigational lighthouse. Nowadays the term "beacon" has taken on a much broader connotation and is used to refer to radio transmitting systems that are primarily aids to navigation or avigation.

In general beacons may be classified under the following categories: *fixed beacons*, *fixed course-setting beacons* (*radio ranges*), *instrument-landing-system* (*ILS*) *beacons*, and *omnidirectional rotating directive beacons*.

Fixed beacons are characterized by single fixed radiating patterns and are used for homing or flying courses to or from the beacon, for marking a point or area on the ground, for establishing a holding pattern near airports for traffic control of aircraft, and for obtaining bearings or lines of position.

The *homing beacon* radiates in a nondirectional pattern. Any aircraft or ship within reception range, and equipped with direction-finding apparatus (see above), can take bearings on the beacon from the vehicle. Broadcast stations can also be used for this purpose. Frequencies below 1750 kc are normally used for this service.

The *marker beacon* radiates 75-Mc rf energy in a narrow vertical conical or fan-shaped pattern. Conical markers are known as *Z* markers and are located at four-course A-N radio ranges. *Fan* markers serve to furnish aircraft with a check as to progress along airways, to mark junctions of two radio range courses, and to designate "holding" points along airways of airport approaches and to mark obstructions. *Outer* and *middle* markers indicate points along the runway extension for "let-down" procedures on ILS. The fact that his aircraft is passing over a marker beacon is indicated to the pilot by a characteristic blinker light on his instrument panel and/or audio signal over his headphones.

Examples of **fixed course-setting beacons (radio ranges)** still in operation are the *four-course A-N range*, operating in the 200- to 400-kc region and the *visual-aural range* (VAR), operating in the 108- to 118-Mc band. Both are rapidly being replaced with VOR and TACAN stations.

The *four-course range* produces its four courses by keying two figure-of-eight antenna patterns with alternate interlocked Morse code characters of A ($\cdot$–) and N (–$\cdot$). The two patterns are directed at approximately right angles to each other. The position of a course is determined by aurally comparing the relative strengths of the two code signals, A and N. When an aircraft is exactly on course, the interlocking of the two code characters produces a steady monotone of 1,020 cps, interrupted periodically by station identification. No special equipment other than a radio receiver is required in the aircraft.

The *visual-aural two-course range* has two visual courses 180° apart created by the overlapping of two field patterns essentially cardioid in shape, one modulated by 90 cps and the other by 150 cps. On course is indicated by a zero-center meter which is centered when the two modulations, and hence the two patterns, are of equal magnitude. The aural courses are also 180 degrees apart, at right angles to the visual courses, and are produced by the alternate interlocked Morse code keying of the letters A and N in a manner similar to the four-course range.

Instrument-Landing-System (ILS) Beacons. These systems consist of two major parts: a *localizer unit*, providing a course for horizontal (azimuthal) guidance, and a *glide-path* unit, which furnishes equisignal course guidance in the vertical plane inclined 2 to 4° with the horizontal. The localizer operates in the 108- to 112-Mc band and produces an equisignal course along the runway centerline extended by the overlapping of two beam-shaped patterns modulated at 90 and 150 cps. The glide-path unit operates in the 332.6- to 335.0-Mc band at the same modulator frequencies. In the aircraft the output of the localizer receiver actuates one "needle" of a zero-left-right crosspointer indicator and the output of the glide path receiver actuates the other. An instrument-landing approach is made by keeping the crosspointer meter needles centered.

Omnidirectional Rotating Directive Beacons. Omnidirectional radio-range beacons provide information by means of which an aircraft equipped with suitable equipment can determine its bearing to or from the station. An aircraft that carries both distance-measuring equipment and omnidirectional range receivers can determine both its bearing and its distance from a given beacon.

VHF Omnidirectional Range (VOR), operating within the band of 108 to 118 Mc, provides bearing information by rotating, in space, a cardioid-shaped variable-phase antenna pattern at the rate of 30 rps. This cardioid pattern is generated either by fixed antennas fed by a goniometer or by antenna systems containing a rotating element. To enable the aircraft to determine its bearing, a reference 30-cps signal is transmitted omnidirectionally on a frequency-modulated subcarrier. The detected output of the omnirange receiver is two 30-cps signals whose phase difference depends upon the bearing of the aircraft with respect to the station. The two signals are in phase when the receiving antenna is north of the station. The phase of the variable signal lags the reference signal by the number of degrees the receiver antenna is moved around the station in a clockwise direction.

The phase displacement of the two signals is measured in the aircraft receiver and may be displayed on various types of instrumentation as the bearing to or from the VOR station. The VOR navigation system permits a pilot to fly any desired course to or from the selected ground station. It is the ICAO (International Civil Aviation Organization) standard short-distance azimuthal navigation aid.

TACAN is a tactical air navigation beacon used by the U. S. military services and can provide both distance and bearing simultaneously, by a rotating cardioid-shaped pattern superimposed on the pulsed transmissions used for distance measuring. TACAN equipment in the aircraft provides the pilot simultaneously with distance and bearing information from the TACAN station. Distance information is also obtained from the TACAN facility by DME (Distance-Measuring Equipment) only, or VOR-DME equipped aircraft.

The TACAN azimuth system is similar to that of the VOR in that a 15-cycle cardioid pattern is employed giving coarse bearing information. Superimposed on this pattern, however, is a sinewave component with a frequency of 135 cps whose phase gives fine bearing information. This arrangement results in a 9° phase change in the fine bearing signals for each degree the receiving antenna moves around the TACAN station. A ro-

tating antenna is used to generate the radio frequency pattern in space.

TACAN, like the VOR system, permits the pilot to fly any desired course to or from the selected ground station. In addition, the distance function provides continuous fix and progress information along the selected course.

VORTAC systems combine both TACAN and VOR at co-located sites so that aircraft carrying either TACAN or VOR-DME equipment can be serviced.

Course Line and Pictorial Computers utilize VOR-DME or TACAN bearing and distance information to provide a pictorial or chart display of the aircraft's position with relation to the station or instrumentation, which permits the pilot to select and fly any course to or from a "way" point within the coverage of the station being used. In other words, the Course Line Computer permits the pilot effectively to move the TACAN or VORTAC station to any point, the way point, within the coverage of the station and fly to or from that point on any course as though that way point were the station location. The Pictorial Display permits similar flying merely by laying out the desired course on the display chart.

The Consol Beacon is a low frequency navigational system providing accurate bearings to aircraft out to distances of 1,000 miles in the day time and 1,500 miles at night. The system was developed by Germany early in World War II under the name of "Sonne." The British, and later the Americans, used it under the name of Consol. The major advantage of the system is that it is capable of giving accurate bearings over long distances without requiring any special receiving euipment other than a low-frequency receiver. Its greatest disadvantage is that it takes a long time to obtain a reading of the bearing (from 30 seconds to a minute); moreover, the system does not produce a visual presentation of the bearing data and cannot be readily adapted for automatic use.

The basic system consists of three radiators spaced 3 wavelengths apart. By proper adjustment of relative phases and amplitudes of the radiator currents a multilobe antenna pattern is created that is shifted during the keying cycle. During the operation of the consol cycle the phases of the outside radiators are changed continually in steps of 3° per second. During each phase change a complete 180° phase reversal takes place such that a dot-dash pattern is produced. A slow rotation of the equisignal lines (due to the intersection of adjacent patterns) results so that at the end of a keying cycle the dot-and-dash patterns become completely interchanged.

A bearing is determined by counting the number of dot and dash characters that precede and follow the on-course signal. Specially prepared charts are available to convert these counts into bearing from each station. Under normal conditions accuracies of better than 1° are possible. However, because of the numerous ambiguities it is necessary to know the bearing to the station to within 20°.

Navarho—Navaglobe. Navaglobe is the name applied to a long-distance low-frequency navigational aid devloped by the USAF and the ITT Laboratories. When distance capability is added in addition to bearing, the system is known as Navarho.

Navaglobe operates at a frequency of 100 kc and makes use of three antennas disposed at the corners of an equilateral triangle. In operation two out of the three radiators are energized simultaneously, producing a figure-of-eight pattern with a shallow null. A synchronized signal is produced at the start of each keying cycle by energizing all three radiators. By comparing the relative amplitudes of the three patterns, the bearing from the station can be obtained with a 180° ambiguity. A wattmeter-type square-law resolver is used to translate the received keyed signals into a bearing indication.

To provide distance information both the ground station and the receiving station must be provided with stable reference oscil-

lators having stabilities of $1:10^9$. A 200-cps beat frequency resulting from the simultaneous transmission of two carriers from the ground station provides the basis for the distance measurement. The phase between the transmitted 200-cps tone and one produced by the internal stable oscillator provides the required information for distance measurement.

FRED MOSKOWITZ

Radar-Beacon Systems and Distance-Measuring Equipments (DME)

Radar beacons are named by analogy with the older beacon lights of ocean navigation. Beacons of both sorts are identifiable radiators located at key geographical points known to the observing navigator or pilot and used for determination of position. The radar beacon radiates in the VHF and higher wave bands and is observed by means of some form of radar.

The simplest form of radar beacon is a passive reflector, of which the corner reflector and Luneberg lens are examples. The radar operator may determine his correct distance to (and more or less proximate bearing from) such a beacon by ordinary radar techniques. This beacon has no frequency limitation and is available for interrogation by all radars. It is identifiable only insofar as its return signal stands out above the surrounding clutter.

The more elaborate radar beacon is an active device, virtually a radar turned end for end. Designations are secondary radar, racon, and transponder. The associated primary radar, known as an interrogator-responsor, must be specially designed to match this beacon. The interrogator (comparable to a radar transmitter) sends out a pulse which is received by the transponder on a receiver corresponding to a radar receiver. The output of this receiver triggers a pulse transmitter (of different frequency) in the transponder into operation, one pulse transmitted for each pulse received. This pulse is received back at the primary radar on a receiver, here known as a responsor, and from there on may be treated as any ordinary radar return. Thus, most of the elements of a radar are present in a transponder, but the sequence of operation is reversed and transmitter and receiver are on different frequencies.

The great advantage of the transponder over the simple radar lies in the greatly increased intensity of the returned signal. Whereas the intensity of a true radar echo varies inversely as the fourth power of the distance to the target, the intensity of the synthetic echo from the transponder varies inversely only as the square of the distance to the transponder. This gain in intensity may be utilized to extend the useful range of the primary radar out to the radio horizon and to ensure improved reliability and precision of operation.

The transponder beacon responds only to a matching interrogator. The two must be matched for frequency, pulse repetition rate, and, in some cases, pulse form and pulse coding; and this match must be established for both the going and the return signals. Moreover, the frequency and the coding of the return signal are usually made different from those of the going signal. The pulse repetition rate is preserved. Obviously the transponder has many means of identifying itself to the responsor, as does also the interrogator to the transponder.

It is customary, but not obligatory, in a transponder to employ the same antenna for reception and transmission. This entails some form of TR (*q.v.*) switch and blocking of the receiver during transmission. In general, the antenna is nondirectional in azimuth, as the beacon may be required to respond to interrogation from any azimuth.

Within a transponder there is an appreciable time delay between reception and transmission, for all receivers require a build-up time, as does also the pulse-shaping mechanism. The over-all time delay back to the interrogator is thus increased.

To reduce the observed delay to true time of propagation (and then to true distance), this instrument delay must be known beforehand and subtracted. Special construction such as automatic gain, must be employed in the transponder to preserve the delay precisely at its preassigned value.

The combination of airborne interrogator-responsor and ground-based radar beacon in a system of aeronautical navigation is known as DME (distance measuring equipment). Presentation is made on a dial reading directly in miles.

In navigation, determination of position must rest largely on the determination of some three elements of a triangle. Since, with radar, determination of distance is much more accurate and convenient than determination of angle, it is logical to use for the three elements DME readings to two beacons as two of the sides, together with the known separation of the beacons as the third side. The two beacons may be interrogated on a time-sharing basis. Computation of a fix based on the three elements may be accomplished by automatic computer. Although greater accuracy is obtained with distances from two DME stations, in practice, distance from a single TACAN or VORTAC station (together with bearing) is used to determine aircraft position.

In high-density traffic, consideration must be given to the possibility of simultaneous interrogation of the same beacon by two or more interrogators, with possible disruption of operation for all concerned. This problem is ingeniously solved in the TACAN DME system by reliance on a partly random pulse repetition rate, time sharing, and signal intensity.

The frequencies employed by radar beacons have been put in the VHF and UHF bands for a variety of reasons. The most cogent argument for this choice runs as follows: Precise distance determination requires a short rise time of pulse. A pulse of short rise time generates a wide frequency spectrum. Wide frequency bands are allocated only at UHF and VHF or above.

Rebecca-Eureka is a British navigation system in the VHF band, a forerunner of DME. Rebecca is the airborne interrogator-responsor and Eureka the ground-based radar beacon. The navigator attempts to fly a course such that his distances to two beacons remain equal.

Shoran was originally an American navigation system in the VHF band similar to Rebecca-Eureka, but it is obsolete as a navigation aid. The Shoran equipment and name have, however, been taken over for a system of geodetic surveying of superior accuracy. Two transportable radar beacons are required: one is located at a known point in a geodetic net, the other at a point to which the net is to be extended. The airborne interrogator-responsor is flown at constant altitude on any reasonably straight path that crosses the line joining the two beacons (preferably, near its midpoint and at an oblique angle), interrogating the two alternately. The paired distances so determined are subtracted one from the other. That instant at which the difference is a minimum is the instant of line crossing, and the sum of the two distances observed at that instant is the distance between the two beacons. For the accuracy required, elaborate corrections must be made for the elevation of the interrogator, the curvature of the earth, and the refraction of the atmosphere. By the use of Shoran, base lines of several hundred miles may be established across utterly inaccessible terrain. It was with Shoran equipment and an accurately taped base line that Aslexson in 1950 made one of the best determinations of the velocity of electromagnetic propagation (light) that has ever been made. Shoran-like equipment on S-band under development is to be known as Hiran.

EPI (electronic position indicator) is a distance-measuring system of interrogator-responsor and transponder operating at 1850 kc carrier frequency and 60 μsec pulse length. It is in use by the U.S. Coast and Geodetic Survey for hydrographic survey-ing. The interrogator is aboard ship. Two beacons are sited on shore.

The *Tellurometer* is a cw phase-comparison system for land surveying. A master and remote station are required, both transmitting on FM. Distance is measured by phase comparison of the modulations.

The *Geodemeter* is also a cw phase-comparison system for land surveying using intensity modulated light beams. The phase comparison is made at the modulating frequencies. The remote station is a passive reflector.

Hyperbolic Navigation and Surveying Systems

These systems are classed together because they report position with reference to a pair of transmitting stations in a system of quasihyperbolic coordinates.

An American example of such a system is *Loran* (*long range navigation*). In this system a master and two slave transmitting stations are spaced several hundred miles apart at fixed known locations. The master at A (Fig. 1) transmits a pulsed signal, which, upon arrival at one of the slave stations, B, is received and triggers that station to transmit a similar pulse on the same frequency. A direct time-difference reading is obtained at the receiver by matching pulses from the master and slave stations.

Let the time of travel of signal from A to B be β; let the time used up between arrival

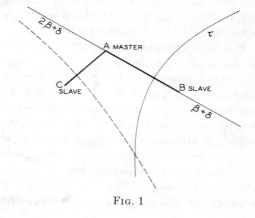

Fig. 1

of signal at B and start of the new pulse be δ. Thus the pulse from B starts after that from A with a delay of $(\beta + \delta)$. This delay is held constant. Consider an observer on the line AB extended beyond slave B, and let him receive the pulses from master and slave and compare their times of arrival. Always, on this line segment, the slave signal follows the master signal with a delay of $(\beta + \delta)$, and only on this line segment will the delay ever be $(\beta + \delta)$. However, on the segment of AB extending beyond A, the delay always amounts to $(2\beta + \delta)$, and only here will it ever amount to so much. These two loci are limiting cases of the general case. Consider the locus of position on the earth where the time delay of slave signal behind master signal has any constant value τ between $(\beta + \delta)$ and $(2\beta + \delta)$. That locus on a flat earth is a parabola with axis along the line AB and vertex somewhere between A and B. On a spherical earth the locus is just a little different. For a given pair of stations, a family of such loci are overprinted on a map of the region in which the stations are located, each hyperbola being identified by its respective delay time.

A second slave station at a third location C similarly is triggered by station A to transmit pulses. All three stations transmit on a common frequency, but the AC pair distinguishes itself from the AB pair by operating on a different pulse repetiton rate. The AC pair determines a second family of hyperbolic loci on the map. The members of the two families mutually intersect, forming a grid. Thus a navigator by the observation of two time delays determines a fix.

Readings are made by the navigator on a double-trace cathode-ray tube with sweep recurrence rate set at the pulse recurrence rate of the station pair to be observed. In the tube the two signals are automatically routed to different traces. The navigator adjusts a built-in delay on one sweep until the two pips representing the two signals are brought to coincidence. The delay adjustment is read to yield the time delay between the pair of signals as received. The master signal is distinguished from the slave signal by the delay δ being chosen so that a slave signal always follows its fellow master signal at an interval less than half the pulse repetition rate. (It leads the next succeeding master signal by an interval greater than half the pulse repetition rate.)

Standard Loran (*Loran-A*) employs the frequencies 1850, 1900, and 1950 Mc. A chain of Loran stations runs down the Atlantic coast of North America and supplies a standard navigation aid over much of the Atlantic Ocean for both ships and aircraft. Other chains cover much of the Pacific Ocean. The daytime range of Loran-A is 300–800 nautical miles (depending on time of day and season). Night coverage may extend to 1500 miles with the use of "one-hop-E" sky waves. Loran signals reflected from the ionosphere are usable, if allowance is made for extra time delay and if confusion with ground wave is not too great. If within range, the ground-wave signal alone is used.

A low-frequency Loran chain operating on 100 kc was set up in 1948 in the Arctic, but failed owing to fuzziness of pulses and multipath interference. In a later military development, *Cytac*, the faults of the earlier equipment are overcome by means of cycle matching within the pulse and by gating out the sky wave. This system is now known as *Loran-C*.

Gee is a short range hyperbolic navigation system operating on VHF similar to Loran.

The outstanding British hyperbolic navigation system, *Decca*, is a cw phase-comparison system. Two stations, master and slave, transmit (in the 75- to 85-kc band) on different but harmonically related frequencies. The transmissions at the slave are locked in frequency and phase on the master. At a distant observing station the two signals are recieved on separate receivers, multiplied to a common frequency (their least common multiple), and the phases of the two common frequency signals compared. The phase delays depend on delay times of transmission as in the case of Loran. Similarly the loci of constant phase difference are quasi-hyperbolas, here known as Decca lines. As with Loran, a second family is required, necessitating a third station on a third frequency similarly locked to the master. A third receiver and a second phase comparator are required at the observing station. Decca lines are overprinted on a map and the fix is read off as with Loran.

In each family of Decca lines there is a multiplicity of lines all having the same phase. This leads to an ambiguity of positioning, which must be resolved. The space between two lines of zero (or zero and 360°) phase difference is called a lane. There may be some 200 lanes in a family. In order to distinguish the lanes, the common frequency is in effect reduced periodically, giving fewer greatly broadened lanes. The precision of fix is greatly broadened but is still sufficient for the navigator to decide in which of the narrow lanes he is located.

In actual navigation the course starts from a known lane and the phase comparator integrates the number of lanes passed through during travel, so that lane identification is usually relatively simple.

Decca was developed primarily for ship navigation, but is also used in Europe for aircraft navigation. A chain of stations covers the European side of the Atlantic Ocean and the Mediterranean.

Dectra is an LF hyperbolic system employing techniques closely associated with those already described for the Decca system. Dectra differs, however, in that it is designed to provide service only along a narrow predetermined route rather than omnidirectionally. A pair of stations, master and slave, are located at each end of the route to be covered. One pair at a time is used to provide course or track position. Information from both pairs or from one pair and a stable oscillator in the aircraft provides distance information through a phase measuring technique, provided the distance indicator is set at a reference point and signals are not lost during the flight.

Lorac and *Raydist* are both American hyperbolic phase-comparison systems de-signed for hydrographic and land surveying. The phase comparison is made in an audio frequency beat signal obtained by interference between several carriers. They operate in the 1600- to 2500-kc band.

Radio Web is a hyperbolic navigation system using independent frequencies from the two stations. These frequencies carry square-wave modulation, and time coincidences are observed rather than phase coincidences.

Radux Omega is a long-range hyperbolic phase-comparison system for navigation, under development by the U. S. Navy. It employs two frequencies in the 10- to 14-kc band, which are transmitted from two interlocked base stations in time-sharing cw.

Rana is a cw hyperbolic phase-comparison system intended for hydrographic surveying, a development of the French Navy. It employs sums and differences of a group of four frequencies all close together (1600–1760 kc).

PAUL B. TAYLOR

Flight Directors

Flight Director is the name given to avigation instrumentation of varying complexity that assists the pilot in the solution of his avigation problem. In essence, it tells him how to move his aircraft controls so as to keep his aircraft on or return it to the desired flight path in cross country and instrument approach flying. The complexity of the system varies with the type of aircraft to be controlled, the type of service for which the craft is used and the modes of control planned in the design of the system. Greatest use of flight directors is made during the final portion of the instrument approach to a landing where the greatest flying precision is required.

The flight-director systems' electronic computers receive information from a combination of VOR-ILS or TACAN avigation receivers; air speed, altitude, yaw, pitch, and roll rate sensors; a vertical gyro; a magnetically stabilized gyro compass; and from the control panel operated by the pilot. The computer output signals operate instruments that tell the pilot how to manipulate the aircraft controls (ailerons, elevators, and rudder) to fly the selected flight path.

Information presented to the pilot on instruments normally includes: horizon plus degree of bank and nose up or down attitude of the aircraft; deviation from glideslope and localizer courses; flags to warn of receiver or computer malfunctioning; heading; and command steering indications. A number of these indications are generally combined in two instruments to facilitate easier visual observation by the pilot. Most computers automatically correct for wind drift on VOR and ILS courses. For example, in an ILS approach the computer receives localizer displacement, bank, and heading command that includes all the necessary corrections to account for crosswinds.

THOMAS JASKI

Doppler Radar

The Doppler effect, i.e., the apparent shift in frequency experienced when radar signals are reflected from a target moving relative to the radar has a special application in navigation. The airborne navigation system known as Doppler radar is based upon the determination of the velocity of the aircraft relative to the earth's surface by reference to the shift in frequency shown by a radar signal reflected from the surface. By means outlined below it is possible to derive the direction of motion of the aircraft (relative to the compass or other orientation system carried by the aircraft) as well as the true ground speed. If a continuous input of such data is available, accurate navigation can be performed by dead reckoning, or by relatively simple computers, without the uncertainties introduced by forecast or intermittently measured wind vectors. This facility, being self-contained in the aircraft, is particularly valuable over remote areas where assistance from naviga-

tional systems depending on ground stations is inadequate.

In practice, current Doppler systems employ two or more fixed beams directed downward from the aircraft with an angle of depression of the order of 60°. Beamwidths of a few degrees are achieved at the allocated frequency of 8,800 Mc. In plan the beams are offset from the longitudinal axis of the aircraft. From such beam configurations a comparison of the frequency of the received signals with that of the transmitted signals as measured in each beam provides the basis of the solution of the geometry of the aircrafts motion relative to the surface. Certain adjustments are necessary to allow for variations in the aircraft's attitude, and inaccuracies follow inevitably if the surface is subject to motion, as is the case with the sea due to wind and currents. Small errors are also caused by variations in the scattering properties of the surface as they effect the angle of incidence of different parts of the beam. Nevertheless, considerable accuracy is possible and system limitations are imposed rather by the difficulty of measuring the reference orientation than by the Doppler determinations.

Various methods of signal transmission have been employed to achieve efficiency and accuracy. The simplest form of transmission would be unmodulated continuous waves, but because of the difficulties caused by direct coupling of the transmitter into the receiver it is more usual to use a frequency or pulse-modulated transmission. The extraction of intelligence from the received signals is a problem of some complexity, and is conveniently combined with a partial solution of the navigational problem. Thus, the basic output of a Doppler system is normally *true ground speed* and *drift angle*. In more advanced systems further processing is carried out in a computer combining the Doppler radar input with those of the gyro-compass and sometimes the airspeed indicator. The output of such systems is a presentation of such data as: (1) present position in geographical coordinates; (2) distance and course to destination or next way point; (3) distance gone and actual track being made good; and (4) wind vector. Such a computer continuously integrates the basic input data and performs all necessary corrections and computations. An important feature in this connection is the *memory* facility which is incorporated in the computer to maintain the record using last available data in the event of temporary interruption of input from the Doppler radar. Such interruptions occur as a result of the failure of the signal owing to poor surface reflectivity—a condition occasionally experienced over smooth seas.

R. T. H. Collis

Cross-references: *Air-Traffic Control, Altimeters, Antennas, Automatic Pilot, Doppler Navigation, Geophysical Prospecting, Inertial Guidance and Gyroscope, Missile Guidance, Propagation, Radar, Radar Displays, Sonar*

NETWORK SYNTHESIS

Approximation

Most network-synthesis techniques in the frequency domain are based on operations on a function of the complex frequency variable p. In addition, this function is usually required to be in the form of a ratio of polynomials with real coefficients (also called a rational fraction). The specifications for the network that is to result from this synthesis, however, are usually given as restrictions on the magnitude and/or phase of the function over a certain range of frequencies. Thus, it is necessary to be able to "approximate" these specifications in the form of a rational fraction before synthesis procedures can be applied.

An example of the procedure may be seen in the approximation of an ideal low-pass filter magnitude specification: $F(j\omega) = K$, $0 < \omega < \omega_c$; $F(j\omega) = 0$, $\omega_c < \omega$. One solution to this specification might be a magnitude characteristic that is "maximally flat" at $\omega = 0$, i.e., a function with as many derivatives as possible set equal to 0 at $\omega = 0$.

For a function with numerator and denominator polynomials of given complexity, this specification may be accomplished by selecting coefficients of these polynomials in such a way that successive terms of a MacLaurin series for the function are equated to zero. If a function $F(p)$ with no finite zeros is determined in this manner it is referred to as a "Butterworth" function. The poles of the product $F(p) F(-p)$ are equally spaced on a circle centered at the origin of the complex frequency plane. The poles in the left half of the plane may be selected to form the desired rational fraction. If $F(p)$ has n poles and is frequency normalized so that the 3-db-down frequency is 1 rad/sec, then

$$| F(j\omega) |^2 = \frac{1}{(1 + \omega^{2n})}$$

A procedure similar to the above may be used to determine the coefficients of a rational fraction such that the phase of the function is linear with frequency, thus providing a "maximally flat delay" approximation. The approximations approach the desired characteristic more closely as the complexity of the approximating function is increased.

Another frequently used approximation to the ideal low-pass normalized filter magnitude characteristic is the function

$$| G(j\omega) |^2 = \frac{1}{1 + \epsilon^2 C_n^2(\omega)}$$

where the C_n are Chebychev polynomials. This function is frequently referred to as an equal-ripple function, since in the passband the magnitude of the function varies between limits set by the coefficient ϵ. The poles of the product $G(p) G(-p)$ are located on an ellipse whose axes are the real and imaginary axes of the complex frequency plane. The poles in the left half of the plane may be selected to form the desired rational fraction. In general, if the magnitude characteristic is the one being approximated, the equal-ripple characteristic provides better filtering than the Butterworth or maximally flat magnitude characteristic described above. It is possible to develop equal-ripple characteristics in both the pass- and stop-band through the use of elliptic functions. It is also possible to extend approximations of the type discussed above for low-pass filters to high pass, band-pass and band-stop filters by means of appropriate transformations of the complex frequency variable.

The potential analogy is another useful means of approximation. It is somewhat unique in that it provides considerable insight into the result of the approximating procedures. Consider the logarithm of a rational fraction which is itself a function of the complex frequency variable. Since the real and imaginary parts of this logarithmic function satisfy Laplace's equation, they may be conveniently represented by the analogy of an electrostatic field in two dimensions. Physically, a sheet of some appropriate resistive material may be used. The logarithm of the magnitude of the rational fraction may be represented by the electric potential, and the phase by the flux. The poles and zeros of the rational fraction are simulated by uniform current distributions into and out of the two-dimensional field. The effect of different pole and zero locations on the magnitude of the resulting transfer function is thus easily observed by measuring the potential distribution along an axis corresponding with the $j\omega$ axis. The phase may be determined from the potential gradient across this axis. It is possible to make further conformal transformations of the logarithmic function to simplify some of the geometrical problems (e.g., the accessibility of points at infinity, etc.). Other potential analogs are also possible, for example poles in the complex frequency plane may be represented by electric dipoles in the potential analogy, with the complex residue determining the dipole moment and orientation. Potential measurements along the $j\omega$ axis can then be made to determine the real and imaginary parts of the function under consideration.

A more general and abstract framework from which to view the approximation problem is provided by orthogonal polynomials and Padé approximants. If a weighted error criterion (e.g., a weighted mean-square deviation) is selected, an approximation to the desired function (the magnitude-squared function) may be formed from a set of orthogonal polynomials based on the specified weighting function. In general, the approximation improves as the number of orthogonal polynomials used is increased. The set of orthogonal polynomials can then be represented by Padé approximants, the choice of the various approximants of equal order being made on the basis of the properties of the function being approximated.

L. P. HUELSMAN

Realization

The present discussion is limited to realization of prescribed rational-fraction-type input and/or transfer immittances with one- and two-port networks which are passive, bilateral, linear, and time invariant. Two-port networks are represented by the equivalent pi network (y_{11}, y_{22}, y_{12} parameters), the equivalent tee network (z_{11}, z_{22}, z_{12} parameters), or by the chain (A,B,C,D) parameters. In the case of a symmetric network, the symmetric lattice equivalent is the most convenient with which to deal because of its generality (where it is usually hoped that the resulting lattice may be reduced to a more desirable unbalanced form).

In any given design, numerous constraints may be imposed as, for example, unavoidable shunt capacitance, need for a common ground, requirement for a definite load resistance, avoidance of transformers, and so on. In addition, high power efficiency may require use of a lossless network or perhaps frequencies are so low that inductance is prohibited altogether. Many of these constraints impose limitations on allowable transfer functions. The designer must be fully aware of such limitations in order to avoid wasting time in attempting to accomplish the impossible.

Network design is greatly simplified if only two of the three kinds of elements occur and if source and load impedances, if any, may somehow be handled separately from basic parameters (y_{11}, z_{22}, etc.). Thus design of RC networks is simplified if source and load resistors, if any, are included as parts of the basic parameters. A lossless network is of itself not of much interest, but when one or both of the terminations are resistors, it becomes of considerable practical value. For such situations, the RLC network has R limited to terminations and the RLC problem can then often be reduced to the simpler two-element (LC) network.

Design techniques that involve all three elements are best handled with reference to the general lattice or to the chain parameters. In the lattice method, we write the transfer function and identify various parts of the expression with the lattice arm impedances, assuming these to be positive-real functions. In this, a (nonunique) separation of a Hurwitz polynomial into two such polynomials may be required. In the case of the chain parameters, we observe that a cascade of two-ports may be analyzed in terms of a product of chain matrices pertaining to the individual stages of the cascade. Thus if the given over-all system matrix may be factored in a suitable manner, a complicated prescribed system may be reduced to a cascade of several easily realized sections. One especially simple case of matrix factorization (but one that may be analyzed with more elementary notions) occurs with the constant-resistance network which may be realized as a lattice or by means of two impedances which complement one another. If complementary impedances are realized with lossless R-terminated networks, filters that provide complementary transfer characteristics are also defined.

For most design techniques, we write the pertinent (given) transfer function in terms of the z or y parameters and then seek to identify individual parameters. In particular, we attempt to find a suitable z_{11}, z_{22}, y_{11}, or y_{22}. Once this has been done, a lad-

der network or a quasi-ladder network may be developed by synthesizing an input immittance in such a manner that desirable transmission zeros are created. Principal techniques for synthesizing a prescribed transfer function are essentially equivalent to synthesis of an input immittance. As previously stated, lattice design may reduce similarly.

The process of finding a suitable input immittance is sometimes a trial-and-error one in which no unique and optimum procedure can be defined. In the case of the R terminated lossless network with ideal source drive, however, the process may be unique. In the case of lossless networks with resistance terminations at both ends, an indirect method involving input reflection coefficient may be required.

Realization of an input impedance (or admittance) involves separating Z into additive parts Z_1 and Z_2 or Y into additive parts Y_1 and Y_2. The usual attempt is to have both parts be positive-real functions and thus the realization of Z or Y is converted to two simpler problems. One of the additive parts may represent a series (shunt) impedance which creates some desired transmission zero; or, this impedance may only be specified in amount such that zeros of the remainder impedance (admittance) allow a subsequent step to be performed in which the remainder admittance (impedance) may be separated into additive parts in order to create a desired transmission zero. The well-known Foster and Cauer networks for two-element-kind networks are the most elementary examples of this process. In principle, any RLC ladder network that has no mutual inductance is obtainable as described.

Prior to separating Z or Y into additive parts, both numerator and denominator may be multiplied by the same arbitrary surplus factor. This procedure may facilitate certain designs, although for general transfer-function realization no standard procedure has been specified. If interest is restricted to an input impedance, one type of separation into additive parts with a special surplus factor obtains the Bott-and-Duffin network, which is capable of realizing any positive-real function without the use of mutual inductance (although the required number of circuit elements may be inefficiently large).

Several other techniques involve separation of Z into additive parts one or both of which may not be positive-real. Subsequent to determination of the relevant nonphysical network, the various elements may be combined such that the result is realizable. The Brune network results in this manner by combining negative inductance into a transformer as also is accomplished in the case of Darlington types "C" and "D" sections. Nonladder but realizable sections such as twin-tee networks may be found in an analogous manner such that the equivalence is to ladder network sections which involve non-realizable elements. The very complete generality of separation techniques which involve non-positive-real parts is pointed out. Every physical two-port network has an equivalent tee and an equivalent pi, although the equivalent by itself may not be realizable.

The subject of network realization is a highly technical and involved one. For more data, reference should be made to various current textbooks and to the principal journal of the field, namely, *IRE Transactions on Circuit Theory*.

J. L. STEWART

Cross-references: *Filters, Network Theory*

NETWORK THEORY

Generalized Equations and Topological Analysis

Introduction and Terminology. A brief treatment of the analysis of networks containing resistances, inductances, capacitances, and independent sources is presented below. The voltage-current conventions and symbols are indicated in Fig. 1. The problem of network analysis is to determine the voltages and currents in the several branches

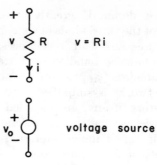

Fig. 1

of a network. A *branch* is defined here as having one single passive element. Let the total number of branches in a network be b. Clearly there are altogether $2b$ unknowns, namely: the b branch voltages and the b branch currents. Since for each branch the voltage is related directly to the current (Fig. 1), it is sufficient to determine the b unknowns (usually either b currents or b voltages). An *oriented graph* is a graph in which each branch has an arrow to indicate the positive direction of the branch current. Once the direction of the branch current is established, the direction of the branch voltage is specified as in Fig. 1. A *node* is defined as a terminal where two or more branches meet. The total number of nodes of a graph is denoted by n_t. A *tree* is defined as a subgraph (parts of a complete graph) formed by any set of branches of a network that connects all the nodes but does not form any loops. Any closed circuit of branches is a *loop*. The branches which belong to a tree are called *tree branches*. From the definition of a tree it is clear that the number of tree branches is equal to $n = n_t - 1$. The branches other than tree branches in a graph are called *links*. The total number of links in a graph is denoted by l. Clearly

$$l = b - n$$

A *cut set* is a set of elements that dissociate two main parts of a graph.

The Complete and Independent Descriptions. (1) *Current Basis.* Consider first the b branch currents of a network. Following the aforementioned classification, one has l link currents and n tree branch currents. We shall show that not all b currents are independent. Actually, there are only l independent currents (the link currents). The tree branch currents can always be expressed in terms of the link currents. This means that the l link currents form a complete and independent set. *Independent* refers to the fact that the link currents may be arbitrarily chosen independent of each other. *Complete* refers to the fact that in order to express any branch current in terms of the link currents one needs in general all the link currents. Thus, in network analysis, one only has to determine l link currents first. The reason is as follows: In a network, if all the links are left open, i.e., all the link currents are zero, from the definitions of tree and links, clearly, there are no more loops in which currents can circulate. Thus, all branch currents are zero. The fact that setting all link currents zero automatically forces all branch currents to be zero indicates the dependency of tree branch currents on the link currents. Hence, there exists, at most, l independent current variables. Moreover, it can be shown that there are exactly l independent current variables. Suppose that there are fewer, say $l - 1$, independent variables only; one should then be able to make all branch currents zero by setting $l - 1$ link currents zero. This, however, is impossible, since if one link is still closed, there is always one circulating loop left.

(2) *Voltage Basis.* It can be shown that n tree branch voltages form a complete and independent set. That is, the link voltages can always be expressed in terms of the n tree branch voltages. The proof is similar to the above case. Here, the argument is as follows: If one sets the n tree branch voltages to zero by shortening out all the tree branches, clearly, all branches are shorted and all branch voltages are forced to be zero.

In network analysis, one can either determine l link currents first and then obtain the rest of the unknowns, or determine n tree branch voltages first. The first one is referred to as the *loop analysis* and the second is the *cut set analysis.* Since for a given network the number of links is in general not equal to the number of tree branches, either method may prove to be better than the other.

Loop Analysis. In loop analysis l link currents are the independent variables. It is shown that by Kirchoff's voltage law one can write a set of l independent equations. Thus, one can solve for the l unknowns from l independent equations. The rest of the branch currents are expressed in terms of the l link currents. The method is illustrated by the following example.

Consider the network as shown in Fig. 2. The oriented graph is shown on the right. First, a tree is picked as shown in Fig. 3. The independent variables are the link currents i_1, i_2, i_3, and i_4. They can be identified as the branch currents

$$j_1 = i_1$$
$$j_2 = i_2$$
$$j_6 = i_3$$
$$j_7 = i_4$$

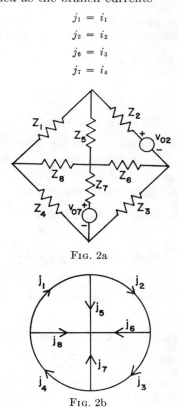

Fig. 2a

Fig. 2b

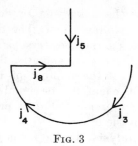

FIG. 3

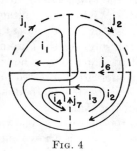

FIG. 4

The loops are drawn as shown in Fig. 4. In drawing the loops we note that each loop contains *one* and only *one* link. The tree branch currents are then expressed as the linear combinations of the four link currents

$$j_3 = i_2 - i_3$$

$$j_4 = i_2 - i_3 - i_4$$

$$j_5 = i_1 - i_2$$

$$j_8 = -i_1 + i_2 - i_3 - i_4$$

Kirchoff's voltage law is next used to write four independent equations. The self and mutual impedances are determined immediately. The four equations are

$$(Z_1 + Z_5 + Z_8)i_1 - (Z_5 + Z_8)i_2 + Z_8i_3$$
$$+ Z_8i_4 = 0$$

$$-(Z_5 + Z_8)i_1 + (Z_5 + Z_2 + Z_3 + Z_4 + Z_8)i_2$$
$$- (Z_3 + Z_4 + Z_8)i_3 - (Z_4 + Z_8)i_4 = -v_{02}$$

$$Z_8i_1 - (Z_3 + Z_4 + Z_8)i_2 + (Z_3 + Z_8 + Z_6)i_3$$
$$+ (Z_4 + Z_8)i_4 = 0$$

$$Z_8i_1 - (Z_4 + Z_8)i_2 + (Z_4 + Z_8)i_3$$
$$+ (Z_4 + Z_8 + Z_7)i_4 = v_{07}$$

Summary. In loop analysis, the following steps are needed.

(1) Pick a tree (thus fix the link current variables).

(2) Draw the loops. Keep in mind that a loop contains one and only one link.

(3) The Kirchoff voltage law is next written by inspection.

(4) If other branch currents are required, they can be written as linear combinations of the link current variables.

Cut Set Analysis. In cut set analysis, the n tree branch voltages are the independent variables. It can be shown that by the use of Kirchoff's current law one can always write a set of n independent equations from which the variables are solved. The process is the complete dual of the loop analysis.

Summary. In node analysis the following steps are needed.

(1) Pick a tree and label the tree branch voltage variables.

(2) Draw and number the nodes and cut sets for writing Kirchoff's current law. Keep in mind that one node or cut set contains one and only one tree branch.

(3) The Kirchoff current-law equations are written by inspection.

E. S. KUH

Mesh-Node Analysis

Mesh (or loop) analysis is the technique commonly used for the analysis of networks on a current basis, that is, to determine the current flowing in each branch of a network. Node analysis is the technique employed for analysis on a voltage basis, that is, to determine the voltage across each branch of the network.

In the analysis of any particular network either one or the other of these techniques may lead to the simplest solution, i.e., the least number of unknown quantities to be determined. In mesh analysis the number of unknown quantities to be determined is equal to the number of independent mesh currents in the network, whereas in node analysis the number of unknown quantities to be determined is equal to the number of independent node pair voltages of the network. If b is the total number of branches of a network, n_t the total number of nodes, and s the number of separate parts, i.e., the number of parts not conductively coupled, then the number of independent node pair voltages is

$$n = n_t - s$$

and the number of independent mesh currents is

$$l = b - n_t + s$$

In general n and l are not equal.

Thus the first step in the analysis of a given network is to determine whether mesh analysis or node analysis will lead to the smaller number of unknown quantities. Once this has been determined analysis proceeds by whichever technique is indicated.

Mesh Analysis. The first step in mesh analysis is the choice of an independent set of mesh currents, which can be done in a number of different ways. One method is to choose the meshes successively such that each new mesh includes at least one branch not already included in a mesh. If the l meshes are chosen in this way then the l mesh currents always form an independent set. The meshes can be chosen in other ways but in any case the mesh currents must form an independent set. In many cases it is not necessary to know all of the currents in the network but only the currents in particular branches. In such cases the computations may be reduced by choosing the meshes in such a way that only one mesh current flows in the branch of interest. In this way the number of unknowns to be determined is held to a minimum.

After the meshes have been established, a positive sense of current flow is assumed for each mesh. If the network contains any current sources they may be either converted to their Thévenin equivalent voltage sources or considered to form extra meshes whose currents are fixed by the sources.

The next step in the analysis is to apply

Kirchoff's voltage law to each mesh. The result is a set of l equations in the l unknown mesh currents. The equations can be expressed concisely as

$$\sum_{j=1}^{l} Z_{kj}I_j = E_k \quad (k = 1, 2, \cdots, l)$$

where

Z_{kk} = impedance of the kth mesh with all other meshes open circuited
= self impedance of the kth mesh
Z_{kj} = impedance common to the kth and jth mesh
= mutual impedance of the kth and jth meshes
I_j = jth mesh current
E_k = sum of voltage sources in the kth mesh

This set of equations can then be solved for the unknown mesh currents. Mesh analysis is illustrated by the following example. For the network of Fig. 5 we obtain

$$b = 5, n_t = 4, s = 1, n = 3, l = 2$$

Thus $l < n$ and mesh analysis is indicated. One possible choice of meshes and positive sense of current flow is as shown in Fig. 5. Applying Kirchoff's voltage law we obtain

$$I_1Z_1 + (I_1 - I_2)Z_2 = e_1 - e_2$$

$$(I_2 - I_1)Z_2 + I_2(Z_3 + Z_4 + Z_5) = e_2 - e_3$$

or rearranging

$$(Z_1 + Z_2)I_1 - Z_2I_2 = e_1 - e_2$$

$$-Z_2I_1 + (Z_2 + Z_3 + Z_4 + Z_5)I_2 = e_2 - e_3$$

Thus we have self and mutual impedances

$$Z_{11} = Z_1 + Z_2 , \quad Z_{12} = Z_{21} = -Z_2$$

$$Z_{22} = Z_2 + Z_3 + Z_4 + Z_5$$

The two equations can be solved to obtain the unknown currents I_1 and I_2 .

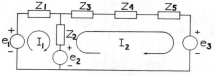

Fig. 5

Summary. The steps in carrying out the mesh analysis of a network are as follows.

(1) Choose an independent set of mesh currents and assign positive sense of current flow.

(2) Apply Kirchoff's voltage law to each mesh.

(3) Solve the resulting set of equations for the mesh currents.

Node Analysis. The first step in node analysis is the choice of an independent set of node pair voltages, usually accomplished by choosing the grounded point or any convenient point in the network as a datum node and using the voltages between each of the other nodes and the datum node as the voltage variables. If the network consists of more than one part then a datum node must be assigned for each part. If the network contains voltage sources they may be either changed to their Norton equivalent current sources or considered to form extra nodes whose voltages are fixed by the sources. After choosing the node pairs a polarity is assumed for each node pair voltage. The next step is to apply Kirchoff's current law to obtain the network equations in terms of the unknown node pair voltages. The result is a set of n equations in the n unknown node pair voltages, expressed concisely as

$$\sum_{j=1}^{n} Y_{kj} V_j = I_k \quad (k = 1, 2, \cdots, n)$$

where

Y_{kk} = admittance across the kth node pair with all other nodes short circuited to the datum node

= self admittance of the kth node pair

Y_{kj} = admittance common to the kth and jth node pair

= mutual admittance of the kth and jth node pairs

V_j = voltage across jth node pair

I_k = sum of current sources at the kth node pair

The technique is illustrated by the following example. For the network of Fig. 6 we obtain

$$b = 5, \quad n_t = 3, \quad s = 1, \quad n = 2, \quad l = 3$$

Thus $n < l$ and node analysis is indicated. One choice of datum node and node pair voltages is indicated in Fig. 6. Applying Kirchoff's current law we obtain

$$V_1 Y_1 + (V_1 - V_2) Y_2 = i_1 - i_2$$

$$(V_2 - V_1) Y_2 + V_2 (Y_3 + Y_4 + Y_5) = i_2 + i_3$$

or after rearranging

$$(Y_1 + Y_2) V_1 - Y_2 V_2 = i_1 - i_2$$

$$Y_2 V_1 + (Y_2 + Y_3 + Y_4 + Y_5) V_2 = i_2 + i_3$$

Thus we have self and mutual admittances

$$Y_{11} = Y_1 + Y_2, \quad Y_{12} = Y_{21} = -Y_2$$

$$Y_{22} = Y_2 + Y_3 + Y_4 + Y_5$$

The node pair voltages V_1 and V_2 are obtained by solving this set of equations.

Summary. The steps in carrying out the node analysis of a network are as follows.

(1) Select a datum node and identify the node pair voltages.

(2) Apply Kirchoff's current law at each node.

(3) Solve the resulting set of equations for the node pair voltages.

J. D. PATTERSON

Time-Domain Analysis

The time-domain analysis of finite, linear, lumped networks is based upon the various forms of the superposition integral. The most useful form of superposition integral is the convolution of two functions $f(t)$ and $g(t)$

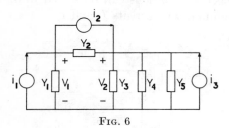

FIG. 6

of which the most general form is defined by

$$f * g[t] = \int_{-\infty}^{\infty} f(\tau)g(t - \tau)\, d\tau \tag{1}$$

If, as in many applications, $f(t)$ and $g(t)$ are zero for $t < 0$, Eq. (1) takes the form

$$f * g[t] = \int_{0}^{t} f(\tau)g(t - \tau)\, d\tau \tag{2}$$

By a simple change of variable we see that the convolution is a commutative operation, that is $f * g = g * f$. By a theorem of mathematics (Titchmarsh's theorem), if the convolution in Eq. (2) is zero, then at least one of f or g is zero. However, this result is not valid for Eq. (1), in general, as can be seen by taking $f(t) = t/(t^2 + 1)$, $g(t) = 1$ which has

$$\int_{-\infty}^{\infty} [\tau/(\tau^2 + 1)]\, d\tau = 0$$

Because of this result, the $*$ in Eq. (2), but not in Eq. (1), can be treated as a multiplication symbol for which the operation of division can be defined. In conjunction with the ordinary operation of addition of two functions we then have an algebraic system (called a field) which behaves under the ordinary rules of algebra but which can be used to solve linear networks. Using this method, which is due to the Polish mathematician Mikusiński, solutions to networks for which excitations or responses are not Laplace transformable can be obtained.

The convolution can arise in several ways. For the first of these consider a linear network with a single excitation x_1, a single response x_2, and a finite number of lumped elements. We can write

$$a_n(d^n x_1/dt^n) + \cdots + a_0 x_1 \tag{3}$$
$$= b_m(d^m x_2/dt^m) + \cdots + b_0 x_2$$

Let the excitation be a unit impulse applied at time τ, denoted by $\delta(t - \tau)$. The corresponding response, called the impulse response, will be denoted by $h(t, \tau)$; here t is the time of observation of the response; τ is the time of excitation. By the meaning of the impulse we see that any other exci-

tation can be written in the convolution form

$$x_1(t) = \int_{-\infty}^{\infty} x_1(\tau)\delta(t - \tau)\, d\tau \tag{4}$$

By the linearity of the network the response due to $x_1(t)$ is then found by the superposition (addition or in this case integration) of the outputs due to the individual inputs $x_1(\tau)\delta(t - \tau)$. The output is then given by the following superposition integral:

$$x_2(t) = \int_{-\infty}^{\infty} x_1(\tau)h(t, \tau)\, d\tau \tag{5}$$

If the network is time-invariant (constant a's and b's in Eq. 3), a simple shift in the time scale for the excitation function (from t to $t - \tau$) results in a simple shift in the time scale for the response function or in this case we can write $h(t, \tau) = H(t - \tau)$. Equation (5) is then in the convolution form

$$x_2(t) = \int_{-\infty}^{\infty} x_1(\tau)H(t - \tau)\, d\tau \tag{6}$$

Equation (1) can then be physically interpreted in the following manner. For a linear, lumped, finite, time-invariant network the response is given by the convolution of the excitation with the impulse response. Equation (3) shows that the network is causal (that is, no output occurs before an input is applied). If the excitation is zero until $t = 0$ the convolution can be written in the form of Eq. (2), because of the causality of the network. The impulse response $H(t - \tau)$ is usually quite easily found; however, for time-varying networks $h(t, \tau)$ is difficult to compute. Probably the most important uses of this method occur when x_1 is a random signal. In this case the statistical properties are most easily found in the time domain, the transform methods being less convenient to apply.

As a second illustration, consider a linear network that can be described by a system of ordinary differential equations. By a process similar to that used in setting up operational amplifiers, the network can be described in first order matrix form

$$(dy/dt) = A(t)y + f(t) \tag{7}$$

Here y is a column vector with n entries, called the state variables, $A(t)$ is an $n \times n$ matrix, and $f(t)$ is a column vector of forcing functions. The state variables can be chosen as currents in inductances and voltages across capacitances. If A consists of functions continuous for $0 \leq t < \infty$ then the corresponding homogeneous equation (Eq. 7 with $f = 0$) has a unique solution, subject to the initial conditions $y(0)$. Let $Y(t)$ be an $n \times n$ matrix solution of the corresponding homogeneous equation with y replaced by Y, subject to $Y(0) = 1_n =$ unit matrix of order n. The solution of Eq. (7) can then be shown to be given by

$$y(t) = Y(t)y(0) + \int_0^t Y(t)Y^{-1}(\tau)f(\tau) \, d\tau; \, t \geq 0 \quad (8)$$

If A is a constant matrix (that is, a time-invariant system) then $Y(t)Y(u)$ and $Y(t + u)$ are both solutions of $dZ/dt = AZ$ subject to $Z(0) = Y(u)$. By the uniqueness property these solutions are identical and letting $t = -u$ we see that $Y(-t) = Y^{-1}(t)$. Thus

$$Y(t)Y(-\tau) = Y(t)Y^{-1}(\tau) = Y(t - \tau)$$

and Eq. (8) becomes

$$y(t) = Y(t)y(0) + \int_0^t Y(t - \tau)f(\tau) \, d\tau; \, t \geq 0 \quad (9)$$

Thus the general solution of a finite, linear, lumped time-invariant network can be broken into two parts, the free response and the forced response. The forced response is obtained as the convolution (of Eq. 2) of the forcing function with the fundamental matrix Y. An explicit form for Y is

$$Y(t) = e^{At} = \sum_{i=0}^{\infty} (1/i!)(At)^i$$

This power series can only feasibly be evaluated by the use of the eigenvalues of A.

This procedure just described is conveniently applied to the analysis of networks with computers. It also serves as an excellent tool for general studies of networks. For this the state variables can be visualized geometrically to yield results on such topics as stability and optimum means of excitation.

Two-Port Networks

A two-port network is a network in which the terminals are associated in two pairs, as shown in Fig. 7. Here terminal pair one is commonly considered as an input port and terminal pair two is taken as an output port.

Because the two port interrelates signals at one point in a system to those at a different point, they occur in the analysis and synthesis of most electrical systems. Some specific examples of their use can be found in the design of vacuum-tube and transistor amplifiers, interstage networks, filters, and power transmission systems.

The behavior of linear, time-invariant two ports can be described by various parameter matrices. The most common of these are defined in the following manner (here V_1, V_2, I_1, I_2 are Laplace transformed variables):

Impedance Matrix, Z

$$\begin{bmatrix} V_1 \\ V_2 \end{bmatrix} = \begin{bmatrix} z_{11} & z_{12} \\ z_{21} & z_{22} \end{bmatrix} \begin{bmatrix} I_1 \\ I_2 \end{bmatrix}$$

Admittance Matrix, Y

$$\begin{bmatrix} I_1 \\ I_2 \end{bmatrix} = \begin{bmatrix} y_{11} & y_{12} \\ y_{21} & y_{22} \end{bmatrix} \begin{bmatrix} V_1 \\ V_2 \end{bmatrix}$$

Transmission Matrix, T (sometimes called the chain matrix, $ABCD$ matrix, or general circuit parameters)

$$\begin{bmatrix} V_1 \\ I_1 \end{bmatrix} = \begin{bmatrix} A & B \\ C & D \end{bmatrix} \begin{bmatrix} V_2 \\ -I_2 \end{bmatrix}$$

h Parameters, H

$$\begin{bmatrix} V_1 \\ I_2 \end{bmatrix} = \begin{bmatrix} h_{11} & h_{12} \\ h_{21} & h_{22} \end{bmatrix} \begin{bmatrix} I_1 \\ V_2 \end{bmatrix}$$

g Parameters, G

$$\begin{bmatrix} I_1 \\ V_2 \end{bmatrix} = \begin{bmatrix} g_{11} & g_{12} \\ g_{21} & g_{22} \end{bmatrix} \begin{bmatrix} V_1 \\ I_2 \end{bmatrix}$$

Normalized Scattering Matrix, S

$$\begin{bmatrix} V_1 - I_1 \\ V_2 - I_2 \end{bmatrix} = \begin{bmatrix} s_{11} & s_{12} \\ s_{21} & s_{22} \end{bmatrix} \begin{bmatrix} V_1 + I_1 \\ V_2 + I_2 \end{bmatrix}$$

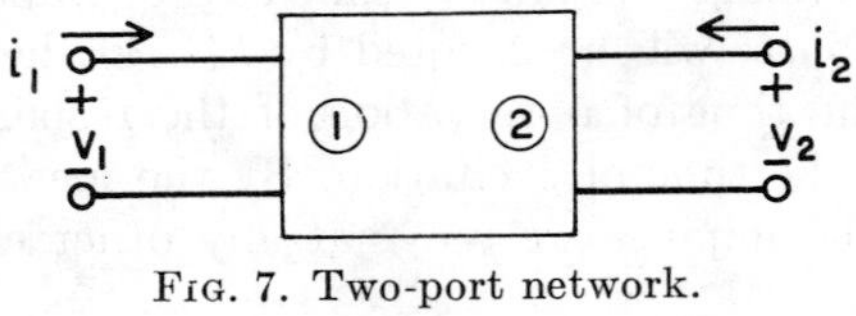

FIG. 7. Two-port network.

Z is called the open-circuit impedance matrix since z_{ij} can be found by performing a measurement with one of the ports open-circuited; for instance $z_{11} = V_1/I_1$ when $I_2 = 0$. Similarly, Y is called the short-circuit admittance matrix, since y_{ij} can be found by performing a measurement with one of the ports shorted. Although Z and Y have the dimensions of impedance and admittance, such is not the case for the general circuit, the h, or the g parameters. Thus h_{11} is the short-circuit impedance seen at port one, whereas h_{21} is the short-circuit current transfer ratio. These latter three matrices are then classified as hybrid parameters. Of the hybrid parameters, the h parameters are especially useful in transistor-amplifier design, since the h_{ij} can easily be measured. For general studies, as well as for synthesis, the scattering matrix is useful, since it exists for all passive networks (excluding several pathological cases). In the definition of S the $V_i + I_i$ and $V_i - I_i$ can be physically interpreted as incident and reflected waves on infinitesimally long transmission lines of unit characteristic impedance connected to the ports (each loaded in 1 ohm); s_{11} and s_{22} are then reflection coefficients, and s_{12} and s_{21} are transmission coefficients, all under unit terminations.

By solving the various equations given above the parameter matrices can be inter-related. If we use $1_2 =$ unit matrix of order two, we find, for instance, that

$$Y = Z^{-1}$$

$$S = (Z - 1_2)(Z + 1_2)^{-1} = (1_2 - Y)(1_2 + Y)^{-1}$$

$$Z = (1_2 + S)(1_2 - S)^{-1}$$

Besides expressing S in terms of Z or Y, the second of these equations shows that S becomes $-S$ in going from a given network to its dual.

In working with two ports it is advantageous to use the parameters which are appropriate to any interconnections which may be encountered. Some of the most useful interconnections with the appropriate matrix operations are illustrated in Fig. 8. Besides these connections, a series input with a

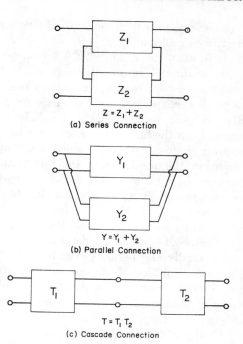

$$Z = Z_1 + Z_2$$
(a) Series Connection

$$Y = Y_1 + Y_2$$
(b) Parallel Connection

$$T = T_1 T_2$$
(c) Cascade Connection

FIG. 8. Representative two-port interconnections.

parallel output connection gives the addition of H matrices; a parallel output with a series input connection yields the addition of G matrices. When using the connections of Fig. 8, care must be exercised to insure that the component two ports are described by the given matrix before and after the connection is made.

The theory of the synthesis of two port finite passive networks has been developed to a considerable degree. Before stating the conditions that allow synthesis, it is necessary to introduce some notation. Let $p = \sigma + j\omega$ be the complex frequency variable, a superscript tilde denote matrix transposition, a superscript asterisk denote complex conjugation, and a subscript H denote the Hermitian part of a matrix (that is, $A_H = \frac{1}{2}[A + \tilde{A}^*]$).

With these, we know that a Z matrix (and by duality Y) can be synthesized by a lumped, finite, passive two port if and only if

(a) the elements of Z are rational in p with real coefficients, and

(b) every principal minor of Z_H is non-negative for all p in Re $p > 0$.

If, as in most cases, we require a reciprocal network then Z must satisfy $Z = \tilde{Z}$. If, as also frequently occurs, we desire a lossless network (i.e., no resistors) then we require $Z(p) = -\tilde{Z}(-p)$. Physically, condition (a) results from the fact that we are considering a finite number of real-valued elements, condition (b) results from the fact that a passive network must be stable with the average power input in the sinusoidal steady state nonnegative. From the fact that this power must be zero for a lossless network, $Z(p) = -\tilde{Z}(-p)$ can be derived.

An equally and perhaps even more useful set of realizability conditions can be given for S. Thus S can be realized by a finite number of lumped, passive elements if and only if

(c) the elements of S are rational with real coefficients

(d) the elements of S are analytic in Re $p \geq 0$

(e) every principal minor of $1_2 - \tilde{S}*S$ is ≥ 0 for all p on Re $p = 0$.

If the network is to be reciprocal then $S = \tilde{S}$, and, if the network is to be lossless, $\tilde{S}(-p)S(p) = 1_2$. In many cases it is easier to check the realizability conditions on S than those on Z. The importance in having realizability conditions on S stem from the fact that S can be advantageously used to (1) synthesize passive networks, (2) synthesize terminated filters, (3) find all equivalent networks, and (4) evaluate the performance of image parameter filters.

It should be observed that the above conditions usually require ideal transformers and that only very limited knowledge exists concerning two-port synthesis without transformers. Further, similar "necessary" conditions exist for distributed parameter networks; however, no general synthesis method exists in this case.

Besides the two-port descriptions listed above, there is another set of parameters which are extremely useful for filter design. These are the image parameters, which are defined through Fig. 7 in the following manner. Let port two be terminated in an impedance Z_{I2} and port one fed by a voltage source of internal impedance Z_{I1}. If, under these conditions, the output impedance (that is, the impedance looking away from the load into port two) is also Z_{I2} and the input impedance (seen looking away from the source into port one) is Z_{I1}, the two-port is said to be image matched. This serves to define the image impedances Z_{I1} and Z_{I2} and shows that

$$Z_{I1} = \sqrt{z_{11}/y_{11}}, \quad Z_{I2} = \sqrt{z_{22}/y_{22}}$$

If, as in filter theory, the two port is reciprocal then one other quantity is needed to characterize the two port. This is taken as the image transfer function Γ, which is defined by

$$e^{-\Gamma} = \sqrt{Z_{I1}/Z_{I2}} \, \frac{V_2}{V_1}$$

(calculated under an image match)

Since $V_1 = Z_{I1}I_1$ and $V_2 = -Z_{I2}I_2$ under an image match, this is seen to yield

$$2\Gamma = \ln\left[-V_1I_1/V_2I_2\right] \text{ (under an image match)}$$
$$= \ln\left[(\sqrt{z_{11}y_{11}} + 1)/(\sqrt{z_{11}y_{11}} - 1)\right]$$

The first of these illustrates the analogy between Γ and the propagation constant of a transmission line.

ROBERT W. NEWCOMB

Linearity

A circuit element is said to be *linear* if the amplitude of the current through the element is directly proportional to the amplitude of the voltage across the element. A circuit composed of linear elements is called a *linear circuit*. A circuit need not necessarily be reciprocal in order to be linear.

The current through a linear element and the voltage across it always contains the same steady-state sinusoidal frequency components. This is not true for a nonlinear element. For example, the current-voltage characteristic of a nonlinear resistor might be bent (Fig. 9). Then if a sinusoidal voltage is applied, the response current is flattened on one side as shown. Although the applied voltage would consist of only one frequency component, the response current would have a Fourier series representation containing a number of frequency components. Another example of additional frequencies introduced by nonlinear elements is the "crosstalk" that can occur in communication systems when a bad connection or a bad amplifier tube introduces nonlinearities into what is supposed to be a linear transmission system. These frequency-mixing effects cannot occur if all of the circuit elements are linear and time-invariant.

In some nonlinear circuits the steady-state response to a steady-state driving signal is not unique. Various different steady-state responses may result, depending on how the driving signal was first applied. In the case of a linear circuit the steady-state response is always unique.

The distinction between a nonlinear capacitance and a linear, time-varying capacitance should be noted. A nonlinear capacitance varies with time as influenced by the applied signal, whereas a linear, time-varying capacitance varies in some fixed manner regardless of the applied signal. If a linear capacitance has a sinusoidal variation with frequency f_c, a signal applied at another frequency f_a causes responses at f_a and various sideband frequencies, the primary ones being $(f_c \pm f_a)$. However, if the applied signal is sinusoidal, the signal- and sideband-frequency responses are also sinusoidal, and their amplitudes are proportional to that of the applied signal.

Also important is the fact that linear circuits obey the *superposition theorem*. This theorem may be stated as follows: *The voltage or current response of a linear circuit to a number of generators applied at the same time at any points in the circuit is equal to the sum of the individual responses due to the generators applied separately.** This property can be very helpful in analyzing linear

* Of course, if a generator is removed it must be replaced by its internal impedance.

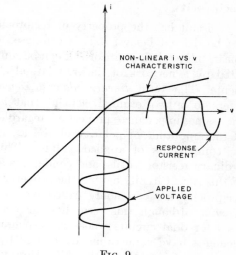

NON-LINEAR i VS v CHARACTERISTIC

RESPONSE CURRENT

APPLIED VOLTAGE

Fig. 9

circuits with more than one generator. Another useful result of this property is that the circuit response to a driving signal consisting of a Fourier spectrum of signal components can be computed by summing the individual responses to the signal components. Fourier integral and Laplace transform methods of circuit analysis are based on this superposition property of linear circuits.

Many circuit elements will become strongly nonlinear if the driving signal is large enough. Examples are vacuum tubes, inductors with iron or ferrite cores, and microwave devices using ferrimagnetic resonance in ferrite material. In numerous cases the nonlinearity of the elements is not apparent at very low signal levels (i.e., the performance of the device can be predicted accurately for small signals by representing it with linear parameters), but at somewhat higher signal levels a linear theory is inadequate. Thus, it is common to represent such devices whenever possible by a *small-signal* theory that represents the device as being linear. Such an approximate theory gives great simplification in the analysis of the device as compared with that required for a large-signal, nonlinear analysis. In many nonlinear cases an accurate solution is feasible only by computer methods.

Reciprocity

A circuit has the property of reciprocity (to be defined below) if it is composed of linear, bilateral elements or if it can be simulated by a network of linear, bilateral elements. The term *linear, bilateral element* refers to a two-terminal element that has the same impedance properties regardless of the amplitude or polarity of the ac and dc components of applied voltage. Thus, ordinary resistors, coils, and condensers are of this sort. Circuits having the property of reciprocity are commonly called *reciprocal circuits*, although this term has been also used for dual circuits whose corresponding elements have values that are related by a specified reciprocal relationship. However, the former meaning will be understood in what follows.

Reciprocal circuits obey the *reciprocity theorem*. It says, in effect, that: *If a voltage or current source is placed at one location in a reciprocal circuit while the current or voltage response, respectively, is measured at another location in the circuit, if the locations of the driving source and measured response are interchanged, the measured response is the same.* This theorem is illustrated by Fig. 10. When the voltage source E is on the left, the current response at R_2 is indicated by I and the solid arrow on the right. Then if the voltage generator is moved to the right, the current I through R_1 is the same as the current which previously flowed through R_2. The theorem applies to a voltage source and a current response or to a current source and a voltage response, but not in general to a source and response of the same type. This is easily seen from Fig. 10 if we hypothesize the cases where $E = 5$ v, $I = 2$ amp, $R_1 = 15$ ohms, and $R_2 = 25$ ohms. With the generator at the left the response voltage across R_2 is $IR_2 = 50$ v; with the voltage generator moved to the right the response voltage across R_1 is $IR_1 = 30$ v. Thus, transfer impedances or admittances for transmission in opposite directions in a reciprocal circuit are the same, but transfer voltage or current ratios for transmission in opposite directions may not be the same.

The source voltage or current referred to in the reciprocity theorem is that of an idealized zero-impedance voltage generator or an idealized infinite-impedance current generator. In actual experiments, the generators used usually have finite internal impedances that must be accounted for in applying the theorem. Thus, again from Fig. 10, if E and $R_1 = 15$ ohms on the left represents the Thévenin equivalent circuit for the generator, when this generator is removed it must be replaced by a load having an impedance equal to the 15-ohm internal impedance of the generator. When the generator is moved to the right the $R_2 = 25$-ohm resistor must be removed and the generator inserted along with a 10-ohm resistor so as to give the generator an effective internal impedance of $R_2 = 25$ ohms. Under these conditions the reciprocity theorem applies.

The reciprocity theorem also applies to radiating systems except for certain cases where the medium of propagation is anisotropic or nonlinear. Thus, the reciprocity theorem applies to a voltage applied at one antenna and the induced current in a second antenna. As a consequence of this fact, the receiving and radiating patterns of a given antenna are the same.

An active network with negative resistances as the active elements are reciprocal, but an active network using typical vacuum-tube amplifier stages is not. Nonlinear circuits generally do not obey the reciprocity theorem partly because nonlinearities usually cause the elements to have different characteristics for one polarity of applied voltage than for the other. Also, the signal levels at the various nonlinear elements depend partly on the location of the gen-

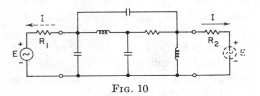

Fig. 10

erator, so that the nonlinear effects are different when the generator and measured response locations are reversed.

GEORGE L. MATTHAEI

Cross-references: *Amplifiers, Coupled Circuits, Equivalent Circuits, Filters, Laplace and Fourier Transforms, Network Synthesis, Nonlinear Circuits, Oscillators, Switching Circuits*

NEURISTOR

Neuristor, derived from "neuron," names a class of structures that exhibit *attenuationless* "signal" propagation, as in the propagation of the chemical burning zone along a simple fuze, or the propagation of the ionic discharge along a nerve axon. Distributed, "one-dimensional" electronic lines, exhibiting such propagation, can be synthesized; arbitrarily complex digital computer systems can be synthesized using such lines exclusively.

Attenuationless propagation does not violate energy conservation, since as the signal propagates, energy flows into the line. A line consists essentially of a distributed, triggerable, active element. When any portion of line is triggered, some or all of the locally available energy is converted into a form for triggering the next portion of line. Thus, in a chemical fuze, if the temperature anywhere exceeds threshold, combustion raises the local temperature enough to activate the next portion of line. A fuze cannot be re-used. The axon recovers after each discharge, and can be re-used indefinitely. Neuro-physiologists call the recovery time the "refractory period."

Neuristor lines can be synthesized in many ways. For example, in a "rechargeable" fuze, burning stops when the available energy is depleted, and recovery implies energy restoration. In an axon, discharge stops not because of energy depletion, but because of "inactivation" of the membrane. In both types, the recovering portion of line is refractive, requiring at least a minimum spacing between successive pulses. Even more

important, oppositely directed pulses are destroyed upon collision, since at that instant, the line is refractive on both sides of the collision point.

Two methods of interconnecting lines to form neuristor networks appear important: In a triggering junction, connected portions of two or more lines become simultaneously activated, as in a knot of fuzes; when a discharge arrives at the junction on any line, it generates a discharge on every connecting line. In a refractory junction, connected portions exhibit mutual refractoriness, but not mutual triggering. Thus, where two parallel lines meet in a refractory junction, one pulse on either line will pass the junction without initiating a pulse on the coupled line, but two pulses, one on each line, attempting to pass each other on the junction are destroyed, since the lines are mutually refractive. This provides a powerful logical inhibition function, which together with the "fan-out" capability of the triggering junction, provides full capability for digital logic synthesis.

Neuristors may be of particular interest in highly miniaturized logic systems because (1) only one "device" is necessary, and (2) nonplanar logic networks can be constructed in a plane, in the sense that lines can cross in a plane (cf. a railroad crossing) without signal interaction.

H. D. CRANE

Cross-references: *Neuron*

NEURON

Electronic and mathematical models of biological neurons are designed to duplicate logical and learning operations known (or postulated) to be functions of living nerve cells. Such functions include the ability to perform logical operations, and the ability to learn or modify nerve cell response based upon experience. Logical functions are known to be performed by some animal optic nerve fibers which, for example, respond only to a pattern of local convex illumination. Learning is exemplified by the classical conditioned reflex.

Certain properties of biological neurons make the above functions possible. A neuron may be considered a binary device, being either active or inactive at any instant. When active, the cell generates an electrical impulse which is transmitted down branching fibers to endings called *synaptic junctions* terminating on or near other nerve cells. When inactive, no signal occurs. A neuron becomes active whenever impulses arriving simultaneously at incoming synaptic junctions create a potential which exceeds the *threshold* of the cell. Synaptic junctions are either *excitatory* or *inhibitory*, depending upon whether they tend to cause or prevent cell activity. The synapse is postulated as the site of permanent memory, which consists of small changes in synaptic strength (or attenuation) occurring over large numbers of such junctions. The change occurs due to the relative activity of input (transmitting) and output (receiving) nerve cells.

Electronic neural models abstract and formalize the above properties. Binary cell states are assumed to change only at discrete time intervals, usually at a synchronous rate. Cells receive multiple inputs and produce outputs which drive a number of other cells. Each input is weighted (or attenuated) by a multiplicative factor corresponding to synaptic strength. The state of a neuron at any instant of time is determined by the state of its inputs and their weights at the previous instant. If the N binary input signals to a neuron are denoted by x_1, $x_2, \cdots x_N$, and synaptic weights by $W_1, W_2, \cdots W_N$, the model is considered to be active (e.g., $+1$) if

$$\sum_{i=0}^{N} W_i x_i \geq 0 \qquad (1)$$

and inactive (e.g., -1 or 0) otherwise. The threshold is represented by W_0 and an input x_0 which is always $+1$. Excitatory synapses are represented by positive weights, inhibitory by negative weights.

The input configurations, consisting of binary combinations of the variables x_1, $x_2 \cdots x_N$, may be regarded as patterns or as entries in a truth-table. The neuron response to each is a decision that the pattern either is or is not a member of some class.

Equation (1) corresponds to the definition of digital decision element circuits variously termed linear logic, summation or majority logic devices. If binary-valued input voltages, e_1, e_2, $\cdots e_N$ are applied to a summing circuit through conductances G_1, G_2, $\cdots G_N$, the sum voltage is

$$e_s = \frac{e_1 G_1 + e_2 G_2 + \cdots e_N G_N}{G_0 + G_1 + G_2 + \cdots G_N} = \sum_{i=1}^{N} e_i G_i' \quad (2)$$

If e_s drives a discriminating device (e.g., transistor switch) whose output is one value for $e_s \geq 0$, and another for $e_s < 0$, then (1) is mechanized. Linear logic elements for digital applications employing resistor weighting, as in the NOR circuit, restrict (1) to positive weights. Circuits in which weight is represented by turns on a magnetic core permit both positive and negative values. The diode AND and OR gate may also be regarded as a realization of (2) with, however, nonlinear conductances G_i.

Not all 2^{2^N} possible input-output relationships or classification schemes which can be specified for N input variables can be realized by single-stage neuron models. That is, the desired activity for each of 2^N configurations of input signals may be such that no solution exists for the weights W_i, under the conditions of (1). For example, with $N = 3$, only 104 of the possible $2^{2^3} = 256$ functions can be realized. If the values that can be assumed by the weights are restricted in any way (e.g., positive only), the number of realizable functions is further reduced. Finally, in the case of positive, equal, nonlinear weighting, as with diodes, only the functions AND and OR are realizable.

Learning on the part of a linear-logic neuron model is defined as convergence to a specified input-output relationship, starting from any other condition, based only upon the repeated occurrence of input configurations and corresponding desired responses. Learning can occur only when a solution exists for the weights W_i, given the input-output relationship and (1). The weighting components must possess the ability to change value according to certain rules, as follows. Let the solution for the weights be denoted by the vector $\mathbf{W}^*$, consisting of the elements W_0^*, W_1^*, $\cdots$ W_N^*. Let the kth input configuration be denoted by the vector $\mathbf{X}(k)$ composed of elements $x_1(k)$, $x_2(k)$, $\cdots$ $x_N(k)$, and the desired output by $D(k)$. Then by (1) the sign of $\mathbf{W}^* \cdot \mathbf{X}(k)$ must agree with the sign of $D(k)$. This may be written $\mathbf{W}^* \cdot \mathbf{X}'(k) > 0$ for all k, with $\mathbf{X}'(k) = \mathbf{X}(k)D(k)$. Thus the solution vector $\mathbf{W}^*$ possesses a positive projection upon all modified pattern vectors $\mathbf{X}'(k)$. The actual weight vector $\mathbf{W}$, consisting of weights W_0, W_1, $\cdots$ W_N, must therefore move toward a similar position. Various methods exist for giving $\mathbf{W}$ the required motion. It has been shown, for example, that increasing $\mathbf{W}$ in the direction of $\mathbf{X}'(k)$ whenever $\mathbf{W} \cdot \mathbf{X}'(k) < 0$, will produce the desired result. In terms of the individual elements of $\mathbf{W}$, this corresponds to changing W_i by an amount proportional to

$$\Delta W_i = x_i[D(k) - A(k)] \tag{3}$$

in which $A(k)$ is the actual output of the linear logic neuron model in response to the kth input pattern. The final value of W_i then becomes the integral of (3).

JOSEPH K. HAWKINS

Cross-references: *Computer Applications, Logic Circuits, Magnetic Cores, Medical Electronics, Neuristor*

NEUTRINOS

The neutrino is postulated as a fundamental elementary particle having zero charge, a mass less than 0.002 that of an electron, a spin of $\frac{1}{2}$, and following Fermi statistics. It was hypothesized in 1927 by Pauli who assumed it was created and emitted in processes involving electrons. The neutrino was postulated to account for the apparent loss of energy in the beta decay process. Microcalorimetric measurements of the heat given up in the beta decay process indicated that the effective energy in heating is the mean energy of the beta particles in its spectrum. It appeared, therefore, that an energy E_{max} was given up at each disintegration, but only a variable fraction of this energy was ever measured. A neutrino spectrum was postulated to account for this loss of energy, so that its spectrum is the inverse of the beta spectrum of a particular nuclear decay. In this way, the sum of the two spectra for any nuclear decay process is E_{max}. The neutrino, having no charge or appreciable mass, could not react with matter and, therefore, could not be measured in the calorimeter experiment.

Nuclei which have a large neutron excess, that is, a high neutron-to-proton ratio, tend to give beta emission. This is illustrated by the following equation: $n \rightarrow p + \beta^- + \eta$, showing the decay of a neutron in the nucleus to give a proton, an electron and a neutrino. Those nuclei which have a low neutron-to-proton ratio tend to be positron emitters and are characterized by the equation: $p \rightarrow n + \beta^+ + \eta$, showing the decay of a proton in a nucleus to give a neutron, a positron, and a neutrino. The process of K-capture, which is in competition with positron emission, is given by: $p + \beta^- \rightarrow n + \eta$. The neutrino would be emitted for the hypothetical positron capture given by: $n + \beta^+ \rightarrow p + \eta$.

The mass of the neutrino is taken into account in the following equation for negatron emission, where M_z and M_{z+1} are the initial and final nuclei in the beta decay: $\Delta E = (M_z - M_{z+1} - \eta)c^2$. Also, for positron emission, the mass of the neutrino enters into the equation: $\Delta E = (M_z - M_{z-1} - 2m_0 - \eta)c^2$. Thus, it is seen that the disintegration energy is shared between the electron and the neutrino. The sum of the energies of the electron and the neutrino is constant for each particular decay.

In 1956, Reines and Cowan of the Los Alamos Scientific Laboratory announced the experimental detection of the neutrino. Their apparatus consisted of more than 1000 gallons of hydrocarbons and water containing dissolved cadmium and a bank of 330 photomultiplier tubes. The source of neutrinos was a plutonium-producing reactor of the Atomic Energy Commission's Savannah River plant. The counting rate of detection was two or three neutrinos per hour.

JEROME BREWER

Cross-references: *Nucleonics*

NEUTRON DIFFRACTION

Since 1936, it has been known that neutrons, like electrons and x-rays, may be diffracted by crystals, and thus provide an additional technique for the analysis of the structures of solids. The first experiments utilized a radium-beryllium source of neutrons, which were by no means of constant velocity and hence of wavelength. With the development of nuclear reactors, neutrons have been made available in sufficient numbers to allow collimation into beams and segregations into narrow energy bands. Most of the neutron diffractometers are to be found in such laboratories as those at Argonne National Laboratory; Oak Ridge; Chalk River, Canada; and Harwell, England. As in the case of electrons, the equivalent wavelength λ of neutrons is given by $\lambda = h/mv$, where h is the Planck constant, and m and v are respectively the mass and velocity of the neutrons. If neutrons, after a number of collisions with atoms in a reactor at temperature T, escape from it, the root-mean square velocity is given by $\frac{1}{2}mv^2 = \frac{3}{2}kT$, where k is Boltzmann's constant. It follows that $\lambda^2 = h^2/3mkT$, and wavelengths are 1.55 Å at 0°C and 1.33 Å at 100°C.

The beam is "white" or contains many wavelengths with no characteristic spectra, as in the case of x-rays; it is monochromatized in accordance with the Bragg law $\lambda = 2d \sin \theta$, by means of a crystal with interplanar spacing, d, of planes parallel to the crystal surface. In order to assure a beam of "slow" or thermal neutrons, the beam is slowed with borated paraffin and of course detected and counted in a BF_3 (B^{10} isotope enriched) proportional counter, boron having a very high absorption coefficient.

The specimen, usually powder, is contained in an aluminum cylinder or box, since aluminum has a very low absorption coefficient. Thus a powder diffraction pattern is registered that is in many ways very similar to the corresponding x-ray diffraction patterns. There are important differences, however, as in the fact that the coherent neutron-scattering amplitude varies little with atomic number in contrast with proportionality to atomic number of x-ray scattering amplitude; but for many elements the absolute values are of the same order of magnitude within a factor of 10. For hydrogen and deuterium the neutron amplitudes are greater than those for x-rays—a fact that leads to one of the valuable contributions of neutron diffraction, namely, the ability to locate the positions of hydrogen atoms, which is usually not possible with x-rays.

Another difference lies in the vastly smaller absorption coefficients in crystals for neutrons than for x-rays, notable exceptions being boron, cadmium, gadolinium, and other rare earths. Much fundamental theoretical and experimental work has been devoted to the evaluation of nuclear cross sections with respect to effectiveness of neutron scattering. This cross section is measured in barns (1 barn $= 10^{-24}$ cm²). The total scattering cross section θ for the nucleus is the sum of two terms: $\theta = \Sigma + S$, where Σ is the cross section for coherent scattering, i.e., scattering that is coherent with that of other nuclei and that can produce interference, and S is the cross section for incoherent scattering.

Applications of neutron diffraction, based upon unique and significant information, are chiefly in three classes: (1) structural investigations of solids, which aim to discover the positions of light atoms, particularly hydrogen atoms and hydrogen bonds in electron density contour maps of hydrides, ice and salts, ammonium salts, and organic compounds; (2) problems such as are often met in alloy systems, which require a distinction to be made between atoms of neighboring atomic numbers, and which have closely similar scattering amplitudes for x-rays; and (3) investigations of magnetic materials, in which advantage is taken of the additional scattering of neutrons by atoms which possess magnetic moments.

Attention is called to an entirely different analytical application of thermal neutrons, namely, the activation of radioactive isotopes in samples irradiated with these neutrons, and the detection of these radioactive species with extreme sensitiveness. For this purpose, neutron activation cross-section values are also available that indicate to the analytical chemist the relative probability with which a given radioisotope will be formed when a substance is exposed to a source of neutrons.

GEORGE L. CLARK

Cross-references: *Electrons, Electron Diffraction and Scattering, Ion Scattering, Isotopes, Neutrons, Nucleonics, Radiation (Ionizing), X-rays*

NEUTRONS: see RADIATION (IONIZING)

NOISE CHARACTERIZATION AND MEASUREMENT

When describing the performance of an amplifier or an oscillator, one feature of vital interest is the amount of noise added to the signal in the amplification or generation process. The ultimate threshold sensitivity of the amplifier, for example, is a direct function of the amount of noise generated in the amplifier itself. It becomes imperative, therefore, to set up standards of description from which absolute sensitivity of an amplifier can be determined and comparisons of the relative merits of various amplifiers can be made.

Amplifier Noise

Currently, there are two figures of merit in popular use to describe the noise performance of an amplifier. One is called the *noise figure* of the amplifier, for which the symbol F is used, and the other is the effective *noise temperature*, or T_e of the amplifier. The latter description has evolved in recent years with the advent of the very low-noise microwave amplifiers such as the maser and parametric amplifier because it was generally felt that a more graphic representation was needed for these devices. The basic difficulty with the more widely accepted *noise figure* was its asymptotic approach to a value of unity for devices with very low noise.

The noise figure is defined as the ratio of the signal-to-noise power ratio at the input of the amplifier to that at the output:

$$F = \frac{S_{in}/N_{in}}{S_{out}/N_{out}} = \frac{N_{out}}{N_{in}S_{out}/S_{in}} \quad (1)$$

S_{out}/S_{in} is the power gain of the device, and N_{in} is the thermal noise power delivered by a matched source, and can be written

$$N_{in} = kTB \quad (2)$$

where k is Boltzmann's constant, T is the temperature of the source in degrees Kelvin, and B is the effective bandwidth of the amplifier.

For purposes of comparison, the noise figure must be referred to a standard source temperature which is taken to be 290°K. When the noise figure measurement is performed at some ambient or source temperature other than 290°K, it must be converted by use of the formula

$$F_0 = 1 + \frac{T_1}{T_0}(F_1 - 1) \quad (3)$$

where F_0 is the standard noise figure, F_1 is the measured noise figure, T_1 is the ambient temperature, and T_0 is the standard 290°K.

Returning to the definition of F, it is noted that the noise at the output of the amplifier can be written

$$N_{out} = GN_{in} + N_A$$

where G is the power gain and N_A the portion of the noise generated in the amplifier. Substituting this into (1) at $T = T_0$,

$$F_0 = 1 + \frac{N_A}{GkT_0B} \qquad (4)$$

Note that as N_A becomes very small with respect to kT_0B, as is the case for many of the new devices, the noise figure approaches unity asymptotically.

To circumvent this difficulty, the effective noise temperature T_e of an amplifier was defined as the internally generated noise power N_A of the amplifier referred to the input terminals, i.e., regarded as if it were excess noise present at the input terminals over and above the thermal noise coming in with the signal. It is defined by the equation

$$N_A = GkT_eB \qquad (5)$$

and is an absolute figure of merit in that it is independent of the specification of some reference temperature. The relation between noise figure and noise temperature is established by substituting (5) into (4), giving

$$F_0 = 1 + \frac{T_e}{T_0} \qquad (6)$$

The noise figure is usually expressed in decibels and the noise temperature in degrees Kelvin.

Another extremely useful concept is that of the *threshold sensitivity* of an amplifier. However, threshold sensitivity depends on the environment of the amplifier and therefore cannot be used as a figure of merit in the comparison of amplifiers. The threshold sensitivity is simply the minimum discernible signal power that can be detected in a particular application. It is usually taken to be that signal power which, at the output of the amplifier, is equal to the noise power output in the same situation. By combining (1) and (3), N_{out} and thus S_{min}, the threshold signal, are determined for the particular situation in which the thermal noise delivered with the signal is from a source with an apparent temperature T_1. In terms of noise figure of the amplifier, the minimum discernible signal is

$$GS_{min} = N_{out} = GkB[T_1 + T_0(F_0 - 1)] \qquad (7)$$

or, alternatively, in terms of noise temperature,

$$GS_{min} = N_{out} = GkB[T_1 + T_e] \qquad (8)$$

Note that for relatively noisy amplifiers (i.e., $F_0 \gg 1$ or $T_e \gg T_0$) the minimum discernible signal depends critically on the amplifier characteristics, whereas for very-low-noise amplifiers (i.e., $F_0 \approx 1$ or $T_e \ll T_0$), it is relatively insensitive to amplifier characteristics for normal values of T_1. Thus it is essential to know the environmental temperature T_1 in order to make a realistic estimate of the noise capabilities needed for an amplifier in a particular application.

Certain other factors also enter into the ultimate sensitivity of an amplifier in a particular application. Some of them are attenuation between the source and the amplifier, noise figure of amplifiers that follow the initial stage of amplification, or attenuation between the cascaded amplifiers. Mismatch or reflections at the various ports also adversely affect the sensitivity but will not be treated here.

When it is desired to find the composite noise figure of cascaded amplifiers that have known individual gains and noise figures, the basic noise-figure definition is applied as follows: Letting the gain and noise figure of the first and second amplifier be G_a and F_a, and G_b and F_b, respectively, the noise output of the cascaded amplifiers becomes

$$N_{ab} = G_aG_bkT_0B + (F_a - 1)G_aG_bkT_0B \\ + (F_b - 1)G_bkTB \qquad (9)$$

The first term represents the amplified input thermal noise, the second term the excess noise generated in the first amplifier and amplified in the second, and the third term the excess noise generated in the second amplifier. Substituting into (4) and rearranging, we obtain for the over-all noise figure of the cascaded amplifiers

$$F_{ab} = F_a + \frac{F_b - 1}{G_a} \qquad (10)$$

Note that for high G_a, the composite noise

figure is essentially determined by that of the first amplifier. A similar procedure will allow calculation of the noise figure of any number of cascaded amplifiers. The expression is readily converted to noise temperature through use of (6).

Familiarity with the somewhat subtle concept involved in attenuating noise is necessary for accurate determination of the overall noise performance of a system of amplifiers and attenuators. Since the networks under consideration are all matched and the addition of attenuation does nothing to upset the match, the noise power present at the input of the network following the attenuation must be at least kTB watts (T is the temperature of the attenuator) regardless of the amount of attenuation. Stated briefly, this means that only the excess noise above the thermal noise can be attenuated. If a source of noise generating $XkTB$ watts is fed to an attenuator having $10 \log L$ decibels of series attenuation, the noise power present at the output of the attenuator is given by

$$N = \frac{(X - 1)kTB}{L} + kTB \qquad (11)$$

Note that N approaches kTB as L approaches infinity. As a consequence of this unusual behavior, the attenuator cannot be designated as a stage with given gain and noise figure to be used in the cascaded networks formula; indeed, it is found that application of (1) to an attenuator yields an expression for noise figure that depends upon the level of incident noise.

To determine the effect of an attenuator on system sensitivity, it should be lumped with an adjacent amplifier to form a stage. Consider an amplifier with noise figure and gain F_a and G_a, respectively, followed by an attenuator having $10 \log L$ db of series attenuation. The composite gain is G_a/L and the noise power at the output, assuming kT_0B input noise, is

$$N_{aL} = \frac{(F_a G_a - 1)kT_0B}{L} + kT_0B \qquad (12)$$

applying (1), the composite noise figure is

$$F_{aL} = F_a + \left(\frac{L - 1}{G_a} \right) \qquad (13)$$

This expression is valid as long as $G_a/L > 1$. Consistent applications of such techniques allow evaluation of the ultimate sensitivity of any combination of system elements. Extreme care must be taken when elements involving loss (attenuators, mixers, converters, etc.) are considered.

Oscillator Noise. Since an oscillator generates not only a fixed frequency but also some noise sidebands, a measure of its quality is the relative purity of its output spectrum. In general, a good low-noise amplifier when used in an oscillator application also performs well as a low-noise oscillator. Since standards for noise output of oscillators are difficult to set up, absolute figures of merit as such for oscillators are not in common use.

Measurement of Amplifier Noise. Most methods for measuring noise figure or temperature of an amplifier make use of broadband standard noise sources which deliver a white noise spectrum whose level is very accurately determined. Temperature-limited diodes are generally used for frequencies below 1500 Mc; argon discharge lamps have become standard at higher frequencies. The excess noise above thermal noise of an argon source is given in db by

$$P_{excess} = 10 \log \left(\frac{T_D}{T_0} - 1 \right) = 15.28 \text{ db} \qquad (14)$$

where T_D is the temperature of the discharge.

The basis for several of the standard methods for measuring noise figure is obtained by rewriting (1) as follows:

$$F = \frac{\dfrac{S_{in} + N_{in}}{N_{in}} - 1}{\dfrac{S_0 + N_0}{N_0} - 1} \qquad (15)$$

the measurement is performed by feeding the output of the noise source into the amplifier as a signal, and noting that

$$\frac{S_{in} + N_{in}}{N_{in}} = \frac{T_D}{T_0} \tag{16}$$

and therefore the expression for noise figure is just

$$F = \frac{\left(\dfrac{T_D}{T_0} - 1\right)}{\dfrac{S_0 + N_0}{N_0} - 1} = \frac{\left(\dfrac{T_D}{T_0} - 1\right)}{\dfrac{P_0}{N_0} - 1} \tag{17}$$

P_0 is the noise power at the amplifier output measured with the source turned on and N_0 the noise power output with the source off. Thus the simple ratio of these two levels, which can be determined accurately with square-law detectors or suitable attenuator arrangements, serves to determine the noise figure completely. Several automatic noise figure meters are now commercially available which use the same basic measurement principle by square-wave modulating the noise source and appropriately measuring and displaying the amplitude of the noise pattern at the output of the amplifier.

D. C. FORSTER

Cross-references: See following entries; also *Masers, Parametric Amplification, Signal Fluctuation and Noise*

NOISE GENERATION

Noise generators are used primarily for the measurement of noise figure. This requires the generation of accurately known noise powers at very low levels (4×10^{-22} to 4×10^{-19} w/cps). It is a problem to measure such low levels of power. A useful noise source would be one whose noise output is directly related to a measurable quantity. A second useful type would be one whose output is essentially independent of operating conditions. Both types are discussed below. Noise diodes, resistors or transmission-line terminations, and gas-discharge tubes are the most commonly used noise sources.

An important noise-source characteristic is the level of the noise. A resistor operating at room temperature ($290°K$) has an available noise power per cycle of $kT_0 = 4 \times 10^{-21}$ w/cps. Noise sources are normally specified as to the amount of excess noise. Thus a source whose total noise output was $11 \times kT_0$ would be specified as having 10 db of excess noise or

EXCESS NOISE = 10 log (Available

source noise $- kT_0)/kT_0$

Another important characteristic is the ability to control the noise output on an on-off basis. This ability is important in noise-figure measurements. Factors affecting the accuracy of the noise-source output are considered below.

Resistors or Terminations. The noise output of a resistor or termination is determined by its temperature. In order to know the noise power accurately it is necessary to measure its temperature accurately. Another means is to immerse the termination in a liquid of accurately known temperature, such as liquid helium. The termination has to be connected to a device at room temperature to be useful. If the accuracy is not to be degraded the termination must be at a uniform temperature. For highest accuracy, corrections for the losses in the temperature-transition region must be calculated and depend on the specific conditions. The noise output is flat with frequency to the extent that the termination is flat with frequency. Switching must be accomplished by mechanical means to achieve any useful speed.

Cold terminations are used in measuring very-low-noise devices where a higher noise termination would tend to mask the device noise.

Hot terminations are most commonly used as a primary standard by organizations such as the U. S. National Bureau of Standards in the calibration of noise sources.

Thermionic Diodes. Thermionic diodes operated temperature limited make excellent noise sources at the lower frequencies. The excess noise is 10 log ($20\, I_{DC}\, R$) where I_{DC} is the plate current in milliamps and R is the load in ohms across which the noise voltage is developed; I and R can be measured very accurately.

Two effects limit the frequency to which noise diodes are useful. One effect is the plate-to-cathode capacity and the lead inductance combination, which limit the 5722 diode to about 100 Mc where the excess noise has increased by an amount of the order of 0.15 db. The L1262A noise diode is designed such that when properly matched at the 50-ohm level it operates to 600 Mc with the same order of accuracy. In this case the second limiting factor, transit time, compensates for the lead inductance and capacity effects. A coaxial diode (TT-1) is available that operates up to 3000 Mc. At this frequency the theoretical correction is about a 3-db reduction in noise from transit-time effects.

There is no switching problem with diodes as it is just a matter of switching the diode plate voltage. This makes them very useful in noise-figure measurements.

As a practical matter noise diodes are useful to frequencies around 500 Mc. With the exercise of proper precautions they make very accurate noise sources. In addition they have the advantage that the noise is directly related to the current. They make a very inexpensive noise source but for a reasonable life cannot generate as much noise as a gas discharge noise source. They are also limited in the peak rf power that they can withstand.

Gas-Discharge Tubes. The gas-discharge noise source is one whose noise output is essentially independent of operating conditions. For those unfamiliar with the devices, they are essentially like fluorescent lights (*q.v.*). Actually fluorescent lamps make quite good noise sources, although they are temperature sensitive, as the vapor pressure of mercury is a function of temperature.

Argon and neon are the most commonly used gases for gas-discharge noise sources. The noise output can be varied somewhat in the manufacture of the device by controlling the gas pressure and diameter of the

glass tube. Most argon noise sources are currently specified as 15.2 ± 0.5 db and most neon noise sources as 18.0 ± 0.5 db. The actual variation from tube to tube is more nearly 0.1 to 0.2 db. National Bureau of Standards is currently working to determine the noise output level more accurately by comparison measurements with a hot load.

Operating conditions have little effect on the noise output. The tubes operate at currents from 100 to 200 ma and the noise varies about 0.004 db/ma for argon and about 0.007 db/ma for neon. The noise output is very flat with frequency and limited only by the ability to couple rf to the discharge. One noise tube is used in different rf structures as a noise generator from 200 Mc to 12 kMc.

In the frequency range from 200 to 4000 Mc the gas-discharge tube is normally placed inside a helix that serves as the rf coupling structure. A single co-ax source covers this frequency range with some correction for insertion loss at the high- and low-frequency ends.

The other most common type of noise source uses waveguide as the rF coupling structure. In this case the tube is inserted into the guide in the E plane at about a 10° angle to the axis of propagation. Such sources provide flat noise output over the full waveguide band with proper design.

For a gas discharge noise source the noise output may be a function of the rf insertion loss with the discharge off and with the discharge on. This is normally a small correction. The

EXCESS NOISE CORRECTION

$$= 10 \log \left[\frac{\alpha_s}{\alpha_c + \alpha_s} \right] [1 - e^{-2(\alpha_c + \alpha_s) l}]$$

where α_c is the cold-loss constant and $\alpha_h = \alpha_c + \alpha_s$ is the hot-loss constant; l is the coupling length.

Gas discharge sources are normally used from 200 Mc to about 4 kMc in co-ax and are currently commercially available to about 50 kMc in waveguide mounts. They can be readily switched, are relatively inexpensive, have good accuracy, have relatively high noise output, and can withstand relatively high rf power.

HOWARD C. POULTER

Cross-references: *Fluorescent Lights, Gases, Noise Characterization and Measurement. Noise in Semiconductors, Noise (Statistical Theory), Noise (Thermal), Resistors*

NOISE IN ELECTRON BEAMS

An electron beam is a stream of electrons with a velocity distribution that is small compared with its average velocity and has a cross section of linear dimension that is small compared with the length of the stream. Electron beams are used in microwave amplifiers and oscillators, such as traveling-wave tubes, klystrons, backward-wave tubes of the O and M types, and beam-type parametric amplifiers. Here, we shall discuss the noise in beams as it affects the performance of these tubes.

In low-level amplifiers, the noise in the electron beam gives rise to output noise additive to the signal. In oscillators it may also cause phase and amplitude modulations of the signal. The common sources of noise in all of these tubes may be described as follows:

(1) The electrons are emitted from the cathode randomly in time. The number of electrons emitted within any time interval of given length is distributed according to a Poisson distribution. The emission from different areas of the cathode is uncorrelated.

(2) The electrons are emitted at different velocities. The velocity distribution is Maxwellian for thermonic emission from a properly processed low-noise cathode.

The fluctuations in the current and velocity distribution as they exist in the stream leaving the cathode may be modified through the action of a potential minimum that is present in all low-noise guns that operate in the space-charge-limited regime. A potential minimum lowers the noise to a value below that which would be observed under temperature-limited emission, at frequencies below the plasma frequency at the potential minimum. Above this frequency, it does not possess this noise-smoothing effect.

It is believed that further modification of the noise in the beam may occur in the region just beyond the potential minimum where the electrons travel at a low average velocity compared with the velocity fluctuations in the beam.

Consider O-type (longitudinal-beam) tubes, in which the electron motion is predominantly rectilinear (along the beam axis) and the circuit fields couple, for the most part, to the axial motion of the beam. A beam of moderate space charge drifting at a constant velocity with no impressed rf circuit fields propagates space-charge waves as a result of the space-charge forces between electrons and the inertia of the electrons. All of these waves have group velocities in the direction of the dc beam velocity. Among these space-charge waves, the two that are of lowest order have the largest rf current for a given energy. For thin beams used in low-noise tubes these two waves are the most important ones because they couple most strongly to any circuit surrounding the beam. One of these waves has a phase velocity larger than the dc velocity of the beam and is called the "fast" wave, the other has a phase velocity smaller than the dc beam velocity and is called the "slow" wave. When the fast wave is excited on the beam, the energy carried by the beam is higher than that in the unexcited beam; when the slow wave is excited the energy transported by the beam is lowered. A microwave circuit with power gain has to couple more strongly to the slow wave so that the energy transported by the beam at the exit of the tube is lower than that carried by the entering beam. From considerations based on energy conservation, it can be shown that strong coupling of the circuit to the slow space-charge wave calls for correspondingly strong coupling to the circuit of an excitation in the slow wave. This coupling establishes fundamentally the limiting noise performance attainable with a given beam.

The noise emerging from the electron gun excites the fast and slow space-charge waves in the drift region following the electron gun. If the beam drifts freely without applied rf fields, the spatial beat between the space-charge waves leads to periodic variations with distance in the rms longitudinal noise current. Such variations were first predicted by J. R. Pierce and measured by C. C. Cutler and C. F. Quate. The velocity fluctuations also vary periodically with distance, the maximum velocity fluctuation occurring where the minimum rms current is found, and vice versa.

The relative excitations of the fast and slow space-charge waves may be changed within limits by adjustments in the average velocity of the beam before its entry into the drift region. Guns used for low-noise beams have several electrodes between the cathode and anode which control the potential at the beam position for the purpose of effecting such changes in the average beam velocity.

In general, the amplifier rf structure couples to both space-charge waves. However, coupling to the slow wave is essential if gain is to be achieved. Therefore, coupling to noise in the slow wave is unavoidable. The least amount of noise associated with the slow wave, which cannot be removed by cancellation with correlated noise in the fast waves, is at any particular frequency proportional to $\frac{1}{2}(S - \Pi)$, where S and Π are parameters determined entirely by the interaction in the multivelocity region of the electron gun. After the beam has passed the potential minimum, the value of S-Π cannot be lowered by any dc operation or by linear (small-signal) rf operations predominantly affecting the axial motion of the beam. The optimum (lowest) achievable excess noise figure of a longitudinal beam amplifier is

$$F_{opt} = 1 + \left(1 - \frac{1}{G}\right) \frac{2\pi}{kT_0} (S - \Pi)$$

where G is the available gain, T_0 is the standard temperature, and k is Boltzmann's constant. The ways in which S-Π can be reduced in the multivelocity region of the gun are not entirely understood and are still being studied.

The limiting noise figure is achieved only if all other sources of noise, such as beam interception (partition) noise, noise of secondary electrons and electrons reflected from the collector, and thermal noise from circuit losses are negligible. In experimental tubes these sources of noise can be made small compared with the beam noise. The recent terminal noise figures on high-gain tubes at S-band are 2.6 db, reported by B. D. Israelsen and E. W. Kinaman, and 2.5 db reported by G. Hodowanec and H. J. Wolkstein.

A similar principle is active in all strictly linear beam amplifiers that have transverse, as well as longitudinal, rf motion and beams with curved dc trajectories. The excitation of the slow waves always leads to a decrease of the beam energy flow, and amplification is always achieved by means of coupling to a slow wave. The intrinsic noise from the slow wave cannot be removed by dc or linear rf operations on the beam. This noise sets the lower limit on the noise performance of the tube. The only low-noise amplifier employing coupling to the transverse motion of the electron beam that has been built so far is a UHF amplifier with a noise figure of 6 db, reported by Robert Adler.

Noise in high-perveance, high-current longitudinal beams may not be explained in such simple terms. It has been found experimentally that the rms noise current in a longitudinal beam grows as a function of distance to values that are many times those of shot noise. The only explanation at the present time attributes this effect to amplification resulting from beam scalloping and cross-modulation effects when large-amplitude saturation sets in. Since high-perveance, high-current beams are not used in low-noise tubes, this phenomenon has not been studied exhaustively.

Similar effects occur in crossed-field devices and are heralded by the onset of large sole currents. The magnitude of the observed noise has not yet been explained by any known gain mechanism. Crossed-field devices are not used as low-noise amplifiers, but the large noise observed at times may lead to undesirable noise modulations of the output signal.

Amplifiers that excite the beam with a large (pump) excitation at a frequency higher than the signal frequency do not depend upon coupling to a slow wave for achieving gain and can couple to a fast wave instead. The noise can (in principle) be completely removed from fast waves. Adler has reported a noise figure of 0.6 db at 500 Mc and at 900 Mc achieved with amplifiers that have a quadrupole pumping field and coupling to the fast cyclotron wave. Quite recently, A. Ashkin has measured an effective input noise temperature T_e of 58° K ± 10° on a similar amplifier at 4 kMc. The noise bandwidth (the bandwidth within which T_e is less than 116° K) was 14 Mc. The beam parametric amplifiers tend to have a rather narrow bandwidth.

HERMANN A. HAUS

Cross-references: *Backward-Wave Tubes, Electron Guns, Klystron, Noise Characterization and Measurement, Noise in Vacuum Tubes, Traveling-Wave Tubes*

NOISE IN SEMICONDUCTORS

Noise in semiconductor material is of a threefold nature: (a) Like metallic conductors these materials show thermal noise, determined by the absolute temperature T and the (differential) resistance R of the sample; (b) spontaneous fluctuations in gain or loss of free charge carriers (electrons and holes) in any volume element or at the surface or junction boundaries cause the current through the specimen to fluctuate; and (c) noise may occur owing to carrier fluctuations which are not (themselves) spontaneous but are induced by some other random mechanism (modulation noise).

Thermal noise. According to Nyquist's formula the spectral intensity of the mean-square open-voltage fluctuations in a bandwidth Δf is $\overline{v^2} = 4kTR\Delta f$, or for the short-circuited current fluctuations $\overline{i^2} = 4kTG\Delta f$. Though strictly valid only in thermal equilibrium this formula appears to hold also when a current is passed through the sample and even in photoconductors which are strongly illuminated; T and R refer to operating conditions. In bulk semiconductors thermal noise is attributed to velocity fluctuations of the charge carriers arising from scattering within conduction and valence bands. It is also called *Brownian* noise or *Johnson* noise. In junction diodes and transistors the Nyquist formula appears to be the limiting form shot noise takes when the external (or net) current through these devices becomes zero. Hence, in these cases thermal noise is not additional to the noises discussed below, except for the small (mean-square) voltage generators that have to be inserted in series with ohmic parts of the device, e.g., $4kTR_{bb}'\Delta f$ in series with the base resistance of a transistor.

Generation-recombination noise, shot noise, diffusion noise are all forms of "electronic noise" which partially overlap. In bulk material the carrier densities fluctuate owing to the statistical nature of the generation, recombination and trapping processes involved. In photoconductors part of these fluctuations may be traced back to the fluctuations in the incident radiation field (photo-induced g-r noise). In semiconductors g-r noise is essentially thermal in origin and can be calculated from irreversible thermodynamics or from the kinetic equations for injected carriers, which can also be represented by an equivalent electrical circuit. The carrier density fluctuations give rise to conductivity fluctuations and these in turn to current fluctuations. If the generation-recombination process can be expressed with a single relaxation time (life time) τ, then the noise is of the form $\overline{i^2} = 4I^2\alpha\tau\Delta f/ n_0(1 + \omega^2\tau^2)$ where $\omega = 2\pi f$ and α is a number depending on such factors as the mobility ratio, the carrier ratio p_0/n_0, and the fractional ionization degree of donor and acceptor levels. Appreciable g-r noise occurs only in close to intrinsic materials or in some extrinsic materials mostly at low temperatures. It may determine the detection limits of infrared photoconductive cells like gold-doped germanium at 77°K and PbS at room temperature and below. Minimum detectable radiation intensities are often ranging from $10^{-10} - 10^{-12}$ w for a detector area of 1 cm². When surface recombination or sweep-out of carriers occurs, ambipolar diffusion noise may modify and complement the g-r noise.

In semiconductor devices containing p-n junctions the nature of the noise is the same but the effect is quite different. G-r fluctuations and diffusion of minority carriers (e.g., holes in the base region of a p-n-p transistor) manifest themselves only in the current flowing through the external circuit by means of their effect on the injected current pulses across the junction from areas immediately adjacent to the junction. Therefore, a picture may be given in which we deal only with the currents flowing across the junction, quite analogous to shot noise in vacuum tubes. Those parts of these currents which are carried off at the electrodes at the next region show full shot noise according to Schottky's formula; however, injected carriers which subsequently escape across the next junction or return to their region of origin by diffusion cause additional noise at high frequencies since diffusion is a relatively slow process. The effect is related to the high frequency conductance G of the junction and in transistors also to the hf current amplification factor α. The noise can be represented by a voltage generator in series with the emitter junction $\overline{v_e{}^2} = (4kTG_e - 2eI_e)|Z_e|^2$, a current generator in parallel to the collector

$$\overline{i_c{}^2} = 2\,e(I_c - |\,\alpha\,|^2 I_e)\Delta f,$$

and a cross correlation which is small for low frequencies; the subscripts e and c refer to emitter and collector, and Z_e is the emit-ter junction impedance. Trapping in the emitter junction may cause additional noise. The noise figure is of the usual form $F = A + BR_s + C/R_s$, where R_s is the source resistance. If the transistor is fed from a low impedance source it is advantageous to operate at relatively large emitter currents (a few milliamperes); for high impedance sources I_e should be small (microamperes).

In tunnel diodes forward and reverse currents give independently full shot noise though some anomalies have been observed.

Modulation noise. Semiconducting bars as well as semiconducting devices often show a large amount of noise that can be roughly expressed by $\overline{i^2} = A I^\beta \Delta f/f^\gamma$ where $\beta \simeq 2$ and $\gamma \simeq 1$. The origin of this "$1/f$ noise" (or flicker noise) is not understood in its details. With improvement of surface conditions this noise has gradually gone down; in many transistors it does no longer show up above ~ 1 kc and in homogeneous bulk specimen it often appears only below 10 cps. "Slow-surface states" and at times dislocation lines have been made responsible for the very low frequencies exhibited by this noise. From experiments in a magnetic field (Hall noise) it was found that the majority carriers mainly contribute to the noise, though other experiments still cast doubt on this fact. In diodes and transistors the $1/f$ noise may be represented by generators $\overline{v_e{}^2}$ and $\overline{i_c{}^2}$ as for shot noise; however, in contrast to shot noise these generators are nearly fully correlated. Poor contacts or granular materials like carbon resistors may generate a large amount of noise which is also of a $1/f$ nature and which may still be observable at 1 Mc. Temperature fluctuations and random impurity diffusion are other examples of modulating mechanisms.

K. M. VAN VLIET

Cross-references: *Brownian Motion, Noise Characterization and Measurement, Semiconductors*

NOISE IN VACUUM TUBES

Noise in vacuum tubes, as in other electron devices, is a designation for the unwanted fluctuations of voltage or current that interfere with the desired signal. The fluctuations of importance to this discussion are the ones introduced by the tube itself, and especially those having a generally random character. Thus spurious oscillations, which introduce one or more interferences of substantially single frequency, are not generally included under this heading. Microphonics, introduced by the vibration of certain tube elements, or other mechanical sources of disturbance such as loose connections, may introduce quasi-random interferences and so are sometimes included in this subject, but are most frequently considered separately as the remedies are in mechanical design.

The sources of noise in vacuum tubes which have true statistically random properties, and which are most often of concern are the following:

(1) Shot noise in the emitted current.

(2) Partition noise arising when a portion of the current is collected.

(3) Ion noise arising from residual gas which is ionized by collision with the electrons.

(4) Secondary-emission noise arising from statistical fluctuations in any important secondary-emission current.

(5) Flicker noise in vacuum tubes at relatively low frequencies.

(6) Induced-grid noise in space-charge-controlled tubes at relatively high frequencies.

(7) Very large excess noises of unknown origin found in crossed-field (magnetron) type tubes.

The phenomenon of *shot noise* is in a sense the most fundamental and most accurately predicted of the above-listed sources. Pure shot noise arises because the emission of electrons from a cathode is a statistical phenomenon, so that instantaneous currents fluctuate in random fashion about the average. These fluctuations give rise to measurable rf currents or voltages in any finite bandwidth. The phenomenon was predicted

by W. Schottky in 1918, and is expressed by the formula

$$\overline{i^2} = 2eIB$$

where $\overline{i^2}$ is the mean-square fluctuation current measurable in bandwidth B when average current I is flowing, and e is the electronic charge, 1.59×10^{-19} coulomb. The above is measurable in a diode, triode, or multielement tube operating under temperature-limited conditions, if there are no other complications from the other sources of noise listed.

If a cathode is space-charge limited, as it generally is in grid-controlled tubes, the shot noise is appreciably modified by the space-charge effects (*q.v.*) because of a smoothing or compensation effect occurring at the potential minimum. This smoothing is a very significant phenomenon, reducing noise to only a few percent of the pure-shot value given above. This effect is often expressed by multiplying the pure-shot noise formula above by a smoothing factor Γ^2, where Γ^2 lies typically between 0.02 and 0.05. An approximate and more convenient formula for the space-charge smoothed noise in a diode, triode, or other space-charge-controlled device is

$$\overline{i^2} = 0.644 \, (4kT_c gB)$$

where T_c is cathode temperature, k is Boltzmann's constant (1.38×10^{-23} joule/°K) and g is the transconductance of the multielement tube or small signal conductance of the diode.

Both of the above equations apply at frequencies low enough so that the transit time of electrons across the device is a negligible fraction of a period of the rf effects under consideration. Values of measured shot noise are also modified by transit-time effects when the transit time is comparable with a period of the frequency components of interest. This phenomenon is relatively complicated and the effects depend upon the type of tube being considered as well as the particular current studied. However, at very high frequencies it can be said that the transit-time effects nullify the effects of space-charge smoothing and noise approaches at least the pure-shot value given above.

Shot noise also excites noise waves along an electron beam and thereby introduces interference into the circuit of such beam-type devices as traveling-wave tubes, klystrons, or magnetron amplifiers. (These phenomena are discussed in detail in the article on Noise in Electron Beams.) It should be noted, however, that the beams of crossed-field (magnetron) type devices may have noise powers many orders of magnitude higher than the pure-shot level, as noted in item (7) above. The reasons for this finding are not now very clear, but it is known that the large excess noises of this type occur when the transverse magnetic field is near a space-charge-limited cathode, and appear to be eliminated when the cathode is either temperature limited, or shielded from the transverse magnetic field.

Partition or interception noise is introduced when a portion of the current is collected on some intercepting electrode, with the remainder passing on to be used in the device. This phenomenon results from the fact that the capture of electrons just grazing the electrode is a statistical phenomenon because of the random velocities of these electrons. The classical low-frequency formula for the noise to the nth element of a multielement device when current is collected on several of the elements is as follows:

$$\overline{i_n^2} = \left[1 - \frac{I_n}{I} (1 - \Gamma^2) \right] 2eI_n B$$

where I_n is the dc current to that element, I is the total emitted current, and other quantities are as in the formula for space-charge-reduced shot noise given above. It is to be noted that if either the space-charge smoothing factor Γ^2 approaches unity, or if the current I_n to the electrode of consideration is a small part of the total current, the noise to that electrode approaches pure shot-noise value. Partition noise is also very much complicated by transit-time effects at

high frequencies, and only approximate theories for these effects have been worked out.

Of the other sources of noise, *ion noise* arises because collision ionization is also a statistical phenomenon, but this source can be reduced to unimportant levels by proper vacuum techniques. *Secondary-emission* noise arises because that source of emission is also statistical. It is of course a fundamental phenomenon in devices such as photomultipliers using this type of emission. However, as secondary emission is suppressed in most other vacuum devices, the noise sources from it are likewise of lesser importance. *Induced-grid noise* is a phenomenon of importance in grid-controlled tubes operating in the transit-time regime, and results from the transit-time-induced grid currents. These currents produce noise voltages by virtue of the grid circuit impedance, and in turn modulate the beam with additional noise.

The *flicker effect* is an important and limiting source of noise in audio, sub-audio, and dc amplifiers, yielding noise powers much greater than the pure-shot value in these ranges. The power from this source is approximately inversely proportional to frequency, so that it is not of much importance above the audio range. The theory of the phenomenon is not completely understood, but Schottky ascribed the effect to foreign atoms arriving at and departing from the emitting surface with random times spent at the surface. Other theories have stressed additional random changes in the surface conditions of the emitter, and as in Schottky's theory can predict spectra approximately as observed. Thus the phenomenon may include a variety of surface effects of the above types.

The noise introduced by the vacuum tube from all of the above sources is generally characterized by the noise figure, which is the signal-to-noise ratio at the input of the device (in power) divided by the signal-to-noise ratio at the output. Noise figures less than 1 db are attainable at the lower rf frequencies, and of a few decibels in the microwave range. The noise behavior of grid-controlled tubes is also sometimes characterized by a "noise-equivalent resistance." This is the value of a fictitious resistance which, if introduced between cathode and control grid, would add thermal noise equal to the noise actually introduced by the tube. Values of this resistance may vary from a few hundred to several thousand ohms. Pentodes and tetrodes, in this class of tubes, are generally much noisier than triodes because of partition and secondary-emission noise introduced by the collected currents on the positive grids.

A very complete discussion of most of the above sources, plus excellent bibliographies, are given in L. D. Smullin and H. A. Haus, eds., *Noise in Electron Devices*, Wiley, 1959.

J. R. WHINNERY

Cross-references: *Noise Characterization and Measurement, Noise Generation, Noise in Electron Beams, Noise (Statistical Theory), Noise (Thermal), Secondary Emission, Space-Charge Instabilities, Thermionic Emission*

NOISE (STATISTICAL THEORY)

The statistical properties of noise vary widely with the type of noise. For example, the statistics of noise due to randomly occurring clicks are quite different from those of the roar of a large waterfall. For the sake of convenience, we shall speak of the noise as a voltage $v(t)$.

A record of $v(t)$, say a long oscillogram, may be analyzed to obtain various statistical properties of the noise. However, such a record is not usually available, or even if it is, one may wish to compare it with theory. In any case it is desirable to have a mathematical model of the noise, i.e., an expression for $v(t)$ containing random variables as parameters. An example is the shot-noise representation,

$$v(t) = \sum_{k=-\infty}^{\infty} F(t - t_k) \qquad (1)$$

where $F(t)$ is the response to an event, say

an electron arrival of the plate of a diode, occurring at time 0, and t_k is the time of occurrence of the kth event. The events are assumed to occur independently at random (more precisely, they form a Poisson process). An important result associated with (1) is Campbell's theorem,

$$\bar{v} = \text{ave. } v(t) = \nu \int_{-\infty}^{\infty} F(t)\, dt$$

$$\sigma^2 = \text{ave. } [v(t) - \bar{v}]^2 = \nu \int_{-\infty}^{\infty} F^2(t)\, dt \qquad (2)$$

where ν is the expected number of events per second.

The averaging process indicated in (2) may be performed in two ways, either (i) over time t with the arrival times t_k fixed or (ii) regarding the t_k's as random variables and averaging over them at a fixed time t. These are special cases of "time" and "ensemble" averages, respectively. Experimentally observed noise statistics are generally time averages of some sort. On the other hand, when one is given a representation for $v(t)$, ensemble averages are usually easier to compute. For a wide class of noises there are good reasons for assuming the two types of averages to be equal (the "ergodic hypothesis") unless $v(t)$ contains periodic or other terms which make the ensemble average vary with t. Even in the second case, ensemble averages are informative.

Power Spectrum. As its name indicates, the power spectrum measures the distribution of the noise power over the frequency range from zero to infinity. Imagine a noise voltage $v(t)$ to be composed of a great many sinusoidal components as suggested by its Fourier series expansion for a long period $(0,T)$ of time. Suppose further that $v(t)$ is applied to a resistance of 1 ohm. Each component of the resulting current dissipates its share of power, and the total power dissipated is the sum of the powers dissipated by the components. From the theory of Fourier series the nth component is

$$a_n \cos \omega_n t + b_n \sin \omega_n t, \quad \omega_n = 2\pi nt/T \qquad (3)$$

Its frequency is $f_n = n/T$ and, from $a_n -$

$ib_n = 2S(f_n,T)/T$, its average power is $2 | S(f_n,T) |^2 T^{-2}$ where

$$S(f,T) = \int_0^T v(t) \exp(-2\pi i f t)\, dt \qquad (4)$$

The power spectrum $w(f)$ of $v(t)$ is then given by the limit of

$w(f)\Delta(f)$ = Average power dissipated by all components in the narrow frequency band $[f - (\Delta f/2), f + (\Delta f/2)]$.

In taking the limit, the period length T is first made infinite, so that the number (approximately $T\Delta f$) of components in Δf becomes infinite, and then Δf is made to approach 0. Recasting the same argument in terms of Fourier integrals leads to

$$w(f) = \lim_{\Delta f \to 0} \lim_{T \to \infty} \frac{1}{\Delta f} \int_{f-(\Delta f/2)}^{f+(\Delta f/2)} \frac{2 | S(f',T) |^2}{T}\, df' \qquad (5)$$

When a representation for $v(t)$ is given, such as (1) for shot-noise, $w(f)$ may be computed from

$$w(f) = \lim_{T \to \infty} \langle 2 | S(f,T) |^2 T^{-1} \rangle \qquad (6)$$

where $\langle \ \rangle$ denotes the ensemble average obtained by averaging over the random parameters in the representation.

A second approach to the power spectrum avoids the difficulties associated with the limiting processes in (5) by defining it as

$$w(f) = 4 \int_0^\infty \psi(\tau) \cos 2\pi f \tau\, d\tau \qquad (7)$$

Here $\psi(\tau)$ is the autocorrelation function of $v(t)$, i.e., the time average of $v(t)v(t + \tau)$, with τ held fixed. Equation (7) and its inverse,

$$\psi(\tau) = \int_0^\infty w(f) \cos 2\pi f \tau\, df \qquad (8)$$

are known as the Wiener-Khintchine relations. The definition (7) is suggested when Parseval's theorem from the theory of Fourier integrals is applied to $S(f,T)$.

In many cases the easiest way to compute $w(f)$ is to compute $\psi(\tau)$ first and then take its Fourier transform (q.v.) to obtain $w(f)$.

When a representation for $v(t)$ is known, one may compute the autocovariance $\langle v(t)$ $v(t + \tau) \rangle$ by averaging over the ensemble with t and τ held fixed. Then $\psi(\tau)$ is given by the time average of $\langle v(t)v(t + \tau) \rangle$. Often the autocovariance is independent of t and gives $\psi(\tau)$ directly.

Gaussian Noise. Most of the theory of noise is concerned with an idealized type called "Gaussian noise." Shot noise in vacuum tubes and resistance noise are generally assumed to be Gaussian. Gaussian noise may be regarded as the limit of shot noise, represented by (1), when the expected number ν of events per second becomes infinite.

When ν is small the individual responses or pulses $F(t - t_k)$ in (1) tend to stand out by themselves and the shot noise becomes "impulse noise." When ν is large there is much overlapping of the individual responses, many terms in (1) contribute appreciably to $v(t)$ at a given time, and the distribution of $v(t)$ tends to be Gaussian (i.e., normal) by virtue of the central limit theorem of probability.

For Gaussian noise with power spectrum $w(f)$ the probability density of $v(t)$ is

$$p(v) = (2\pi\sigma)^{-1/2} \exp[-v^2/(2\sigma^2)] \qquad (9)$$

$$\sigma^2 = \overline{v^2(t)} = \psi(0) = \int_0^\infty w(f)\, df \qquad (10)$$

The second and higher order probability densities are also Gaussian. For example, the probability that $v < v(t) < v + dv$ and $u < v(t + \tau) < u + du$ when t is selected at random is $du\, dv$ times

$$p(u,v) = (2\pi\sigma^2)^{-1}(1 - \rho^2)^{-1/2} \exp\left[\frac{-u^2 - v^2 + 2\rho u v}{2\sigma^2(1 - \rho^2)}\right]$$

where σ^2 is given by (10) and

$$\rho\sigma^2 = \psi(\tau) = \int_0^\infty w(f) \cos 2\pi f \tau\, df.$$

It is sometimes convenient to represent Gaussian noise as the sum

$$v(t) = \sum_{n=1}^\infty c_n \cos(\omega_n t + \varphi_n) \qquad (11)$$

where $\omega_n = 2\pi f_n$, $f_n = n\Delta f$, $c_n{}^2 = 2w(f_n)\Delta f$, and the φ_n's are independent random phase angles distributed uniformly over $(0,2\pi)$.

The representation (11) shows that when Gaussian noise is passed through a filter the output is still Gaussian with an altered power spectrum. This follows from the fact that the sum of φ_n and the phase shift produced by the filter is a new random angle which is again distributed uniformly over $(0,2\pi)$, and can play the role of a new ϕ_n.

In many technical applications one is interested not only in the fraction of time $v(t)$ exceeds v, namely

$$P(v) = \int_v^\infty p(x)\,dx \qquad (12)$$

where $p(x)$ is given by (9), but also in the number of times N_v per second $v(t)$ crosses upward across the level v. By working with the joint probability density of $v(t)$ and its time derivative $v'(t)$ one can show that

$$N_v = N_0 \exp\,[-v^2/(2\sigma^2)],$$

$$N_0 = \frac{1}{2\pi}\left[\frac{-\psi''(0)}{\psi(0)}\right]^{1/2} = \sigma^{-1}\left[\int_0^\infty f^2 w(f)\,df\right]^{1/2} \quad (13)$$

where $\psi''(\tau)$ is the second derivative of the autocorrelation function $\psi(\tau)$. As an example, take $w(f) = w_0$ for $0 \le f \le f_b$ and $w(f) = 0$ for $f > f_b$. Then (10) gives $\sigma^2 = w_0 f_b$ and from (13) it is seen that the expected number of zeros per second of $v(t)$ is $2N_0 = 2f_b/\sqrt{3}$.

The intervals during which $v(t)$ remains above a given level v vary in length. Some results regarding the distribution of these lengths are available, in particular for $v = 0$, but up to the present no really satisfactory expression for the distribution function is known.

Gaussian noise for which $w(f)$ is constant for all frequencies from 0 up to some indefinitely high frequency beyond the range of interest is called "white Gaussian noise." This is approximated in nature by resistance, or Johnson, noise.

Narrow-band Gaussian Noise. When the power spectrum $w(f)$ is zero except in a narrow (compared to the midband fre-

quency) frequency band, $v(t)$ behaves roughly as a sine wave of midband frequency whose amplitude fluctuates at a rate proportional to the bandwidth. The representation (11) for $v(t)$ may be written as

$$v(t) = R(t)\cos\,[\omega_0 t + \theta(t)] \qquad (14)$$

in which the envelope $R(t)$ and the phase angle $\theta(t)$ vary slowly in comparison to $\cos \omega_0 t$, ω_0 being $2\pi f_0$ and f_0 the midband frequency (or some convenient value close to it).

The probability that $R(t) \ge R$ at a time t chosen at random is $\exp\,[-R^2/(2\sigma^2)]$, the cumulative Rayleigh distribution function. The median value of $R(t)$ is $\sigma(2\ln 2)^{1/2} = 1.1774\sigma$. The values of $\theta(t)$ are distributed uniformly over $(0,2\pi)$. Methods similar to those leading to (13) give an expression for N_R, the number of times per second $R(t)$ crosses upward across the level R. For example, if $w(f)$ has the constant value w_0 in a narrow frequency band of width β and is zero outside the band, N_R is equal to $(\pi/6)^{1/2} (\beta R/\sigma)\exp\,[-R^2/2\sigma^2]$, where $\sigma^2 = \beta w_0$.

In many technical problems a signal is also present with narrowband noise. This suggests the study of the statistical properties of a sine wave plus Gaussian noise. For example, it may be shown that the probability density of the envelope of

$$P\cos \omega_0 t + v(t) \qquad (15)$$

is $R\sigma^{-2}I_0(RP\sigma^{-2})\exp\,[-(R^2 + P^2)/(2\sigma^2)]$, where $I_0(z)$ denotes the Bessel function of order zero with imaginary argument, and σ is the rms value of $v(t)$ given by (10). Some information is also available concerning the phase angle $\theta(t)$ of (15) and its time derivative $\theta'(t)$, the latter being of interest in FM since $\omega_0 + \theta'(t)$ is the "instantaneous frequency" of the wave in radians per second.

Noise Through Nonlinear Devices. When a voltage $V_i(t) = P\cos pt + Q\cos qt$ is applied to a nonlinear device having no memory, the output $V_0(t)$ is the sum of modulation products having frequencies $mp \pm nq$, m and n being integers. When the input voltage $V_i(t)$ is Gaussian noise, the output consists of the sum of the modulation products corresponding to the sine waves in the representation (11) for $V_i(t)$.

One method of computing the output power spectrum $W(f)$ is to consider the average power due to the modulation products in the elementary frequency band $(f, f + \Delta f)$. However, it is generally simpler to compute the autocorrelation function $\psi(\tau)$ of the output $V_0(t)$ and then take its Fourier transform (7) to obtain $W(f)$. Quite often only terms corresponding to low-order modulation products need be retained. When $V_i(t)$ is of the form (15) where the sine wave frequency is in the narrow band of noise, some statistical properties of the low-frequency portion of $V_0(t)$ may be obtained from those of the envelope $R(t)$.

As an example, suppose (15) is applied to a square-law device such that $V_0(t) = V_i^2(t)$. The dc component of $V_0(t)$, obtained by squaring $V_i(t)$ and taking its time average, is $2^{-1}P^2 + \sigma^2$ where σ^2 is given by (10). The component of frequency $2\omega_0 t$ in $V_0(t)$ has the amplitude $P^2/2$, and the low-frequency portion of $V_0(t)$, including the dc, is $R^2(t)/2$. The autocorrelation function for $V_0(t)$ is the average value of $V_i^2(t)V_i^2(t + \tau)$ and turns out to be

$$\psi(\tau) = (2^{-1}P^2 + \sigma^2)^2 + 8^{-1}P^4 \cos 2\omega_0\tau$$
$$+ 2P^2\psi(\tau) \cos \omega_0\tau + 2\psi^2(\tau)$$

where $\psi(\tau)$ is given by (8). The first two terms of the right correspond respectively to the dc and $\cos 2\omega_0 t$ components of $V_0(t)$. The last two terms correspond to the continuous portion $W_c(f)$ of the power spectrum of $V_0(t)$. Application of (7) and the convolution theorem for Fourier integrals (q.v.) leads to

$$W_c(f) = P^2[w(f - f_0) + w(f + f_0)]$$
$$+ \int_{-\infty}^{\infty} w(x)w(f - x)\,dx$$

with the understanding that $w(-f) = w(f)$ and $\omega_0 = 2\pi f_0$.

For the special case in which the power spectrum $w(f)$ of the Gaussian noise $v(t)$ is

equal to w_0 in the narrow-band $f_0 - 2^{-1}\beta < f < f_0 + 2^{-1}\beta$, $W_c(f)$ consists of two parts, one around $f = 0$ and the other around $f = 2f_0$. The low-frequency part of $W_c(f)$ is the sum of a rectangular portion plus a triangular portion. The rectangular portion is equal to $2P^2w_0$ for $0 < f < 2^{-1}\beta$ and to 0 for $f > 2^{-1}\beta$. The triangular portion is equal to $2\beta w_0^2(1 - \beta^{-1}f)$ for $0 < f < \beta$ and to 0 for $f > \beta$. These two portions may be regarded as (noise components) $\times$ (sine wave) and (noise components) $\times$ (noise components) modulation products, respectively.

STEPHEN RICE

Cross-references: *Interference, Markov Processes, Noise Characterization and Measurement, Random Processes, Signal Fluctuation and Noise*

NOISE (THERMAL)

Noise generated in resistive media because of random motions of the current carriers in the resistive material is commonly called thermal noise, or, alternatively, *Johnson* or *Nyquist* noise. Most engineers are familiar with the equivalent circuit of a resistor used when one wishes to consider the noise voltage that appears across the open terminals of the resistor. The common equivalent circuit in use is simply an ideal noise free resistor equal in value to that of the actual resistor in series with a noise voltage generator whose RMS output is given by

$$V = \sqrt{4kTRB} \tag{1}$$

In this equation, k is Boltzmann's constant (1.38×10^{-23} joule/°K), T is the temperature of the resistor in °K, R is the resistance value in ohms, and B is the bandwidth of the circuit in question. This circuit can be converted to its Thévenin equivalent by the usual techniques.

What is the basic mechanism by which this noise voltage is generated? In essence, the charge carriers, which we shall assume to be electrons, are in rapid motion because of the heat energy of the resistor. As one would expect, they also undergo repeated collisions with the atoms of the material. Each electron, during its travel between collisions, induces a current in the resistor's external circuit that is proportional to the velocity and direction of travel. By considering the statistical average of the currents that flow in a wire that short circuits the resistor, it is found that the spectral density of the short-circuit current at low frequencies is simply

$$i^2 = 4\,kT/R \qquad (2)$$

This expression is the basis for the equivalent circuits that have been discussed.

If the resistor and its equivalent noise generator are connected to a load resistor of the same value, the noise power dissipated in the load resistor because of the noise voltage of the first resistor is, by straightforward circuit considerations,

$$P_L = kTB \qquad (3)$$

This is known as the *available noise power* of the resistor and is only delivered to a matched load.

Thermal Noise In Transmission Lines. More fundamental treatments involving quantum thermodynamics show that the terminating resistor will supply to any mode or degree of freedom an *available noise power* given by

$$P_L = \frac{hfB}{\exp\,(hf/kT) - 1} \qquad (4)$$

where h is Planck's constant (6.625×10^{-34} joule-sec) and f is the frequency. If the wires connecting the two resistors discussed in the previous paragraph are regarded as a short section of transmission line which supports one traveling-wave mode in each direction, then the previously determined results are seen to be entirely consistent. Note in Eq. (4) that only for very high frequencies and very low temperatures does the quantity hf/kT become comparable to unity. For ordinary temperatures and even at microwave frequencies, $hf/kT \ll 1$, and Eq. (4) is accurately approximated by Eq. (3). In some of the more recent work at very

low temperatures and high frequencies such as in the maser (*q.v.*), and even in the room-temperature laser (*q.v.*), this approximation cannot be made and the available thermal noise is found to be much less than kTB.

Many of the problems faced by the microwave engineer do not involve lumped-circuit elements such as resistors but distributed systems such as lossy transmission lines or waveguides. In such systems, as previously indicated, it is best to consider the noise power delivered to each propagating mode by the matched termination. This power is, as previously implied, also given by Eq. (4). Its magnitude can be determined from thermodynamical considerations of an antenna connected to a perfectly terminated transmission line, both of which are enclosed in an isothermal blackbody enclosure. Planck's hypotheses concerning the quantum nature of blackbody radiation are needed to properly predict the spectral distribution of the thermal energy.

The effects on the signal-to-noise ratio of propagating signals along lossy transmission lines are of particular interest. Qualitatively, one sees that the thermal noise associated with the mode is continually being attenuated but also replenished by each element of the line. Thus one expects the signal-to-noise ratio to decrease along a lossy transmission line. If the signal fields are attenuated as $\exp\,(-\alpha z)$, the signal power is attenuated as $\exp\,(-2\alpha z)$. Thus the decrease in power is given by

$$\frac{dP}{dz} = -2\alpha P \qquad (5)$$

If the transmission line is perfectly matched at each end, and one examines the noise power flowing across an arbitrary plane normal to the line, he will find a noise wave traveling to the right and another to the left. Each will carry the same amount of noise power, and this power is again

$$P_N = kTB \qquad (6)$$

if we assume $hf/kT \ll 1$. The amount of noise power absorbed from a given wave in a distance dz is simply $2\alpha kTB$ as given by Eq. (5). Since our fictitious arbitrary plane can also be to the right of the element dz, $2\alpha kTB$ must also be the amount of noise power generated by the distributed loss in the element dz. The differential equation which describes the noise generating and absorbing properties is thus

$$\frac{dP_N}{dz} = -2\alpha P_N + 2\alpha kTB \qquad (7)$$

which has the solution

$$P_N(z) = A \exp(-2\alpha z) + kTB \qquad (8)$$

The constant A must be determined by matching boundary conditions at $z = 0$. Assuming that the thermal noise at the driving point of the transmission line is $xkTB$, then $P_N(z)$ is given by

$$P_N(z) = (x - 1)kTB \exp(-2\alpha z) + kTB \qquad (9)$$

Since the signal propagation along the line is described by the equation

$$S(z) = S(0) \exp(-2\alpha z) \qquad (10)$$

the signal-to-noise power ratio can be written

$$R(z) = \frac{S(z)}{P_N(z)} = \frac{S(0)}{kTB[(x - 1) + \exp(2\alpha z)]} \qquad (11)$$

Since the denominator is always larger than $xkTB$, the signal to noise ratio decreases monotonically down the line.

D. C. FORSTER

Cross-references: *Noise Characterization and Measurement, Noise in Semiconductors, Noise (Statistical Theory), Statistical Mechanics*

NOMOGRAPHY

A nomograph (often called nomogram, alignment chart, or line coordinate chart), in its simplest and most common form, is a chart in which a straight line intersects three scales in values that satisfy an equation or a given set of conditions. This definition suggests the three principal advantages of the nomograph: its essential simplicity, the rapidity with which it can be used, and its

accuracy. As for essential simplicity, the complexity of the calculation may be reflected to some extent in the design and to a greater extent in the construction of the chart, but to only a minimum degree in its use. Interpolations are usually made along closely graduated scales rather than vaguely in a confusing network of curves; and unskilled individuals, with no knowledge whatever of the underlying theory, can perform involved computations by nomograph as readily as can the trained chemist, chemical engineer, or the nomographer himself.

Usually a calculation can be made nomographically in merely the time needed to draw a straight line, with a straightedge, between two points on a sheet of paper; instances of calculations that require *minutes* by slide rule and *seconds* by nomograph are common. Nomographs are usually direct-indicating, a feature that contributes significantly to their accuracy of use, since it obviates outside operations and "pointing off." Almost any desired degree of precision can be attained when proper attention is given to the design of the chart, its size, and the type of graduations employed.

Construction of a nomograph requires (1) a knowledge of the equation that connects the variables or of linear relationships, of the same type, between two of the variables for each value of the third, (2) knowledge of the ranges covered by these variables, (3) identification of the particular case with one of the standard type forms, and (4) determination of suitable moduli or unit representations to be used in laying off the desired scales. Most of the equations of practical value of engineers are of the following forms:

Type	Equation
A	$f(x) = F(y) + \phi(z)$
B	$f(x) = F(y) \cdot \phi(z)$
C	$f(x) = \psi(x) \cdot F(y) + \phi(z)$
D	$f(x) = F(y)/\phi(z)$
E	$\phi(z) = a + b F(y)$

where, in standard notation, $f(x)$, $\psi(x)$, $F(y)$, and $\varphi(z)$ represent any functions of the variables x, y, and z, and where a and b depend

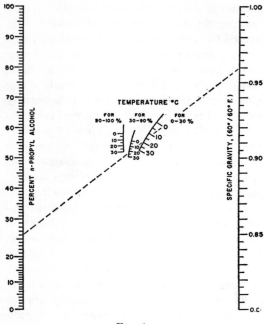

FIG. 1

For a more complete treatment of nomography, see *Nomography and Empirical Equations*, Reinhold, 1962; 2d ed.

D. S. Davis

NONLINEAR CIRCUITS

Electric circuits containing one or more nonlinear element are designated as nonlinear circuits. A nonlinear circuit element is a device that does not obey the principle of superposition. Nonlinear circuits or circuit elements may be classified as resistive or reactive depending upon whether they dissipate or store energy. However, most circuits and many circuit elements are neither strictly resistive nor reactive. They can also be classed as either active or passive: a passive circuit being one for which the net energy flow into the circuit considering all accessible ports is always non-negative. (Any circuit which is not passive is active.)

A complete description of a one-port resistive circuit can be given in the form of a v-i or i-v characteristic as shown in Figs. 1 and 2. If the characteristic is confined to the first and third quadrants of the v-i plane, the circuit is passive (Fig. 1), otherwise it is active (Fig. 2). A characteristic having a region of negative slope is termed a *negative-resistance* device. (Incremental resistance is defined as dv/di.) Figure 1 illustrates a *current-controlled* negative resistance; Fig. 2, a *voltage-controlled* negative resistance.

Similarly, one-port reactive elements are described by charge-vs-voltage (q-v) or flux-

upon x, but are defined by tables or plots rather than by a mathematical expression.

These forms are really closely related. Type B becomes the same as Type A when the equation is written in the logarithmic manner. When the equation for Type D is solved for $F(y)$, it is seen to be similar to that for Type B; when a and b are identified with $f(x)$ and $\psi(x)$, respectively, Types C and E are recognized as the same. The distinctions between the types are rather in the manner in which the charts are constructed. Type A usually calls for parallel, uniform scales; parallel, logarithmic scales characterize Type B; Types C and E frequently result in parallel y and z axes and in a curved x axis; parallel y and z axes connected with a diagonal x axis are characteristic of Type D. Numerous nomographs deal with four, five, or six variables instead of only three, so that combinations of these types are common.

In the accompanying typical nomograph the broken index line shows that the specific gravity, relative to water at 60°F, of 26% n-propyl alcohol is 0.960 at 15°C.

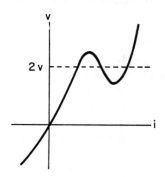

FIG. 1

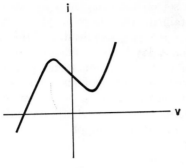

Fig. 2

linkage-vs-current (λ-i) characteristics. An incremental definition of capacitance (dq/dv) or inductance ($d\lambda/di$) is used for these elements.

Some typical resistive nonlinear two-terminal circuit elements are vacuum and semiconductor diodes, thermistors, thyrite, incandescent lamps, tunnel diodes, gas diodes and the "cryosar." The latter three are negative-resistance devices. In addition, all multiterminal semiconductor, vacuum, and gas-filled devices are basically nonlinear resistive circuit elements; e.g., transistors, triodes, tetrodes, thyratrons, etc. Among the latter, the last two exhibit negative-resistance characteristics. Commonly used nonlinear reactive elements are the "varactor" (a nonlinear capacitor), saturable reactor, and various devices constructed with "square-loop" magnetic materials.

Since nonlinear circuits may contain all types of circuit elements, they can exhibit an infinite variety of behavior. The following paragraphs describe the more important types of fundamentally nonlinear behavior.

Resistive Circuit Phenomena. Any nonlinear resistive n-port can be described by a set of n implicit algebraic equations,

$$f_j(v_1, v_2, \cdots, v_n, i_1, i_2, \cdots, i_n) = 0 \quad j = 1, 2, \cdots, n$$

These equations need not be solvable uniquely for any particular variable, nor need they be single-valued functions. Networks having specified functional relationships at specified ports can generally be synthesized using ideal diodes and linear elements. (An ideal diode is an element which is a short circuit for one direction of current flow and an open circuit for the other direction.) Although the resultant functional relationships will always be piecewise-linear, they can usually be made to approximate the required functions to the desired degree of accuracy.

Simple resistive one-ports and two-ports having single-valued functional characteristics find application in analog function generators, multipliers, dividers, logarithmic amplifiers, and in various pulse and digital circuits; e.g., clippers and gate circuits.

Multivalued functional relationships can be used to produce circuits which exhibit more than one state of stable equilibrium. Negative-resistance elements as well as nonlinear multiterminal devices can readily be made to exhibit such multi-stable behavior. For example, a 2-v source connected to the element of Fig. 1 would form a bistable circuit. The Eccles-Jordan "flip-flop" circuit is probably the best-known example of a multistable circuit.

Self-Sustained Oscillations. Oscillations can occur in either conservative or nonconservative nonlinear circuits. A parallel combination of a capacitor and inductor, one or both of which are nonlinear, and neither of which are lossy, oscillates in a *nonisochronous* manner, i.e., the frequency depends upon the amplitude of oscillation. Such behavior is typical of conservative nonlinear systems (e.g., the frictionless pendulum) and is fundamentally different from linear oscillation, which is always *isochronous*.

In nonconservative systems oscillations can usually be classed as either of the "quasi-harmonic" or relaxation type. Quasi-harmonic nonlinear oscillators are characterized by almost-sinusoidal waveforms of fixed amplitude and frequency. They differ from strictly linear oscillations in that the amplitude is fixed by the nonlinear elements in the circuit rather than being dependent upon initial conditions. In most oscillators of this type a high-Q linear tank circuit is the frequency-determining part of the system (e.g., a tuned LC combination, a crystal, a tuning fork, or a material exhibiting a sharp molecular, atomic, or nuclear resonance). An associated nonlinear resistive active circuit serves to fix the amplitude by supplying energy to or extracting energy from the tank circuit. Amplitude stabilization is generally accomplished by means of the non-linearities in a vacuum tube or transistor, or by a two-terminal element: typically, a lamp.

Relaxation oscillations are characterized by highly irregular and often discontinuous periodic waveforms. The frequency of oscillation, being highly dependent upon the resistive nonlinear elements in the circuit, is generally not particularly stable. Such oscillators usually comprise highly nonlinear elements (often with negative-resistance characteristics) in conjunction with one or more reactive elements. The reactive elements are not normally in a tank circuit configuration. The device of Fig. 2, when connected to an inductor, would constitute a simple relaxation oscillator. Applications of relaxation oscillators occur primarily in the pulse and digital field: astable multivibrators, sawtooth sweep circuits, timing circuits, etc.

The Van der Pol equation

$$x'' - \epsilon(1 - x^2)x' + x = 0$$

describes most of the essential features of oscillations in nonconservative systems. It expresses in normalized form, the behavior of a linear tank circuit together with a negative resistance element having a cubic $v\text{-}i$ characteristic. The Van der Pol equation describes to a good approximation the behavior of a very large class of practical oscillators, categorized as "negative resistance oscillators." For $\epsilon \ll 1$ the periodic solutions are quasi-harmonic; for $\epsilon \gg 1$ they are of the relaxation type.

Periodically Excited Circuits. A nonlinear circuit driven by a sinusoidal source generally exhibits a periodic response of the same frequency as the excitation. If the nonlinearities are small, the resultant waveform is approximately sinusoidal, in which

case a set of frequency response curves can be obtained. The shape of the curves depends upon the amplitude of the driving function. Hysteresis effects, sometimes known as "jump" phenomena, can often be observed in such response curves. These phenomena, unique to nonlinear circuits, are characterized by sharp discontinuities in the amplitude and phase characteristics as well as multivaluedness of these curves.

Under certain conditions, which are easily produced experimentally, subharmonic responses may occur; i.e., periodic responses whose periods are integral multiples of the excitation period. This phenomenon is utilized in the "parametron" (q.v.), a binary memory element.

Self-sustained oscillators which are periodically excited at a frequency in the neighborhood of their natural frequency are subject to *entrainment*. For certain amplitudes of the forcing function the frequency of oscillation shifts from the natural to the forced frequency. All synchronized oscillators (e.g., recurrent oscilloscope sweeps, phase-locked devices) utilize the entrainment phenomenon.

Frequency Conversion. Various types of nonlinear circuits are used throughout communication systems to effect frequency conversion. Frequency multiplication is often achieved by a nonlinear resistive network with a sharply saturating characteristic. Astable multivibrators triggered at a frequency several times their natural frequency are used as frequency dividers. Frequency shifting, i.e., modulation and demodulation (q.v.) is accomplished in a wide variety of ways, using either multiterminal devices or simple combinations of diodes and linear elements, as in the peak detector, for example.

Parametric and maser amplification (q.v.) provide additional examples of frequency conversion through the medium of nonlinear elements. In all such devices energy is supplied at one frequency, the "pump" frequency, and extracted at the signal frequency. A set of analytical relations derived by Manley and Rowe govern the flow of power in a broad class of nonlinear frequency-conversion circuits.

Methods of Analysis. No one method of analysis is adequate to deal with all nonlinear problems. Of the many methods used to treat nonlinear circuits some of the more important are: linearized equivalent circuits, piecewise-linear models, phase plane techniques, perturbation, iteration, various numerical methods, and quasi-harmonic techniques: e.g., describing functions, equivalent linearization and the method of first approximation of Kryloff and Bogoliuboff. The choice of method depends upon the type of circuit, the form and accuracy of solution required and the availability of automatic computers.

THOMAS E. STERN

Cross-references: *Network Synthesis, Network Theory, Oscillators, Systems (Nonlinear)*

NORTON'S THEOREM: see NETWORK THEORY

NUCLEAR MAGNETIC RESONANCE

The earliest attempts to observe NMR were carried out by Gorter and Broer, but chiefly owing to the choice of an unfavorable substance, no experimental result was obtained. NMR was first observed in molecular beams by Rabi, Zacharias, and Kusch (1938), and in neutron beams, by Alvarez and Bloch (1940). These measurements are fundamental in our understanding of nuclear structure, and have led to a remolding of emphasis on molecular-beam studies. While resonance studies of beams have continued to add to our knowledge of elementary particles, a more universal employment of resonance techniques—employing solids and liquids—were discovered somewhat later.

In 1946, Bloch, Hansen, and Packard at Stanford, and Purcell, Torrey, and Pound at Harvard independently observed NMR in solids and liquids. The techniques of the two

groups were sufficiently different for Bloch to name his observation "nuclear induction," whereas Purcell used "nuclear absorption." Both methods of observation are important; the nuclear induction procedure is more sensitive, but also more critical to adjust, while the Purcell measurement of resonance absorption is reasonably sensitive and simpler to operate.

Bloch, in essence, observed the voltage induced in a coil whose axis was perpendicular to the quasistatic magnetic field. The induced emf is due to the transitions of the resultant magnetization vector **M** of the nuclear spins. Because nuclei have magnetic moments which are a few hundred to thousands of times smaller than electrons, Bloch observed the resonances at a frequency of about 8 Mc rather than the kilomegacycle frequencies used in electron resonance. A schematic of the Bloch, Hansen, and Packard apparatus is shown in Fig. 1. The rf and magnetic-field modulation force the magnetic moment of the sample to process in the proper direction to induce a voltage in the detector coil. A reversal of magnetization (adiabatic fast passage) occurs because of the swing past the resonance region by the 60-cps magnetic field modulation. One observes the "off diagonal" elements of the energy matrix. That is, the signal occurs during the transition. The analysis and experimental description of nuclear induction appears in the *Physical Review* (1946).

NMR, as observed by Purcell, requires essentially the same apparatus, but the receiving and transmitting coils are not placed perpendicular to each other. The apparatus used by the Harvard group has been improved by experience; a schematic may be found in an article by Bloembergen, Purcell, and Pound, *Physical Review* (1946). The angular frequency ω for absorption is the same for either method and is given by

$$\omega = \gamma H \tag{1}$$

where γ is the gyromagnetic ratio characteristic of the nuclear species, and H is the static magnetic field. In order to observe the

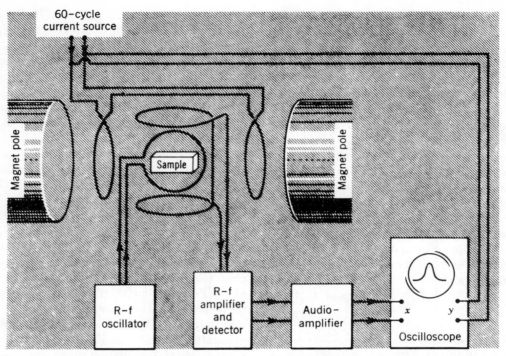

FIG. 1. A schematic of the nuclear induction apparatus of Bloch, Hansen, and Packard. (Reproduced from *Masers*, by J. R. Singer, with permission of the publishers, John Wiley and Sons, New York, 1959.)

resonance a static field of a few thousand to 30,000 oersteds or more may be employed. Observations are easier at the larger fields due to the larger resonance signal intensities. The rf frequencies employed vary from a few to 60 Mc in order to satisfy Eq. (1).

Almost the only atomic substances which do not exhibit NMR are those with even-even nuclei—that is, an even number of protons and an even number of neutrons—as these materials have no nuclear magnetic moment. Literally thousands of chemical materials have been proved with NMR. The information obtained has provided new insight in nuclear structure, atomic organization and nuclear-electron interaction. Some of the information is obtained very indirectly, e.g., the frequency for nuclear resonance is shifted slightly by magnetic interactions of the nuclei and the electrons. These shifts are keys to understanding of matter and go by such names as the chemical shift and Knight shift (NMR frequency shifts dependent upon the environment of the atoms). Recently, NMR has been utilized to measure flow rates of blood and other liquids with the elimination of any need to insert any device into the flow channel (J. R. Singer, *Journal of Applied Physics*, 1960).

NMR has, as some of its applications, nuclear structure determinations, chemical structure determinations, nature of chemical bondings, analysis of chemicals, biological structure investigations, and flow measurements of blood and other fluids.

J. R. SINGER

Cross-references: *Electron Paramagnetic Resonance, Microwave Spectroscopy*

NUCLEONICS

Nucleonics is the name proposed by Z. Jeffries of the Manhattan District in 1944 to describe the general field of nuclear science and technology. As popularly used it encompasses not only the study of the atomic nucleus, but also related physical techniques, instrumentation, radiochemistry, and the applications of radioisotopes. In its strict technical sense it refers only to the first of these topics and is so used here.

Prior to 1900 atoms were considered to be unalterable and indivisible entities of which the elements were composed. With the discovery of the nuclear transmutations resulting from the radioactive decay process, however, it became apparent that atoms themselves possessed internal structure.

Upon observing that in passing through matter alpha particles (q.v.) were scattered through larger angles than the then current concepts of the atom would predict, E. Rutherford (1871–1937) suggested that the atom actually consisted of a small, heavy, positively charged nucleus surrounded by negative charges of the same magnitude. Further observations and theoretical refinements have led to the now generally accepted concept that the nucleus also contains elementary particles, i.e., neutrons, which are electrically neutral and have a mass of 1.00897, and protons, which are positively charged and have a mass of 1.00812. Stated in simple form, then, the atom consists of a positively charged nucleus, containing neutrons and protons, surrounded by a number of negatively charged electrons sufficient to provide electrical neutrality. Although this concept of the atom has not been in serious question for almost 50 years, complete understanding of the forces which hold the neutrons and protons together has not yet been achieved.

In 1927 Aston found that experimentally measured isotopic weights differed slightly from whole numbers. From this he was led to the concept of the *packing fraction*, which is defined as the algebraic difference between the isotopic weight and the mass number divided by the mass number. Although the theoretical significance of the packing fraction is difficult to assess, it does lead to some interesting conclusions with respect to nuclear stability. A negative packing fraction derives from a situation where the isotopic weight is less than the mass number, implying that in the formation of the nucleus from its constituent particles some mass is converted into energy. Since an equivalent amount of energy would be necessary to break up the nucleus into its constituent particles again, a negative packing fraction suggests a high order of nuclear stability. By the same reasoning, a positive packing fraction indicates nuclear instability. As can be seen from Figure 1, stable elements with mass numbers above about 175 and below about 25 have positive packing fractions. It is interesting to note that the packing fractions of both hydrogen and uranium are positive.

Actually, a comparison of the isotopic weight with the mass number as is done in determining the packing fraction is somewhat artificial. A rigorous determination of the mass-energy interconversion in the formation of an atom would seem to require a calculation of the difference between the sum of the masses of the constituent particles of the atom and the experimentally measured isotopic weight. The value of the mass difference thus obtained is the *mass defect*. The energy equivalent of this mass difference as derived from the Einstein equation yields a measure of the binding energy of the nucleus. Division of the binding energy of a nucleus by the number of nucleons (the total number of protons and neutrons) therein yields the binding energy per nucleon. As indicated in Figure 2, in stable isotopes the binding energy per nucleon decreases with increasing mass number, a fact which is important in nuclear fission. Secondly, the binding energy per nucleon derived in the manner described above is an average value, whereas each additional nucleon added to the nucleus has a binding energy less than those which preceded it. Thus, the most recently added nucleons are bound less tightly than those already present.

Additional considerations regarding nuclear stability may be gleaned from a consideration of the odd or even nature of the

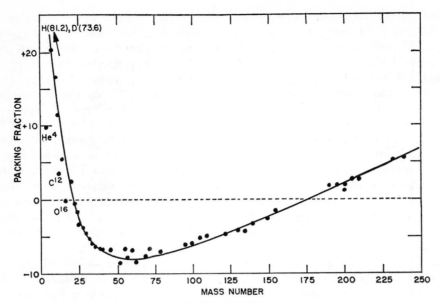

Fig. 1. Packing fraction curve.

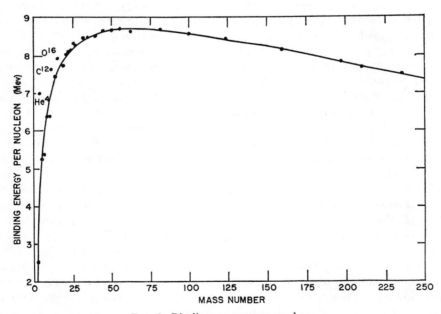

Fig. 2. Binding energy per nucleon.

numbers of protons and neutrons in the nucleus. According to the *Pauli exclusion principle,* no two extranuclear electrons having an identical set of quantum numbers can occupy the same electron energy state. The application of this principle to the nucleus leads to conclusions that at least are not at variance with observations of nuclear stability. Thus, one may infer that no two nucleons possessing an identical set of quantum numbers can occupy the same nuclear energy state. It would appear, then, that both protons and neutrons which differ only in their angular momenta or spins may exist in a nuclear state. The exclusion principle requires, therefore, that only protons having opposite spins can exist in the same state. The same consideration applies to neutrons. Accordingly, two protons and two neutrons might occupy the same nuclear energy state provided the nucleons in each pair have opposite spins. Such two-proton—two-neutron groupings are termed "closed shells," and by virtue of their proton-neutron interaction impart exceptional stability to nuclei which are made up of them. The nuclear forces in closed shells are said to be "saturated" by which it is meant that the nucleons therein interact strongly with each other, but weakly with those in other states. Since like particles tend to complete an energy state by pairing of opposite spins, two neutrons of opposite spin or a single neutron or proton also might exist in a particular energy state.

Any of the above conditions may be achieved when the nucleus contains an even number of both protons and neutrons, or an even number of one and an odd number of the other. Since there is an excess of neutrons over protons for all but the lowest atomic number elements, in the odd-odd situation there is a deficiency of protons necessary to complete the two-proton—two-neutron quartets. It might be expected that these protons could be provided by the production of protons via beta decay. As a matter of fact there exist only four stable nuclei of odd-odd composition, whereas there are 108 such nuclei in the even-odd form and 162 in the even-even series. It will be seen that the order of stability, and presumably the binding energy per nucleon, from greatest to smallest, seems to be even-even, even-odd, odd-odd.

Although the existence of binding energies holding the nucleus together has been demonstrated, the problem of defining the nature of these forces presents itself. Clearly, repulsive electrostatic forces must exist between protons. These forces are "long range" in effect. To achieve nuclear stability, compensating attractive forces also must exist.

It has been concluded that "short-range" attractive forces exist between protons, neutrons, and protons and neutrons. The (p-n) attractive forces are considered to be of the greatest magnitude; the (n-n) and (p-p) forces are of lesser intensity, with the latter decreased by virtue of electrostatic repulsion. When the number of protons in a nucleus is greater than twenty, it is found that the ratio of neutrons to protons exceeds unity. The additional short-range attractive forces provided by the excess neutrons, therefore, may be considered as compensating for the long-range electrostatic repulsive forces between the protons. Nevertheless, when the number of protons exceeds about 50, the short-range forces are insufficient to counteract the electrostatic forces completely, with the result that the binding energy per each additional nucleon decreases.

Unfortunately, the nature of the short-range attractive forces between nucleons remains essentially unresolved. An interpretation of them has been presented by Heisenberg, however, in terms of wave-mechanical exchange forces. Thus, if the basic difference between the proton and neutron in a system composed of these two particles is considered to be that the former is electrically charged while the latter is not, then the transfer of the electric charge from the proton to the neutron results in an exchange of individual identity but not a change in the system. That is to say, the system still is composed of a proton and neutron, despite the fact that the particles have exchanged their identities. Since the system itself has the same composition, it must possess the same energy after the exchange as it did before. One of the principles of wave mechanics is that if a system may be represented by two states, each of which has the same energy, then the actual state of the system is a result of the combination, i.e., resonance, of the two separate states and is more stable than either. In the proton-neutron system under discussion, the energy difference between the "combined" state and the individual states may be considered as the "exchange energy" or "attractive force" between the particles. In an extension of Heisenberg's proposal Yukawa has postulated that the exchange energy is carried by a new particle which has been given the name *meson* (*q.v.*). Particles having the properties attributed by Yukawa to mesons have been identified in cosmic rays.

Nuclear Fission. With these concepts of nuclear structure and stability, however imperfect, the process of nuclear fission of uranium can now be considered. Although fast neutrons (greater than 0.1 Mev) can cause fission in both Uranium 235 and Uranium 238, thermal neutrons (about 0.03 ev) are effective only with Uranium 235. Uranium 238 is unsatisfactory as a fissionable material for most purposes, however, since it has a high probability for "resonance capture" of fast neutrons, which is a nonfission process. It is instructive to ponder why Uranium 235 fissions with thermal neutrons and Uranium 238 does not. It will be recalled that the binding energy for an even-even nucleus exceeds that for an even-odd. Consequently, the addition of a neutron to Uranium 235, which yields an even-even compound nucleus, will contribute a greater binding energy than in the case of Uranium 238, where an even-odd compound nucleus would be produced. Calculations yield a value of 6.81 Mev for the additional neutron in the former case, and 5.31 Mev in the latter. Using Bohr and Wheeler's calculations, it is found that the activation energy for fission is 5.2 Mev for Uranium 235 and 5.9 Mev for Uranium 238. Thus, the binding energy for an additional neutron in Uranium 235 exceeds its fission activation energy, whereas it is less in the case of Uranium 238. It can be seen then that Uranium 235 fission is energetically feasible with thermal neutrons, whereas the fissioning of Uranium 238 is not.

It will be recalled that the binding energy per nucleon decreases with increasing mass number. To state it differently, a greater amount of energy is released in the formation of nuclei of intermediate mass number from their constituent nucleons than is the case in nuclei of high mass number. Thus, energy is released in fission because the binding energy of the high-mass-number Uranium 236 compound nucleus is less than that of the intermediate-mass-number fission products formed. The total energy thus liberated in fission is about 200 Mev. Of this the kinetic energy of the fission products accounts for 160 Mev. These fragments, being of significantly lower atomic number, require fewer neutrons for stability than they actually contain immediately after fission. These excess neutrons, therefore, are "boiled off" the fission fragments, the process occurring in two distinct phases. In the first phase "prompt" neutrons of about 2 Mev energy are released within 10^{-12} sec after fission occurs and take up about 7 per cent of the fission energy. Subsequently, after several seconds, additional "delayed" neutrons with about 0.5 Mev energy are boiled off the fission products. These neutrons play an extremely important role in the control of the chain reaction in nuclear reactors (*q.v.*).

Measurements made by Zinn and Szilard indicate that an average of 2.3 neutrons are released per fission. If in each fission, therefore, at least one of the released neutrons caused the fissioning of another uranium nucleus, there would result a series of fissions, i.e., a self-sustaining chain reaction. The establishment of this condition basically depends upon two related factors: (1) the number of neutrons lost by escape from the geometrical confines of the system, and (2) the number that are used up in nonfission processes, such as capture by Uranium 238. Loss by escape is proportional to the surface area of the system. A sphere, for example, would provide a maximum volume of fissionable material for a minimum surface area. Loss by capture may be controlled by the use of uranium suitably enriched in the 235 isotope. Thus, the quantity, quality, and configuration of the system may be varied until a "critical" mass is obtained. Under these conditions, there is a constant number of neutrons in the system, that is to say, the "reproduction factor" is unity.

Fusion. In 1932 Cockcroft and Walton,

using an accelerator, bombarded Lithium 7 with protons and obtained Helium 4. The reaction was accompanied by an energy release of 17.3 Mev.

$$_1H^1 + _3Li^7 \rightarrow 2\,_2He^4 + 17.3\ Mev$$

This was the first demonstration of nuclear *fusion*, i.e., the production of elements of higher atomic number (e.g., He) from elements of lower atomic number (e.g., H). As in the case of the fission reaction, energy is released because the binding energy of the proton is less than that of the alpha particle produced.

Unlike the fission reaction, in which there is no electrostatic repulsion to the approach of the uncharged neutron to the target nucleus, the fusion reaction requires the coalescence of two positively charged nuclei. It is clear that at least one of the reacting particles must possess exceedingly high energy to overcome this potential barrier. A temperature of about 20 million degrees centigrade is necessary to effect the reaction:

$$_1H^3 + _1H^2 \rightarrow _2He^4 + _0n^1 + E \qquad (I)$$

and even higher energy is required in the case of

$$_1H^2 + _3Li^6 \rightarrow 2\,_2He^4 + E \qquad (II)$$

Although the Atomic Energy Commission has not released information concerning "thermonuclear devices" discussions of it available in the open literature are of interest. Several writers have postulated that a conventional fission bomb provides the energy necessary to initiate reaction (I) and this in turn furnishes sufficient energy to trigger reaction (II). These authors believe it would not be feasible to employ a sufficiently large initial charge of tritium to make a practical device and therefore conclude that the neutron produced in reaction (I) reacts with the Lithium 6 employed in reaction (II) to yield further quantities of tritium:

$$_3Li^6 + _0n^1 \rightarrow _2He^4 + _1H^3 \qquad (III)$$

Assuming this to be the case, only a small initial charge of tritium would be necessary since the additional quantities produced in reaction (III) would be available to react with deuterium as per reaction (I). Thus, they envisage a type of "chain reaction" involving the sequence I → II + III → I. Although it would appear from this scheme that the reaction, once started, is not amenable to moderation, it was revealed at the Geneva Conference in 1955 that work is in progress in several countries on a controlled thermonuclear reaction.

JOSEPH E. MACHUREK

Cross-references: *Atoms, Fission, Fusion, Isotopes, Protons, Thermodynamics*

NYQUIST DIAGRAM: see SYSTEMS (LINEAR)

O

OPERATIONS RESEARCH

Operations Research (OR) is the application of research (i.e., scientific) techniques to operations (i.e., to management problems as distinguished from straightforward technical problems). It has been variously defined as "the scientific approach to operational problems for the greater fulfillment of objectives," "a scientific method of providing executive departments with a quantitative basis for decisions regarding the operations under their control," and "the application of scientific methods, techniques, and tools to problems involving the operations of systems so as to provide those in control of the operations with optimum solutions to the problems." (These definitions are taken from three leading books whose titles contain the words "operations research".) Although the difficulty of defining OR is proverbial it is clear that OR is an important activity; one need only cite the International Federation of Operations Research Societies, with eleven national members, of which the largest, the Operations Research Society of America, has over 3,000 practitioners as members.

OR was born about 1940 when a group of British scientists, including Nobel laureate P. M. S. Blackett, was asked to aid in developing operational methods for using the new tool of radar, and were extraordinarily successful in doing so. Operations research groups were employed with great success by all branches of the service in the U.S. during World War II, and in the following years the activity spread to civilian occupations; for example, in the early 1950's, OR people showed how to reduce the cost of inventory without increasing shortages and how to reduce the cost of toll booths while reducing waiting times at the booths, and made valuable contributions to many similar problems of allocation and scheduling.

The steps in an OR problem are most typically: a background study, including a first formulation of the problem (which is usually incorrectly stated at the beginning, and is continually refined); choice of a measure of effectiveness; elaboration of a mathematical model; gathering data to validate, and supply parameters for, the model; solution of the mathematical problem, including judicious approximations to render it soluble, in an attempt to maximize the chosen measure; implementation, and evaluation, of the recommendations arising from such solution. Of course these steps may be difficult to separate, or even recognize, in practice; and of course they vary greatly from one problem to another. Furthermore, it is all too easy to confuse the solution of the mathematical model with OR as a whole, particularly in writings and courses on OR, since the mathematics is at least readily definable. Thus, OR is often linked with such important tools as construction of Monte Carlo models, simulation, linear programming (*q.v.*) and queueing theory. Nonetheless, choices of appropriate problem statements, figures of merit, and mathematical idealizations, and questions of implementation and evaluation, are often more significant, and in practice more difficult.

A classical example of OR in World War II concerned the search for German submarines in the Atlantic Ocean by shore-based U. S. aircraft. These aircraft had been spending most of their time looking for submarines fairly close to shore, because it was easier, and because most of the enemy submarines had, in fact, been found close to shore. The OR team, however, was able to show that the only reason most sightings had been close to shore was because the preponderance of searching effort was close to shore; appropriate reduction of the data demonstrated conclusively that the number of sightings per hour of search increased greatly as the distance from shore increased. The recommendation to conduct more search far from shore was implemented, and the number of sightings increased greatly.

This example is by no means trivial. The true situation was not obvious to the operational commanders, partly because the pertinent data were hidden in an enormous mass of records, and partly because the correct questions had never been asked. This is a common problem. C. W. Churchman has said: "It is amazing that 90 per cent of the work in OR is the gathering of cost information. Not just for new businesses, but for old businesses as well, the really important cost information does not exist. For example, any outsider can see immediately that the data most relevant to running a railroad isn't collected. Railroads don't know the relative costs of hauling different commodities. Railroads have never even determined how long a train should be. . . . I don't know of a single company that collects the proper data on the total time required to process products. It is impossible to state whether cutting delays from 90 to 60 days is worthwhile." (The important point here is the common unavailability of relevant data.) Thus we can see that OR is in some sense an approach or a state of mind, in the sense that asking the correct questions is often more important than supplying the correct answers.

Another, more recent example of OR success concerns the "transportation problem." Here one has, for example, a number of factories, each of which must ship a given number of units each month, and a number of warehouses, each of which must receive a certain number of units each month (the numbers may vary widely). The transportation cost from each factory to each warehouse is also given. The problem is to distribute the necessary goods in the cheapest fashion. This problem may be formulated mathematically in several forms (one of which is a linear programming form), and is then susceptible to exact solution, generally on a medium-sized computer.

This particular problem is almost ideal, because the model may be formulated with little or no approximation, and because exact costs are available. When one must estimate the cost of customer attitudes, or, worse, the cost of a human life, or the value of deterring a war, the situation is far more difficult. In some cases, the problem involves large numbers of variables, so that even if the parameters were known (and they are likely to be very uncertain) the problem would be hopelessly complex. Consider the design of a battlefield surveillance system, where the variables include many tactical and strategic situations, various weather and visibility conditions, and so forth. How is one to rank in value such desiderata as accuracy, precision, timeliness, reliability, coverage, range, security, feasibility, cost, and logistic supportability? Worse, how does one combine them to obtain a parameter that one wishes to maximize if one could in fact construct a model of reasonable accuracy that was capable of manipulation?

Even in such difficult situations, it is the almost unanimous opinion of those who have had experience in such matters that OR can help. An objective and quantitative study of the situation by technically trained persons cannot hurt, except for the cost (which is frequently trivial compared to the over-all system cost), and in most cases it has given valuable insight and aid to the system managers.

Although most universities now offer courses in OR, and a few offer degrees in this field, most OR men are trained in one of the classical disciplines—usually a heavily mathematical discipline such as physics or chemistry, or mathematics itself. In addition to mathematical knowledge (especially probability), the OR practitioner must have an understanding of the experimental method, a creative imagination, and an interest in broad problems. OR is most typically performed by teams of men, with many different disciplines represented on the team.

Because of its very success, the nature of OR changed markedly during the 1950's. Instead of presenting the OR man with a finished piece of equipment (which was never optimal) and asking him how to use it, OR has been brought into the earliest phases of system design. Thus the OR man, who classically disdained "hardware" considerations and concerned himself solely with operations, has become more and more a system designer. System evaluation, as performed by OR, now typically takes place during the design phase, before equipment is built, quite as often as it takes place during practical operation of the same equipment. Thus, OR is becoming almost indistinguishable from "system engineering."

ROBERT E. MACHOL

Cross-references: *Information Theory, Systems*

OPTICAL MASER: see LASER

OPTICS

Geometrical Optics

Geometrical optics may be understood as the craft of the optical engineer. Historically, the limitations of available materials and of mathematical and computational tools have not forestalled the invention of a succession of elegant and incisive analytical views of optical systems. These mathematical methods describe the geometry of sets of rays as they are refracted or reflected at the surfaces of lenses, prisms, or mirrors, taken singly or in groups. In general, the function of the devices under study is to form an image. Certain very limited cases do exist in which the problem can be ideally satisfied with very simple specifications of the elements involved. For example, rays parallel to the axis of a concave mirror of parabolic

section are reflected so as to converge to a point. Such an explicit solution to the imaging problem is quite rare. Even allowing aspheric surfaces, several surfaces and (in refractive systems) several different glasses will be required.

The following is limited to systems comprising lenses centered on an axis. The concepts are readily generalized to mirror systems. Almost invariably the lens surfaces are spherical because such surfaces can be ground and polished to the high accuracy required.

A ray is defined as the normal to a wavefront. An infinite set of rays originates at each point of a real object or would converge to a point of a virtual object. Those rays that then pass through the optical system (or component) may converge to the corresponding real image point or appear to have come from the corresponding virtual image point. The rays, before entering the optics, are described in object space; on emerging, in image space. In an ideal system the intersection in image space of any pair of rays from one object point must occur at the image of the point. The end parameters are the same when a ray is traced in reverse; i.e., image and object may be interchanged without affecting the trace.

If the only rays considered lie close to the axis and have little obliquity, the expression of their path and of the slope of the refractive surfaces encountered can be simplified by $\sin \theta = \theta$. First-order theory is based on this simplification and on Snell's law of refraction, in which the paraxial properties of lenses can be defined: The primary focal point is such that any ray through it emerges, after passing through the system, parallel to the axis. By extending the entering and the emerging ray segments, an intersection point is obtained that lies in the primary principal plane. Rays entering parallel to the axis trace to the secondary focal point and likewise define the secondary principal plane. If the medium before entering has an index n, and the final medium an index n', the primary and secondary focal lengths that are measured from the focal points to the corresponding principal planes give $n'/n = f'/f$.

The term "back focal length" refers to the distance from the vertex of the last element to the secondary focal point.

The primary nodal point is a point on axis such that any entering ray segment that can be extended through it emerges as though through the secondary nodal point with equal obliquity.

Distances to object (s) and image (s') planes are measured from the principal planes and satisfy the relation:

$$\frac{n}{s} + \frac{n'}{s'} = \frac{n}{f} = \frac{n'}{f'}$$

If the medium through which the ray passes before entering the systems and after emerging is the same, the two nodal points coincide with the principal points, and the two focal lengths are equal.

All these first-order parameters may be determined and manipulated comparatively easily. The properties of rays more distant from the axis, and more oblique, are obviously of greater importance. However, since the paraxial rays are always present, one method of examining the collective performance of the larger set of rays consists in extending the expressions used to describe the system, and seeking equality with the paraxial expressions.

In third-order theory, $\sin \theta$ may be replaced by $\theta - \theta^3/3!$. The terms in θ correspond to those of first-order theory. The remaining terms are arranged as five sums, known as the Seidel terms. By manipulating the shape factors of the components, the spacing, the position of apertures, etc., one then attempts to cause the Seidel sums to vanish in order. As this objective is achieved, the ray trace reverts more and more to coincidence with the first-order parameters established by the paraxial rays, and the aberrations are minimized. The following five monochromatic aberrations are corrected consecutively as the five Seidel sums are made to vanish consecutively.

(1) *Spherical* aberration is due to the excessive bending power of the outer zones of lenses on rays parallel to the axis.

(2) The second aberration is called *coma*, from the comet-shaped, blurred image of an off-axis object point.

(3) *Astigmatism* is also an off-axis aberration. It causes the image of object lines that would intersect the axis to occur in a plane other than that of the image of lines perpendicular to them.

(4) *Curvature of field* refers to the fact that, unless corrected, the points in an object plane perpendicular to the axis are mapped to image points lying on a curved surface.

(5) *Distortion* is the defect due to magnification in the field margins unequal to the paraxial magnification. It is called *barrel* distortion or *pincushion* distortion depending on the appearance of the image of an object made up of orthogonal lines.

Chromatic aberration is caused by the change of index of refraction with wavelength, i.e., dispersion. It is commonly corrected by combining negative and positive elements made of glasses of high and low dispersive powers.

Optimum design of an optical system is achieved by making the most judicious compromises consistent with the application. A telescope objective requires low spherical aberration, low chromatic aberration, low coma. A camera lens is sensitive to astigmatism, field curvature, distortion. A condenser group may have deliberate aberrations if they assist in obtaining uniformity of screen illumination.

The more sophisticated lenses can and do approach the resolving power limits owing to diffraction. For telescopes this (angular) limit is conveniently expressed as a function of the diameter of the entrance pupil and of the wavelength: $\theta = 1.22\lambda/D$.

For microscopes of high power, the separation S of two resolved points is found from the angle $(2i)$ which the entrance pupil subtends at the object, $S = \lambda/(2n \sin i)$, the object being in a medium of index n. In the electron microscope (*q.v.*), S is much smaller, but the increase in resolution is limited by a much smaller i and by system aberrations. In general, there are many analogies between electron optics and light optics; one should note, however, that electron lenses lack the distinct boundaries of glass lenses, that the range of indices is far greater in electron optics, that magnetic and electrostatic lenses (or prisms) can exist in the same space, and that the electron wavelength decreases with increased velocity.

JAMES A. OGLE

Physical Optics

Physical optics deals in general with the nature of light and the interaction of light with matter. Many of the phenomena in this classification may be dealt with by the use of wave theory. Let the wave be described by $Ae^{j(\omega t - \mathbf{k}\cdot\mathbf{r})}$, where A is the amplitude of the disturbance, the frequency is $\nu = \omega/2\pi$, and k is the propagation vector. The expression $(\omega t - \mathbf{k}\cdot\mathbf{r})$ is the phase of the wave. Intensity is proportional to the square of the amplitude.

Two or more waves of light may interfere and show an intensity distribution that is not a simple addition of the intensity of each wave when the phase difference of each wave is constant. The phase of a wave is initially determined by the source.

When the phase difference is a constant, then the waves are produced by coherent sources. A light source has many emitters randomly sending out wave trains of 10^{-8}-sec duration (excluding lasers, *q.v.*). For observations over a longer time interval, a single coherent source is necessary. When two waves from a coherent source with the same frequency are superposed, the intensity is given by

$$I = \left| A_1 e^{j(\omega t - \mathbf{k}\cdot\mathbf{r}+\delta_1)} + A_2 e^{j(\omega t - \mathbf{k}\cdot\mathbf{r}+\delta_2)} \right|^2$$

$$= A_1^2 + A_2^2 + 2A_1A_2 \cos \delta$$

where $\delta = \delta_1 - \delta_2$ is the phase difference of the two waves at the point of interference.

For $A_1 = A_2$, the intensity varies between 0 and $4A^2$.

Geometrical optics considers only the rectilinear propagation of light rays. Thus, an aperture blocking a wavefront should sharply define the boundary of the emerging wave. On a small scale this is not true—the wavefront is diffracted around the edge of the geometrical shadow. The intensity distribution is then a result of interference caused by the variation in path length of the different rays. Interference and diffraction are artificially divided according to whether the effect is due to a number of interacting beams or a summation of elements across a wavefront. The term *Frauenhofer* diffraction is limited to the diffraction of plane wavefronts, whereas all other diffraction phenomena are called *Fresnel* diffraction.

It is shown in electromagnetic theory that the propagation factor k is related to the medium in which the wave traverses by

$$k = \frac{\omega}{v} = \frac{n\omega}{c} = \frac{\sqrt{\epsilon\mu}\,\omega}{c}$$

where v is the velocity of light in the medium, n is the index of refraction, ϵ is the dielectric constant, and μ the permeability of the medium. For optical frequencies $\mu = 1$ and the index of refraction $n = \sqrt{\epsilon}$. The value of ϵ for optical frequencies is not the same as the dc value.

Dispersion, the variation of the velocity of light in matter with frequency, can be described as a change in ϵ with frequency.

Reflection and refraction in dielectrics and conductors are described by Fresnel's equations, in which the interaction of light and matter is treated by the use of ϵ. For metals ϵ is complex and the conductivity σ at the frequency of the light is the imaginary component.

The transverse wave motion of light is apparent in polarization phenomena. Polarization by the use of Polaroid films, a dichroic material, is accomplished by the selective absorption of all amplitude components parallel to a particular direction in the material. A phenomenological description of dichroism depends on the use of a complex dielectric constant $\epsilon = \epsilon' - j\epsilon''$. The imaginary component is proportional to the conductivity σ at that frequency, which is different for the two directions in the dichroic material. The real part, ϵ', may also be different for the two directions. Many substances show anisotropic optical properties. Again, a phenomenological description of events is obtained by the use of a tensor dielectric constant in the material equation $\mathbf{D} = \epsilon\mathbf{E}$. For dielectric, nonabsorbing crystals the components of the tensor ϵ are all real and the interaction phenomenon is called double refraction or birefringence.

A uniaxial, doubly refracting crystal exhibits two indices of refraction depending upon the direction of polarization of the light. The *ordinary* ray is polarized in a direction perpendicular to the plane containing the optic axis and has a constant velocity in all directions. The *extraordinary* ray is polarized in a plane containing the optic axis and has a velocity that depends on its direction in the crystal. These two velocities may be represented by a sphere and an ellipsoid of revolution about the optic axis. Light incident on the crystal decomposes into two beams. The ordinary ray, polarized perpendicular to the optic axis, behaves in a normal fashion. The wavefront of the extraordinary beam is tangential to elliptical wavelets. The extraordinary ray from the origin to the point of tangency of the wavefront diverges in general from the ordinary ray.

In addition to double refraction, quartz shows optical activity, or the ability to rotate plane-polarized light; this phenomenon can be considered as a difference in velocity for right- and left-handed circularly polarized light, which add up to plane polarized light.

Many materials that are normally isotropic in their optical properties can be made anisotropic by the application of mechanical stress, magnetic, or electric fields. Photoelasticity is the field of study of stresses which can be detected by the resulting double refraction in a polariscope. The Faraday and Cotton-Mouton effects are the result of anisotropy induced by magnetic fields, as is the Kerr magneto-optic effect. The Kerr electro-optic effect is the double refraction resulting from the application of an electric field to suitable matter. All of these effects may be described by the use of proper components in the tensor dielectric constant.

Molecular optics deals with the various models proposed to develop these tensor components on the basis of more fundamental concepts of matter. In general, the models are of a quantum-mechanical nature.

REXFORD G. ALEXANDER

Cross-references: *Dielectric Theory, Electromagnetic Theory, Electron Optics, Faraday Effect, Kerr Effect, Refractive Index*

OSCILLATORS

Harmonic Oscillators

Harmonic oscillators are electronic subsystems that generate continuous waves in which each cycle is almost sinusoidal, and successive cycles are nearly identical in magnitude and period. A great majority of harmonic oscillators are *nonlinear* in the sense that some internal current or voltage is markedly nonsinusoidal. The output wave of such oscillators is usually nearly sinusoidal as a result of the smoothing or filtering action of the reactive elements which control the frequency of operation.

A typical and important example of the nonlinear harmonic oscillator is shown in Fig. 1. Under normal operating conditions a relatively large and nearly sinusoidal voltage

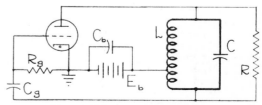

FIG. 1. LC harmonic oscillator.

exists across the *resonator* or *tank circuit* consisting of the inductor L and the capacitor C. The rectifying action of the grid produces a substantial direct voltage across the *grid leak* R_g which biases the tube to such an extent that current flows in the plate circuit only for a short period during each cycle. These pulses of current drive the tuned circuit and produce the useful output.

Power is drawn from the dc supply, represented by the battery E_b. Part of this power is dissipated at the electrodes of the tube, in R_g, and in the parasitic losses of the resonator. However, a substantial fraction of the primary power is available as a useful output to the load R, which is ordinarily coupled inductively rather than directly to the tank circuit. The *efficiency* of power conversion is often of interest and is usually taken as the ratio of the power delivered to the load to that drawn from the dc source. Efficiency values as high as 80 per cent are not uncommon.

In most oscillators the constancy of the frequency of the output is the most important property, and a great deal of work has been done to improve this characteristic. The principal factors that cause frequency variation are changes in the tube and tank circuit parameters owing to applied voltages, temperature, and aging. The influence on frequency of changes in the tube or other active device can be greatly reduced by reducing the losses of the resonator and adjusting the impedance level so that the energy stored in the resonator is large compared to that supplied per cycle. In practice, this requirement means that the useful power output is reduced to the vanishing point and the selectivity Q of the resonator is made as high as possible.

Quartz crystal resonators are greatly favored for frequency stabilization because they have very large values of Q (upwards of 10^4), low values of temperature coefficient (less than $10^{-6}/°C$) and little variation with aging. At frequencies in the microwave region the natural resonances of ammonia, cesium, and rubidium molecules are used for frequency stabilization. Tuning forks and resonators using magnetostriction (*q.v.*) are also sometimes used for frequency control.

Another important example of the non-linear harmonic oscillator is the phaseshift circuit shown in Fig. 2. The frequency stability of this circuit is relatively poor and deteriorates rapidly at frequencies above about 50 kc. However, the complete absence of inductance permits the construction of oscillators which are extremely light, compact, and cheap.

Oscillation occurs at a frequency such that the phase-shift of the three cascaded RC sections just balances the 180° phase-shift inherent in the vacuum tube. A triode with an amplification factor in excess of 29 is required if the three capacitors and associated resistors are all equal. However, the required amplification factor is considerably reduced if the impedance levels of the RC sections are progressively increased (for example, $R_3 = 2R_2 = 4R_1$ and $C_1 = 2C_2 = 4C_3$), or if the number of sections is increased.

Unless some special provision is made, the amplitude of oscillation will always increase to such a level that it is limited by saturation in the tube or transistor used. The nature and degree of this saturation due to nonlinearity is extremely important in determining the harmonic content and other characteristics of a particular oscillator.

In an important class of harmonic oscillators, commonly referred to as linear oscillators, the level of operation is fixed by a thermistor or bias control system with a response time that is very long compared to the period of one cycle. Such oscillators are useful in signal generators and other special

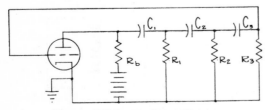

FIG. 2. RC harmonic oscillator.

applications because they have good frequency stability and the harmonic content of the output is extremely low.

Though a constant level of output is ordinarily desirable, it is sometimes necessary to *modulate* the output of an oscillator. The simplest way of producing amplitude modulation is by varying the applied voltage in conformity with the desired output variation. The principal drawback of this method is that a considerable amount of undesirable *incidental frequency modulation* is produced. In other situations it is desirable to vary or modulate the frequency while maintaining the amplitude constant. The common feature of the many arrangements used for this purpose is that the reactance or phase-shift of some portion of the oscillator is made sensitive to the modulation voltage.

Noise of thermal or other origin adversely affects the behavior of oscillators by introducing slight irregularities between the amplitudes and periods of successive cycles. Thus the fundamental component of output has a finite spectral width rather than being a discrete line. At ordinary frequencies and power levels the line width is very small and the effect relatively unimportant. However, the sensitivity of microwave superheterodyne receivers is reduced by noise in the local oscillator. And noise sets demonstrable limits on the accuracy and precision to which frequencies can be generated and measured.

WILLIAM A. EDSON

Relaxation Oscillators

Relaxation oscillators are oscillators with at least two distinct regions of operation in a complete cycle of oscillation. These distinct regions are due to highly nonlinear circuit operation, which produces a nonsinusoidal waveshape. Relaxation oscillators require the following: one or more nonlinear active devices having power gain over some frequency range, one or more energy storage elements, and a source of power. A necessary condition for oscillation is that the circuit should be unstable over a portion of its volt-ampere characteristics, i.e., in this region the free response of the circuit grows with time.

The operation of the relaxation oscillator can be divided into two types of regions, the unstable or regeneration regions and the passive decay or relaxation regions. In the regeneration regions the active devices supply power to the passive part of the circuit, which is moved farther away from its equilibrium conditions. The equilibrium conditions for an oscillator with only dc supplies are zero current flowing through the capacitors, zero voltage across the inductors. The end of the regeneration region is reached when, owing to the nonlinear characteristics of the circuit, it is no longer unstable. In the relaxation regions the energy-storage elements charge or discharge toward their equilibrium conditions. The relaxation process must bring the oscillator back into an unstable region. Many relaxation oscillators have two regeneration regions and two relaxation regions in a complete cycle of operation. Often the time spent in the relaxation regions is much longer than the time spent in the regeneration regions. Thus the period of oscillation and the output waveshape are determined largely by the relaxation process.

Some suitable active devices for use in relaxation oscillators are vacuum triodes and pentodes, transistors (*q.v.*), thyratrons (*q.v.*), and negative-resistance devices such as glow tubes (*q.v.*) and tunnel diodes (*q.v.*). Some energy storage elements that may be used are capacitors, inductors, and sections of transmission lines.

The junction transistor *blocking oscillator* shown in Fig. 3 is an example of a relaxation oscillator with a rectangular output voltage. The important energy-storage element is the transformer magnetizing inductance. If the transistor is initially off (zero collector current) then V_{bb} raises the base voltage to a positive value which brings the transistor into its active region. The resulting collector current is regeneratively fed back through

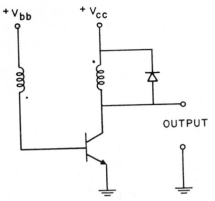

Fɪɢ. 3. Transistor blocking oscillator.

the transformer to the base until the transistor becomes saturated. A relaxation region follows, which lasts until the transformer magnetizing current is reduced to the value that brings the transistor back into the active region. The second regeneration region switches the transistor to the off state and another relaxation region follows. This second relaxation region lasts until the base voltage of the transistor rises to a positive value. The diode prevents the collector voltage from rising above V_{cc} and helps to discharge the transformer magnetizing current in the second relaxation region.

Another relaxation oscillator with a rectangular output voltage is the astable *multivibrator*. This oscillator consists essentially of a two stage resistance-capacitance coupled amplifier with the output of the second stage RC-coupled to the input of the first stage. The circuit is biased so that it has no stable states. Both the blocking oscillator and the astable multivibrator have nearly 100 per cent positive feedback. A simple sawtooth oscillator consists of a glow tube, resistor, and capacitor in series. The capacitor is fed by a constant-current source. If the supply current is less than the value required to sustain the glow tube in conduction, the voltage across the glow tube is a sawtooth.

Some important properties of relaxation oscillators are the output waveshape, the period of oscillation, the stability of the period, the amplitude, and the amplitude stability.

The most commonly required waveshapes are rectangular and sawtooth. An oscillator with a rectangular output waveshape has two regeneration regions and two relaxation regions per cycle of operation. An oscillator with a sawtooth waveshape has one regeneration region and either one or two relaxation regions per cycle of operation. The sawtooth oscillator has two relaxation regions if the output waveform consists of a constant segment, a rising segment, and a rapidly falling segment. The first two segments are produced by relaxation regions, the third by a regeneration region. For either a nearly rectangular or nearly sawtooth waveshape the ratio of regeneration time to relaxation time must be small.

Often the period is easily calculated if it is nearly equal to the relaxation time. Calculation of the period is much more difficult if both the regeneration and relaxation times are significant. The duration of the period can change with variations in the element values owing to aging and environmental changes. Ordinarily the active-device parameters are most susceptible to change. In this case the stability of the period is increased if its dependence on the active-device parameters is reduced. Noise decreases the stability of the period, primarily by introducing an uncertainty in the voltage or current level that determines the start of the regeneration region.

An important property of a given oscillator configuration is its minimum obtainable period of oscillation. Active devices with good high-frequency characteristics, and circuit elements with small values of stray shunt capacitance and lead inductance, are required for an oscillator with a short period of oscillation. As the period of oscillation decreases, the relaxation time decreases and the regeneration time usually increases slightly. Near the minimum period of oscillation the regeneration and relaxation times are of the same order of magnitude, which degrades both the quality of the waveshape and the stability of the period.

The impedance level of the active devices is important when the period of oscillation is either very long or very short. A high impedance is required for a long period if the relaxation time is controlled by the charge or discharge of a capacitance. For very short periods, stray shunt capacitance slows the regeneration time, thus increasing the period. A low impedance level reduces the effect of stray shunt capacitance by decreasing the associated time constants.

The maximum amplitude is limited by the characteristics of the active devices. Good amplitude stability can be obtained with sharp nonlinearities in the operating characteristics of the active devices or by the use of limiting diodes.

DAVID K. LYNN

Cross-references: *Amplifiers, Class A, AB, B, C Operation, Frequency Standards, Modulation and Demodulation, Network Theory, Nonlinear Circuits, Pulse Generation, Sequential Circuits, Switching Circuits*

OSCILLOSCOPES

The cathode-ray oscilloscope is an instrument that displays changing events, in the form of a graph traced on the fluorescent screen of a cathode-ray tube. The display is usually presented in terms of XY coordinates, with time represented horizontally from left to right, and the electrical analog of the event, by a vertical displacement up or down from some zero point (the abscissa and ordinate, respectively).

As the oscilloscope has come into greater use, it has been required to permit more and more accurate measurements of time and amplitude, directly from the display if possible. The engineering efforts to meet these requirements have resulted in sophisticated instruments that are actually small "systems." For example, some instruments meant for broad general-purpose laboratory use contain more than 150 vacuum tubes and semiconductors.

The events that the oscilloscope displays are usually referred to as signals, and the signal parameters determine the requirements the instrument must satisfy. The design of any instrument should reflect the desired range of signals it is expected to handle. For instance, an instrument to deal with a narrow range of uniformly repetitive signals will be quite simple compared to one that is expected to deal with arbitrary signals. Such signals impose the most stringent design requirements, as there is no way of anticipating the *time* of signal occurrence, *how soon* it will occur again (if ever), its *duration*, and its *character* or *content*.

A signal that occurs only once, or whose duration is very short compared with the time until its next occurrence, presents a special problem; how can *all* of such a signal be seen when it must initiate a chain of complex events in order to be displayed? The answer to this special problem in most cases permits viewing almost any other kind of signal.

An oscilloscope consists of three basic elements (four if the common power supply is counted): cathode-ray tube, time base generator, and vertical deflection amplifier. For best performance in a given situation these elements must be designed to go with one another.

The case of a single signal illustrates the relationship between these basic elements. The time relations involved required that the signal to be observed not appear on the vertical deflection plates of the cathode-ray tube until the sweep signal has been impressed on the horizontal deflection plates. Clearly the desired signal must be "held up," stored, or somehow delayed until the sweep generator is well started and the electron beam in the cathode-ray tube is flowing. Normally, this delay is taken care of in the vertical amplifier by an artificial transmission line that requires a large amount of time for the signal to traverse compared to the onset of the signal.

Signal amplifiers in the cathode-ray oscilloscope are usually required to portray accurately both the dc level at which a signal may occur and the signal itself, no matter how transient it may be. At the present time signals as short as 10^{-10} sec are of interest and present-day vacuum-tube amplifier techniques are incapable of handling such a range of signals. This problem has been met in several different ways. Basically, they all reflect the fact that electrical currents and signals take time to move from place to place—whether through the space inside a cathode-ray tube or along a conductor from one component to another. This fact makes it possible to space out electrical elements physically so that they will influence the same electron or signal at different times. Consequently, we can apply the same deflecting field to the same electron or amplify the same signal a number of times in successive instants. Sizable improvements in bandwidth at a given deflection sensitivity in a cathode-ray tube, or in gain at a given bandwidth in an amplifier, are possible in this way. Devices designed in this way are usually referred to as "distributed deflection-plate" cathode-ray tubes or "distributed" amplifiers.

Another way in which an apparent increase in bandwidth can be obtained is by the sampling method. If a signal occurs continuously, it is possible to generate a very sharp voltage pulse whose occurrence is related in time to the signal in question. This pulse is then combined with the signal at successively later instants (in relation to some arbitrary point on the signal), and a series of voltage pulses is developed whose amplitude varies in the same manner as that of the signal in question, but whose duration is expanded by as much as is desired. In other words, a signal of very short duration can be expanded into one of long duration, which can be handled by conventional amplifier techniques. An effective increase in bandwidth of as much as 100 times can be obtained by this method.

In at least one respect the oscilloscope differs from most other instruments: it is expected to display the changes in some phenomena *without distortion* in either time or magnitude. In contrast with most other instruments, it does not deal with only one aspect of a phenomenon, such as an average value, a peak value, the time between two events, the number of events, etc. In these cases the attributes of no concern can be distorted if necessary to facilitate handling and dealing with the desired attributes. The oscilloscope, however, must display the "way" in which something changes and it should be essentially passive in the way it "processes the information" between the receiving of it and the displaying of it.

Consequently, the use of the oscilloscope implies that it "displays" precisely what is put into it. (Otherwise it would not be very useful!) This is not absolutely possible in the general case because certain signals whose characteristics fall near or outside the range of the oscilloscope amplifiers are distorted to some degree. Such distortion is inevitable and the problem is to agree on what kind of distortion is acceptable.

Ordinarily, bandwidth has been considered to be the criterion of performance of an amplifier. However, when an amplifier is dealing with arbitrary signals it is nearly impossible to adjust it to give undistorted response over the whole range of performance by using bandwidth testing techniques. The most effective method that has been developed to test for such response is by the use of step functions or square waves. A step function is a "no-time" transition from one voltage level to another. A square wave is simply a series of step functions "alternating" between two levels of voltage in a regular manner. The value of a square wave is that its quality can be evaluated by eye with a precision unmatched by most conventional, easily used bandwidth-testing techniques. Once the criteria of distortion have been agreed upon, evaluations can be made which are limited only by the skill of the viewer.

Several kinds of distortion of a step function may occur in an amplifier. For instance, it can be adjusted to give the shortest possible risetime, since the step function rises in "no time." Although such an adjustment gives the best possible reproduction of the actual transition, it also causes the signal to "overshoot," adding something to the display that was not present in the original signal. Conversely, the amplifier can be adjusted so that the rapid rise is completely obscured and the result is a gradual transition from one voltage level to another with no distortion of stable voltage levels. However, there is an optimum region of performance where the transition takes place as rapidly as is possible under the circuit conditions but with no overshoot. In this situation the circuit itself determines the response to a step function, the deteriorated portion can be computed from the observed risetime and the known amplifier risetime and, most important, there is never any question whether a particular element of the display is due to the amplifier or is present in the signal. If something is present in the display, it is present to at least that degree in the signal. It *may* be present to a greater degree than the display indicates, in which case it can be estimated to a risetime about one fifth that of the amplifier.

The problem of determining fidelity of response resembles a merry-go-round. The testing square wave must be of high enough quality to avoid contributing any distortion of its own. *How do we know?* Only by having a measuring system with capabilities much better than the testing square wave. *How do we know this measuring system is good?* By having a testing, etc., etc.

These are some of the exceedingly difficult problems facing the oscilloscope designer when he seeks to design an instrument that operates near the limits of technological capability.

J. E. DAY

Cross-references: *Amplifiers, Cathode-Ray Tubes (Display), Pulse Generation, Radar Displays, Solid-State Displays, Storage Tubes, Television, Television (Color).*

P

PACKAGING

The major problems in electronic packaging are those of component connection, system interconnection, and heat transfer or removal. These problems become increasingly acute when reduction in equipment volume is required at no reduction in system capability or complexity. The digital-data processor, as one class of machines in particular, emphasizes these problems.

Why the digital-data processor should lead in these areas is evident when its system operating requirements are compared with those of communication equipment. In this latter class the information is processed in series by (in general) changing its frequency as a single-line operation. Except for some operator control in selection of the exact functions to be performed, the machine operating sequence is fixed by the original design. By contrast, the digital data processor requires information on many lines to perform the desired function. This operation is under the control of other parts of the machine so that the desired function and direction is provided at each step. Another point of difference may be found in that data processors, such as a high-speed parallel digital computer, require from 30,000 to 50,000 components.

The other requirements of physical assembly and environmental protection can be met by the usual mechanical design procedure. But for the proper solution to the problems originally stated, the design must be based on the considerations of the whole machine. To illustrate, consider the design of a digital computer. From the nature of the application some measure of system complexity can be derived. Next, the number of functional elements, and hence the total number of components, can be estimated. The physical design can now be started, based on specifications of volume, environmental conditions, speed of operation, and cost.

These last two items may need further explanation. Speed of operation in a digital computer is generally taken as the time interval between successive operations. When, because of the physical size of the machine, the time it takes to communicate from one part to another becomes an appreciable part of this basic time period, it can become a limitation on the upper speed of operation. Line delays of the order of 3–4 nanoseconds (ns) per foot of length may be expected for twisted pair wires. Delays of 2 ns/ft occur in coaxial cable. Another aspect of speed is initial current necessary to charge the stray capacity associated with each foot of interconnecting wiring. This drain on the source driver can limit the number of loads the driver can service, which in turn may set the requirement for either a larger driver or additional drivers. In either case the cost and size of the machine may have to be increased to handle the stray capacity needs.

The effects of cost are not only in the purchase of the components but also in the method of assembly; materials for cabinets and structure; shop floor space for assembly, erection and test; and in handling and shipping. It may be difficult to assign a dollar value to each of these factors, but they all press in the direction of making the machine as compact as possible.

At this point the general size, number of components, and class of components to be used have been determined. The determination of size of the circuit board and the function or group of functions to be performed on each can be determined from the system design. By means of a graphical layout of the function requirements and their interconnection, the necessary adjustments in grouping and localization can be made. The threefold objectives of this work are as follows:

(1) To arrive at an initial interconnection scheme that results in a reasonable density of wires. In particular, to avoid congestion and exceptionally long lengths.

(2) To group the related functions required on each board so as to facilitate the interconnection requirements. In making this grouping, one must consider the generalization of the design so that a minimum number of different boards are required. This generalization may lead to the inclusion of some parts that are not always used, but this loss is expected to be made up in the reduced cost of designing and producing fewer types.

(3) Having determined the types of boards required, one can place a limit on the number of connections necessary between the board and the interconnection plane. If miniaturization is an objective, the number of connections and the minimum distance between connections sets the least size of one of the board dimensions independently of the component size.

The minimum size of the circuit board can now be determined. From objective (3) the length is fixed; from the requirements of the functions to be performed and the size of components the area is fixed; and from the considerations of interconnection the minimum distance between boards is fixed.

The two major techniques for the fabrication of boards have been (1) to use printed-circuit boards with the component leads inserted into the board and dip-soldered or (2) to use welded connections between component leads.

The question of the reliability of connections made by these techniques has been one of the strong motivations in the development of deposited-in-place components and connections. This is not to say that these techniques, when practiced correctly, do not yield excellent results but that the desire is to remove the separateness of each opera-

tion and to decrease the total number of connections. By going directly from the element of one component to that of the other, the number of connections is cut in half.

The heat-transfer problem is one that requires increasingly more attention as system volume is decreased. For open-card construction in cabinets, it is usually sufficient to circulate ambient air. As component density is increased, cold plates and/or refrigerated air is required. Ultimately, however, the air space has to be removed if anything like the packaging density inherent in the component is to be achieved in a system. Replacement of convective heat transfer through air by conductive transfer through metal can result in a volume reduction by a factor of 10 to 15 without a change in component size.

Circuit construction in what may be taken as essentially two dimensions favors the transfer of heat since it provides the maximum surface area for the volume contained. Even when the circuits are capsulated, the maximum distance to a surface is one-half of the thinnest dimension.

In order that inclusion of the heat exchanger may be effective without unduly increasing the volume of the system, the heat exchanger must be allowed for during the initial design phase. Since methods for heat removal ultimately depend upon the exact nature of the application, what to do with the heat once it is extracted from the electronic package has to be resolved to comply with the intended use. For example, in a ground-based installation it may be sufficient to use water through the heat exchanger. In other applications, a coolant may already be available (cold plates, liquid nitrogen). If the total operating period is fixed, then expendable coolants may be employed. In this case it is only necessary to supply a sufficient volume of coolant so as to limit the temperature during the operating period.

STANLEY SCHNEIDER

Cross-references: *Integrated Circuits, Miniaturization, Modular Construction, Printed Circuits*

PARAMAGNETISM

Substances containing particles with a permanent magnetic moment μ have paramagnetic properties. These particles are, in general, ions of the transition elements of which those of the iron group and the group of the rare-earth metals are the most important. In the partly filled electronic shells in these ions the electronic magnetic moments, which may be orbital and (or) spin moments, do not compensate each other, so that a net magnetic moment results. These magnetic dipoles are oriented in a magnetic field H. However, because of the thermal agitation this orientation is only partial. According to quantum theory only discrete orientations of the moment with respect to the magnetic field are possible, such that the component μ_H of the magnetic moment in the direction of the field has special values, corresponding to the values $-\mu_H H$ of the dipolar magnetic energy. The numbers of dipoles in one of these energy states are proportional to $\exp(\mu_H H / kT)$, where k is Boltzmann's constant and T the absolute temperature. The total magnetic moment σ of a group of N dipoles is therefore

$$N \sum [\mu_H \exp(\mu_H H / kT)] / \sum [\exp(\mu_H H / kT)],$$

represented in Fig. 1. For not too large values of H/T (and when one is not working in the temperature region of liquid helium this condition is practically always fulfilled) only the beginning of the curve is realized and σ is proportional to H/T (Curie's law). For large values of H/T one approaches the state of paramagnetic saturation, where all dipoles are oriented in the direction of the magnetic field and which can be realized for some salts at liquid helium temperatures.

So far only the magnetic energy has been taken into account. But attention should be given to the fact that, in general, the energy depends also on the orientation of the dipole with respect to the lattice, that is, to the crystalline electric field caused by the surrounding ions or molecules. Water molecules are often very important in this respect. Also, the magnetic interaction can play a role, and sometimes an exchange interaction. The result is that in first approximation Curie's law can often be replaced by a Curie-Weiss law: $\sigma = CH/(T - \theta)$ or $\chi = C/(T - \theta)$, where $\chi = \sigma/H$ is called the magnetic susceptibility and C and θ are constants. Here as in Curie's law C proves to be $N\mu^2/3k$.

From the measurements of χ as a function of temperature (e.g., by determining the force on a sample in an inhomogeneous field), the values of the magnetic moments of the ions can be calculated and, what is more important, information can be obtained on the crystalline field.

In switching on a magnetic field, the dipoles in a sample in this field change their energy. As the heat exchange with the lattice is not instantaneous, it gives rise to relaxation effects. These effects can be studied in alternating fields parallel to a static field. The absorption and dispersion effects, found in these circumstances, are the most pronounced when the frequency of the field corresponds to the relaxation time.

In an alternating field perpendicular to the static field paramagnetic resonance can be studied.

J. VAN DEN HANDEL

Cross-references: *Diamagnetism, Electron Paramagnetic Resonance, Ferromagnetism, Magnetism*

PARAMETRIC AMPLIFIERS

Beam-Type Parametric Amplifiers

Parametric amplifiers convert power from an ac source (the pump) at frequency f_p into

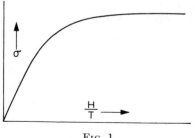

FIG. 1

power proportional to an input signal at frequency f_s. They are important in electronic communication systems because they add less noise to the input signal than conventional amplifiers, which convert dc power into signal power.

Electron-beam parametric amplifiers are very similar in their principles of operation to traveling-wave tubes (q.v.); a thermionic cathode generates an electron beam, which interacts with the electric field on a distributed (or lumped) circuit so that net electronic gain results. In a traveling-wave tube, the electric field alternates at the signal frequency only; in an electron-beam parametric amplifier, an additional electric field that alternates at the pump frequency also interacts with the electron beam, making possible very low-noise gain over relatively broad bandwidths, at least in principle. As in traveling-wave tubes, there are three types of electron-beam parametric amplifiers: longitudinal-field, transverse-field, and crossed-field devices. The usual frequencies of operation range from about 100 Mc to over 4 kMc; higher frequencies are possible, but require increasingly smaller microwave circuits, which are difficult to fabricate.

To understand the low-noise properties of an electron-beam parametric amplifier, consider the normal modes of propagation on an electron beam. These modes generally occur in pairs, with positive and negative kinetic power, respectively. A mode has positive kinetic power when the power contained in the electron beam with the mode propagating exceeds the power contained in the unexcited beam, and a mode has negative kinetic power when the excited beam's power is less than an unexcited beam's power. If a negative-kinetic-power mode with the proper phase constant is coupled to an adjacent circuit, electromagnetic power is induced on the circuit. The circuit and the beam are the only carriers of ac power, and the circuit power is always positive. If the circuit power has increased, the power in the beam must have decreased, i.e., the magnitude of the negative kinetic power mode

must have increased. This interaction leads to the exponential gain of traveling-wave tubes. A mode with positive kinetic power couples to a passive circuit in the same manner as two passive circuits couple. If the phase velocities of the circuit and the electron-beam mode with positive kinetic power are identical, then in one-half a coupling wavelength, all energy on the beam mode is transferred to the circuit, and vice versa.

The above results also hold for noise power in the beam modes generated by thermionic emission. Noise power in a negative-kinetic-power mode is amplified by coupling to a passive circuit, but noise in a positive-kinetic-power mode can be completely coupled off the electron beam while signal power to be amplified is simultaneously coupled onto the beam's positive-kinetic-power mode.

Analysis shows that the positive-kinetic-power mode can be amplified only by parametric means. Moreover, the interaction between the electron beam modulated at f_s and the pump field which alternates at f_p produces modulation of the beam at least one new frequency, $f_p - f_s = f_i$, the so-called idle frequency. Similarly, any excitation of the beam at the idle frequency produces a corresponding excitation of the beam at the signal frequency. An important consequence of power transfer between these two frequencies is that noise must be coupled off the beam at both the signal and the idle frequencies for low-noise amplification, otherwise noise at the idle frequency is transferred to the signal frequency, spoiling the device performance. If the beam interaction becomes nonlinear, noise can be transferred to the signal frequency from additional frequencies also; this nonlinear interaction has prevented certain electron-beam parametric amplifiers from being low-noise devices in practice. In most electron-beam parametric amplifiers, the signal and idle frequencies are kept within the band of frequencies at which noise has been coupled from the positive kinetic-power mode of the beam; i.e., f_p is approximately twice f_s. In this degenerate mode of operation, one coupler therefore suffices.

An electron-beam parametric amplifier may be divided into three interaction regions. In the input-coupler region, noise is coupled from a positive kinetic power mode of the electron beam, and an input signal is simultaneously coupled onto this mode. In the pump region, the signal that modulates the beam is amplified parametrically; and in the output-coupler region, the signal is coupled from the beam to a circuit, and transmitted to the load where it is to be utilized. It is crucial that no noise is added to the electron beam mode after it enters the input coupler, if low-noise amplification is to be achieved. Noise can be added if electrons in the beam are intercepted by any circuit element before leaving the output coupler (partition noise). Beam noise can also be transferred from other frequencies to the signal frequency, as mentioned earlier, by nonlinear effects, or in some cases, by an improper centering of the electron beam in the pump circuit. The pump can also couple two modes on the electron beam; if one of these modes contains noise, part of this noise generally appears at the output of the amplifier, with a corresponding decrease in signal-to-noise ratio. However, it has been recently shown that this parametric coupling of modes allows the noise to be coupled *from* the *negative* kinetic power modes on an electron beam. A noise-free negative kinetic power mode can in principle give exponential (traveling-wave-tube) gain with essentially a 0-db noise figure.

The most successful electron-beam parametric amplifier proposed so far is the transverse-field, cyclotron-wave amplifier of Adler, Hrbek, and Wade. This amplifier is unconditionally stable and gives 30 db gain with a double-channel noise-figure of about 1 db at 500 Mc. Its bandwidth of approximately 10 per cent is determined by the input and output couplers, which are called Cuccia couplers, and consist of two parallel metal plates spaced symmetrically about the beam axis. As the electron beam passes between these two plates, the alternating electric field generated between them by the input signal increases the radius of cyclotron rotation in direct proportion to the signal. This cyclotron motion is amplified by an electric field at the pump frequency impressed on the electrodes of a quadrupole structure, through which the beam next moves. Opposite electrodes of the quadrupole are excited in phase, adjacent electrodes are in quadrature. The maximum cyclotron radius, and therefore the gain, is limited by interception. The amplified beam next passes between the plates of a coupler identical with the input coupler, where the signal is transferred to the circuit and delivered to the output load.

T. E. EVERHART

Diode Parametric Amplifiers

Parametric amplification takes place when the value of a reactive element in a circuit supporting a signal frequency is varied in such a fashion that energy from a source external to the signal circuit is stored in the reactive element and enhances the signal. Such amplification can take place through the medium of the voltage-dependent capacitance associated with the junction between the p- and n-type material in a special semiconductor diode called a *varactor*.

A mechanical model of such a parametric or reactance amplifier would be one in which the plates of a capacitor in a resonant circuit are mechanically separated each time the charge storage is maximum and restored to their original position each time the charge is zero. A periodic motion of the plates, with a corresponding periodic change in the value of the capacitance, would then occur at twice the frequency of the signal voltage. The fact that an alternating force must be applied to vary the reactive element is a fundamental aspect of parametric amplification.

In the varactor, layers of charge at the junction are periodically displaced by the application of an alternating voltage across the terminals of the device. This operation corresponds to varying the capacitance in the equivalent circuit of the varactor. Since there is only a small displacement of the charge, the capacitance can be varied at extremely high frequencies—well into the microwave and possibly millimeter region.

Various forms of parametric amplifiers are possible. One simple embodiment consists of two resonant cavities, one for the signal and one for the pump, with a single diode mounted in such a way that the fields in both cavities can act on the junction. The amplifier in this form is a one-port device, but a circulator may be used to separate input and output.

If the frequency of the ac source or pump is exactly twice that of the signal, as in the mechanical model described above, energy can be transferred from the pump to the signal only if the two voltages have the proper phase relationship. Since this relationship is difficult to achieve in practice, the signal frequency is usually made lower than half the pump frequency and the signal circuit is designed with sufficient bandwidth to support a resonance at a third frequency equal to pump minus signal frequency; or a third resonant circuit may be added. The operation is then called nondegenerate and the third frequency is called the idler, lower-sideband, or difference frequency. Power is also extracted from the pump at the idler frequency but the phase relationship between pump and signal is now automatically maintained.

To increase the bandwidth, the circuitry of the single-diode amplifier may be modified or a number of diodes may be used as lumped elements in transmission lines which support signal, idler, and pump frequencies. This form of the amplifier is called a traveling-wave parametric amplifier and has an advantage over the single diode amplifier of being unilateral and broadband. In theory, a distributed junction could be used and has been analyzed, but no equivalent semiconductor device has been fabricated.

If the varactors used in parametric amplifiers were purely reactive, no noise would be introduced in the amplification process. There is, however, a resistance of the order of a few ohms in series with the capacitance associated with the junction. Thermal noise originates in this resistance but is small compared to the shot noise associated with electron flow in vacuum tubes. Noise figures of the order of 1 db can be obtained with parametric amplifiers at room temperatures and lower noise figures can be obtained by cooling the varactor.

Some of the fundamental limits on the performance of the varactor parametric amplifier are quite logically determined by the characteristics of the diode. Of great importance is the ratio of the reactive to the resistive component of the varactor impedance at the operating frequency. The frequency at which the quality factor Q becomes equal to unity is referred to as the cutoff frequency f_{co} of the varactor. Since the capacitance is a function of bias voltage, Q and f_{co} are also voltage dependent. Since the capacitance decreases monotonically with reverse bias, the maximum cutoff frequency is associated with maximum reverse voltage applied to the varactor. Capacitance values less than 1 $\mu\mu f$ can be achieved and the series resistance can be of the order of a few ohms so that cutoff frequencies of 100 kMc are typical of what has been achieved. With further improvements in varactors, this figure will no doubt be increased considerably.

Of importance in achieving high cutoff frequencies is the type of semiconductor material used, the area of the junction, and the way in which the junction is formed. These factors influence the values of capacitance and resistance achieved and the change in capacitance available with change in voltage. For maximum performance in an amplifier it is also extremely important that the electrical contacts to the junction and the packaging of the unit should introduce as little fixed reactance as possible. In very-high-frequency amplifiers the semiconductor element may have no packaging, but be mounted directly in the circuit.

SHIRLEY W. HARRISON

Solid-State Parametric Amplifiers

The bulk properties of solid state materials can be used in place of the more common diode or electron beam, to provide the time-varying reactance of a parametric amplifier, and may offer advantages in some applications. The transverse rf magnetic susceptibility of ferromagnetic materials depends on the strength of the rf magnetic field, and ferroelectric materials exhibit a nonlinear electric susceptibility (dielectric constant). By applying a strong rf pumping field, a time-varying reactive element can thus be obtained. Since parametric amplifiers are primarily used for their low-noise properties, at frequencies where the noise performance of conventional amplifiers deteriorates, uhf and microwave devices are of greatest interest.

Ferromagnetic Amplifier. For high-frequency applications, a ferromagnetic insulator such as ferrite or garnet is commonly used. The sample is placed in a microwave circuit, and the combination of sample and circuit must support the pump, signal, and idler frequencies. These frequencies must fulfill the relation $f_p = f_s + f_i$, for regenerative operation. Frequency conversion is also possible, if $f_p = |\pm f_s \pm f_i|$. A dc field is applied to magnetize the material, and it is convenient to discuss this device in terms of the magnetization vector $\mathbf{M}$, which provides coupling between the signal and idler modes. Two principal classes of amplifier can be differentiated by the relative orientation of rf pump magnetic field and dc polarizing field.

Transverse Pumping. With the pump field at right angles to the dc field $\mathbf{H}$, the magnetization is driven in precession about the dc field at the pump frequency and describes a cone of precession angle θ between $\mathbf{M}$ and $\mathbf{H}$. Usually the uniform mode of precession is used as the pump mode. A large precession angle is desirable for parametric amplifica-

tion; therefore, the circuit is tuned to f_p and the dc field is adjusted for ferromagnetic resonance. Then $\theta = h/\Delta H$, where h is the pump field strength and ΔH is the uniform-mode linewidth.

Four types of transverse pumping operation have been proposed, using different circuit and sample properties to provide the necessary resonant modes.

(1) Electromagnetic (EM) type: The microwave circuit is made resonant to the signal and idler frequencies f_s and f_i. If one mode has a magnetic field component along $\mathbf{H}$, and the other mode has a transverse component, these modes are coupled by the precessing magnetization driven by the pump.

(2) Semistatic (SS) type: The ferromagnetic sample has many modes of oscillation, called magnetostatic modes, in which the magnetization precesses with different phase in various parts of the sample. One of these modes can be used as signal or idler mode. Efficiency is greater than in the EM type, because more stored energy is within the sample.

(3) Magnetostatic (MS) type: Both signal and idler modes can be magnetostatic modes of the sample, but parasitic oscillations of unwanted magnetostatic mode pairs limits the use of this type.

(4) Modified semistatic (MSS) type: The uniform mode of ferromagnetic resonance can be used as idler, with the pump at a higher frequency. Efficiency is not as high as for SS operation, because the pump is not at ferromagnetic resonance, and θ is diminished.

The performance of these various types of amplifier is summarized in Table I, which shows the threshold pump-field strength h_{th} at which the amplifier gain becomes unity, an approximate expression for the maximum filling factor F of each type of device, and the maximum voltage gain-fractional bandwidth product $g^{1/2}B$ determined by parasitic oscillations of sample modes (spin waves).

Frequency conversion can be obtained by coupling a load to the idler, and techniques

TABLE I. Properties of transverse-pumped ferromagnetic amplifier.

Type / Performance	EM	SS	MS	MSS
$h_{th}/\Delta H$	$\dfrac{1}{F_{EM}}\dfrac{2\pi f_s/\gamma}{4\pi M}\dfrac{2}{\sqrt{Q_1 Q_2}}$	$\dfrac{1}{F_{SS}}\sqrt{\dfrac{\Delta H_2}{4\pi M}}\dfrac{1}{\sqrt{Q_1}}$	$\dfrac{1}{F_{MS}}\sqrt{\dfrac{\Delta H_1}{4\pi M}}\sqrt{\dfrac{\Delta H_2}{4\pi M}}$	$\dfrac{1}{F_{MSS}}\dfrac{2\pi f_s/\gamma}{\Delta H}\cdot\sqrt{\dfrac{\Delta H}{4\pi M}}\dfrac{1}{\sqrt{Q_1}}$
F	v/V	$\sqrt{v/V}$	1	$\sqrt{v/V}$
$g^{1/2}B(\beta Q_1/2)$	$\tfrac{1}{2}F_{EM}^2 Q_1 Q_2 \dfrac{4\pi M\Delta H_k}{(2\pi f_s/\gamma)^2} - 1$	$2F_{SS}^2 Q_1 \dfrac{\Delta H_k}{\Delta H_2} - 1$	$2F_{MS}^2 \dfrac{(\alpha\Delta H_k)^2}{\Delta H_1\Delta H_2} - 1$	$2F_{MSS}^2 Q_1 \dfrac{\Delta H_k}{\Delta H} - 1$

Q_1, Q_2 are unloaded Q of signal and idler cavities; ΔH_1, ΔH_2 are magnetostatic mode linewidths; ΔH_k is spin wave linewidth; v is sample volume; V is cavity volume; $\gamma/2\pi = 2.8$ Mc/oersted; α,β are parameters of order unity. Other notation is defined in the text.

have been proposed to obtain amplification at a frequency higher than the pump frequency. It has also been suggested that spin wave resonances in thin metal films, or acoustic modes of the sample, might be used.

Most experimental devices have employed pump frequencies of 5 to 10 kMc. In EM operation, the lowest reported threshold pump power is 500 w, using manganese ferrite, and typical observed $g^{1/2}B$ is about 30 Mc. Operation of the SS type has been reported with only 40 w of pump power. Performance of the MSS type is comparable to EM type, both in pump power, and operating parameters. Superregenerative operation has also been demonstrated, with very high gain. No satisfactory noise figure data have been obtained on these devices, because pulsed operation was used to avoid sample heating. An MS type amplifier has not been achieved.

Longitudinal Pumping. In a configuration with h parallel to H, and with signal and idler provided by magnetostatic modes, the low pump power of MS operation is retained. Parasitic oscillations do not interfere with amplification because only certain pairs of modes can be pumped parametrically in this arrangement. These modes are determined by the frequency condition $f_p = f_s + f_i$. and by selection rules on magnetostatic mode indices. The threshold pump field strength is

$$h_{th} = (1/F_L)\sqrt{\Delta H_1\Delta H_2}(2\pi f_p)/(\gamma 4\pi M)$$

where F_L depends on the magnetostatic mode pair used, and may be near unity. For optimum signal circuit loading, the gain-bandwidth product is approximately

$$g^{1/2}B = \gamma\sqrt{\Delta H_1\Delta H_2}/2\pi f_s.$$

In this amplifier, pumping cannot occur at the difference frequency $f_p = |f_s - f_i|$.

Experimental results have been reported on two amplifiers. Both used an yttrium iron garnet sphere ($\Delta H = 0.3$ oersted), with the $3\bar{1}1$ and 310 magnetostatic modes as signal and idler. Pump frequency was in X-band, and less than 0.5 w pump power was required. Signal and idler frequency were about half pump frequency, but operation was nondegenerate. Gain of 20 db was observed, with bandwidth 50 to 100 kc. The measured noise figure was about 13 db, although sample temperature rose to nearly 400°K. Sources of noise are not clear at this time, and may be improved by cooling the sample.

Resonant-type amplifiers have limited bandwidth and poor gain stability. To overcome this, traveling-wave ferromagnetic amplifiers have been proposed, but no experimental work has been reported.

Ferroelectric Amplifier. The use of ferroelectric materials in parametric amplifiers has also been proposed. One possibility is to construct straightforward analogs of the various diode amplifiers. A different approach is to make a very small cavity of ferroelectric material and place it in waveguide where the parameters are modulated by the pump electric field. For $(BaSr)TiO_3$ material, dimensions would be of the order of a millimeter in the microwave region. Gain of 20 db is predicted at about 5 kw of pump power. By diluting the material with a nonferroelectric material, the dielectric constant can be reduced to permit larger sample dimensions and larger fractional changes in the dielectric constant. Calculated pump power is thus reduced to about 1 w. A traveling-wave configuration in stripline should give 20 db gain with about 200 w of pump power, using the diluted barium-strontium titanate.

Nonlinear behavior of ferroelectric materials has been observed at microwave frequencies, and signal mixing has been accomplished, but no operable microwave parametric amplifiers have been reported.

RICHARD W. DAMON

Cross-references: *Coupled-Mode Theory, Ferroelectricity, Masers, Millimeter-Wave Generation, Noise, Traveling-Wave Tubes*

PARAMETRON

The parametron is a digital computing element based on the principle of parametric oscillation and was invented by E. Goto in 1954 at the University of Tokyo (*Proc. IRE*, August 1959). A scheme similar to the parametron has also been proposed independently by the late Professor von Neumann (*ibid.*, April 1959).

A parametron element is essentially a resonant circuit in which either the inductance or capacitance is made to vary periodically. The magnetic parametron of Fig. 1(a) consists of coils wound on two magnetic ferrite cores $F1$, $F2$, a tuning capacitor C, a damping resistor R and a input trans-

former T. Each of the cores has two windings, which are connected in a balanced configuration so that the exciting current of frequency $2f$ and applied to coils 1, 1' varies the tuning inductance L periodically at frequency $2f$. Similarly, in the capacitive parametron of Fig. 1(b), an exciting voltage of frequency $2f$ is applied between the neutral point of two nonlinear capacitors C', C'' and the neutral point of the tuning inductance L so that the effective tuning capacity varies periodically at frequency $2f$. In each type, the circuit is made to resonate at frequency f and oscillation at frequency f, which is the $\frac{1}{2}$ subharmonic of the exciting frequency $2f$, is generated in the resonant circuit. This kind of phenomenon is generally called parametric oscillation since the oscillation is energized by varying the value of the circuit parameters, L or C in the above case. In a mechanical system, a playground swing is one of the most familiar examples of this phenomenon. The following will give an intuitive explanation of the phenomenon. Because of the balanced configuration and the difference of the frequencies, voltage with exciting frequency $2f$ is not induced in the resonant circuit. On the other hand, if a weak resonant current of frequency f exists in the resonant circuit, voltages at beat frequencies $2f \pm f$, the difference being of the same frequency f as the resonant current, are induced owing to cross modulation. If the resonant current has an appropriate phase relationship to the exciting current, the phase of the induced voltage is in the positive-feedback direction so that the resonant current increases very rapidly and reaches a stationary amplitude.

The subharmonic parametric oscillation thus generated has a remarkable property in that the oscillation is stable in either of two phases which differ by π radians. Utilizing this fact, a parametron represents and stores one binary digit, "0" or "1", by the choice between these two phases "0" or "π" radian. The stationary oscillation of a parametron is extremely stable, and if one should try to change the state of an oscillat-

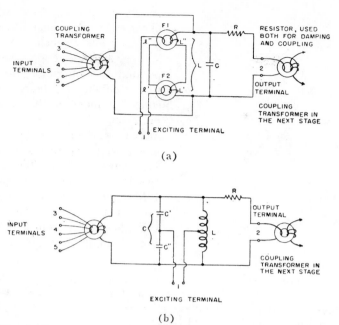

(a)

(b)

FIG. 1. Circuit diagram of parametrons; (a) magnetic type, (b) capacitive type.

ing parametron from one state to another just by applying a control voltage directly to the resonant circuit, a signal source as powerful as the parametron itself would be necessary. This difficulty is got around by providing a quenching means for the oscillation, and making the choice between the two modes, i.e., the rewriting of information, by a weak control signal applied at the beginning of each build up period as shown in Fig. 2. This fact may be regarded as a kind of amplification since the phase mode of oscillation of large amplitude is determined in accordance with the phase of a very weak control signal and the amplifying mechanism may best be understood as superregeneration

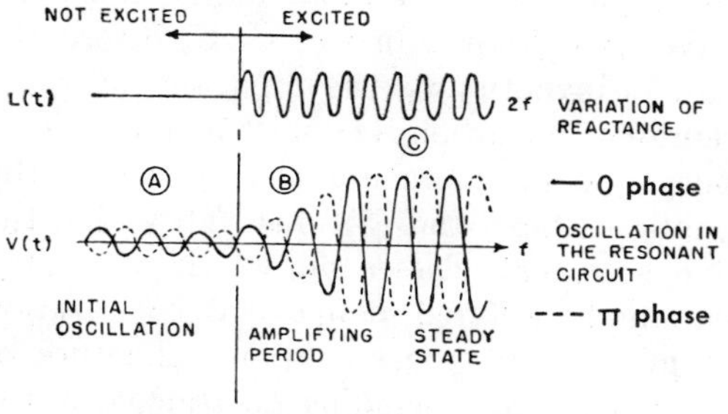

with the phase quantized to either of two values, 0 or π radian.

Usually, the parametrons in a digital system are arranged in three groups, labeled I, II, and III, and the oscillations of each group are simultaneously (and the oscillation of different groups successively) interrupted in a cyclic manner by switching the exciting currents of each group as shown in Fig. 3. The interruption of oscillations causes the superregenerative action and the cyclic interruption gives a unilateral nature to the transmission of information, namely from group I to II, II to III, and III to I.

Parametrons can perform logical operations on the basis of a majority principle. Figure 4 shows a fundamental majority circuit, in which the output oscillations of three parametrons X, Y, and Z of group I are applied to parametron U of group II as its

FIG. 2. Oscillation of parametrons.

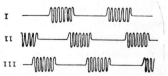

FIG. 3. The exciting current of three groups, I. II, and III.

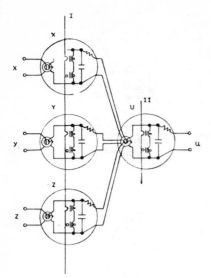

FIG. 4. A majority circuit.

small initial oscillation voltage. As the algebraic sum of the voltages from X, Y, and Z serves for the effective input to U, the phase of U is determined in accordance to the majority of phases of the former three. AND and OR operations are included in the majority operation. Fixing one input, say Z, to a constant "0" we obtain an AND circuit for the remaining two inputs X and Y. Similarly, fixing Z to "1," an OR circuit is obtained. Negation is made very simply by reversing the polarity of coupling. Hence, by combining the above basic circuits we can construct any complicated digital systems such as general-purpose computers with a single component—the parametron.

At present all of the commercially available parametrons in Japan are of magnetic type and are made of ferrite material. Extreme long life, high reliability, and low cost are believed to be the merits of the ferrite parametrons; they have already been applied to computers, telegram and telephone exchange devices, numerically controlled machine tools, and to scientific equipments.

The present ferrite parametrons are rather slow in speed (about 100-kc clock) and high in power consumption (about 100 mw). These demerits, however, may be improved by future development. Capacitive parametrons, especially those utilizing the nonlinear capacity of backbiased semiconductor p-n junctions, are believed to be most suited for very high speed operation. Sterzer reports parametric subharmonic oscillation at microwave frequencies. The replacement of ferrite cores by metallic thin films is also very promising. Compared to ferrite parametrons, metalic thin-film parametrons may have much wider operating temperature range, say from $-273°C$ to $200°C$, higher operating speed, several tens of megacycles pump and 1 Mc clock, and lower power consumption (less than 1 mw). The main problem of thin-film parametrons is in the mass production technique of uniform thin films.

EIICHI GOTO

Cross-references: *Digital Computers, Ferrites, Logic Circuits, Parametric Amplifiers, Switching Circuits*

PATENTS

A patent, under United States law, is the grant to its owner of the right to exclude others from the use of an invention for 17 years from the date of issuance of the patent. In consideration of this grant, the patentee discloses the invention so clearly and completely that the public will know how to practice the invention after the patent expires. Also he pays fees to the Government at the time of filing the patent application and of issuance of the patent, these fees now being $30 each.

For *patentability* the invention (1) must not have been published in any country or in public use in the U. S., in either case for more than 1 year prior to the date of filing the application for the patent; (2) must not have been known in the U. S. before the date of invention by the applicant; (3) must represent invention; (4) must be useful for a purpose not immoral and not injurious to the public welfare; and (5) must fall within the five statutory classes on which only may patents be granted, namely (a) composition of matter, (b) process (of manufacture or treatment now including treatment of the human body), (c) machine, (d) design (ornamental appearance), or (3) plant produced asexually, tuber-propagated plants being excluded.

Special regulations relate to atomic energy developments and subjects directly affecting national security. No U. S. patent on any subject is valid if the subject matter is disclosed in an application for patent filed abroad earlier than 6 months after filing the U. S. application, unless permission for export of the information is obtained from the Patent Office.

Systems of doing business and also *scientific principles*, as distinguished from the application of those principles, are not patentable.

The *test for invention* is unobviousness, at the time the invention was made, to a person having ordinary skill in the art to which the invention pertains and knowing all that has gone before, as shown by publication any where or public use in the U. S. When reliance for patentability is placed on a new mixture of components that have been used separately, it must be shown that there is some unexpected coaction between the ingredients and not just the additive effects of the several materials. It is not necessary, however, for the unobvious result to be the principal result sought from the mixture; where the over-all therapeutic effect, for instance, is evident in advance, a surprising result may arise in the preservation of one ingredient by another.

The *inventor* is the one who contributes the inventive concept in workable detail, not the one who demonstrates it or tests it, unless the experimenter must supply some inventive or unobvious step to make the concept operative. When error arises in the initial designation of inventor without deceptive intent, an inventor's name may be added or, in the case of joint inventors, subtracted, these changes being permissible after the application is filed or even after the patent is issued or suit filed thereon. Proper credit for inventions promotes morale in a research organization.

Patent rights of the employee are commonly stated in a contract. In the absence of such contract, the rights for various classes of employees under various circumstance will be understood to be as follows:

(1) The employee is not hired to make inventions. He makes an invention on his own time and with his own materials; the invention belongs to him. He makes the invention on his employer's time and with the employer's materials; the invention belongs to the employee but the employer has a shopright to use the invention in his own factories without extra payment to the employee.

(2) The inventor is employed for research or under other circumstances showing that making inventions is a part of the work normally expected of him. The invention belongs to the employer if it is in the particular field of work assigned to the employee.

Data for the patent application, whether the data are presented orally or in writing, should include: brief discussion of the closest prior art; difference from it and the unobvious result of the change from what has been done before; the general properties necessary for each of the classes of components or reactants in a chemical case and at least three specific examples of each class; ranges of proportions for each class of materials that may be used without loss of operability of the invention; ranges of temperatures, times, or other conditions, if any, that are critical; several examples illustrating in diverse manners methods of practicing the invention successfully, including the best manner; and sketches in case a drawing is required and unless the inventor is to confer personally with the attorney or his draftsman. In all such presentations, the inventor should use the technical form and avoid unnecessary legalistic language.

In *interpreting patents*, claims are considered to cover all that they do not exclude. Adding to a process or composition a step or an ingredient not recited in a claim does not avoid infringement of the claim. Omitting an essential part of the claim, on the other hand, does ordinarily avoid the claim.

Interferences are declared by the Patent Office when two or more applicants seek patent on the same invention. The first inventor, to whom the patent will issue, will be the one who first reduced the invention to practice and tested it adequately for the intended use, if such test is required to show the utility. The inventor who first conceived of the invention (and can prove as much by having disclosed it to another who is not a joint inventor) may advance his reduction to practice to the date from which he began to exercise continuous diligence in work on the invention and continued diligent up to and including the time of actual reduction to practice.

Licenses may be exclusive, in granting to one party the sole right to an invention, or nonexclusive. An exclusive license excludes the patent owner himself from practice of the invention. Licenses may be for all or part of the U. S. License agreements should identify the parties to the agreement and the invention to be licensed, state the amount of royalty or other compensation and the periods of payment, and give the licensor the right to inspect the accounts to verify the reports of royalty due when calculated from the extent of operations under the invention and also the right on due notice to cancel the license (or convert it from exclusive to nonexclusive) if payments fall below a stated minimum sum.

Infringement is the unauthorized making, using, or selling of the invention within the U. S. Contributory infringement arises from actively inducing another to infringe, as by supplying a part or component only of what is recited in the claims, provided it is a material part of the invention, the supplier knows that the part or component is especially made for the infringing purpose, and the part or component has no other commercial use for noninfringing purpose.

Validity of a patent is necessary for infringement, either primary or contributory. Validity will be assumed in the absence of proof to the contrary, the proof attempted being usually that the invention does not meet one at least of the requirements set forth above for patentability.

Liability for patent infringement when a patent is held valid and infringed shall be damages adequate to compensate the patent owner for the infringement. In no case will the damages be less than a reasonable royalty plus interest and costs as fixed by the court. In the absence of particularly unfavorable circumstances, such as continued infringement after a court holding of infringement and injunction thereagainst, the damages are ordinarily about the same as a reasonable royalty. A great disadvantage of infringing, as contrasted with taking a license in advance, however, is the possibility of being enjoined from continued use of the invention, regardless of the amount of royalty then offered, if the suit goes against the infringer. Moreover, those who believe in patents should support the patent system by willingly compensating the patent owner for rights that have doubtless cost him money or research or both to acquire. Reputable companies generally seek to avoid knowingly infringing valid patents.

In general, patenting inventions is preferable by far to negotiating for license or standing the cost and hazard of suit after patents are taken by others. Patenting should be considered as the anchoring step for each successful phase of a research. Small companies sometimes overlook this step, although protection by patents is more vital to them than to large concerns which, in any event, derive some measure of protection from their size and reputation and from the amount of capital necessary for damaging competition with them.

ROBERT CALVERT

Cross-references: *Economics of Electronics Industry*

PAY-TV: see TELEVISION [SUBSCRIPTION (PAY) TV]

PENTODES: see ELECTRON TUBES (CONVENTIONAL)

PERMANENT MAGNETS

Permanent-magnet materials are characterized by relatively large magnetic hysteresis which permits the magnet to support a magnetic field external to itself after the removal of the magnetizing field. The satisfactory application of permanent magnets to any device requires a knowledge of the magnetic properties and characteristics that enable them to function satisfactorily in such a unit. It is also important to understand the physical properties and manufacturing limitations of these materials in order to choose magnet materials that are adaptable to the physical and mechanical requirements of the device.

The fundamental properties of magnet materials are described by the *hysteresis* loop. The most useful curve is that portion of the hysteresis loop in the second or fourth quadrants, called the *demagnetization curve*. The *energy-product* curve is a plot of the product of B and H at any point on the demagnetization curve.

The point on the demagnetization curve at which the magnet operates depends upon its coefficient of self-demagnetization in the case of a magnet alone, or upon the permeance of the magnetic circuit in the case where other magnetic materials form a portion of the magnetic circuit. A line drawn from the origin through the operating point is called the operating or shear line of a particular magnet design. The slope of the shear line is a function of the permeance of the circuit external to the magnet per unit of magnet volume.

If the external permeance of a magnet is decreased, the operating point moves irreversibly along the demagnetization curve to some point of lower induction. Upon restoring the external permeance to its original value, the operating point recoils along the lower branch of a minor loop to a new point at the intersection of the minor loop with the shear line through the original operating point. This new operating condition represents a permanent loss of external energy, which can only be restored by remagnetization of the magnet under the original conditions. Since the minor loops of most permanent-magnet materials are extremely narrow they are usually depicted as a straight line representing their average slope or incremental permeability. The effects of recoil and irreversible change can also occur in a magnet with fixed external permeance when subjected to demagnetizing forces.

Elementary considerations in the design of permanent magnets involve the selection of a suitable magnet alloy for the application, followed by the determination of the proper magnet dimensions and shape. The selection of the magnet alloy for a specific application depends primarily on its magnetic properties. Other properties of the magnet alloy, such as physical strength and machinability, are usually secondary.

The calculation of the optimum size and shape of a magnet for a specific application is sometimes difficult. However, the examination of certain fundamental relationships of the magnet circuit permits a fairly close approximation to optimum conditions. The relationship between the operating slope, the total permeance and the permeance of the space occupied by the magnet is expressed as

$$\text{Slope} = \frac{P_t}{P_m} = \frac{l_m}{A_m}(P_g + P_l)$$

where

P_t = total external permeance
P_m = permeance of the space occupied by magnet
P_g = permeance of the air gap
P_l = leakage permeance
l_m = length of the magnet
A_m = area of the magnet

By adjusting magnet dimensions and leakage permeance it is possible to provide for operation of the magnet at or near its maximum energy product. The ratio of the total permeance to the useful permeance may be defined as the leakage factor, k:

$$k = \frac{P_t}{P_g} = \frac{P_g + P_l}{P_g}$$

In practical designs leakage factors of from 1.1 to several hundred may be encountered.

The number of commercial applications for permanent magnets has become very large, and is growing rapidly, largely owing to the advent of the Alnico magnet materials, and to the large variety of special magnet alloys becoming available in recent years. Magnet applications can be broken down into a number of types which present more or less similar characteristics of design and operation, although not necessarily of size, shape or configuration of magnetic circuit.

A. *Fixed Gap Without Demagnetizing Force or Varying Reluctance Present.* Magnets of this type have essentially a fixed operating point and are not subjected to either stabilization or recoil of any appreciable amount. Magnet applications with magnets or assemblies whose useful field is more or less concentrated in one or more useful gaps include the following: loudspeakers, microphones, meters, galvanometers, magnetron fields, gyrator magnets, magnetic pickups, head sets, hearing aids, coin separators, beta-ray spectrographs, sound-powered telephones, and nuclear resonant fields. Magnet applications containing magnets or assemblies without well-defined gaps include the following: compasses, compass compensators, ion traps, cathode-ray focusing, musical instrument pickups, traveling-wave-tube fields, klystron tube fields, beam switching tube fields, traffic signal controls, arc blowouts, and magnetic separators.

B. *Fixed Gap with Demagnetizing Forces and/or Varying External Reluctance Present.* Magnets and assemblies of this type have either an appreciable amount of demagnetizing force opposing the magnet field or variable shunting across the fixed gap. Either

stabilization or recoil, or both, are present in these designs. The following types of applications are included in this group: speedometers, tachometers, watt-hour meters, eddy current drives, hysteresis drives, magnetic damping devices, telephone ringers, polarized relays, voltage regulators, reverse current cutouts, adjustable nuclear resonant fields, and adjustable beta-ray spectrograph fields.

C. *Variable Gap.* Magnets of this type are always subject to recoil since their external reluctance varies as the gap varies. In some variable gap applications, the magnet is not subjected to demagnetizing influences from opposing fields. The following applications are examples: holding magnets, thermostat switches, magnetic conveyors, magnetic chucks, magnetic friction clutches, limit switches, magnetic door latches, magnetic rolls, and sheet spreaders. Other variable-gap applications subject the magnet to demagnetizing fields in addition to the normal stabilizing influences and recoil. The following types of applications are included in this group: generators, motors, alternators, magnetos, salient-pole magnetic drives, and hysteresis motors.

J. E. MITCH AND F. DEMPSEY

Cross-references: *Magnetic Cores, Magnetism*

PHASE-SPACE REPRESENTATION

The phase-space representation of a dynamical system provides a means for depicting possible motions of the system which is closely related to the Hamiltonian formulation of the equations of motion. Phase-space representation has, therefore, an advantage over other methods for diagrammatically depicting the properties of a dynamical system in that general theorems of Hamiltonian dynamics assume their simplest form in this representation.

Consider, for simplicity, a system with one degree of freedom characterized by a time-independent Hamiltonian function $H(p,q)$, where p is the momentum variable conjugate to the configuration variable q.

"Phase-space" now reduces to a plane mapped by coordinates q and p. We now see that a point of phase-space represents not only the instantaneous configuration of a system but also its instantaneous state of motion; this combination may be termed the "state" of the system.

Following the motion of the dynamical system, the state changes and the representative point moves in phase space according to the canonical equations

$$\frac{dp}{dt} = -\frac{\partial H}{\partial q}, \qquad \frac{dq}{d\,} = \frac{\partial H}{\partial p} \qquad (1)$$

The representative point thereby maps out a curve of phase-space which we term a "trajectory." We now see from Eq. (1) that *one and only one trajectory passes through each point of phase space*. We may note that, in consequence, *trajectories cannot cross in phase space*.

If the Hamiltonian is time dependent, the values of dp/dt, dq/dt depend not only on p and q but also on t. Hence this case is rather more complicated and we shall not consider it here. We may, however, note that some simplification is achieved in the important case that the Hamiltonian is periodic in t. If the state of the system is plotted in the phase plane only at appropriate periodic time intervals $t = t_1, t_2, \cdots$, then there exist curves, which may be appropriately referred to as "trajectories," with the property that if the representative point lies on a trajectory at any one instant $t = t_n$, then it lies on the same trajectory for the entire sequence of times $t = t_1, t_2, \cdots$. It is again true that one and only one trajectory passes through each point of phase space, hence much of the theory of time-independent Hamiltonians may, with appropriate modification, be applied to Hamiltonians that are periodic in time.

We may expect that a set of trajectories in phase space may be represented by an equation of the form

$$f(p,q) = \text{constant} \qquad (2)$$

Hence trajectories in phase space are closely related to the "constants of the motion." In the simple case we are considering, the only constant of the motion is the energy E of the system. Since, for any state, the energy is given by the value of the Hamiltonian, we may infer that the set of trajectories is expressible as

$$H(p,q) = E \qquad (3)$$

This may be confirmed by means of Eq. (1). Even in more general cases, it is possible to obtain important information about the topology of trajectories in phase space by examination of the energy and other constants of the motion.

One of the simplest and most important aspects of the topology of trajectories concerns *stability*. We find, for instance, that the two Hamiltonian functions

$$H = \frac{1}{2m}\, p^2 + \frac{1}{2}\, m\omega^2 q^2 \qquad (4)$$

$$H = \frac{1}{2m}\, p^2 - \frac{1}{2}\, m\alpha^2 q^2 \qquad (5)$$

lead to contours as shown in Figs. 1 and 2, respectively. The first diagram represents a *stable* system, since the variation of p or q

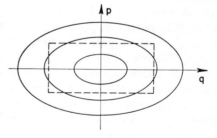

Fig. 1

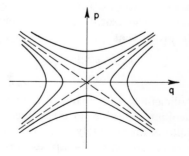

Fig. 2

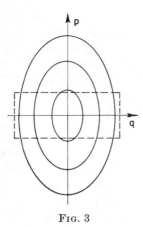

FIG. 3

is bounded for any initial condition. The second diagram, on the other hand, represents an *unstable* system since, for any nontrivial initial condition, we must expect p and q to increase without limit. We may confirm this interpretation of the phase-space diagram by forming, by means of Eq. (1), the equations of motion appropriate to (4) and (5). Note also that we may distinguish, by means of the phase-space diagram, between "weak focusing" and "strong focusing," as exemplified by Figs. 1 and 3, respectively.

One theorem of classical dynamics that lends itself to particularly simple interpretation in the phase-space representation is *Liouville's theorem*. This theorem states, in the present context, that the area of any closed contour in the phase plane remains constant, the contour being assumed to develop in time according to the equations of motion (1). We may verify this theorem by noting that the areas of two corresponding small contours are related by the Jacobian of the transformation. Hence we need to prove that

$$\frac{\partial[p(t_2),\, q(t_2)]}{\partial[p(t_1),\, q(t_1)]} = 1 \qquad (6)$$

It is sufficient to prove that, if $t_2 = t_1 + \Delta t$, the Jacobian contains no term linear in Δt. This follows immediately from Eq. (1).

We may consider, as an example, the focusing of a beam of electrons by a static electromagnetic field, allowing t to measure distance along the axis of the beam and q displacement transverse to the axis, so that p is a measure of the angle of inclination of an electron trajectory to the axis. Since a beam contains electrons with many different values of p and q, it may be represented, for any value of t, by some region of the phase plane. If it is possible for the beam to be focused to a point, the beam is said to constitute a "normal congruence." Hence we see that *a normal congruence is represented in the phase plane by a region of zero area*, that is, by a point or by a curve. We may note, however, that this curve may not enclose any region of phase space, for it would then be impossible for the curve to shrink to a point.

We may also introduce the idea of "matching" of a beam to a focusing system, the condition being that the configuration of the beam should be unchanged during its propagation through the focusing system. A beam which emerges from a gun with defined transverse dimensions and defined transverse velocities may be represented by a contour in the phase plane such as the rectangles indicated in Figs. 1 and 3. In neither case is the beam perfectly matched to the focusing system, but we can see that the matching is much better for the case of Fig. 1 than for that of Fig. 3. The condition for perfect matching is that the beam should be represented by a region of the phase plane bounded by an "energy" contour of the focusing system.

Closely associated with Liouville's theorem is the *adiabatic theorem*, which, in terms of our present formalism, may be expressed as follows. We consider a number of different time-developments of the same dynamical system, all with the same energy. Then, at any time, the representative points of these time developments lie on the same energy contour; we may say that the points are "evenly spaced" around the contour, if, after a certain time, each point has moved to the position which the next originally occupied. The adiabatic theorem now asserts that, if the dynamical system as represented by the Hamiltonian function changes slowly and aperiodically with reference to the oscillation period of the system, then a set of points originally evenly spaced around an energy contour will, after this slow adiabatic variation, still be spaced evenly around an energy contour. The final energy contour must, by virtue of Liouville's theorem, embrace the same area of the phase plane as the original energy contour. Thus, if the Hamiltonian is such and changes in such a way that the initial and final sets of contours are those shown in Figs. 1 and 3, and if the original set of representative points originally lie on the bold-line contour of Fig. 1, then they will finally lie on the bold-line contour of Fig. 3.

The above theorem may again be exemplified by consideration of the focusing of an electron beam. If an electron beam is originally matched to a focusing system and is represented by the bold-line contour of Fig. 1, it follows from the adiabatic theorem that a slow change in the focusing system which modifies the phase contours into these shown in Fig. 3 has the result that the beam remains matched to the focusing system and is finally represented by that part of the phase plane bounded by the bold-line contour of Fig. 3. The structure just described represents a "beam condenser," since the non-uniform focusing system through which it has passed has compressed the transverse dimensions of the beam.

P. A. STURROCK

Cross-references: *Accelerators, Electron Optics*

PHONETIC TYPEWRITING

The phonetic typewriter is an experimental device which automatically prints words spoken into a microphone. The output of the machine is phonetic, corresponding exactly to the sound of the spoken syllables rather than to the accepted spelling of the written word. Thus the device is regarded as a potential aid for specialized or informal communication, such as note-taking, internal memoranda, inventory listings, etc., rather than for formal correspondence. In addition, its operating principles are adaptable to a variety of voice-control techniques for many types of machine operation.

The operation of the phonetic typewriter is based on the fact that spoken sounds, while extremely complex, contain characteristics of frequency, amplitude, and time that distinguish any one sound from all others. Thus, for example, the vowel sound "I" exhibits through its duration a change in the relationships of frequency and amplitude totally unlike those which occur through the duration of any other spoken sounds, such as "see," "U," or "er." The phonetic typewriter incorporates at a key stage in its operation a means for sampling each syllable sound at intervals through its duration to determine these characteristic frequency and amplitude changes, and thus to identify the particular syllable.

The complete phonetic typewriter incorporates the following basic sequence of operations:

(1) conversion of speech sounds into corresponding electrical variations by means of a conventional microphone;

(2) amplification and compression of the electrical variations to achieve a relatively constant level, regardless of whether the incoming sound is soft or loud;

(3) analysis of the resulting signals to determine the changes through time of the frequency-amplitude relationship, thus identifying the particular syllable sound;

(4) comparison of the analyzed syllable pattern with patterns stored in the machine memory; and

(5) activation through the memory of a sequence of typewriter keys corresponding phonetically to the letters in the syllable.

In the basic system, developed by H. F. Olson and H. Belar, the first two of these steps are performed with conventional circuitry. The remainder of the process is then carried out in the following manner.

The composite signal from the compressor-amplifier goes simultaneously to nine tuned amplifiers. Eight are tuned to pass different narrow frequency bands in the audio spectrum, thus providing means for analyzing the frequency content of each sound. The ninth amplifier is used to activate the system by triggering a time-sequence switch if the energy level of the incoming sound is high enough.

Through the time-sequence switch, the output signals from the eight frequency-selective amplifiers are fed successively at 0.2-sec intervals to five sets of individual relays, each containing eight coils. In each of the successive switching positions, any of the amplifier outputs with sufficient amplitude will close the corresponding relays. Since the frequencies and amplitudes vary with time through the duration of the original spoken sound, this technique provides a means for converting the unique frequency-amplitude-time relationship of each syllable into a correspondingly unique pattern of closed relays. This pattern appears in the form of lighted squares on a "spectral memory display," providing a visible record of the relays that have been actuated by the sound. The display is useful for analyzing and establishing the code which plays a prominent role in the succeeding steps.

The pattern from the spectral display is next fed to a "syllable memory." This unit consists of a number of relays, each corresponding to a different syllable pattern. The capacity, or "vocabulary," of the phonetic typewriter is determined by the number of such memory elements installed in the system. The appearance of a pattern in the spectral display closes only the particular memory relay associated with that pattern—so that the spoken "I," for example, will close the "I" memory relay and no others. Each of the different memory relays, in turn, is connected through a time-sequence switch to the appropriate key solenoids of the typewriter. When the memory relay closes, the time-sequence switch causes the typewriter to print the particular sequence of letters forming the syllable.

The first experimental model of the phonetic typewriter, developed in the middle 1950's, had a "vocabulary" of ten syllables. A subsequent model, now used in laboratory experiments, contains 100 syllables in its memory. Studies now being undertaken with the system are aimed at such improvements as added flexibility, so that the phonetic typewriter will respond reliably to variations in the pronunciation of words.

R. K. Kilbon

Cross-references: *Storage, Visible Speech*

PERMEABILITY: see MAGNETISM

PHASORS: see COMPLEX NOTATION

PHOSPHORS: see ELECTROLUMINESCENCE; FLUORESCENCE

PHOTOCELL

A large variety of photocells (here used to describe all sorts of photosensitive devices) with a wide diversity of characteristics is in existence. This variety can be grouped into a relatively small number of classes, which is based on an even smaller number of physical phenomena underlying the device operation.

The first phenomenon present in all photosensitive devices is the *photoelectric effect*, based on light absorption by photon-electron interaction. This photon-electron interaction is a "one photon-one electron" process, in which the photon is annihilated by transfer of its total energy to the electron. This energy is imparted to the electron as potential energy plus some kinetic energy. In the photoelectric effect, this potential energy results in the removal of the electron from a bound state in the crystal lattice. In the case of a metal, where the electron is mobile in a half-filled conduction band, this means overcoming the work function (*q.v.*) and liberating the electron from its bond to the lattice as such (ionization, *q.v.*). This process is called the "outer" photoelectric or *photo-emissive* effect. In an insulator or semiconductor, the "inner" photoelectric or *photoconductive* effect is found. In this effect, the electron is freed from its tight bond to a lattice site, expressed by a state in a filled or nearly filled valence band, and is brought to a mobile bond within the lattice, expressed by a state in the conduction band.

The second phenomenon, the *photovoltaic* effect, is present only in some photosensitive devices. It leads to the partial utilization of the potential energy imparted to the electrons from the absorbed photons. In the case of the outer photoelectric effect, a second electrode of lower work function than the illuminated and emitting electrode, placed at a sufficiently short distance so as to avoid limitation of the current flow through space charges, permits such energy utilization in an electrical load connected across the two electrodes. With the inner photoelectric effect, pairs of mobile charges of opposite polarity are created—electrons and holes— which normally recombine in a relatively short time. If a potential gradient is present within the lattice near the location of the carrier generation, then the mobile charges may be separated, permitting energy utilization in a load connected across the two regions of the lattice which are separated by the potential gradient (p-n junction, surface barrier, etc.).

A third phenomenon applied is *charge multiplication*, leading to increased sensitivity. Charge multiplication can be achieved by collision-ionization in a gas, or through secondary emission from the surface of an electrode, both applicable with the outer photoelectric effect. In the case of the inner photoelectric effect, charge multiplication (*avalanche* effect) can take place within the region of built-in potential gradient, especially when this gradient is enhanced through an externally applied voltage.

The outer photoelectric effect leads to the class of vacuum phototubes, often designated

as *photocells*, in which the electrode spacing is large so that space-charge effects have to be overcome by application of an external voltage; to the class of *gas-filled photocells* utilizing ionization multiplication; and to the class of *photomultipliers* having a multitude of electrodes for secondary emission. The outer photoelectric effect also underlies the operation of the class of photoelectrolytic or (for short) *photolytic* cells, where either an electrode or a "dye" is the photoemitter, and where the electrolyte reduces space-charge effects, permitting photovoltaic operation. The outer photoelectric effect is also present in some solid-state photovoltaic devices, like all "blackwall-" cells in which the spectral response extends towards the long-wavelength side of the absorption edge of the semiconductor. Examples are the Cu_2O_2-Cu and CdS-Cu cells.

The inner photoelectric effect is the sole basis of operation for the class of *photoconductive* cells. The class of *photovoltaic energy converters*, often called solar cells, is based on the photovoltaic effect, as their name indicates. So is the class of *solid-state photodiodes*, which, however, are normally not operated in the photovoltaic mode, since output signals of larger voltage can be obtained by the application of bias. Avalanche-type charge multiplication can also be utilized. The inner photoelectric effect is also utilized in the classes of 3- and 4-layer phototransistors. It replaces carrier injection from an electrical input as in normal transistor operation by carrier generation from an optical input, to obtain corresponding output signals.

The multitude of photosensitive devices is in existence because of their wide variety of characteristics, making individual types especially suitable for specific applications. The spectral response of the devices can be varied, since it is determined by either the work function of the metal in the case of the outer photoelectric effect, or by the width of the energy gap between valence and conduction band of the semiconductor in the case of the inner photoelectric effect. Increased sensitivity through charge multiplication is mostly accompanied by reduced speed of response, as is higher voltage gain obtained through increased circuit resistance (RC time constant). In general vacuum or gas-filled phototubes are extremely high-resistance devices (10^{11}–10^{12} ohms) giving small current signals, whereas the photovoltaic devices have low resistances (10^0–10^4 ohms), but give large current signals. High speed of response is available in both types. The phototube is most suitable as an input device for a vacuum tube; the photovoltaic device provides a more suitable input for a transistor circuit. Both are useful for photometric applications, besides their general use as detectors, counters, etc. The photomultiplier with its extreme sensitivity forms a detector for special cases. The photoconductive cells have medium resistance, and give medium current output. They can operate relays directly. Their current-voltage characteristic is linear like that of a resistor, but its slope varies with the amount of impinging radiation. The photodiodes fall into the same resistance and output current range, but their current-voltage characteristic approximates that of a pentode with the current varying with the input signal, but being rather independent of the applied voltage.

MARTIN WOLF

Cross-references: *Energy Conversion, Photoelectric Emission, Photoconductivity, Photovoltaic Effect, Semiconductors, Solid-State Displays*

PHOTOCONDUCTIVITY

Photoconductivity deals with changes in the electrical conductivity of a material as the result of absorption of photons (either light or X-rays, ultraviolet, infrared, etc.). Photoconductivity generally involves an *increase* in conductivity as a result of such absorption. It is possible in special cases for the conductivity to be decreased by the absorption of suitable radiation; this phenomenon has been called negative photoconductivity.

The absorption of photons with sufficient energy to produce free electrons and/or holes in a material results in an increase in the number of charge carriers that can carry current under the influence of an applied electric field. This increased conductivity continues until the carriers freed by photon absorption can no longer move through the material. The termination of the increased conductivity may result either from the freed carriers giving up their energy and returning to their un-excited state (recombination), or by the freed carriers passing out of the material at one electrode, without being replenished at the opposite electrode.

The key parameter in determining the photosensitivity (i.e., the change in conductivity per photon absorbed) is the *lifetime* of the free carriers. This lifetime varies by many orders of magnitude among different materials, and may even vary over many orders of magnitude in a single material, as the types of imperfection dominating the recombination processes are altered by chemical or physical treatment. If free carriers are being excited at a rate of F cm^{-3} sec^{-1}, then the number of photo-excited free carriers per cm^3, Δn, is given simply by:

$$\Delta n = F\tau \qquad (1)$$

where τ is the lifetime of the freed carriers. The corresponding change in conductivity, $\Delta\sigma$, is given by:

$$\Delta\sigma = \Delta n e\mu = Fe\tau\mu \qquad (2)$$

where μ is the carrier mobility and e is the electronic charge.

A distinction is frequently drawn between primary and secondary photoconductivity. Primary photoconductivity occurs when the only carriers involved in the increase in conductivity with photo-excitation are the carriers initially excited. When the initially excited carriers recombine or pass out of the material at the electrodes, the primary photoconductivity process is terminated. If the *gain* of a photoconductor is defined as the number of electrons passing between the electrodes per photon absorbed, it is clear that the maximum gain of primary photoconductivity is unity. Secondary photo-conductivity occurs when carriers enter the material from one of the electrodes, replacing similar carriers that have passed out of the material at the opposite electrode, to maintain charge neutrality in the material. The current flow is therefore terminated only by recombination, and not by loss of carriers at the electrodes. The maximum gain of secondary photoconductivity is much larger than unity, values of 10^4 being common, and is limited only by the maximum electric field that can be applied without initiating field-injection of carriers from the electrodes.

Another important property of a photoconductor is its speed of response, i.e., the speed with which changes in conductivity can follow changes in photo-excitation. An upper limit to the speed of response is set by the lifetime of free carriers, and hence by the desired photosensitivity. In many practical cases, however, the observed speed of response is much less than this upper limit, because of the trapping and thermal release of carriers from imperfections. If the number of photo-excited free carriers is much less than the number of photo-excited trapped carriers, then the speed of response is determined primarily by the time required for release of carriers from traps and not by the lifetime for recombination.

As a tool for research into the nature of solids, photoconductivity is important, since its effects depend strongly on the number and types of imperfection that are present. As a useful phenomenon in its own right, photoconductivity is also important, and the uses of it are increasing daily. Photoconductors are frequently used in single-crystal form, but many applications requiring large-area photosensitive surfaces have led to the development of photoconductors in the form of evaporated layers, sintered layers, and microcrystalline powders. Photoconductors are widely used as radiation detectors over a wide portion of the electromagnetic spectrum. Typical examples are CdS, which has a long-wavelength-limit of sensitivity at 0.51 microns, and is normally an insulator; GaAs, which has a long-wavelength-limit of sensitivity at 0.91 microns, and requires considerable care in preparation to be an insulator rather than a semiconductor; Ge, which has a long-wavelength-limit of sensitivity at 1.8 microns, and is a semiconductor; PbS, which has a long-wavelength-limit of sensitivity at 3.1 microns, and is a semiconductor; and InSb, which has a long-wavelength-limit of sensitivity at 8 microns, and is a highly conducting semiconductor.

Photoconductors are also used as radiation-controllable electronic switches, in applications ranging from street lighting to computers, and as radiation-controllable variable resistances, in applications ranging from film sound reproduction to picture reproduction. Photoconductors have been widely used in the Vidicon (q.v.) form of the television camera and in various techniques for electrophotography, where the dissipation of the charge on an insulator by illumination is utilized. In conjunction with electroluminescent materials, photoconductors have been used in light amplifiers, X-ray intensifiers, and various picture and information display systems.

REFERENCE

R. H. BUBE, "Photoconductivity of Solids," New York, John Wiley & Sons, Inc., 1960.

RICHARD H. BUBE

Cross-references: *Image Intensifier, Photocell, Photomultiplier, Photovoltaic Effect*

PHOTOELECTRIC EMISSION

Photoelectric emission occurs when the absorption of light results in electrons being released from a material into vacuum or a second material. The emitting materials are usually solids. However, photoelectric emission can also be obtained from gases and liquids.

In 1905 and 1906, Albert Einstein (1879–1955) established the basic laws of photoelectric emission and, in so doing, made a great contribution to modern quantum physics. Einstein conceived of light as

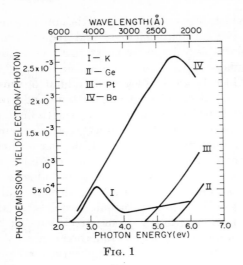

Fig. 1

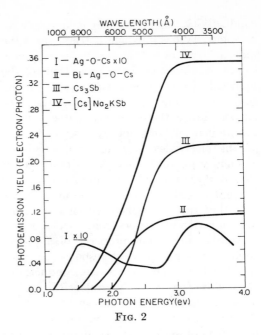

Fig. 2

quantized particles (photons) having energy $h\nu$,* where h is Planck's constant and ν is the frequency of the light. He stated that photoelectric emission was the result of the absorption of single photons by single electrons. For example, if an electron bound by an energy E_b absorbs a photon of energy $h\nu$, it may escape from the host material if $h\nu > E_b$. After emission, the maximum kinetic energy of this electron is $h\nu - E_b$. Einstein's laws also predict that the emission current is directly proportional to the intensity of the incident light, which agrees with experiment.

Photoelectric emission from a solid may be looked upon as a three-step process. In the first step, the electron absorbs an incident photon. This excitation process may occur at some distance from the surface. During the second step, the electron moves through the crystal to the vacuum interface and may lose energy through collision processes. The third step is the escape of the electron over the potential barrier, i.e., the emission of a photoelectron.

Corresponding to these three steps, the photoemissive characteristics of solid are determined by the type and density of energy

* Although Planck had previously introduced quantized oscillators for the blackbody problem, he clearly did not conceive of the quantization of radiation.

levels from which electrons can be excited, by the rate at which electrons lose energy as they move through the crystal, and by the height of the surface barrier. These parameters vary considerably from material to material; however, certain general statements can be made for metals and semiconductors.†

In the visible and near ultraviolet ($h\nu \leq 8$ ev, i.e., $\lambda \geq 1550$ Å) metals have, at the most, efficiencies of about 5×10^{-3} electron per incident photon. In this spectral region semiconductors have maximum efficiencies varying between 5×10^{-3} and 0.3 electron per incident photon depending on the material. In general, the greater the ratio of band gap energy to electron affinity (the energy difference between the bottom of the conduction band and the vacuum level), the greater the photoemission efficiency. For wavelengths smaller than 1000 Å, the efficiencies of metals rise to values as high as 0.15 electron/photon.

An important parameter of a photoemitter is its threshold of response. In accordance with the Einstein law, this parameter is de-

† The term "semiconductor" in used here for both semiconductors *and* insulators.

termined by the difference in energy between the highest lying filled electronic states and the vacuum level. For metals the threshold roughly corresponds to the work function (*q.v.*). It varies from about 1.9 ev (7000 Å) for Cs to about 5.4 ev (2300 Å) for Pt. For semiconductors, it varies between about 1.0 ev (Ag-O-Cs) and 12 ev (LiF). The response curves of typical metals and semiconductors are shown in Fig. 1. Figure 2 hows the response curves of the four materials that have proven most useful in detecting light in or near the visible region of the spectrum. All of these materials are semiconductors.

Photoelectric emitters have found use in many devices, including photomultipliers (*q.v.*), television camera tubes, and "electric eyes." With the advent of space technology, there is an increased interest in "solar blind" phototubes, i.e., detectors that are sensitive to the ultraviolet radiation but not to visible solar radiation.

W. F. SPICER

Cross-references: *Field Emission, Photocell, Secondary Emission, Thermionic Emission, Work Function*

PHOTOMULTIPLIER

Photomultipliers make use of the phenomena of photoemission and secondary-electron emission in order to detect very low light levels. The electrons released from the photocathode by incident light are accelerated and focused onto a secondary-emission surface (called a dynode). Several electrons are emitted from the dynode for each incident primary electron. These secondary electrons are then directed onto a second dynode where more electrons are released. The whole process is repeated a number of times depending on the number of dynodes. In this manner, it is possible to amplify the initial photocurrent by a factor of 10^8 or more in practical photomultipliers. It is, therefore, evident that the photomultiplier represents an extremely sensitive detector of light.

The major characteristics of the photomultiplier with which the user is generally most concerned are as follows:

(a) Sensitivity, spectral response and thermal emission of photocathodes.

(b) Amplification factor.

(c) Noise characteristics and the signal-to-noise ratio.

Sensitivity, Spectral Response, and Thermal Emission of Photocathodes. Many different types of photocathodes are being used in commercially available photomultipliers. The most important photocathodes in present-day use are listed in Table 1. Typical spectral response curves of these photocathodes are shown in Fig. 1.

Amplification Factor. The amplification factor in a photomultiplier depends on the secondary emission characteristics of the dynode and to some extent on the design of the multiplier structure.

Most secondary-emission surfaces used in commercial photomultipliers fall into two classes:

(1) Alkali metal compounds, e.g., cesium-antimony.

TABLE 1. Characteristics of Common Photocathodes.

Photocathode	RETMA Code Number	λ_m (at max.) in Å	λ_0 (1% of max.) in Å	Quantum Efficiency (at λ_m)	Average Thermionic Emission at 25°C in amp/cm²	Average μa/lumen (2870°K tungsten source)
Cs-O-Ag	S-1	8,000	12,000	0.005	10^{-11}	10–20
Cs-Sb(O) opaque	S-4	4,000	7,000	0.25	10^{-14}	60–100
Cs-Sb(O)	S-11	4,500	7,000	0.20	10^{-14}	40–80
Cs-Ag-Bi	S-10	4,500	7,500	0.10	10^{-13}	40–60
Na-K-Sb		4,000	6,200	0.20	10^{-16}	30–60
Na-K-Cs-Sb	S-20	4,250	8,250	0.25	10^{-14}	150–180

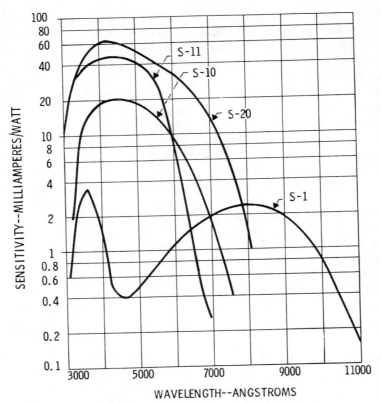

Fig. 1. Spectral response characteristics.

(2) Metal oxide layers, e.g., magnesium oxide on silver-magnesium alloy.

The alkali metal compounds have higher gain at low primary electron energy (of the order of 75 v). The metal oxide layers show less fatigue at high current density of emission (i.e., at several microamperes per square centimeter or higher).

Table 2 lists some characteristics of the common dynode surfaces.

The multiplier structures may be divided into two main types, dynamic and static.

The dynamic multiplier in its simplest form consists of two parallel dynode surfaces with an alternating electric field applied between them. Electrons leaving one surface at the proper phase of the applied field are accelerated to the other surface where they knock out secondary electrons. These electrons in turn are accelerated back to the

TABLE 2. Characteristics of Common Dynode Surfaces.

Surface	Maximum Secondary Emission Ratio	Primary Voltage for Maximum Ratio
Cs-Sb	8.0	500
Cs-Ag-O	5.8–9.5	500–1000
MgO (on AgMg)	9.8	500
BeO (on CuBe)	3.5–5.5	500–700
BeO (on NiBe)	12.3	700
Al_2O_3	1.5–4.8	350–1300

first plate when the field reverses, creating still more secondary electrons. Eventually the secondary electrons are collected by an anode placed in the tube; if they are not, a self-maintained discharge occurs. In practice, dynamic multipliers have been replaced by static ones mainly because the latter have better stability and are easier to operate.

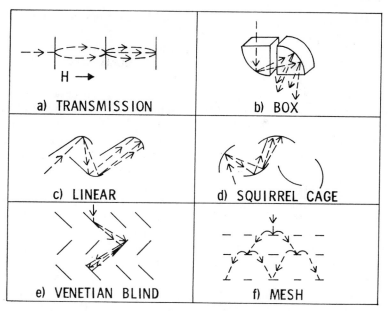

Fig. 2. Various multiplier structures.

The static multipliers may be either magnetically or electrostatically focused.

Figure 2a illustrates one type of multiplier structure using *magnetic* focusing. Primary electrons impinging on one side of a dynode cause the emission of secondary electrons from the opposite side. These electrons are then focused onto the next dynode by means of the axial magnetic field.

Figures 2(b)–(f) illustrate the more common types of *electrostatic* multiplier structures. The structures shown in Fig. 2(b), (c), and (d) actually use focusing from one stage to the next. The structures in (e) and (f) are unfocused.

The unfocused electrostatic structures have less sensitivity to stray electric and magnetic fields. The focused structures, especially (c) and (d) in Fig. 2, can be made to have very short transit-time spreads. Often special accelerating electrodes are placed between the dynodes to improve their transit time spread and space-charge characteristics. At 200–300 v/stage the transit time spread may be less than 10^{-9} sec and peak pulse outputs of the order of 200 ma may be drawn before nonlinearity owing to space-charge saturation sets in.

In the normal operating range the over-all amplification G of the multiplier is proportional to V^{β}, where V is the over-all voltage and β is a constant of the order of seven.

Noise Characteristics and the Signal-to-Noise Ratio. It is necessary to distinguish between two types of noise in photomultipliers, dark and shot noise.

The *dark noise* in photomultipliers is caused mainly by the following:

(1) leakage current across insulating supports,

(2) field emission from electrodes,

(3) thermal emission from the photocathode and dynodes,

(4) positive ion feedback to the photocathode, and

(5) fluorescence from dynodes and insulator supports.

By careful design and construction of the photomultiplier it is possible to limit the dark noise principally to (3).

Associated with the photocurrent from the photocathode is *shot noise*. There is also shot noise from secondary emission in the multiplier structure. The mean-square shot noise current $\overline{i_n{}^2}$ at the anode is given to a close approximation by

$$\overline{i_n{}^2} = 2eG^2\overline{i_p}b\Delta f$$

where e is the electronic charge, G is the amplification, $\overline{i_p}$ is the average photocurrent, Δf is the bandwidth of the system, and b is a factor equal to approximately 1.5 which accounts for the shot noise created in the multiplier. The signal-to-noise ratio S/N is then given by

$$S/N = \frac{G\overline{i_p}}{\sqrt{\overline{i_n{}^2}}} = \sqrt{\frac{\overline{i_p}}{2eb\Delta f}}$$

Uses of Photomultipliers. One of the major uses of photomultipliers is in the scintillation counter where in combination with a fluorescent material it is used to detect nuclear radiation. Other applications include use in facsimile transmission, spectral analysis, photometry, automatic quality control, and many other areas where low light levels must be detected.

B. R. Linden

Cross-references: *Noise, Photocell, Photoelectric Emission, Scintillation Counters, Secondary Emission*

PHOTOVOLTAIC EFFECT

The photovoltaic effect obtained its name from experiments with voltaic cells, which E. Becquerel performed in 1839, and in which he observed a change of potential when one of the electrodes was illuminated. The name photovoltaic effect is in general applied to the phenomena leading to the direct conversion of a part of the energy absorbed from impinging photons into usable electrical energy. However, the name has also found a restrictive use for devices having this same property, but being prepared only from semiconducting materials utilizing the inner photoelectric effect, and containing a p-n junction or surface barrier.

Both the inner and the outer photoelectric effect can lead to photovoltaic behavior, and cases are known where both effects contribute simultaneously.

In the case of the outer photoelectric or photoemissive effect, the electrons leave the photocathode and enter either through a vacuum, an electrolyte, or a direct interface into a second electrode (anode) of lower-work-function material which may also be a semiconductor. If the electrodes are connected by a zero-resistance external circuit, the electrons can return from the second electrode to the photocathode via this circuit (short-circuit current).

Without a conducting connection between the electrodes, a negative charge and an associated potential (open-circuit voltage) build up on the anode, rendering the kinetic energy of the emitted electrons insufficient for reaching the anode.

In the inner photoelectric effect, electrons are energetically raised from their state in the valence band across the forbidden gap into a mobile state in the conduction band, leaving an also mobile positive charge called hole in the valence band. If the semiconductor is extrinsic, a large number of mobile charge carriers of one type (majority carrier) is continually present owing to ionized impurity atoms. Photon absorption results in an increase in the number of majority carriers and in generation of minority carriers, so that the material remains electrically neutral. The mobile charges wander about randomly in the material. After a certain time interval from their generation, statistically called minority-carrier lifetime, the holes and electrons recombine, giving off energy mostly to the lattice in form of heat or by photon emission.

A necessity for the photovoltaic effect is a built-in electric field, present in the material owing to a gradient of the fixed charges associated with ionized impurity atoms in the lattice. Mobile charges entering this space-charge region drift across it or are repelled depending on their polarity. This action leads to depletion of the minority carriers on the boundary of the space-charge region. Carriers become majority carriers and cannot recombine after crossing the space-charge region and to diffusion of the minority carriers towards the space-charge region due to the density gradient thus established. Carriers become majority carriers and cannot recombine after crossing the space-charge region. This flow of charges continues through a zero-resistance outside circuit connected through ohmic contacts to the material on both sides of the space-charge region. The magnitude of this short circuit current is

$$I_L = \int_0^\infty N(\lambda)\gamma(\lambda)\, d\lambda$$

where $N(\lambda)$ is the number of photons incident on the surface of the device per square centimeter and second in the interval $d\lambda$ around the wavelength λ, and $\gamma(\lambda)$ is the over-all collection efficiency which is determined chiefly by the reflection and absorption coefficients, the minority carrier lifetime and mobility, and geometry factors; it is the basis for the spectral response, which depends through the listed quantities strongly on the energy gap of the material.

In open circuit, the majority-carrier concentration is increased, leading to a decrease of the potential difference across the space-charge region, which is synonymous with applying forward bias to a diode. The result is a steady-state condition with a current across the space-charge region equal in magnitude to the light generated current I_L, but in opposite direction. This mechanism leads to the basic equivalent circuit of a current generator parallel-connected with a diode, and to the equation describing the current voltage characteristic:

$$I = I_0 \left[\exp\left(\frac{q}{AkT}\,V\right) - 1 \right] - I_L$$

where I and V are terminal current and voltage, respectively, q the electronic charge, k Boltzmann's constant, T absolute temperature, A a dimensionless constant between 1 and 3, and I_0 is the saturation current according to rectifier theory as applicable to the specific device, which depends on temperature and material properties, and particularly on the height of the potential barrier of the space-charge region. The latter can be a p-n junction obtained by diffusion, alloying or growing, or a surface barrier at the transition to a different type of material, formed by chemical reaction or adsorption, and deposited by a multitude of processes such as chemical, electrolytic, pyrolytic, vacuum, or plasma deposition.

The photovoltaic effect is normally associated with high speed of response, limited only by the minority-carrier lifetimes, and by the RC time constant connected with the capacitance of the space-charge region and the circuit resistance, but not by slow trapping effects like many photoconductors.

Major application of the photovoltaic effect is made in the photovoltaic solar energy converters, photovoltaic sensors or readout cells, photo diodes, and photo transistors.

MARTIN WOLF

Cross-references: *Energy Conversion, Photocell, Photoelectric Emission, Photoconductivity, Semiconductors, Solid-State Displays*

PICKUP: see SOUND RECORDING

PICTORIAL DISPLAYS: see RADAR DISPLAYS

PIEZOELECTRICITY AND PYROELECTRICITY

Piezoelectricity is the generation of an electric moment by a change of stress applied to a solid. Wherever it occurs, the converse piezoelectric effect (strain proportional to an applied electric field) is also observed. The first definite demonstration of piezoelectricity is due to J. and P. Curie in 1880. Their studies included quartz and Rochelle salt, which are today the two most important piezoelectric crystals.

Piezoelectricity cannot occur in any material that has a center of symmetry. Its occurrence is limited to 20 out of the 32 crystal classes; substantially all optically active substances crystallize in one of these piezoelectric classes. Piezoelectric crystal classes are found in every crystal system, including two classes in the cubic system. Eighteen independent coefficients are needed to describe all possible piezoelectric interactions between electric field and mechanical stress components in a crystal without any symmetry. The symmetry axes and planes which define the various crystal classes reduce this number drastically for most well-known crystals. The table lists only the largest coefficients for some important piezoelectric crystals. These coefficients measure the piezoelectric charge density in micro-microcoulomb/square meter per applied stress in newton/square meter, and conversely the strain in microns/meter caused by an applied electric field in kilovolt/millimeter. It should be emphasized that piezoelectricity is an electrostatic phenomenon giving small electric charges on insulating bodies resulting in comparatively high voltage.

Pyroelectricity is the generation of an electric moment in an insulating body by a change of temperature. Specifically, "true pyroelectricity" is the generation of such an electric moment due to a homogeneous change in temperature. From principles of symmetry, it can be derived that such true pyroelectricity can occur only in substances having a unique polar axis. Such axes occur in single crystals of only ten symmetry classes. The best-known mineral crystal showing pyroelectricity is tourmaline. Twenty times more pyroelectric charge is generated by lithium sulfate monohydrate; in this crystal the charge developed per °C change is 76×10^{-6} coul/m². Inhomogeneous temperature changes can produce stresses which create "false pyroelectricity" in crystals belonging to classes which are piezoelectric but not truly pyroelectric.

Pyroelectricity and piezoelectricity can also occur in polycrystalline or amorphous substances which have become anisotropic by external agents. This is true especially of "ferroelectric" ceramics in which preferred orientation of electric moments has been induced by treatment in strong electric fields.

The practically most important ferroelectrics are Rochelle salt and barium titanate. In Rochelle salt single crystals, the ferroelectric phenomenon is apparent in the high value and strong temperature dependence of the piezoelectric effect. In barium titanate, piezoelectric effects occur only below 120°C, the Curie point. Polycrystalline (ceramic) barium titanate preparations show very strong piezoelectric effects in this temperature range after they have been exposed to a high electric field. This poling process is a close analog to the magnetizing of polycrystalline ferromagnetic materials, and the resulting piezoelectric effect is analogous to the magnetostrictive response of a magnetized ferromagnetic material.

Solid solution ceramics, especially those containing lead titanate and lead zirconate, have been found to give improvements over barium titanate ceramic in magnitude of piezoelectric effect, temperature range, and stability.

Applications. The most widespread application of piezoelectric materials is in con-

PIEZOELECTRIC COEFFICIENTS

The unit is 10^{-12} coul/newton $= 3 \times 10^{-8}$ esu/dyne.

Substance	Temp.	Coefficient*	Value
Quartz o	r.t.	d_{11}	2.3
Tourmaline	r.t.	d_{33}	1.8
Rochelle salt	30°C	d_{14}	500.
K_2 tartrate·$\frac{1}{2}$ H_2O	r.t.	d_{36}	23.2
$Li_2SO_4H_2O$	r.t.	d_{22}	15.0
$NH_4H_2PO_4$	27°C	d_{36}	48.0
KH_2PO_4	27°C	d_{36}	21.
Ethylene diamine tartrate	r.t.	d_{36}	18.4
$BaTiO_3$ crystal	r.t.	d_{31}	36.
$BaTiO_3$ ceramic	27°C	d_{33}	190.
	27°C	d_{31}	78.

* The first subscript denotes the direction of the electric field in respect to the crystal axes. The second subscript denotes the stress component involved; 1 to 3 indicates compressional, 4 to 6 shear stress.

verters of mechanical signals into electric signals such as in phonograph pickups, microphones, underwater listening devices (hydrophones), vibration pickups, and accelerometers. The converse piezoelectric effect is utilized in underwater sound generators (sonar) and other sources for sonic and especially for ultrasonic vibrations. For all these applications high piezoelectric effects are desired; hence crystals of Rochelle salt or $NH_4H_2PO_4$ (known as "ADP" for ammonium dihydrogen phosphate), and barium titanate ceramics are used. The former have advantages owing to their low mechanical compliance, whereas the latter is outstanding in ruggedness and the availability of complex shapes.

Equally important applications of piezoelectric crystals depend on their reaction upon the electric circuits used to set them into mechanical vibrations. In this type of application, both the direct and converse piezoelectric effects are involved and the closely controllable mechanical resonance is impressed on the electric circuits. Crystals are thus used to control precisely the frequency of radio signals and to separate the voice channels of multi-channel telephony. In these applications, quartz is used almost exclusively in view of its great mechanical stability and the extremely low temperature coefficients of resonant frequency for quartz plates of certain special orientations. Processes for growing quartz crystals by hydrothermal synthesis have recently been developed; these manufactured crystals are substantially identical with natural crystals in their frequency-control properties. Engineering applications of pyroelectricity remain to be developed.

HANS JAFFE

Cross-references: *Ferroelectricity, Frequency Standards, Transducers, Underwater Sound, Ultrasonics*

PLASMA

A plasma is defined as an ionized gas in which there are equal numbers of positively and negatively charged particles; that is, a plasma is an ionized medium with no net charge. Therefore, space-charge forces do not play a major role in the macroscopic properties of a plasma.

Physical Properties. The characteristic length used to differentiate plasmas from the general classification of ionized gases is the Debye shielding distance. This distance, the Debye length, λ_D, is given by

$$\lambda_D = \sqrt{\frac{\epsilon_0 k T}{n_0 e^2}}$$

where ϵ_0 is the dielectric constant of free space, k is Boltzmann's constant, T is the electron temperature, n_0 is the number density of electrons; and e is the electronic charge. This length is approximately the distance in which the thermal energy of the electrons is balanced out by the electric potential energy created by the positive space charge of the ions. Within this distance the electrons diffuse away from the ions because of their relatively large random energy. Outside of this distance the electrons are held by the space-charge forces of the positive ions, so that the ionized gas is neutral for distances greater than λ_D. If the ionized medium is large in extent compared to λ_D, it is then called a plasma. Within most plasmas λ_D is, at most, of the order of 1 mm in length.

Many plasmas are weakly ionized, so that the number of neutral particles is several orders of magnitude greater than the number of electrons or ions. Owing to the thermal energy of these constituents, collisions between different particles occur. In general, these collisions can be classified as elastic and inelastic collisions. The elastic collisions are those in which no change in the internal energy of the molecules is involved, which usually implies that an electron colliding elastically with a molecule loses very little of its original energy. A typical example of such a collision is the case of an electron colliding with a neutral particle of large mass. In this case momentum is transferred to the electron as a result of the collision. Because of the much heavier mass of the neutral molecule, compared with the electron, very little energy is lost by the electron. Inelastic collisions are usually taken to be those in which the internal energy of one of the colliding particles is involved. Typical examples are the cases of an electron striking a neutral particle and either ionizing or exciting the particle. In this case, the electron loses an appreciable portion of its original energy in the process.

Electrons may be lost from a plasma in a variety of ways. They may attach to neutral particles, forming negative ions; they may recombine with positive ions, forming neutral particles; and they may diffuse through the plasma and strike the container walls, thus being lost by wall recombination. In order for plasma neutrality to be maintained, similar loss mechanisms must occur to the positive ions.

The Boltzmann equation is used to describe the distribution of the constituents of an ionized gas in configuration and velocity space. This is a differential equation for the number density of particles in phase space. Once having determined the distribution functions (q.v.) of the electrons, ions, and neutral particles, through solutions of the Boltzmann equation, it is normally assumed that one can describe all of the properties of a plasma.

A plasma is usually created through a process called breakdown. In the presence of an electric field sufficient energy may be imparted to the free electrons to produce ionizing collisions, and a discharge may then be produced. Breakdown is usually said to occur when the electric field is of such strength that it produces an ionization rate that slightly exceeds the rate at which electrons are lost through the previously described mechanisms.

A gas can also be ionized by heating its constituents to such a temperature that ionization will be produced simply through the thermal motion of the gas particles.

Electromagnetic Wave Interactions.

A plasma can be represented as having a dielectric constant given by

$$\frac{\epsilon}{\epsilon_0} = \left[1 - \frac{\omega_p^2}{\nu^2 + \omega^2} + j\, \frac{\omega_p^2 \nu/\omega}{\nu^2 + \omega^2} \right]$$

where $\omega_p = n_0 e^2/m\epsilon_0$ is the plasma frequency and ν is the electron-neutral particle collision frequency for momentum transfer. The plasma frequency is the frequency at which the electrons would oscillate about their rest positions if they were displaced from this position by an external force. When electrons are displaced from their rest positions, a restoring force is established, owing to the coulomb force between the electrons and the ions that have been left behind. The electrons then tend to return to their original positions, thus maintaining charge neutrality, and oscillate about their original positions owing to inertial effects.

One can see that the effects of a plasma are always to reduce the dielectric constant below that of free space (in the absence of the dc magnetic field). The fact that ϵ is complex implies that the medium can attenuate the wave since k, the propagation constant of the wave, is given by

$$k^2 = \mu_0 \epsilon \omega^2$$

It can be seen that this absorption vanishes at $\nu = 0$. Collisions, therefore, are the mechanism by which an electric field can impart energy to the electrons, since in the absence of collisions, the electron velocity is 90° out of phase with the electric field. For $\nu/\omega \ll 1$, the medium appears as a high-pass filter with a cutoff at $\omega = \omega_p$.

In the presence of a dc magnetic field the dielectric constant is a tensor. For the case of an electromagnetic wave propagating in the same direction as the direction of the dc magnetic field, the wave splits into right and left circularly polarized waves. The dielectric constant in such a situation is given by

$$\frac{\epsilon_\pm}{\epsilon_0} = \left[1 - \left(\frac{\omega_p^2}{\omega} \right) \frac{(\omega \mp \omega_c) - j\nu}{(\omega \mp \omega_c)^2 + \nu^2} \right]$$

where ϵ_+ is the dielectric constant of the medium for the right-hand circularly polarized wave and ϵ_- is the dielectric constant of the medium for the left-hand circularly polarized wave; ω_c is the electron cyclotron frequency given by $\omega_c = -(e/m)B_0$, where B_0 is the magnitude of the dc magnetic field. In the limit of zero collision frequency the propagation constant of the waves propagating in the ionized plasma is given as

$$k_{\pm} = \frac{\omega}{c}\left[1 - \frac{\omega_p^2}{\omega(\omega \mp \omega_c)}\right]^{1/2}$$

For $\omega > \omega_p$ a wave propagates through the medium, and for $\omega < \omega_p$ it does not. For the right circularly polarized wave, propagation occurs (k_+ is real) for all values of ω, for $\omega < \omega_c$, and also when ω is greater than ω_+. The left circularly polarized wave propagation occurs only for $\omega > \omega_-$; that is, the medium acts as a high-pass filter for the left circularly polarized wave with a stop band when ω is less than ω_- (Fig. 1). The medium acts as a stop-band filter for the right circularly polarized wave when the stop band exists in the region $\omega_c < \omega < \omega_+$; ω_+ is defined by

$$\omega_{\pm} = \pm(\omega_c/2) + [(\omega_c/2)^2 + \omega_p^2]^{1/2}$$

For the case of propagation in the direction perpendicular to the direction of the dc magnetic field, the propagation constant $k_{\perp}$ is given by

$$k_{\perp} = \frac{\omega}{c}\left[1 - \frac{\omega_p^2(\omega_p^2 - \omega^2)}{\omega^2(\omega_p^2 - \omega^2 + \omega_c^2)}\right]^{1/2}$$

In this case the medium acts as a filter with stop bands in the regions

$$0 < \omega < \omega_- \quad \text{and} \quad \sqrt{\omega_c^2 + \omega_p^2} < \omega < \omega_+.$$

The propagation characteristics of a plasma are indicated schematically in the figure.

Microwave Applications. From the propagation characteristics of a plasma it can be seen that the electron density and the electron-neutral particle collision frequency control propagation phenomena. In other words, these properties of an ionized gas could be used to produce microwave devices, such as attenuators, phase shifters, isolators, and switches. In addition, when an intense electromagnetic field is incident upon a plasma, the plasma may exhibit nonlinear effects. These nonlinear phenomena can be used to produce a harmonic generator.

One form of controlled thermonuclear reactor is a highly ionized, confined plasma at a high temperature (see below). The above-described microwave interactions with an ionized medium are currently being used in thermonuclear work as diagnostic tools. By measuring the attenuation and phase shift of a wave passing through an ionized gas one can then relate these measurements to the electron density and the electron-neutral particle collision frequency. In this way microwave interactions with a plasma may be used as diagnostic tools for the worker in the field of thermonuclear devices.

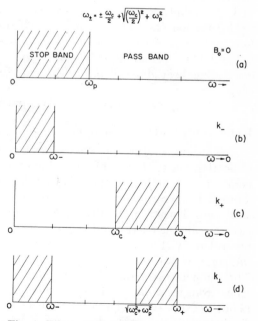

Fig. 1. Filter characteristics of the medium for the various waves.

When a supersonic vehicle re-enters the earth's atmosphere a shock wave is set up around the vehicle. This region is at a high pressure and high temperature. Because of the high thermal energy within the shock wave it is highly ionized. Such an ionized medium can modify the radar cross section of the re-entry vehicle; it can cause absorption of signals transmitted to or from the vehicle; it can change the radiation pattern of the antennas on the vehicle; and it can, in general, disrupt communications with the vehicle. For this reason plasmas and their interactions with electromagnetic waves must be taken into account when designing communications equipment for use with such a vehicle.

Energy Conversion. A typical attempt at converting heat into electrical energy is through the use of a cesium plasma diode. By introducing cesium into a diode, and operating the cathode and anode of the diode at elevated temperatures, a cesium plasma can be produced. This cesium plasma results in increased emission from the cathode, since the cathode is no longer space-charge limited. In addition, the cesium lowers the work function (*q.v.*) of the cathode. Therefore, increased efficiency of the diode is obtained. This technique shows promise for converting heat directly into electrical energy.

ROMAYNE F. WHITMER

High-Temperature Plasmas

A high-temperature plasma is the result of heating matter to a sufficiently high temperature so that in general it is completely ionized. The temperature required to achieve this state depends primarily upon the first electron binding energy and only secondarily upon density. For laboratory pressures this temperature is about 5 ev (1 ev = 11,600°K). The temperature required to strip all electrons from an atom of atomic number Z is about $10Z^2$ ev. When equilibrium is achieved (including radiation) the degree of ionization is defined by the Saha equation,

$$\log \frac{Pf^2}{1 - f^2} = -0.434 \frac{E_i}{kT}$$
$$+ \frac{5}{2} \log T + \log g + 3.67 \tag{1}$$

where

f = fractional ionization
p = pressure in atmospheres
g = ratio of statistical weights of bound to free states (about $\frac{1}{2}$)
E_i = ionization potential in ev
kT = temperature in ev

If equilibrium is not achieved, as for instance no radiation, then a detailed balance between ionization by collision and recombination must be calculated. (See, for instance, L. Spitzer, Jr., *Physics of Fully Ionized Gases*, Interscience Publications, New York, 1956.)

The pressure of a high-temperature plasma depends upon the energy content:

$$P = \tfrac{2}{3} NkT \tag{2}$$

where N = total number of ions and electrons and kT = thermal energy per particle. In addition, blackbody radiation contains energy and exerts a pressure

$$E_{rad} = P_{rad} = aT^4 \text{ ergs/cm}^3 \text{ (dynes/cm}^2) \tag{3}$$

where $a = 137$ and T is in ev.

The energy and pressure of equilibrium radiation is so high that high-temperature laboratory plasmas must be formed without radiation equilibrium, which is achieved by using gases of low atomic number (hydrogen or helium) and at low density $N \leq 10^{17}$/cc. In order for the pressure to be feasibly small, a plasma at thermonuclear temperature (10 kev) must be less than 10^{15}/cc. At such low density and high temperature, collisions between particles are very rare. The coulomb cross section for scattering is given by

$$\sigma \cong \frac{6 \times 10^{-14} \ln \Lambda}{E^2} \text{ cm}^2 \tag{4}$$

where E is particle energy in ev and $\ln \Lambda$ is weakly dependent upon density and temperature, generally of order 10. In a thermonuclear plasma $T = 10$ kev, $N \cong 10^{15}$/cm³, and the mean free path between collision is

$$\lambda \cong \frac{1}{N\sigma} \cong 1.5 \text{ km} \qquad (5)$$

Such small cross sections for scattering lead to rapid thermal transport and low electrical resistivity. The thermal conductivity becomes

$$K = 2.24 \times 10^8 T^{5/2} \frac{\text{ergs}}{\text{sec (ev temp) cm}} \qquad (6)$$

For a vessel whose dimension is less than a scattering mean free path, the thermal energy content of the plasma is conducted to the walk at the mean thermal speed of the particles,

$$V_{ther} = \sqrt{\frac{KT}{2M}} \text{ cm/sec} \qquad (7)$$

where kT is in ergs/particle and M is the mass in grams.

The electrical resistivity is

$$\eta = 0.05 \, ZT^{-3/2} \text{ ohm-cm} \qquad (8)$$

where T is in ev and Z is the ion charge; and twice this resistivity for current transverse to a magnetic field. A plasma at 1 kev temperature has the conductivity of copper. With no containment a thermonuclear plasma would cool by conduction to the walls in a time

$$\tau = D/V_{ther} \text{ sec} \qquad (9)$$

where D = diameter of vessel.

This time is approximately 10^{-6} of the time needed to recreate the energy content by thermonuclear reactions. Therefore a magnetic field is used to isolate thermally and contain a high-temperature plasma. To contain a plasma the energy density of magnetic field

$$W = \frac{B^2}{8\pi} \qquad (10)$$

must be greater than the plasma pressure $(\frac{2}{3})NkT$. The fraction of the total pressure due to the plasma is

$$\beta = (\tfrac{2}{3})NkT/[(B^2/8\pi) + (\tfrac{2}{3})NkT] \qquad (11)$$

A plasma can escape a magnetic field by diffusion which is the magnetic skin depth time

$$\tau = \frac{4\pi L^2 10^{-9}}{\beta\eta} \text{ sec} \qquad (12)$$

where $\mathfrak{N}$ = resistivity (7) and L = dimension of magnetic field. Since the resistivity is small for high-temperature plasmas, the containment time may be many seconds.

Collisions among particles leads to thermalization, so that the time for thermalization of a non-Maxwellian distribution of a particular species of atomic number A and charge Z, by collisions between similar particles becomes

$$\tau = \frac{1.42 \times 10^7 A^{1/2} T^{3/2}}{nZ^4 \ln \Lambda} \text{ sec} \qquad (13)$$

where T is in ev and the time for thermalization of particles $A_1 Z_1$ to particles $A_2 Z_2$ becomes

$$\tau = \frac{7.3 \times 10^6 A_1 A_2}{(n_1 + n_2) Z_1^2 Z_2^2 \ln} \left(\frac{T_1}{A_1} + \frac{T_2}{A_2} \right)^{3/2} \text{ sec} \qquad (14)$$

A plasma can escape from a magnetic field by hydrogmagnetic instabilities that permit a change in configuration of plasma and field such as to lower the total energy of the system. Hydromagnetic instabilities are avoided by forming magnetic-field and plasma configurations in such a way that any perturbation raises the total energy.

In general an instability grows in the time of the transit of sound across the wavelength of the instability. In equilibrium, sound speed is close to the thermal speed (6) of the heavy ions, but for nonequilibrium conditions sound speed becomes the classical value:

$$C = \sqrt{\frac{\gamma P}{\rho}} \qquad (1 \leq \gamma \leq 2) \qquad (15)$$

where γ = ratio specific heats, P = total pressure including electron and ions separately, and ρ the density. If the total pressure includes the magnetic field pressure $B^2/8\pi$, then the resulting sound speed is called the Alfvén speed and is the speed of propagation of a hydromagnetic wave.

A high-temperature plasma can cool without coming in contact with a cold wall by the emission of radiation. Equilibrium blackbody radiation $(C/3)aT^4$ ergs/cm²sec would cool a high-temperature laboratory plasma too fast for observation. Nonequilibrium radiation may arise from:

(1) Bremsstrahlung (*q.v.*), where an electron emits a photon on being inelastically scattered from an ion. The emitted power is:

$$P_B = 1.53 \times 10^{-25} Z^3 n_i^2 T^{1/2} \text{ ergs/cm}^3\text{-sec} \quad (16)$$

with T in ev.

(2) Impurity radiation, where an electron inelastically scatters off a bound electron state raising the bound electron (of the parent ion or atom) to an excited state. Line emission occurs in the return transition to the ground state. For impurity atoms that are not completely stripped of bound electrons ($10 Z^2 \geq kT$ in ev) the impurity radiation is approximately $10^5 P_B$ per impurity atom.

(3) Partial blackbody microwave emission (synchrotron radiation). Up to the cyclotron frequency and in the bands near the higher harmonics (up to 10th) a high-temperature plasma is partially opaque to microwaves and therefore emits as a "partial" black body in this frequency region. The emitted power depends upon both volume, density, temperature, field and surface area, but per unit area is approximately

$$P \cong 2 \times 10^{-22} T^2 B^3 \text{ watts/cm}^2 \quad (17)$$

with T in ev, B in gauss.

(4) Charge exchange, which may cool a magnetically confined plasma rapidly by allowing a fast energetic ion to charge-exchange with a cold neutral atom, thereby becoming a fast neutral and reaching the wall in a straight line. A low-energy ion is left behind in the plasma. The cooling time becomes

$$\tau = \frac{1}{n\sigma V_{th}} \quad (18)$$

The charge exchange cross section is a function of energy and atomic species, but can be as large as 10^{-14} cm².

STIRLING A. COLGATE

Cross-references: *Characteristic Frequencies, Energy Conversion, Fission, Gases, Ionization, Magnetohydrodynamics (MHD)*

PLASMA FREQUENCY: see CHARACTERISTIC FREQUENCIES

PLASMA PROPULSION

The development of plasma propulsion is motivated by the need for space-vehicle propulsion systems with exhaust velocities far greater than those attainable with chemical rockets. For a fixed thrust, an increase in exhaust velocity results in a smaller expenditure of propellant mass. Depending upon the particular mission considered, the ratio of the useful payload to initial mass of the rocket is correspondingly increased.

The exhaust velocity is conventionally expressed in terms of the *specific impulse* I_{sp}. It is likely that plasma-propulsion systems will be developed with I_{sp} ranging from 1000 to 20,000 sec. The optimum I_{sp} depends mainly upon the mission (including the time allowed for the trip) and upon the mass/power ratio of the power plant needed to supply the electrical energy. Devices with an I_{sp} of 1000 to 2000 sec are useful for attitude stabilization of communication satellites and for lifting satellites from a low-altitude orbit to a 24-hr orbit. An I_{sp} from 3000 to 20,000 sec is optimal for extended missions within the solar system.

Similar performances are anticipated for *ion propulsion* (*q.v.*). Plasma propulsion is likely to be less efficient in the range of high I_{sp}, but offers the advantage of a wider choice of propellants (ion propulsion is limited to using mainly alkalis) with good storage and handling characteristics. Other anticipated advantages are a higher thrust per unit area owing to the absence of space-charge limitation, and possibly a wider useful range of specific impulse.

Thrusts of the order of 1 lb have been obtained with laboratory devices operating in the lower range of I_{sp}. Early applications to space vehicles envisage thrust levels of only a fraction of a pound, corresponding to accelerations of $10^{-4}g$ or less. Chemical or nuclear boosters are therefore needed to put the vehicle first into a low-altitude orbit, from which it can ascend slowly in a spiral path until escape velocity is reached. The time required to enter a new orbit about an earth-near planet exceeds several months.

Anticipated power requirements are of the order of a few to hundreds of kilowatts, depending upon the application. Nuclear and solar energy sources are being considered. The successful application of plasma propulsion hinges largely upon the development of light-weight power-conversion methods (electrostatic generator, thermoelectric, and thermionic devices). In the lower range of I_{sp}, cooling by direct thermal radiation and regenerative cooling suffices; at high I_{sp}, a cooling cycle is required.

The weight of the propulsion unit is only a small fraction of the combined weights of energy source and conversion equipment, and therefore not of critical importance. However, the efficiency with which electric energy is converted into kinetic energy of the propellant is crucial, since it directly affects the weight of the power plant. In the range of low I_{sp} (arc jet), efficiencies exceeding 50 per cent have been demonstrated with laboratory devices; at high I_{sp}, the present-day efficiency is less than 30 per cent.

The propellant is accelerated either by means of expanding an arc-heated *plasma* through a supersonic nozzle (arc jet), by imparting a momentum to the plasma by means of magnetic fields (crossed-field accelerator, rail accelerator, etc.) or by a combination of both methods. The magnetic devices depend upon the *ponderomotive force* to accelerate the plasma. As a consequence of the high particle density, the *Debye shielding distance* is small compared with the physical dimensions. Except for thin sheaths on electrodes and insulators, electric forces are therefore absent and play no role in the acceleration.

Arc Jet. The usual configuration is co-axial, with the two electrodes separated by an annular gap across which the arc strikes, and through which the propellant flows. The inner electrode is usually the cathode, made of thoriated tungsten or some other refractory. Liquid-cooled copper or uncooled refractory metals are used for the anode.

In one version, the arc is confined by the throat region formed by the anode and strikes to the diverging portion of the nozzle, resulting in an increased voltage gradient and arc temperature. Anode-spot motion to prevent anode burnout can be increased by introducing the propellant with a swirl, or by means of an axial magnetic field. In the case of poly-atomic propellants, the energy required for dissociation represents an important loss mechanism. Owing to the relatively low density, recombination in the nozzle is incomplete. Specific impulses of 1000 to 2000 sec have been obtained with gases of low molecular weight.

Crossed-Field Accelerator. Characteristic for these devices is an externally applied magnetic field, with lines of force substantially perpendicular to the discharge current. The resulting ponderomotive force is perpendicular to both field and current, and is in the direction of motion of the plasma. The propellant flows through a rectangular channel, bounded by two electrodes facing each other. At low current densities, there is a tendency for the arc to strike in the channel boundary layer. Magnetic field strengths of several thousand gauss are typical.

The same general principle is utilized in the *T-tube*, which is operated as a pulsed device. The arc current is supplied by a repeatedly charging and discharging capacitor bank. The magnetic field is provided by the return conductor for the arc current. In other experiments, the capacitors discharge through a metallic wire which is vaporized (*exploding-wire* technique).

Rail Accelerator. The electric discharge

takes place between two parallel, plane conductors (rails) or surfaces of revolution. The magnetic field associated with the discharge current drives the current front along the rails. In one mode of operation, the space between the electrodes is initially filled with gas at a low pressure; the moving current front then produces a propagating shock wave, which compresses and ionizes the gas. In other devices of this type, a puff of gas is admitted through a fast acting valve into the vacuum between the electrodes and is accelerated by the discharge. Maximum velocities corresponding to a specific impulse of 20,000 sec and higher have been obtained in pulsed operation.

Traveling-Wave Accelerator. The principle of operation is somewhat analogous to that of an induction motor. A time-varying magnetic field is produced either by multiphase windings, by sequentially switched coils, or by means of a transmission line. An attractive feature of this type accelerator is the absence of electrodes and the possibility of isolating the plasma from the walls by means of magnetic fields.

RUDOLF X. MEYER

Cross-references: *Energy Conversion, Ion Propulsion, Plasma, Satellite Electronics*

POLAR MOLECULES

The term "polar" is applied to molecules in which there exists a permanent separation of positive and negative charge, or dipole moment. Such a moment was first postulated by Debye for organic molecules with structural asymmetry, to explain certain of the observed electrical properties. He chose for his model the simplified picture of an electric dipole contained in a spherical molecule, free to rotate into alignment with an applied electric field, subject, of course, to the viscous drag of the surrounding medium and to collisions with other molecules owing to their thermal motion. Then the net dipole moment per mole (molar polarizability) is calculated statistically on the basis of the average fraction of the dipoles oriented in the direction of the field. At ordinary temperatures and field strengths the electrical energy involved in the orientation is much smaller than the thermal energy kT; therefore, a very small fraction of the dipoles are actually aligned with the field. The polarizability per unit volume is

$$P = N \left(\alpha + \frac{\mu^2}{3kT} \right) \tag{1}$$

where μ is the dipole moment, N is the number of dipoles per unit volume, and T is the absolute temperature. The *polarizability* α represents the induced moment per molecule (as opposed to the permanent moment) resulting from the distortion of electron orbits by the applied field. For nonpolar molecules it is the only contribution; it corresponds to the optical polarizability as measured by the refractive index. The above expression is an approximation in that it does not take into account the short-range interaction of the dipoles with one another or saturation effects at high field strengths.

As the frequency of the electric field is increased, a point is reached at which the molecular dipoles are no longer able to oscillate in phase with the field because of the retarding effect of the viscous medium. This effect leads to a diminution of the polarization, and at sufficiently high frequencies the contribution of the dipoles to the polarization vanishes. At the same time the out-of-phase component of the orientation appears as a current in phase with the applied field, giving rise to a dielectric loss which is indicative of the dissipation of energy in the material. This phenomenon is known as *anomalous dispersion* and may be characterized by a frequency or relaxation time that is a function of the molecular size and shape, the viscosity of the medium, and the temperature. Dispersion may also be observed as a function of temperature at constant frequency because of the variation in relaxation time as a consequence of the temperature dependence of the viscosity.

The molar polarizability may be related

to the dielectric constant ϵ' by the approximate equation of Clausius and Mosotti:

$$\frac{\epsilon' - 1}{\epsilon' + 2} = \frac{P}{3\epsilon_0} \qquad (2)$$

where P is the polarizability per unit volume. At optical frequencies the polarizability is related to the refractive index n by replacing ϵ' by n^2 in the above expression. The measurement of dipole moment may therefore be accomplished by a determination of dielectric constant in the vapor phase or in dilute solution. In the latter case the molar polarizability is extrapolated to infinite dilution to eliminate the effects of intermolecular interactions. The dipole moment is obtained from the temperature coefficient of the polarization, as may be seen from Eq. (1). Alternatively a companion measurement of the optical refractive index may be made in order to determine α; the difference between the total polarization and the optical contribution is then taken to represent the dipole contribution from which μ is calculated. Dipole moments are usually expressed in terms of debye units (1 debye $= 10^{-18}$ esu $= \frac{1}{3} \times 10^{-29}$ MKS).

The relationships between the dipole moment and dielectric constant fail for concentrated solutions or pure polar liquids because they do not take into account the interaction between neighboring dipoles, which generally increases the total moment. The calculations have been extended by Onsager, Kirkwood, and others to include this effect. The results are expressed in terms of a correlation factor which is a measure of the extent of nonrandom orientation of the dipoles, i.e., the tendency of the dipoles to aggregate parallel or antiparallel to one another. Experimental determination of this quantity yields some insight into the structure of polar liquids.

Another source of information regarding the structure of polar liquids lies in the determination of relaxation times. As indicated above, the relaxation time is determined by the size and shape of the molecule and the microscopic viscosity of the medium. For complicated molecules or high polymers the frequency dependence is generally characterized by a distribution of relaxation times rather than by a unique value as a result of the orientation of molecular segments of various sizes. Information regarding the freedom of orientation within the molecule may thus be gained.

In the solid state most crystalline polar compounds exhibit low dielectric constants because the rotational freedom necessary for dipole orientation has been frozen out. A few compounds, notably long-chain derivatives, show a persistence of high dielectric constant to temperatures below the melting point, indicating rotational freedom in the solid. At some lower temperature, characteristic of a further first- or second-order transition, this rotation ceases and the dielectric constant drops. Dielectric-constant measurement has frequently been used as a method of detecting these transitions in polar compounds.

DAVID EDELSON

Cross-references: *Dielectric Theory, Dipole Moment, Electromagnetic Theory, Molecules, Refractive Index*

POLARIZATION: see PROPAGATION

POPOV, ALEKSANDR STEPANOVICH (1859–1905)*

A. S. Popov was born on March 4, 1859, in Turynskie Rudinki in the Perm government of Russia, the son of a clergyman. He studied first for the priesthood, but in 1877 he enrolled at the University of St. Petersburg to study mathematics. He graduated in 1882 and after a year of postgraduate studies in mathematics and physics accepted a position at the Naval School in Kronstadt, and also taught electrical engineering and physics at the Naval Engineering College there from 1890 to 1900. In 1889, stimulated by the experiments of Heinrich Hertz, he proposed

* This material is based in part on an article in vol. 34 of the Great Soviet Encyclopedia.

A. S. Popov. (*Taken from Bolshaja Sovetskaja Encyclopedia*, v. 34.)

that electromagnetic waves could be used to receive signals. He began his own experiments in this field in 1894, using a receiver with a metal-powder coherer of his own design and increasing its sensitivity by the addition of a wire; equipped with this antenna, the receiver was sensitive enough to record atmospheric discharges and thus acted as a storm detector. Instruments based on this invention were installed in St. Petersburg in 1895 and in Nizhni Novgorod in 1896. In the same year, Popov demonstrated radio transmission and is said to have transmitted the first radio message, consisting of the two words "Heinrich Hertz." In an article published in the January, 1896, issue of the Journal of the Russian Physical-Chemical Society, entitled "Device for detection and registration of electric oscillations," Popov included a schematic diagram and a detailed description of a radio receiver, thus antedating Marconi's first publication. In 1897, Popov succeeded in obtaining transmission over a distance of 5 km in secret experiments carried on for the Russian Admiralty. Although hampered by unfavorable economic conditions, Popov persuaded the Admiralty

to install radio communications between ships and between ship and shore stations, but the equipment was insufficient to supply the entire fleet; for the Russo-Japanese War of 1904–05 the Russian Naval Command hurriedly had to supply its ships with apparatus of German manufacture.

Popov was widely recognized by his contemporaries, being elected vice-president of the Russian Physical-Chemical Society in 1904 and receiving a Premium of the Russian Technical Society in 1898 for the construction of his receiver and for its practical application to meteorology and radio transmission. At the Fourth International Technical Congress in Paris in 1900 he received a diploma with a gold medal. He died on December 31, 1905, without receiving the full international recognition that continued participation in the early years of radio development would have brought him; but in recent years his achievements have been brought to the attention of the entire world through the efforts of his countrymen, who regard him as the inventor of radio.

CHARLES SUSSKIND

Cross-references: *Historical Background of Electronics*

POSITRONS

The *positron* is an elementary particle having a rest mass of about $\frac{1}{1840}$ of that of a neutron and a unit positive charge. Its symbol is e^+ or β^+. Its rest mass is 0.000584 mass unit, compared with that of the neutron of 1.008937 mass units. The spin value of the positron is $\frac{1}{2}$ and it obeys Fermi statistics. Its magnetic momentum is 1.00118 Bohr magnetons. The existence of the positron is fleeting, as it soon interacts with an electron at rest and both particles are annihilated to produce two photons of equal energy, 0.511 Mev, which is equal to the rest-mass energy of an electron. These two photons are directed exactly opposite one another to insure the conservation of momentum.

C. D. Anderson was the first to discover these particles when he observed them in cloud-chamber photographs of cosmic radiation. When photons having energies greater than 1.022 Mev strike thin materials of a high atomic number, a positron-negatron pair is produced. The energy of the photon is transferred to the creation of masses of the pair and their resulting kinetic energies. This interaction is represented approximately by the following relation:

$$E_\gamma = 2m_0c^2 + E^- + E^+$$

The rest energy of the positron or negatron is m_0c^2. Both a positive and a negative particle must be produced to maintain conservation of charge. The tracks of the positron-negatron pair were seen in the cloud chamber by applying a magnetic field at right angles to the direction of the photons. The tracks of the pair were deflected by the magnetic field in opposite directions, indicating unlike charges.

As seen from the above equation, the energy E_γ of the photon must be greater than 1.002 Mev for the production of the positron-negatron pair, since this is the value of the rest energy $2m_0c^2$. Energy of the photon in excess of this value is divided in kinetic energies between the positron and the negatron. This division is not equal, as for low energies of the photon, the positron has a little more kinetic energy than the negatron. This fact is due to the unsymmetrical Coulomb interaction between the catalyzing nucleus and each particle. However, as the energy of the photon increases, these differences in kinetic energies tend to disappear. The particles tend to be ejected in the same direction as that of the initiating photon. This phenomenon is particularly noticeable at higher energies.

The production of the positron-negatron pair is sometimes referred to as the "materialization" of radiation. There is a tendency for a nucleus to emit a positron and thereby reduce its charge by one unit if, in the nucleus, the number of neutrons is small in comparison to the number of protons. Positron emission can occur only if the difference between the initial and final nuclei is greater than $2m_0c^2$. The process of positron emission is described by the following equation:

$$\Delta E = (M_z - M_{z-1} - 2m_0 - \eta)c^2$$

Here ΔE is the kinetic energy of the positron, M_z and M_{z-1} are the initial and final nuclei, respectively, and η is a neutrino. It is obvious, then, in order to have positron emission, an energy must be available between the initial and final nuclei equal to 1.022 Mev. An example of positron emission is given by the following equation:

$$_{29}\text{Cu}^{64} \rightarrow {}_{28}\text{Ni}^{64} + {}_{+1}e^0 + {}_0\eta^0 + Q$$

where Q is the sum of the kinetic energies.

A given nucleus, with a relatively large proton-to-neutron ratio, may decay by K-capture instead of by positron emission when it possesses 1.022 Mev for disintegration. This competition between K-capture and positron emission is especially pronounced for the heavier nuclei. An example of this phenomenon is $_{29}\text{Cu}^{64}$, which decays both by K-capture and positron emission, both producing $_{28}\text{Ni}^{64}$.

In 1935 Dirac postulated a concept in regard to positrons, positron annihilation, and pair production. This theory permitted the energies of the free electron to be predicted. This concept consisted of a positive continuum above the value of m_0c^2 and a negative energy continuum below the value $-m_0c^2$, with both continuums symmetrical about the axis, $E = 0$. The annihilation of the positron and the negatron is described graphically by a displacement from the value, $+m_0c^2$, to $-m_0c^2$. In this model, pair production is conceived of as a displacement of a point a certain distance below $-m_0c^2$ in the negative continuum to a point an equal distance above $+m_0c^2$ in the positive continuum.

JEROME BREWER

Cross-references: *Atoms, Electrons, Nucleonics*

POTENTIOMETERS

The name "potentiometer" has gained acceptance over the more appropriate name "voltage divider." The device "meters" electrical potential, using "meter" not in the usual sense of "measuring" but rather in the sense of "proportioning," the meaning in the term "metering valve."

A potentiometer's function is to divide an available input voltage in a predetermined or desired fashion. It has at least three terminals, one at each end of the resistance unit, and one for the movable brush that supplies the variable output. It is thus distinguished from a rheostat (*q.v.*, which often looks superficially the same) by usually having three terminals instead of only two. Exemplary specific uses are: (1) to adjust voltage on a vacuum-tube electrode; (2) as manual volume control; (3) as a calibrating adjustment in many circuits; (4) in analog computers; (5) as essential parts of transducers.

Potentiometers have a number of characteristics which are usual, definitive, or of particular importance: (1) low power dissipation; (2) many sizes, as determined by power, resolution, or conformity; (3) usually, low brush current; (4) good resolution; (5) low brush noise; (6) resistance and tolerance; (7) specific resistance-rotation characteristic—for example, linear, exponential, logarithmic, parabolic (square-law), sine-cosine, reciprocal, empirical, etc.; (8) linearity or conformity to specified curve; (9) frequency characteristic; (10) occasionally, minimal torque; (11) sometimes, continuous rotation; (12) special mechanical features.

Many resistive materials may be used, but most usual material is in the form of metal alloy wire. Many alloys are available having different combinations of characteristics, for example, resistivity, temperature coefficient, thermal emf against copper, hardness, corrosion resistance, etc. Best corrosion resistance at elevated temperatures requires the use of precious-metal alloys. Others in use are: metal filament, deposited on substrate in various ways; nonmetallic filaments, in-

cluding carbon-based mixtures; solid homogeneous material, as molded or laminated pieces in which the resistive material is uniformly distributed throughout an insulating host or binder.

Potentiometers are made in single- or multi-turn versions. The former may be arranged for continuous rotation. The latter yield large angles of rotation and are capable of high resolution and good linearity.

In wire-wound potentiometers, mandrels on which wire is wound may be round or flat. Most multi-turn and many single-turn units employ Kohlrausch windings in which the resistive wire is wound over a large (say $\frac{1}{8}$-in. diameter) copper wire having a heavy synthetic enamel coating. Most single-turn units employ windings on flat rectangular cards of flexible synthetic laminate.

If the resistance-rotation characteristic is not linear, several winding methods are employed. Turns may be spaced nonuniformly on Kohlrausch or flat-mandrel windings. Flat mandrels may be shaped and wire turns spaced uniformly or nonuniformly. Several sections of a flat rectangular mandrel may be wound with different rates of angular resistance change, approximating a curve by several secants. A similar result may be obtained by tapping a uniform winding and shunting the sections differently.

Method of brush actuation is usually rotary, but translational units are built in large numbers.

Frequency characteristic is often important; it is determined by magnitude of residual L and C. Best results are obtained by minimizing L and C. Failing that, compensating methods are available that ameliorate but do not cure the difficulty. Inductance is kept low by reducing the area of each turn, as by a thin mandrel. Capacitance is vastly increased by Kohlrausch windings on copper and by metal cases, whereas Kohlrausch windings on extruded synthetic insulators, windings on flat insulating mandrels, and cases of insulating material minimize capacitance.

The particular application of a given potentiometer dictates the inclusion of many types of available special features: (1) precious-metal contacts to help control electrical noise; (2) ganging of several units on one shaft; (3) phasing such ganged units versus one another; (4) tracking among such ganged units; (5) bringing out taps at desired angles; (6) concentric mounting of two units, yielding separate actuation; (7) low operating torque; (8) hermetic sealing; (9) special shaft details, such as diameter, length, flatting, projections front and rear; (10) special mounting details, such as single-hole or servo mounting.

A specialized multi-turn variety is available having so-called "infinite resolution" in which the brush ingeniously traverses a helically wound single (not Kohlrausch) resistive wire.

In commerce, potentiometers divide commonly into three rough categories: (1) military precision class, very expensive and usually made to order; (2) laboratory-grade semiprecision units, stocked in many versions having established demand, at medium prices; (3) commercial nonprecision units as used in radio sets, stocked in many varieties at competitive low prices.

P. K. McElroy

Cross-references: *Indicating Instruments, Resistors, Rheostats*

POULSEN, VALDEMAR (1869–1942)

Valdemar Poulsen was born on November 23, 1869, in Copenhagen, the son of a civil servant (later judge). He attended school in Christianshavn, showing a predilection for physics (but not mathematics) and in 1890 embarked upon the study of medicine. The subject did not interest him, but he could not switch to the study of engineering because of his classical secondary education and entered industrial employment instead, first in a machine shop and then in the Copenhagen Telephone Co.'s engineering department. During this employment he conceived the method of magnetic wire re-

cording, but attempts to capitalize upon this invention, both in Denmark and in the U.S., failed owing to the lack of satisfactory amplifiers.

In 1902 he developed the arc generator ("Poulsen arc") for producing high-frequency continuous oscillations that played an important role in the development of radio transmitters. This device was based on the "singing arc" of William Duddell (1872–1917), who had first shown in 1899–1900 that an arc could be used in conjunction with a tuned circuit to produce oscillations. Poulsen extended the frequency range of the device by providing a suitable atmosphere. He adapted existing radio systems, which were devised for spark generators, to the cw arc generator, and made practical radiotelephony (*q.v.*) possible for the first time. The system was adopted all over the world; Poulsen transmitters were installed by the U.S. and British navies, as well as in France, Germany, and other countries. Not until vacuum tubes came to be used in transmitters during the 1920's did the Poulsen arc gradually lose its importance to radio communications.

Poulsen received many honors and honorary degrees. The Gold Medal of the Danish Academy of Technical Sciences is named in his honor. He died in 1942.

Charles Susskind

Cross-references: *Historical Background of Electronics*

PRECISION COMPONENTS: see MINIATURIZATION

PRINTED CIRCUITS

Prior to World War II most electronic equipment was constructed for the radio or communications industry. It was assembled laboriously by interconnecting the various circuit components mounted on terminal boards or sheet metal chassis with hook-up wire and hand-soldered joints. The tremendous growth in the military electronics industry during and after World War II, plus the growth of television, electronic data processing, and industrial electronics in general, made necessary the creation of new methods of assembly for electronic equipment. Hand-wiring of individual components was too costly, too unreliable and did not allow miniaturization in such critical applications as proximity fuzes (*q.v.*), aircraft communication equipment, and missile guidance computers.

Two broad but diverse approaches were followed to solve the problem. In one an effort was made to print the components of the circuit as well as their interconnections. The other method provided a means of mounting and interconnecting conventional electronic components by printing conductors on insulating boards. These two broad approaches have paralleled each other; rather than competing with each other they have been complementary. The name "printed circuits" covers both types.

Work begun at the National Bureau of Standards resulted in circuits printed on small ceramic wafers containing printed resistors, capacitors, and conductors. A silver-powder ink was silk-screen stencil-printed on the surface of the ceramic. After oven firing the fused printed silver lines had almost the conductivity of solid silver foil. Resistors were applied by screen-printing inks made of carbon and resin mixtures in small rectangles between the silver conductors. Capacitors were formed by printing silver ink areas on opposite sides of the ceramic. If high capacity was needed ceramic with high dielectric constant, such as barium titanate, could be used as a substrate. Subminiature tubes were used with these resistor-capacitor networks by soldering their leads to the fired silver conductors.

After World War II this technique was commercialized and used by several companies in the preparation of small resistor-capacitor networks for the radio and television industry. These networks, coated with a protective resin, were provided with a multiplicity of leads or tabs at one edge so that they could be wired into circuits just as conventional axial lead components.

It was not found economical, however, to put a large number of resistors or capacitors into such a circuit since the yield of finished parts in manufacturing dropped off rapidly as the number of components increased. A typical network might contain 3 capacitors and 4 or 5 resistors on a plate 1 x $\frac{3}{4}$ in. in area.

A great many variations on this basic idea have been explored since World War II. Resistors have been laid down by vacuum evaporation of metals. Capacitors have been made in multiple layers by alternate deposits of conductors and dielectrics. The incorporation of active semiconductor elements in the ceramic or glass wafers and deposition of interconnections to these elements has been shown to be feasible. The patterns for the conductors and the dielectric and resistive films have been formed usually either by evaporating through masks or stencils or by covering the entire surface and then masking and removing unwanted areas by chemical etching.

The second approach to providing a printed circuit was simply a means of interconnection for conventional components. The type of printed circuit or (as it is more commonly called) printed wiring board used in this assembly method is an insulating board usually about $\frac{1}{16}$ in. thick carrying a conductive metal pattern laid out in such a fashion that it makes the desired connections between resistors, capacitors, transistors, tubes, etc. that are mounted on the board. Connections between the leads or tabs of the components and the printed wiring board are made by inserting the leads into holes that go through lands or pads in the metallic conductor, then making the connections between the conductor pattern and the leads by soldering. An advantage of this assembly method is that all of the soldered joints may be made at once by dipping the underside of the printed circuit board with the components mounted in a pot of molten solder.

Many methods of placing the conductive metal pattern on the plastic insulator have been proposed but only three have been commercially useful. By far the largest percentage of the over 100,000,000 printed wiring boards manufactured each year are made by the etched-circuit process. This basic idea was originally conceived by Dr. Paul Eisler in England in the early 1940s. Instead of attempting to "print" conductors Dr. Eisler concluded that it would be better to laminate a thin metal foil over the entire surface of a plastic sheet, then lay down an acid resist on the surface of the metal clad sheet by one of the well-known printing processes. After chemically etching away the unprotected copper the printed resist could be removed, leaving a conductive metal pattern on the surface of an insulator. By starting with foil on both sides of the insulator two-sided parts are made. In a variation of this process the reverse of the desired pattern is printed with the resist material; then another metal such as solder, silver, or gold is electroplated on the copper not protected by resist, the plating resist ink is removed, and the unwanted copper is etched away with a solution that does not attack the electroplated metal. It is possible in this way to provide metal patterns with special electroplated metal finishes for plug-in connectors, switches, commutators, and the like.

Since this etching process used the techniques of already well-established businesses, namely the laminated plastic industry for the production of the foil-clad laminate, and the printing industry for the methods of applying the resist ink, it saw rapid and widespread acceptance. Set-up costs are low since it is only necessary to make a master drawing suitable for photographing and to prepare printing tools such as screen stencils or offset printing plates. Circuits can be made by this method on both rigid and flexible materials. Sizes can vary from a tiny thumbnail part up to 3 x 4 ft. Etched circuits have found application in everything from radio sets to missile-guidance computers. Virtually every new electronic device being designed today uses etched wiring in one form or another.

The two other techniques for making printed wiring that have attained commercial usage involve electroplating (q.v.) and stamping. In the plating process the insulator is coated with an adhesive, then with a thin copper film over its entire surface. The reverse of the desired conductor pattern is printed in ink and the conductor pattern is built up by copper plating. After the removal of the resist and the thin copper film under it the remaining circuit is very similar in appearance to the etched circuit. The advantage of this process is that it uses a less expensive raw material and provides two-sided circuits at small additional cost.

In the stamped-circuit process a heated die with sharp edges delineating the circuit pattern is brought down with great pressure on an adhesive-coated copper foil placed on top of an insulator. The pattern is die-cut from the copper foil and the desired conductors are adhered to the insulator surface when the heated die softens and then cures the adhesive coating on the copper. This process has been used primarily for very long run applications where low price is important and tooling costs are unimportant. A typical example would be wiring for an automobile instrument panel.

R. L. SWIGGETT

Cross-references: *Miniaturization, Packaging*

PROBABILITY

Probability is a branch of mathematics which models physical situations involving uncertainty. The uncertainty may be implicit in the physical situation (as in the description of the emission of particles from a hot body) or introduced by the investigator (as when one talks about the distribution of prime numbers throughout the integers).

If an experiment, real or imaginary, may materialize in two or more outcomes under conditions which are, to the best of one's knowledge, identical, the outcome is said to be subject to chance. Probability is the numerical measure of chance.

A variable whose occurrences are subject to chance is a *random*, or *stochastic*, variable. Such variables are either discrete or continuous (combinations occur and are treated by a mixture of the considerations governing each). For a discrete variable consider the total number of possible outcomes on each trial of an experiment. Let a fraction of these outcomes p correspond to the outcome value k (values are not in this case limited to number; the outcome may be an attribute such as red, tall, etc.). The probability of k is p. A function of k which describes the distribution of the probability of outcome over values of k, say $p(k)$, is called a probability distribution. For the discrete case, if $p(k) = 0$, k is impossible; if $p(k) = 1$, k is certain to happen.

One of the central problems of probability applications is the derivation of the probability distribution of a function of a variable when some underlying probability for the variable is assumed. Thus, if it is known that on a single trial of an experiment, the chance of success is p and of failure is $1 - p = q$, then it may be shown that for n trials, the probability of exactly k successes is

$$p(k) = \binom{n}{k} p^k q^{(n-k)}$$

This distribution, the binomial, is a most important discrete variable distribution. Another is the Poisson distribution given by

$$p(k) = \frac{e^{-m}m^k}{k!}$$

where m is the mean number of occurrences per unit (of space, or time) and k is the exact number of successes in a unit chosen at random.

For continuous variables, the probability of outcome is distributed by means of a probability density function. Such functions distribute probability over the range of a chance variable in the same way that a mass distribution function distributes load over a beam in mechanics. Important continuous distributions are the *uniform* distribution,

$$p(x) = \frac{1}{l} \text{ [for } 0 \le x \le l]; \; p(x) = 0 \quad \text{otherwise}$$

and the *normal* distribution

$$p(x) = \frac{1}{\sqrt{2\pi}\sigma} e^{-(x-\mu)^2/2\sigma^2} \quad \text{[for } -\infty \le x < \infty].$$

where μ is the mean and σ the root mean square of x.

The probability of any interval in x containing an outcome is

$$\int_{\text{interval}} p(x)\, dx$$

In a fashion similar to the way in which points exist even though they have no length, if $p(x) = 0$, the outcome x may still occur. Any distribution, discrete or continuous, is subject to two restrictions:

$$p(x) \quad \text{or} \quad p(k) \ge 0$$

and

$$\int_{\substack{\text{all} \\ \text{values} \\ \text{of } x}} p(x)\, dx \quad \text{or} \quad \sum_{\substack{\text{all values} \\ \text{of } x}} p(k) = 1$$

To derive various probability results certain fundamental notions and theorems are used. For two outcomes A and B, we may speak of the probability that A and B both occur. When the occurrence of one does not depend on the occurrence of the other, $P(A \text{ and } B) = P(A) \cdot P(B)$. The probability of A or B occurring is $P(A \text{ or } B) = P(A) + P(B)$. If B's probability depends on whether A occurs, let $P_A(B) = $ probability that B occurs given that A has already occurred. Then $P(A \text{ and } B) = P(A) \cdot P_A(B) = P(B) \cdot P_B(A)$. If $P(A) = P_B(A) = P_{\bar{B}}(A)$ (where $\bar{B}$ is the nonoccurrence of B) then A and B are said to be independent. If A and B are not mutually exclusive, $P(A \text{ or } B) = P(A) + P(B) - P(A \text{ and } B)$.

In the application of probability to the physical world, there are several modes of use. The theory may be used to describe some physical process, an underlying distribution assumed, and the consequences of the assumptions derived and subsequently experimentally tested. If the latter holds in test, the results may be applied. Thus, in shot noise theory the events occurring in time (particle emission) are assumed to be independent and equiprobable in every infinitesimal interval of time. From these two assumptions one may show that the Poisson distribution governs the outcomes. Then results may be derived concerning the distribution of voltage levels, circuit performance, etc., based on assumptions concerning the physical relationships between particle emission and voltages. Finally, the predictions may be checked in the laboratory.

In another mode, probability may be used as the model of the occurrence of the outcomes of experiments. In this case, we may assume the distribution of the experimentally observed variable and derive the distribution of certain calculable indices or statistics. Thus we may evaluate the probability distribution of the mean, the root mean square (standard deviation), or other functions of the observations. On this basis, we may evaluate the chance that a certain outcome (or set of outcomes) will be observed. Turning the problem around, after having observed certain outcomes, we may ask what is the probability that any assumed hypothesis was responsible for the observed result. This inverse problem is the problem of inference in mathematical statistics, which rests on a foundation of probability theory.

But probability serves as the basis for many other endeavors. Directly from the statistical theory of inference, the mathematical theory of communication, or information theory, is developed. To see that the problem is of a similar nature, we note that the originally generated signal is mixed during transmission with a certain amount of noise (uncertainty is introduced) and at the receiving end we must make an inference concerning the origin of the received signal. The whole fabric of signal detection theory is based upon probability.

Signal detection theory is only a subclass of a larger set of problems concerned with decision in the presence of uncertainty and the science of decision theory is itself based on probability. Further, waiting line theory (useful in switching problems for telephone work), game theory (useful in problems of conflicting aims), artificial intelligence theory (developing in the study of thought process), time series study (useful in economics, communications, and elsewhere), all are based on probability theory for descriptions of the stochastic process involved.

Two more special, and related, uses of probability are worth noting. The physics problem of particle birth and death can of course be modelled as a stochastic process with probability theory. But as the problem gets complicated the analytic approach breaks down. However, as the process complicates, it is feasible to describe it mathematically and set it in motion on a digital computer, thus "simulating" it. In general, probability plays a strong role in simulation in deriving useful and realistic models.

The related use is somewhat more subtle. To indicate it, the problem of Buffon's needle is useful. Assume a very large table with a set of parallel lines drawn on it at successive distances apart. Toss a needle of length d onto the table making the position (of the needle center), and the angle (of the needle with the lines), uniformly distributed random variables. Then it may be shown that the probability that the needle will intersect a table line is $2/\pi$. But if this is so, then by repeatedly performing this experiment, π may be evaluated. Such an evaluation is called a Monte Carlo calculation. Many problems ranging from the solution of sets of simultaneous equations to the solution of partial differential equations may be solved by the Monte Carlo method (*q.v.*) and the underlying theory for the method is probability theory.

HARRY H. GOODE

Cross-references: *Decision Theory, Distribution Functions, Information Theory, Signal Detection, Statistical Communication Theory*

PROGRAMMING: see COMPUTER PROGRAM-
MING; LINEAR PROGRAMMING

PROPAGATION

General Considerations

The discussion of propagation phenomena in general media requires a rather elaborate and sophisticated mathematical formalism. For a detailed treatment of those disturbances that fall into a category of wave phenomena, an electromagnetic theory (*q.v.*) of characteristics whose origin lies in the subject of partial differential equations has long been available.

Two viewpoints are of interest for an understanding of the mechanism of propagation of an electromagnetic wave: the macroscopic phenomenological theory of Maxwell and the microscopic theory of Lorentz. The Maxwell theory avoids the explanation of what happens to the individual charged particles that constitute the medium in which the phenomena are taking place; the influence of the medium is accounted for by means of factors called constitutive parameters. The effect of the electric field of equal numbers of oppositely charged particles that make up the medium is accounted for by the permittivity ϵ. The effects of the motions of the charges comprising the medium on the fields are taken into account in the following manner: the motion of the unbound charges is subsumed under the conduction current by means of a conductivity σ; the translational motion of the bound charges is subsumed in the electric-displacement field by means of the permittivity ϵ; and the rotational motion of the constituent charges is subsumed in the magnetic-induction field by means of the permeability μ.

This representation of the dynamical behavior of the constituent charges by means of the parameters ϵ, μ, and σ has proved to be of great practical importance, since one can separate the study of the macroscopic behavior of the fields from that of the macro-scopic behavior of the constituents of the medium in which the fields are present. In many media these constitutive parameters can be determined by empirical means much more easily than by theoretical considerations. For such media the macroscopic theory is clearly most suitable.

In an ionized gas (in contrast to media made up of neutral molecules) it is difficult to measure the constitutive parameters. The difficulty arises from the fact that the space charges present and the boundary condition imposed by the measuring apparatus affect each other significantly. To determine these parameters a knowledge of the dynamical behavior of the microscopic constituents is required, which leads us to the second point of view, the exhaustive microscopic theory of Lorentz. This theory attempts to describe all electrical phenomena in terms of the elementary positive and negative charges comprising the medium. The theory dispenses with the concept of the material medium and considers only the ensemble of negative and positive charges (which actually constitute the medium) in free space. More specifically, the theory postulates that in all permeable bodies there exists a large number of charged particles of very small size, which are separated from each other by free space. Conducting bodies are imagined to be constituted of a large number of free particles capable of being moved through the body under the action of an electric force. Nonconducting or weakly conducting bodies are considered to be made up of particles bound to their positions of equilibrium by an elastic force. Even though they are displaced from their equilibrium positions this displacement is not very large (small oscillations). It is also postulated that the medium has no net charge, so that the positive and negative charges balance exactly. When particles are displaced from their equilibrium positions, the medium becomes polarized.

The Lorentz theory further assumes that the free-space displacement current exists not only in the empty space between the particles but also within the particles themselves. The action of the material medium participates in this theory if we consider the motions of the charged particles under the influence of the electromagnetic forces as a fundamental concept. If each particle has a charge q and a mass m, then under the action of the electric force the particle is displaced from its equilibrium position, and at time t has a velocity of magnitude v. However, the moving charge produces a current $q\mathbf{v}$, and if there are N such particles per unit volume, they give rise to a convection current density $Nq\mathbf{v}$ (by $\mathbf{v}$ we understand the *time-average* value of the charge velocity). The average convection current density can be written as $Nq\mathbf{v} = \rho\mathbf{v} = \mathbf{J}$ regardless of whether the charges are free or bound.

For varying fields, it is not clear *à priori* whether this total current is a conduction current proportional to the electric intensity and in phase with it, or a displacement current proportional to $\dot{\mathbf{E}}$ and out of phase with the electric intensity $\mathbf{E}$ by $\pi/2$. Consequently, the total current density must be written as the sum of the free-space displacement current and the material convection current.

Let us summarize the two views: the Maxwell theory describes the phenomena in terms of the equations

$$\nabla \times \mathbf{E} + \dot{\mathbf{B}} = 0 \tag{1}$$

$$\nabla \times \mathbf{H} = \mathbf{J} + \dot{\mathbf{D}} \tag{2}$$

$$\nabla \cdot \mathbf{D} = \rho \tag{3}$$

$$\nabla \cdot \mathbf{B} = 0 \tag{4}$$

supplemented by the relations

$$\mathbf{B} = \mu\mathbf{H} \tag{5}$$

$$\mathbf{D} = \epsilon\mathbf{E} \tag{6}$$

$$\mathbf{J} = \sigma\mathbf{E} \tag{7}$$

The Lorentz microscopic theory describes the electromagnetic phenomena by the same set of Maxwell's equations as given above, but since there is no medium in this point of view, the relations (5, 6, 7) must be given in vacuo,

$$\mu = \mu_0 \; ; \quad \epsilon = \epsilon_0 \tag{8}$$

and the current density is given directly in terms of the moving charges:

$$\mathbf{J} = \sum_k q_k\mathbf{v}_k / \text{volume of region} \tag{9}$$
$$\text{containing charges}$$

Maxwell's equations relate the fields to the charges and their motions, but since these motions are not known, it is necessary to supplement them with the dynamical equations of motion for the charges. These equations have the form, for each particle q_k,

$$\frac{d(m_k\mathbf{v}_k)}{dt} = q_k(\mathbf{E} + \mathbf{v}_k \times \mathbf{B}) \tag{10}$$

where $\mathbf{B}$ is the *total* magnetic induction field evaluated at the position $\mathbf{r}_k$ of the kth particle and $\mathbf{E}$ is the *total* electric field evaluated at $\mathbf{r}_k$. These fields can consist in part of external fields, and in part of fields due to the q_k's themselves.

The set of equations (1–10) must be solved simultaneously for the dynamical behavior of the charges, and from this behavior we can derive the constitutive parameters for the macroscopic model of the medium.

In the Lorentz theory, the motion of the electrical charges is described in terms of the polarization vector (dipole moment per unit volume) rather than in terms of the convection current. In this case the polarization vector $\mathbf{P} = Nq\mathbf{r}$, $\mathbf{r}$ being the average displacement of the charged particles. Consequently, $\mathbf{J} = \dot{\mathbf{P}}$.

In order to discuss propagation in plasmas (*q.v.*) the relationship between the polarizations (or the current density) and the electric intensity must be added to Maxwell's equations; this completed set we call the Maxwell-Lorentz equations.

In the ionized gas, the electrons and ions are detached completely from their parent molecules; no elastic forces bind them as in the case of a solid body such as a crystal; the particles have no free period of oscillation of their own. But under the influence of an applied force, they are disturbed by collisions with the neutral molecules. In the collision process some of the energy of motion of the electrons and ions is converted into energy of random motion of particles, i.e., heat energy. The charged particles are therefore losing energy continually and this loss can be represented as a resistance to their motions. This simple model of a resistive mechanism is incorporated into the equations of motion of the charged particles as a damping force.

The electron theory of Lorentz gives some idea of the mechanism by which the charged particles alter the phase velocity of a propagating electromagnetic wave field. Consider a semi-infinite medium separated by a plane interface from the free space, and imagine an electromagnetic wave field propagating in free space impinging upon the medium. The electromagnetic wave traveling through the free space between the particles excites the charged particles and causes them to oscillate so that they essentially become small dipole oscillators, the wave field governing their phase of oscillation.

At each point either in or external to the region in which the particles are contained, the secondary waves radiated by the oscillators interfere with the original wave field and with the other radiated waves; the sum of all the waves is a resultant field at the point. Moreover, it is the resultant field that acts on the particles at the given point which causes them to vibrate. The total intensity at any point is the vector sum of the intensity of the original wave field and the resultant intensity due to all the oscillating particles. According to this picture, in general, the emerging wave has its phase velocity altered. Reflective waves are treated in a similar manner.

Plane Wave Fields: Dispersion Relations. Consider the kind of waves that an unbounded homogeneous medium can support, in the presence of a uniform (in space-time) externally applied magnetic field. Although this is not the most general situation, a great many of the salient features may be culled from it. The Maxwell-Lorentz equations, together with the postulated

magnetic field, permit us to examine the existence of simple plane wave fields, i.e., field quantities proportional to $\exp(-j\mathbf{k}\cdot\mathbf{r})$ where $\mathbf{k}$ is the wave vector whose components are in general, complex. For fields with harmonic time dependence, the above assumptions lead to the condition for propagation which takes the form

$$\Delta(\mathbf{n}, \omega, \cdots)\mathbf{E} = 0 \qquad (11)$$

The condition for propagation is thus seen to reduce to the question of the existence of nontrivial fields, i.e., $\mathbf{E} \neq 0$. The necessary and sufficient condition for this is simply the vanishing of the determinant

$$\Delta(\mathbf{n}, \omega, \cdots) = 0 \qquad (12)$$

which expresses an algebraic relation between the wave normal direction $\mathbf{n}$ (defined through $\mathbf{k} = k\mathbf{n}$, k a complex scalar) and the impressed frequency ω of the wave field. The other factors not specifically indicated are functions of the parameters of the medium itself. This algebraic relation is often called a "dispersion relation," since it is a relation for ω. It is only when this condition is fulfilled that a propagating plane wave field is possible. This condition also implies an equation for the refractive index of the medium. The same considerations that led to this relation also leads to a relation between the displacement field $\mathbf{D}$ and the electric field $\mathbf{E}$, in the form

$$\mathbf{D} = \epsilon_0 \varepsilon' \mathbf{E} \qquad (13)$$

where ε' is a tensor whose structure for a particular choice of coordinate system (applied magnetic field co-directional with the x_3-axis) is

$$\varepsilon' = \begin{pmatrix} \epsilon_1 & j\epsilon_2 & 0 \\ -j\epsilon_2 & \epsilon_1 & 0 \\ 0 & 0 & \epsilon_3 \end{pmatrix} \qquad (14)$$

Here, the $\epsilon_j (j = 1, 2, 3)$ are complex valued and are functions of the parameters of the medium. If the medium is magneto-ionic (ions, electrons, and neutral molecules) and if collisions take place only between the charged species and the neutrals comprising the medium, the ϵ_j are rational functions of the medium parameters and the dispersion relation is also called the Appleton-Hartree equation, both of whom derived the relation independently.

The fact that the dispersion relation of such a medium depends upon the direction of the wave normal direction and ω makes the fourth-degree algebraic equation defining the refractive index complicated in practice. Theoretically, two indices are defined; the medium is doubly refracting in this case, analogous but certainly not identical with propagation in certain crystals, and this plasma crystal optics analogy can be advantageously exploited.* The propagating wave fields associated with each index are called, respectively, the *ordinary* mode, because it is least effected by the applied magnetic field; and the *extraordinary* mode. These two modes are linearly independent, i.e., one of them cannot be expressed as a simple multiple of the remaining one. Both modes in passing through the medium undergo attenuation and rotation of their respective planes of polarization; the so-called Faraday effect (q.v.) is present here as in some crystals. This effect is used in electron-density determinations, since the density can be expressed in terms of the angle of rotation of these planes. The planes of polarization of each mode rotate opposite to each other.

Two important parameters (characteristic frequencies, q.v.) are involved in discussing propagation: (1) the *plasma* frequencies of the constituents ω_j, defined by

$$\sqrt{N_j e^2 / \epsilon_0 m_j},$$

where subscript j stands for the type of species (electron, ion, etc.), N_j is the number density, m_j its mass, and e the electronic charge; and (2) the gyro or *Larmor* frequency defined by $\Omega_j = B_0 e / m_j \omega$, where B_0 is the magnitude of the applied magnetic field and ω is the impressed wave frequency.

* See, for instance, J. Brandstatter, "The Propagation of Waves and Rays in a Plasma," McGraw-Hill Book Co.

The plasma frequency is essentially a resonant frequency and is more closely tied to the concept of collective motion or plasma oscillations. The Larmor frequency is a well-known concept and is substantially the frequency with which a charged particle "winds" itself about the externally applied magnetic field in the absence of collisions. If $\omega > \omega_j$ for all j, propagation is possible; if the medium consists only of electrons, the above condition is well known in ionospheric radio wave propagation.

Plasma Waves. For a more complicated description of the medium, other modes of propagation are possible. If the Lorentz force equation is extended so as to include pressure gradients (temperature effects are naturally included in the description by simple use of the gas laws), a hydrodynamic model of the gas results; and since this model is coupled to the electrodynamic equations through the Lorentz force term, we speak of magnetohydrodynamics (q.v.) or (to be more inclusive) magneto-fluid dynamics and its various synonyms. To see the effect of this coupling, we should recall that a completely incompressible perfect fluid with no magnetic field imposed cannot support any wave-like disturbances, as is obvious on physical grounds. This result is also clear on mathematical grounds in which the velocity potential satisfies Laplace's equation whose solutions are certainly not wave-like. If now the fluid is still incompressible but conducting and with a magnetic field imposed upon it, wave phenomena are now possible; the resulting waves are called magnetohydrodynamic and include both longitudinal and transverse types.

In the high-frequency limit these waves yield the usual radio waves mentioned above; in the low-frequency limit the resultant waves are no different in principle. However, because of the coupling of the more extensive hydrodynamic model with the electrodynamic field equations, the intermediate frequency region is naturally more complicated. The conditions for propagation (i.e., the dispersion relations) can no longer be readily discussed in general. The coupling, on the other hand, opens up a vast new area of investigation of wave phenomena, the existence of plasma waves, which was investigated initially by the astrophysicist Alfvén. In the case of an unbounded homogeneous medium, it is possible to treat, in a systematic way, the propagation of plane wave fields.

The conclusions drawn from the extensive hydrodynamical model in the low-frequency limit are also obtainable from a simpler point of view. For a magneto-ionic medium and $\omega \ll \omega_p$, Astrom and others deduced the properties of plane wave propagation by elementary considerations and arrived at the same results as Alfvén. The energy associated with the extraordinary mode proves to be propagated along the magnetic field lines. This manner of propagation sheds light on whistlers, a low-frequency natural phenomenon that exhibits similar properties, as discussed under **Radiation (Terrestrial)**. It is also worthwhile noting that since the dielectric tensor is in general nonsymmetric, the condition of reciprocity (interchange of transmitter and receiver) does not hold as in the isotropic case in which ϵ reduces to a single scalar quantity. Finally, in the homogeneous unbounded case, the mean Poynting vector is *not* co-directional with the wave normal direction of either mode.

Nonhomogeneous Media. In nonhomogeneous, nonmagnetic media whose dielectric tensor varies in only one direction, the problem of calculating the wave fields can be reduced to the calculation of a Hertzian vector potential function, which satisfies an integral-equation relation. Here, one can employ variational techniques similar to those used by Schwinger, Levine, and others to find approximate solutions. Numerical techniques based on matrix theory have likewise been exploited. General reflection and transmission matrices are byproducts of this problem. Other attempts to deal with this kind of problem, particularly for a

doubly refracting medium separated from free space by a horizontal plane, are based on the ideas of Booker *ei al.* A plane wave penetrating the medium from free space below splits into an ordinary and extraordinary wave. Because of the inhomogeneity of the medium the penetrating waves which start at the plane interface generate along their path two ascending and two descending waves, the latter because of postulated internal reflections. The four waves so produced have different wave normal and Poynting vector directions. Snell's law is valid for both the ordinary and extraordinary waves. The inhomogeneous character of the medium causes the four waves, each of different elliptical polarization, to be coupled to each other. K. Suchy has shown that in the general nonhomogeneous medium, with no assumptions of stratification, Maxwell's equations reduce to a pair of coupled equations which has its simplest structure for a certain class of curvilinear coordinates. He has also treated the propagation of electromagnetic waves in absorbing, anisotropic, inhomogeneous, and unbounded media and studied in some detail the transition from the full vector wave equation with arbitrary wavelength λ to small values of λ but nonvanishing.

Ray-Theoretic Approach. The study of propagation in anisotropic, inhomogeneous media becomes amenable to analysis by means of a ray theory. Under the assumption that the wavelength λ is very much smaller than some characteristic dimension of the medium it becomes possible to replace the more complicated vector field equations defined through the Maxwell-Lorentz system by a much simpler structure. By analogy with the homogeneous case, $\mathbf{E}$ is taken to be proportional to

$$A(\mathbf{r}) \exp \left[j \left(\omega t - \omega \int \mathbf{M} \cdot d\mathbf{r} \right) \right]$$

where $\mathbf{M}$ is in general a complex-valued vector. The $\mathbf{H}$ field is expressed similarly. If this expression is used in the vector wave equation for $\mathbf{E}$ we are led to a system with the following structure:

$$(\mathbf{L} - \boldsymbol{\varepsilon})\mathbf{E} = 0 \qquad (15)$$

where $\mathbf{L}$ is a matrix whose elements contain the differential operators $\partial^2/\partial x_i \partial x_j$, and are complex. The condition for propagation is still the vanishing of the determinant $|\mathbf{L} - \boldsymbol{\varepsilon}|$, which is now a nonlinear partial differential equation of the second order for the three components of $\mathbf{M}$. The matrix $\mathbf{L}$ is known as the "Eikonal matrix" and the above dispersion equation constitutes a generalization of the usual Eikonal equation or equation of geometrical optics. To understand the significance of the Eikonal equation we consider a scalar wave equation whose spatial dependence f is of the form,

$$\nabla^2 f + \left(\frac{\omega M}{c}\right)^2 f = 0. \qquad (16)$$

By taking $f(\mathbf{r}) = A(\mathbf{r}) \exp[-2\pi j \psi(\mathbf{r})]$ and setting both the real and imaginary parts to zero, we obtain two nonlinear partial differential equations for the determination of both A and ψ. If both of these functions vary slowly within a distance of a wavelength these equations simplify and one can find ψ without having also to find A. The resulting expression under these conditions for ψ is the Eikonal equation

$$4\pi^2(\nabla\psi)^2 = \left(\frac{\omega M}{c}\right)^2 \qquad (17)$$

whereas that for A takes the form

$$\nabla\cdot(A^2\nabla\psi) = 0 \qquad (18)$$

We can now easily relate ψ to $\mathbf{M}$; indeed we put

$$\psi = \psi_1 - j\psi_2, \quad \mathbf{M} = \mathbf{u} - j\boldsymbol{\chi} \qquad (19)$$

and in general both ψ and $\mathbf{M}$ are functions also of frequency. The complex phase ψ is defined through

$$\psi = \int_{p_0}^{p} \nabla\psi\cdot d\mathbf{r} = \frac{\nu}{c}\int_{p_0}^{p} \mathbf{M}\cdot d\mathbf{r} \qquad (20)$$

where $d\mathbf{r}$ is a real vector and ν the frequency.

The vector $\mathbf{u}$ is normal to the family of surfaces ψ_1 = constant, and $\boldsymbol{\chi}$ is normal to the family ψ_2 = constant; these surfaces are in general distinct, and therefore we put

$$2\pi\psi_1 = \frac{\omega}{c}\int_{p_0}^{p} \mathbf{u}\cdot d\mathbf{r} \qquad (21)$$

$$2\pi\psi_2 = \frac{\omega}{c}\int_{p_0}^{p} \boldsymbol{\chi}\cdot d\mathbf{r} \qquad (22)$$

To find expressions for the magnitude of μ and χ we have

$$M^2 = (\mathbf{u} - j\boldsymbol{\chi}) = P - jQ \qquad (23)$$

which is equivalent to

$$\mu^2 - \chi^2 = P; \quad 2\mu\chi\cos\theta = Q \qquad (24)$$

where θ is the angle between $\mathbf{u}$ and $\boldsymbol{\chi}$. These two relations yield

$$\begin{aligned}\mu^2 &= \tfrac{1}{2}\{[P^2 + (Q/\cos\theta)^2]^{1/2} + P\}\\ \chi^2 &= \tfrac{1}{2}\{[P^2 + (Q/\cos\theta)^2]^{1/2} - P\}\end{aligned} \qquad (25)$$

the first expression defines a refractive index surface, and the second, an extinction index surface.

The equation defining A suggests a conservation law (equation of continuity) as applied to a fictitious fluid. By analogy we consider $A^2\nabla\psi$ proportional to the current density of this fluid, and an application of the divergence theorem gives

$$0 = \int_V \nabla\cdot(A^2\nabla) \, dV = \int_S A^2\nabla\psi\cdot\mathbf{n} \, dS \qquad (26)$$

where V is some volume containing the fluid and bounded by a surface S with outward drawn normal $\mathbf{n}$. If we consider this fluid to have (material) density proportional to A^2 and velocity proportional to grad ψ, then the above expression states that A^2 is conserved in time. If we assume that $|A|^2$ is a measure of the energy localized in the wave at each point, that grad ψ is proportional to the energy flux at each point, and is directed along the ray associated with the wave; then it appears as if the energy is a fluid which is conserved as it flows along the rays. Thus, the rays appear as trajectories of energy, a thin pencil of rays being analogous to a tube through which the energy flows.

In a homogeneous, anisotropic, but non-absorbing medium the concept of ray is defined as the trajectory whose direction is the same as that of the mean Poynting vector. This direction, as mentioned previously, is not the same as the wave normal direction. The task of defining the ray direction becomes more difficult for a nonhomogeneous, anisotropic, absorbing, and dispersive medium. It can be shown that starting with the concept of a pulse in such a medium, one can derive extensions or generalizations of the usual Fermat's principle. This principle states that in a nonabsorbing, isotropic medium characterized by an index μ_r, a function of position only, the path of a so-called light ray makes the integral of μ_r between two fixed points assume a stationary value. The pulse concept for the general case leads to the following stationary principles:

$$\delta \int \pmb{\mu}_r \cdot d\mathbf{r} = 0$$

$$\delta \int \pmb{\chi} \cdot d\mathbf{r} = 0 \qquad (27)$$

$$\delta \int \frac{\partial}{\partial \omega} (\omega \pmb{\mu}) \cdot d\mathbf{r} = 0$$

where δ is the symbol of variation. In the nonabsorbing case the first of Eqs. (27) gives the phase path, which is always normal to the surfaces of constant phase. Similarly, the trajectory of the amplitude surfaces is also normal to the surfaces of constant amplitude. For the absorbing case we retain these two definitions. This means that $\pmb{\mu}_r$ is always tangent to a path element of the phase trajectory and $\pmb{\chi}$ is tangent to a path element of the amplitude trajectory. These path elements are denoted, respectively, by $d\mathbf{r}_p$ and $d\mathbf{r}_a$. The pulse principle permits us to define, in addition to the above surfaces, the surfaces of constant group amplitude. These surfaces are distinguished from those of constant wave amplitude and constant wave phase. If $d\mathbf{r}_g$ denotes an element of the path along which the group amplitude

propagates, then the stationary principle for this path takes the form

$$\delta \int \pmb{\mu}_r \cdot d\mathbf{r}_g = \delta \int \frac{\partial}{\partial \omega} \omega \pmb{\mu}_r \cdot d\mathbf{r}_g = 0 \qquad (28)$$

and in general the direction of the vector $\partial/\partial\omega(\omega\pmb{\mu}_r)$ is not parallel to $d\mathbf{r}_g$. The vector $\partial/\partial\omega(\omega\pmb{\mu}_r)$ is the basis for the definition of the group velocity. By definition, the displacement of the center of the wave group in a time dt is

$$\mathbf{v}_g dt = d\mathbf{r}_g \qquad (29)$$

where $\mathbf{v}_g$ is the group velocity. If we define a vector $(\mathbf{v}_g)^{-1}$ (symbolic meaning only), such that

$$\mathbf{v}_g \cdot (\mathbf{v}_g)^{-1} = 1 \qquad (30)$$

it is not difficult to show that

$$(\mathbf{v}_g)^{-1} = \frac{1}{c} \frac{\partial}{\partial \omega} (\omega \pmb{\mu}_r) \qquad (31)$$

We take the path of energy propagation to be the path of group amplitude. This condition is certainly plausible when we consider that the energy of a field is usually proportional to the square of the amplitude of its oscillations.

In the case of an electromagnetic field it is not so clear that the group path is also the energy path if this energy is measured by the mean Poynting vector, and the conditions under which this holds requires careful analysis.

The question naturally arises as to how one actually calculates a ray path in the general case. The answer has been available for a long time. Hamilton's work in optics actually provides a *modus operandi* for the practical calculation of the ray paths. Fermat's principle provides the starting point; we assume that the medium is characterized by an index function $m(\mathbf{r}, \pmb{\alpha}, \omega)$ called the ray refractive index. This function depends on position $\mathbf{r}$, direction $\pmb{\alpha}$, and frequency ω, and is a homogeneous function of the first degree in $\pmb{\alpha}$. The rays are defined as those curves such that

$$\delta \int_{p_0}^{p} m \, ds = 0, \qquad (32)$$

where s is the parameter of arc length. The anisotropy is defined through the direction α which is normalized so that

$$\boldsymbol{\alpha}\cdot\boldsymbol{\alpha} = \frac{dr}{ds}\cdot\frac{dr}{ds} = 1 \tag{33}$$

that is, α defines the tangent to the ray. In the isotropic case this dependence is lacking and $m(\mathbf{r})$ is invariant with respect to proper rotations. Usually we do not know $m(\mathbf{r}, \boldsymbol{\alpha}, \omega)$ but rather $\mu_r(\mathbf{r}, \mathbf{n}, \omega)$ where $\mathbf{n}$ is the wave normal direction, as in the Appleton-Hartree equation. Thus it is desirable to attempt to express the ray path through the phase refractive index μ_r. This is accomplished by constructing a Hamiltonian defined by

$$H(\mathbf{r}, \boldsymbol{\sigma}, \omega) = \frac{|\boldsymbol{\sigma}|}{\mu_r(\mathbf{r}, \mathbf{n}, \omega)} = 1 \tag{34}$$

which is a homogeneous function of the first degree in $\boldsymbol{\sigma}$, where $\boldsymbol{\sigma} = \partial m/\partial \mathbf{r}$ is a vector in the direction of $\mathbf{n}$. It can be shown that the rays which satisfy Fermat's principle with m as index are identical with those satisfying

$$\delta \int_{p_0}^{p} \boldsymbol{\sigma}\cdot d\mathbf{r} = 0 \tag{35}$$

whose variations are subject to the constraint $H(\mathbf{r}, \boldsymbol{\sigma}, \omega) = 1.*$ The latter is Hamilton's principle and is fully equivalent to Fermat's principle. It follows from Hamilton's principle that the rays satisfy Hamilton's canonical equations

$$\frac{d\mathbf{r}}{dt} = \frac{\partial H}{\partial \boldsymbol{\sigma}}, \frac{d\boldsymbol{\sigma}}{dt} = -\frac{\partial H}{\partial \mathbf{r}} \tag{36}$$

where t is a parameter along the path. Equations (36) are six simultaneous first-order nonlinear ordinary differential equations. Subject to initial conditions these equations have a unique solution. The advantage of defining the rays in terms of the first order system as above are many, particularly from a computational point of view. The rays can be calculated for rather general media, and no assumptions of stratification

* Brandstatter, loc. cit.

are needed. The form of Hamilton's equations can easily be found for any coordinate system by tensor methods. Finally, we mention that a systematic study of ray propagation is possible without alluding to wave concepts although the ray-wave duality is implicit.

J. J. BRANDSTATTER

Ionospheric Propagation

The term ionosphere is applied to that part of the terrestrial atmosphere between about 50 and 1000 km above the earth in which free electrons are produced by the interaction of extraterrestrial (primarily solar) radiation with the atomic and molecular constituents of the earth's atmosphere. (See, for instance, K. Rawer, The Ionosphere, New York, Ungar, 1956.)

Ionospheric radio propagation was first demonstrated by G. Marconi (q.v.) when he found, in 1901, that signals were received in Newfoundland from a transmitter in England. The equipment most commonly used for studying the ionosphere is the ionosonde. This is a radar device which measures the time taken for a pulse of radio waves to travel up to the ionosphere and back as a function of frequency (1 to 25 Mc). The highest frequency reflected from a given layer, at normal incidence, is known as the critical frequency.

It has been shown with the ionosonde that the ionosphere consists of a number of regions within which layers of electrons may be produced. The approximate height ranges of the various regions and the layers that may be observed are given in Table I.

TABLE I

Region	Height Range (km)	Layers
D	50–90	
E	90–150	E1 E2 Es
F	over 150	F1 F1½ F2

Little is known about the structure of the D region although there is evidence which suggests the existence of more than one layer. The E1 layer is always present during the day at all seasons and its behavior is subject to close solar control. The E2 layer occurs frequently only in certain parts of the world. The Sporadic E (Es) layer consists of relatively dense patches of electrons on the order of a few tens of kilometers in horizontal extent. It is probable that several different phenomena are placed in this classification. Sporadic E phenomena are exhibited primarily by day in some parts of the world and mainly by night in others.

The F1 layer is similar to the E1 layer in that it is subject to close solar control, but most of the evidence from electron density profiles indicate that the F1 and F2 are never distinct layers. During the night hours the ionization in the F region is usually called the F2 layer. However, this is somewhat a matter of definition since the night F layer is sometimes continuous with the F1 layer.

The F2 layer exhibits a number of conspicuous irregularities when compared with the E1 and F1 layers. For instance the critical frequency reaches its maximum well after noon and, in temperate latitudes, the maximum value is greater in winter than in summer. Furthermore, there is a marked geomagnetic control of the critical frequencies.

An F1½ layer is often seen during the daytime at low latitudes during high sunspot activity.

The whole ionosphere is subject to a marked long-term variation associated with the sunspot cycle. One effect is an increase in the critical frequencies of the E, F1, and F2 layers and higher absorption in the D region with increasing sunspot number. This effect permits the use of higher frequencies for communication at times of sunspot maxima than is possible at sunspot minima. Although during the period of maximum solar activity the lower frequency limit of the usable radio spectrum is in-

creased by the enhanced D region absorption, the over-all effect is an improvement in propagation conditions.

The propagation of radio waves in the ionosphere is influenced by the following:

(1) wave frequency,
(2) electron density,
(3) earth's magnetic field, and
(4) electronic collisions.

The effect of the ionosphere on the refraction of a wave decreases with increase of frequency but increases with increase of electron density. The main effect of the earth's field is to split up an incident wave into two characteristic waves known as the ordinary and extraordinary waves. (See J. A. Ratcliffe, The Magneto-Ionic Theory, Cambridge University Press, 1959.) Moreover, the ray paths are deviated, the extraordinary wave toward the magnetic equator and the ordinary wave away from the magnetic equator. At vertical incidence the deviation of the ordinary ray, for a magnetic dip angle of about 70°, can amount to as much as 50 km at the level of reflection in the F2 layer. The deviation of the extraordinary ray under the same conditions, is about 10 km. At oblique incidence the deviations are, in general, small. For instance, over an east-west path in the United States they are of the order of 1 km.

Ionospheric absorption is brought about by electronic collisions mainly in the D region where the collision frequencies are large. Since the refractive index (q.v.) in the D region is nearly unity for waves which penetrate to and are reflected by the higher layers, the absorption is called nondeviative. It decreases with increase of wave frequency. Hence, the higher the frequency the stronger the signal reflected from the E and F regions. In general, the extraordinary wave is absorbed more strongly than the ordinary wave, especially in the vicinity of the electron gyrofrequency which varies from about 0.8 Mc at the magnetic equator to about 1.6 Mc at the poles. The daytime absorption of radio waves of medium frequency (500 to 1500 kc) is so great that standard broadcasting stations a few hundreds of miles apart can operate on the same frequency without mutual interference. At night, when the sun's ionizing influence is reduced, the electron density in the D region (and hence the absorption) decreases and propagation of medium frequency waves to relatively long distances is possible.

The upper frequency limit for radio communication by ionospheric refraction is set by the electron densities in the reflecting layers and by the layer heights. For any frequency above the critical frequency there is a maximum angle of elevation above which reflection is not possible. The minimum ground range is known as the skip distance. Within this distance the only signals that can be received are those due to ground-wave propagation (see below) and those scattered from ionospheric and ground irregularities. Furthermore, for a given distance of transmission, there is an upper limit to the frequency that can be reflected from the ionosphere. This frequency is known as the maximum usable frequency (MUF) and the distance is the corresponding skip distance. To aid the communications engineer select the optimum communications frequencies for any circuit, radio propagation laboratories issue predictions of monthly median ionospheric parameters, months or even years in advance; for instance, in Series D of the Central Radio Propagation Laboratory. To allow for day-to-day fluctuations it is customary to take, as the optimum frequency, 85 per cent of the maximum usable frequency.

High-frequency (3- to 30-Mc) ionospheric propagation is characterized by irregular and deep amplitude fading and, in certain regions of the world (e.g., the auroral zone), by long periods of excessive absorption resulting in traffic blackout. The chief advantage of high frequencies is the relative simplicity of the equipment required for long distance communication.

These defects in reliability of high-fre-

quency ionospheric propagation may be largely overcome by the use of low frequencies or very high frequencies. Low-frequency waves, propagated via the lower boundary of the D region, are not affected by ionospheric disturbances to the same degree as the high-frequency waves and are characterized by relatively slow fade rates. The chief disadvantages are the limited usable bandwidths and the relatively large transmitter installations required.

Very high frequencies (30–300 Mc) are propagated via the ionosphere (80- to 95-km level) by a process of forward scatter from inhomogeneities in the electron distribution. Only single-hop transmission (maximum distance about 2000 km) is feasible; for longer distance communications relay stations are required. Furthermore, since the scatter process is relatively inefficient, large transmitted powers and high gain antennas are necessary.

KENNETH DAVIES

Tropospheric Propagation

Radio waves propagated through the troposphere* are influenced primarily by its dielectric properties, the conductivity being very small except in high electric fields where breakdown occurs (as in lightning discharges). Propagation is characterized by refraction, absorption, and scattering. Except near absorption lines, the tropospheric refractive index is independent of radio frequency and can be determined from air temperature, pressure, and humidity. It varies linearly with the last two of these quantities, and is approximately inversely proportional to temperature. It differs from unity by no more than a few parts in 10^4, but this amount is sufficient to cause appreciable refractive bending. The bending of a radio ray is usually in a downward direction since vertical gradients of refractive index are likely to be steeper than horizontal

* The lower 30,000 ft or so of the earth's atmosphere characterized by mixing of the air at various levels, direct influence of the earth's surface, and the presence of clouds and precipitation.

gradients. In fact, where temperature increases, and moisture decreases with altitude, it is possible for the downward ray curvature to exceed the earth curvature. In such cases, low-angle rays are trapped, and a "ducting" condition is said to occur. Such a condition may lead to phenomenally large radio and radar ranges (over 1000 miles) since the waves follow around the curvature of the earth.

Absorption bands of practical importance in the earth's atmosphere are centered at frequencies of 22, 60, and 119 kMc, the first of these being due to water vapor, and the other two, to oxygen. At sea level these bands give rise to attenuation rates of 0.2, 20, and 2.7 db/mile, respectively. Above 150 kMc, sea-level absorption becomes prohibitive at almost all radio frequencies. The above magnitudes are sufficiently formidable to limit surface propagation to short distances, though the 22- and 119-kMc absorption is not strong enough to prevent earth-to-space propagation. Consequently the frequency range above 20 kMc has enjoyed little application in the past, but will doubtless receive considerably more in the future. Not only does the attenuation associated with each absorption line diminish with altitude as the air density decreases, but the absorptive regions between lines, which are filled by collision broadening, open up even more rapidly. Liquid water, in the form of clouds or rain, is more intensely absorptive than atmospheric gases. Furthermore, the thermal noise radiated by any strongly absorbing constituent can be a nuisance to sensitive receiving systems.

Higher-power transmitters, more sensitive receivers, and increasingly greater antenna gains have made practical transmission over earth-bound distances exceeding line-of-sight even under nonducting conditions. Small inhomogeneities in the atmospheric dielectric constant caused by layer formations and by turbulence scatter a portion of the transmitted wave through small angles, permitting reception well beyond the horizon, out to several hundred miles. Such

reception is characterized by signal levels more than 50 db below the free-space value and by relatively rapid fading (several fades per second). Fluctuations of a few degrees in angle of arrival are present and lead to a failure to realize the anticipated gain of a fixed narrow-beam antenna. There is also an associated bandwidth limitation of a few megacycles.

Other tropospheric effects include Rayleigh scattering from cloud droplets and from precipitation, which permit the tracking of weather formations by radar techniques. Finally, mention should be made of "angels" observed on radar scopes,—echoes often unaccounted for, though frequently caused by birds and insect swarms.

A. T. WATERMAN, JR.

Ground-Wave Propagation

The term "ground-wave propagation" is ordinarily applied to propagation of radio signals along the surface of the ground at distances such that atmospheric refraction, ionospheric reflection, direct transmission, and scatter do not contribute the major part of the signal. Regions always exist where the various mechanisms contribute simultaneously. The distance for which ground-wave propagation predominates is a function of frequency, with the ground wave important much farther at lower frequencies. In the VLF range the ground wave may be important to thousands of kilometers, whereas at UHF it is only significant a few kilometers. In the standard broadcast band, the ground wave is the primary propagation method in the daytime, but at night ionospheric reflections are stronger beyond a distance of a few tens of kilometers. The result is increased coverage for stations at the low-frequency end of the band.

Theoretical studies of ground-wave propagation preceded the discovery of the ionosphere. In 1909 Sommerfeld solved the *plane-earth* problem, although many authors expanded his work in later papers. Although the solutions for the *spherical-earth* problem were known before 1909, it was not until

1918 that Watson transformed these solutions to a practical form. His work, too, was later expanded by numerous authors.

The *plane-earth* results are easier to apply than those for *spherical earth*. The approximation involved in using the former is valid to distances of about $10\lambda^{1/3}$, where the distance is measured in kilometers and the wavelength in meters. Beyond that distance the spherical-earth formulas must be used— and the results should be compared with fields of other modes of propagation.

For a vertical short dipole at the surface, the variation of the vertical surface electric field is given by $E_z = 2(E_0/d)f(\rho)$, where E_0 is the field strength that would exist at 1 km if the antenna were in space, d is the distance in km, and $f(\rho)$ is a function of the *numerical distance* ρ. The function $f(\rho)$ is too involved to present here, since it is given by different approximations in different regions. Figure 1 shows the function. The abscissa is the *magnitude* of the numerical distance and the parameter is the *phase* of the numerical distance. Thus $\rho = pe^{jb}$.

For vertical polarization, the basis for the numerical techniques shown in Fig. 1 for

computing the numerical distance is the definition

$$\rho = jkd \left[1 - \sqrt{\frac{1}{1 + k^2/k_E{}^2}} \right]$$

where k is the wave number $(2\pi/\lambda)$ for air, and k_E is the wave number

$$[\omega\sqrt{\mu(\epsilon + \sigma/j\omega)}]$$

for earth.

For large numerical distances, $f(\rho)$ may be approximated by $\frac{1}{2}\rho$; thus, the variation of field strength with distance goes from inverse first power near the transmitter to inverse square at large distances where the plane earth approximation is still valid. For a highly conducting ground

$$\rho \approx \frac{\omega k r}{2\sigma}$$

so that the attenuation associated with a particular value of ρ occurs at a distance from the transmitter inversely proportional to frequency.

For fields in the region where the spherical-earth formulas must be used, the reader should consult the references. An indication

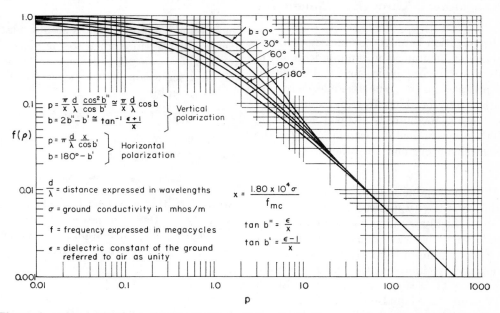

Fig. 1. Ground-wave attenuation factor $f(p)$. (After F. E. Terman, Radio Engineers' Handbook, New York, McGraw-Hill Book Co., 1943.)

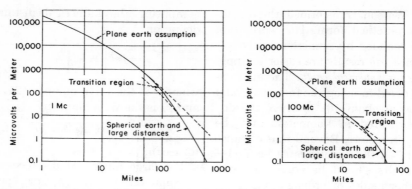

Fig. 2. Typical ground-wave field-strength variation for 1 kw transmitted from a short vertical antenna. (After F. E. Terman, Radio Engineers' Handbook, New York, McGraw-Hill Book Co., 1943.)

of the changeover is given by Fig. 2. Actually at 1 Mc, the ionospherically reflected wave predominates, especially at night at the extreme distances shown. On the other hand, this mechanism is not available at 100 Mc, so that the spherical-earth calculations give the field beyond the horizon until their level is comparable with either *tropospherically scattered* or *ionospherically scattered* signals, beyond which distance the scattered signal predominates because of a slower rate of decrease with distance.

Propagation Through Conducting Media

Propagation through conducting media is important in submarine communications, in subterranean communications and geophysical prospecting (*q.v.*), in the ionosphere, and in the study of skin effect and shielding. A conducting medium is defined as one in which the conduction current exeeds the displacement current; i.e., where

$$\sigma > \omega\epsilon$$

with σ the conductivity in mhos/meter and ϵ the permittivity in farads/meter.

In a highly conducting medium (good conductor), the wave equation is the same as the equation of diffusion or heat conduction, and techniques developed for these fields may be used to solve electric problems. The plane wave equation is the same as that for the RC transmission line, so that tech-

niques developed for such lines may also be applied.

The wave equation for electric fields in a conducting medium is, for the general (and for the steady-state ac) case

$$\nabla^2 \mathbf{E} = \mu\sigma \frac{\partial \mathbf{E}}{\partial t} \qquad \nabla^2 \mathbf{E} = j\omega\mu\sigma\mathbf{E} = \gamma^2\mathbf{E}$$

where $\mathbf{E}$ is the electric field in volts/meter and μ is the permeability in henrys/meter. From this we find

$$\gamma = \alpha + j\beta = \sqrt{j\omega\mu\sigma} = \sqrt{\frac{\omega\mu\sigma}{2}}(1 + j)$$

nepers and radians/meter. The attenuation factor α is therefore equal to the phase factor β. The *skin depth* is defined as the depth for an attenuation of one neper (8.69 db) and is given by

$$\delta = 1/\alpha = 1/\sqrt{\pi f\mu\sigma} \text{ meter}$$

The wavelength of this highly attenuated wave is given by

$$\lambda = 2\pi/\beta = 2\pi/\alpha = 2\pi\sqrt{2/\omega\mu\sigma} \text{ meter}$$

Note that the wavelength does *not* vary inversely as the first power of frequency. The velocity of propagation is a function of frequency in conducting media:

$$v = \sqrt{\frac{2\omega}{\mu\sigma}}$$

A most important point is that the attenuation in nepers is equal to the phase shift in radians, so that there is an attenuation of 2π nepers/wavelength (or 55 db/wavelength).

Communication between points in a conducting medium near a boundary with a nonconducting medium is accomplished by the wave traveling from transmitter to boundary, being refracted almost 90° at the boundary, and being "leaked" back into the conducting medium where the receiver is located.

R. K. Moore

VLF Propagation

Very-low-frequency (VLF) radio wave propagation (10 to 100 kc) is characterized by low attenuation of the ground wave and almost mirror-like reflection of the sky wave from the ionosphere at heights of 60 to 90 km. VLF waves below 25 kc propagate in a waveguide-like mode between sharply bounded limits produced by the lower edge of the ionosphere and the surface of the earth. Above 25 kc the propagation model is more complicated owing to stratification of the ionosphere.

VLF field strength at a distance measured along the surface of the earth is the sum of the ground and sky waves. The individual components of the composite wave may be received by suitably selected and oriented antennas permitting the measurement of the magnitude and phase relative to each other. An interference pattern of received field strength as a function of distance results when the components are of comparable magnitude.

The waves suffer attenuation owing to spreading and absorption of energy in the ionosphere and at the earth's surface. The loss in the ionosphere exhibits regular diurnal, seasonal, and solar variations and is subject to sudden ionospheric disturbances and magnetic storms. Energy absorption is lowest at night, in winter, and in the years of the sunspot cycle having the lower sun-

spot numbers. Diurnal changes occur around sunrise and sunset. There is a sudden decrease in the effective reflection coefficient about 1 hr before ground sunrise, remains fairly constant throughout the day, and increases rapidly near sunset. The reflection coefficient is greater for lower frequencies and for oblique incidence.

Differences in East-West and North-South propagation have been observed and are thought to be due to the direction of the earth's magnetic field relative to the transmission path and the fact that the condition of the ionosphere due to the sun's illumination is substantially the same along North-South paths. Also, in North-South transmission, the propagation path is usually away from the auroral zones.

At short distances, $D < 300$ km, the ground-wave signal predominates. Sky waves at these distances are approximately circularly polarized. At intermediate distances where both the ground and sky waves are of comparable magnitude, the resultant signal shows large changes in amplitude and phase. The received signal may be either stronger or weaker during daylight than at night, depending upon the distance, frequency, and season. At greater distances, $D > 400$ km, the sky wave is approximately linearly polarized and is surprisingly constant in its propagation characteristics. Long-distance sky-wave propagation suffers different amounts of attenuation at different frequencies. There is a pronounced daytime attenuation band around 4 kc which drops to about 3 kc at nighttime. The magnitude is also lower. There is a broad attenuation null in the order of 15 to 20 kc favoring these frequencies for long-distance transmission. Above 30 kc, there is a gradual rise in both the daytime and nighttime attenuation. The 100-kc daytime attenuation factor is approximately nine times greater than for 15 kc and the corresponding nighttime ratio is about seven to one.

Earl G. Goddard

Radio Effects of Aurorae

For many years it has been known by users of high-frequency radio communications circuits that paths traversing the auroral zones are subject to rapid fading and absorption at times of magnetic disturbance. In recent years study of auroral effects by radio methods has greatly enhanced our knowledge of the detailed phenomena occurring in high latitudes. It is now possible to distinguish several types of events affecting radio propagation.

The visual aurora is a result of the emission of streams of corpuscular matter from the sun. The ionized particles approach the earth with velocities of the order of 1000 km/sec, and arrive about 3 days after their ejection from a solar disturbance. The mechanism of interaction of the stream with the earth's magnetic field remains uncertain, and the trapping and dumping of particles in the radiation belts probably plays an important role. The result is that particles of increased energy are able to penetrate the earth's magnetic field within two bands, the northern and southern auroral regions, at high magnetic latitudes. The interaction of the particles with the earth's atmosphere instigates the production of the observed line and band light emissions. At the same time, changes in atmospheric electron density and collision frequency occur that produce radio scattering and absorption effects. The changes in ionospheric conductivity and electric-field strength caused by the aurora produce changing ionospheric currents, and magnetic fluctuations observable at the ground. The northern auroral zone, in which these effects are most easily noted, is roughly definable as the region from magnetic latitude 60° to 70 or 80°. The region of higher latitude constitutes the polar cap. A similar auroral zone exists in the southern hemisphere, but is in a difficult region observationally.

Near the auroral zone radio wave absorption events occur every day or so at times, and commonly last several hours or more. At 30 Mc, the absorption experienced by a radio wave may range from 1 to 20, 30, or occasionally more decibels; it varies inversely as the square of the radio frequency. The absorbing regions occur in patches that are typically several hundred kilometers in extent. Some uncertainty exists about the height of the absorbing regions, but they are believed to lie between 50 and 100 km in altitude. The intensity of the absorption in decibels correlates with the degree of magnetic field disturbance, and is strongest during pulsating and flaming aurorae. At present it is not clear whether the absorption is produced entirely in the D-region owing to an increased electron density caused by bremsstrahlung (*q.v.*) X-rays formed by energetic bombarding electrons, or whether an increased collision frequency in the E-region caused by electric fields may be important.

A second type of high-latitude radio wave absorption event takes place across the polar caps, primarily during the daytime. This type of event starts within minutes or hours after a large solar flare, and may persist rather uniformly in time and space for days. Low-energy cosmic-ray (*q.v.*) protons of solar origin cause the absorption by producing increased D-region ionization.

Radar studies with mono- and bistatic systems have greatly expanded our knowledge of the scattering properties of auroral ionization. Echoes have been received at frequencies as high as 900 Mc. However, at lower frequencies much stronger scattered signals can be obtained. Echoes from auroral ionization are characterized by a rough fading at about ten times the frequency associated with normal ionospheric echoes, and by field alignment. When the ray from the radar to the ionization meets a geomagnetic field line at right angles, echoes are much stronger than if the ray deviates from perpendicularity by more than a few degrees. Doppler studies of auroral echoes show a frequency shift associated with east-west motion at speeds of the order of 500 m/sec. Auroral echoes are most frequently found at heights near 110 km, although echoes have been obtained at much greater heights. As yet, the electron densities responsible for the scattered signals are not specifiable, because of uncertainty concerning details of the scattering process.

The effect on communications of the scattering and absorption of radio signals passing through the auroral zone is serious. High-frequency ionospherically propagated circuits are subject to garbling because of the characteristic high auroral fading rate, and to partial or complete black-out for extended periods because of the absorption effects. Signals from satellites or radio stars suffer intense scintillation upon passing through the auroral zone. At 500 Mc scintillation is noted about half the time. Rapid fading is accompanied by a continual fluctuation in the direction of arrival of the signals. Ionospheric scatter communication circuits are less troubled by auroral effects because the signals are scattered at lower heights, and do not enter the main auroral-height region. However, the low-lying ionization produced by solar cosmic-ray events does affect ionospheric scatter circuits. At times radio communication can be supported by auroral scatter signals on a particular frequency when normal high-frequency communications have dropped out. For many years radio amateurs in the United States have reported that garbled but usable signals can occasionally be obtained by directing their antennas toward the auroral zone, rather than along the great circle, at times when the operating frequency exceeded the conventional maximum usable frequency. At times of intense auroral activity, the primary means for preserving high-frequency communications between points on opposite sides of the auroral region is to re-route the transmission circuits to utilize paths at lower latitudes. The use of very low frequency signals that are reflected from the bottom of the ionosphere is also possible.

L. A. MANNING

Cross-references: *Electromagnetic Theory, Extraterrestrial Radio Sources, Radar, Radiation (Terrestrial), Radiometeorology*

PROTONS

Protons are the fundamental unit of positive electrical charge, the value of this charge being 1.60×10^{-19} coulomb. This is the same as the charge on the electron but opposite in sign. The mass of the proton is 1.6729×10^{-27} kg, which is 1836.57 times the mass of the electron. A single proton forms the nucleus of the hydrogen atom. The nuclei of other atoms also contain protons, the number of protons in the nucleus being equal to the atomic number of the element.

Protons are attracted to neutrons with enormous forces at small distances, although these forces are not apparent at large distances of separation. For instance, two protons combine with two neutrons to form a helium nucleus, the distance of separation of the particles being of the order of 4×10^{-15} m. At this distance, the force of repulsion between the protons due to Coulomb's law is of the order of 3 pounds! Yet we know that this is a very stable nucleus and, therefore, the force of attraction between the particles must be considerably stronger.

Protons can be accelerated to great speeds in various devices such as the cyclotron and have been used as projectiles for inducing artificial nuclear disintegrations. The first nuclear reaction induced by accelerated particles involved striking a lithium nucleus with a high-speed proton to produce two helium nuclei.

R. T. ELLICKSON

Cross-references: *Accelerators, Atoms, Nucleonics*

PROXIMITY FUZES

A proximity fuze is a device that causes the explosion of a military missile upon its approach to within a preset distance from a suitable target. Proximity fuzes have been developed for almost all U.S. weapons that fire an explosive round, ranging in size from long-range rocket-borne missiles, through conventional artillery shells, down to small-bore cannon rounds. At the discretion of a field commander the proximity fuze usually may be replaced with a time fuze or an impact fuze.

Various approaches have been taken to achieve the action-at-a-distance upon which the operation of a proximity fuze depends. Most prevalent is the radio type, in which the fuze consists, in essence, of a short-range radar set. Practically all the basic systems, such as fixed-frequency pulsed, FM-CW, FM-Doppler, and CW-Doppler, which have found use both in radar systems and in aircraft altimeters, have also been adapted to proximity fuzing. Each system possesses its own advantages and weaknesses in terms of reliability, resistance to electronic countermeasures, compactness, cost, and simplicity; none is outstanding for all applications.

Electromagnetic radiation in the optical region, including both infrared and ultraviolet, has also been employed successfully for fuzing. Although optical systems can be made very effective for specific applications, they are capable of far less flexibility and sophistication than are the various radio systems. Electrostatic and magnetostatic fields, and acoustic energy, have also been employed for target range detection, but the use of such systems is very restricted.

The component parts of a radio fuze consist of (1) a transmitter, (2) a receiver, (3) one or more antennas, often but not always used in common by the transmitter and the receiver, (4) a range sensing detector, (5) target discrimination detectors, (6) a firing circuit, (7) power supplies, and (8) safety and arming devices. (Safety devices are used to prevent explosion of the round in the event specified malfunctions of the fuze occur; arming devices are employed to prevent the fuze from becoming active until the round has travelled a specified distance after being fired.)

In the past proximity fuzes were very simple, and indeed still are on the smallest weapons; recently the trend has been toward greater complexity, in an effort to attain increased target discrimination and increased resistance to countermeasures. This trend

has emphasized the need for ever more reliable components, and has forced state-of-the-art advances not only with regard to reliability, but also with regard to reproducibility, minimum size and weight, maximum efficiency, and ability to function in extreme thermal and vibrational environments. One may gage the mechanical requirements placed on fuze design by considering that the fuze must withstand the shock and vibration associated with firing from a mortar, howitzer, cannon, etc.

There is probably no aspect of modern weaponry that places greater demands upon operational equipment than does proximity fuzing. The lack of reliable components has occasionally forced the fuze designer to redundancy, i.e., the use of multiple fuzes within the same weapon.

In certain cases, particularly those involving the smaller weapons, the cost of manufacture of a proximity fuze is comparable with the cost of the remainder of the explosive round, using a time or impact fuze. However, in all cases the increased cost of the round with proximity fuze is more than offset by the increased effectiveness of the round, usually by a substantial factor. Thus, in terms of accomplishing a given military objective, the use of proximity fuzes actually reduces the total cost of the necessary rounds. To this advantage may be added the fact that proximity fuzes, because of their greater effectiveness, also increase the morale of the fighting man who must rely upon them.

As the larger missiles grow ever more complex and sophisticated it is likely that the proximity fuze will gradually merge with the guidance system, eventually ceasing to exist as an independent entity. As in the past, the effectiveness of future fuzing systems will continue to be limited almost entirely by the availability of components capable of meeting the severe operational demands, and by the imaginations of those whose task it is to achieve action at a distance.

W. E. WATERS

Cross-references: *Altimeters, Countermeasures, Missile Guidance, Radar*

PULSE CODE MODULATION (PCM)

PCM belongs to the class of quantized pulse modulation systems that represent a continuous message by a finite number of discrete signal levels. Each allowable signal level nearest to the amplitude of a message sample is coded into a discrete pattern of pulses whose positions are equally spaced in time. This pulse packet is called a word. In its most common form, binary PCM, a pulse may take on either of two waveforms depending upon whether it represents a one or a zero. Thus, if 128 levels are used to interpolate the continuum of message amplitudes, a combination of seven binary digits constitutes a word. The 128 binary words are in a one to one correspondence with the 128 allowable levels. In general, b^n levels can be achieved with an n-digit, base-b code.

Time-division multiplexing may be employed conveniently to interleave words from several channels between two successive words of a given channel.

Terminal Operations

From the above abstract picture it can be seen that the basic ingredients in the processing of messages by a PCM terminal preparatory to transmission are the sequential operations of:

(1) Sampling and multiplexing

(2) Quantizing or coding

At the receiving terminal the received pulse train is decoded, routed to the proper channel (demultiplexing) and the original analog signal closely reconstituted by a low-pass filter. In addition, timing signals must be generated to program these functions.

Sampling and Multiplexing. Conversion of a message that is a real, continuous function of time into a PCM signal involves first sampling the message at discrete time intervals. The sampling rate is chosen, in accordance with the Sampling Theorem (*q.v.*), to be slightly greater than twice the highest frequency "of consequence" in the spectrum of the time function. The phrase "of consequence" is introduced above to point out that usually this frequency cannot be specified as precisely as would seem to be required by the Sampling Theorem. The choice depends on the application and the message under consideration. For example, in good-quality speech transmission an 8-kc sampling frequency is common.

Sampling thus converts the message into a series of equally spaced pulses whose amplitudes are identical with those of the original message at the sampling instants. PAM signals* from several channels are multiplexed in time and applied sequentially to the coder.

Quantizing or Coding. The coder accepts the PAM signal with a continuous range of amplitudes and approximates each amplitude with the discrete level closest to it. This process results in a round-off error (like that in any approximation process) whose extreme values are plus or minus one-half of the spacing between levels. This error is commonly called quantizing noise and is the principal source of noise in a well-designed PCM system. The size of the smallest quantum (distance between levels) is based on the allowable quantizing noise for the lowest level signal that must be faithfully reproduced. This error may be made arbitrarily small by employing a large number of equally spaced steps to cover the desired range. However, as the number of steps is increased the coding operation becomes more complex and the bandwidth required for transmission increases. The later point follows from the fact that if b^n is the number of steps used in the coder and $f_{c\downarrow}$ is the highest frequency in the message to be transmitted, then $nf_{c\downarrow}$ is the minimum required bandwidth per message (again according to the

---

* PAM signals are considered throughout as a convenient prelude to PCM although PDM and PPM may be used prior to quantizing to yield PCM.

sampling theorem). A more attractive procedure for many applications is to taper the step size such that many small steps are utilized for coding the low-level signals, whereas a smaller number of large steps are employed for the most robust signals. In this way the required transmission bandwidth may be conserved.

When the input signal is much larger than a single quantum step, the quantizing errors are practically uncorrelated and in the case of uniform step size equally likely to lie anywhere within plus or minus half a quantum step. The rms value of the quantizing noise is then $1/2\sqrt{3}$ times the step size. Since the number of levels is b^n, the ratio of peak-to-peak signal to rms noise is

$$R = 2\sqrt{3}\, b^n \qquad (1)$$

which in decibels becomes

$$20 \log R = 10.8 + n\,(20 \log b) \qquad (2)$$

As noted previously n is directly proportional to the transmission bandwidth. Therefore, in PCM the ratio (in decibels) of signal to quantizing noise varies linearly with the bandwidth. In the information theoretic sense this is an efficient "trade."

Transmission

Following these terminal operations the pulse train may be shaped further to match the peculiarities of the transmission medium. Alternately, the PCM pulses can modulate a carrier to produce one of the compound transmission schemes such as PCM-AM or PCM-FM. In considering PCM transmission attention is focused on baseband transmission, although (with appropriate modulators and demodulators) the comments are equally applicable to RF systems.

The salient feature of PCM transmission, specifically binary transmission, is the yes-no nature of the transmitted signal. In the simplest case a binary *one* is represented by a pulse of amplitude V and a binary *zero* by no pulse. In principle all that is required at a repeater site is the recognition of the presence or absence of a pulse. For interference owing to noise and crosstalk less than $V/2$ (threshold of error) the binary signal can be reconstructed without error and sent anew to the next repeater. Therefore, the over-all transmission-system requirements are nearly equal to the requirements between repeaters. This result is in contrast with an analog-transmission system where the repeater-to-repeater requirements are considerably more stringent than the over-all requirements as a result of the accumulation of systematic distortion and noise.

Signal-to-Noise Requirements. If the interference becomes larger than the threshold, errors are made. Some idea of the required signal-to-noise ratio for a given probability of error may be obtained if it is assumed that white noise is the only source of interference to a 1,0 pulse train. For this situation Table 1 applies.

TABLE 1

Peak Signal-to-(rms) Noise Ratio (db)	Probability of Error	For a Pulse Rate of 10^5/sec this Corresponds to One Error Every
13.3	10^{-2}	10^{-3} sec
17.4	10^{-4}	10^{-1} sec
19.6	10^{-6}	10 sec
21.0	10^{-8}	20 min
22.0	10^{-10}	1 day
23.0	10^{-12}	3 months

The most important conclusion from the above table is that a definite *threshold* occurs below which the errors are significant and beyond which errors are vanishingly small. A modest increase of signal power beyond that required at threshold serves to reduce errors to negligible importance. This feature is characteristic of the class of systems that achieve freedom from noise by using a wide transmission bandwidth. As noted previously the way in which PCM makes this trade is particularly efficient.

Reconstructive Repeaters. The repeaters that make the pulses almost as good as new are usually composed of three basic building blocks; namely, the three R's. The first block performs preliminary signal *Reshaping*. It takes the incoming pulse train that has been dispersed by the transmission medium and corrupted with additive noise and interference and shapes it to the point where the digital-decision process can take over. Basically this initial function involves a compromise between approaching a desirable pulse shape and removing the interference. The amplitude decision made by the *Regenerator* must be made under the control of a timing gate. This *Retimer* is used to sample the incoming train at the time a pulse peak is expected and also to maintain proper pulse spacing. Pulse jitter must be controlled to prevent the conversion of this undesired PPM to intolerable crosstalk at the receiving terminal. Timing jitter and its accumulation in a chain of repeaters is an important problem in PCM transmission.

A separate timing wave may be transmitted along with the pulse train or timing may be extracted from the pulse train itself as in self-timing repeaters.

Summary

PCM is a quantized pulse modulation system characterized by:

(1) Favorable trade between S/N and bandwidth.

(2) Rugged performance in a noisy dispersive medium due to the use of reconstructive repeaters.

REFERENCE

H. S. Black, Modulation Theory, Van Nostrand, 1953; Chap. 19.

M. R. AARON

Cross-references: *Bandwidth Reduction, Coding and Coding Circuits, Modulation and Demodulation, Multiplexing*

PULSE GENERATION

Low-Power Pulses

Pulse waveform generators are of several types, varying with the particular application.

(1) *Step waveform* is used for adjustment of resistance-capacitance compensated attenuators for flat frequency response, in conjunction with an oscilloscope. In addition, step waveform is frequently applied to a video amplifier to make peaking adjustments for least transient overshoot. See also *Square-wave* signal below.

(2) *Impulse waveform* can be shown mathematically to be the sum of two steps having opposite polarity and separated by an insignificant time difference. This signal is often used for measuring sensitivity of high-frequency receivers.

(3) *Pulse waveshape* is the summation of a positive and a negative step waveform separated in time by the length of the pulse. Pulse waveshape is commonly encountered in electronic control and instrumentation. For example, digital counters normally are made to count random pulses. Pulse waveform is also required for radar and sonar drive, for oscilloscope blanking, television synchronization, computer gating and switching circuits, electromedical stimulus, and other applications.

(4) *Square-wave* signal is commonly employed to demonstrate low- and high-frequency performance of video amplifiers, audio amplifiers, transformers, etc. Tilt in the top of the square wave indicates a deficiency in low-frequency response; spiking, ringing, or sluggish rise indicates improper high-frequency bandpass. The square wave can be considered as the sum of a series of step waveforms of alternating polarity. A square-wave generator is therefore a repetitive step generator.

(5) A *pulse train* of two or three consecutive pulses is commonly used to test the performance of high-speed digital or binary counters.

(6) The *sine-squared* test signal applies to testing television equipment. Deficiencies in signal transmission affect test signal height and shape. The sine-squared signal may be viewed as a modified impulse waveform.

Waveform *generators* are characterized by their output amplitude, rise time, repetition rate, output impedance, and triggerability or syncability.

Following are the common circuit devices for generating pulse waveforms:

(1) A mechanical switch generates a step signal, subject to the limitations of contact bounce and resulting multi-closures. Pulse waveform can be obtained from a simple switch by discharging a fixed length of coaxial cable through the switch into a matched load. These simple waveforms are readily differentiated by either inductance-resistance or resistance-capacitance techniques to produce a type of impulse. Contact bounce commonly results in two or more output signals per operation. Coaxially arranged mechanical switches may produce 10^{-10} sec rise time and excellent waveshape except for contact bounce.

(2) Mercury switches produce closures free from contact bounce. Presence of a mercury puddle or unnecessary contacts may produce small complications in waveshape in the sub-nanosecond range. Rate of operation is normally much slower than 1000 cps.

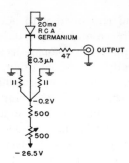

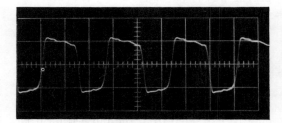

Fig. 2. Tunnel diode free-running at nearly 20 Mc as displayed on 100-Mc oscilloscope at 20 ns/cm and 0.1 v/cm vertical.

(3) Vacuum-tube or transistor multi-vibrators supply the majority of common pulse and squarewave signals. Rise times below 10 ns require careful design. High repetition rates are possible.

(4) Blocking oscillators are potent power sources for rapid-rise pulses. Transistor or vacuum-tube circuits can readily generate pulses of less than 1 μsec duration. Clipping and amplification techniques may be used to help provide the necessary output shape.

(5) Transistor avalanche is very rapid, as seen in Fig. 1. Duration of the pulse output is established by the length of charge cable selected. Substituting 50 ohms and 0.01 μf for the charge cable produces a step output having an RC decay.

(6) Tunnel diodes are useful in the range 0.2 to 1 v depending upon load impedance, diode current, and choice of semiconductor material. Tunnel diode risetime may be less than 0.2 ns for fast units. Free-running tunnel diode waveshape is shown in Fig. 2. Frequency of oscillation may be adjusted by L_1.

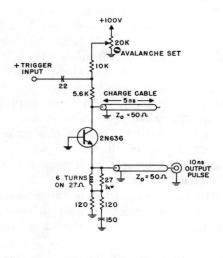

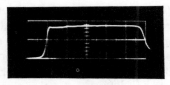

Fig. 1. Avalanche of 2N636 transistor produces risetime of less than 0.5 ns on sweep of 2 ns/cm. Vertical sensitivity 10 v/cm.

An over-driven wideband amplifier may be used to improve the rise-time of a slow pulse, or to enhance power level. The net risetime of cascaded clipping stages generally is limited by circuit capacitance to the 1- to 10-ns range.

CLIFF MOULTON

High-Power Pulses

High-power pulsers include those which deliver to the load peak power in excess of 1000 w at voltages above 1000 v. Generally the output waveform is essentially rectangular.

The primary applications of high power pulsers are radar, high-energy particle accelerators, fusion devices, hypersonic wind tunnels, and high-voltage surge test applications. In radar applications, the loads are typically triodes, tetrodes, magnetrons, amplitrons, klystrons, or traveling-wave tubes. In accelerator applications the loads are typically magnets, deflection plates, electron-gun structures, and the same types of rf sources as are used in radar applications. In fusion devices the loads are typically magnets or plasmas and in wind-tunnel applications the loads are typically high-pressure gases.

High-power pulsers comprise three basic elements: an energy storage device, a switch, and a load. In all present-day applications the limitations imposed on high-power pulsers in terms of peak power, average power, peak current, average current, ratio of average power to peak power (duty cycle), interpulse period, and pulse repetition rate are imposed by the switching device. The switch almost always limits pulser capability.

High-power pulsers naturally subdivide into two classes: Class 1, where all the stored energy is delivered to the load each pulse, and Class 2, where only a small portion of the stored energy is delivered to the load each pulse. Class 1 pulsers include line-type modulators, magnetic pulsers, and impulse generators or single-shot pulsers. Class 1 pulsers generally employ a triggered commutation device such as a hydrogen thyratron, ignitron, spark gap, or less commonly a semiconductor or magnetic pulsactor. Switches for Class 1 pulsers must be capable of passing high peak currents and are turned off only when the forcing voltage is removed or reversed. Class 2 pulsers generally use a high-vacuum (hard) tube switch to control the power to the load by means of a space-charge-control electrode. Switches for Class 1 pulsers are relatively low-impedance devices compared with those of Class 2 and therefore have relatively high peak current capabilities combined with low voltage drop.

Typical switch characteristics are pertinent. A representative large thyratron can deliver 50 Mw of peak power and 30 kw of average power with peak pulse currents up to 2000 amp. Large ignitrons have been used as switches up to 60 kv and can pulse thousands of amperes at average currents high compared to spark gaps or thyratrons. Spark gaps have been built to hold off voltages as high as megavolts and switch currents up to mega-amperes. Many spark-gap applications have been in single-shot systems because of severe limitations due to erosion. Present-day vacuum tubes used in hard-tube pulsers are typically capable of not much more than 125 kv at 1000 amp. Tubes are being developed that can hold off voltages up to 350 kv. Hard-tube switches have operated at pulse lengths up to several milliseconds and have been made to control average powers up to several hundred kilowatts in the load.

Energy storage devices include fly wheels, capacitors, and inductors. Magnet pulsers drawing energy from fly wheels with power levels of 100 Mw peak and 5 Mw average at pulse widths up to seconds and pulse rates up to 20 pps are not uncommon. Most high-speed pulsers use capacitors as energy storage devices. Capacitive energy storage systems with energies up to millions of joules have been built.

Loads for pulsers include either plate-pulsed triodes or tetrodes, grid-pulsed triodes or tetrodes, cathode-pulsed magnetrons, amplitrons, klystrons, or traveling-wave tubes, and grid-pulsed klystrons or traveling-wave tubes. Both Class 1 and Class 2 pulsers are used with all types of loads. Class 2 pulsers are most widely used with loads that have control electrodes.

In pulsing any given type of load, Class 1 pulsers are always more efficient than Class 2 pulsers because the switching devices used carry higher current at lower internal voltage drop. Both types of pulsers have great flexibility in terms of variable pulse amplitude and repetition rate. Because the switch in Class 2 pulsers is easier to turn off, Class 2 pulsers have much greater flexibility in variable pulse width systems. Also, because of deionization time problems, Class 1 pulsers suffer interpulse period limitations that are not imposed on Class 2 pulsers. Pulse shaping is more easily accomplished with Class 2 pulsers.

Exemplifying the rapid increase in power levels in recent years is the comparison between the highest power radar pulsers of World War II operating at 10 Mw peak and 3 kw average power and systems being built today with up to 150 Mw peak and 4 Mw average power.

E. M. Goldfarb
H. G. Heard
A. J. Morris
J. P. Swanson

Cross-references: *Accelerators, Oscillators, Oscilloscopes, Radar, Switches*

PUPIN, MICHAEL IDVORSKY (1858–1935)

M. I. Pupin was born on October 4, 1858, at Idvor in the Banat, now part of Yugoslavia, of peasant parents. He received some training in his home district but his first formal education took place in Prague, where he did not particularly distinguish himself. He decided to emigrate to America and arrived in New York in 1874. He supported himself by menial tasks, at the same time studying for the entrance examinations of Columbia University, which he entered

in 1879. He graduated in 1883, and became an American citizen in the same year. In 1885, after a couple of years at Cambridge, he went to Berlin to study under Hermann von Helmholtz (1821–1894) and G. R. Kirchhoff (1824–1887). He received the Ph.D. in 1889 and returned to teach mathematical physics in the Department of Electrical Engineering. He worked on gaseous discharges and on a number of engineering problems, including the analysis of higher harmonics inherent in ac magnetization. This work led to his discovery of the LC tuned circuit, which he devised by analogy with Helmholtz's resonator method of analyzing complex sound waves. Again by analogy with the problem of vibrating strings he implemented the suggestion made by Oliver Heaviside (*q.v.*) and others that the efficiency of long transmission lines could be improved by increasing the distributed inductance. (Such lines were for a time known as "pupinized" lines.) He also contributed to the development of X-ray fluoroscopy and made improvements in various phases of radio transmitters. E. H. Armstrong (*q.v.*) was one of his pupils.

He remained at Columbia until his retirement in 1931, but after World War I he devoted himself largely to public affairs and to writing; his best-selling autobiography, *From Immigrant to Inventor*, earned him the Pulitzer prize in 1924. He was elected to the National Academy of Sciences. He died in New York on March 12, 1935. The physics laboratory at Columbia is named in his honor.

Charles Susskind

Cross-references: *Historical Background of Electronics*

PYROELECTRICITY: see PIEZOELECTRICITY AND PYROELECTRICITY

PYROMETERS

Radiation pyrometers generally measure the magnitude of radiant energy from a hot object over some portion of the visible or

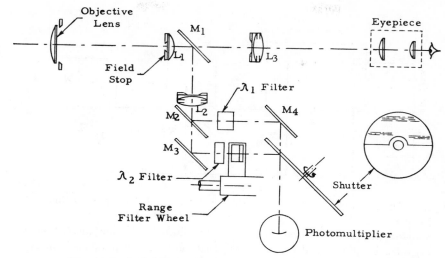

Fig. 1. Optical drawing of automatic two-color pyrometer.

infrared spectrum; this quantity is related to the temperature of the target area by the appropriate integration of Wien's spectral radiation law,

$$W(\lambda) = \epsilon(\lambda,T)C_1\lambda^{-5}e^{-C_2/\lambda T} \qquad (1)$$

where

$W(\lambda)$ = emittance from target at the wavelength λ

C_1 and C_2 are constants

T = target temperature in deg K

$\epsilon(T,\lambda)$ = emittance of target surface at T and λ

It is evident from Eq. (1) that if a pyrometer is calibrated with a blackbody target with $\epsilon(\lambda,T) = 1$, its readings will be in error when the target is not a black body, i.e., $\epsilon(\lambda,T) \neq 1$.

A *two-color* optical pyrometer measures the *ratio* of radiant energy in two discrete narrow bandwidths in the visible spectrum. To a good approximation, the output of a two-color pyrometer may be expressed as follows:

$$E_0 = W_2/W_1 = K_1\epsilon_2/\epsilon_1 e^{-n/T} \qquad (2)$$

where

$n = C_2[(1/\lambda_1) - (1/\lambda_2)]$

λ_1 and λ_2 are the peak wavelengths of the two narrow spectra of the instrument

K_1 = constant determined by electrical and optical parameters

ϵ_2 and ϵ_1 are target emittances at λ_2 and λ_1, respectively

The purpose of the two-color technique is to minimize or eliminate errors in temperature readings for "greybody" radiators, where

$$\epsilon_2(T,\lambda_2) = \epsilon_1(T,\lambda_1) \neq 1 \qquad (3)$$

Similarly, errors owing to attenuation of radiant energy in the transmission path are minimized provided the relative spectral characteristics are not affected.

A typical equipment is described below that instruments Eq. (2) in a stable manner by means of an electronic feedback circuit.

Optical Design

Figure 1 is the optical drawing of the sensor head. The objective lens collects radiant energy from the target field. The beam-splitter assembly divides this energy into two beams, which pass through a narrow-band red filter whose peak wavelength is λ_1 (approximately 640 mμ) and a narrow-band blue-green filter with a peak wavelength λ_2 (approximately 470 mμ).[1] The

[1] Other wavelengths may be used, not necessarily in visible spectrum. The wavelengths mentioned are considered near optimum for temperatures between about 1000° and 3000°C.

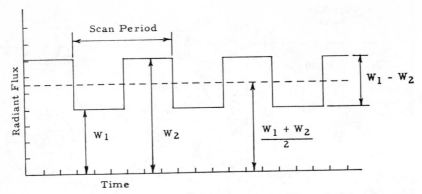

Fig. 2. Waveform of radiant flux on photomultiplier cathode vs time.

rotating shutter alternately passes the λ_1 and λ_2 energy to the photomultiplier sensor at a rate determined by the angular speed of the drive motor and the number of sectors in the shutter. The waveform of the energy incident on the photomultiplier cathode as a function of time is approximately as shown in Fig. 2.

The partially silvered mirror M_1, lens L_3, and the eyepiece are a secondary part of the optical system which permits visual examination of the target field.

Electronic Design

The photomultiplier current is proportional to the magnitude of energy incident on its cathode; therefore, its current output as a function of time is identical in form to the function shown in Fig. 2. In the steady state, the photomultiplier current is seen to consist of two components: an average or dc component

$$I_{DC} = \frac{G_1 W_1 + G_2 W_2}{2} \qquad (4)$$

and an ac component with peak-to-peak value

$$I_{AC} = G_1 W_1 - G_2 W_2 \qquad (5)$$

where G_1 and G_2 are photomultiplier sensitivities in terms of unit current/unit of energy at λ_1 and λ_2, respectively.

I_{DC} is constrained to remain constant and independent of the magnitudes of W_1 and W_2 by means of a dc feedback loop that automatically changes the dynode voltage of the photomultiplier (Fig. 3). Note that the high voltage is divided between the

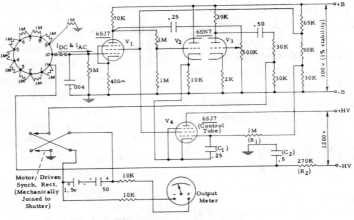

Fig. 3. Electronics schematic of two-color pyrometer.

photomultiplier and the control tube V_4, since these elements constitute a voltage divider circuit with respect to ground. When the control-tube plate-to-ground voltage increases or decreases there is a corresponding decrease or increase in the photomultiplier-dynode voltage. The control-tube plate voltage, in turn, is a function of its grid-cathode voltage. Any change in I_{DC} is amplified by V_1 and coupled by V_2 to the cathode of V_4. The plate-ground voltage of V_4 is thus caused to change and alter the dynode voltage in a manner that tends to maintain I_{DC} virtually constant.[2] Therefore, for practical purposes,

$$I_{DC} = G_1 W_1 + G_2 W_2 = \text{constant} \qquad (6)$$

Substituting Eq. (6) into Eq. (5) yields

$$I_{AC} = K_2 \frac{1 - (W_2/W_1)(G_2/G_1)}{1 + (W_2/W_1)(G_2/G_1)} \qquad (7)$$

where K_2 is a constant

[2] I_{AC} and other alternating currents must be filtered out of the dc feedback circuit; C_1, C_2, R_1, and R_2 serve this purpose.

I_{AC} is amplified further by V_3 and is then synchronously demodulated by an electro-mechanical switch mechanically coupled to the shutter-drive motor. The synchronously demodulated signal E_0' is related to temperature by the following equation:

$$E_0' = K_2 \frac{1 - (\epsilon_2/\epsilon_1)K_1\, e^{-n/T}}{1 + (\epsilon_2/\epsilon_1)K_1\, e^{-n/T}} \qquad (8)$$

Equation (2) has been substituted for W_2/W_1. Equation (8) is not identical to Eq. (2), but it achieves exactly the same objective.

SUMNER ACKERMAN

Cross-references: *Thermal Detectors, Thermal Radiation*

QUALITY CONTROL: see RELIABILITY AND QUALITY CONTROL

QUEUING: see CONGESTION AND WAITING SYSTEMS

R

RADAR

The word *radar*, coined as a code name in World War II, was derived from the phrase *RA*dio *D*etection *A*nd *R*ange. This phrase, expanded to include direction, well indicates the salient features of the most widely used forms of radar. Not all forms of radar involve range determination or direction finding however, and the term radar as now used can be applied to any system that:

(1) radiates radio frequency signals;

(2) receives from a distant source, radio frequency signals that are in some way systematically related to the original signals;

(3) derives from the relationship between the received and transmitted signals, one or more characteristics of the distant source —such as its range, direction, size, relative velocity—or even, quite simply, its existence.

Types of Radar. Radars may be classified in several ways:

(1) By function: search, surveillance, tracking, heightfinding, etc. (although of course, a given radar equipment often performs more than one function).

(2) By the method by which the relationship between the transmitted and received signals is distinguished: pulsed, continuous wave (cw), doppler, frequency modulated, matched filter, or coded systems; or by combinations of these possibilities.

(3) According to whether the received signal is an echo, as in *primary* radar; or a responding transmission from a device carried in the target, as in *secondary* radar.

(4) By application: marine, air traffic control (*q.v.*), weather, etc.

(5) By the characteristics of the beam or scanning method: pencil beam, fan beam, mechanical scan, electronic scan, tracking, "lock-on" follow, etc.

(6) By the relative location of the transmitter and receiver: the simplest and by far the most common systems are "monostatic," with the transmitter and receiver co-located. In "bistatic" systems they are separately located and it is also possible to have more than one transmitter or receiver so separated in a single system.

Basic Range and Direction-Finding Radars A. *General Principles*. Such radars depend upon three fundamental factors:

(1) that radio energy is propagated at uniform and known velocity;

(2) that radio energy is propagated in effectively straight lines, the direction of which can be controlled or recognized; and

(3) that radio energy may be re-radiated or "reflected" to a greater or lesser degree by objects or matter intercepting the transmitted energy.

The capacity of an object to "reflect" radio energy depends upon a number of factors: the dielectric properties of the material of which it is made, its size and shape, and the frequency of the incident radio energy. When energy from a sufficiently powerful transmitter is intercepted by an object the latter will re-radiate a given amount of radio energy. This energy can be detected by a sufficiently sensitive radio receiver adjacent to the transmitter. Because radio energy is propagated in effectively straight lines, the direction from which the reflected energy is received may be determined by employing a receiving antenna capable of discriminating the angle of arrival of signals. In practice it is usual to employ a similarly directional antenna for the transmitter and a single antenna is commonly used by both transmitter and receiver. The efficiency or *gain* of an antenna in either role is defined as the ratio by which its performance in a *given* direction exceeds that of a completely non-directional (isotropic) antenna. The greatest directivity, and hence highest gain, is achieved by antennas having a narrow beam. The advantage of employing a narrow-beam antenna for both transmission and reception is thus obvious. To obtain extended coverage it is then necessary to scan the antennas in one or more planes. (It is sometimes convenient to employ a relatively broad beam in one plane to facilitate scanning.) In any case, it is not possible to obtain infinite gain, the beam of transmitted energy is always divergent, and its intensity (as is also true in the case of reflected energy) varies inversely with the square of the distance.

Radio energy propagates at the velocity of light c. By measuring the time t taken by radio energy to reach a target and be reflected back to the radar, the range R of the target is readily determined ($R = \frac{1}{2}ct$). A radar must accordingly incorporate a timing device to determine the interval that elapses between the emission of a quantum of radio energy and the reception of its "reflection" back from a distant target. In *pulse radar*, which is by far the most common form, this measurement is achieved by transmitting discrete pulses of radio energy of durations of the order of microseconds. The *pulse repetition frequency* (prf) is arranged so that the reflected signals from the most distant targets expected is received before the next pulse is transmitted. This system offers the additional advantage that the signal actually transmitted can be of very high power although the *average* power transmitted is some orders of magnitude lower. In continuous-wave (cw) radar, the transmitted signal is continuous but in a commonly employed variation the signal is modulated in frequency to enable the time delay of the returned signal to be distinguished.

The indication of the presence, location and range of a target detected by the radar techniques is presented on one of several possible radar displays (*q.v.*). Most of them employ a cathode-ray tube (*q.v.*), a device that lends itself particularly well to a graphical presentation of the radar data. In the Plan Position Indicator (PPI), for example, radar echoes are presented as bright points or areas

on the face of the tube, having the same position relative to the origin (usually the tube center) as the target objects have to the radar site (Fig. 1). Various aids to interpretation are employed, such as range markers and other range-measuring devices, and azimuth and directional markers. These are frequently electronically produced indications that also appear on the face of the tube. A variety of other presentations are in use and great ingenuity has been shown in meeting operational needs.

B. *The Radar Equation.* The "radar equation" provides a convenient expression of the fundamentals of radar detection and propagation. It may be stated as

$$P_r = \frac{P_t G}{4\pi R^2} \times \sigma \times \frac{1}{4\pi R^2} \times A_r \times k$$

$$\text{(1)} \quad\quad \text{(2)} \quad \text{(3)} \quad\quad \text{(4)} \quad \text{(5)}$$

where

P_r = received power
P_t = transmitted power
G = gain of transmitting antenna
σ = "reflectivity" of the target
A_r = effective area of receiving antenna
R = range
k = atmospheric attenuation

The term (1) represents the power density at range R, and thus (1) $\times$ (2) is the power reflected by the target. This power, re-radiated back to the radar, yields a power density at the radar of (1) $\times$ (2) $\times$ (3). Multiplied by (4) this density yields the power that would be available at the antenna terminals under free-space conditions. In practice this power is reduced by atmospheric attenuation, (5), experienced over the total path $2R$. The target will be detected if the power received P_r exceeds the minimum signal detectable by the receiver. The latter level is determined by a number of factors and strictly includes all aspects of display, observation, etc.

C. *Radar Equipment.* Radar components and circuitry are too varied and complex to describe in detail. The basic principles of range and direction-finding radars are il-

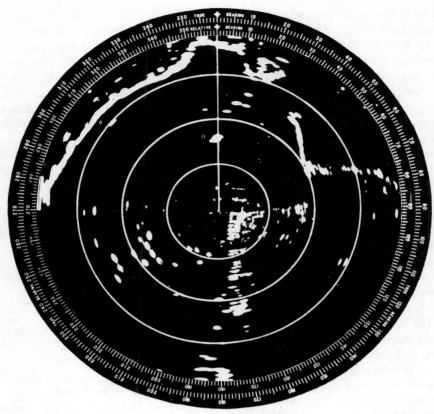

Fig. 1. Typical marine radar display. This 16-in. plan-position-indicator presentation shows shore installations and shore line, channel markers, and other shipping as seen by radar in a ship maneuvering in a harborage. (*Courtesy Raytheon, Inc.*)

lustrated in Fig. 2, however, in which the major units of a simple, pulsed radar are shown together with a diagram of the pulse sequence in time.

Doppler Techniques. Radio energy reflected by a moving target that has a component of motion along the line of sight relative to the radar exhibits an apparent variation in frequency on reception due to the Doppler effect. This phenomenon, orig-

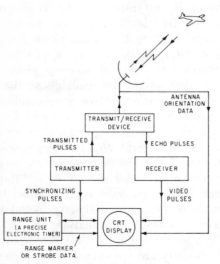

Fig. 2a. A simple pulsed radar system.

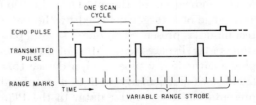

Fig. 2b. Pulse time sequence.

inally described in terms of acoustic waves, occasions a shift in frequency f_d, which is proportional to the relative radial velocity v and the original frequency f_0 :

$$f_d = \frac{2v}{c} f_0$$

In pulsed radar applications, such variations in frequency are too small to be significant and lie well within the bandwidth of the system. In special applications, with equipment designed to distinguish small differences in frequency between the transmitted signal and its echo, advantage is taken of this effect to determine relative radial velocity. A particularly valuable application is employed in the aircraft navigation technique commonly called "doppler radar" or more accurately "doppler navigation" (*q.v.*).

Use has been made of the doppler technique to distinguish between moving and fixed targets and also to distinguish the speed of targets. Although of particular value in the case of aircraft targets (with their high speeds) the technique can be used on targets having much slower speeds. One application is the determination of the speed of automobiles from a stationary transmitter/receiver; this technique is currently widely used in the enforcement of traffic laws. The doppler effect is also being employed experimentally in meteorological studies where the motion of hydrometeors reveals their fall rates or yields information on air movements. Doppler techniques are also of special importance in analyzing radar signals from very distant moving targets where beam divergence precludes any useful resolution by conventional methods. A particularly interesting example of this has been the contribution made by doppler techniques in the study of the moon's surface.

Radar Applications. The more common applications include the following.

A. *Marine Radars.* Simple PPI radars providing plan presentation showing other ships, coastlines, bouys, and other features, for navigational purposes.

B. *Harbor Radar.* Shore-based systems providing similar navigational facilities for the operation of shipping in harbors and their approaches.

C. *Air-Surveillance Radar.* PPI radars, often complemented by height finding facilities, used in the surveillance and control of air traffic in civil applications and in the detection of aircraft and missiles in defense applications.

D. *Approach-Control Radar.* Special application of (C) to enable aircraft approaches and landings to be carried out under the direction of a ground-based radar operator.

E. *Fire-Control Radars.* Precision ranging and tracking radars used in gun laying or missile direction. May be used in ships, ground, or airborne installations.

F. *Weather Radar.* To detect the presence, location, and (with certain qualifications) the intensity of precipitation. Ground installations make possible the detection and tracking of storms, and airborne weather radars alert pilots to the presence of severe weather in and near their path.

Mention should also be made of recent applications of special interest.

G. *Radar in the Space Age.* In recent years, large radars have been used to investigate the nature of the upper atmosphere and have been instrumental in studying ionospheric and auroral phenomena. They have also been used to observe the large numbers of meteors entering the earth's atmosphere from outer space.

Radar has also played a vital role in tracking earth satellites and in making important measurements of their orbit paths.

Radar is also making contributions in astronomy and radar returns have been obtained from the Moon, Venus, and the Sun. By these means it is possible to make studies of radio propagation in space and investigate such features as the surface roughness of the Moon and its libration motion.

Past, Present, and Future. A. *Applications*. As originally conceived, radar was a device to overcome the limiting effects of darkness and atmospheric obscurity on man's vision. It was soon found that with its special capacity for measuring *range* and the readiness with which direction could be enumerated, radar opened up new concepts of perception. Not only was man now able to see with measured precision independently of visibility, but he could now "see" such objects as aircraft at ranges far in excess of those possible even under ideal optical conditions with normal vision. Until relatively recently, technical development was concentrated on improvement of this capacity to "see" more precisely, with greater resolution, less ambiguity, and at greater ranges than hitherto. Although the problems of presentation were by no means neglected, emphasis was for long on improvements in performance, i.e., to increase the capacity to detect smaller targets at greater range.

In its principal applications, namely in aviation and marine navigation, radar has completely changed the basis on which operations were formerly conducted, and is now a fundamental factor in such operations, both in peace and in war. Because of the increased volume of air and sea traffic and the manner in which each unit can and indeed expects to operate with radar assistance, the over-all aspect of radar applications is now changing.

Current developments are particularly concerned with the problems of *utilization* of radar data. Although the quest for improved *acquisition* of such data continues, the emphasis is now on new methods of processing and presenting radar data; modern radar applications are as much concerned with supplementing man's mind and understanding as were the earlier applications with aiding his vision. Thus, although the basic radar principles continue to apply, present and future developments involve the substitution of the computer for the familiar CRT visual presentation stage.

B. *Technical*. The search for performance has involved a constant stream of invention and development. New techniques and components have met the continuing challenge for increased precision and flexibility and increased ability to detect more distant and smaller targets. The former requirement has led to great advances in the knowledge of electromagnetic propagation and the use of an increasing portion of the frequency spectrum.

For example, experimentation is active in the utilization of propagation of millimetric wavelengths which are expected to have special importance in radar applications in the rarified atmosphere of outer space; and the recent development of the laser (*q.v.*) has opened up frequencies from the visible and near visible spectrum. Antenna design has kept pace with such developments and is making great advances in such areas as rapid scanning by electronic control of the shape and direction of the beam.

In the search for increased detection range performance two approaches are possible first, to increase transmitter power; and second, to improve receiver sensitivity. Although much effort is being devoted to the development of ever more powerful transmitting tubes and components, the most promising advances appear to lie in the field of receiver development. Here the problem is to reduce noise and improve amplification factors. Low noise-amplifiers such as masers (*q.v.*), parametric amplifiers (*q.v.*), and the general application of solid-state devices are all playing their part.

Another area in which advances are being made is the development of information theory and the application of this to signal detection techniques to extract the maximum intelligence from the radar signal. These techniques include various forms of signal integration and such techniques as the analysis of the information within a single pulse. The utilization of current intelligence to program and control the scan is also a technique from which much is expected.

RONALD T. H. COLLIS

Cross-references: *Air-Traffic Control, Altimeters, Antennas, Doppler Navigation, Navigation and Navigational Systems, Radar Astronomy, Radar Displays, Radomes, Sonar, TR and ATR Tubes*

RADAR ASTRONOMY

The very beginning of the radar art, in the 1920's, is associated with its application for probing into space. The first radar target was the earth's ionosphere, the ionized layers of gas 50 to 500 miles high that support long-distance, high-frequency radio communications. The wartime use of radar for the detection of ships and planes did not come until about 15 years later, but the improvements in radar technology during the war years had profound influence on its later astronomical applications.

In "radar astronomy" man-made radio signals are sent into space from powerful radio transmitters and large antennas. This radio energy may be affected in many ways by the bodies and gaseous regions that it encounters. If a small portion of this energy is scattered back to the earth and is picked up by an antenna and receiver, study of the characteristics of the returned energy may reveal new information about the regions and bodies that were encountered. Radar astronomy differs from radio astronomy in that the source of the radio waves is under our control in the former, whereas in the latter only the natural radio emissions from the cosmos are received and studied. The control inherent in the use of our own signals in radar astronomy makes possible many new measurements, but the energy loss resulting from the two-way path from earth to target back to earth is likely to limit radar studies to the confines of the solar system.

Radar studies have already been made of the ionosphere, auroras, meteor trails, artificial satellites, the moon, Venus, and the sun. In the future it should be possible to investigate Mars, Mercury, and the major planets (Jupiter, Saturn, Uranus, and Nep-

tune) by radar, as well as close asteroids and comets. In addition it should be possible to measure characteristics of the solar corona, solar streams of gas, and the interplanetary medium by radar.

It is interesting to note that our technical capability for making important radar studies of the solar system is developing at about the same pace as our capability in astronautical exploration using rocket probes. These two techniques should not be viewed as alternate methods of space exploration, however, since the salient fact is that they are complementary, and both should be developed for a well-rounded program. Radar can help pave the way for later astronautical exploration by determining distances with precision, by measuring surface features on the moon and planets, by making first-order measurements of planetary atmospheres, and by monitoring the changes of the interplanetary medium. Radar may be used to measure some phenomena with low precision but continuously for comparison with high-precision but transient measurements made by rocket probes. Radar measurements from powerful systems on the ground can help determine the optimum design of the small radar systems to be put aboard the rocket probes for close study of the planets. Radar-astronomy facilities would also be invaluable for maintaining communication with distant rocket probes. And in at least one instance, radar can probe a region (the solar corona) where the rocket probe cannot venture.

For the detection and study of the moon, terrestrial planets, giant planet cores, and asteroids it is important to use relatively short wavelengths to realize the greatest advantage from large antennas and low-noise receiving devices, such as masers (*q.v.*) and parametric amplifiers (*q.v.*). For the detection and study of the sun, the ionospheres of the earth and planets, solar streams of gas, and the interplanetary medium long wavelengths must be used since only they are affected strongly by tenuous ionized gases. From obvious physical differences the former objects are called hard targets and the latter, soft targets.

One of the most important reasons for probing the hard targets with radar is to measure distances very accurately. The basic unit of measurement in the solar system, the mean distance of the earth from the sun, was known from optical astronomy to an accuracy of only one part in a thousand. Thus the estimate of the "astronomical unit" might have been in error by 100,000 miles. The accurate measurement of range is fundamental to radar. Strong radar echoes from a planet or asteroid will make possible a greatly improved value for the astronomical unit. Significant improvement has already been made from the first radar studies of Venus.

By measuring the changes in the echoes from hard targets accompanying changes in wavelength, wave polarization, and aspect of the surface, it may be possible to determine the electric and magnetic properties of the surface material, the average roughness of the surface (i.e., whether it consists of sand, boulders, mountains, or water waves), and the presence or absence of features of uniform orientation and length, such as vegetation.

Once sufficiently sensitive systems are available, the great resolving power of radar could be used to measure the above surface features over relatively small areas. On Mars, for example, it should be possible to map in some detail the size and shape of the optically faint surface markings and determine something about their electrical and physical characteristics. More is now known about Mars than any other planet, save the earth, but much more will surely be discovered from careful radar studies.

Since Venus is covered by optically opaque fog, essentially nothing is known about its solid surface. Radar waves will penetrate the fog and be reflected from the surface. With only relatively coarse resolution in radar range and Doppler frequency it should be possible to determine the large-scale surface features, to see if there are oceans, con-

tinents, polar ice caps, and mountain ranges. These same measurements would also show the length of the Venusian day and the tilt of the axis.

It is to be expected that some of the planets have ionospheres, magnetic fields, and radiation belts. If so, radar studies at long wavelengths might be used to measure their characteristics. A special problem is encountered here because the wavelength used must be short enough to pass through our own ionosphere, yet long enough to be reflected by the ionosphere of the distant planet.

Interplanetary space is far from being a complete void. It is estimated that there may be on the order of 1000 electrons/in.^{3} in the space between the planets. Inside the great solar streams of gas the number may be a hundred times greater. While this represents a very tenuous region, much better than the most perfect vacuum produced by man, it should be possible to measure the density of the interplanetary medium using long-wavelength radar echoes from the moon and planets.

Future radar studies of the sun should be perhaps the most fruitful area of investigation in radar astronomy. From long-wavelength studies that include radar resolution in range, Doppler frequency, and angle, much new information should be obtained about the changing features of the solar corona and how the sun produces great streams of ionized gas that envelop the earth and cause the auroras, ionospheric and magnetic storms, communication blackouts, and at least one of the radiation belts around the earth.

At the present time (1961), radar systems consisting of antennas measuring up to 1000 ft in diameter and transmitters having power outputs up to 10 Mw are being readied for studies in radar astronomy. Complex electronic computers and low-noise receivers are also vital parts of such radar systems since they make possible the detection and study of extremely weak echoes. Continuing developments of these various electronic components will soon allow us to bring essentially all of the solar system under the direct scrutiny of man-made radio probes.

VON R. ESHLEMAN

Cross-references: *Extraterrestrial Radio Sources, Propagation, Radar*

RADAR DISPLAYS

A radar set is basically a sensor. Its function is to obtain information about the physical environment within its range of operation. The most commonly derived information is the distance or range to a given object. In addition, the angular bearing or direction of the object, often called the target, is usually determined. Relative angular or lineal elevation and relative velocity of the target are frequently obtained.

The radar information is sometimes processed and fed directly into a computer. Alternatively, it is recorded on tape or film for later use or analysis. The most common arrangement by far, however, is to display the desired information to a radar observer. The instrument used for this purpose is the radar indicator which usually is a cathode-ray tube (CRT). The electronic traces on the CRT, together with suitable overlays and scale markings, constitute the *radar display*.

Basic Displays. *A-Scope.* Historically the oldest radar display, the A-scope (Fig. 1) shows target range and, within limits, the amplitude of the target echo. The A-scope, which is simply an oscillographic presentation of the radar return, is used when angular information is not required or is provided from another sensor. For example, the A-scope might show range to targets directly in front of a radar equipped aircraft, or to targets whose angular position is determined for the radar with an optical sight or infrared sensor.

Plan-Position Indicator. The plan-position indicator (PPI) displays bearings to the targets as angles and ranges as the radial

distances to the target echoes (Fig. 2). Since radar measures absolute range, the relative locations of targets are correct only for those in the same horizontal plane with the radar. Without some form of compensation, an aircraft target at 60° elevation appears at twice the true ground range. Similar distortions are present in an airborne ground-mapping PPI, and can be minimized or eliminated by the use of special nonlinear range sweeps on the CRT.

Sometimes only a portion of the complete azimuth is of interest or available. Examples are the localizer display of a GCA

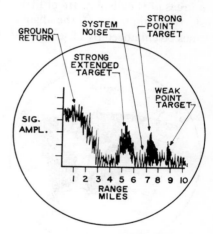

Fig. 1. A-Scope.

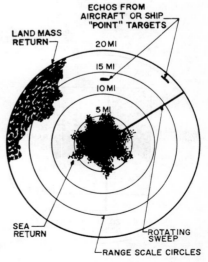

Fig. 2. PPI.

radar or the display of a nose-mounted airborne weather radar. In such cases, a sector PPI display is used with the sector angle usually but not necessarily corresponding to the actual coverage.

For ground installations, the PPI angular reference is fixed and usually north oriented. Airborne and shipborne PPI displays can either be north-oriented or vehicle-oriented, depending upon the application. The sector PPI for the nose-mounted weather radar obviously must be vehicle oriented.

A frequent variation seen with both full and sector PPI displays is off-centering. If certain areas of the display are of little or no interest, the remainder of the display can sometimes be enhanced by off-centering. The

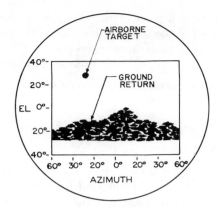

Fig. 5. C-Scope.

advantage is the enlargement of the areas of interest without distortion. Figure 3 shows an off-center sector PPI as a display for an airborne ground mapping radar.

B-Scope. Like the PPI, the B-Scope (Fig. 4) displays range and azimuth angle. However, the use of a rectilinear coordinate system causes considerable distortion, particularly for close-in mapping. The B-Scope is useful where close-in target resolution is important, and the most common usage is in airborne fire-control radar.

C-Scope. Unlike the displays described so far, the C-Scope (Fig. 5) does not display range. It is a rectilinear presentation of the azimuth and elevation angles to the target. In order to achieve a useful signal-to-noise ratio, the radar return is usually range-gated prior to display. That is, only a small segment of the available range is displayed at a time. The setting of the range gate, then, provides an indication of range.

Radar Indicators and Auxiliary Circuitry. The radar indicator usually consists of a suitably packaged CRT and the required auxiliary circuits. The CRT can be either a magnetically or an electrostatically deflected type. Deflection circuits are of two types. One type moves the CRT spot in synchronism with antenna beam position and the other provides a linear spot deflection with time. The latter constitutes the range trace and the spot must travel each nautical mile calibrated on the display in

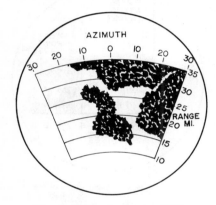

Fig. 3. Off-center sector PPI.

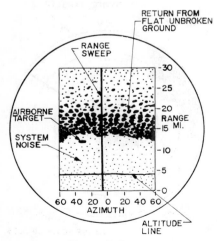

Fig. 4. B-Scope.

12.6 μsec. Finally, there must be video amplifying and blanking circuits to convert the received signals into the correct form to drive the CRT and to blank or turn off the CRT beam during retrace time. In the case of the A-Scope, the video amplifier output is used to deflect the CRT spot vertically in conjunction with a horizontal range sweep. A variety of other display circuits for generating special symbols and for time-sharing displays on one CRT have been devised.

Conventional CRT Displays. A great many special radar displays have been designed and used. The glide slope display on a GCA radar is essentially a sector PPI which indicates elevation rather than azimuth angles. Special sector PPI displays for airborne radars indicate only those targets above a horizontal plane adjustable in distance below the aircraft, thus providing a terrain clearance display. A unique form of a C-Scope, called a profilometer, indicates the elevation of the highest terrain at each azimuth in front of an aircraft. Special forms of the B-Scope indicate relative target speed instead of range. In addition, many displays are modified, frequently as different modes of operation of one indicator, by scale factor changes and off-centering.

There is another class of displays, usually superimposed on a conventional display, in which certain auxiliary information is presented. Some of the information thus presented is derived from the radar, and some is provided from other sensors or a computer.

Color Displays. Frequently, more information is available for display than can effectively be presented on a conventional CRT. The use of color provides an additional information channel. A typical application using a PPI display on a color CRT presents elevation information by changing color of the targets. Although this is an effective means of providing additional information, the limitations of the human observer must be recognized. The human eye can distinguish color differences very well but has a poor capability to identify a single color on an absolute basis. On such a display, then, the observer could readily determine relative target elevations, but the absolute elevation of a single target could not reliably be determined with accuracy.

Stored Displays. Early CRT's used phosphor screens with relatively short persistence. In other words, light is emitted from the electronically exited phosphor for only a short time after the excitation is removed. The decay time of screens using phosphors, such as the P-1, is of the order of milliseconds. A typical radar has a range sweep of 100 to 1000 μsec, a pulse repetition frequency of 200 to 4000 pps, and an azimuth scan rate of 25 to 100 deg/sec. An A-Scope display appears continuous and relatively bright because the repetition rate is well above the eye's flicker threshold, the phosphor persistence is long compared to the range sweep time, and the radar information does not change significantly from pulse to pulse. Displays that present angular information, however, paint a given target echo at a rate well below the eye's flicker rate, and to have a useful display greater phosphor persistence or storage is required. The P-7 cascaded or two-layer phosphor and later the single-layer P-19 were developed to fulfill this requirement. These phosphors have decay times of several seconds depending upon the ambient light level. In a very dark room, the P-19 traces can be seen for several minutes after the removal of excitation.

Where the application allows the reduction of ambient light levels, the long-persistence phosphors provide an excellent display. There are many applications, however, where the ambient light cannot be controlled. Even where control is possible, it would be better if normal ambient light levels could be used to permit better performance of other tasks. Consequently, recently developed practical storage tubes having very high screen brightness have found use in many radar displays.

Non-CRT Displays. The CRT is a series device; information is accepted and written on the screen sequentially. Storage tubes provide a parallel output, but the input remains serial. Certain radars inherently provide a parallel output. In such cases, the parallel outputs must be time-shared and fed sequentially to the CRT display. The complexity of this arrangement has created much interest in the possibilities of a parallel input display. In its most elementary form, such a display might take the form of a solid-state display (*q.v.*) comprising two grids of parallel wires, oriented at right angles, with an electroluminescent layer between the two grids. Signals on any orthogonal pair of wires "turn on" the light at their intersection. Recent developments in the field of electroluminescence (*q.v.*) have made such displays much more feasible than before. However, the problems of low brightness, poor resolution, and the requirement for high signal voltage must be overcome before this type of display can find wide application. An additional advantage of this display is its thinness. Less than 1 in. thick, it fits in a crowded instrument panel much better than the long CRT.

Human Factors

Display-Observer Relationships. The radar observer is frequently required to perform difficult tasks of detection and recognition of aircraft or ground targets under adverse conditions of time, fatigue, noise, ambient light, and personal danger. It is essential for the radar display to be designed with the human operator as a foremost consideration. Some of the more important parameters involving the display-observer relationship are as follows:

Display dimensions	Display persistance
Resolution	Ambient light
Viewing distance	Display distortion
Display brightness	Dynamic range
Display color	

In selecting the optimum combination of parameters for a particular display application certain characteristics of the human observer should be taken into account. For example, the acuity or resolving power of the human eye is equal to approximately 1' of arc. Thus two point sources of light separated by an angular subtense of 1' can just barely be distinguished as two spots rather than one by an observer with normal vision. However, in order for an observer to identify an object by its shape, the object usually must subtend an angle of at least 20'. Thus, in determining the required size and resolution of a CRT display and the proper viewing distance, the human characteristics just mentioned become practical limiting design considerations.

Similarly, the dynamic range of the eye is often an important factor in determining display and ambient lighting requirements. The total dynamic range of the human eye, including its marvelous ability to adapt to light and darkness, is some 100 db, ranging from about 10^{-6} to 10^4 millilamberts. However, the instantaneous dynamic range is a small fraction of the total range, since the eye adapts to gross changes in light relatively slowly. Although the instantaneous dynamic range of the eye thus exceeds by far that of any present-day CRT display, ambient light must be controlled sufficiently to allow the eye to adapt so that its momentary dynamic range covers the range of light intensities emitted by the display.

Another important consideration is the manner in which the eyes move in scanning a display. Eye movements are neither continuous nor systematic. The eyes move in quick, saccadic jumps from one fixation point to the next. The patterns of movement are irregular, and the points of fixation are not uniformly distributed over the whole display area. More attention is given to some areas than others. Displays should be designed either so as to direct the observer's attention appropriately, or so that the observer's natural eye-movement habits are not a critical factor in the task.

An example of the former is the use of a small circular "target marker" to indicate the position at which a target is most likely to appear on an interceptor radar display.

This is particularly important if a standard CRT with a relatively rapid phosphor decay is used, thus requiring the operator's eyes to follow a moving trace to detect targets. An example of the latter approach is the use of a storage tube with selective erasure which presents all signals with no decay until they are erased and replaced by new signals, thus making eye-movement patterns less important in detection.

Detection of Targets. In using a mapping or weather radar, the primary observer task is recognition. Certain other systems, such as GCA, stress interpretation and control. In the case of the search radar, the primary task is detection of targets. Search radars are usually operated at their limit. That is, targets are detected at the maximum possible range and more range is always desired. Detection must occur, then, with very weak signals. Consequently, every means has been sought to enhance the signals on the display.

It is not the weakness of the signal *per se* that causes the difficulty, since the signal could be amplified. It is the signal-to-noise ratio that is important. The noise or interference is of two types. One is the noise (*q.v.*) inherent in the radar receiver and is often called thermal noise. The other is the return from unwanted targets such as sea or ground echoes.

Much effort has been spent on studies of display optimization for improved detection of targets in thermal noise. It has been shown that optimum values of CRT bias and video drive exist for any given display and indicator. Probably the most important improvement can be gained through signal integration. This process takes advantage of the fact that in the addition of two or more successive returns, the correlated signals add directly, whereas the uncorrelated noise, random in time and amplitude, adds as the square root. Thus, a signal, undetectable in noise, might be enhanced to the point of detection by adding the echoes from successive transmitted pulses. Such signal integration was first obtained by the use of long-persistence phosphor screens and A-Scope displays, the integration occuring in the phosphor. Storage tubes can be used to perform this function and several correlators have been devised that perform the function prior to the display.

Since the noise or clutter from unwanted targets is not random, signal integration does not improve detection here. The best display solution for this problem is to improve the dynamic range and resolution to allow detection based upon recognition of target characteristic, i.e., shape or movement, in an unsaturated display.

HOWARD G. WILSON AND STANLEY N. ROSCOE

Pictorial Displays

Pictorial displays for airborne navigation purposes are designed to answer two questions, "Where am I?" and "How do I get from here to there?" To provide the answers, the displays utilize several data sensors to obtain the necessary information. These data are, in general, magnetic heading (usually from a gyro stabilized compass); slant range and bearing (from Omni-DME or TACAN ground stations) or grid coordinate displacement (from a dead-reckoning computer); localizer displacement (from an instrument landing system); and several manually set parameters such as desired heading, desired radial to a station, or runway heading.

The displays process these data and furnish the operator information in one of two forms which have been assigned specific titles by general usage:

(1) Horizontal Situation Indicators: devices solving the navigational problem with a specific and unique solution based on triangulation.

(2) Map Displays: devices solving the navigational problem by simultaneously presenting all possible solutions by imaging position and orientation on a map.

Some examples of each type are currently manufactured by several of the aircraft instrument or electronic industries. A

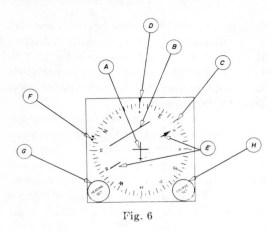

Fig. 6

general example of each is described and taken through a representative flight path to illustrate function and operation.

Horizontal Situation Indicator (HSI). The design of the indicator (Fig. 6) is such as to reduce the navigation situation to a simple triangulation problem since the aircraft position is always definable with respect to a line or point in space. A fixed aircraft symbol *A* in plan view, with its nose pointing upward, is located in the center of the indicator to represent the actual aircraft. A movable course bar *B* representing desired flight path or positional reference line in space is located underneath the aircraft symbol. The displacement and orientation of this bar with respect to the fixed aircraft symbol represents the space relationship of the aircraft to the desired track or reference line. This space geometry is then related to earth coordinates by surrounding these elements with a rotating compass rose *C*. Magnetic heading of the aircraft is then read at the index marker *D* at the top of the display. The alignment of the course bar with respect to the compass rose is accomplished by the arrowhead and tail markers *E* which rotate with the bar. Desired magnetic heading is portrayed by a command marker *F* which may be positioned around the periphery of the compass rose. After positioning, the command marker rotates with the compass rose. Knobs for manually selecting desired heading *G* and course *H*

complete the display. (Where greater accuracy is required, a three-digit counter may be coupled to the course setting knob for a digital readout of runway heading or desired course.)

In a typical flight, the pilot flies a specified heading until he intercepts a radial to a ground TACAN station, flies the radial into the station, turns onto the prescribed heading to intercept an instrument landing system localizer beam, and then flies the beam to the runway.

Figure 7 illustrates how the aircraft and indicator appear at the start of the example. The operator has placed the heading command marker on 347° (his present heading) and the course bar has been set to 292° (desired radial to the station). The course bar has displaced itself ahead of the aircraft symbol to indicate that the desired radial is ahead of the actual aircraft. In Fig. 8, the aircraft is nearer the desired radial to the station and the course bar has started to move towards the aircraft symbol on the display. This display indicates to the pilot that he must prepare to turn left to capture the selected radial.

Figure 9 shows the aircraft about halfway through the turn onto the TACAN

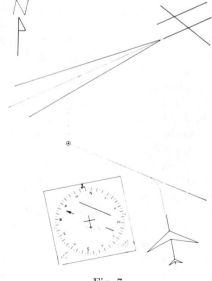

Fig. 7

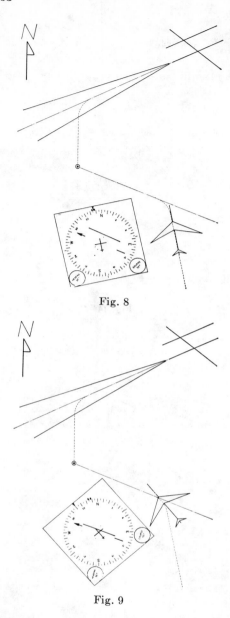

Fig. 8

Fig. 9

the aircraft nears the TACAN station (indicated by a distance reading on a distance measuring equipment indicator approaching zero) and the pilot sets in a new desired heading of "N" on the command marker. At the same time he sets the course bar to the runway heading of 64°. Figure 11 shows the situation just prior to the aircraft turning to the new heading.

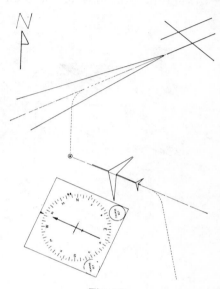

Fig. 10

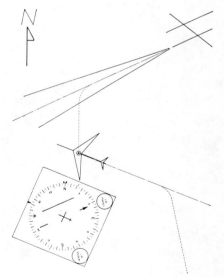

Fig. 11

radial. The course bar is almost aligned with the arrowhead and tail, the magnetic heading has changed to 320°, and the command marker (still set at 347°) has rotated to the right with the compass rose.

Complete capture of the desired TACAN radial is illustrated by Fig. 10. The course bar and arrowhead and tail are exactly aligned and magnetic heading corresponds with the selected radial (292°). In Fig. 11,

As soon as the turn to the desired heading is completed (Fig. 12), the command marker is aligned with the index marker at the top of the display and the course bar is again displaced ahead of the aircraft symbol. When the aircraft intersects the outer edge of the localizer beam, the course bar begins to move towards the aircraft symbol (Fig. 13). This is the cue to the pilot to begin his turn to the right to capture the center of the beam.

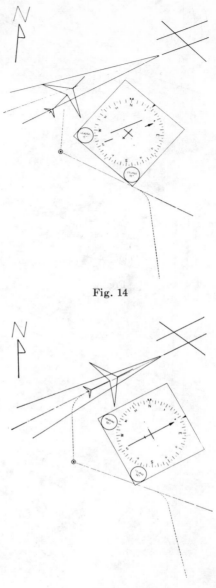

Fig. 14

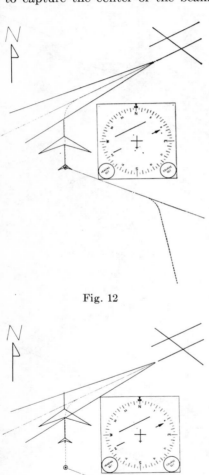

Fig. 12

Fig. 13

Fig. 15

As the aircraft turns, the display assumes the configuration shown in Fig. 14. The course bar is moving closer to the aircraft symbol. Capture of the center of the localizer beam is illustrated in Fig. 15. Just before landing, the horizontal situation indicator appears as seen in Fig. 16.

The preceding figures and descriptions completely illustrate all the functions of the

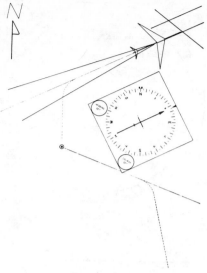

Fig. 16

have been used, and are recommended, for different phases of a flight.

Assuming the same example as in the case of the HSI, we shall now fly the same path using a map display for our navigation indicator.

At start of the flight path (Fig. 18), magnetic heading 353°, desired radial 292°. Approaching desired radial (Fig. 19). Halfway through turn on to radial (Fig. 20). Magnetic heading 320°. On desired radial inbound to station (Fig. 21). Magnetic headiing 292°. Near TACAN station preparatory to turning to new heading to intercept localizer beam (Fig. 22). Outbound from TACAN station. Magnetic heading "N" (Fig. 23).

Intercepting edge of localizer beam (Fig. 24). Preparing to turn right into center of

HSI. To simplify the illustrations it was necessary to orient the display such that its 12 o'clock position always paralleled the nose of the aircraft. Understanding of the display and its space orientation may be enhanced if the page is rotated such that the nose of the aircraft is always up with respect to the reader.

Map Displays. Map displays provide basic navigation data by imaging a symbol, representing the aircraft, on a map of the terrain over which it is flying. Different methods for presenting this situation have been developed by various manufacturers. They include mechanical, "hot wire," and optical imaging techniques as well as oriented and nonoriented symbols. In a representative example (Fig. 17), the display elements consist of a chart *A*, a symbol representing the aircraft *B*, an aircraft heading marker *C*, and a compass rose *D*. The chart, with its center representing a ground Omni-DME or TACAN station, is a stationary reference in an orientation of magnetic north up. The position and heading of the aircraft are continuously given by the aircraft symbol, with a precise readout of magnetic heading obtainable by means of the heading marker and compass rose. Various scales of charts

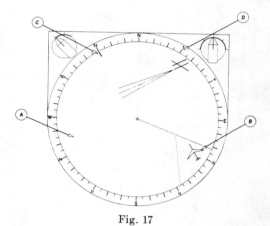

Fig. 17

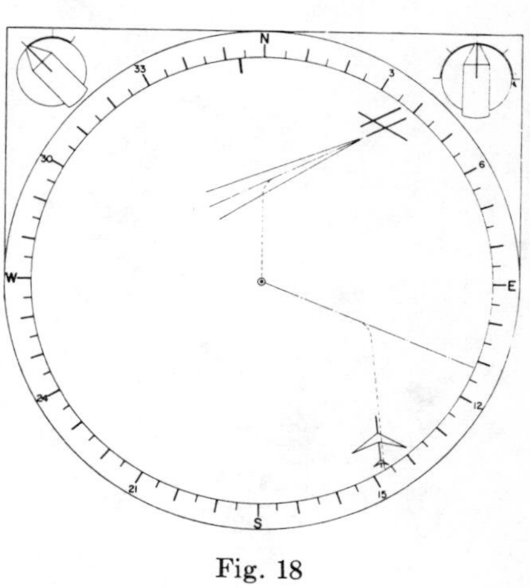

Fig. 18

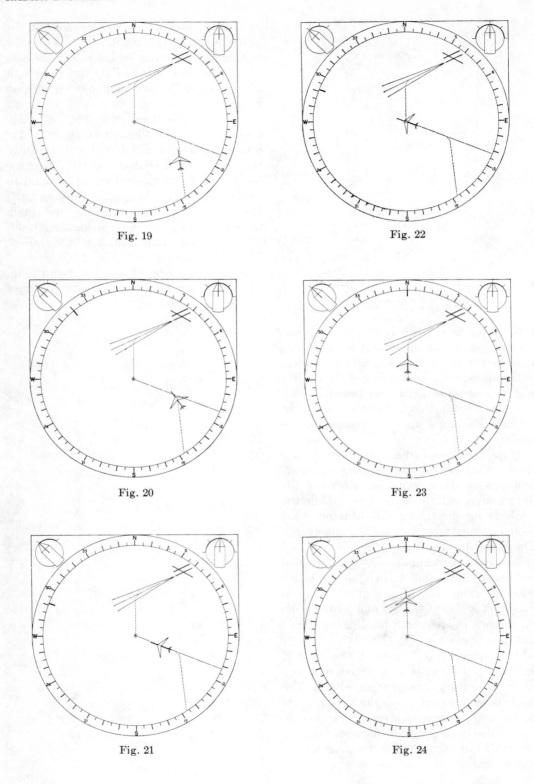

Fig. 19

Fig. 22

Fig. 20

Fig. 23

Fig. 21

Fig. 24

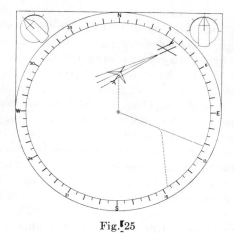

Fig. 25

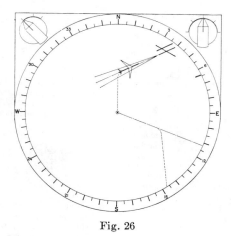

Fig. 26

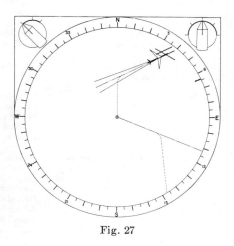

Fig. 27

beam. Halfway through turn onto localizer center line (Fig. 25). Localizer center line captured (Fig. 26). Inbound to runway. On course just prior to landing (Fig. 27).

The preceding example illustrates the functional operation of the map display. The shortness of the descriptions associated with the figures is an indication of the simplicity of interpreting the display. Variations of the basic map display include:

(1) Fixed aircraft symbol with a map that translates for position and rotates for heading.

(2) An aircraft symbol that rotates for heading and a translating map for position.

(3) Fixed position symbol with a translating map. (No heading orientation.)

(4) Fixed map with translating position symbol. (No heading orientation.)

GLENN WEATHERSPOON

Cross-references: *Air-Traffic Control, Automatic Pilot, Cathode-Ray Tubes (Display), Doppler Navigation, Navigation and Navigational Systems, Radar, Solid-State Displays, Sonar*

RADIATION (IONIZING)

Radiation in the oldest and strictest sense is the process in which energy is emitted in accordance with the classical theory by a body in the form of electromagnetic waves possessing a frequency ν and wavelength λ, with vibrations transverse to the direction of propagation. This definition includes the radiant energy associated with the electromagnetic spectrum ranging from the highest energies (shortest wavelengths) of secondary cosmic rays, the γ-rays from radioactive disintegrations of atomic nuclei, and X-rays (which now may be generated at millions or billions of volts), on down through ultraviolet rays, visible light, infrared, radio or Hertzian, and very long electric waves. All these waves, seemingly so different in methods of excitation and in properties, even though the origin in all cases may be termed the unrest of electric charges, are actually identical in every respect except length. All have the same velocity of propagation, namely, 3×10^8 m/sec; all may be refracted, reflected, diffracted, and polarized, which are properties of waves. But in many other phenomena these radiations manifest themselves as corpuscular quanta, or chargeless and massless *photons*, thus indicating a dual and seemingly incompatible nature which can be depicted not with familiar models of everyday life, but only mathematically by the Schrödinger wave-mechanics equations. The various ranges of the electromagnetic spectrum are summarized in Table 1.

In modern concepts the term "radiation" also includes energy emitted in the form of particles which possess mass, with one exception, and may or may not be electrically charged positive or negative. Beams of such particles may be considered as "rays," which also have wavelike properties and thus the same dual nature as photons described above. These particles include photons, neutrons, electrons, neutrinos (massless), mesons and other "strange" particles, and their *antiparticles*. The list of known elementary particles is given in the article on antiparticles (*q.v.*). The charged particles may all be accelerated and very high energies imparted to beams in the particle accelerators such as cyclotrons, betatrons, synchotrons, and linear accelerators.

TABLE 1.—RANGE OF ELECTROMAGNETIC WAVES*

Type	Octaves	Wavelength Range, Å (1 Å = 10^{-10} m)	Generation	Detection	Type	Octaves	Wavelength Range, Å (1 Å = 10^{-10} m)	Generation	Detection
γ-rays	—	0.001–1.4 0.06–0.5 used in radiology	Emitted when atomic nuclei disintegrate (radioactivity)	As for x-rays but more penetrating	Infrared rays	9	7,700–4 × 10^6	Heat radiations	Heating effects on thermocouples, bolometers, etc.
X-rays	14	0.006–1019 0.0001 and less in betatron	Emitted as result of ejection of electrons from inner atomic orbitals by radiation (electrons, photons)	*a.* Photography *b.* Phosphorescence *c.* Chemical action *d.* Ionization *e.* Photoelectric action *f.* Diffraction by crystals, etc.	Solar radiation	—	Limiting wavelengths reaching earth 2,960–53,000		
					Hertzian waves	28	1 × 10^6 to 3 × 10^{14}		
					Short Hertzian	17	1 × 10^6 to 1 × 10^{11}	Spark-gap discharge oscillating triode valve, etc.	Coherer. Spark across minute gaps in resonant receiving circuit. Reflected, refracted, diffracted.
Ultraviolet rays	5	136–3,900	Radiated from very hot bodies and emitted by ionized gases	Same as x-rays *a–e* reflected, refracted by finely ruled gratings	Radio	11	1 × 10^{11} to 3 × 10^{14}	Same	Coherer. Conversion to alternating current. Rectification with or without heterodyning and production of audible signals.
					Broadcasting band	—	2 × 10^{12} to 5.5 × 10^{12}		
Visible rays	1	3,900–7,700 Violet 3,900–4,200 Blue 4,220–4,920 Green 4,920–5,350 Yellow 5,350–5,860 Orange 5,860–6,470 Red 6,470–7,700	Radiated from hot bodies and emitted by ionized gases	Sensation of light; same as ultraviolet rays	Electric waves	—	3 × 10^{14} to 3.5 × 10^{16}	Coil rotating in magnetic field	Mechanical. Electrical. Magnetic. Thermal effects of alternating currents.

* From Clark, "Applied X-Rays," 4th ed., McGraw-Hill Book Co., N. Y.

The word "ionizing" in the title actually imposes a limitation upon this topic of radiation, for only rays of all types with sufficiently high energies, i.e., with large values of $h\nu$, where h is the Planck quantum action constant and ν the frequency, are able to ionize (electrify) or cause electrons to be ejected from atoms or molecules of irradiated gases, liquids, or solids.* In general such ionizing agents are X-ray and γ-ray photons, accelerated electrons (β-rays), protons (also deuterons from deuterium H^2, tritons from tritium H^3, α-particles or He ions, and ions of even heavier atoms), and neutrons emitted by atomic nuclei. Ionization is indicated not only electrically but also by emission of radiation—optical spectra when outer valence electrons are ejected at relatively low energies, and X-ray spectra following removal of electrons from inner electron shells (the K-series spectrum, for example, corresponding to the innermost or K orbital). Chemical and biological effects of radiation often are due to free radicals that may exist momentarily in the ionization or excitation by radiation. Of course in some cases of very high energies of bombarding particles nuclei may undergo fission, or fusion with the bombarding particle to synthesize new nuclides (for example Lawrencium[103], newly added to the Table of Elements, from element 98 bombarded by ions of element 5).

GEORGE L. CLARK

Basic Interactions

Radiations of a large class, called ionizing, which interact with matter in its many forms and lead to a wide variety of "observed" or expressed effects have a similar basic interaction pathway. The common bases for discussion of both the nature and origin of these radiations, as well as of their fate in target matter, are the great systemizations of the structure of matter: the periodic table of elements, and the table of isotopes (q.v.) or nuclides.

Unstable and Stable Matter. Nuclear species (nuclides) can be represented on a chart of p, the number of protons in the nucleus (also called atomic number Z) vs the number of neutrons n in the nucleus. Of the more than 1200 such entries, less than 300 are *stable* with respect to nearby nuclides. The stable configurations are those in which intranuclear attractive and repulsive forces are most nearly in balance. Nuclides outside the region of stability undergo *radioactive decay*, with characteristic *half lives*, to achieve such stability, by emitting particles (including photons) that carry away the excess nuclear excitation energy. These particles or "radiations" (most commonly alpha, beta, or gamma), if inside or contiguous to some given matter, interact with it. Besides radioactive isotopes, other sources of similar radiations include fission or fusion reactions (based on another type of nuclear instability), accelerators, and cosmic rays. Regardless of the source of any given radiation (applied to a given target), the basic interaction depends only upon the fundamental properties of the irradiating particle itself.

Ionizing Radiations. The principal ionizing radiations are summarized in Table 2. Although only the gamma (or X-) rays are electromagnetic in character and thus waves or "radiations" in the classical sense, the distinction between ionizing "radiations" and "particles" is often not made. It is also often difficult to make a clear distinction between ionizing and nonionizing electromagnetic radiations, particularly in condensed phases. The ionization potential of gaseous elements, i.e., the energy required for removal of the first electron, varies from 3.9 ev (Cs) to 24.6 ev (He). Comparable values are not well known for most complicated molecular systems or liquid- and solid-state systems, but are probably in or near this general range. Although ultraviolet

---

* "Ionizing" radiation is intended in the present volume to be distinguished from "nonionizing" radiation, i.e., radio waves; the distinction is largely drawn from the effects of radiation on biological substances, and is not meant to be an exact one.

TABLE 2

Name	Sym-bol	Location in atom	Relative rest mass	Charge
Proton (H¹)⁺	p	nucleus	1	+1
Neutron	n	nucleus	1	0
Electron	e	outer shells	0.00055	−1
Beta⁻ (electron)	β	Ejected during dynamic decay processes	0.00055	−1
Beta⁺ (positron)	β⁺		0.00055	+1
Alpha (He⁴)⁺⁺	α		4	+2
Gamma* (photon)	γ	"	0.0	0

* X-rays of equal energy are identical, but of extranuclear origin.

and even visible light can in special cases cause ionizations, the general assumption is that more energetic X- or gamma radiation is required to insure ionization. Hence the name "ionizing radiation" is reserved for electromagnetic radiation at least as energetic as X rays and for charged particles of these energies. Neutrons also lead to ionization, but for other reasons, described below.

Basic Action. From the standpoint of *interaction* of these radiations, the most significant aspect of target matter is its electronic structure. Though most of the mass of an atom resides in the nucleus, the nuclear diameter, less than about 10^{-12} cm, is a small fraction of the atomic size of about 10^{-8} cm. The electrons, each of which is of the order of nuclear size or larger, are systematically distributed throughout the extranuclear atomic volume. Therefore, the target presented by matter to penetrating radiations is that of a sea of electrons in space interspersed here and there with an occasional nucleus.

Charged particles "see" principally the atomic electron clouds, both because of the relative size of electrons and because they act to screen out the nuclear charge. Direct nuclear interactions are of prime importance to nuclear physics, but because of their rarity (except at very high energies) they are rela-

tively unimportant for interaction considerations. An energetic charged particle plowing through this cloud pushes or pulls out electrons by simple electrostatic action, i.e., ionizes. For each ion pair formed it is known or assumed that about 33 ev is absorbed, for all such radiations in all types of matter. These ionizations are generally believed to occur in groups of one primary ionization and perhaps two secondaries induced by the rapidly moving primary ions (especially the electrons). The tracks of secondary ionizations, often extending outward from the track core, are known as *delta rays*. Associated with the ionizations are other, less energetic events known to occur with radiations of lower energy. Perhaps one-third to one-half of the total energy lost is dissipated as molecular *excitations*. Thus the 33-ev figure is a composite for both the ionization and for the several associated excitations. (Note: The exact details of this primary process, particularly for liquids and solids, are still a matter for discussion.)

The geometrical distribution of these events varies with the type and energy of radiation and the target material. It is generally described in terms of the *ionization density*, or more properly the energy loss per unit track length (dE/dx) denoted Linear Energy Transfer (LET) or sometimes Rate of Loss of Energy (RLE). From qualitative electrostatic considerations the higher the *charge* of the incident radiation and the lower its *velocity* (i.e., the longer it is near the target electrons), the greater is its LET along the track. For most of the track length LET depends approximately on the square of these particle parameters, i.e.,

$$\frac{dE}{dx} \propto \frac{(\text{charge})^2}{(\text{velocity})^2} \tag{1}$$

Thus, with reference to Table 2, a 1-Mev proton with the same charge magnitude as a 1-Mev electron travels much slower (kinetic energy = $\frac{1}{2}mv^2$), so that it has a higher LET than the electron and exhausts its energy after traveling a shorter distance. Likewise, comparing alpha particles and protons of the same velocity, the alpha particle with its double charge has a four times greater LET and correspondingly shorter range. By this argument alone, positrons and electrons should behave identically. The usual fate of positrons, however, is the mutual annihilation with an electron (its antiparticle, *q.v.*) resulting in two gamma rays.

Since the targets are the electrons in matter, the LET is the greater the higher the target electron density, so that we can write for (1),

$$\frac{dE}{dx} \propto \frac{(\text{charge})^2}{(\text{velocity})^2} NZ \qquad (2)$$

where N is the number of target atoms/cc and Z the number of electrons/neutral target atom (i.e., atomic number). More complete theoretical expressions of the general form of (2) have been worked out by Bethe, Block, and others. The form of target matter (gas, liquid, or solid) does not enter explicitly in (2).

Associated or Post-Ionization Events. Subsequent to the primary and secondary molecular ionizations and excitations, a number of events can occur that depend rather strongly on the form of the target material, including

(1) dissociation of molecules and formation of free radicals (species with unpaired electrons, hence great chemical reactivity; e.g., in water, H, OH, HO_2);

(2) recombination of ions and radicals, leading to no net change;

(3) dispersion of energetic ions and radicals, and reaction with other species present or with each other;

(4) nondiffusion migration of electronic excitation to energy "sinks," e.g., in macromolecules or crystals; and

(5) eventual degradation of the excess absorbed energy to heat (insignificant from the standpoint of effects).

For many systems the basic interactions must be considered only the initiators of a complex sequence of later events. In a living organism, the ultimate manifestations are such diverse phenomena as mutation, sterilization, or death.

As electron speeds are increased (energies above 1 Mev) another mechanism of energy loss becomes significant: bremsstrahlung (*q.v.*). The expression equivalent to (2) for this type of process has the form:

$$(dE/dx)_{rad} \propto NZ^2E$$

Electromagnetic Radiation (X, Gamma). If one were to extend the idea of the above relation between LET and particle charge and velocity, one might expect photons with no charge (and with the velocity of light) to ionize much less densely than charged particles. This is indeed the case, though for different reasons, since nuclear interaction now becomes important. Three mechanisms are to be noted:

(1) Photoelectric effect. Low-energy photons can give up all their energy to a bound electron, forming an ion pair and disappearing in the process. (Generally unimportant above 1 Mev.)

(2) Compton scattering. For medium-energy photons (0.5–5 Mev) this elastic collision process predominates, leading to ejection of a recoil electron plus the partially degraded (longer wavelength) photon.

(3) Pair production. Photons of highest energy most often interact by forming an electron-positron pair in the field of a nucleus, and disappearing in the process. The absolute energy threshold for this process is the rest mass energy of the pair: 1.02 Mev.

Mechanisms (1) and (3) increase in importance with higher powers of absorber Z. The net result of all three processes is the formation of (charged) ion pairs and in particular of electrons having energies ranging up to the photon energy but on the average only a fraction of this maximum. The discussion on charged particles thus applies to X- or gamma-ray action also.

Neutrons. Because of their lack of charge, neutrons do not interact electrostatically either with orbital electrons or with nuclei. They do interact with nuclei, however, in various other ways.

Fast neutrons (up to a few Mev), lose energy primarily by elastic collisions with other nuclei. From considerations of momentum transfer, this process is most efficient for target nuclei of about the same mass (i.e., protons in hydrogenous materials), though other light nuclei are also effective. On the *average*, about half the initial neutron kinetic energy is transferred to the protons, so that fast-neutron bombardment looks (to a hydrogenous material) like bombardment with fast protons of half the neutron energy. In addition to such simple collision processes, fast neutrons also induce nuclear reactions in certain elements, leading to emission of particles or photons, with their previously described interaction.

After about 20 collisions, neutrons are no longer sufficiently energetic to eject recoil protons but have become "thermalized," i.e., they act (for a short time) like a gas in thermal equilibrium with its surroundings (energies of about $\frac{1}{40}$ ev).

When a neutron has become thermalized and wanders into a nucleus, it is quite often captured, momentarily yielding an excited isotope of the original nucleus. Nuclei usually lose their excitation by emission of particles or characteristic gamma rays. Thus, even an uncharged slow neutron gives rise to the release of ionizing radiation inside a material being irradiated. In living tissue slow neutrons commonly are captured by H^1 nuclei with emission of an energetic gamma ray, and by N^{14} nuclei with emission of an energetic proton.

Comparison of the Radiations. Diverse electromagnetic and particulate radiations thus have in common as their basic interaction (or closely following upon it) the production of molecular ionizations (and excitations, dissociations, free radicals) inside target matter. They differ in the *geometry* of these events (especially in LET), a difference that leads to wide variations in range or penetrating ability and thus in the subsequent reactions leading to the final expression of the radiation effect.

The slower, more highly charged, heavy particles (such as alphas) travel in straight-line tracks ionizing densely along the track and exhibiting discrete ranges characteristic of the particle energy. Lighter, less highly charged particles such as electrons have their tracks more easily deflected and therefore have less precisely specified ranges in matter (although they have a maximum range). With a lower ionization density, however, they travel much farther than heavy charged particles of the same energy. X- or gamma rays interact causing release of electrons in matter but at widely spaced intervals and in a random fashion; they have a still lower ionization density (LET) and much longer "range." (Since the resultant of all their absorption processes is a roughly exponential attenuation in matter, their "range" must be described in terms of a parameter such as "half thickness," the thickness of material that reduces incident intensity to 50 per cent.) X-ray interaction has been likened to a "shotgun" effect in contrast to the "rifle" effect from incident heavy charged particles. Neutrons, which only interact with nuclei, may have either high or low LET. Their penetration in matter is great though difficult to specify well except in terms of specific materials. For much of their path, *fast* neutrons also are attenuated roughly exponentially.

The approximate range r or half thickness $d/2$ is given in Table 3 for several 1 Mev radiations in water.

Finally, a variety of conventional particle and wave interactions (such as reflection, transmission, and refraction) are also experienced by the above radiations. Moreover, many other more or less ionizing radiations have been omitted from this discussion, including mesons, (*q.v.*), hyperons,

TABLE 3

$\alpha(r)$ (cm)	β^- (max r) (cm)	γ ($d/2$) (cm)	Neutrons ($d/2$) (cm)
0.0007	0.4	10	5–10

heavy cosmic particles, large fission and spallation products, and antiparticles (q.v.). Their relative interactions can be quite well predicted from their composition, charge, and velocity, and the above considerations.

HOWARD C. MEL

Damage to Materials

Radiation can consist of either charged or uncharged particles. Examples of charged particles are helium nuclei or alpha particles, high-energy electrons such as beta rays and positrons, mesons, and protons. Uncharged radiation particles might be high-energy photons or gamma rays, high- and low-energy neutrons, and neutrinos. Of these particles, the neutrons are the most significant in inflicting damage to electronic materials. Since the neutron is uncharged and is relatively heavy, it is able to penetrate deeply into solid materials and can collide with many atomic sites before losing energy. Neutrons are generally classified as slow or fast neutrons according to their particle energies.

The measure of neutron radiation is flux. This flux is analogous to magnetic or light flux and is the number of particles per unit volume n, multiplied by the average speed of the particle v, and expressed as units of nv. When considering the effect of neutron radiation on materials both the history of the radiation or integrated flux or dosage in units of nvt and the intensity of the radiation or dose rate in units of nv must be specified. Gamma radiation, which is also of interest in considering radiation dosage, is normally measured in roentgens.

The two effects produced by irradiation of electronic materials are (1) the transient effect from ionization of the material and (2) the permanent effect, caused by two closely related types of changes called transmutations and atomic displacements. A transmutation is a change in energy character of an atomic structure caused by interaction with a radiation particle. In semiconductors this mutation is manifested by the introduction of new energy levels in the forbidden gap, similar to an impurity atom substitution for an intrinsic atom in the crystal structure. Atomic displacement is the dislocation of an atom from a structure by collision with a radiation particle. After displacement defects occur, some of the atoms in interstitial sites may be returned by normal thermal processes to a lattice vacancy, and thus repair the defect or anneal. Many electronic materials experience annealing, especially at high temperatures.

Semiconductors. Semiconductors (q.v.), because of the regular crystal structure and the high degree of purity required in most devices, are the most vulnerable to degradation by irradiation. Germanium and silicon transistors and diodes, which depend on minority-carrier transport, are sensitive to transient damage by neutrons and protons and to some extent by electrons and gamma particles. Electrically, the most common effect is malfunction caused by spurious outputs resulting from the radiation-induced carrier injection. At about 30 ev of energy in the radiation particle permanent damage occurs. The new induced impurity levels, interstitial atoms, and vacant lattice sites cause a reduction in minority-carrier lifetime by providing recombination sites and a change in carrier concentrations due to trapping and impurity conduction. The electronic effect on transistors (q.v.) is a reduction in current amplification and an increase in collector-base reverse current. In diodes (q.v.), higher leakage current and a poorer forward conduction is noted. Germanium is more radiation resistant than silicon because the intrinsic carrier mobility is about twice as high in germanium, so that more degradation can occur before the device suffers electrically. Since minority carrier lifetime is most important in the base region of a transistor, those devices with extremely thin base construction are least affected electrically. In addition, fast neutron and gamma bombardment raise the temperature of a solid significantly so that a device may fail by over-dissipation rather than by radiation-inflicted damage itself.

Two types of present-day semiconductor devices are somewhat radiation resistant. The tunnel diode (*q.v.*), which employs the tunneling effect of majority carriers across an abrupt junction, is one such device. In these diodes the material is degenerate owing to the high impurity doping, about 10^{19} impurities per cubic centimeter, and there-

TABLE 4. RADIATION TOLERANCE OF ELECTRONIC COMPONENTS

Component Type	Device	Threshold Neutron Flux (n/cm²)	
		Integrated	Fast[1]
Semiconductor	Gallium Arsenide		
	Tunnel Diodes		5×10^{16}
	Germanium		
	Diodes	10^{13}	
	Transistors	10^{13}	
	Tunnel Diodes		10^{16}
	Silicon		
	Diodes	10^{12}	
	Transistors	10^{12}	
	Tunnel Diodes		10^{15}
	Silicon Carbide		
	Diodes	10^{15}	
Resistors[2]	Carbon		
	Composition	10^{18}	
	Film	10^{18}	
	Metal Film	10^{18}	10^{15}
	Wirewound	$10^{19\ 3}$	10^{18}
	Carbon Potentiometer	10^{15}	
Capacitors	Aluminum		
	Electrolytic	10^{15}	10^{12}
	Boron		
	Electrolytic	10^{13}	10^{10}
	Ceramic	10^{18}	10^{15}
	Glass	10^{18}	10^{15}
	Mica	10^{18}	10^{15}
	Mylar	10^{17}	10^{14}
Capacitors	Paper-oil	10^{15}	10^{12}
	Paper-solid	10^{16}	10^{13}
	Polystyrene	10^{17}	10^{14}
	Tantalum		
	Electrolytic	10^{15}	10^{12}
Vacuum Tubes[4]	Ceramic		10^{19}
	Gas Tubes[5]		1.5×10^{13}
	Miniature		
	Receiving	10^{18}	5×10^{15}
	Photomultiplier[5]		10^{12}
	Power Tubes		10^{18}
	Subminiature		
	Receiving	10^{18}	5×10^{15}

Table 4—*Concluded*

Component Type	Device	Threshold Neutron Flux (n/cm²)	
		Integrated	Fast[1]
Insulators[6]	Anodized		
	Aluminum	10^{17}	
	Formex	10^{16}	
	Mycalex	10^{17}	
	Mylar	10^{16}	
	Nylon	10^{14}	
	Phenolic (Bakelite)	10^{13}	
	Polyester	10^{16}	
	Polyethylene	10^{16}	
	Polyvinyl Chloride	10^{16}	
	Silicone Resin	10^{17}	
	Silicone Rubber (phenyl)	10^{16}	
	Teflon	10^{12}	
Magnetics	Inductors		
	Ferrite		10^{17}
	Metallic Tape		10^{15}
	Storage Cores		
	Ferrite		10^{16}
	Metallic Tape		10^{14}
	Transformers		
	Ferrite	10^{20}	10^{17}
	Nickel-iron		10^{15}
	Silicon-iron		10^{17}
Crystals and Ferroelectrics			
	Barium Titanate	10^{13}	
	Quartz	10^{16}	
	Rochelle Salt	10^{12}	
	Triglycine Sulfate	10^{13}	
Miscellaneous	Batteries	5×10^{13}	

[1] Fast neutron flux tolerance is typically 10^3 less than integrated in this table. Both will be listed if measured.

[2] Fast flux tolerance depends strongly on circuit dissipation and resistor wattage.

[3] Highest experimental flux value reported.

[4] Boron-free glass envelopes and thoriated type cathodes used where applicable.

[5] Transient ionization not considered here as component failure.

[6] The resistance may decrease drastically during transient ionization. Silicone varnish or polyester coating helps to prevent this occurrence.

fore displacement damage is not very significant even at very high neutron intensities. In addition, since the minority carrier is not employed in the tunneling action of the device, the transmutations are not significant. The diode thermal-response portions of the device are affected and another current of unknown character called excess current is also affected by radiation. The increasing value of excess current eventually causes tunnel-diode failure.

Another type of semiconductor device which is resistant to radiation damage is the field-effect device. Since this device operates on majority carrier voltage pinch, the radiation damage, which strongly affects minority carriers, is not pertinent.

Inorganic Materials. In general, inorganic materials are more radiation resistant than organic materials with the exception of semiconductors. Most inorganic material damage is due to displacements caused by fast neutrons. Glass-to-metal seals used in electron-tube manufacture (q.v.) are vulnerable to radiation damage. Relay contacts, switches, and connectors employing gold or silver are more susceptible to radiation damage (owing to the large neutron-capture cross section of these materials) than those using aluminum, tin-plated steel, or copper alloys. In most cases inorganic-material damage is not a handicap since organic material damage usually occurs at lower radiation levels.

Organic Materials. Gamma radiation is in many cases more damaging than neutron radiation in organics. The radiation causes changes in various properties of the materials owing to displacements, destruction of a molecular bond, radical formation, polymerization, liberation of gas, and other chemical changes, especially if an active atmosphere is present. Natural rubber, for example, cracks and decomposes under ozone. In dielectric oils, two things occur. First, hydrogen and possibly methane gas are liberated, as well as many other gases in smaller amounts. Second, polymerization occurs resulting in the formation of a gel with the corresponding increase in viscosity which may cause failure in the particular device (e.g., in a time-delay relay). Silicone oils (phenyl type) are more radiation resistant since corrosive gases are not liberated. The aromatic hydrocarbon oils such as polyphenyl ethers can withstand up to 10^{15} neutrons/cm^2 before serious damage is incurred. Teflon, nylon, and commercial silicone rubbers are damaged at about the same radiation level as semiconductors, but high phenyl silicone rubbers are much more resistant to damage.

Radiation Table. Table 4 lists typical electronic components and approximate neutron radiation levels at which degradation becomes serious.

LLOYD M. LAMBERT

Measurements, Dosimetry, Hazards

Measurements. All radiation detectors utilize, in some way, the phenomenon of ionization, which is the formation of positive and negative charges when an atom is struck by an incoming charged particle or photon. Radiation detectors may be classified according to the method utilized in detecting this ionization. These categories are:

(a) The Geiger counter, proportional counter, and ionization chambers (q.v.);

(b) the cloud chamber and bubble chamber;

(c) photographic emulsion; and

(d) the scintillation counter (q.v.) and Cerenkov counter.

Detectors in category (a) are seldom used in high-energy physics research, but find their widest application in industry, in radiological monitoring, and in low-energy research. The cloud chamber and photographic emulsion are frequently used in cosmic ray research. The bubble chamber, the scintillation counter, and the Cerenkov counter, as well as the photographic emulsion, are the principal detectors employed in present-day high-energy physics.

The detectors in category (a) are usually referred to collectively as "ionization instruments," although it must be borne in mind that all radiation detectors utilize ionization in some manner. The reason for this designation is that the detectors in this category produce an electrical signal as a direct consequence of the production of ionization, whereas in the other types of detectors the ionization serves to initiate or trigger a release of energy or brings about a transformation of energy by some other mechanism. This secondary release of energy is then recorded.

An ionization instrument is basically an enclosed vessel containing a gas. The walls of the vessel are metalized and form the outer electrode. A central electrode is connected to an amplifier and counting circuit. When a charged particle enters the vessel through one of its walls the gas inside is ionized, producing electrons and positive ions. The electrons quickly travel toward the central electrode, while the positive ions migrate slowly to the outer electrode. By using an electronic detecting circuit with a short time constant, one can record the pulse due to the electrons and then ignore the ion pulse. Although the "ionization instruments" are basically the same, each instrument mentioned in (a) operates at a different applied voltage on the central electrode—the applied voltage of the Geiger counter being the greatest and the applied voltage of the ionization chamber being the smallest.

The scintillation counter, on the other hand, consists of a transparent material, called a scintillator, that emits a flash of light when it is struck by a charged particle, viewed by a photomultiplier tube which gives an electrical pulse when the flash of light strikes it. In choosing a scintillator, several factors must be considered. They are:

(a) its speed;

(b) its light yield;

(c) its sensitivity to various types of radiation;

(d) the linearity of its response to different types of radiation;

(e) its density—number of nuclear events occurring in its volume; and

(f) its ease of manufacture.

Finally, considering the cloud chamber and bubble chamber, it is to be noted that both of these instruments are track imaging devices. In the former case, an incoming particle produces a track of droplets in a supersaturated gas, whereas in the latter case the track consists of tiny bubbles in a superheated liquid.

The above-mentioned instruments measure most of the biologically important radiation coming from radioactive isotopes, i.e., alpha, beta, and gamma rays. Neutrons are also of great biological importance; however,

owing to their lack of an electric charge they require specialized measuring techniques.

Dosimetry. Radiation as it applies to biological problems is measured in the following units:

(a) Curies

(b) Roentgens

(c) Roentgen Equivalent Physical

(d) Rad

(e) Roentgen Equivalent Man

The roentgen is especially convenient for measuring X- or gamma rays. Since it applies to air, it is not necessarily directly applicable to tissue nor is it applicable to types of radiation other than X- or gamma rays. In order to produce a unit that is useful in tissue, the roentgen equivalent physical (rep) has been defined on the basis of energy absorption by a gram of tissue. For example, if a beam of X- or gamma rays producing one roentgen in air, at a certain distance from the source, is allowed to fall on 1 g or 1 cm³ of tissue, at the same distance from the source, then approximately 90 ergs are released in this gram of tissue. The rad rounds off 90 ergs per gram to 100 ergs/g.

In order to take into account that other types of radiation are capable of releasing 100 ergs/g of tissue, and are also capable of producing entirely different biological effects, the roentgen equivalent man (rem) has been introduced. This is the amount of radiation, of an unspecified type, which produces the same biological effect as one roentgen of X- or gamma rays.

Low-level radiation dose rates are often expressed in terms of the unit "millirem per year." It is to be noted that when dealing with tolerance dose rates two values are always listed—the nonoccupational tolerance of 500 mrem per year, and the value 5,000 mrem per year, based on the criterion that a person receiving this dose beginning at the age of 18 and extending through his working life will suffer no observable effect.

Hazards. It is to be remembered that the dose rate plays quite an important part with reference to biological effects, as can be seen from Table 5.

TABLE 5

(a) *Effect vs Dose for Fullbody Radiation Received in a Few Days*

1 rem	No detectable change
10 rem	Blood changes are detectable
100 rem	Some injury—no disability
200 rem	Injury and some disability
300 rem	Injury and disability
450 rem	50% deaths in 30 days
600 rem	100% deaths in 30 days
10,000 rem	50% deaths in four days
1,000,000 rem	Quick death (less than one day)

(b) *Effect vs Various Dose Rates of 250-kv X-Rays*

r/day	Time	Result
500	2 days	100% deaths
100	—	average 15 days survival
10	1 year	some deaths
½	several years	drop in life span

At low dose rates, where no obvious injury is produced in a short time, the important effects thought to be caused by radiation are leukemia, cancer, cataracts, and genetic changes. These long-term effects plus others lead to an over-all reduction in life expectancy. Actually radiation injury, if it does not produce a specific disease, can be thought of as an accelerated aging process. Biological systems especially sensitive to radiation are the lymphatic glands, the small intestines, the bone marrow, the lenses of the eyes, the gonads, and unborn children.

ROGER WALLACE

Processing of Materials

Ionizing radiation can be used for preservation processes (see below) and for production of materials. In the production processes the ions and free radicals produced by absorption of radiant energy are used to promote chemical reaction. Synthesis reactions, polymerizations of various kinds, and vulcanization are among the effects that can be promoted by radiation. (Throughout this article we shall refer to ionizing radiation defined above simply as radiation. When other forms of radiant energy are mentioned, they will be explicitly identified.) The potential advantages of radiation processing over conventional techniques lie principally in the following areas: (a) Formation of ions under all temperature conditions. Ion formation is ordinarily possible only at extremely high temperatures. (b) Controlled formation of ions and radicals at selected temperatures. (c) Promotion of reaction using free radical mechanisms without introduction of extraneous materials as free radical former or "catalyst." (d) Promotion of reaction in solids with control of the reaction zone.

Reaction efficiency is measured in "G values." G is defined as molecules of product per 100 ev of energy absorbed in a reacting mixture. For most simple reactions G values range from 1 to 3. For acceptance in industrial processing, the radiation must produce large G values or a great increase in some desirable property.

Primary Uses. Synthesis reactions have been demonstrated. For example, the formation of benzenehexachloride from benzene and chlorine proceeds as well under the "catalytic effect" of radiation as under the influence of ultraviolet light. Reported G values for this system approach 100,000 under the most favorable conditions. Other syntheses reported include the oxidation of benzene to phenol, the formation of ethylene glycol from methanol, the formation of hydrazine from ammonia, and the fixation of nitrogen as nitrogen dioxide or nitric acid. Of these synthesis reactions using radiation, none has been utilized for commercial production to date.

Polymerization of monomers, cross linking of polymers, and graft and block polymerization are all promoted by radiation. The major commercial processes utilizing radiation depend upon the cross linking of polyethylene. The principal results of the cross linking are (a) raising of the softening temperature and (b) a change in tensile strength and elastic properties. Heat sterilizable bottles and other objects, improved insulating coating for wire (*q.v.*), and freeze bags for poultry are all produced in commercial quantities by subjecting ordinary polyethylene to radiation. These cross linking reactions, along with the sterilization of sutures and the treatment of raw wool to destroy anthrax bacteria, make up the bulk of the application of radiation processes in current commercial use.

Graft and block polymerization studies are still in the research stage. In these polymerizations, various techniques are used to produce radical reactions at the surface of a polymer so that a different polymer is formed from monomers on the surface of the original polymer. One related research area is the treatment of wood with combinations of chemicals and radiation to produce greater strength, water repellancy, rot resistance, and other desirable properties.

Biological Systems. Special processing of biological systems has been accomplished using radiation. Through irradiation of the screw worm fly, the males have been made sterile, and thus the capacity to reproduce greatly diminished. By careful spreading of the sterile males throughout the Southern U. S. A., the damage caused by this pest has almost been eliminated. Genetic mutations have been caused in plant organisms; research is evaluating the improvements in crop yield, disease resistance, and other factors among the plants favorably affected by radiation.

Radiation Sources. Many processes that can be initiated with radiation can also be initiated by simple chemical catalysts, light, or heat. The relatively high cost of radiation today restricts its use. The use of radiation is limited to those cases where the ordinary initiators are difficult to apply. Sources of radiation now used in the processing of materials include particle accelerators (*q.v.*; electron or X-ray beams from machines of the resonant transformer and linear accelerator types are in greatest use) and reactor-produced isotopes (Cobalt 60). In addition, future processing may be done with separated fission product isotopes (Cesium 137), spent reactor fuel elements, other reactor-produced isotopes, and the nuclear fission process. In the last case, the reacting materials must be introduced into a nuclear reactor and brought into intimate contact with the fissioning uranium or plutonium fuel, which must be in such form that a sizable fraction of the recoil path of the particle formed in fission is in the reacting substance and not in the fuel. If this is true a large fraction of the fission energy can be used in ion and radical formation, thus promoting chemical reactions as well as producing heat.

Sterilization of Food

Ionizing radiation can be used in place of other types of energy to pasteurize or sterilize foods. By interacting in complex ways with the large organic molecules and the aqueous mediums of microorganisms, radiation destroys them directly by ionization and indirectly by creating free radicals which give rise to destructive reactions.

The preservation of food by high-energy radiation has been under investigation in the United States and in many foreign countries for several years. In the United States, the U. S. Interdepartmental Committee on the Radiation Preservation of Foods has coordinating functions over all government activities in food irradiation. The major research in food irradiation has been conducted by the U. S. Army Quartermaster Corps. This organization has concentrated on the problems of producing sterilized food packages suitable for consumption by military personnel and capable of long storage without refrigeration. The U. S. Atomic Energy Commission has recently embarked on studies of irradiation preservation of foods designed to prolong shelf life or to reduce refrigeration requirements of the more perishable items such as fish and fruits. Commercial organizations have also contributed research to the program. Despite the progress made to date, much research remains before a complete food irradiation system acceptable to the U. S. Food and Drug Administration and the consumer is developed.

Radiation Dose. Various types of organism are important in food technology, and various radiation doses* are needed for protection of the foodstuffs treated. The required dose has not been exactly determined for all foods. The sprouting of tuberous plants can be inhibited by doses of 10–20,000 rad. Insects and parasites which infest grain can be inhibited in growth or completely destroyed by doses of 25–50,000 rad. Pasteurization of foods in which the more sensitive spoilage organisms are destroyed and others greatly depleted in number requires 100,000 to 500,000 rad. Complete destruction of the spores of resistant microorganisms, for example, Cl botulinum, requires doses of 2–5,000,000 rad. Enzymes are inactivated only at very high doses (10,000,000 rad).†

Deleterious Radiation Effects. Combined with the beneficial actions of ionizing radiation which can preserve meats, fish, and other agricultural products, are some deleterious effects of the radiation. Chemical changes are produced in the materials treated, and these changes are revealed through changes in the appearance and texture of the products and through odor and flavor changes. Some materials, such as powdered milk, are very sensitive to radiation treatment, noticeably deteriorating in flavor with small doses. Others, such as shrimp and chicken, are very little affected even at high doses (2–5,000,000 rad). The food processor using radiation is faced with the problem of achieving the proper degree of preservation before the odor and flavor changes make the product unacceptable. Possible changes in nutritional content and the possibility of the formation of harmful chemicals are currently being evaluated through research sutdies which include extensive animal feeding programs. No proof of toxic effects due to irradiation has been found in the experimentation so far published.

Radiation Sources. Many sources of ionizing radiation can be used to preserve foods; the considerations that apply are similar to those discussed under Processing of Materials above.

Beta-ray sources have been proposed for surface sterilization applications. However, to use these sources requires solution of many difficult technical problems in radiation source design and product manipulation.

E. M. KINDERMAN

Cross-references: *Accelerators, Alpha Particles, Antiparticles, Bremsstrahlung, Cerenkov Radiation, Cosmic Rays, Gamma Rays, Infrared, Mesons, Neutrinos, Positrons, Radioactivity, X-rays*

RADIATION PROCESSING: see **RADIATION (IONIZING)**

RADIATION (TERRESTRIAL)

Terrestrial radiations may be classified into two major categories, (1) those which occur in nature, and (2) those which are man-made. Radiated noise, whether it originates in nature or is man-made, continues to be one of the basic limitations to satisfactory radio reception. The intelligent establishment and effective utilization of present-day radio systems requires a thorough understanding of radio noise and its characteristics.

Natural noise may be divided into atmospheric, solar, galactic, precipitation, and thermal. The characteristics of each determine the portions of the radio spectrum where they become limiting factors. Below 15 Mc and particularly in the LF and VLF ranges atmospheric noise radiated by lightning discharges is usually the most predominant. The radiation produced by such discharges possesses specific characteristics that have been measured and can be used to predict the expected noise levels for practically any given frequency, time, and geographical location.

---

* Radiation dose is expressed here in terms of energy absorbed in the foodstuffs treated. The common unit of dose, the rad, represents the absorption of 100 ergs/g of material.

† Combinations of blanching (for enzyme inactivation) and radiation sterilization have been proposed.

In order to establish a quantitative basis for the evaluation and use of noise data the short-time variations of instantaneous noise power are averaged over a period of several minutes. This average power level is relatively constant during a given hour, except during sunrise and sunset. The hourly levels vary with time of day and tend to follow particular diurnal and seasonal patterns. Changing propagation conditions result in varying noise levels. The nighttime noise at the lower frequencies is high owing to noise from distant storms being propagated via the ionosphere. Ionospheric absorption is high during the daytime with a resulting reduction in noise from distant sources. The noise that is received is primarily from local storms. Local storms tend to occur during the afternoon hours and the resulting diurnal variation usually has the following pattern: low noise during the morning, a moderate increase in the afternoon, and the maximum level at night. The seasonal variation at tropical and temperate latitudes causes the noise to be highest in summer and lowest in winter.

The radiated fields of lightning discharges exhibit considerable variation in their waveforms. However, the waveforms are sufficiently similar in form and amplitude variations to permit the use of statistical analysis to obtain quantitative data. While individual sferics have individual waveforms the majority are found to fit into the following general classifications that aid in their identification, comparison, and study:

(1) *Reflection.* Contains a series of five or more pulses spaced in time by intervals which support the theory of successive reflections from an ionosphere of constant height.

(2) *Peaky Short.* Contains five or fewer pulses which decrease rapidly in magnitude.

(3) *Smooth Short.* Contains five or fewer smooth oscillations of rapidly decreasing amplitude, which nevertheless join to give a continuous variation in electric field.

(4) *Quasi-Sinusoidal.* Contains six or more smooth oscillations with several of comparable amplitude.

The mechanism by which a lightning discharge takes place is very complex. In the pre-discharge period which is approximately 1 msec in duration there are short pilot and leader strokes which radiate energy from 10 to 40 kc. The leader stroke is followed by the main or return stroke which results in the flow of a current of around 20,000 amp. The main stroke is composed of lower frequency components that are radiated in 100 to 200 μsec. The frequency spectrum of the radiation component is triangular in shape with a broad peak near 5 kc. Below 5 kc the radiated energy decreases with decreasing frequency and above it drops off at a rate approximating $1/f$.

The combination of VLF propagation characteristics, which possess a pronounced absorption band centered around 4 kc, and the spectrum of lightning discharges results in the received noise energy having a broad maximum around 10 kc. As the distance between the source and receiver increases the noise energy between 15 and 20 kc is enhanced. As the frequency increases the magnitude of the received noise becomes more dependent upon propagation via the ionosphere and possesses the same diurnal and seasonal variations as other signals that propagate in the same way. Around 15 Mc the atmospheric noise drops to a level comparable to galactic noise for regions in the lower and middle latitudes. In the higher latitudes, where very low critical frequencies are encountered, galactic noise may be the principal source of noise at frequencies as low as 1 Mc. Above 30 Mc thermal and man-made noise predominate.

Precipitation noise or static at ground receiving stations is caused by induced discharges usually produced during storms when dust, snow, rain, or ice crystals are blown against the receiving antennas or nearby structures. This same phenomenon requires special treatment of the antennas used with the radio receiving equipment in fast-moving aircraft.

High-voltage power transmission lines, electric motors, industrial machinery, diathermy machines, and ignition systems are typical sources of man-made noise. The characteristics of the different sources vary depending upon their origin. Propagation is generally by conduction via power lines or by ground-wave propagation from the source and hence is relatively unaffected by diurnal or seasonal variations.

EARL G. GODDARD

Whistlers

A whistler, or whistling atmospheric, is a naturally occurring transient electromagnetic disturbance lasting about 1 sec and appearing predominantly in the VLF range of 0.3 to 30 kc. It is caused by dispersion of a lightning-produced impulse which enters the ionosphere and travels into the opposite hemisphere along a line of force of the earth's magnetic field. Such line-of-force paths may extend to heights as great as five earth radii from the center of the earth.

For most whistlers the high frequencies travel faster than the low, so that at the receiver the frequency falls with time. For some whistlers, particularly those observed at high latitudes, the curve of frequency vs. time exhibits a minimum value at the so-called "nose" frequency. Above this frequency time delay *increases* with frequency. Detection of this behavior generally requires a suitable spectrum analyzer.

The time delay between the initiating lightning impulse and the resulting whistler is typically of the order of 1 sec, and it generally increases markedly with geomagnetic latitude. A quantity called "dispersion" is often used to describe the time delay and is given by $D = t\sqrt{f}$ sec$^{\frac{1}{2}}$ where t is the time delay at frequency f. At frequencies low compared with the minimum value of electron gyro-frequency along the path, D tends to be independent of frequency.

A whistler which has traveled once over its dispersive path is called a "short" or "one-hop" whistler and its source is usually located in the hemisphere opposite to that of the observer. A whistler traveling twice over its dispersive path is called a "long" or "two-hop" whistler, and its lightning source is generally in the observer's hemisphere. Echoes of a one-hop whistler have time delays in the ratios 1:3:5:7, etc; of a two-hop whistler, 2:4:6:8, etc. Many whistlers exhibit several components which appear to have been excited simultaneously by a single lightning impulse. These "multipath" whistlers are thought to arise from the trapping of energy in ducts of enhanced ionization aligned with field line paths of different lengths.

Whistlers are heard more often at night than during the day, probably because of the higher D-region absorption in daytime. Whistlers occur most frequently at middle latitudes. They are practically never heard on the geomagnetic equator where the earth's field is horizontal, or from very high geomagnetic latitudes where the field lines extend to very great distances.

Whistlers can be observed with very simple equipment consisting of a loop or long-wire antenna, audio amplifier, and loudspeaker. No detector is needed. Whistler-mode signals excited by VLF transmitters radiating 50 kw or more are readily detectable.

Certain properties of the ionosphere can be deduced from whistler data. From the frequency-time curves of whistlers it is possible to determine separately the location of the path of propagation and one or two parameters describing the electron density along the path of propagation. Analysis of whistler data indicates that electron density in the outer ionosphere is roughly proportional to magnetic field strength and at five earth radii has a value of the order of 100 per cm^3.

Related to whistlers is another class of natural transient phenomena known as VLF emissions, including such types as dawn chorus, hiss, quasi-constant tones, and various discrete events. These noises are most prevalent in the auroral regions and show a strong association with magnetic disturbance. Certain types have been found to correlate in occurrence with visual aurorae. VLF emissions occasionally appear to have been "triggered" by strong whistlers; such events are called "interactions."

VLF emissions are thought to be generated within the ionosphere and to travel in the whistler mode. Various theories of generation have been advanced, based on such mechanisms as Cerenkov radiation (*q.v.*), traveling-wave interaction, and gyro-frequency radiation.

R. A. HELLIWELL

Cross-references: *Extraterrestrial Radio Sources, Propagation, Radar Astronomy, Radiometeorology*

RADIATION HAZARDS (NONIONIZING RADIATION)

Most of the experimental work to date supports the belief that the chief effect of radio frequency energy on living tissue is to produce heating. Consequently, exposure to rf radiation should probably present no hazard unless overheating is a possibility. Within carefully prescribed limits, the heating effect of radio waves may actually be beneficial; in fact, this is the basis of diathermy, which has long been employed therapeutically. The use of diathermy is so widespread and so well accepted a part of medical procedure that the FCC has assigned seven frequencies for the operation of medical diathermy equipment.

Heating is a function of the strength of the rf power density, that is, the average power flow per unit area (usually expressed in milliwatts per square centimeter). It is also a function of time. The heating may take place near the surface or deep within the body, the depth of penetration being related to frequency. Frequencies in the region 200 to 900 Mc penetrate deeply, whereas S-band (1500–5200 Mc) and X-band (5200–11,000 Mc) frequencies used by radars produce heating at or near the surface.

Heating effects, depending on frequency, are (1) a general rise in body temperature, similar to fever, or (2) something more localized, akin to the cooking process in a radar oven, where a steak can be cooked from the inside out. The human body can compensate for a certain amount of heating of the first type through perspiration, if the temperature rise is not too sudden. Consequently, the hazard may be somewhat less in cool weather than on an extremely hot day when the body's cooling mechanism is already working at full capacity. Compensating mechanisms for coping with the second type of heating are less adequate.

Circulating blood acts as a coolant, so that localized heating is least serious in parts (such as muscle tissue) that are well equipped with blood vessels. Heating is more of a danger to the brain, the testes, and the hollow viscera. The most widespread publicity has related to the effect of microwave radiation on the eyes. The viscous material within the eyeball is affected by heat as is also the white of an egg, which is transparent at room temperature but becomes opaque white when warmed slightly. In the eyes as in the egg white the process is irreversible.

As the surface of the human body is more generously supplied with sensory nerves than the interior, a feeling of warmth may give a warning in case of over-exposure to frequencies that produce surface heating. If the frequencies are such as to cause a general rise in body temperature, the resulting sensation of discomfort may or may not be perceived in time to provide adequate warning. In the case of localized microwave heating deep within the body, it is still less likely that any warning sensations would be noted before damage was done.

Power densities required to maintain "tolerable" temperatures in different portions of the body under normal conditions have been estimated by several investigators. Typically, T. S. Ely and his colleagues at the Naval Medical Research Institute in 1957 concluded that the "tolerable" temperatures could be maintained by the absorption of 100 mw/cm² for the whole body, 155 mw/cm² for the eye, and 5 mw/cm² for the testes. H. P. Schwann and Kam Li of the University of Pennsylvania have studied the absorption and reflection coefficients of tissue and present well-founded arguments in support of tolerance values for total body irradiation near 10 mw/cm².

On the basis of these and other well-documented reports, there appears to be general agreement in industry and the Armed Forces on 10 mw/cm² average power density as an upper limit for safe whole-body exposure of humans to rf radiation.

More detailed technical aspects of the problems associated with microwave radiation hazards may be found in a recent survey article (*Proc. IRE*, February 1961).

W. W. MUMFORD

Cross-references: *Cooking (Electronic), Electric Shock, Heating (Electronic), Medical Electronics, Radiation (Ionizing)*

RADIATION MEASUREMENTS (NONIONIZING RADIATION)

The subject of electromagnetic radiation measurements may be conveniently divided into two parts: field-strength measurements and microwave radiometer measurements. Field-strength measurements are generally made for the purpose of determining the fields (in volts per unit length) generated by transmitting equipment; microwave radiometers measure the blackbody or other radiation emitted by passive objects, such as celestial bodies, and are usually calibrated in terms of temperature, a function of the power emitted.

(The term "nonionizing radiation" is used in this volume to refer to radio waves, as distinct from α, β, γ, radiation and the like. It is, of course, recognized that radio waves can actually produce ionization, e.g., of gases.)

Field-Strength Measurements

Field-strength measurements (for a general reference see Terman and Pettit, *Electronic Measurements*, McGraw-Hill, New York, 1952; 2d ed.) may employ a standard or calibrated antenna, in which the induced voltage V delivered by the antenna is a known function of the field strength E. The induced voltage may be measured in a number of ways; the field strength can then be calculated directly. A second method of measuring field strength involves the use of a standard field generator which generates a field of known strength. This field strength is then compared with the field strength of the radio wave being measured. When very strong fields are being measured, standard antennas with vacuum-tube voltmeters, or bolometers (*q.v.*), may be used.

Standard Antenna Method Using Receiver with Calibrated Intermediate Frequency Attenuator. This method of measuring the field strength with a standard antenna involves the use of a superheterodyne receiver connected to the standard antenna, and a means for introducing a calibrating signal from a signal-frequency oscillator into the antenna circuit (generally by means of a small coupling coil in series with the antenna). The IF amplifier of the receiver is provided with a calibrated attenuator, and a microammeter following the second detector. The signal is tuned in for maximum response, and the attenuator is adjusted to a value α_1 such that a convenient deflection on the microammeter is obtained. The signal-frequency oscillator is turned on at the frequency of the incoming signal and is adjusted to a known voltage V_0 (commonly 1 v) at the input to the receiver, as determined by an auxiliary vacuum-tube voltmeter. The IF attenuator is readjusted to a new value α_2, to obtain the original reading on the microammeter. The incoming signal voltage *at the receiver input* is then $(\alpha_2 - \alpha_1)$ db less than V_0, and is gretaer than the actual voltage induced in the antenna by a gain factor representing the resonance effects in the antenna circuit. In order to determine this gain factor, a switch is provided for connecting the signal-frequency oscillator directly to the input of the receiver. A third reading is taken under these conditions and the attenuator is readjusted to a value α_3, to obtain again the same reading on the microammeter. The gain

TABLE I. RELATION BETWEEN FIELD STRENGTH AND POWER OR INDUCED VOLTAGE, FOR
VARIOUS TYPES OF STANDARD ANTENNAS*

Type of Antenna	Relationship		Remarks
Loop	$V = 2\pi EN \dfrac{A}{\lambda}$	(1)	$L < \dfrac{\lambda}{12}:\quad f < \dfrac{f_0}{3}$ Wave plane-polarized in plane of loop; loop oriented for maximum response
Half-wave dipole	$V = \lambda E/\pi$	(2)	
Doublet antenna	$V = EL/2$	(3)	$f < \dfrac{f_0}{3}$
Vertical grounded antenna	$V = EL/2$	(4)	$L \ll \lambda/4$
Vertical grounded antenna	$V = EL/4$	(5)	$L = \lambda/4$
Horn or parabola	$E = \sqrt{\dfrac{480\pi^2 P_r}{\lambda^2 G}}$	(6)	$Z_a = Z_L$; $R_c \ll R_R$

* *Definition of Notation.*

A = Area of loop
E = Field strength, volts per unit length
f = Frequency of operation
f_0 = Self-resonant frequency of antenna
G = Antenna gain relative to an isotropic radiator
L = Length of doublet or vertical grounded antenna: or largest dimension of loop
N = Number of turns in loop

P_r = Load power, watts
R_c = Conduction or loss resistance of antenna
R_R = Radiation resistance of antenna
V = Induced voltage, volts
Z_a = Internal impedance of antenna
Z_L = Load impedance
λ = Wavelength, m

factor is $(\alpha_2 - \alpha_3)$ db. The voltage actually induced in the antenna by the field being measured is then $(2\alpha_2 - \alpha_1 - \alpha_3)$ db below V_0.

Standard Antenna Method Using Substitution of Voltage. Field strength may also be measured with a standard antenna by connecting a sensitive radio receiver to the standard antenna and tuning the receiver to the signal with the loop oriented for maximum reception. The receiver gain is adjusted to give a convenient deflection on a microammeter connected at the output of the second detector. The loop is then oriented for minimum signal. A known voltage from a signal generator, at the signal frequency, is introduced in| series with the loop acrnss a resistance having a low value. The signal generator is adjusted until the microammeter indicates the same output as that produced by the incoming signal. The known voltage delivered by the signal generator is

then equal to the voltage induced in the antenna by the incoming signal.

Characteristics of Standard Antennas. When using the standard antenna method of field measurement, the relations shown in Table I exist between induced voltage or load power and field strength, for various types of antennas.

Standard-Field-Generator Method. A standard-field generator comprises a portable oscillator connected to a transmitting antenna of known characteristics. The output is calibrated in terms of current, or power radiated, so that the free-space field strength at any distance d can be calculated in accordance with the relationships shown in Table II for various types of antennas. The standard-field generator is generally used in conjunction with a receiver equipped with a receiving antenna, an IF attenuator, and a microammeter following the second detector.

The transmitting antenna is oriented so

TABLE II. RELATION BETWEEN FIELD STRENGTH AND ANTENNA CURRENT OR RADIATED POWER FOR VARIOUS TYPES OF STANDARD FIELD GENERATOR ANTENNAS*

Type of Antenna	Relationship		Remarks
Loop	$E = \dfrac{120\pi^2}{d}\, N\, \dfrac{A}{\lambda^2}\, I_a$	(7)	
Short vertical antenna	$E = \dfrac{60\pi}{d}\, \dfrac{h}{\lambda}\, I_a$	(8)	Top loaded to give uniform current: $h < \dfrac{\lambda}{10}$
Half-wave dipole	$E = \dfrac{60 I_a}{d} = \dfrac{7.02}{d}\, \sqrt{P_a}$	(9)	
Directional antenna	$E = \dfrac{5.48}{d}\, \sqrt{P_a G}$	(10)	

* *Definition of Notation.*
Same as Table I, with the following additions:
 d = distance, m
 I_a = standard field generator antenna current, amperes
 h = height of antenna, m
 P_a = power radiated by standard field generator antenna, watts

that the direction of arrival of the test and standard waves is the same at the receiving antenna. The IF attenuator is adjusted successively for a convenient identical microammeter reading while receiving the test and standard signals, respectively. The field strength of the test signal is then below the known field strength produced by the standard signal generator by an amount equal to the difference in db between the two readings of the attenuator.

The presence of ground affects the field existing at the receiving antenna, which may vary from 0 to twice the free-space value shown in Table II, owing to interference effects. Corrections must be made for this effect.

Microwave Radiometers

A microwave radiometer (for a general reference see D. B. Harris, *Microwave J.* 3: April, May, June 1960) is, in effect, an extremely sensitive radio receiver. This receiver is provided with a highly directional antenna usually incorporating a paraboloidal reflector, and the technique of observation consists of directing the antenna at the object, or region of space under observation,

and reading the power picked up by the antenna (generally noise power) as indicated in circuits and equipment associated with the output circuit of the receiver. McCoy, Hepperle, Giberson, and Ringeon have developed the relationships existing between the temperature of the body under observation and the observed receiver input power (Research Rep. CRR 102, Collins Radio Co., 1949).

Under normal conditions the noise power received from a celestial body by a radiometer is considerably lower than the ambient noise of the radiometer receiver. Special circuitry is therefore required, as outlined under Instrumentation.

Blackbody Radiation. From Planck's radiation law it can be shown that the noise power received from a *gray* body is

$$P_R = \frac{1}{4\pi}\, akT\Delta f \int_\Omega G(\theta,\phi)\, d\Omega \qquad (11)$$

where

a = the absorptivity of the emitting body

k = Boltzmann's constant (1.38×10^{-23} joule/°K)

T = temperature of emitting body in °K

Δf = bandwidth of radiometer

$G(\theta,\phi)$ = power gain of radiometer antenna in the direction (θ,ϕ), with respect to an isotropic antenna

Ω = angle subtended by source at radiometer antenna

If the emitting body is a perfect blackbody, $a = 1$. It is noted that, in accordance with this theoretical relationship, P_R as a function of T is independent of frequency, unlike the ordinary radio-transmission case between two antennas, where P_R as a function of the transmitted power varies directly as the square of the wavelength. This theoretical result is modified in practice when observing celestial bodies, as the spectral index x, defined as a function of the power $P(f)$ emitted at frequency f by the equation

$$P(f) \propto f^{-x} \tag{12}$$

may actually vary from 0.5 to 1.5, in the case of nonthermal radiation.

In Eq. (11), the antenna gain can be evaluated for certain types of antennas. If the source completely encloses the antenna, the value of the integral is 4π and the total power received is

$$P_R = akT\Delta f \tag{13}$$

This relationship is also applicable to the case where the source is sufficiently large to fill the entire pattern of the antenna even without enclosing the antenna proper on all sides.

If the source is much smaller than the beam, the gain may be considered constant over the solid angle, the value of the integral is $G(\theta,\phi)\Omega$, and the power received is

$$P_R = akT\Delta f G(\theta,\phi)\Omega \tag{14}$$

where $G(\theta,\phi)$ is the peak gain of the antenna in the direction of the radiating source.

The beam width and the source are of comparable size in the case of solar and lunar observations. It can be shown that, under these conditions, when using a paraboloidal antenna of the "tapered feed" type, the value of the integral is $4\pi \times 0.533$ and the power received is

$$P_R = 0.533akT\Delta f \tag{15}$$

Instrumentation. Conventional superheterodyne receivers, provided with output meters calibrated in terms of the power received and therefore of temperature, are satisfactory for certain kinds of radiometrical observations, generally at low frequencies, and where the temperature of the source is high, as in the case of the sun. The level of blackbody radiation in the microwave region, is, however, generally below the noise level of the receiver, and in this case special instrumentation is required, such as the radiometer receiver developed by R. H. Dicke (*Rev. Sci. Instr.*, July 1946). In receivers of this type, the inherent receiver noise is cancelled out by comparing the noise power received from the antenna with the noise power received from a reference source, or "attenuator," operated at a known temperature. Generally these receivers switch from the antenna to the attenuator periodically, and, after integration over a sufficient period of time, the indicated output is closely equal to the difference between the "temperature" of the antenna and the temperature of the reference source. A typical Dicke radiometer receiver performs the switching operation by periodically inserting a reference attenuator into the antenna waveguide.

It can be shown that the output meter reading of a Dicke radiometer is proportional to temperature, and that the indicated temperature is

$$T_i = \Gamma aT - T_a \tag{16}$$

where

$$\Gamma = \frac{1}{4\pi} \int_\Omega G(\theta,\phi) \, d\Omega$$

a = the absorptivity of the emitting body
T = temperature of the emitting body
T_a = temperature of attenuator

from which we obtain, for the temperature of the body being observed,

$$T = \frac{T_i + T_a}{\Gamma a} \qquad (17)$$

This result applies in the absence of intervening absorptivity between source and antenna.

The "equivalent antenna temperature," defined as the temperature T_e that would be assumed by a resistance connected in place of the antenna in order to produce the observed reading, is

$$T_e = T_i + T_a \qquad (18)$$

Substitution of this relationship in (17) yields

$$T = \frac{T_e}{\Gamma a} \qquad (19)$$

The sensitivity of a radiometer, in terms of the minimum temperature differential which can be observed, is limited by the root-mean-square temperature fluctuations in the output meter, which can be shown to be given by

$$\Delta T = \xi T_a F \left(\frac{b}{\Delta f}\right)^{1/2} \qquad (20)$$

where

F = over-all receiver noise figure expressed as a power ratio

Δf = receiver IF bandwidth in cps

b = bandwidth of low-pass filter in cps

T_a = temperature of modulating wheel, assumed to be the standard reference temperature $T_0 = 290°K$ in this case

ΔT = rms temperature fluctuations of the output meter in degrees K

ξ = a constant

The constant ξ, as determined by various investigators, may vary from 0.69 to 5.65, depending upon the shape of the passbands and other factors.

Equation (20) shows that if the IF bandwidth is fixed at 8.0 mc, the rms temperature fluctuations of the output meter (and accordingly the sensitivity) will vary from approximately 0.083°K to approximately 0.83°K, over a range of low-pass filter bandwidths from 0.01 to 1.00 cps. This sensitivity can be improved by employing low-noise traveling-wave amplifiers, thereby reducing F and increasing Δf, to obtain a predicted sensitivity limited by statistical noise fluctuations of the order of 0.01°K. Further improvement can be attained by introducing an artificial noise source into the antenna circuit, and balancing this noise source against the noise received from the reference source in the absence of a signal. This scheme, which generally employs a fixed reference resistor and a ferrite switch in place of the rotating attenuator of the Dicke radiometer, reduces the effect of gain variations in the circuitry.

Observations made with the radiometer equipment described are too numerous to summarize in this article. A good reference on the subject is the Paris Symposium on *Radio Astronomy*, R. N. Bracewell, ed., Stanford University Press, 1959.

Donald B. Harris

Cross-references: *Antennas, Extraterrestrial Radio Sources, Interferometer Method (Optical), Radiation (Terrestrial), Refractometer*

RADIO ASTRONOMY: see EXTRATERRESTRIAL RADIO SOURCES: RADAR ASTRONOMY

RADIO COMPASS: see NAVIGATION

RADIO LINKS

Radio relay systems have expanded enormously since 1947, in response to constantly growing demand for wideband communication facilities. In the United States alone, microwave radio links in 1960 provided over a third of the long-distance telephone circuit miles, and over 85 per cent of the intercity television circuit miles. Their applications fall into two categories:

(1) national and international communication networks (multichannel telephony, radio and television, digital data, facsimile, etc.); and

(2) civil and industrial control systems (fire, police, forestry, highways, pipelines, electric power lines, and railways).

Wideband radio links are mainly low-power "line-of-sight" repeaters about 30 miles apart, operating at microwave frequencies (from 1 to 12 kMc, approximately). They are supplemented by high-power "over-the-horizon" repeaters, about 200 miles apart, usually at frequencies between 0.5 and 2 kMc. In addition, shortwave radio plays an important role in overseas telephony and telegraphy.

Line-of-sight Relay Systems. In the United States, the Bell System has developed and uses three microwave relay systems. Their characteristics are typical of national integrated networks in many countries, and will serve to illustrate current practice in this field.

hundred such telephone signals or one television signal, is frequency-modulated on an IF carrier, 70 and 74.1 Mc, respectively. It is then translated up to the microwave band, amplified, and combined with other microwave channels to enter the transmitting antenna. At each repeater, the rf channels are converted back down to the IF band for amplification, and each is retransmitted in a microwave frequency band different from the received frequency. In addition, the polarization of adjacent channels alternates between horizontal and vertical. These measures help avoid adjacent-channel interference and feedback at repeaters.

In the TJ system, the message baseband is applied directly to the repeller of the transmitter klystron, to produce a frequency-modulated microwave carrier. At each repeater, the microwave signal is converted to

Microwave Relay Networks in the Bell System

	Code Name		
	TD-2	TH	TJ
Service	Long-haul (4000 miles)	Long-haul (4000 miles)	Short-haul (up to 200 miles)
Frequency (Mc)	3700–4200	5925–6425	10,700–11,700
Average repeater hop (miles)	30	30	10 to 30
Max. no. of broadband channels	12 two-way (2 protection)	8 two-way (2 protection)	6 two-way (3 protection)
Two-way channel capacity	600 telephone or one TV	1860 voice	240 voice or one TV
Transmitter tube	Triode, 0.5 w output	Traveling-wave tube, 5 w output	Klystron, 0.5 w output

The TH system supplements the older TD-2 system and usually uses the same antennas and towers. Partly because of its higher power level, it has greater channel capacity (with the same signal-to-noise ratio). The TJ system was designed for short-haul routes and to supplement existing wire and cable facilities.

All three systems use frequency-division multiplex. Telephone messages are generally stacked side by side in the form of single-sideband suppressed-carrier signals, 4 kc apart. In the TD-2 and TH systems, the entire base-band, consisting either of several

IF, amplified, and demodulated to baseband, before passing to the transmitter. This method makes it convenient to drop and add telephone channels at any repeater.

On long-haul routes such as the TD-2 and TH systems, where more than 125 repeaters may be used in tandem, the antennas must provide at least 65 db discrimination against the rearward direction, to prevent interchannel interference. In addition, there are routes where two or all three of the relay systems are in use simultaneously. Thus the antennas must be capable of supporting 4, 6, and 11 kMc in both polarizations. These requirements are met by the horn-reflector antenna and circular waveguide feed. This antenna consists of a rectangular horn terminated by a narrow sector of a paraboloid and its window, the whole antenna resembling a huge sugar scoop. A network of directional couplers and tapered sections distributes the different polarizations and frequency bands. Channel filters and isolators are used to separate or combine the channels in each band.

On short-haul or secondary routes, parabolic-dish antennas with rectangular waveguides are generally used. Along the TJ system, however, most paraboloids are employed in a "periscope" arrangement, in which they are mounted vertically on the roof of the repeater station and the beam is transmitted via a reflector atop a tower.

Beyond-the-Horizon Transmission. Radiowaves can be reflected or forward-scattered high above the earth and thereby propagate hundreds or thousands of miles. Between 4 and 22 Mc, they are reflected by the ionosphere with very little loss. Multiple reflections from the earth and ionosphere permit shortwave propagation half-way around the earth. Although subject to severe multipath fading and magnetic-storm blackouts, these waves are extensively used in overseas and ship-to-shore telephony, usually with a capacity of four voice channels for overseas service.

There are two different types of scatter transmission:

(1) Ionospheric scatter, utilizing either turbulence at the lower edge of the E-layer or meteor-trail scatter (25 to 60 miles high). This has been used for long-distance (600 to 1200 miles), narrow-band transmission of telegraph or slow facsimile (*q.v.*), at frequencies of 25 to 60 Mc.

(2) Tropospheric scatter, at about a mile above the earth, useful over a wide frequency band (100 to 10,000 Mc) over distances of 100 to 400 miles.

Both forms of scatter propagation are subject to slow and rapid fading, caused by atmospheric changes and multipath transmission, respectively. Tropospheric scatter systems are reliable and moderately broadband, provided very large antennas and high-power transmitters are employed with space and/or frequency diversity to combat random fading. Their cost, relative to that of line-of-sight radio links, may be justified when long stretches of rugged terrain or water must be bridged. Tropospheric scatter links are widely employed in northern Canada and Alaska, as elements of radar and civil communications networks. Others are in operation between Florida and Cuba, Florida and Nassau (185 miles each), and between Sardinia and Minorca (240 miles). They have capacities typically of about 100 two-way telephone circuits or one television channel.

Future Trends. Recent advances in rocket technology and low-noise amplifiers (masers and parametric amplifiers, *q.v.*) have spurred experimentation and planning on the use of artificial earth satellites as relays. They might take the form of a few active repeaters in equatorial orbits 22,400 miles high, where they would be stationary with respect to the earth, or a larger number at lower altitude where at least one repeater would be visible to both land stations at all times. Another possibility would be to place a large number of passive reflectors in low-altitude orbits, and use high-power transmitters to ensure a usable signal at the distant receiver. The most attractive application for a satellite-relay system appears to be in transoceanic transmission of multichannel telephony and high-quality television transmission.

Growth projections of overland communications traffic indicate eventual saturation of the frequency band available for microwave relay systems. Long before then, it may become economical to employ low-loss circular waveguides in the millimeter-wavelength region for transcontinental broadband circuits. Operating at frequencies from 35 to possibly 100 kMc, with signal attenuations of 3 db per mile or less, such waveguide systems give promise of opening up a new interference-free band about 60,000 Mc wide, five times the entire developed radio spectrum.

W. W. RIGROD

Cross-references: *Antennas, Propagation, Satellite Communications*

RADIOACTIVITY

Radioactivity is the spontaneous transformation of one nuclear species into another, accompanied by the emission of corpuscular or electromagnetic radiation. The process may be associated with secondary phenomena such as the emission of conversion or Auger electrons, X-rays, delayed neutrons and annihilation radiation. The number N of nuclei of a given radioactive species decreases in time t according to the fundamental law $N = N_0 e^{-\lambda t}$ where λ is a constant characteristic of that species.

The term was coined in 1898 to describe the mysterious penetrating radiations from uranium, thorium, and other materials associated with them in their minerals. The *primary* natural radioactivities include Th^{232}, U^{235}, and U^{238} which are the surviving remnants of a primordial stock produced some 5 to 10 billion years ago. The *secondary* natural radioactivities, such as radium, are shorter-lived radioelements which are present today only because of their recent formation from Th^{232}, U^{235}, or U^{238}. All known secondary radioactivities belong to the three heavy-element families of radioactivities. The chief other primary natural radioelements are K^{40}, Rb^{87}, and Sm^{147}.

By methods of artificial transmutation it has been possible to make radioactive isotopes of every element including 11 synthetic elements beyond uranium. Over 900 such species are known.

The chief types of radioactive transformation include beta, alpha, and gamma decay and spontaneous fission. The fundamental bases of these can be briefly explained as follows:

Beta decay is the process whereby an unstable nucleus transforms itself into a more stable nucleus of the same mass number by converting one of its protons into a neutron, or vice versa. The transforming nucleon undergoes one of the following processes:

$$N \to P + \beta^- + \nu$$

$$P \to N + \beta^+ + \nu$$

$$P + e^-_{orbital} \to N + \nu$$

The symbols N and P refer to neutron and proton, β^- and β^+ to electron and positron, ν to the neutrino and $e^-_{orbital}$ to a planetary electron outside the nucleus. The first process is referred to as negative beta decay (or negatron emission), the second to positron emission, and the third to orbital electron capture. The radioactive nucleus contains many nucleons but the fundamental transformation involves a single nucleon. The relative and absolute stability of two nuclei of the same mass number is determined by the balance between the specifically nuclear forces and the disruptive Coulomb force of the protons pushing against each other. This balance is sensitively affected by the neutron/proton ratio.

Alpha decay is the spontaneous ejection from the nucleus of a clump of nucleons consisting of two neutrons and two protons. This clump is called an alpha particle and is identical with the helium nucleus. The energy for the transformation comes from the fact that the mass of the initial nucleus is greater than the sum of the masses of the daughter nucleus and the separated alpha particle. This energy condition exists for all the heavy elements but not for light elements. According to classical concepts an alpha particle cannot escape because of the repulsive Coulomb force it experiences at the nuclear surface. In quantum mechanical theory the alpha particle can "tunnel" through this repulsive barrier. Radioactive decay by emission of protons, or of clumps of nucleons other than alpha particles, is theoretically possible but alpha emission is much more probable because of the specially great binding energy of the alpha particle.

Nuclear fission becomes energetically possible when the mass of the nucleus is greater than the total mass of the products into which it might divide. Nuclei do not fission instantaneously because considerable energy must be put into the distortion of the nucleus before the Coulomb repulsive energy of the protons in the two "halves" of the nucleus is great enough to tear the nucleus apart against the restoring tendency supplied by the nuclear force. In classical theory the nucleus in its ground state has not enough energy to overcome this distortion energy barrier. In quantum mechanical theory, however, this barrier is subject to a "tunneling." Decay by spontaneous fission by this tunneling mechanism is appreciable only for the synthetic elements above uranium.

Alpha and beta decay and fission often leave the product nuclei in excited states. The great majority of these states are de-excited by the emission of electromagnetic radiation called *gamma radiation*. The detailed pattern of the gamma emission may be quite complex if many excited states are involved. Usually, the time of gamma emission is an immeasurably short fraction of a second so that the gamma emission can be considered a secondary phenomenon of the radioactive decay.

In some cases gamma ray emission is delayed, which gives rise to the phenomenon of nuclear isomerism. Nuclear isomers are two or more nuclear species containing the same number of neutrons and protons, but which nonetheless exhibit distinct properties for measurable periods of time. The measurable periods of time may range from fractions of seconds to billions of years. Isomerism is associated with the occurrence of close-lying states of excitation differing widely in angular momentum content.

The various types of radioactive decay are independent processes so that two or more of them may occur in a collection of identical nuclei.

EARL K. HYDE

Cross-references: *Alpha Particles, Fission, Gamma Rays, Radiation (Ionizing)*

RADIOMETEOROLOGY

Radiometeorology is the study of:

(1) the nature and causes of the dielectric structure of the troposphere and stratosphere, and that structure's effect on radio propagation; and

(2) meteorological phenomena by radio and radar methods.

In the rf band (30–30,000 Mc the refractive index $(1 + 10^{-6}N)$ of the atmosphere is given by

$$N = 77.5 \, PT^{-1} + 370,000 \, eT^{-2}$$

where P = total pressure in millibars,
T = air temperature in degrees Kelvin, and
e = partial water vapor pressure in millibars.

For centimetric waves, water-vapor and oxygen absorption become important; also, precipitation causes attenuation through scattering. Precipitation and absorption aside, the refractive index decreases with height in the first two kilometers or so above ground at the general rate $-dN/dh = 40/km$, somewhat faster than the 30/km valid for homogeneously mixed air. In temperate latitudes and fair weather, profiles of N vs height generally show unreproducible wiggles of $\pm 1 - 3N$, plus approximately reproducible steps of 5–80 N-units, believed to represent wavy horizontal stable interfaces between airs of different densities.

A radio ray traveling through a nearly horizontally stratified atmosphere is deflected from a rectilinear path according to Snell's law; radar determinations of aircraft height need corrections for local weather on line-of-sight links. Several ray-paths may be possible between fixed antennas; these paths vary in electrical length to produce fading.

A ray traveling horizontally in air where $-dN/dh = 157/km$ continues parallel to the curved earth; atmospheric layers of greater $-dN/dh$ form ducts that convey ratio energy in a wavelength-dependent, waveguide-like fashion around the curve of the earth. Owing to the refractive irregularities, energy is scattered out of (and into) ducts. The rough surface of the ground or ocean also scatters energy from ground-based ducts, so that a duct is always less effective as a waveguide than theoretically deduced from an N-profile.

In duct-free atmospheres, dielectric irregularities scatter radio energy around the earth so that fields fall off at 0.1 db per nautical mile of range, starting from a level 40 to 80 db below free space at ranges 50 to 100 km beyond the radio horizon. Fields depending on or affected by irregularities fade accordingly at rates about proportional to rf because of regular and turbulent air motions. The scattered rays arrive at the receiving antenna with a variety of arrival angles so that narrow-beam antennas are less effective than in line-of-sight operation. In addition, rain, thunderheads, lightning, and frontal passage increase fade rates and affect signal level.

Ducts are formed over most of the oceans owing to saturation at the water surface; stronger ducts are formed when dry air flows over water and in general below subsiding air, as in trade windbelts or often in polar regions.

The ground is cooled through nocturnal radiation in deserts or by thundershowers; the stable, cooled air overlying such ground often forms a surface duct. In general, a temperature inversion or other cause of atmospheric stratification corresponds to a large local value of $-dN/dh$ and hence to a duct.

In air-to-air and air-to-ground radio, atmospheric effects become severe when rays are approximately horizontal, i.e., travel for large distances through a given regime of dN/dh. Reflection of a ray nearly tangent to an N-inversion is nearly perfect and the inversion can prevent line-of-sight communication between aircraft; the jet stream may be associated with similar effects.

The long-range aim of that part of radiometeorology concerned with propagation is the ability to predict from synoptic data, using dynamical meteorological principles and Maxwell's equations, the behavior of

radio signals over specific links at specific times. Here one must eventually know the shape and magnitude of dielectric irregularities in stable and "mixed" conditions, as function of air history and wind field, to all scales and with various conditions of surface energy and humidity flux. Improved ground-based instrumentation and research aircraft can give more than the piecemeal data now available; field-measuring aircraft are useful in determining the relative or joint importance of ducting and random single or multiple scatter in a specific regime, also an open problem.

Radiometeorology, as a study of meteorological phenomena, employs radar echoes to provide information. The principal target is precipitation, and the signal strength is related to the intensity of rain or snow. The return from precipitation-free water cloud is about 60 db below that from rain. Wavelengths of 0.86, 3.2, 5.7, and 10 cm are used; the shorter wavelengths yield much greater sensitivity, but 0.86 cm is hopelessly impaired by rain, and 3.2 cm, although most used for rain, provides patterns that are seriously distorted in the case of heavy rain. At wavelengths 10 cm and longer returns are received from lightning but with a persistence of only a fraction of a second. The greatest use of weather radar in the study of severe storms, anywhere in scale between tornado and hurricane; here radar-equipped aircraft are coming into use as are pulse-doppler radars for indicating wind velocities.

Vertically pointing radars are becoming important in studying cloud development and motions of dielectric irregularities. Radiometeorology has not yet developed to the stage where point-to-point radio signal behavior is a useful indicator of weather.

REFERENCES

L. J. Battan, "Radar Meteorology," University of Chicago Press, 1959 (*J. of Res. of Nat. Bureau of Standards.* vol. 64D, pp. 607–627).

WILLIAM S. AMENT

Cross-references: *Propagation, Refractometer*

RADIOMETRY: see RADIATION MEASURE-
MENTS (NONIONIZING RADIATION)

RADIOTELEGRAPHY

Radiotelegraphy represents the oldest and still one of the most common methods of signaling by means of radio frequencies. Early experimenters were first able to determine the presence of the radio frequency wave and soon utilized a code similar to that developed by Samuel F. B. Morse (1791–1872) for his land-line telegraph for communications purposes. The code used in radio telegraphy is commonly referred to as the International Morse Code and has been modified from Morse's original code to provide a better match to the characteristics of rf equipment and environment. The fact that radiotelegraphy has persisted since the very first experiments with radio frequencies would lead one to believe that it possesses certain inherent desirable qualities. Chief among these are the simplicity of the equipment involved and the ability of the human operator to utilize the signals under very trying conditions. Figure 1 represents the basic elements of the radiotelegraphy system. Coded signals are generated by a transmitter which consists of four basic parts: a keying circuit, an oscillator, buffer

amplifiers, and a power amplifier. The last is connected to the antenna system. Very frequently this antenna system is made directional when used in point-to-point circuits in the high-frequency region. The signal then propagates in the medium and is exposed to a number of deleterious factors. These may be briefly classed as impulse noise, interfering man-made signals, propagation effects, and random noise. At the receiver the signal is picked up on an antenna system which again may be directional and passed through a selective filter amplifying stage and then to a series of converters that progressively convert the signal to intermediate frequency stages for amplification and filtering. The last of these converters reduces the frequency of the rf signal to an audible tone, usually near 1,000 cps for presentation to the operator in a headphone or a loudspeaker. The operator then transcribes the signals by hand or by the use of a typewriter, although other transcription means are used as will be described later.

Some brief insight into the reasons why the radiotelegraphy system is organized in the way it is may be of merit. First of all, the transmitter is usually organized in the separate stages in order to isolate the independent problems. The most important is

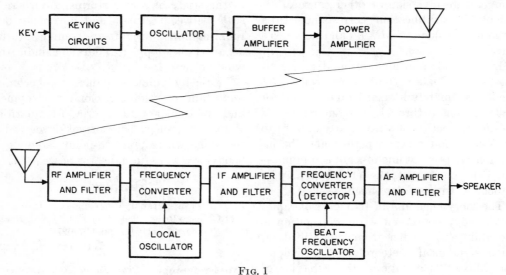

Fig. 1

frequency control. The radiotelegraph signal is inherently a narrow-band signal; therefore, a high degree of frequency stability on the part of both the transmitter and receiver allows the use of narrow filters and thus allows gains against the various forms of interference and noise. Isolation of the oscillator stage from the power amplifier is necessary in order to reduce instabilities and the effects of variation in power amplifier loading. The power-amplifier stage is required to be stable and efficient, producing as it may powers up to hundreds of thousands of watts. The keying circuit is required to shape the pulses corresponding to the dots and dashes in such a way that their bandwidth is the minimum required to provide the clean on-off shape that appears distinct to the human ear of the receiver. The receiver is most frequently of the superheterodyne type. This allows excellent stability and selectivity to be achieved in a receiver which covers a wide frequency range, which is very often the case. In the very-low-frequency and low-frequency bands frequently only one conversion is required before the last conversion to audio frequency However, in the higher portions of the high-frequency band triple conversion is often used. The maximum amount of selectivity is introduced in each one of the stages of the receiver that is compatible with tracking problems in a tunable receiver. The bandwidth of the final amplifying stages of the receiver may be as low as 100 cps. Although the signal bandwidth is considerably lower, the filtering characteristics of the human ear are such that smaller bandwidths cause a degradation in performance, especially with weak signals or in the presence of impulsive noise. Many receivers used for radiotelegraphy incorporate limiting stages, preferably in the wider-band amplifying stages in order to prevent impulsive excitation of the later narrow-band receiver portions. Receivers used for radiotelegraphy are normally equipped with manual controls for gain in the rf amplifying portions of the receiver. If they are provided with means of automatic

gain control these circuits are designed with fast attack times and long release times, in order to prevent the receiver from attempting to follow the slow-speed variations in signal strength of the manual keying.

High-speed radiotelegraphy, at speeds up to 60 and 100 words per minute, uses some additional and different techniques. When these signals are to be transcribed by manual operators, they are first recorded on an oscillographic tape recorder, as a form of line recording, referred to as an "undulator." These tapes are then transcribed visually by operators using typewriters. Since the audio signals are not used directly and the recorders are not as well adapted to signals of varying strength as the human operator, frequency-shift keying is frequently used for these signals. Recent developments in automatic transcription equipment have provided automatic printing of these high-speed Morse radiotelegraph signals. Since these signals are developed at the transmitter by automatic tape keying equipment, they are quite regular in speed and well adapted to automatic transcription. Equipment has been developed that automatically transcribes hand-transmitted characters over a wide range of speeds. The equipment is quite complex and is only used in special applications.

The manual transmission of Morse radio telegraph signals continues to provide a means for emergency and low-speed communications which has not been supplanted by a mechanized means. The equipment is very minimal and inexpensive and has a capability of operating under extenuating circumstances, which makes it continue to be attractive in situations where the employment of manual operators is not a prohibitive burden.

D. F. Babcock

Cross-references: *Radiotelephony, Teletype*

RADIOTELEPHONY

Radio telephony is concerned with the transmission of audible sounds, such as speech or music, by means of rf energy. To accomplish the transmission, the sounds must be first converted into electrical signals, amplified, and filtered, and then used to modulate or control a source of rf energy. In cv systems three parameters of the rf energy may be modulated: amplitude, phase, and frequency. In addition, simultaneous modulation of amplitude and phase, in proper relationship, results in what is known as "single-sideband" modulation. Radiotelephony signals can also be transmitted by means of pulsed rf energy. Various parameters of the pulsed signals may be modulated, either singly or in combination, e.g., pulse width, pulse repetition frequency, pulse position, and pulse amplitude. Pulse systems are utilized primarily in the uhf and microwave spectra where the sources of rf energy are more adaptable to pulse-modulation techniques and the required greater bandwidths are more readily available. At the receiving end of a radiotelephone link the rf signals must be amplified, filtered, and demodulated. The form of the demodulator is the inverse of the modulator, with the overall goal of reproducing the electrical input signal to the transmitter in an optimum form for the intended user. The basic criteria involved are usually intelligibility, linearity, dynamic range, frequency response, and susceptibility to impulse and random noise. The signals after demodulation are amplified and filtered and converted to audible sounds by means of earphones or a loudspeaker.

The reasons for choosing a system of modulation for a given application may involve a consideration of the bandwidth available; the fidelity required, i.e., a high signal-to-noise ratio, a high degree of linearity, a wide dynamic range and a wide frequency response; the type of rf energy source available; the disturbing effects of the rf propagation medium, e.g., Doppler frequency shifts, fading, impulse noise, etc.; the limitations on primary power and rf power available; and the required cost and complexity of equipment required. The most common system in use is amplitude modula-

tion, which was demonstrated by R. A. Fessenden (1866–1932) in 1906, and is in worldwide use for broadcasting in the medium- and high-frequency spectra. It provides moderate fidelity in this frequency range, where bandwidth is very limited. It is however, susceptible to impulse noise and fading as the distance between the transmitter and receiver exceeds several hundred miles in daylight and smaller distances at night. Long-distance high-frequency broadcasting is almost exclusively amplitude modulation at present as a result of the limited bandwidth available and the simple receiving equipment in existence. Single-sideband broadcasting has recently proved to be superior to amplitude modulation when selective fading is severe but the more complex receiving equipment has limited its application to point-to-point relay of broadcasts. In 1936 E. H. Armstrong (*q.v.*) demonstrated that bandwidth could be exchanged for signal-to-noise ratio by the use of frequency modulation. The necessary bandwidth is only available in the very-high-frequency spectrum and above. At present frequency modulation is used in many areas of the world to provide a broadcast service with a high degree of fidelity, though limited to line-of-sight propagation. Frequency modulation also provides a high degree of invulnerability to impulse noise and fading.

In addition to its use for broadcasting, radiotelephony finds wide use as a communications medium where instantaneous and direct information flow is required. Such applications as air/ground/air, mobile/fixed-base, and point-to-point communications are primarily concerned with the intelligibility of the message to the receiving operator. In these applications the fidelity criteria may be purposely limited to improve intelligibility in the presence of impulse noise and of adjacent-channel interference, or to increase the average level of modulation. The effects of impulse noise are often reduced by the use of limiters which set a definite upper level on the dynamic range of the receiving equipment and thus prevent the high peaks of impulse noise from appearing in the receiver output. Adjacent-channel interference, and also the effects of random noise, can be reduced by reducing the system bandwidth to the minimum allowable for intelligibility, usually 300 to 2700 cps for the audio frequency signal. The average level of modulation can be increased by the use of compression and expansion (*q.v.*) which can reduce the dynamic range of the input audio signal. Amplitude modulation is universally used for air/ground/air communications, both in the high-frequency and very-high-frequency spectra. Both frequency modulation and amplitude modulation are used for mobile/fixed-base communications, although the former is restricted to the very-high-frequency spectrum and above. Frequency modulation offers good protection against the impulse noise caused by auto ignition systems in this service. In high-frequency point-to-point communications applications amplitude modulation has been used extensively. However, telephone companies have used single sideband since 1923. The use of single sideband is now becoming more general and many civil and military networks have been developed using it. Single sideband has three distinct advantages over amplitude modulation: less power is required by elimination of the carrier, selective fading causes much less severe distortion of the received signal, and the receiver bandwidth is less than half that for amplitude modulation. The main disadvantage of single sideband is the more complex equipment required, mainly the result of the small frequency tolerance allowed.

One disadvantage of radiotelephony, the lack of privacy, has been reduced for links that require it by the development of speech privacy systems. These systems destroy the intelligibility of the signal for the unintended listener by a combination of frequency band inverters and time segment inverters. Such devices add considerable complexity to the system and may decrease intelligibility and naturalness in the received signal.

The speech signal requires a bandwidth much wider than that required by an optimized system carrying the same message information. Extensive research effort has been devoted to techniques for analysis of the speech signal into significant quanta, coding these quanta for transmission over digital transmission links, decoding the received digital signals, and synthesizing a replica of the original signal that is intelligible to the human ear and mind. The best known of such systems is the channel Vocoder (*q.v.*) of the Bell Telephone Laboratories that accomplishes a 10:1 bandwidth compression with small loss in intelligibility but complete loss of identification of the speaker.

D. F. BABCOCK

Cross-references: *Compression and Expansion, Multiplexing, Radio Links, Radiotelegraphy, Vocoder*

RADOMES

A radome is a dielectric housing designed to provide protection for an antenna against wind, rain or other weather conditions, and to provide streamlining in the case of airborne vehicles. Ideally, such a radome would transmit completely all of the incident energy without amplitude loss or distortion to the antenna beam pattern. In actual practice, however, such performance is never perfectly obtained and some of the energy is lost either by reflection or by absorption loss in the dielectric material. In addition, differential phase delays across the antenna aperture caused by curved surfaces can drastically affect side-lobe structure and can alter the shape and direction of the main beam. The latter effect is particularly objectionable in the case of boresighting radomes where the antenna is used for tracking or guidance.

An analysis of the antenna-radome as an electrical boundary value problem is so complex that it can be rigorously solved only in a few idealized simple cases and is seldom, if ever, used in actual design. Instead an approximate analysis is used in which the curved surface is replaced by an infinite flat sheet and the antenna field distribution by a plane wave. In this way the transmission, reflection, and phase delays can be computed as a function of incidence angle and polarization. Two types of polarization are considered, one in which the electric field vector is perpendicular and the other, parallel, to the incidence plane. The actual antenna-radome structure is then analyzed to determine the range of incidence angles involved, and a design is chosen that provides satisfactory transmission for both polarizations over this range of angles. Once this goal has been achieved, phase perturbations are usually taken into account as secondary corrections.

Transmission losses through a plane flat sheet are caused by (1) reflections, and (2) absorption losses. Electromagnetic reflections occur at each interface between two different dielectric media. The over-all reflection from the flat structure is a superposition of all of the interface reflections taking into account their individual phases and amplitudes. Wall thicknesses are chosen so as to provide partial or complete cancellation of these individual reflections. Absorption losses are minimized by the use of low-loss dielectric materials.

The principal radome types may be summarized as follows:

(1) *Homogeneous Thin Wall*. The simplest form of radome is a laminated or molded structure in which the electrical thickness d_e is small compared to the free space wavelength λ_0, that is

$$d_e = d \sqrt{\epsilon'} \leq \frac{\lambda_0}{10} \qquad (1)$$

where d is the mechanical thickness and ϵ' is the relative dielectric constant.

This type of radome is particularly useful for frequencies up to several kilomegacycles, but becomes excessively physically thin in the upper centimeter region.

(2) *Half-Wave Homogeneous Wall*. Perfect transmission is obtained from a lossless dielectric sheet at an incidence angle θ, pro-

vided the thickness is

$$d = \frac{\lambda_0}{2 \sqrt{\epsilon' - \sin^2 \theta}}$$

At this thickness the phase of the interface reflections from each surface is such that complete cancellation occurs. If the dielectric is lossy, perfect transmission is not possible; however, maximum transmission occurs at approximately the same thickness as for the lossless case.

The half-wave radome, which is usually a fiberglass laminated structure, is particularly suitable in the middle and upper microwave region. Because of its excellent structural strength and high temperature properties it has found wide use in supersonic aircraft and missile applications.

(3) *The Single Sandwich*. The single-sandwich wall consists of a sheet of low-density foamed or honeycomb core material faced on both sides by thin higher-density laminated skins. The structure has an excellent strength-to-weight ratio and good electrical characteristics because of low reflections from the thin skins and core material of the low dielectric constant. The transmission is further improved by choosing a core thickness such that the skin reflections tend to cancel. Structures of this type are used from low frequency all the way up to 17 kMc.

(4) *The Double Sandwich*. The double sandwich is a five-layer structure, essentially two single sandwiches back-to-back. This structure has greater mechanical strength than the single sandwich. In addition, the double sandwich can be designed to transmit over a larger range of incidence angles than is possible with the single sandwich.

(5) *The Inverted Sandwich*. The inverted sandwich has skins having a lower dielectric constant than the core material. Generally, the design is arranged so that the skins are a quarter-wave thick and have dielectric constant equal to the square root of that of the core. This provides matching into and out of the core material leaving the transmission independent of the core thickness. This pa-

rameter is then available for making any necessary phase corrections.

E. O. HARTIG

Cross-references: *Antennas*

RANDOM PROCESSES

The theory of random, or stochastic, processes is generally defined as the "dynamical" part of probability theory in which one studies a collection of random variables (called a stochastic process) from the point of view of their interdependence and limiting behavior. A stochastic process is one which is developing in time in a manner controlled by probabilistic laws. Examples of stochastic processes are provided by the path of a particle in Brownian motion (*q.v.*), the growth of a population such as a bacterial colony, the fluctuating numbers of electrons and protons in a cosmic-ray shower, the fluctuating output of gasoline in successive runs of an oil-refining mechanism, and the fluctuating current in a network due to thermal noise (*q.v.*) or shot noise.

A stochastic process (or a random process) is best defined as a family $\{X(t), t \epsilon T\}$ of random variables. The set T is called the index set of the process (the Greek letter ϵ is to be read "belongs to" or "varying in"). No restriction is placed on the nature of T. However, two important cases are when $T = \{0, \pm 1, \pm 2, \cdots,\}$ or $T = \{0, 1, 2, \cdots,\}$, in which case the stochastic process is said to be a *discrete-parameter* process, or when $T = \{t: -\infty < t < \infty\}$ or $T = \{t: t \geq 0\}$ in which case the stochastic process is said to be a *continuous-parameter* process.

There are two main ways in which one defines a stochastic process $\{X(t), t \epsilon T\}$. One way of describing a stochastic process is to give a formula for the value $X(t)$ of the process at a given time t, in terms of a family of random variables whose probability distribution is known. The stochastic process

$$\{X(t), t \geq 0\},$$

defined by $X(t) = A \cos \omega t + B \sin \omega t$, where ω is a known frequency and A and B are independent random variables is an example of a process defined by an explicit formula.

It seems plausible that a stochastic process $\{X(t), t \epsilon T\}$, defined on an infinite index set T, can for practical purposes be adequately represented by some finite number of ordinates. Consequently, a second way of describing a stochastic process $\{X(t), t \epsilon T\}$ is to specify the joint probability law of the n random variables $X(t_1), \cdots, X(t_n)$ for any integer n and n points $t_1, t_2, \cdots, t_n$ in T. To specify the joint probability law of the n random variables $X(t_1), \cdots, X(t_n)$ one may specify either (i) the joint distribution function, for any n real numbers $x_1, \cdots, x_n$,

$$F_{X(t_1), \cdots, X(t_n)}(x_1, \cdots, x_n)$$
$$= P[X(t_1) \leq x_1, X(t_2) \leq x_2, \cdots, X(t_n) \leq x_n]$$

or (ii) the joint characteristic function, for any n real numbers $u_1, \cdots, u_n$,

$$\varphi_{X(t_1), \cdots, X(t_n)}(u_1, \cdots, u_n) = E[\exp i(u_1 X(t_1) + \cdots$$
$$+ u_n X(t_n))] = \int_{-\infty}^{\infty} \cdots \int_{-\infty}^{\infty} \exp i(u_1 x_1$$
$$+ \cdots + u_n x_n) \, dF_{X(t_1), \cdots, X(t_n)}(x_1, \cdots, x_n)$$

The theory of stochastic processes is mainly concerned with the study of various *standard types* of stochastic processes, especially Markov processes and stationary processes.

A stochastic process $\{X(t), t \epsilon T\}$ is said to be (strictly) stationary if for any set of indices $t_1, \cdots, t_k$ in T, and any h in T, the k-dimensional random vectors $(X(t_1), \cdots, X(t_k))$ and $(X(t_1 + h), \cdots, X(t_k + h))$ are identically distributed. Intuitively, a stationary process is one whose distributions remain the same as time passes.

EMANUEL PARZEN

Cross-references: *Information Theory, Markov Processes, Probability, Statistical Communication Theory*

RANDOMLY VARYING SYSTEMS

By a randomly varying system, one understands a system some or all of whose internal characteristics are changing in a nondeterministic manner, i.e., the unforced system can be represented by an ensemble of equations indexed by the element ω of a sample space Ω. Thus, for example, the system may have a representation as a linear differential equation with random processes as coefficients. We are here concerned chiefly with the *stability* of systems described by random differential (or difference) equations rather than measurement, identification, optimization, etc.

In general, the problem of stability is to determine the extent to which a set of properties of a system remains invariant under a specified set of disturbances or alterations on the system, on the initial conditions, etc. If the system is random, the properties of interest must be appropriately specified so as to take into account the random nature (i.e., the dependence on ω) of the system state vector. Thus, for deterministic systems, a common stability problem is the study of deviations of the state vector from a given equilibrium state when initial conditions are close to this equilibrium state; the various stability concepts are generated by imposing requirements that the magnitude of the deviations remains small for all time, that it returns to zero as $t \rightarrow \infty$, that it satisfies uniformity conditions with respect to initial conditions, etc. For random systems, the deviation is measured in some stochastic sense, e.g., in probability, almost surely (with probability one), almost uniformly (in ω), in the ith mean, etc. Thus to every concept of stability in the deterministic case and every stochastic "distance function," there is a corresponding concept of stability in a stochastic sense.

Thus, let $\mathbf{x}(t, t_0, \mathbf{x}_0)$ be the state vector characterizing a deterministic system at time t and satisfying the initial condition

$$\mathbf{x}(t_0, t_0, \mathbf{x}_0) = \mathbf{x}_0$$

and assume, without loss of generality, that

$\mathbf{0}$ is an equilibrium state, i.e., $\mathbf{x}(t, t_0, \mathbf{0}) = \mathbf{0}$. Then the zero equilibrium state is called stable if to every $\epsilon > 0$ and t_0, there corresponds a $\delta(\epsilon, t_0) > 0$ such that

$$\|\mathbf{x}(t, t_0, \mathbf{x}_0)\| < \epsilon \quad (*)$$

for all $t \geq t_0$ and all $\|\mathbf{x}_0\| < \delta$. For a random system [with $\mathbf{x}(t, t_0, \mathbf{0}) = \mathbf{0}$ almost surely], the zero equilibrium state is called stable almost surely if it is stable for every ω contained in a set of probability one. Replacing $(*)$ by $E\|\mathbf{x}(t, t_0, \mathbf{x}_0)\| < \epsilon$ yields the definition of stable in the mean norm; replacing $(*)$ by $E \sum x_i^2(t, t_0, \mathbf{0})$ yields the definition of mean-square stability though quite often only one component of the vector $\mathbf{x}$ (e.g., the "error") and boundedness with respect to inputs rather than changes in initial conditions, are considered. The author has defined and investigated some relationships among the various types of stability for random systems.

For the deterministic linear vector system $\dot{\mathbf{x}} = \mathbf{A}(t)\mathbf{x} + \mathbf{b}(t)$, there exist well-known theorems relating the properties (such as exponential boundedness of the norm) of the fundamental matrix with the property "bounded solutions for every bounded $\mathbf{b}(t)$." Some extensions to the random case have been considered by the author and provide a partial justification for considering only the free ($\mathbf{b} \equiv 0$) system in stability analyses of such random systems.

For random *linear* systems with continuous parameter variations, some results are available. For first-order systems Rosenbloom has expressed the output moments in terms of the characteristic function of the indefinite time integral of the parameter process. He shows, in particular, that if the parameter process is Gaussian, then for a step input the first and second output moments may approach ∞ whereas the output approaches one in probability as $t \rightarrow \infty$. Tikhonov has considered the first-order case where the input and parameter processes are jointly Gaussian. For the linear system with all coefficients constant except for one which is perturbed additively by independent (of the input) white noise, Bergen has shown that the mean-square error (output minus input) is always larger with than without white noise, and has found necessary and sufficient conditions for the mean-square error to remain bounded. Samuels (*IRE Trans., PGIT*, May 1959) considers linear systems with dependent parameter processes and an independent input and arrives at specific results in some special cases. Zadeh (*J. Math. & Phys.*, April 1953) has investigated a very general class of random linear systems admitting of a certain integral representation and demonstrated an integral relation between the output covariance and the input and "system" covariance functions similar to that for deterministic linear systems.

The stability of random linear systems with piecewise-constant parameters has been investigated in some detail. For the nth order vector differential equation $\dot{\mathbf{x}} = \mathbf{A}_k\mathbf{x}$, $t_{k-1} \leq t < t_k$, $k = 1, 2, \ldots$, Bergen (*IRE Trans., PGAC*, September 1960) has found necessary and sufficient conditions for asymptotic stability in the second moment when $\mathbf{A}_k$ alternates between two possible values and $\{t_k - t_{k-1}\}$ is an independent random process. The author has investigated the asymptotic stability in the ith moment for the case where $\{\mathbf{A}_k(t_k - t_{k-1})\}$ is a finite Markov chain. In both cases above, it can be shown that asymptotic stability in the mean norm implies almost sure asymptotic stability, whereas the converse is false.

Bertram and Sarachik (*IRE Trans., PGIT*, May 1959) have extended "Lyapunov's Second Method" to random systems. By working with the expectation of the total time derivative of the Lyapunov function along the system trajectories and measuring stability in the sense of the mean norm, they have arrived at theorems analogous to those in the deterministic case.

Behram H. Bharucha

Cross-references: *Markov Processe, Probability, Random Processes, Systems*

REACTORS

A nuclear reactor is a device to produce energy and neutrons by means of a fission chain reaction. During the process of nuclear fission, matter is converted to equivalent energy according to Einstein's law $E = mc^2$. Also during fission some 2.5 neutrons on the average are emitted, one of which is necessary to maintain the chain reaction, i.e., to cause another fission. The energy released per fission is 200 Mev, or about 0.1 per cent of the original mass of the nucleus is converted to energy. This is many million times the energy release per reacting atom in chemical reactions. The available stored energy in 1 lb of fissionable material is equivalent to several thousand tons of coal or high explosives.

The neutrons emitted during fission are all-important since they are the means by which the chain reaction sustains itself.

An average cycle in a fission chain reaction may be described as follows. In the reactor core (the region containing fissionable material), a neutron is absorbed and causes a fission to take place yielding 200 Mev of energy and 2.5 neutrons. The energy appears primarily as kinetic energy of the fission fragments, the remainder in the form of emitted neutrons, beta particles, and gamma rays (*q.v.*). Nearly all of the energy is immediately converted to heat in the fuel region. The neutrons emitted now migrate or diffuse about in the core in a random-walk manner due to scattering by the nuclei of the core materials. They are degraded in energy by such collisions if light nuclei are present. Eventually they die by one of three processes. They may be absorbed in a fissionable nucleus to further the chain, they may be absorbed in a nonfissionable nucleus, or they may leak out of the core region. The first two processes depend upon the material composition of the core. The third depends also upon the size of the core.

The competition of these three processes determines the neutron economy of the reactor. If on the average one of the emitted neutrons causes another fission to take place, the chain will be sustained and go on indefinitely. More generally, if k (usually termed the multiplication factor) is the average number of fissions caused by the neutrons emitted from a previous fission, then the chain reaction following one fission can be represented by:

$$1 + k + k^2 + k^3 + k^4 + \cdots$$

If $k < 1$, each successive term in this series is smaller, the chain dies out, and the reactor is called sub-critical. If $k = 1$, the chain just maintains itself and the reactor is critical. If $k > 1$, the terms increase, the chain increases and the reactor is super-critical. Another frequently used term the reactivity or ability of the reactor to maintain a chain is defined as $(k - 1)/k$. The reactivity is then less than zero for a sub-critical reactor, equal to zero for a critical reactor, and greater than zero for a super-critical reactor.

An alternative and completely equivalent definition of the multiplication factor k can be made: let

P_f = probability a neutron dies by capture causing a fission

P_c = probability a neutron dies by non-fission capture

P_L = probability a neutron leaks from the core

ν = average number of neutrons emitted by fissioning nucleus

Then $k = \nu P_f$, or since $P_f + P_c + P_L = 1$,

$$k = \nu \left(\frac{P_f}{P_f + P_c} \right) (1 - P_L)$$

The value of $P_f/(P_f + P_c)$ is determined solely by the material composition of the core. The value of $(1 - P_L)$ is determined primarily by the size of the core. In designing a reactor consideration must be given to both of these terms. If $P_f/(P_f + P_c) < 1/2.5$ the reactor can never be critical even if $P_L = 0$. Care must be taken that nonfission capture is sufficiently small, which limits the type and amount of nonfissionable materials present in the core. Once its composition is fixed the core must be made sufficiently large, which reduces the leakage probability P_L, so that the product of all three terms equals unity. This requirement determines the critical size or mass of the core.

To start up, run at power, and shut-down a reactor one must have some means of varying the multiplication factor or reactivity of the core. Usually, the amount of a strong neutron absorber in the core is varied by means of insertable rods or vanes. In operating a reactor one starts from a shut-down condition where $k < 1$ and the chains are not self-sustaining. Absorber is withdrawn from the core until k is slightly greater than one. With an external source to initiate them, the fission chains slowly grow so as to increase the number of fissions per second until the desired power level is reached. Absorber is then inserted until $k = 1$ and the power level then remains constant. To shut down, absorber is inserted into the core to make $k < 1$ and the fission rate then dies away.

Reactors are classified according to their primary function.

Power reactors are designed to make use of the energy liberated during fission. This energy appearing as heat may be used to generate steam to run turbines, or as process heat for industrial operations. The enormous capability of reactors for high power production over long periods of time with a small amount of fuel makes them particularly attractive as propulsion power plants and for generation of electrical power where standard fuels are difficult to obtain.

Breeder and *converter reactors* are designed to use the excess neutrons in the chain reaction to produce fissionable material. A so-called fertile material such as U^{238} beta-decays upon neutron capture to Pu^{239}, a fissionable isotope suitable for reactors. Breeders form more fissionable material than they burn. Converter reactors form less though they are much easier to design. Either type may also be a power reactor designed to perform both functions.

Research and *test reactors* are designed to make use of the excess neutrons also. However, here the neutrons are used to perform neutron physics experiments, study radiation damage, test other reactor components, and produce artificial radioisotopes.

Any reactor system consists of several principal functional parts peculiar to such systems.

(a) Fuel. The fissionable material distributed throughout the core usually in the form of rods or plates, completely clad by metal to prevent the release of fission products.

(b) Reflector. A thick blanket of a material (D_2O, Be, BeO, or C) placed around the core to decrease neutron leakage or, if made of fertile material, to produce new fissionable material.

(c) Moderator. Materials of light atomic weight and small capture cross section (H_2O, D_2O, Be, BeO, C) used in the core to reduce the neutron energy rapidly and thus to increase the probability of causing a fission. The fuel is sometimes dispersed uniformly throughout the moderator to form a so-called homogeneous reactor.

(d) Control System. A remotely controlled means of varying k, usually by motion of strong neutron absorbers into and out of the core, but sometimes by varying the reflector thickness. For safety reasons all reactors have some means of decreasing k very rapidly to provide a quick shut-down called a scram. This action may be necessary if the power level is rising too rapidly, the power level is too high, or there is some malfunction of the over-all reactor system.

(e) Nuclear Instrumentation. Consists of detectors to measure the neutron density in the vicinity of the core and hence to indicate the power level of the reactor.

(f) Shielding. Because of the radiation of neutrons and gamma rays from the core, massive shielding is required. Biological shields of water or concrete protect personnel from the core radiation. Thermal shields usually of lead or iron with appropriate cooling absorb the major portion of the core

radiation, thus preventing thermal shocks from the deposition of this energy in structural components or the biological shield.

A. J. KIRSCHBAUM

Cross-references: *Fission, Isotopes, Nucleonics*

RECIPROCITY: see NETWORK THEORY

RECTIFIER TUBES

In a rather restricted sense rectifiers permit the conversion of ac to a unidirectional current by physical properties that allow current to flow in only one direction upon the application of an alternating voltage. In this sense the ideal rectifier would have zero resistance in the forward direction and infinite resistance in the inverse direction.

Rectifier tubes may be classified into two general groups: the vacuum and the gaseous rectifier. Both types possess infinite resistance during the inverse cycle, since they conduct no current during this part of the cycle. During the conducting cycle, vacuum tubes are characterized by an almost constant value of resistance, whereas gaseous tubes are characterized by a substantially constant voltage drop.

The high-vacuum rectifiers belong to the diode class of tubes, that is there are two electrodes, the plate and the cathode. The cathode may be either of the filamentary type and directly heated or it may be a cathode-heater type heated by a separate heater, usually mounted within a cylindrical cathode sleeve.

In a high-vacuum type of rectifier operating in the usual space-charge-limited region the current is proportional to the voltage across the tube raised to the three-halves power. The forward resistance of the tube, which is the ratio of the voltage applied to the tube to the current, is equal to $1/KV^{1/2}$; K is the perveance, a constant equal to $I/V^{3/2}$. For many applications, the forward resistance may be considered to be a constant.

With the gaseous type of rectifier the tube may be filled with mercury vapor or an inert gas such as neon or argon. The gas pressure within the tube would be in the range from 10^{-3} mm of Hg to as high as 50 mm of Hg for some applications. The rectifier tube starts to conduct only when the voltage equals the breakdown voltage, which depends on the type of gas, pressure, and electrode spacing. During conduction, a constant voltage drop exists between the cathode and the anode. Conduction ceases when the voltage becomes less than the extinction value, which may be only a few volts less than the value for breakdown.

One type of gaseous rectifier is the hot-cathode gas-filled diode. The maximum current that is obtainable in this type of tube is the saturation thermionic emission from the cathode enhanced by the effect of the electric field at the surface of the cathode. The only function of the gas in these tubes is to provide ions for the neutralization of space charge, thereby permitting the current to be obtained at much lower voltages than are necessary in vacuum tubes. The most commonly used gas is mercury vapor. The gas pressure within the tube is then a function of the mercury-vapor condensation temperature.

Another class of gaseous rectifiers is of the mercury-pool type. The cathode of these rectifiers consists of a mercury pool. Electrons enter the arc through a cathode spot, which wanders on the surface of the pool of mercury. The discharge in this type of rectifier must be initiated by means of a starting electrode. Ignitrons belong to the mercury-pool classification, and comprise a starting or igniting electrode to initiate the arc during each cycle.

A keep-alive electrode to which a steady arc is maintained at all times is used with single-anode units, since otherwise the tube would be extinguished during the negative half cycle of an applied alternating voltage. Keep-alive electrodes are not a necessity for the larger size units which are designed to operate on polyphase ac circuits, since these tubes have a separate anode for each phase and an arc is continuously maintained within the tube.

A more general definition of a rectifier tube would also include the more recently developed *microwave-type rectifiers*. Because of the high frequency of microwaves the electron transit time in a diode would be equal to several cycles. As a result of the transit time corresponding to several cycles the net electron flow in one direction is very greatly reduced. However, by the use of any of several microwave interaction processes the electrons can absorb energy from the microwave source. This energy can then be converted to useful dc power.

One characteristic of a microwave type of rectifier that is different from conventional rectifiers is that a low tube resistance is not particularly desirable. The input resistance of the tube during operation must be matched to the characteristic impedance of the input line in order to have the maximum microwave power absorbed by the electronic space charge. If the resistance is either too low or too high the microwave power is reflected and does not even enter the rectifier.

One type of microwave rectifier is somewhat similar to a magnetron in the physical structure, but the method of operation, the operating conditions, and the design approach are radically different. The rectifier is composed of a circular re-entrant slow-wave network, a cathode concentric with the anode structure, and an axial magnetic field similar to a magnetron.

Electrons move out from the cathode under the action of the radial component of the microwave electric field. The electrons travel only a small fraction of the anode to cathode spacing before they are deflected by the magnetic field and are locked in phase with the traveling wave on the slow-wave circuit. The electrons are drawn to the anode only where the peaks of the traveling wave exceed the Hartree threshold voltage, the voltage which is required for electrons to flow to the anode while moving in synchronism with a traveling wave. Electron current, thus, flows from the cathode to the anode even though the dc anode voltage may be negative with respect to the cathode if the microwave voltage, which is determined by the input microwave power and the impedance of the circuit, is sufficiently large. The output of the microwave rectifier thus has the proper polarity to function as source of dc power.

To achieve high efficiency the electrons must drift slowly toward the anode in order to minimize the power which would be dissipated on the anode due to electron bombardment. For this reason relatively high values of the magnetic field intensity and microwave circuits with a relatively slow phase velocity are required.

JAMES B. THOMAS

Cross-references: *Diodes (Semiconductor), Electron Tubes (Conventional), Ignitrons, Magnetrons, Thyratrons*

RECTIFIERS (SOLID-STATE)

Rectifiers convert alternating current into direct current. They can be fashioned from a wide variety of systems, but of great theoretical and practical importance are those that employ semiconductors, a group of solid-state materials with unique and extremely interesting properties.

Solid-state rectifiers, therefore, are distinguished from those that utilize liquids (such as the electrolytic rectifier) and those that make use of gases, vapors, or a vacuum (such as the mercury-arc rectifier and the various types of electron tubes). Mechanical rectifiers, vibrators, and synchronous converters, which employ mechanical motion for their operation, are not considered as solid-state rectifiers.

Because of their simplicity of operation, relatively small size, ruggedness, reliability, absence of moving parts and of heated filaments, and the ability to operate even in severe mechanical and thermal conditions, solid-state rectifiers have become increasingly important.

Solid-state rectifiers can be classified into point-contact, barrier layer, and monocrystalline junction types. Examples of each of these types are the germanium microwave diode, the selenium rectifier, and the silicon p-n junction, respectively.

One of the first widely known solid-state rectifiers was the galena (PbS) crystal, used for the detection of rf waves in the early days of radio history. Often called a "cat's whisker," it employed a thin pointed metal wire pressed lightly against a sensitive spot on the crystal surface. This *point-contact* type of rectification had been observed in the 19th century for contacts between metals and various naturally occurring sulfides. In the early part of our present century it was found that other materials, such as silicon, silicon carbide, tellurium, and germanium, also displayed point-contact rectification. It is now recognized that these materials are semiconductors.

After the development and improvement of electron tubes, the use of crystal detectors in radio sets was abandoned, only to be resurrected with the advent of World War II and the need for a detector in radar and other high frequency circuits. An intensive research program, utilizing scientists from various disciplines, culminated in the modern point-contact diodes which utilize highly purified monocrystals of germanium and silicon. At present, newly developed semiconductors, such as gallium arsenide and indium antimonide, are being investigated for superior point-contact diodes.

Until a few years ago, the most important area type of rectifier was the *barrier layer* type, also known as the dry-disk or metallic rectifier. The last term is actually a misnomer since the device depends on the properties of a polycrystalline semiconductor layer, and especially of the junction between this layer and one of the contact electrodes. At this junction, a barrier or blocking layer is believed to exist that permits easy current flow in one direction (forward) but more or less resists it in the opposite (reverse) direction.

The development of the barrier-layer type

of rectifiers was largely an empirical one in which a considerable amount of art and of "trade secrets" were involved. The best known examples of the type are the magnesium-copper sulfide, the copper oxide, and the selenium rectifier. The last has almost completely displaced the other two types.

The selenium rectifier is actually the oldest large-area rectifier, having been first produced in 1883, but large-scale development did not begin until about fifty years later. Basically, it consists of a layer of selenium sandwiched between a baseplate of aluminum (originally iron) and a sprayed-on counterelectrode of a fusible alloy, such as the tin-cadmium-bismuth eutectic. To enhance the blocking characteristics, an artificial barrier layer is often deposited between the top selenium surface and the counterelectrode. The exact nature of the blocking mechanism is not yet completely understood despite the considerable amount of investigational effort that has been expended.

Although displaced to some extent by the modern germanium and silicon counterpart, the selenium rectifier is still widely used. Blocking voltages are limited to about 45 v per cell, but recent research has greatly improved the forward characteristics. In addition, the selenium rectifier is noted for its ability to withstand large momentary current overloads and surges of excessive back voltage.

The most exciting development in rectifier technology, however, has been the development of the p-n junction type, largely as a result of the intensive studies conducted on single-crystal semiconductors during and since World War II. Germanium and silicon rectifiers, for instance, have higher blocking voltages and a much greater current-density rating than the other types of rectifiers and, consequently, are much more efficient. Furthermore, the p-n junction is fairly amenable to critical analysis, and the theories that have been advanced to describe it have contributed in large measure to the rapid progress that has been made in development and application.

Germanium and silicon rectifiers are available commercially in a host of styles and sizes. Load-current ratings range from milliamperes to almost 1000 amp; peak reverse voltages can be obtained up to 1000 v or more. There is great need, however, for standardization in package design and in electrical characteristics.

The silicon rectifier, with its very low reverse leakage current and its high operating temperature, appears to be displacing the other types, particularly for power applications. Although the germanium unit has a lower forward voltage drop and is therefore more efficient, especially where very large current loads are involved, these advantages are offset by the need to keep its operating temperature below about 85°C. The silicon rectifier, on the other hand, can be operated to almost 200°C with much higher blocking voltages. Semiconductors that are presently being studied promise to provide rectifiers operable up to 500°C or more. Some are new compounds like gallium phosphide; others, like silicon carbide, are being reinvestigated in high-purity, single-crystal forms.

Rectifier cells can be connected in series to withstand greater voltage and in parallel to handle more current, but there are problems of unbalance that have to be considered. In many cases, it is possible to utilize shunt resistors and capacitors to provide proper division of voltage and current.

The solid-state rectifier is also used in a number of ways that exploit some of its special characteristics. The Zener or avalanche diode, for instance, is designed to utilize the rapid increase in reverse current that occurs above the breakdown voltage. The steep voltage-current curve can provide excellent voltage regulation against current change. Likewise, the large variation in rectifier capacitance with applied reverse voltage is utilized in "variable-capacitance diodes" for automatic frequency control and in variable frequency oscillator designs.

Finally, p-n junctions can be alternated and combined in a number of ways to produce a wide variety of devices. A three-layer arrangement (pnp or npn), for instance, can yield a transistor, while a four-layer structure semiconductor (pnpn, *q.v.*) can be fashioned into a "controlled rectifier." The latter can control a large load current by means of a small gating current, and is in reality a semiconductor thyratron (*q.v.*).

C. A. ESCOFFERY

Cross-references: *Diodes, Parametric Amplifiers, Rectifier Tubes, Semiconductor Manufacture*

REFINING (ELECTRONIC)

Electron-bombardment melting provides a high-vacuum environment combined with a noncontaminating energy source. This unique combination of characteristics has made it possible to prepare ultrapure specimens of substances with relatively high melting points and intense chemical activity in the molten state. Both "floating-zone" refining for the preparation of relatively small quantities of ultrapure materials, and electron-beam furnaces for melting and casting operations on a commercial, or tonnage, scale of production make use of the advantages offered by these environmental factors.

From a metallurgical point of view, the electron-beam melting system is interesting in that it provides for (1) high-vacuum at the surface of the melt, (2) stirring of the melt, (3) control of the degree of superheating above the melting point, and (4) control of the length of time the metal is molten. The effect of electron-beam melting upon the composition of various reactive metals is significantly different from changes occurring in other types of melting systems operating at higher pressures. In experiments performed to date, all metals have been purified to a greater extent than is at present possible in vacuum arc melting, vacuum induction melting, or vacuum sintering operations.

Devolatilization reactions proceed more rapidly and to a greater extent under high-vacuum conditions. The mechanism of purification via devolatilization reactions is a function of the physical chemistry of each particular system. The most important parameter is the relation between the vapor pressure of the metal in the molten state and the corresponding vapor pressures of the impurities. A useful general rule is that the volatilization of impurities proceeds at economically rapid rates if the equilibrium vapor pressure of the particular species is greater than 10^{-2} mm of Hg. The degree of purification achieved depends on such factors as the pressure over the melt, the residence time in the molten state, and the amount of superheat above the melting point.

Many purification reactions do not proceed at significant rates at the melting point of the base material. For example, the deoxidation of hafnium proceeds very slowly at its melting point. If it is superheated several hundred degrees, however, appreciable clean-up is achieved in a reasonable time. The degree of superheat is also important in the case of zirconium. It has the lowest vapor pressure at the melting point of any refractory or transition group metal. This property permits superheating of it to about 800°F above the melting point without serious loss of metal by evaporation. Such a melting operating results in the volatilization of low-vapor-pressure impurities, not otherwise removable, with a corresponding decrease in hardness. No change in hardness can be obtained without superheating. In general, a long residence time at a superheated state is more effective in achieving the volatilization of impurities than multiple melts.

Tantalum is an example of a material that reacts ideally in electron-beam melting. Because of its high melting point (about 5400°F) almost all impurities are removed by evaporation. Triple-melted tantalum consistently has residual contents of oxygen, nitrogen, and carbon of less than 20 ppm.

The development of electron bombardment furnaces for melting and casting emerged from laboratory to commercial scale when large quantities of refractory metals were required for nuclear-reactor, aircraft, and space-vehicle construction. The scale-up was supported by concurrent development in the auxiliary fields of high-vacuum technology and electronics. Advancements in the design and construction of electron guns (*q.v.*), power supplies, electron circuitry, and vacuum-system components have all contributed an important part in the rapidly increasing scale of electron-beam-furnace operations.

In the design of electron-beam furnaces, both laboratory and commercial scale, the vacuum system is basic to the operation. It must provide a sufficient pumping speed so that high vacuum conditions can be maintained at economic rates of melting. This requirement is particularly true of commercial scale furnaces.

With the heating and fusion of the melt stock, gases and vapors of various kinds are evolved. The space between the cathode and the anode no longer conducts a current as determined by either emission or space-charge limitations, but is rather a circuit element characterized by an impedance that is continuously varying between wide limits. The electronic circuitry for an electron beam furnace must provide a controller combining over-all circuit current limiting with a cathode emission limiter that must maintain steady operation even through transient local discharges.

Electron-beam furnaces of 600 kw capacity and capable of producing ingots 20 in. in diameter by 70 in. long are now in operation. Production figures run to tonnage quantities of refractory metals and alloys as well as nickel superalloys and special grades of steel.

Electron-beam furnaces are also being used in floating-zone refining operations for growing small single crystals as well as in "Czochralski" type crystal-growing operations for the production of relatively large single crystals of ultra-high purity from molten materials supported in cold-mold, "skull" crucibles.

C. D'A. HUNT

Cross-references: *Semiconductor Manufacture, Vacuum Techniques, Welding (Electronic), Zone Melting*

REFRACTIVE INDEX

The refractive index of any substance is the measure of its ability to refract light. When light passes from one medium into another there is usually a change in its velocity which causes a change in its direction (unless the light ray is normal to the surface of the second medium). The refractive index, commonly represented by n, is equal to the sine of the angle of incidence divided by the sine of the angle of refraction, or $n = (\sin i)/(\sin r)$.

As an approximation it is true that the denser any substance is the higher is its index of refraction. For example, the index of vacuum being taken as unity, the index of air is 1.0003, that of water is 1.333 (for sodium light), that of crown glass is 1.608, and that of diamond is 2.4195.

Like a wave moving on the surface of smooth water, light moves through a medium like air by means of vibrations at right angles to its path; but the wave on the water moves only by means of vibrations at right angles to the surface of the water, whereas a ray of light in air moves forward by means of vibrations in all directions at right angles to its path. Light travels in this way through any substance that has no oriented internal structure, that is, through any gas or liquid or amorphous solid, like glass. It even travels in the same way through crystalline solids if they have an internal structure that is exactly the same in three directions at right angles to each other, that is, if they are isometric, like diamond and rock salt. But some isometric crystals of relatively low symmetry (having no center of symmetry) produce a *rotation* of the vibration plane of polarized light. This rotation cannot be produced by crystals of any crystal system if they have a center of symmetry. The amount of rotation produced varies greatly; for example, a plate one millimeter in thickness produces a rotation of 3.1° if it is $NaClO_3$ (isometric), 21.7° if it is quartz, (hexagonal), and nearly fifteen times as much if it is cinnabar (hexagonal HgS).

The most important feature of a microscope adapted to the study of refractive indices is a device for changing ordinary light into light vibrating in a single plane. Such an instrument was first made and described by William Nicol in 1828 and is therefore commonly called a nicol, even though in recent years a Polaroid plate can be used instead of the transparent cleavage piece of calcite used by Nicol. Each microscope has two such nicols, one below the stage, called the polarizer, and the other above the objective, called the analyzer. When the vibration plane of the analyzer is at right angles to the vibration plane of the polarizer (and both are in use) they are described as crossed nicols. In a polarizing microscope the lower nicol (or polarizer) is placed below the condenser, and the upper nicol (or analyzer) is easily inserted or removed from the path of the light above the objective. The light emerging from the lower nicol vibrates in the north-south plane of the microscope, and light from the upper nicol vibrates in the east-west plane. Since vibration in a north-south direction has no component in an east-west direction, no light can pass through the microscope when both nicols are in place in this crossed position and there is no object between them to change the vibration direction of the light.

Most isometric crystals (like amorphous solids) produce no change in the vibration direction of the light emerging from a polarizer, and therefore such light cannot pass through the analyzer and the crystals are dark in all positions of rotation (between crossed nicols) on the stage of a polarizing microscope. Such substances are called *isotropic*.

The refractive index of any substance varies inversely with the velocity of a light ray in it, and that velocity depends upon the vibration direction rather than on the direction of propagation. Any substance in which light vibrates with equal ease in all directions has only one index of refraction. But light does not vibrate with equal ease

in all directions in any crystalline solid unless the crystals are isometric. However, there is one (and only one) direction of propagation of light in tetragonal and hexagonal crystals in which the light does vibrate with equal ease in all directions at right angles to the path; this single direction is the direction of the vertical crystal axis (c), which is also known as the optic axis. Such crystals are optically uniaxial, and are considered to be optically positive if the slow ray vibrates in the direction of c axis and negative if the fast ray vibrates in that direction.

Two principal indices of refraction are recognized for any uniaxial solid: one for a ray vibrating in any direction which is at right angles with the vertical crystal axis (the optic axis), called the ordinary ray O; and the other, for a ray called the extraordinary ray E, which vibrates parallel to the vertical crystal axis. Optically positive uniaxial crystals have the index of the extraordinary ray greater than that of the ordinary ray, and optically negative uniaxial crystals have the reverse condition. Any ray vibrating in a direction intermediate between these two directions has an index between the two values mentioned.

Three principal refractive indices are recognized for crystals with lower symmetry (i.e., orthorhombic, monoclinic, and triclinic). Such crystals are optically biaxial because they have two directions of transmission analogous to the optic axis of a uniaxial crystal. The bisector of the acute angle between these optic axes is called the acute bisectrix, and is designated X if it is the vibration direction of the fastest ray, or Z if it is the vibration direction of the slowest ray transmitted by the crystal. The obtuse bisectrix is then designated Z or X, respectively, and the direction perpendicular to X, Z, and the plane of the optic axes, is the optic normal Y. By generalization of the uniaxial case, a biaxial crystal is considered positive if Z is the acute bisectrix, otherwise negative. The principal refractive indices are commonly designated α (or n_x), β (or n_y), and γ

(or n_z), corresponding to the vibration directions X, Y, and Z. A complete optical description of a biaxial crystal requires in general six independent quantities giving the directions of X, Y, and Z, and the magnitudes of the associated refractive indices. However, in monoclinic crystals one of these directions must coincide with the symmetry-direction, and in orthorhombic crystals all three of them must coincide with the three mutually perpendicular symmetry-directions. In general, any ray of light passing through a biaxial crystal is resolved into two components with mutually perpendicular vibration directions. These components are transmitted with different velocities and correspondingly different refractive indices n_1 and n_2, which are always within the following limits:

$$n_x \leqq n_1 \leqq n_y \leqq n_2 \leqq n_z .$$

Any crystal, which is not isometric and does not have an optic axis in the axis of the microscope, has two (and only two) directions of vibration for the light passing through it. These two directions are at right angles to the path of the light and also at right angles to each other. If these two directions are N-S and E-W, the crystal is dark between crossed nicols. When turned 45° from such a position the vibration directions are NW-SE and NE-SW and the crystal transmits the maximum amount of light (though the light is nearly the same through a considerable angle about this position). Each of the two rays in the crystal is divided into two rays upon entering the upper nicol, one component vibrating N-S and the other E-W. The N-S components cannot pass through the analyzer. The E-W components from the two rays of the crystal unite; but they have followed different paths in the crystal because of the differences in refraction expressed by the difference in the refractive indices. Therefore, the two rays of light differ in phase and some parts of the spectrum are (more or less) obliterated and other parts more or less reinforced. The resultant "interference color" depends upon two factors, namely, the difference between the two indices of refraction of the crystal for the two rays (that is, the *birefringence*) and the thickness of the crystal where the light passes through it.

A. N. Winchell
and Horace Winchell

Cross-references: *Dielectric Constant, Optics*

REFRACTOMETERS

An important instrument for studying the radio refractive structure of the troposphere is the radio refractometer. Various types of these instruments have been developed and widely used to study refractive phenomena throughout the troposphere and lower stratosphere. Most data have been obtained with instruments in which the resonant frequency of a cavity resonator exposed to the ambient atmosphere is continuously compared with a sealed fixed-frequency cavity resonator. The change in difference frequency between the cavity resonators is directly proportional to the change in refractive index of the atmosphere to which the open sampling cavity resonator is exposed. Use of this technique at X-band frequencies has made possible the development of sensitive and accurate radio refractive index instruments. Variations of atmospheric refractive index of less than one part in 10^8 (i.e., 0.01 N unit) are measurable. Recording instruments of either the amplitude-time or X-Y type are used to display the data. For X-Y records the Y displacement is normally made proportional to altitude and the X axis is used to record refractive index. Thus, refractive index profiles are plotted directly.

The use of refractometers in aircraft installations has made possible measurements of atmospheric refractive structure over wide areas (often inaccessible to ground-based instruments such as the radiosonde) in relatively short time periods. From such measurements meteorologists are now learning more of the nature of small-scale properties of the atmosphere. These include horizontal gradients, vertical gradients, small inhomogeneities, convective columns, etc.

One of the special uses of the radio refractometer has been in studying water vapor gradients and general variability in the atmosphere and particularly in clouds. Since the instrument has a very short response time (of the order of 0.01 sec) relative to other meteorological devices used for measuring water vapor content, its use has led to important new understandings of the detail structure and characteristics of various type clouds.

CULLEN M. CRAIN

Cross-references: *Propagation, Radiation Measurements, Radiometeorology*

RELATIVITY

In 1905 Albert Einstein (1879–1955) enunciated the *theory of relativity* to explain the negative result of the Michelson-Morley experiment, which attempted to measure absolute motion through space. The theory of relativity, which is based on the *principle of relativity*, requires that the concept of space and time as unrelated independent quantities must be modified. As a result of these modifications several important and fundamental relationships that connect physical quantities occur and must be taken in account in the study and design of some modern electronic devices.

The theory of relativity, which deals with the way that observers in a state of relative motion describe physical phenomena, is divided into two categories: (1) the *general* theory of relativity, which deals with observers that are in an arbitrary state of motion, and (2) the *special* theory of relativity, which deals with observers that are in relative motion along a straight line at uniform speed.

General Theory of Relativity. A detailed discussion of the postulates of general relativity and consequences resulting therefrom are beyond the scope of this article and only a brief description will be given.

The essential features of the general theory are that (1) when properly formulated, the laws of physics will have the same form (i.e., they will be *covariant*) for observers in an arbitrary state of motion in any space-time coordinate system, and (2) it is not possible to distinguish by experiment between a gravitational field and the force field set up within an accelerating box that is in a region free of a gravitational field (*principle of equivalence*).

A consequence of these postulates is that space time has a curvature that must be taken into account when dealing with motion in accelerating systems or in gravitational fields. The facts that the paths of light rays are bent when they pass through a gravitational field and that the wavelength of light emitted from atoms located in a gravitational field is shifted from the zero-field value are experimentally verified examples that serve to illustrate effects explainable by the general theory.

Special Theory of Relativity. Although the general theory of relativity is important in understanding and unlocking the secrets of the universe, it is the special theory of relativity that finds extensive application in the modern laboratory.

The relationships connecting the various physical quantities may be formulated from two basic postulates:

(1) When properly formulated, the description of a physical phenomenon cannot depend in any way on the absolute speed of translational motion of the coordinate frame in which the phenomenon is being described.

(2) The speed of propagation of an electromagnetic wave is a constant for all observers that are in a state of translational motion along a straight line at constant speed, and is independent of the speed of the source of the wave.

The Lorentz transformation, which forms the basis of the mathematical description of the special theory of relativity, states that as a consequence of the above two postulates, time must be regarded on an equal basis as one coordinate of a four-dimensional space with the usual Cartesian coordinates for the other three dimensions. Furthermore, time and the coordinate along which the reference frame is translating are related in a linear fashion. This linear relationship is known as the Lorentz transformation:

$$x' = \gamma(x - \beta ct); \quad y' = y$$
$$t' = \gamma[t - (\beta x/c)]; \quad z' = z$$

where primes denote quantities in the system moving with velocity v along the x axis, $\beta = v/c$, and $\gamma = [1 - (v^2/c^2)]^{-1/2}$.

Relativistic kinematics relates velocities of objects as measured by one observer to those measured by another observer who is in relative motion along a straight line with respect to the first. If the velocity in the moving system is denoted by u', the velocity u as seen by the observer in the unprimed system is

$$u_x = \frac{u_x' + v}{1 + (u_x'v/c^2)}$$

$$u_{y,z} = \frac{u_{y,z}'}{\gamma[1 + (u_x'v/c^2)]}$$

These equations illustrate that if we give an object in the moving system a velocity $u_x' = c$ (the velocity of light) and allow the two systems a relative velocity $v = c$, the object still only has a velocity $u_x = c$ as measured by the stationary observer. This demonstrates that the speed of light is the *upper* limit of physically attainable speeds of objects.

With the same notation, the transformation of components of acceleration are:

$$\frac{du_x}{dt} = \left[\gamma\left(1 + \frac{u_x'v}{c^2}\right)\right]^{-3} \frac{du_x'}{dt'}$$

$$\frac{du_{y,z}}{dt} = \left[\gamma\left(1 + \frac{u_x'v}{c^2}\right)\right]^{-2} \frac{du_{y,z}'}{dt'}$$
$$- \frac{u_{y,z}'v}{\gamma^2 c^2}\left(1 + \frac{u_x'v}{c^2}\right)^{-3} \frac{du_x'}{dt'}$$

Two other interesting consequences of the Lorentz transformation relation between space and time are the *relativistic time dialation* and the *Lorentz-FitzGerald contraction.*

The relativistic time dialation expresses the fact that the time interval between two events occurring at the same location in the moving reference frame appear to have occurred at different locations in the stationary reference frame as well as at different times. The two observers will therefore disagree as to the time interval between these events

$$\Delta t = \gamma \Delta t'$$

where Δt is in the stationary system and $\Delta t'$ is in the moving system. Each observer will find that a clock in the other observer's system is running slower than his own.

The Lorentz-FitzGerald contraction expresses the fact that the length of an object x' as measured by an observer in the moving reference frame will appear to be shorter to an observer in the stationary reference frame

$$\Delta x = \frac{\Delta x'}{\gamma}$$

This contraction occurs only in the direction of motion.

Relativistic dynamics describes the resulting motion of material bodies that have velocities that are a significant fraction of the velocity of light whenever these bodies are acted on by force.

One point of view of relativistic dynamics that can be taken is to define a *rest mass* of a body as that measured by an observer in whose reference frame the body is stationary. The first postulate of special relativity requires that momentum in an isolated dynamical system be conserved where this momentum is defined as the scalar mass times the vector velocity u. As a consequence of this point of view, the scalar mass m is now a function of the translational velocity u

$$m = m_0[1 - (u^2/c^2)]^{-1/2}$$

where the rest mass m_0 is the same for all observers. This is referred to as the relativistic variation of mass with velocity.

The transformation equations for the components of force using the notion of a scalar mass follow from the time rate of change of momentum

$$\mathbf{F} = \frac{d}{dt}(m\mathbf{u})$$

If the components of force in the prime or moving system are F_x', F_y', F_z', the components in the stationary system are given by

$$F_x = F_x' + (u_y'F_y' + u_z'F_z')\frac{v}{c^2 + u_x'v}$$

$$F_{y,z} = \frac{F'_{y,z}}{1 + \dfrac{u_x'v}{c^2}}$$

Relativistic electrodynamics deals with the transformation of Maxwell's equations from a stationary to a moving reference frame so that the first postulate of special relativity is satisfied. The transformation equations for the components of the electromagnetic field as seen by the moving observer are

$$B_x' = B_x \qquad\qquad E_x' = E_x$$

$$B'_{y,z} = \gamma\left(B_{y,z} \pm \frac{\beta E_{z,y}}{c}\right) \quad E'_{y,z} = \gamma(E_{y,z} \mp \beta c B_{z,y})$$

where the lower sign goes with the second subscript. The electric charge density transforms

$$\rho' = \rho\gamma\left(1 - \frac{\beta u_x}{c}\right)$$

If the field components are known in the moving system and desired in the stationary system change the sign of β and interchange primed and unprimed quantities.

The force acting on a particle of charge q follows from these transformation equations since charge must be conserved between the two systems:

$$\mathbf{F} = q(\mathbf{E} + \mathbf{v} \times \mathbf{B})$$

Relativistic Doppler shift related the frequency and wavenumber of electromagnetic waves that have their source in a moving reference frame to the frequency and wavenumber as measured by the observer in the stationary reference frame. For waves that propagate like $\exp[j(\omega t - k_z z)]$ in the stationary system the transformation equations to the moving system consistent with

the Lorentz transformation are

$$\omega' = \omega - k_z v$$

$$k_z' = k_z - \frac{\omega v}{c^2}$$

Although it turns out that the corrections that must be made in a theory to account for the laws of relativity usually do not introduce any new effects, these corrections do make a quantitative difference in the results that must be taken in account in the design of high-power microwave tubes such as klystrons, magnetrons, etc., and in other devices such as electron microscopes, linear accelerators, cyclotrons, and x-ray tubes.

A. W. TRIVELPIECE

Cross-references: *Electromagnetic Theory, Statistical Mechanics*

RELAYS

The relay, one of mankind's first electrical devices, was used practically in telegraphy as early as 1850. The modern relay, properly applied, is one of the most simple, effective and desirable components available. In the majority of instances, it can achieve better reliability, at less cost, than an equivalent solid-state switching complex. The efficiency of modern telephone systems attests to the reliability and longevity of the relay during billions of daily operations.

The relay is a device that permits switching control of one or more circuits to be accomplished by electrical variations in a usually noninterdependent control circuit. In the usual connotation, a relay is an electromagnetic device in which control power is supplied to the coil of a relay motor whose mechanical motion is used to actuate contacts of other circuits. The term is also used to identify other control switching devices which use saturable-reactor, semiconductor, photovoltaic, piezoelectric or electrochemical phenomena.

There are many forms of the electromagnetic relay, various designations being descriptive of particular features. Terminology such as *clapper*, *rotary*, or *plunger* (*solenoid*) is frequently used to describe the motor armature type. The *telephone* type is a special configuration of clapper relay that can have many contacts of varying forms. *Miniature* and *subminiature* refer to size but recently have been identified with a small, hermetically sealed relay designed to endure the rigors of military applications. *Power* relay implies a contact rating of 5 amp or more; however, above 25 amp, the word *contactor* comes into usage.

Variations of the electromagnetic relay extend the general employment. A *latching* relay assumes either of two attitudes when respectively energized and maintains position after control power is interrupted. This type is particularly suitable for pulse operation. Introducing a permanent magnet into the relay magnetic circuit causes polarization, i.e., sensitivity to the polarity of the control signal. A polarized relay which assumes one attitude or another depending on the signal polarity is called a *side-stable* relay and is also a latching relay. If it returns to a neutral center position when de-energized, it is considered to be a *center-stable* relay.

In the *mercury* relay, contact is actually made by liquid mercury in the form of a pool or by mercury-wetted contact faces fed by capillary action. Contact is made in the pool type by tilting the capsule to move the pool to the contact or by moving the contact into the pool using electromagnetic forces. Mercury relays are considered highly reliable and usually bounce free in both low-level and power circuits. They have the disadvantage of being position-sensitive and cannot be overloaded since the mercury converts to vapor and causes continuous conduction.

The *thermal* relay derives its mechanical motion to actuate the contacts from the thermoexpansions of metals heated by the control circuit. Because of its nature, it is particularly suitable as a time-delay relay. Time delay may also be obtained in conventional relays through a shorted-turn coil, mechanical dash-pots, or electronic circuitry. If snap action is not built into the contacts, time-delay relays can suffer from severe contact erosion owing to slow motion.

Sensitive relays describe the many relay forms operating at extremely low control powers, e.g., below 50 mw. Usually, sensitivity is obtained at the expense of size and contact rating. Many sensitive relays operate from a slowly rising current and require built-in snap action for rapid contact transfer. The *meter* relay is an extremely sensitive form using meter movement as a motor; contact is made by the meter pointer. Although delicate and rated for small loads, they offer flexibility because the actuation point can be accurately set or predetermined.

In the *stepping* relay sequential contacts are made through progressive actuation accomplished by controlled pulses to the coil. Many forms exist and uses in programming and counting circuits are unlimited.

A new relay, developed by Bell Telephone Laboratories and coming into great prominence, is the *reed* relay. It consists of two reeds of magnetic materials sealed in each end of a long glass tube in such a way that the reeds overlap at the center of the tube with a small gap. When a coil is placed around the tube and energized, magnetic flux causes the reeds to come together, thereby making contact. These units offer promise of millions of reliable operations at relatively low contact ratings. Reliability can be attributed to simplicity and contact operation in a sealed atmosphere.

Military applications require relays that are small, light, and relatively immune to environment; these relays must have high contact pressure to maintain continuity during shock and vibration, must have larger gaps between contacts to prevent arc-over, and must be hermetically sealed. Military-type relays usually have rotary (balanced) armatures that make the relay motor less susceptible to external forces.

Increased sensitivity can be obtained by a sacrifice in contact rating, size, or environmental immunity. Operate and release time are limited by moving component size or magnetic-circuit configuration. Contact bounce is objectionable since it can reduce contact life or present erroneous information to certain types of circuitry; this condition occurs because of rebound of the motor armature and contacts. Attempts to add components to dampen rebound are difficult, particularly in miniature relays, because of size and the tendency of additional components to affect reliability adversely.

In recent years, there have been breakthroughs in the study of contacts operating in the region below 250 mv, generally referred to as the low-level or dry-circuit region. Contacts operating in this region make physically but not electrically because the voltage is not sufficient to break down the insulating gaseous and chemical films. It is therefore necessary to choose relay and contact materials to minimize these effects. Contact materials of gold or gold alloys are the best; silver, metals of the platinum group and nonnoble metals are totally unsuitable. Alloys of silver and metals of the platinum groups make excellent contacts for low- and medium-power loads. Refractory materials such as tungsten or molybdenum are more suitable for high-power loads but require exceedingly high contact pressures, which prevent their incorporation in small relays.

Louis D. DeLalio

Cross-references: *Circuit Breakers, Connectors, Contacts, Sequential Circuits, Switches, Switching Circuits*

RELAY SYSTEMS: see SYSTEMS (NONLINEAR)

RELIABILITY AND QUALITY CONTROL

Quality Control

Statistical quality control is the use of probability theory in quality inspection problems. In lieu of basing decisions on rule of thumb or intuition, the laws of probability are used to make a scientific, objective estimate in contrast to the biased and subjec-

tive approaches that are so often used. The principle of quality control is that it is impossible to make or find two objects which are identical; the random effects of many variables in the manufacturing process cannot be absolutely predicted or controlled. For this reason, for most practical cases in quality control it is feasible to assume a Gaussian distribution. The Gaussian distribution is the familiar bell-shaped or "normal curve" with long tails.

The assumption of a normal distribution coupled with a knowledge of such parameters as the mean ($\bar{x}$), dispersion (R), or standard deviation (s) of the tested sample, permits one either to measure the quality of the manufactured product (percent defectives to be expected) or to control, within limits, the various manufacturing processes to insure that a given quantitative quality will be maintained.

Acceptance sampling plans are attributes or variables plans depending upon whether the observed characteristic is a count or a measurement. Sampling plans are also classified as single, double, or multiple (sequential) sampling depending upon the number of groups of items sampled from the submitted lot. Various types of acceptance sampling plans are discussed in the literature. It is sufficient for our purpose to discuss briefly only single sampling plans.

On an attributes basis, a single sampling plan is specified by three members: the lot size N, the sample size n, and the acceptance number a. When the n sample units are randomly selected from the submitted lot and the number of defectives c observed, the decision to accept or reject the lot is as follows: accept if $c \leq a$ and reject $c \geq a$. To evaluate such a plan, it is necessary that we gain some idea of its ability to discriminate between "good" and "bad" lots. The most common method of performing this evaluation is to establish the operating characteristic OC curve for the plan. This curve (Fig. 1) is simply a plot of the "probability of acceptance" against the "fraction defective in the lot."

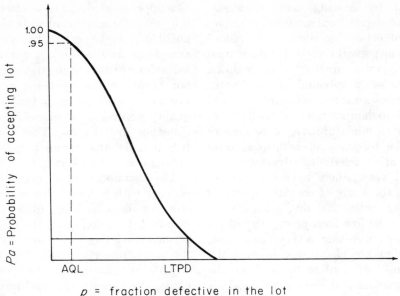

FIG. 1. Operating Characteristic Curve.

Two points of particular interest should be noted: the acceptable quality level (AQL) associated with a 0.95 probability of acceptance and the lot tolerance percent defective (LTPD) associated with a 0.10 probability of acceptance. From knowledge of these plus the desired producer's risk (α) and consumer's risk (β) (α = probability of rejecting a good lot; β = probability of accepting a bad lot) a sampling plan OC curve may be found from documents such as MIL-Std-105A, which will meet the requirements.

If a variables plan were utilized the observed characteristic would be a measurement. Further, at the present time, the only variables plans available require that a normal distribution be assumed for the population from which the measurements are a random sample. Then, the decision (for a two-sided test) to accept or reject is given by: accept if both $\bar{x} + ks \leq U$ and $\bar{x} - ks \geq L$ are satisfied; reject if $\bar{x} + ks > U$ or $\bar{x} - ks < L$, where U and L are upper and lower specification limits and $\bar{x}$ and s are sample mean and standard deviation.

A *control chart* is a graphical device which aids in keeping track of production quality. Control charts usually take the form of Fig. 2 where the plotted points represent values calculated from samples selected from the production processes and the control lines

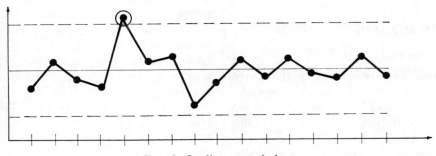

FIG. 2. Quality control chart.

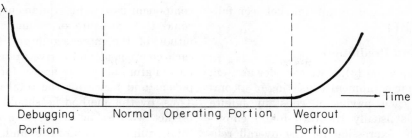

FIG. 3. Common life characteristic curve.

are determined by assessing the inherent variability of the process. No matter what explicit assumptions are made concerning the nature of the process, the same general form of chart always evolves.

In general, charts are utilized to control both adherence (on the average) to a nominal specification and variability among the many items produced. Sometimes one chart accomplishes both of these tasks; in other cases two charts are needed. If the measured characteristics are assumed to be normally distributed, two charts are used: the $\bar{x}$-chart for averages and R-chart for ranges. If the characteristic being controlled is binomially distributed (such as fraction defective) then one chart, the p-chart, will suffice.

Regardless of the exact form of the chart(s), the rules for reaching decisions are the same. The process is said to be out of control if one or more of the following events occur:

(a) A point plots outside of the control limits.

(b) Too many points in succession plot on one side of the center line.

(c) A trend (up or down) becomes apparent as a sequence of points is plotted.

Reliability

Reliability is defined as the probability of adequate performance of a specified function or functions, for a specified time under specified conditions. Thus, reliability may be considered a numeric, capable of measurement and prediction. From studies conducted on complex electronic equipments, it has been found that the smoothed failure rate versus time curve shown in Fig. 3 best represents the life characteristic curve of well-designed equipments.

Actually Fig. 3 is somewhat deceiving since, with most well-designed equipments, the normal operating period of the life curve is much longer than either of the other periods. It should also be noted that the failure rate is constant during the middle portion of the equipment life curve. This fact greatly simplifies the reliability design, prediction, and measurement problems.

Statistical theory indicates that, if failures occur as discrete, single, independent events in time, the probability of exactly x failures in time t is given by the Poisson distribution,

$$p(x,t) = \frac{u^x e^{-u}}{x!} \qquad (1)$$

In this expression, u, is the expected number of failures, or the universe mean number of failures. It is equal to;

$$u = \bar{\lambda}t \qquad (2)$$

where $\bar{\lambda}$ is the average failure rate, or the average number of expected failures per unit time.

If the failure rate is constant, as in the middle portion of figure 3, and we wish to find the probability of zero failures in time t, the Poisson equation becomes;

$$p(0,t) = \frac{\lambda t^0 e^{-\lambda t}}{0!} = e^{-\lambda t} = R(t) \qquad (3)$$

where $R(t)$ is the reliability as previously defined. This is the basic reliability equation also given by;

$$R(t) = e^{-t/m} \qquad (4)$$

where $m = 1/\lambda$ = mean-time-between-failures (MTBF)

Design and Prediction

From equation (3), if we consider an item of electronic equipment consisting of n components, each having a constant failure rate (as is usually the case found empirically), the expression for the overall reliability of the equipment will be given by;

$$
\begin{aligned}
&= R_1 R_2 \ldots R_n = \prod_{i=1}^{n} R_i \\
R_{\text{total}} &= e^{-\lambda_1 t} e^{-\lambda_2 t} \ldots e^{-\lambda_n t} \qquad (5) \\
&= \exp\left[-\sum_{i=1}^{n} \lambda_i t \right] = e^{-t/m}
\end{aligned}
$$

where λ_i is the failure rate of the ith component. Therefore, the overall equipment failure rate is simply the sum of the individual component failure rates.

The equipment mean-time-between-failures (m) is equal to

$$
1 \Big/ \sum_{i=1}^{n} \lambda_i
$$

providing the following assumptions are made:

(1) All components are assumed to be in series, so that if one fails the equipment is considered to have failed.

(2) The failure of one element does not affect the future probability of failure of any other elements.

(3) The equipment failure rate is constant.

It would appear, if one accepts these assumptions, that to make a reliability prediction on an item of electronic equipment, we need only know the failure rates (λ's) of each component. Adding the λ's would provide the λ_T or equipment failure rate and $1/\lambda_T$ would provide the mean-time-between-failures, a measurable quantity. Failure rate versus stress curves for most electronic components are available in handbooks and are constantly being revised as additional data become available. Armed with a complete set of such curves for each

component used in his equipment, a designer could then measure or estimate the magnitude of the more significant stresses on each component and arrive at realistic and meaningful failure rate figures for each component and hence for the total equipment. Thus, by this method he should be able to predict with a fair degree of accuracy the total equipment failure rate and, hence, the MTBF of his equipment. By the same token, this technique permits a designer, given a specific equipment MTBF, to design the equipment scientifically to meet this figure.

It can be seen, therefore, that reliability depends upon the failure rate of the individual component part. Faced with the problem of designing an equipment with a given MTBF, a designer must first perform an analysis as to whether the part failure rates, under the anticipated stresses, will permit meeting the figures. If not, he has the choice of developing more reliable components or reducing the stresses, and hence the failure rates, of those available. If even these measures fail, then more sophisticated design techniques such as parallel redundancy must be used. These techniques are described in detail in the literature.

Measurement

Most time-based reliability test criteria in use today are based mathematically on a constant failure rate assumption related to the normal operating period shown in Fig. 3: in effect, a failure distribution per operating time which is Poisson distributed. If one had a large enough number of samples and were able to test these for long periods of time, the MTBF of the equipment could be determined by:

$$
\text{MTBF} = \frac{\text{Total operating time of all samples}}{\text{Total number of failures}}
$$

Since, in practice, this is not so, one must, on the basis of a limited sample, use statistical processes to estimate the actual equipment MTBF of the equipment. A simple example is given here but the reader is cautioned to consult additional references on reliability testing rather than blindly follow this example, since reliability testing is a complex and controversial process at this time.

Suppose it is necessary to predict from the results of a 200-hr test what the MTBF of an equipment would be if a complete longevity test were run to wearout. The investigator must ask himself, "How likely is the MTBF indicated by the sample to be the actual equipment MTBF for its lifetime?"

If an equipment being measured has an MTBF equal to the specified value (i.e., $m = m_0$) the failure rate of the equipment λ per hour would be equal to λ. Thus if the equipment were tested on the hypothesis that $m = m_0$, one would expect the total failures during a test of length t to be $\lambda \cdot t$. The figures $\lambda \cdot t$ or its equivalent t/m_0 are, thus, the expectancy of failures during a test.

There are standard cumulative Poisson probability charts that list the probability of c or less failures occurring for various expectancies of failure. In the reliability test, the expectancy is t/m_0 which is substituted for p_n in the Thorndike charts. The probability for various numbers of failures can thus be read directly from the chart.

For example, let us assume an equipment specified $m_0 = 100$ hr and it is tested for 200 hr (t). Substituting $t/m_0 = 2$ for $p_n = 2$ in the Thorndike chart, we can read directly that there is only a 12-percent chance of having no failure, a 40-percent chance of having one or less failure, a 68-percent chance of having 2 or less failures, an 86-percent chance of 3 or less, and a 94-percent chance of 4 or less. This last figure can be read that there is only a 6-percent chance that there will be 5 or more failures during the 200-hr test if the actual m equals the specified m_0. Thus if we do have 5 or more failures during the 200-hr test we can conclude with high confidence (94 per cent) that the actual m is not equal to or greater than the specified m_0; thus, the equipment should

be rejected. For additional details on this as well as other approaches such as the chi-squared or sequential technique, the interested reader should consult the literature.

JOSEPH J. NARESKY

Cross-references: *Distribution Functions, Errors in Measurement, Probability, Sampling Theorem*

REMANENCE: see MAGNETISM

RESISTORS

Carbon Composition Resistors

Resistors that are used extensively in commercial and military equipment may be classified into three main categories: composition resistors, precision film resistors and wire-wound resistors. Carbon composition resistors are used in great quantities and are very low in cost. The composition resistors are often much smaller than wirewound or precision film resistors for an equivalent application. These resistors are used in all applications where the initial resistance tolerance does not have to be less than ±5.0%, and the stability does not have to be better than ±5.0% under storage conditions, and ±15% under full rated operating conditions. The high-frequency properties of composition resistors of low wattage rating can be considered as having practically pure resistances in the megacycle region. This property is particularly important since at high frequencies wirewound resistors may have reactances that are of the same order of magnitude as their resistance. Composition resistors are made in two different types of construction. One is called a "slug" type of fixed composition resistor, and the other is generally referred to as a film type.

The "slug" type of resistor is made by mixing carbon and resins in a series of different proportions. These mixtures are molded or pressed into the form of a solid rod. The type of carbon, and its concentration, may be modified to make a wide range of resistance values. The axial lead wires are usually anchored in the molding operation. A sec-

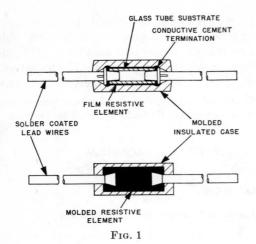

FIG. 1

ond molding operation forms a plastic jacket, usually of phenolic resin, as an insulating case around the lead element subassembly. Obtaining exact resistance values by this process is difficult and generally the finished molded unit may be "binned" into stock in a series of adjacent resistance increments. This binned stock serves as inventory from which units may be withdrawn to fill orders. These resistors are completed by the application of color coding paint bands and testing before shipment. The molded units may be given stabilizing heat treatments before binning in order to develop greater stability. Figure 1 shows a cross section of a "slug" type composition resistor.

The film-type fixed composition resistors are prepared by hot drawing a large tube of glass into a continuous small-diameter capillary form. This small glass tube or filament is coated with a mixture of liquid resins and carbons. The coating is continuously applied and thermally cured. The resistance value of the coating is monitored constantly and corrective feedback information controls the process within allowable resistance limits. Resistance values are varied by changing the composition of the conductive mixture applied to the filament, resulting in a wide range of possible resistance values. The coated and stabilized filament is cut into discrete lengths and talon-headed lead wires

are inserted into both ends of the small tube. The inserted talon leads serve to remove heat from the interior of the resistors by conduction. Permanent electrical connection is made between the lead wire and the resistance film by using a metered amount of an electrically conducting adhesive, which is also subjected to a curing treatment. The subassemblies are molded in specially compounded thermosetting resin jackets, then are tested and color coded. Excellent control of the desired resistance value may be achieved by this continuous process with correspondingly high yield of resistors.

In both processes the final product is sorted into $\pm 5.0\%$, $\pm 10.0\%$, or $\pm 20.0\%$ resistance tolerances. Figure 1 also shows a cross section of a film-type composition carbon resistor for comparison with the "slug" type. The use of colored paint bands around the circumference of the resistors identifies the resistance value and tolerance level. The power rating of a resistor is the amount it can dissipate for long periods of time without greatly changing its resistance value. Composition resistors are generally available in wattage ratings of $\frac{1}{10}$, $\frac{1}{4}$, $\frac{1}{3}$, $\frac{1}{2}$, 1, and 2 w. The resistance values normally made range between 10 ohms and 22 megohms. Below 10 ohms, wirewound resistors are usually preferred; above 22 megohms operation may be somewhat less reliable owing to sensitivity to moisture.

The performance of the two composition resistor types is usually quite similar with but few exceptions. The "skin effect" (*q.v.*) observed in electrical conduction at high frequencies does cause a performance difference at high frequencies. Thus, in measurements at frequencies of up to 400 Mc the "slug type" changes significantly more than the film in the ratio of ac to dc resistance.

SIDNEY J. STEIN

Film Resistors

Film resistors comprise a thin film, normally 10 to 10,000 Å thick. The development of high-stability films has been based on the need for a replacement for wirewound resistors that should have these characteristics:

(1) Precision and stability of wirewound resistors

(2) Smaller size and lower weight

(3) Better high-frequency performance

(4) Lower cost

The principal elements of film resistors are as follows.

Substrate. The support for the film is made of ceramic or glass and normally shaped as a cylinder or tube.

Film. Carbon dispersions, deposited carbon, metal, and metal oxide are some of the more common types of materials employed as resistance films. Formation of the film is by spraying, dipping, evaporation, sputtering, or pyrolitic cracking of gas. This operation is carried out in a controlled atmosphere. The resistance of a film depends on the specific resistance of the material and the film thickness. For a given material the resistance is controlled by film thickness and is characterized in ohms/square, which is inversly proportional to film thickness. The relation between measured resistance and ohms/square is:

$$\text{Ohms/square} = \frac{\text{R measured} \times \text{Rod circumference}}{\text{Rod length}}$$

Spiralling is an operation commonly employed to increase the resistance of a film resistor. By cutting a helical path in the cylinder of film the resistance is raised by as much as 3000 times.

Termination. The terminals of a film resistor are made of a low-resistance conductive material applied to the ends of the rod. This conductor is a base metal such as gold or silver, and is applied by painting, evaporating, or sputtering. To the conductor are attached the metal leads or lugs that serve as the resistor terminals.

Protective Enclosure. To protect the film from environmental conditions, an enclosure is applied. It is in this area that the greatest variety is offered to the user. These enclosures range in order of effectiveness as follows: varnish, molded or encapsulated ther-

mosetting material, solder-sealed ceramic jacket, glass-sealed jacket. It is important to note that there can be wide design variations in any one enclosure that may destroy its effectiveness.

Specifications. Resistor parameters are defined in specifications given by the manufacturer.

Power Rating is determined by physical size and operating temperature. The operating temperature is composed of ambient temperature plus the heat generated in the resistor. The resistor designer can reduce the latter by use of good heat conductors and radiators in the design.

Resistance range of a given resistor size is determined by the upper and lower limits of film thickness. As might be expected, there are quality problems at both extremes. Normal range is from 1 ohm to 20 megohms.

Resistance Tolerance available is normally determined by over-all stability. There would be little value in purchasing a resistor with 1% tolerance if it changed 5% in environmental cycling. By control and sorting it is possible to manufacture film resistors with 0.1% tolerance.

Maximum Operating Voltage is specified on film resistors to limit voltage and thermal deterioration of the high-value thin films. The user should note that a ¼-w, 1-megohm, 300-m.o.v. resistor should never be used with over 0.09 w of power applied.

Temperature Coefficient of Resistance is a measure of the variation in resistance with an incremental change in temperature, commonly expressed in parts per million per degree centigrade. This parameter is determined by the film material and ranges from 0 to 500 p.p.m.

High-Frequency Characteristics of film resistors are good. Film resistors are only slightly frequency dependent. With only a few spirals there is very low series inductance and shunt capacitance. In most cases the ac resistance does not drop until 1 Mc is reached. At this point the reactance from the shunt capacitance becomes predominant. By using unspiralled resistors it is possible to operate in the 100-Mc region without serious loss of resistance.

Voltage Coefficient is a measure of the variation in resistance with voltage and is expressed as percentage per volt. This change is independent of temperature and is very low on high-stability film resistors, of the order of 0.001%/v.

Noise voltages are internally generated emf (Johnson noise) and current-dependent noises caused by resistance variation. Owing to the absence of standard noise measurement equipment it has been difficult to duplicate measurements. It can be stated that good film resistors have noise voltages as low as wirewound resistors, i.e., less than 0.1 μv/v.

Environmental Characteristics are a series of tests devised to simulate the use conditions that a resistor might undergo. Some of these are: temperature cycle, short-time overload, low-temperature operation, terminal strength, dielectric withstanding voltage, insulation resistance, effect of soldering, resistance temperature coefficient, load life, moisture resistance, acceleration, shock, and high-frequency vibration. The ability of a resistor to be subjected to the various environments and exhibit resistance changes within allowable limits is its figure of merit. Film resistors of good design and quality have this ability. The type of enclosures used is the most important factor in reducing resistance changes caused by these tests.

In the past few years giant strides have been taken in the development and improvement of film resistors. Specifications have been upgraded. Although precision film resistors with the stability and precision of wirewound resistors are not yet available, the gap is rapidly closing. The objectives of small size, good high frequency performance, and lower cost have been met.

WALTER RANDOLPH

Wirewound Resistors

A wirewound resistor is an electrical resistance element of wire alloy, of correct size, wound between terminals on a supporting form and suitably protected against mechanical and environmental hazards.

The category into which a particular wirewound resistor is placed is determined by its power rating and intended use. General-purpose low-power fixed-value; low, medium, and high power; and precision wirewound resistors make up the bulk of the wirewound resistors manufactured.

A general-purpose low-power fixed-value resistor is usually produced semi-automatically on machinery that (1) winds resistance wire on either a rigid or flexible mandrel, (2) cuts the wound mandrel to the proper length, and (3) clamps preformed terminals firmly to each end. The range of resistance values obtained by this method of manufacture is from a minimum of less than 1 ohm to a maximum of approximately 10,000 ohms. The resistance value tolerances for this type of resistor are nominally ±5% and ±10%. The type is used in place of carbon composition resistors when the values and wattage ratings are compatible, for commercial applications in television receiver circuits, meters, and test sets where the inductance of the helically wound element is not significant.

Low-, medium-, and high-power wirewound resistors are basically similar in construction. The various power ratings require different sizes of resistance wire or resistance ribbon and suitable coatings of high-temperature silicone, inorganic cement, or vitreous enamel, all of which contribute to the many varied configurations of power resistors manufactured.

Individual resistors are generally wound on ceramic tubes, or in the case of the smaller diameters, on ceramic rods that have had cap and lead assemblies or a preformed lug fastened to each end. The resistor is wound on a machine that allows a regular pitch and uniform tension to be applied to the wire, which has been selected according to type and size from wire charts for the particular type and wattage of resistor required. The electrical-mechanical connection of the resistance element to the terminations is of utmost importance and is usually accomplished by welding or silver soldering. The coating is applied by dipping, spraying, or flowing the material over the resistor and curing until a firm impervious outer shell is formed as a protection against harsh environments.

Power resistors are used in power supplies, magnetic amplifiers, television receivers, resistance loading devices, and electronic control equipment.

Precision wirewound resistors have an initial tolerance of $\pm 0.1\%$ or less and a temperature coefficient of $\pm 0.003\%/\deg$ C or better over a temperature range of -65 to $+125°C$.

Two kinds of construction are used in these resistors, the unenclosed "commercial" types and the enclosed "military" types. Circuit connections are made by means of (1) radial lugs, (2) radial leads, (3) axial leads, and (4) printed-circuit types having both leads on one end. Mounting is accomplished with a through bolt on the radial lug and radial lead types, and by the leads on the axial lead and printed circuit types.

In either the unenclosed or the enclosed type the fine resistance wire (sometimes 0.0005 in. in diameter) is wound on a bobbin consisting of an equal number of sections called "pi's." The wire is wound in reverse directions in each section (reverse-pi winding) to minimize the effective series inductance.

The unenclosed types use nonhygroscopic steatite bobbins and have the windings protected with varnishes, waxes, or sometimes silicone rubber. The terminations must be rugged enough to maintain the tolerance of the resistor in normal use and are made by welding, soft soldering, and brazing. A label of paper or acetate tape is used to identify the unit.

The enclosed types use a plastic bobbin with the same thermal expansion characteristics as the material used for encapsulation or molding of the completed unit to minimize stresses during adverse environmental conditions. Additional precautions are taken; to maintain a constant minimum winding tension, to age the resistors adequately to remove any spurious winding stresses, and to cushion the winding suitably against shrinkage of the encapsulating compound used. The completed resistors are normally marked with an ink that forms a homogeneous bond with the surface of the unit.

Precision wirewound resistors are used in bridge circuits, summing networks, voltage dividers, calibration circuits, and as meter multipliers.

GEORGE W. ENGERT

Cross-references: *Bridges, Color Codes, Noise Generation, Potentiometers, Printed Circuits, Thermistors*

RESNATRON

The resnatron is a high-efficiency class-C grounded-grid amplifier with cavity circuits placed within the vacuum. Gains of 5 to 15 db are obtained with control grids that are very coarse for such high frequencies, 200 to 3000 Mc, with nearly a cycle of transit time. The control-grid bars are several millimeters thick and spaced a similar distance apart. Electrons from a nearby hot cathode are density modulated and focused into a beam that passes through this grounded grid and on through slots in the screen or accelerator grid which likewise is at rf ground. The beam crosses the output interaction field of the anode and penetrates deep into slots in the anode from where it is difficult for secondary electrons to travel to the screen even if the phase of the fields then permitted such movement to begin. The early tetrode resnatrons required a small dc potential between screen and anode to assure this, but in later tetrodes both electrodes were at the same dc potential with respect to the control cavity. There are dozens of beams of electrons located at the voltage maxima of the input and output cavities, and the intervening space between the two cavities is arranged to have a voltage node where the beams pass through the dc potential, to minimize interaction here.

Although the resnatron was used mostly for radar countermeasures (*q.v.*), it was developed originally to supply power to electron linear accelerators (*q.v.*) made of disk loaded waveguide, in 1939. The first high-Q cavity ever driven by a grounded-grid amplifier of any kind was at 500 Mc, using a pentode resnatron coupled through a half-wavelength line. The resnatron was driven by energy obtained from the high-Q load through another half-wavelength line. Thereafter tetrode resnatrons were used with model disk-loaded waveguide high-Q resonator loads up to 1000 Mc, before World War II diverted this effort to countermeasures.

The power, efficiency, gain, and bandwidth of resnatrons is about the same as for amplitrons (*q.v.*), but resnatrons are more expensive and are more difficult to shield. Like klystrons (*q.v.*), resnatrons do not require matching of input and output to avoid reflections and oscillations.

D. H. SLOAN

Cross-references: *Electron Tubes (Conventional)*

RESONATORS AND WAVEMETERS

A resonator is a circuit in which energy is stored in both magnetic and electric fields in such a manner that the energy oscillates from the electric field to the magnetic field with small loss of energy. The amount of energy stored in the electric field is exactly equal to the amount of energy stored in the magnetic field at the resonant frequency. Lumped-constant resonators may consist of an inductor and a capacitor in parallel. Distributed constant resonators may be produced by taking any conceivable type of transmission line and short circuiting it at two points separated by half a wavelength ($\lambda/2$) or multiples thereof. Open-wire lines, coaxial lines, striplines, or waveguides may be used. In the case of coaxial or striplines a resonator may also be obtained by short-circuiting such a line at one end and leaving it open-circuited $\lambda/4$ away. Resonators are also formed from irregular closed shapes including the spherical resonator, the partial coaxial resonator, and resonators of peculiar shapes such as the hyperbolic paraboloid. Each of these resonators must include a portion of its volume which is electrically similar to a capacitor in which energy is stored in the E field and also a section resembling an inductance in which energy is stored in the B field. The resonant frequency of any such chamber will then be the frequency (or frequencies) at which the energy in the magnetic field is exactly equal to the energy in the electrical field.

Open-wire line resonators have been used occasionally as resonators for rough measurement of frequency in the form of the Lecher line. In microwave measurements, coaxial and waveguide resonators are preferred. The advantage of these types is that they are enclosed volumes with a much higher Q owing to the elimination of radiation losses. Coaxial line resonators fit into three categories: the $\lambda/2$ line with short circuits at each end of the line, the $\lambda/4$ line with a short circuit at one end and an open circuit at the opposite end, and the capacitive loaded line with a short circuit at one end and a variable capacitor at the other end for tuning. Waveguide resonators usually consist of cylindrical or rectangular waveguides with short circuits spaced at $\gamma/2$. When a tunable resonator is desired, as in a frequency meter, the $\lambda/2$ cylindrical waveguide resonator provides high Q and is readily adjustable. Hence this type has found use in many types of resonant-cavity wavemeters. The resonant frequency is readily determined for a cylindrical resonator since its resonant wavelength is computed from the formula:

$$\lambda = \left[\left(\frac{K_{lm}}{\pi D} \right)^2 + \left(\frac{n}{2L} \right)^2 \right]^{-1/2}$$

where

λ = free-space wavelength
D = cavity diameter
L = cavity length
K_{lm} = mth root of $J'(K) = 0$ (for TE modes)

$K_{lm} = m$th root of $J(K) = 0$ (for TM modes)

l = number of circumferential field variations

m = number of radial field variations

$n = 1, 2, 3 \cdots$ (for TE modes)

$n = 0, 1, 2 \cdots$ (for TM modes)

An infinite number of modes of resonance exist in circular waveguide resonators of this type just as an infinite number of transmission modes exist. These modes may be plotted for ready use in determining the resonant frequency of the cylindrical cavity from the resonant equation. Such a chart is shown in Figure 1 where $(fD)^2$ is plotted vs $(D/L)^2$. The two commonly used regions for the TE_{111} and TE_{011} modes are indicated on the chart within brackets.

Resonators in rectangular parallelepipeds have approximately the same unloaded Q as those of cylindrical resonators of corresponding volume. Although not practical for a tunable resonator, they find wide usage as resonators in bandpass filters that are used in waveguide systems. Here the resonator is constructed by simply inserting obstacles such as irises into the waveguide at the proper spacing.

Re-entrant resonators such as a partial coaxial resonator or distortions of a coaxial resonator are used in klystrons ($q.v.$) to provide a configuration for the proper coupling of energy to an electron beam. Typical re-

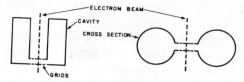

FIG. 2. Re-entrant cavities coupled to an electron beam.

entrant cavities and means of coupling them to an electron beam are shown in Fig. 2. Because of the greater ratio of surface to volume a re-entrant cavity has lower Q than that of a cylindrical or rectangular cavity.

A relatively new type of resonator is the traveling-wave resonator, which is constructed from a directional coupler in which the secondary line output is looped back and connected to the normally terminated end of the secondary arm. When energy is propagating in the primary arm of this directional coupler, energy coupled into the secondary arm continues to circulate around the secondary loop. At frequencies at which the loop path is a multiple of 360° the circulating energy is in phase with the coupled energy. This circumstance results in extremely high E field distributions in the secondary line. This type of resonator is used to generate high-amplitude E fields in testing high-power transmission components when a source of high power is not available. Directional filters are also made from traveling-wave resonators.

Microwave resonators normally have the characteristic that frequency decreases with increasing temperature. The reason for this is that the resonant frequency is a function of the dimensions of the resonator. If a resonator is made completely of one homogeneous material, that material increases in size with an increasing temperature thus increasing the resonant wavelength and decreasing the resonant frequency. Therefore, the resonant frequency is an inverse function of temperature:

$$\Delta F = -\alpha F \Delta T$$

where α is the linear coefficient of expansion of the cavity material. Resonant frequency

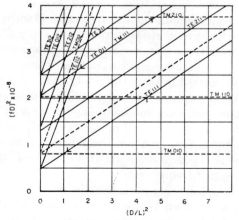

FIG. 1. Mode chart

also varies with relative humidity when a cavity is filled with air.

Resonators are frequently used in band-pass and band-reject filters. Since the input impedance of a resonator is resistive at the resonant frequency and is highly reactive at any frequencies off resonance, this is exactly the characteristic necessary in many types of such filters. Resonators are also used for impedance matching. For instance, a small coupling loop or iris has a relatively low impedance whereas the impedance across opposite faces of a cavity may be extremely high. Hence a resonator can be treated as a transformer of high turns ratio. Resonators are used in most klystrons to couple the electron beam to the output. Resonators are also used in detector mounts and in certain types of waveguide to coaxial adapters to provide the proper impedance variation as a function of frequency to obtain low VSWR.

An important application of resonators is in radar (q.v.) performance testing as in echo boxes. Very large resonators operating in high-order modes, called echo boxes, are coupled to the radar transmission line. When the transmitted pulse reaches the echo box an oscillation increases in amplitude within the echo box. When the transmitted pulse is completed energy is still oscillating from the electric to the magnetic field within the echo box. This oscillation gradually decays in an exponential manner. Meanwhile the radar receiver tuned to the radar frequency receives the decaying signal. The time for the decaying signal to reach noise level is referred to as echo-box ring time. The ring time is proportional to the radar transmitter power and to the receiver sensitivity. Therefore it is a measure of the over-all performance of a radar system. A tunable echo box may be used as a crude spectrum analyzer, since by tuning in the vicinity of the radar frequency a sample of small portions of the spectrum may be obtained. When the amplitude of energy measured in these portions of the spectrum is plotted as a function of frequency an approximation of the transmitted spectrum is obtained.

Certain types of resonators are used to perform frequency control of oscillators as part of the frequency determining network of the oscillator. Resonant cavities have been used to perform the direct frequency control of triodes, klystron oscillators, magnetron oscillators, and various solid-state oscillators. Resonators have also been used to perform the indirect control of many types of voltage-tunable oscillators in AFC loops. Such resonant cavities usually have extreme stability with environmental changes. Cavities are frequently silver-soldered assemblies made of materials with a low coefficient of expansion such as Invar. Cavities have been made with frequency coefficients of expansion of less than $1:10^6$ per °C. These cavities are hermetically sealed and have no frequency variation with atmospheric pressure or relative humidity.

Resonators are occasionally used in the measurement of dielectric constants. The resonant frequency of the resonator is shifted by inserting a sample of dielectric material. The amount of shift is a function of the dielectric constant of the material. The variation in unloaded Q is a measure of the loss tangent of the material.

Resonators are also used as discriminators in frequency-modulated systems.

Resonators as Wavemeters. As mentioned above, Lecher lines, coaxial lines, and cavities have been used as wavemeter resonators. When a resonator is used as an absorption wavemeter it is coupled loosely to a transmission line and at resonance absorbs a small amount of the transmitted energy. A transmission wavemeter has an input coupling and an output coupling. Energy is transmitted through the cavity at resonance. The absorption type of coupling is used for many common test set-ups. However, the two-terminal or transmission-type of wavemeter is preferred for a rapid-tuning wavemeter that permits rapid location of the resonant frequency.

The following table lists the various types of wavemeters that have been manufactured and commonly used in microwave frequency measurements. Included are the frequency ranges used and the accuracies that have been obtained. Other characteristics of various types of cavity wavemeters are also listed.

adjustable calibrating resistors in more complex circuits, often in series with a much larger fixed resistor.

To meet the differing requirements from those of potentiometers, rheostats differ in a

Resonator Type	Physical Characteristics	Frequency Range	Accuracy (%)	Tuning Range	Loaded Q
Lumped constant	Inductance and capacitor in parallel	1–400 Mc	0.2–1.0	1.5:1–3:1	10–100
Lecher line	Open-wire line	50–500 Mc	0.1–0.5	10:1	100–500
Coaxial, C loaded	Shorted line tuned by variable C at open end	200–2000 Mc	0.05–0.2	3:1	500–2000
Coaxial	$\frac{1}{4}$ or $\frac{3}{4}$ λ open one end; $\frac{1}{2}$ λ shorted both ends	0.9–11.0 kMc	0.05–0.2	2:1–3:1	1000–5000
Cylindrical cavity	TE_{111} mode	2.4–220 kMc	0.01–0.25	1.5:1	1000–15,000
Cylindrical cavity	TE_{01n} mode	2.4–220 kMc	0.005–0.1	1.25:1	2,000–100,000

STUART CASPER

Cross-references: *Attenuators and Isolators, Circulators, Coaxial Lines, Frequency Measurement, Microwave Measurements, Waveguides and Waveguide Components*

RHEOSTATS

A rheostat is a resistor for regulating a current by means of variable resistance, derived from "rheo" meaning "current" and "stat" signifying "invariant."

Rheostats, then, are adjustable resistors, distinguished from potentiometers (*q.v.*, which often look superficially the same) by having only two terminals rather than three. So-called "trim pots" are usually used as rheostats in circuit. Rheostats are used for a variety of purposes that require an adjustable resistance which, once adjusted, remains fixed for periods of varying lengths. Some exemplary uses are: (1) for controlling amount of current through another component, such as a heating unit, a motor, a relay. or a vacuum-tube filament; (2) as

number of ways: (1) If a potentiometer is otherwise suitable, it can be used as a rheostat by ignoring a third terminal or connecting it to the brush terminal. (2) They often must dissipate much higher power. (3) Resistance value is often very low for the high-current application. (4) They sometimes embody an off position, thus eliminating the need for a switch. (5) The high power requires different materials or construction, as well as larger size. Cores carrying the resistive material must be heat-resisting ceramic, or even insulated heat-conducting material. Turns of resistance wire, if used, may be anchored by vitreous enamel. (6) High current may require different design and material for the brush takeoff mechanism. (7) Takeoff-brush material and design are more critical because brush carries full rheostat current, whereas potentiometer brush usually carries very little current or none. This current can cause electrical noise during motion and, through heating loss at the contact, induce deterioration by atmospheric corrosion when at rest. (8) Rheostats, more often than potentiometers, have so-called "tapered windings," meaning that the resistance per unit angle varies in predetermined appropriate fashion with rotation. This tapering would be needed, for example, to make an optimum rheostat for feeding a tube heater, say, from a battery.

Rheostats are made in a number of different geometrical embodiments. Most usual is a round one, with central actuating shaft and contact brush traversing a circularly disposed resistance unit, with or without off position at one end. High-wattage rheostats are often made with longitudinally moving brush, with coarse hand or fine helical adjustment means. Resistance element is carried on a form of tubular, or other more suitable, cross section. Plate-type rheostats are used for high power or for larger tapering than is convenient on the circular model. Such a rheostat is not "stepless" like more usual ones, but has separate switch contacts between which fixed resistors are attached and then vitreous-enameled to a substrate. A rotating switch blade selects one of the contacts. Large numbers of so-called "trim pots" are small low-power rheostats with longitudinal brush movement. Cross section is small and rectangular, thus conserving panel or shelf space when large numbers are to be mounted in one location.

Many different resistive materials may be used, but most usual material is in the form of metal alloy wire. Many alloys are available having different combinations of characteristics, for example, resistivity, temperature coefficient, thermal emf against copper, hardness, corrosion resistance, etc. Best corrosion resistance at elevated temperatures requires the use of precious-metal alloys. Others in use are: metal film, deposited on substrate in various ways; nonmetallic films, including carbon-based mixtures; carbon disks; and carbon granules put under varying pressures.

Special mechanical arrangements common to other components having similar methods of actuation are not covered, such as ganging, concentric shaft operation, special shaft machining, etc.

P. K. McElroy

Cross-references: *Potentiometers, Resistors*

RIEKE DIAGRAM

A Rieke diagram is a load diagram plotted on polar coordinates.

In general, the operating characteristics of electron-tube oscillators are functions of the magnitude and phase of the load impedance. A graphical presentation of the power output and frequency as a function of the load impedance or admittance is called a load diagram. When the load diagram is plotted on polar coordinates, it is called a Rieke diagram and the polar coordinate paper used in this application is termed a Smith chart. The major advantage of the Smith chart in this application is the ease of presentation of the characteristics of the oscillator over wide ranges of load admittance. A complete Rieke diagram includes a series of constant-power and constant-frequency contours.

If the oscillator may be represented by a simple parallel RLC circuit, the general forms of these contours on a Rieke diagram may be predicted. The conductance of the equivalent RLC circuit is composed of the positive conductance of the load and the negative conductance of the tube, the electronic conductance. The electronic conductance is associated with the energy conversion by means of the electron stream within the tube. Under equilibrium conditions, the net conductance must be zero. If the electronic conductance is assumed to be a function of the amplitude of oscillation but independent of the frequency, a constant load conductance implies constant electronic conductance and constant power output. Consequently, the constant-power contours coincide with the constant-resistance or constant-conductance circles on the Smith chart. By means of a similar argument, contours of constant frequency may be expected to coincide with the constant-reactance or constant-susceptance circles on the chart. The assumptions contained in the foregoing discussion are not completely fulfilled in practice and experimental Rieke diagrams usually depart considerably from the simple form described.

The Rieke diagram is useful in that it makes possible the choice of a load for a satisfactory compromise between the requirements of power output and frequency stability.

J. G. SKALNIK

Cross-references: *Oscillators, Smith Chart*

S

The responsibility for the safety and health of workers rests with management. Hazardous conditions, processes, or work practices are symptomatic of inefficiency either in the planning or carrying out of industrial operations. If a machine is unsafe, or an operation depends exclusively upon the correct performance of a worker, ultimately an accident will occur, either with or without an injury: production will stop; workers and supervisors will lose time; and if there is an injury, there will be compensation benefits to the injured as well as medical expenses.

Such occurrences therefore increase costs in the same manner as poor quality or excessive waste. Foremen, supervisors, and all levels of management have the direct responsiblity, therefore, to keep them to the absolute minimum.

Except in very small operations where the owner or manager is the only supervisor, it is necessary to establish a policy, and to delegate responsibility for the prevention of injuries and diseases. In an organization of several hundred workers, the staff function for this activity should be delegated to one person. He must be familiar with all of the common hazards found in that type of operation, sources of information, laws and regulations affecting the operations, and methods of reducing the hazards. He should also know the processes in sufficient detail to advise and consult on the training of workers in their jobs.

Standards of Safety. Whether a machine or operation is safe is relative. "Safe" or "safety" is not an absolute value, but rather is either a matter of judgment or of comparison to a known or recognized standard. Such standards may be those set by law or regulation, or by a nationally recognized voluntary standard.

Legal standards of safety are set forth in local codes or ordinances and usually affect building construction, exit facilities, or the amount of pollutants discharged to the atmosphere.

State laws and regulations frequently spell out the legal standards for guarding of machinery, maintenance of tools and equipment, control of toxic and hazardous substances, methods of reporting injuries, amount of compensation benefits, and procedures to be followed in handling claims for benefits as well as medical treatment.

Many voluntary standards are available for reference and guidance. Casualty insurance companies can provide much information. The American Standards Association publishes many standards drafted after thorough study by individuals representing users, manufacturers, professional societies, governmental agencies and labor unions. The National Fire Protection Association publishes standards particularly devoted to fire hazards and their control. The Underwriters' Laboratories test many products for their safety and, if found to meet standards, the products are labeled as having passed these tests. Further information can frequently be obtained through safety councils.

Specific Hazards. (a) The *construction* of the building is important from many points of view. Such matters as exit facilities, enclosed stairways, location of standpipes for fire-hose connections, location and types of elevators, sprinkler systems, and even parking facilities for employees are all factors of significance in preventing injuries.

(b) Potential *catastrophe* hazards such as overloading of floors, explosions due to boilers and unfired pressure vessels, and storage of flammable materials need to be checked constantly.

(c) *Machine* hazards, although not the largest source of injury, contribute the most serious injuries. Standard enclosures of moving gears, pulleys and other moving parts prevent the employees from being caught in them while the machines are operating. The operating area of the machine—frequently called the point of operation—is the greatest potential for serious injuries. Some machines can be protected by providing various automatic or semi-automatic feeding devices. Other machines are extremely difficult to protect because of the nature of the operation. The layout of machines, to conform to the flow of materials and parts, is part of the machine hazard, since poor spacing or overcrowding can cause many injuries.

(d) *Chemical* hazards arise because industrial operations today use many chemicals and so many new combinations are being created each year that it would be practically impossible to list those that are hazardous. Practically all chemicals have some degree of hazard to the person exposed to them. When a chemical is purchased, data should be secured from the supplier concerning its properties and its toxic qualities. Most reliable manufacturers will give instructions on how to control the hazards. Certain chemicals, such as the lighter petroleum distillates, are flammable and must be stored in fireproof containers while in production use, and always placed in a special storage area at the end of the shift.

(e) *Production* methods and processes need to be examined carefully and constantly to make sure the method of performing the operation is the safest possible.

A simple example would be handling parts that are being cleaned by "pickling" in an acid solution. Such parts can be handled mechanically to avoid any personal contact with the solution. Cleaning of storage vessels which require workers to enter such vessels has to be done by following a detailed procedure.

(f) *Lighting, ventilation and noise prevention* are essential to efficient and safe production. The worker who has to strain to see contrasts between materials in poor light becomes fatigued and is more likely to make an error. Similarly, ventilation, which includes both temperature control and humidity, affects the attitudes of workers, which in turn affect their safety. Studies have shown that the frequency of injury in the hot summer months is greater than in other months. Excessive noise can likewise cause irritations as well as injuries. Sounds above the 90-db level are generally considered to be harmful over a period of time. Excessive noise also makes verbal communication difficult.

Training and Education. The training of workers in the correct, safe way to perform their work is vital. Older workers should be given refresher training and should be solicited for ideas on how to eliminate hazards. New workers must be given general indoctrination on their job as a part of the over-all production picture. They must then be shown and checked on the job thoroughly for the first two or three weeks. The reasons for various procedures must be explained.

There are many educational media to keep all workers and supervisors aware of the need for safe conditions and procedures. Bulletin boards, if changed at least each week, company publications, special messages with pay checks in pay envelopes, and direct mailing to the employees' homes are all useful and should be used to provide variation in method.

Interdepartmental contests may be valuable in keeping groups of employees interested in the subject.

Foremen and supervisors need the help of staff personnel in finding hazards, evaluating them and determining means of control. Short, well-prepared meetings for this group can be held at regular times to review injuries that have occurred, their causes and means of prevention. New operations should be discussed well in advance and need to be analyzed for hazards.

Reports. All injuries, even minor first-aid cases, should be recorded giving the name of employee, date and time of injury, and a description of what he was doing when he was injured. These data should be reviewed by the foreman or supervisor as well as the safety engineer or safety director. If the same type of injury occurs a number of times in a department, a careful analysis of the operation is indicated.

All injuries should be carefully investigated to determine the primary cause and what corrective action is necessary to prevent a recurrence. Monthly or quarterly reports of the frequency of injuries by departments, together with a summary of activities, should be prepared by the person responsible for the safety function.

For detailed information on safety and hazards see "Industrial Accident Prevention Manual" (National Safety Council, Chicago) and "Dangerous Properties of Industrial Materials", N. I. Sax, New York, Reinhold Pub. Corp.

A. C. BLACKMAN

Cross-references: *Electric Shock, Radiation (Ionizing), Radiation Hazards (Nonionizing Radiation)*

SAMPLED-DATA SYSTEMS

Any system in an elementary sense can be visualized as a black box with input coming into it and output leaving it. When the input to such a system is available only at discrete intervals of time with no information between two consecutive instants of time, then it is called a sampled-data input, and the system subjected to such an input or to any other signal of this form flowing in it is a sampled-data system.

These signals may arise as a result of the discrete nature of the available information because of the measuring equipment; or they may be purposely introduced, although available at all times, to time-share available continuous information among several systems. The latter application is increasing to provide economic use of equipment.

One of the functions of the black box is to reproduce as much of the continuous signal as possible from the sampled information. Thus the problem of sampling rate and the reproduction function of the black box is important in the information handling of such signals, and the reproduction capacity

of the system. Therefore, the information-theory part of sampled-data systems related to the nature of sampling and to the information content of the discrete signal play an important role in the field of communications and in the design of electronic equipment. Another feature of sampled-data systems relating to information theory is the digital coding and transmission of information at discrete times, which is increasing in importance in view of higher accuracy and reproduction fidelity.

The second feature of sampled data appears in *sampled-data control systems*. The information in such systems appears periodically in sampled form with the sampling period T. One of the major problems in the analysis is the stability study. The characteristic function becomes a function of T in addition to the other parameters of the system. For the design part, problems associated with minimum settling time and dead-beat response, as well as minimum error, are the major factors in effective synthesis.

Further application of sampled-data systems arises in the use of digital computers in time-sharing multiple-control systems. Such systems are designated as *digital control systems*, whose main feature is the introduction of amplitude quantization (in view of the use of analog digital converters) in addition to the time quantization of sampled-data control systems. The use of digital computers in control systems is increasing in importance because of their versatility, weight, multiple-function performance, accuracy, and reliability. The stability analysis of such systems reduces to the stability of nonlinear sampled-data control systems and the design of the computers to enable the system to perform under certain specifications is becoming systematized. In particular, dynamic programming methods are one of the techniques used for effective and practical design. The form of operation of such computers can be quite complex depending on the function required and the sampling scheme used. The most important

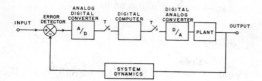

FIG. 1. A typical digital control system.

are the multirate, cyclic-rate and bandwidth-limited digital computers. An illustrative example of a single-rate computer in a control system is shown in Fig. 1.

Another feature of sampled data is its application to the field of applied mathematics. The use of sampled-data theory is increasing in applications to other disciplines such as numerical analysis, approximation of continuous by sampled-data systems, in time-domain synthesis of networks, in pulsed linear or nonlinear circuits, in the operational solution of linear difference equations with constant and periodic coefficients, and finally in the approximate solution of certain nonlinear continuous systems. Of the various techniques developed in the case of investigating sampled-data systems, the Z-transform method is widely used and is finding many applications to the problems cited above.

REFERENCES

E. I. Jury, *Sampled-Data Control Systems*, Wiley, 1958.

J. R. Ragazzini and G. F. Franklin, *Sampled-Data Control Systems*, McGraw Hill, 1958.

J. Tou, *Digital and Sampled-Data Control Systems*, McGraw-Hill, 1959.

E. I. JURY

Cross-references: *Digital Computers, Information Theory, Systems*

SAMPLING THEOREMS

It is often desirable to represent a function $g(t)$ by a set of sample values $g(t_n)$ and interpolating functions $s_n(t)$ such that the interpolation

$$\sum_n g(t_n)s_n(t)$$

approximates $g(t)$ in some specified sense. In uniform sampling—the most frequently

encountered case—$t_n = nT$, and a single interpolating function is used by making $s_n(t) = s(t - nT)$. If $g(t)$ is a (deterministic) function whose Fourier transform vanishes outside the interval $(-W,W)$, perfect reconstruction is achieved if the sampling rate is equal to, or greater than, twice the highest frequency [i.e., $(1/T) \geq 2W$]. A similarly sampled stationary random function with band-limited power spectrum may be reconstructed from its sample values with zero mean square error.

Uniform Sampling of Deterministic Functions. The desired summation

$$\sum_n g(nT)s(t - nT)$$

can be regarded as the convolution of $s(t)$ with*

$$\hat{g}(t) = \sum_{n=-\infty}^{\infty} g(nT)\delta(t - nT) \qquad (1)$$

The modulated impulse train $\hat{g}(t)$ is a convenient representation of the succession of sample values; finding $g(t)$ when $\hat{g}(t)$ is given is equivalent to reconstructing $g(t)$ from its sample values. It is convenient to discuss this process in terms of the corresponding Fourier transforms $G(f)$ and $\hat{G}(f)$. It will be shown that $\hat{G}(f)$ is the sum of periodically repeated replicas of $G(f)$, and that it may be expanded as follows:

$$
\begin{aligned}
\hat{G}(f) &= (1/T) \sum_{n=-\infty}^{\infty} G\left(f - \frac{m}{T}\right) \\
&= \sum_{n=-\infty}^{\infty} g(nT) \exp(-jn2\pi fT)
\end{aligned}
\qquad (2)
$$

If $G(f) = 0$ for $|f| \geq 1/2T$, the functions of the first summation do not overlap, and one may obtain $G(f)$ by multiplying $\hat{G}(f)$ by a rectangular "window function"; that is,

$$G(f) = \hat{G}(f)\left[u\left(f + \frac{1}{2T}\right) - u\left(f - \frac{1}{2T}\right)\right]T \quad (3)$$

where $u(f)$ is the unit step function. Using the second equality of (2) yields

---

* The convolution of $s(t)$ and $\delta(t - nT)$ yields $s(t - nT)$.

$$G(f) = \sum_n g(nT) \left[Tu\left(f + \frac{1}{2T}\right) - Tu\left(f - \frac{1}{2T}\right) \right] \exp\left(-jn2\pi fT\right) \tag{4}$$

The Fourier transform of the bracketed quantity is sinc $(t/T) = [\sin(\pi t/T)]/(\pi t/T)$, and the phase factor following it corresponds to a time delay of nT units. There follows the *Whittaker-Shannon* sampling theorem*

$$g(t) = \sum_{n=-\infty}^{\infty} g(nT) \text{ sinc } [(t - nT)/T] \tag{5}$$

provided that $G(f) = 0$ for $|f| \geqslant 1/2T$.†

Each interpolating function vanishes at all but one sampling points; thus,

$$\text{sinc } (t/T) = 0$$

for all $t = nT$ except $t = 0$. Another significant property is expressed by the orthogonality relation

$$\int_{-\infty}^{\infty} \text{sinc }\left(\frac{t - nT}{T}\right) \text{sinc }\left(\frac{t - mT}{T}\right) dt$$

$$= 0 \quad \text{if} \quad m \neq n$$

$$= T \quad \text{if} \quad m = n$$

It follows that

$$\int_{-\infty}^{+\infty} |g(t)|^2 \, dt = T \sum_{n=-\infty}^{\infty} |g(nT)|^2$$

If $g(t)$ is not strictly bandlimited, the right side of (5) constitutes an approximation $g_{BL}(t)$ obtained by sampling and band-limiting‡ of $g(t)$. Using the first equality of (2), one has:

If $g(t)$ is sampled at $t = nT$ and is subsequently bandlimited to $|f| \leq 1/2T$, the resulting function and its Fourier transform are

* "Kotel'nikov's theorem" in the Russian literature.
† The equal sign may be omitted if $G(f)$ does not contain any impulse functions at $f = \pm 1/2T$, or if the impulses at these two frequencies are equal.
‡ It is, in fact, the response of an ideal lowpass filter of cut-off frequency $1/2T$ to an input given by $\hat{g}(t)$ of (1).

$$g_{BL}(t) = \sum_n g(nT) \text{ sinc } [(t - nT)/T]$$

$$G_{BL}(f) = \sum_m G\left(f - \frac{m}{T}\right), \quad |f| \leq 1/2T \tag{6}$$

Proof of Eq. (2). The first equality of (2) is taken as the definition of the periodic function $\hat{G}(f)$. Its Fourier series expansion

$$\sum c_n \exp\left(-jn2\pi fT\right)$$

is characterized by the coefficients

$$c_n = T \int_{-1/2T}^{1/2T} \hat{G}(f) \exp\left(jn2\pi fT\right) df$$

$$= \sum_m \int_{-1/2T}^{1/2T} G\left(f - \frac{m}{T}\right) \exp\left(jn2\pi fT\right) df$$

A change of variables yields

$$c_n = \sum_m \int_{(2m-1)/2T}^{(2m+1)/2T} G(f) \exp\left(jn2\pi fT\right) df$$

$$= \int_{-\infty}^{+\infty} G(f) \exp\left(jn2\pi fT\right) df$$

The last integral follows from the observation that the integration intervals in the preceding summation are contiguous; it is readily identified as the transform of $G(f)$, evaluated at nT. Thus, $c_n = g(nT)$, and the second equality of (2) is proved. Fourier transformation of (2) yields

$$\hat{g}(t) = \sum_n g(nT) \int_{-\infty}^{\infty} \exp\left(-jn2\pi fT\right) \exp\left(j2\pi ft\right) df$$

and (1) is obtained by recognizing the last integral as a representation of $\delta(t - nT)$.

Uniform Sampling of Random Functions. Let $x(t)$ be a sample function of a stationary random process with autocorrelation function $R_x(\tau) = E\{x^*(t)x(t + \tau)\}$, and define a new random process by the relation

$$y(t) = \sum_{n=-\infty}^{\infty} x(nT) \text{ sinc } [(t - nT)/T] \tag{7}$$

The autocorrelation function of $y(t)$ will be shown to be

$$R_y(\tau) = \sum_{n=-\infty}^{\infty} R_x(nT) \text{ sinc } [(\tau - nT)/T] \tag{8}$$

$R_y(\tau)$ is thus a sampled and bandlimited version* of $R_x(\tau)$, and (6) can be applied to the corresponding Fourier transforms $P_y(f)$ and $P_x(f)$:

$$P_y(f) = \sum_m P_x\left(f - \frac{m}{T}\right), \quad |f| \le 1/2T \quad (9)$$

$P_y(f)$ and $P_x(f)$ are the power spectra of $y(t)$ and $x(t)$, respectively. If $P_x(f)$ vanishes for $|f| > 1/2T$ and has no δ-functions at $\pm 1/2T$, then $P_y = P_x$ and $R_y = R_x$.† In this case, $y(t)$ will be shown to approximate $x(t)$ in the mean-square sense; that is,

$$E\{|\,y(t) - x(t)\,|^2\} = 0 \quad (10)$$

Equations (7) and (10) constitute a sampling theorem for random processes with bandlimited power spectra.

Proof of Equations (8) and (10).

$$R_y(\tau) = E\{y^*(t)y(t + \tau)\}$$
$$= E\{\sum_n\sum_m x^*(nT)x(mT) \text{ sinc } [(t - nT)/T]$$
$$\cdot \text{sinc } [(t + \tau - mT)/T]\}$$
$$= \sum_n\sum_m R_x[(m - n)T] \text{ sinc } [(t - nT)/T]$$
$$\cdot \text{sinc } [(t + \tau - mT)/T]$$
$$= \sum_k R_x(kT) \sum_m \text{ sinc } [(mT - t - \tau)/T]$$
$$\cdot \text{sinc } [(mT - kT - t)/T]$$

Equation (8) is now obtained by using the identity‡

$$\text{sinc } [(x - y)/T]$$
$$= \sum_{m=-\infty}^{\infty} \text{ sinc } [(mT - x)/T] \text{ sinc } [(mT - y)/T] \quad (11)$$

The left side of (10) is equal to $R_y(0) + R_x(0) - E\{x^*(t)y(t)\} - E\{x(t)y^*(t)\}$. Since $x(t)$ is now assumed to be bandlimited, $R_y = R_x$, and it suffices to show that $E\{x^*(t)y(t)\} = R_x(0)$. From (7),

$$E\{x^*(t)y(t)\} = E\{\sum_n x^*(t)x(nT) \text{ sinc } [(t - nT)/T]\}$$
$$= \sum_n R_x(t - nT) \text{ sinc } [(t - nT)/T]$$

---

* The Fourier transform of sinc $[(\tau - nT)/T]$ vanishes for $|f| > 1/2T$.

† Equation (8) is then simply a direct application of (5) to the bandlimited function $R_x(\tau)$.

‡ sinc $[(x - y)/T]$ is a function of x whose Fourier transform vanishes for $|f| > 1/2T$; application of the sampling theorem (5) yields (11).

Since $R_x = R_y$ for the case considered here, (8) may be used to obtain

$$E\{x^*(t)y(t)\} = \sum_k\sum_n R_x(kT)$$
$$\cdot \text{sinc } [(t - kT - nT)/T] \text{ sinc } [(t - nT)/T]$$

and application of (11) yields the desired result.

D. A. LINDEN

Cross-references: *Information Theory, Laplace and Fourier Transforms, Pulse Code Modulation (PCM), Random Processes*

SATELLITE COMMUNICATIONS

Communications by satellites involve the use of both natural and man-made bodies that are made to orbit the earth for communication purposes. This classification includes all communications that are conducted through the use of the moon, man-established passive reflecting dipole belts, reflecting balloons or similar passive objects, and amplifying (active) signal repeaters installed in satellites with various orbit configurations.

Proof that communication was feasible by means of satellites beyond the earth's ionosphere came in 1946 when the U. S. Army Signal Corps established electronic contact with the earth's moon and received reliable electromagnetic echos from that satellite. Subsequent major research by the U. S. Navy established the first operational system using the moon as a passive reflector of communication signals.

In general all man-made satellites, including the earliest Sputniks and U. S. Vanguards, Pioneers, Explorers, etc., have carried means for communicating technical information back to earth by means of radio waves. In many of these systems, command signals from earth-based stations activate mechanisms in, and responses from, the satellites. Thus knowledge has been acquired for developing communications systems for conventional types of information.

On December 18, 1958 an Atlas missile placed in orbit the first satellite designed primarily as a communications experiment. Project SCORE (Signal Communication by Orbiting Relay Equipment) was a collective effort of the Advanced Research Projects Agency, Department of Defense, the U. S. Air Force, the U. S. Army and several U. S. industrial companies. This experiment demonstrated that both voice and teletype messages could be transmitted from earth to satellite, stored on magnetic tape and retransmitted to ground receiving stations when so directed by the ground station. Direct point-to-point message transmissions were also achieved without delay.

The next similar active repeater communications experiment was Project Courier, operational October 4–22, 1960, a collaborative effort of ARPA, U. S. Army, U. S. Air Force, and industry. This experiment greatly extended the communications capability of Project SCORE and attained a traffic handling rate during 5-min. transmission periods of 16.5×10^6 bits of information.

Another important experiment was Project Echo of the U. S. National Aeronautics and Space Administration. On August 12, 1960, a 100-ft-diameter, 130-lb aluminized plastic balloon was launched into a nearly circular orbit 1000 miles above the earth. Much valuable knowledge on the life of balloon satellites, propagation conditions near the horizon, and problems of satellite communications was gained from this experiment. In addition, signals reflecting from this satellite demonstrated two-way telephonic communication between Holmdel, N. J., and Goldstone, Calif.

Following studies of orbiting dipole belts at Massachusetts Institute of Technology an experimental program has been proposed that would use 35 kg of 8000-Mc dipoles orbiting at an altitude of a few thousand kilometers. The study concluded that such belts of reflecting dipoles in suitably designed orbits could provide reflecting media for a large number of reliable international communications circuits of high information-handling capability, would be quite invulnerable to physical damage, and would not cause damage to space vehicles or measurable interference to radio-astronomy observations.

These pioneering efforts managed by U. S. government civilian and military agencies, in collaboration with U. S. industry and scientific institutions, have sought new knowledge and the attainment of new communications capabilities. For military applications the practical objectives were more extensive, flexible, and reliable global communications with greater bandwidth, information-handling capability, and economy. A clear but more distant objective was to provide wholly new possibilities for world communications. More extensive, more facile, and more economical communications systems could draw the earth's population closer together. If this objective is to be accomplished, technical feasibility is only the first step. Economic feasibility must also be proved. Strong probabilities must exist for progressive cost reductions for the future.

Studies by many industry groups have concluded that intercontinental communications by satellites is economically feasible and that strong probabilities exist for continued progressive cost reductions. International telecommunications agreements for frequency usage and other standards, the nature of the national and international structures for the capitalization and management of this business, and the selection of optimum technical systems concepts are yet to be concluded.

U. S. industry has concluded that active (receive-amplify-retransmit) satellites placed in suitable orbits offer the greatest technical and economic feasibility for commercial communication systems. System design and development has been carried on by a number of U. S. companies. Proposed systems fall into three general categories: satellites in random orbits at uniform-orbit altitudes of 2000 to 9000 miles; positioned satellites in precise, controlled equatorial orbits at altitudes from 4000 to 8000 miles; and satellites in a 22,300-mile synchronous, stationary, equatorial orbit (the "24-hr" satellite).

The number of orbiting satellites required

for the first system is influenced by the altitude of the satellites and the amount of tolerable communication outage. Estimates vary from 50 to 120 satellites. The second system requires fewer satellites. Proposals state that with such a system, communication outages can be eliminated between points within a belt about the equator, the width of which depends upon the number of satellites and their altitude. With both systems, if one satellite fails, communications are only partially disrupted. Complex ground facilities for tracking and communications control are essential to switch from one moving repeater satellite to another at precisely the proper time. With satellite repeaters in a synchronous, stationary orbit (22,300-mile altitude), three or four satellites will cover the earth's surface except for the polar regions but an additional three or four satellites probably would be required as "spares" to insure reliability. Orbit adjustment and altitude controls will be required to correct for orbit errors caused by the moon's gravitational field, solar pressure, and anomalies in the earth's nonspherical configuration including triaxial perturbations due to nonuniformity of the earth's gravitational field.

The Department of Defense program (Project "Advent") has been initiated to develop and establish a military communications satellite system employing synchronous (stationary) satellites at 22,300-mile altitudes.

JAMES D. O'CONNELL

Cross-references: *Doppler Navigation, Radio Links, Satellite Electronics, Telemetry*

SATELLITE ELECTRONICS

For centuries man's scientific experiments and traveling capabilities have been largely confined to the earth and its immediate atmosphere. The rapid development of aircraft and more recently of high-performance rockets over the short span of fifty years has expanded our knowledge of the atmosphere surrounding us. In addition, it has provided us with the background to launch satellite and space-probe-bearing

vehicles, to guide them into orbit, and, after performing many preprogrammed maneuvers from commands stored in the vehicle or broadcast from the ground, to effect separation of the powered vehicle from the orbiting satellite payload. The performance capabilities of the launching vehicles places many restrictions on the payload and its included experiments. Currently, size and weight are disturbing limitations; however, they have stimulated rapid progress in electronic component development and circuit design, in transducer designs, in computer and data storage techniques, etc.

The first successful launching of a satellite, Sputnik (I), was announced by the U.S.S.R. on 4 October 1957. It remained in orbit until January 1958 and reportedly carried 184 lb of simple transducers, processing, and radio transmitting equipment for the collection of internal temperatures, pressures, and other parameters essential for future design control. On 3 November 1957 Sputnik (II) attained orbit and remained there until April 1958 carrying a 1,120-lb scientific payload consisting of a dog and instrumentation for cosmic and solar radiation, temperature, pressure, physiological measurements, etc. Its perigee was 142 miles; its apogee was 1038 miles.

After an unsuccessful attempt (Vanguard, 6 December 1957), the U. S. satellite Explorer (I) went into orbit on 1 January 1958 with 18 lb of instrumentation for the measurement and radio transmission of data relating to cosmic rays, micrometeoric impact, temperatures, etc. Its perigee and apogee were 224 and 1573 miles, respectively, and its life expectancy is judged to be about 5 years. This vehicle was responsible for the location of the Van Allen radiation belt.

A 3.3-lb scientific Vanguard payload was launched on 17 March 1958 with a lifetime expectancy of 200 to 1000 years and it is orbiting with a perigee of 409 miles and an apogee of 2453 miles. Its instrumentation for the measurements of temperature, pressure, radiation and geodetic purposes is providing earth-mapping data that have contributed significantly to a new earth shape factor.

Explorer (III), an 18.6-lb U. S. payload, was successfully launched on 26 March 1958 and it remained in orbit until June 1958 reporting Van Allen radiations and cosmic-dust density data. Transducers for detecting micrometeorites, cosmic rays, etc., in this instance were coupled into in-flight tape recorder storage prior to transmission.

The principal milestones for the U.S.S.R. probably are: Sputnik (III), 5 May 1958; Lunik-Mechta, 2 January 1959, a solar orbiting probe carrying a payload weighing 3245 lb for the accumulation of data pertaining to temperatures, pressures, interplanetary matter, solar and cosmic radiation, magnetic fields—reportedly making a 15 months' orbit of the sun; Lunik (II), 12 September 1959, the first successful moon shot that provided photographs of the moon and data to indicate the absence of a magnetic field associated with it; Yuri A. Gagarin, first man to land with his health unimpaired after reportedly orbiting the earth once on 12 April 1961 at a distance of 187.75 miles.

Likewise, representative United States milestones are: Explorer (IV), 26 July 1958; Lunar probe, Pioneer (I) which is detecting oscillation in the earth's magnetic field at altitudes of 70,700 miles; Score, 18 December 1958, which was the first satellite voice relay and carried President Eisenhower's voice; Explorer (VI), 9 August 1959, the first all solar-driven satellite and the first to provide TV pictures of the earth; and on 5 May 1961 Astronaut Alan B. Shepard, Jr. rode the Mercury capsule, launched by a Redstone Rocket, into space and landed for a sea pickup. This was the first time anyone had even brief control over the motions of the space craft while in flight.

On 12 July 1961, in the United States, a missile-detecting alarm system satellite (*MIDAS III*) was placed in orbit as was another weather satellite with television capabilities. And on 20 February 1962 John H. Glenn or-bited the earth three times at an altitude of 120 miles in the Mercury capsule Friendship 7 launched by a 130-ton Atlas rocket, controlling the attitude of the craft in flight.

It is apparent from this fleeting history of satellite experiments that transducers for the physical measurements of temperatures, pressures, electrostatic and magnetic fields, radiation dosages in all forms (i.e., alpha, beta, and gamma, neutron particles, X-rays and ultraviolet, visible and infrared light waves), optical spectra and particle radiation spectra; and of chemical and biological effects relating to metabolism, cardiovascular studies, mutations in this new and severe environment of radiation, minimal pressure and widely fluctuating temperatures, are being used or considered. Generally, the power available for them and their associated electronic systems and subsystems is supplied by solar cells, thermoelectric generators, nuclear batteries, etc. This power is currently only available in nominal amounts for short periods and in very very limited amounts if greater life span is desirable.

Furthermore, although an extremely high degree of system reliability is desired to provide months or even years of life in orbit, the components to provide systems power, the transducers, the associated electronics for amplification, processing storage, and programming prior to transmittal all may be required to endure pressures of the order of 10^{-8} mm of Hg, large temperature variations, extreme vibration and "g" loadings during the launching phase, and radiation dosages now only poorly defined.

Because of these controlling conditions, coupled with a restricted vehicle-lifting capability, miniaturizing circuit techniques utilizing printed circuits; micromodules; solid-state devices such as transistors, and diodes; and radiation detectors such as lead sulfide, lead selenide, and gold and zinc doped germanium have been essential. It is through such miniaturization that one can operate with the weight and size restrictions and also provide a maximum of radiation shielding for a minimum amount of shielding material. A further stimulant for development of solid-state devices results because their employment may minimize the need for moving parts such as slip rings and bearings with their accompanying severe lubrication problems at low pressures.

Finally, the cost of each satellite payload and the nominal probability that a particular launch and orbit will ensue, dictates the need for maximum reliability, optimum circuit designs, the need for time and frequency sharing to service a multitude of transducers, in-flight recording and storage, processing to remove redundant information, and programming of the acquired data for transmittal on command or interrogation.

To date, satellite electronics has been designed with care and precaution, yet the extent that the new and severe environment will affect their extended performance is, as yet, undocumented.

WALTER G. DRISCOL

Cross-references: *Doppler Navigation, Microcircuitry, Miniaturization, Modular Construction, Satellite Communications, Telemetry*

SCALARS: see VECTOR ANALYSIS

SCALERS: see COUNTER AND SCALER CIRCUITS

SCATTER: see PROPAGATION

SCINTILLATION COUNTERS

The scintillation counter represents an improvement, by modern electronic techniques, of one of the first counting methods used in nuclear physics. Sir William Crookes and also Elster and Geitel in 1903 observed that a screen coated with small crystals of phosphorescent zinc sulfide displayed a brilliant luminosity when bombarded by alpha particles. When the surface of the screen was viewed with a magnifying glass, the light from the screen was found to consist of individual flashes of light, or scintilla-

tions. Early experiments proved that each scintillation was caused by a single alpha particle striking the screen. The zinc sulfide screens were found to be insensitive to high-speed electrons and gamma-rays but were sensitive to protons.

A visual observation technique consisting of a ZnS screen viewed through a low-power microscope was used in the first oscillation counters. In a typical visual counter, with a microscope of numerical aperture 0.45 and magnification 50, the faintest scintillations which could be detected were those produced by low-energy alpha particles and corresponded to 300 quanta entering the eye.

In the modern scintillation counter the microscope and human eye combination has been replaced by an efficient photomultiplier tube. The scintillations from the fluorescent screen are converted into electrical pulses at the output of the multiplier tube. A major advance in this new technique resulted from the work of Kallmann, who found that single beta and gamma rays could be detected with counters using large transparent blocks of naphthalene. The original naphthalene phosphor has been superseded by more efficient organic and also inorganic phosphors.

The following list of applications shows some of the possible uses of the photomultiplier scintillation counter.

(a) The detection and energy measurement of ionizing particles with a detection efficiency of 100 per cent under suitable conditions. The flux of particles can range from a few per second to millions per second.

(b) The detection and spectroscopy of x-radiation and gamma-radiation. In general, the detection efficiency is much higher than that of a gas counter or ionization chamber owing to the increased absorption in the phosphor compared with that in the gas and surrounding walls.

(c) The detection and the energy measurement of fast neutrons by recording the scintillations from the fast recoil protons produced in an organic phosphor.

(d) The detection of thermal neutrons by

the scintillations resulting from slow neutron induced nuclear reactions within the phosphor.

Photomultiplier Tubes. The photomultiplier tube used in the scintillation counter consists of a photosensitive surface and an electron multiplier which amplifies or multiplies the initial number of photoelectrons. The most widely used photocathodes are thin surfaces of antimony cesium usually deposited on glass. The spectral response of a typical photocathode enclosed in a glass envelope is shown in Fig. 1.

Since the emission spectra of most phosphors are peaked in the blue, a more precise correlation with scintillation requirements is obtained by using a suitable filter with the tungsten light source.

A thermionic emission at room temperature of 10^{-15} to 10^{-14} amp/cm^2 is observed for antimony-cesium photocathodes. A decrease in the thermionic current by a factor of about 2 per 10°C change in temperature can be produced by refrigeration of the photocathode.

In practically all scintillation counters the photoelectric current is amplified or multiplied in an electron multiplier located in the same vacuum tube which contains the photoelectric surface. By means of the electron multiplier, the initial photoelectric current may be multiplied by a factor of 10^7 without the addition of appreciable noise from the multiplier.

Photomultiplier tubes are very sensitive to magnetic fields. This effect is due to the deflection of the beam of photoelectrons in the region between the photocathode and the first dynode and in the region within the multiplying structure. For example, Engstrom has shown that, in the case of an 5819 tube, a field of 0.8 oersted parallel to the dynode cage axis reduces the tube gain by a factor of about three. Increasing the voltage between the cathode and first dynode reduces the effect, and high-permeability shields help to screen the tube from magnetic fields.

Inorganic Scintillation Phosphors. *Zinc sulfide*, activated with copper or silver, has the highest light conversion efficiency of any known phosphor. A value of about 25 per cent for the ratio of the energy of the emitted quanta to the energy lost in the phosphor by the incident particle is typical for the conversion efficiencies of these phosphors. The silver activated sulfide has a maximum emission near 4500 Å and is well matched to the spectral response of many commercial photomultipliers. The copper activated sulfide has a maximum emission near 5200 Å. The light from these sulfide phosphors has a decay time of the order of 10^{-5} sec and phosphorescence of much longer time duration has been noted. These phosphors in the form of powders show very low transparency to the emitted light and consequently are opaque in thicknesses greater than 25–50 mgm/cm^2. A thin layer of zinc sulfide is relatively insensitive to high energy electrons due to the low specific ionization of these particles. For this reason strongly ionizing particles, such as low energy electrons or alpha particles, can be detected against a background of high-energy electrons or gamma radiation.

Sodium iodide, activated with thallium, is probably the most widely used inorganic phosphor. Since the crystals are highly

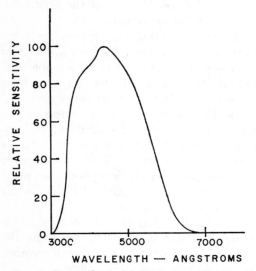

FIG. 1. Spectral sensitivity curve of an antimony-cesium photocathode.

transparent to their emitted radiation, large crystals may be used in scintillation counters. The relatively large absorption coefficient of the iodine component (85 per cent by mass) combined with large crystal size makes sodium iodide particularly suitable for the detection and spectrometry of gamma rays and x-rays. Sodium iodide may also be used as a detector of electrons and heavy particles such as protons and alpha particles.

The emission spectrum, with a peak at 4100Å, is well matched to the spectral response of most photomultiplier tubes. The decay time of the emitted light is 2.5×10^{-7} sec at room temperature, which is adequate for most counting experiments. The energy conversion efficiency is about 8.4 per cent.

Lithium iodide, activated by either thallium or tin, has been used as a scintillation crystal. The crystals have a blue-green emission spectrum and a fluorescent decay time of about 1×10^{-6} sec. A disadvantage of this phosphor is its low light conversion efficiency which is about $\frac{1}{10}$ that of sodium iodide. The most important application of lithium iodide is for the detection of thermal neutrons. Natural lithium contains 7.4 per cent of Li^6, which has a large cross section for the absorption of thermal neutrons in the reaction $Li^6(n, \alpha)H^3$. The product nuclei have a total energy of 4.8 Mev which results in scintillation pulses of constant size which may be detected against a gamma-ray background.

Organic Crystalline Phosphors. Organic phosphors have the following useful generation properties:

(a) The decay time of the emitted light is of the order of 10^{-8} sec.

(b) A high transparency to their fluorescence radiation.

(c) The maximum intensity of the light emitted from most organic phosphors is near the peak of the spectral sensitivity curve of many photomultipliers.

(d) The efficiency of energy-to-light conversion is high, although somewhat lower than that of ZnS (Ag) or NaI (Tl).

(e) The magnitude of the scintillation pulses produced by electrons is proportional to the energy when the energy is greater than 125 kev.

Anthracene has the highest energy-to-light conversion efficiency of the organic phosphors so far studied. For excitation by fast electrons the conversion efficiency at room temperature is about 4 per cent. The fluorescent spectrum excited by ionizing radiation has a main peak near 4450 Å. The decay time of the fluorescence excited by electrons is about 2.7×10^{-8} sec at room temperature.

Stilbene combines a relatively high energy-light conversion efficiency with a very short scintillation decay time of about 7×10^{-9} sec. This phosphor has been widely used in high-speed coincidence experiments where a short resolving time is essential.

Organic Plastic and Liquid Phosphors. Liquid scintillators are useful whenever a large volume and relatively cheap scintillator is required. This type of scintillator is fast and highly transparent to its emitted radiation. At present the most efficient scintillator is a solution of *p*-terphenyl in xylene or in toluene. The scintillation efficiency of this type of scintillator at the optimum concentration of about 4 to 5 gm/liter is about 45 per cent that of solid anthracene. The decay time of the light from terphenyl solutions is 2 to 4×10^{-9} sec. The light emitted from terphenyl solutions for excitation by either ionizing radiation or by ultraviolet light has emission bands in the region 3450 to 3880 Å. Since the emission spectrum is not well matched to the spectral response of most photomultiplier tubes, a wavelength shifter such as alpha naphthyl phenyloxazole is frequently added.

Plastic scintillators have been synthesized by incorporating an organic phosphor into a suitable transparent plastic. As in the case of liquid scintillators, the plastics have relatively high energy-to-light conversion efficiencies and have short decay times. Buck and Swank have described the properties of plastic scintillators formed by the polymerization of styrene and vinylstyrene solutions of organic phosphors. The most efficient scintillator was a polyvinyltoluene plastic with 4-percent terphenyl and 0.02-percent tetraphenylbutadiene. This scintillator gave scintillation pulses 47 per cent as large as those from anthracene under similar conditions. The decay time of the light was less than 8×10^{-9} sec. Plastic scintillators of this type now are available commercially in a wide range of shapes and sizes.

Gas Scintillators. The gas scintillation counter represents the latest development in this field. This type of counter consists of a volume of gas contained in a cuplike container placed over the photocathode of a multiplier tube. The light emitted by gas molecules excited and ionized by the passage of an ionizing particle is detected by the photomultiplier. A scintillation pulse resulting from the de-excitation of the gas molecules is expected to have a time duration of about 10^{-9} sec. The amplitude of the light pulses is proportional to the energy expended by the charged particles and is independent of the charge or mass of the exciting particles.

The gases xenon, krypton, argon, and helium have been used successfully in scintillation counters. Since the light emitted from these gases extends far into the ultraviolet region, a wavelength shifter must be used to convert the shorter wavelengths to a frequency region that matches the spectral response of the photomultiplier. A thin layer of quaterphenyl on the inner surface of the gas cell has been used successfully as a wavelength shifter. The time duration of the scintillation pulses from these gases is about 10^{-8} sec.

The gas scintillation counter appears to offer definite advantages over both organic and inorganic crystals as a detector of heavy charged particles such as alpha particles and protons. The main advantage of the gas scintillator over the organic crystal is the fact that the response is linear with the energy of the heavy particle in the case of the gas but not in the organic crystal. When compared with either ZnS (Ag) or NaI (Tl) the response of a gas scintillator is much more rapid. The low sensitivity of a gas counter to gamma-rays will permit the detection of heavy particles in a large background of radiation.

JAMES S. ALLEN

Cross-references: *Cathode-Ray Tubes, Cathodoluminescence, Electroluminescence, Fluorescence, Ionization Counters, Photomultipliers, Solid-State Displays*

SECONDARY EMISSION

In its most general sense, secondary electron emission refers to the ejection of electrons from matter under the impact of rapidly moving particles such as electrons, ions, or neutral atoms. When the atoms of the material bombarded are in the gaseous state, the phenomenon is more commonly referred to as impact ionization. In electronics, the term is mainly used in connection with the emission of electrons from solids under electron bombardment as in photomultipliers, and for the ejection of electrons at the cathode of gas discharge devices under the action of positive ions.

Historical Background. Secondary emission from solids was first observed with electrons as incident particles. The effect was discovered by Austin and Starke in 1902 in the course of studies on the reflection of fast electrons from metals. Upon increasing the angle of incidence of the primary electrons away from the normal, Austin and Starke observed that the current into the target first decreased to zero and then actually reversed. They concluded that the incident electrons are not only reflected but other electrons are also ejected from the plate such that the total number leaving exceeds the number arriving. The effect was found to be strictly proportional to the number of primary electrons. Furthermore, it was found to be more pronounced for metals of high density, and it was observed to increase rapidly with the angle of incidence. Shortly thereafter, P. Lenard (1903) showed that the secondaries are emitted diffusely, that they possess low

energies of the order of a few volts independent of primary energy or target material, that the yield goes through a maximum at a few hundred volts, and that the
process occurs in insulators as well as metals.
Lenard concluded that the formation process
is fundamentally an atomic one and therefore largely independent of the state of
aggregation. This deduction has been confirmed in recent years.

The emission of secondary electrons from
solids under ion bombardment was first
demonstrated in 1905 by J. J. Thomson
(*q.v.*) and established to be very similar to
the case of electron bombardment by C.
Füchtbauer (1906). The secondaries were
again found to have energies of a few volts,
essentially independent of the nature of the
bombarding ion, its velocity, or the properties of the solid bombarded. Shortly thereafter, N. R. Campbell (1911) established the
same characteristics for the electrons emitted
under α-particle bombardment, the so-called
δ-rays.

**Secondary Emission Under Electron
Bombardment.** The basic features of the
phenomenon as clarified by subsequent in-

vestigations may be summarized as follows.
For all pure metals and elemental semiconductors free from surface oxides or gas contamination, the total yield δ, defined as the
total number of electrons emitted per incident primary electron, never exceeds a value
of about 2. Out of this total, the number of
backscattered electrons per incident primary η may be as high as 0.5 for high atomic
number elements and energies in excess of a
few kilovolts. The distinction between the
two kinds of emitted electrons is based on
their energy distribution. The true secondaries are characterized by their low energies
peaked at about 2 ev for all metals and a
Maxwellian-like energy distribution with a
mean value close to 5 ev independent of
primary energy. The backscattered electrons
above about 50 ev emerge with energies all
the way to the primary energy, but only a
few per cent are truly elastically reflected,
having lost no appreciable energy in the
solid (as indicated in Fig. 1).

The backscattered fraction η is almost constant with changing primary energy for low
atomic number elements ($Z \lesssim 30$), varying
nearly linearly with Z from 0.04 for Be

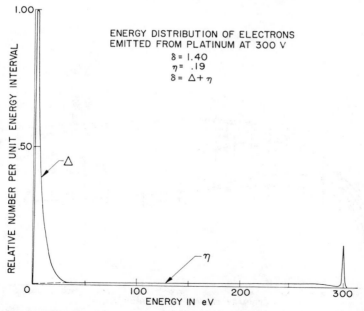

F_{IG}. 1. Typical energy distribution of the electrons emitted from metals under electron bombardment
by 300-v primaries; δ is the total yield, Δ the yield of true secondaries, and η the backscattered fraction.

($Z = 4$) to 0.28 for Ni ($Z = 28$). For heavier elements, η increases slowly with primary energy from values less than for Ni to limiting values as high as 0.45 for Pt ($Z = 78$) above 5 kv. The yield of low energy secondaries $\Delta = \delta - \eta$ starts from zero at a finite voltage in the neighborhood of 10–15 ev and rises to a maximum value in the range of 0.5–1.5 between 100 and 700 v for all metals. Thereafter, it decreases steadily until at energies above a few kilovolts, Δ becomes less than the backscattered fraction η.

In sharp contrast to thermionic or photoelectric emission, neither the onset of emission nor the maximum yield is directly related to the work function (*q.v.*) of the metal. Instead, it has been found that the maximum yield Δ_m increases steadily within each period of the atomic table as successive electrons are added, the alkali metals having the lowest yield in each case as illustrated for the fourth period by Fig. 2.

The presence of surface impurities or oxides can increase the yield considerably, primarily owing to the fact that secondaries can travel larger distances in insulators than in metals, where they lose energy rapidly to the conduction electrons. Measurement of the yield for insulators, such as BaO, MgF_2, MgO, and KCl, have shown that yields of 6 to 10 or higher can be obtained for such materials depending on the method of preparation, the yield remaining well above unity even at primary energies of many kilovolts. It is for this reason that in technical applications in which it is desired to obtain the largest possible yields, one utilizes alloys which upon heat treatment form an oxide layer containing BeO or MgO on their surfaces. The most common of them are alloys of Cu-Be and Ag-Mg.

In addition to the larger mean-free path for secondaries, such complex insulating surfaces often show an additional enhancement of their yield owing to internal electric fields, which act to increase the fraction of electrons able to escape, thus resulting in yields often many times those normally attainable. The presence of charging effects is characterized by a strong increase in the relative number of very low energy secondaries. It is generally accompanied by a time-delay in the emission process long compared

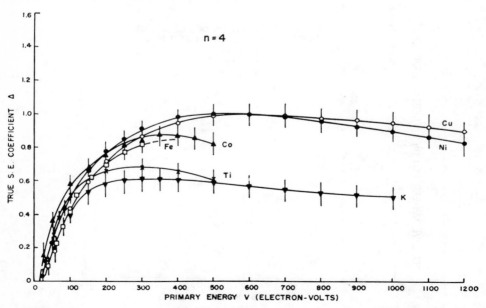

FIG. 2. Typical secondary-electron yield curves for metals. Data shown for elements in the 4th period of the atomic table.

with that for normal secondary emission, which is completed in less than 10^{-12} sec.

Secondary Emission Under Ion Bombardment. As already noted, secondary emission under ion bombardment resembles closely the phenomenon under electron bombardment, especially for very high ion energies, when the velocities of the incident ions exceed the orbital velocities of electrons in the atoms of the solid. The principal difference is the somewhat larger yield for ions, brought about by their greater rate of energy loss and therefore ionization near the surface. For protons, the maximum yield is close to 4 occurring at an incident energy of about 100 kv. For α-particles or helium ions, the maximum yield is almost four times as large since the rate of ionization is proportional to the square of the effective charge. Another important difference in the case of fast ions is that all clean metals show closely the same yield at a given energy, because of a proportionality between the probability of secondary formation and absorption in all metals. Again, the presence of oxide layers can greatly enhance the attainable yield. For ions of very low velocity, the phenomenon becomes more complex since the relative values of the ionization potential and the work function of the solid begin to play a dominant role. The electron-emission process is then determined primarily by the energy made available when an electron from the metal drops into the ionized outer level of the approaching ion, rather than by its kinetic energy and state of charge.

Theory. In contrast to thermionic, photoelectric, and field emission, secondary emission under the impact of high-speed particles is an energetic process for which the usual free-electron model of a metal becomes inadequate. Furthermore, in the case of electrons falling on a solid, the strong inelastic scattering by the large number of more firmly bound electrons is the principal factor determining the depth at which the secondaries are formed. The theoretical description therefore consists of finding an expression for the ionization density as a function of depth,

and then calculating the probability that the secondaries formed will reach the surface. When the primary particle velocity is high, the theory of Bohr and Bethe for the stopping of charged particles in gases may be used to calculate the scattering and ionization of the incident particles. In the special case of high-energy ions, scattering is negligible and a simple theory can be formulated that explains the maximum in the yield as reflecting the maxium in the ionization probability for the atoms of the solid.

For the case of low-energy electrons incident on the surface, it is possible to arrive at an approximate expression for the mean depth at which the electrons have been completely scattered and where most of the secondaries are formed. In view of the known rapid exponential absorption of the secondaries in metals, with a mean-free path of only a few atomic layers and an energy expenditure per secondary formed similar to that for gases ($\sim$30 ev), good agreement with the observed yields is obtained. The shape of the yield curve is found to reflect the opposing effects of an increase in the number of secondaries formed and the decrease in their chance of reaching the surface as the primary energy is increased. In insulators, the escape probability is greater, thus leading to larger yields at high primary energies.

For the case of low-velocity rare-gas ions incident, the band-model of a metal can be used to calculate the energy available for the ejection of a conduction electron when a metallic electron neutralizes the incoming ion. The observed yield and energy distribution of the secondaries can then be accounted for rather well. At the present time, the principal theoretical problem remaining is to establish the precise role of the surface potential barrier in determining the fraction of the secondaries able to escape.

Applications. The principal application of secondary emission in the field of electronics has been in the amplification of weak electrical currents first suggested by J. Slepian in 1917. The most common use is in the intensification of photoelectrons by successive steps of multiplication in photomultiplier tubes, over-all gains of 10^7 being readily achieved at a very small loss in signal-to-noise ratio. The phenomenon also plays an important role in many types of television camera tubes such as the iconoscope (q.v.) and the image orthicon (q.v.), and more recently in image-intensifying tubes based on secondary emission from a series of thin foils. Other important applications exist in storage tubes, magnetrons, and high-gain multiplier receiving tubes. Secondary emission under ion bombardment is a fundamental process involved in most gas-discharge devices, and it is also believed to play an important role in high-voltage breakdown phenomena.

E. J. STERNGLASS

Cross-references: *Distribution Functions, Field Emission, Image Intensifier, Magnetron, Photoelectric Emission, Photomultipliers, Storage Tubes, Thermionic Emission*

SELSYN: see SERVO COMPONENTS

SEMICONDUCTOR MANUFACTURE

The main present-day techniques for the manufacture of semiconductor devices are the alloying and diffusing processes. Earlier techniques, which are now in or near obsolescence, are those used in making the point contact and the grown units (pulled). Although somewhat improved performance devices are obtained by variations of the grown method, such as the melt-back and the rate-grown methods, the technology is now considered obsolete.

Alloy Process. In the alloying process, wafers of the semiconductor of thicknesses of the order of 0.005 in. are prepared that have flat and parallel surfaces.[1] The area of the wafer scales with the current-carrying capacity desired. Two metal dots (usually

[1] Various sources originally referred to transistors produced by this fashion as fused, diffused or fusion-alloy transistors. The generally accepted term now is alloy transistor.

indium in germanium) are alloyed on exactly opposite sides of the wafer. On recrystallizing, portions of the semiconductor near the metal in the molten phase regrow back into the original single-crystal form, but now have some of the metal included in the regrowth layer as an impurity dopant. The dots then have lead wires soldered to them (emitter and collector leads). A ring or tab of metal of the type that has the same polarity of doping as already exists in the base (the wafer in this case) is usually alloyed at the same time the emitter and collector junctions are formed by alloying.

The principal difficulty of this method is in obtaining uniform melting of the emitter and collector so that the uniformity of the depth of the alloying is controllable. Furthermore, the base width is determined by the difference of the original wafer thickness and the sum of the junction depths that the alloying of the two dots produces. Base widths that give alpha cutoff of about 5 to 10 Mc are feasible. Attempts to decrease the base width below this limit result in loss of yield and raise costs prohibitively.

Diffusion Process. The diffusion process refers to introduction of impurity atoms into the solid original crystal by means of the random movement of the impurity atoms that are placed on the surface of the semiconductor wafer. Although the operation takes place at high temperature (1,000 to 1,300°C in silicon) in order to be completed in a reasonable time, there is no melting operation as found in the alloy process.

The impurity atoms are placed on the surface by (1) painting on of compounds containing the desired impurity on the wafer, (2) passing of a carrier gas (that includes in the mixture a compound of the impurity) across the heated wafer, or (3) insertion of the wafer plus compounds containing the impurity into an ampule which is then pumped down, sealed off, and then heated to diffusion temperatures.

The junction areas in diffused devices are controlled by either etching through the diffused layer past the junction (the "mesa" is left where the etching did not take place) or by limiting the area where the diffusant can enter into the parent crystal. The mesaing process is used in forming the collector-base diode of all mesa transistors. The second process uses a relatively thick, thermally grown oxide on the surface of the silicon as a masking medium which was selectively removed by an etching process at the desired junction areas. This process is used in making the emitter junction in double diffused silicon mesa units.

Variations on Alloy and Diffused Devices. In the alloying method, improvements have been obtained by utilizing the diffusion technique to produce a nearly exponential base-impurity profile which provides a drift field in the base region that improves the frequency characteristic. This type of alloy drift has sometimes been known as the diffused-base transistor, the drift-field transistor, or simply as a drift transistor. Another variation is an alloy technique combined with diffusion in which an alloyed emitter produces simultaneously a diffused-base structure.

For the production of surface-barrier transistors the operations begin by electrochemical "machining" of the starting blank from opposite sides so that a very thin base region is obtainable. Then metal contacts are electrolytically deposited at the machined area. By a slight heat treatment (microalloying) the surface barrier contact is converted to an alloy contact as found in the alloy types. Here again, if a diffused impurity of the base polarity is added in the base, one gets the equivalent of an alloyed drift transistor.

Germanium mesa transistors are made with a diffused base region with an alloyed emitter. The double-diffused process, in which both emitter and base are diffused, is usually used in silicon mesa transistors. A significant variant is the double-diffused planar, where the collector base junction is no longer delineated by a chemical etching which forms the so-called mesa. Rather, the collector area is defined by oxide masking and is formed on a flat surface underneath a silicon oxide layer. The final device has both emitter and collector covered and protected by a silicon oxide layer. A further variation that belongs in the diffused field is the epitaxial transistor, which has been combined with the double diffused silicon units (both mesa and planar) and also the diffused base-alloyed emitter germanium mesa. Here the epitaxial (or vapor-growth) process is used to deposit a very thin and relatively lightly doped region over the very heavily doped original wafer of the same polarity. The effective collector resistivity that determines most of the collector spreading resistance is greatly reduced over that of the conventional processing. The thickness and resistivity of the grown film are selected from breakdown voltage considerations.

Lead Attachment. Leads are attached to low-current diodes by soldering one side of the wafer to a flattened pin while a pressure contact is made to the other side. For power devices both contacts are made by soldering.

Leads are attached to mesa and planar types by means of thermal-compression bonding. A fine wire, usually gold, is placed over the contact areas of the emitter and base (these areas are normally metallized) and by application of moderate temperatures and pressures to the wire a weld is made that provides a very low resistance contact that can be stronger than the original wire.

Leads are normally soldered to the alloy metal regions on alloy transistors.

Packaging. The techniques for packaging transistors have evolved considerably since the early use of simple plastic encapsulating methods, which were unreliable owing to moisture penetration to the unprotected germanium junction. Solder-seal packages were an improvement over this type but still were not adequate. Present packaging techniques generally provide hermetic seals similar to that of vacuum-system enclosures. Methods that are used are resistance welding for joining the two separate metal pieces of the enclosure (header and can) and cold welding. A high thermal conductance between the active region of the transistor and the heat sink is an important consideration in packaging power transistors. Thus, the semiconductor element (usually the collector side) is tied thermally and electrically to the case of the transistor. For very high powers a threaded stud is provided so that the device can be bolted onto a heat sink. In many other applications it is desirable to have all elements isolated from the case, and the transistor element is mounted on a tab inside of the enclosure.

In diodes, the coaxial-glass package has been used extensively for low-power applications. In power-rectifier work, one end of the rectifier is connected electrically and thermally to the case which has integral with it a threaded stud that is fastened to the heat sink.

VICTOR H. GRINICH

Cross-references: *Clean Rooms, Diodes (Semiconductor), Four-Layer Semiconductor Devices, Semiconductors, Transistors, Tunnel Diode*

SEMICONDUCTORS

As the name implies, the electrical conductivity of semiconductors is intermediate between that of conductors and nonconductors, or insulators. The ability of any material to conduct electricity requires the presence of mobile charge carriers within the conducting medium. These carriers may be ions or electrons, or both, that are free to move when an electric field is applied. Ionic conduction usually produces gross changes in composition, either in the bulk of the medium or at the electrodes, and is a separate subject in itself. This discussion will be confined to electronic conduction in crystalline solids.

Most metals are good conductors. A 1-cm cube of a typical metal has a resistance of the order of 5×10^{-6} ohm. The resistance of a similar cube of a typical insulator, like diamond, sulfur, quartz, or mica, is many orders of magnitude larger. At room temperature a 1-cm cube of sulfur has a resistance of about 10^{17} ohms. Between these two extremes are semiconductors like PbS, SiC, Cu_2O, Si, Ge, and Se with resistivities in the range from about 10^{-2} to 10^9 ohm-cm. Many properties of semiconductors are in sharp contrast to those of metals. As the temperature is raised, the resistivity of a semiconductor decreases rapidly, whereas that of a metal increases relatively slowly. In general the thermoelectric power of a semiconductor is large compared to that of metals. The conductivity of semiconductors is usually quite sensitive to light, being higher when illuminated than when in the dark. Semiconductors exhibit a more pronounced magnetoresistive effect (change of resistivity in a magnetic field) than do metals. The Hall coefficient is usually much larger for semiconductors than metals.

Clearly semiconductors are basically different from conductors; in fact, at sufficiently low temperatures a perfect crystal of most semiconductors would behave as an insulator. Properties peculiar to semiconductors usually occur as a result of crystalline imperfections that include both lattice defects and chemical impurities. Explanation of differences in the properties of metals, semiconductors, and insulators has been accomplished only in the past twenty years and is a major triumph of the quantum theory of solids.

In order to describe the properties of a molecule, it is necessary to examine the electronic binding structure between the atoms that comprise the molecule. The properties of a crystalline solid similarly depend on the nature of its electronic binding. One approach to the problem, which is perhaps more familiar to the chemist, involves a consideration of different solids in the light of their degree of covalent binding. The bond in the diatomic hydrogen molecule is a characteristic covalent bond. If a third H atom approaches this molecule, it is repelled because there is no close-lying energy level available for the third electron. In other words, from the point of view of valence, the

H_2 molecule is saturated. This is not the case, however, with a typically metallic atom like Li because, though each atom contributes only one electron, there are eight available states of approximately the same energy arising from the 2s and 2p atomic levels. So many levels are available that the Li atom can bind itself to almost as many atoms as can find space about it. The electrons do not belong to any one covalent bond but resonate among all of them. This situation does not lead to a condition of saturated valence, because Li may be pictured as bound to its eight nearest neighbors by eight unsaturated covalent bonds. The bonds are unsaturated because each atom contributes one electron which must participate in eight electron-pair bonds. On a time average there is effectively one fourth of an electron in each bond that could normally hold two electrons. Since the electrons participate in so many bonds, they are highly nonlocalized, and one would expect them to be mobile, and therefore, to contribute to electrical conductivity.

In contrast to this picture for metals is the case of a typical insulator like diamond. Here each atom contributes four electrons with eight close-lying energy states available for binding. In the diamond lattice each atom is surrounded by four nearest neighbors to form a tetrahedral structure. There are just enough electrons to saturate each of the four covalent bonds. As one would expect, the binding energy is much greater than in the case of unsaturated covalent bonds, and an electron is effectively localized in a given bond. The electrons are not mobile and cannot contribute to electrical conductivity.

Electronic binding in an intrinsic (pure) semiconductor is saturated, like that in an insulator, but the binding energy is not as great. An electron can be extracted from a covalent bond more easily. This can occur through the simple expedient of absorption of either heat energy from lattice vibration or incident light of suitable wavelength. When an electron is ejected from a covalent

bond by absorption of thermal or radiant energy, it is free to move throughout the crystal and contribute to conductivity until some other incomplete bond accepts it.

The bond from which the electron was ejected suffers a "hole" or a state of incompletion, and this fact introduces a new concept in the theory of conductivity. The deficient bond readily accepts an electron from a nearby normal bond with the absorption of only a small amount of thermal energy from the lattice. This process can repeat itself, so that there is a random motion of the hole. For each random jump of the hole there is a reciprocal electron motion. Thus in semiconductors there are two quite distinct ways in which electrons can move: the electron of a thermally generated electron-hole pair can move while the hole remains fixed; another electron can move into the hole leaving behind itself another hole, or, what is equivalent, the hole itself can move.

In an electric field a small uniform drift is superposed on the random motions of both electrons and holes and conduction takes place by both processes simultaneously. The electron flow which takes place by virtue of holes is equivalent to a flow of positively charged carriers in the opposite direction. All these results apply equally well to an insulator, the difference being that considerably larger energies are required to produce the electron-hole pair.

In an intrinsic semiconductor there is a hole for each free electron. In an extrinsic semiconductor this is not the case, and the conductivity may be primarily by holes or by electrons. This behavior is brought about by the presence of impurity atoms. An impurity atom which supplies electrons in excess of those required to saturate the covalent binding scheme is called a donor impurity, and the resulting semiconductor is called n-type because the conductivity is primarily by negative electrons. Conversely, an impurity atom that furnishes fewer electrons than are required to complete the binding arrangement is called an acceptor impurity, and the resulting semiconductor is called p-type, because the conduction is due primarily to positive holes. The conductivity of an extrinsic semiconductor is proportional to the concentration of the donor or acceptor atoms. If both acceptor and donor impurities are simultaneously present and uniformly distributed, the conductivity is proportional to the difference of their concentrations. The reason is that the hole furnished by an acceptor atom is readily filled by the excess electron of a nearby donor. Insofar as conductivity is concerned, this leaves the local binding scheme of the crystal negligibly different from that in a pure or intrinsic semiconductor. Semiconductor impurities are usually present in extremely minute concentrations. As little as 10^{-6} atomic percent of arsenic reduces the room temperature resistivity of germanium from 47 ohm-cm to 4 ohm-cm. Such low levels of concentration are beyond the range of ordinary methods of analysis, and the resistivity or Hall coefficient is generally used to measure the impurity concentration.

The energy-band theory is an alternate approach to the description of solids. A molecular orbital type solution is determined for an electron in the periodic field of the lattice and in a self-consistent field due to all the other electrons. This point of view is more convenient for considering dynamic processes in the solid.

The differences in the properties of metals and semiconductors can be readily explained. The small increase in metallic resistivity with temperature is due to increased vibration of the atoms which reduces the electron mobility. This effect is also present in semiconductors but is overshadowed by a much increased generation of current carriers. From a dynamic consideration of the Hall effect, it develops that the Hall coefficient is inversely proportional to the current carrier density. Since the carrier density is much smaller in semiconductors, they exhibit a larger Hall coefficient than metals. The thermoelectric power of a semiconductor is generally larger than that of metals be-cause the carrier density in a semiconductor is a very sensitive function of the temperature. Similarly the photoconductivity of semiconductors arises from the generation of current carriers by incident radiant energy.

Prompted by the success of solid-state theory in elucidating their properties, widespread interest has developed in semiconductors and in a variety of electronic devices based on their properties. These devices, which have wide application, include rectifiers, modulators, detectors, photocells, thermistors and transistors (*q.v.*). Germanium and silicon are the two elements most suitable for use as semiconductors.

HENRY E. BRIDGERS

Cross-references: *Atoms, Electrons, Hall Effect, Semiconductor Manufacture*

SEQUENTIAL CIRCUITS

Sequential circuits constitute that subclass of digital circuits (switching circuits) which depend essentially for their proper operation on memory or delay. In contrast, all other digital circuits, which are called *combinational circuits*, have outputs that are (ideally) functions only of the present condition of their inputs, regardless of the past history of these inputs. Taken together, sequential and combinational circuits are the building blocks from which digital systems (e.g., digital computers, control systems, digital communication systems, etc.) are designed and constructed.

Examples of sequential circuits include such computer subsystems as binary counters, serial adders, shift registers, parity checkers, sequence generators, and sequence detectors. The high-speed memory (storage) of a digital computer may be regarded as a very large sequential circuit, as in fact, may the whole computer itself. Sequential relay circuits are widely used in the automatic control of industrial processes, in interlocks for the protection of equipment or personnel, in telephone switching systems and related applications. In the communication field, sequential circuits are coming to be widely used for the encoding and decoding of digital messages. It may be said that wherever digital signals are to be processed serially, sequential circuits play a crucial role.

Sequential circuits may be made up of the various kinds of digital components such as vacuum-tube or transistor flip-flops, electromechanical relays, and magnetic cores. All such components are *binary*, or two-state devices. They can be, at any one instant, in either of two physically distinguishable states—on-off, conducting-nonconducting, energized-disenergized, unblocked-blocked, etc. Conventionally these states are called the *one* and *zero* states of the devices. When, as with electromechanical relays, only one of the states is physically active in consuming energy, it is customary to refer to the active state as the *one* state, and the passive state as the *zero* state.

Regardless of the physical nature of their basic components, all sequential circuits may be regarded as systems capable of being in any one of a number N of internal states, and possessing input and output terminals by which they communicate with their environment. With binary components, the number N must be a power of two. Thus if a sequential circuit contains n flip-flops (or other similar binary storage devices), then $N = 2^n$. When external inputs are applied to such a circuit, the internal state changes, and signals appear at the output terminals in a systematic manner determined by certain rules built into the circuit.

If the input signals and output signals are represented by the Boolean variables X_1, $\cdots$, X_m and Y_1, $\cdots$, Y_p, respectively, and the internal state is denoted by the Boolean variables S_1, $\cdots$, S_n, then the rules built into the circuit take the form of Boolean equations:

$$Y_j = Y_j(X_1, \cdots, X_m; S_1, \cdots, S_n);$$

$$j = 1, \cdots, p$$

$$S_k' = S_k'(X_1, \cdots, X_m; S_1, \cdots, S_n);$$

$$k = 1, \cdots, n$$

Thus the present outputs depend on the present inputs and the present internal state S_k; the *next* value, S_k', of the internal state is likewise a function of the present inputs and present state. It is through the intermediary of the internal state that the present outputs are made to depend on the past inputs.

Sequential circuits, in fact digital systems generally, may be divided into two main types, *synchronous* and *asynchronous*, depending on how the internal state is permitted to change with time. In synchronous circuits all internal storage elements are prevented from changing state except in synchronism with signals from an internal or external "clock." In asynchronous circuits, each individual storage element proceeds, as it were, at its own speed. The design of asynchronous circuits is necessarily complicated by the need for avoiding undesirable *race* conditions between different storage elements whose states are changing simultaneously. So-called *safe-asynchronous* circuits avoid such race conditions by a design that allows only one storage element to change its state at a time. Thus each action of a safe-asynchronous circuit must await the completion of the previous action before a new change can be initiated. However, such a design procedure is usually too restrictive, and in many practical asynchronous circuits certain types of race conditions, *noncritical races*, may be permitted with a consequent saving in complexity and cost, as well as the achievement of higher speed of operation.

Asynchronous circuits possess an inherent speed advantage over synchronous ones, in that synchronous circuits may proceed at a speed (clock rate) determined by the slowest component used. On the other hand, the speed of asynchronous circuits is determined essentially by the average speed of its components. However, because of the design complications required for asynchronous circuits, the majority of present-day digital computers and related systems are of the synchronous variety.

Autonomous sequential circuits are a special category consisting of those which either possess no input terminals or only a trivial input (such as a clock input). Thus, autonomous circuits exhibit only a sort of free-running, unforced behavior. Binary counters and sequence generators are examples of this type. The Boolean description of autonomous circuits thus simplifies in that the next-state functions S_k' and the output functions Y_j depend only on the present state, $S_1, \cdots, S_n$.

Elaborate logical design procedures have been developed for sequential circuits. Basically, all such procedures attempt to reduce the logical design of sequential networks to that of combinational networks. A typical procedure begins with a set of (verbal or symbolic) specifications for the desired terminal behavior. These specifications are then converted to a *state diagram* (flow diagram, sequence diagram, etc.). Techniques for the reduction and simplification of such diagrams are available. After simplification of the diagram, its vertices (or nodes) representing internal states of the circuit, are *coded*. That is, an assignment of binary variables is made to these nodes in ways suggested by past design experience. This state-assignment procedure is one portion of the whole logical-design process that is still largely a matter of skill and art on the designer's part, rather than a straightforward process for which definite rules can be given. However, once the states have been coded, direct procedures permit the expression of the input-output and next-state relations of the circuit as a set of Boolean equations. Conversion of the coded state diagram into a *flow table* is often used to facilitate this last step. The entries (zeros and ones) in the flow table now constitute a direct expression of the Boolean functions to be realized as a multi-input, multi-output combinational network. Techniques for the realization of such functions constitute a major portion of the logical designer's art. The details of these procedures depend to a very great extent on the specific types of logical components to be used in the circuit. Relay-contact logic, direct-coupled transistors, and cryotrons (*q.v.*) fall into one class for this purpose, whereas diode AND and OR logic, and vacuum-tube or transistor AND and OR logic form another class which must be handled quite differently.

BERNARD ELSPAS

Cross-references: *Boolean Algebra, Digital Computers, Oscillators, Relays, Signal-Flow Graph, Switching Circuits*

SERRODYNE: see FREQUENCY CONVERSION AND SERRODYNE

SERVO COMPONENTS

Servo components are all the components and devices required to construct and operate a servomechanism or servo system. The type and number of components used varies with the mode of operation, the complexity, and the precision of the system. Generally, servo systems are closed-loop feedback systems that can be used accurately to position or regulate devices, machinery, and processes continuously or step-wise. Servo systems are used where direct manipulation of the devices or processes is impractical because of the magnitude of output power required, the precision and speed of operation demanded, or the requirement of remote control; or where such manipulation is uneconomical in terms of human operating time.

Servo components are classified according to their mode of operation into: electrical, electronic, mechanical, pneumatic, and hydraulic components. Frequently a system requires the application of several types of components by this classification, and occasionally most of them.

Within the system servo components are classified according to their function into: input member, output member, differential error detector, controller, and damping or stabilizing device.

The *input member* is the *standard* according to which the output is to be adjusted by the system. The *output member* is the *load* which is so adjusted. This load can be a device to be positioned or controlled, or a process to be regulated. Electrical, chemical, or physical parameters of such a process may constitute the output member of the system.

The *differential-error detector* is a device or circuit designed to compare the standard with the actual position or condition of the load under control, and to produce an *error signal* proportional to the difference between the two. The error signal may relate linearly or nonlinearly (time-varying) to the difference between the standard and the output-condition signal. Frequently the output-condition signal differs in mode from the standard, and the differential-error detector must contain the necessary components for transformation of either one, which can be done by means of active or passive networks; occasionally, the complexity of the relationship requires the use of analog or digital computing devices.

The *controller* of the system comprises the devices needed to respond to the error signal and to produce an output of the magnitude and direction required to bring about changes in device position or process parameters to diminish error-signal level. For continuous process control the controller most frequently includes an amplifier with specific characteristics, and a positioning or controlling device specially matched to the load. The controlling device may have inherent amplifying properties. For stepwise control a servo system frequently contains logic elements that perform the assessment of the requirements for output adjustment, amplifiers, and a positioning or controlling device matched to the load.

The *stabilizing* or *damping* devices are electrical or mechanical components or combinations of components that can modify the *rate* of change in the system, thus reducing oscillation (hunting) and shortening the settling time-constant of the system. Invariably the application of damping de-

vices in the system reduces the over-all accuracy, and their application is a compromise between settling time and accuracy demanded.

In the electronically operated servo systems the input member is some manually adjusted electrical quantity, or an electrical parameter adjusted automatically in a predetermined manner by a program device or as the readout of a computer (analog or digital) that obtains and deals with information from a number of sources to arrive at an appropriate standard of the moment. The devices used to produce the input member signal are not unique to servo systems. If a single activity is the determining factor for the magnitude of the standard, the input signal may be obtained as is the output-condition signal, by means of *transducers*.

Transducers are components that transform physical, chemical, or electromagnetic quantities into an appropriate electrical signal for use in servo system. Typical transducers used in servo systems are (1) *pressure transducers* using diaphragms, bourdon tubes, or bellows to convert pressure into an electrical signal by operating potentiometers, strain gages, piezoelectric devices, variable capacitance, or variable reluctance; thermistors, resistance bulbs, and thermocouples for the direct conversion of *temperature* changes to electrical parameter changes; rotary or linear *potentiometers* to transform position, velocity, or acceleration into electrical signal changes; *gyroscopes* operating potentiometers to transform changes of position into an electrical signal; *rate gyros* to transduce the rate of change of position or attitude; *level gages* which convert immersion of electrodes into a change of capacitance or conductance; *synchro generators*, which produce three-phase alternating signal voltages, the phase and magnitude of which represent and precisely identify angular shaft position; *photoelectric* devices, which convert changes in illumination into signals usable in servo systems. All of these and many other types of transducers become servo components when their primary function is to provide the input signal or the output-condition signal to be compared with each other in the differential-error detector. Many of them are described under the appropriate headings elsewhere in this volume.

The differential-error detector in mechanical systems usually consists of a differential gear train. In electronic servo systems the differential-error detector can be a passive network such as a bridge circuit, or an active network such as a differential amplifier. Transformations required for the differential-error detecting function can be carried out with modulators for dc to ac conversion and demodulators for ac to dc conversion. Changes of magnitude can be accomplished in passive networks. For very complex transformations, computers can be applied. Where the momentary standard is related to a number of parameters of the output condition the use of computers becomes essential, especially when these relationships are nonlinear. The output of the differential-error detector is the error signal which in all cases is in some proportional relationship to the deviation of the output condition from the output condition prescribed by the standard.

The error signal is fed to the controller. The controller contains, generally, an operational amplifier, which amplifies the error signal. Through the application of nonlinear feedback the relationship between input and output of the operational amplifier can be varied.

By such means a large error signal may, for example, be made to produce a proportionally larger output signal than a weak input signal. Operational amplifiers, whether ac or dc, are not in essence different from those used in analog computers. Amplifiers may be constructed with vacuum tubes, gas-filled tubes, transistors, or magnetic amplifiers. The essential features of a servo-system operational amplifier are stability, large gain, and controllable relationship between input and output, generally through the application of feedback. If the opera-

tional amplifier is a dc amplifier, the controller must include a well-regulated power supply for this amplifier.

Where the process control or the positioning function of the system is carried out entirely in a digital manner, the usual amplifier and error detector is replaced or augmented by logic devices. Where the resultant control is to be the result of a number of different inputs such logic-type systems are more economical than the usual continuous control system, provided the inputs can be stated in a binary form.

The controller also contains the positioning device or final control member. This can be a typical servo motor, which usually is an ac motor with several field windings operated out of phase with each other and thereby capable of positioning the armature precisely. The final control member may be an actuator of the solenoid type, or a set of control valves to control subsequent hydraulic or pneumatic activity in the system. In such a case valves with several stages are used in the system, and the valves then have also amplifying properties. Dc positioning may include *amplidynes*, which are rotating "regulators" exploiting armature reaction to obtain great amplification of the amplifier signal.

The final amplifier in the controller may be constructed with vacuum tubes, thyratrons, transistors, or magnetic amplifiers, and is virtually always a push-pull amplifier to provide economical bi-directional control of considerable power.

Damping or stabilizing devices can be introduced into the system at the output, at the error-signal level or both. In mechanical systems the damping device may be a frictional device, such as a dashpot or friction disk, or an electrical device such as an eddy-current damper, a disk rotating in a magnetic field, or an ac servo motor with a dc current in the control winding. A critically damped system is a system in which no oscillation takes place; most systems are underdamped, allowing for minimal oscillation. The greater the damping, the greater is the positioning error. Only undamped systems have zero positioning error; critically damped and undamped systems are theoretical limit cases only.

In electronic systems damping can take place by means of passive networks in the error-signal level, through signal feedback from a tachometer generator driven with the load, through a proportional feedback signal from the amplifier output, or through specific characteristics of the output motor or actuator. The feedback systems are called frictionless viscous damping in contrast to the friction - type viscous damping cited above.

In general, servo components are uncommon electronic, electrical and mechanical components, applied specifically in servo systems where their particular characteristics are employed to achieve the method, accuracy, speed and magnitude of control desired.

THOMAS JASKI

Cross-references: *Amplifiers, Analog Computers, Digital Computers, Feedback Systems, Magnetic Amplifiers, Systems, Transducers*

SERVOMECHANISMS: see FEEDBACK SYSTEMS

SHADOWMASK TUBE: see TELEVISION (COLOR)

SIGNAL DETECTION

The theory of signal detectability is one of a class of theories grouped under the general heading of statistics. The theory utilizes concepts from probability theory, the theory of testing statistical hypotheses, and decision theory to characterize the task of detecting signals embedded in noise.

During World War II Siegert introduced the concept of an "ideal observer" in the detection of signals. In 1954 papers by Van Meter and Middleton and Peterson, Bird-

sall, and Fox presented more sophisticated treatments of this concept based on the work of Grenander, Wald, and others. Recently a thesis by Kotel'nikov, written in 1947, has become known in the U. S. A.: V. A. Kotel'nikov, *The Theory of Optimum Noise Immunity* (New York, McGraw-Hill, 1960). This thesis offers a rather complete treatment of the subject. An extensive treatment of the relevant topics appears in D. Middleton, *An Introduction to the Statistical Theory of Communication* (New York, McGraw-Hill, 1960).

The general theory, in its present form, assumes that with every receiver input $x(t)$ there are associated two numbers: (1) the probability density that the input $x(t)$ arose from noise alone, $f_N[x(t)]$; and (2) the probability density that the input $x(t)$ arose from signal plus noise, $f_{SN}[x(t)]$. It is then proved that the receiver should use a decision rule that calls for accepting the signal as included in the input, $x(t)$, if and only if

$$l[x(t)] \stackrel{df}{=} \frac{f_{SN}[x(t)]}{f_N[x(t)]} \geq \beta$$

where $l[x(t)]$ is the likelihood ratio and where β is a number, or a weighting function. A receiver that has the task of detecting signals in noise must perform two operations: (1) compute likelihood ratios associated with the inputs, and (2) compare these to a number β.

To treat a particular problem, or to design a receiver to perform a particular task, it is necessary to know how to determine the numbers $f_{SN}[x(t)]$ and $f_N[x(t)]$, and to have a method for computing the number β.

The first problem is one of choosing a set of assumptions that permit mathematical manipulation and at the same time agree arbitrarily well with one's intuitive notions of the physical conditions under consideration. In most cases, assumptions permitting mathematical manipulations do not agree in a precise sense with any realizable physical conditions. For example, in order to incorporate a mathematics that can be manipulated into these solutions, finite sampling plans are often introduced. One such plan assumes that both the waveforms arising from noise alone and from signal plus noise are Fourier series bandlimited in the same way over the open interval, 0 to T. This assumption has led to much controversy. Whether or not such an assumption is permissible appears to depend on the particular application involved. Sometimes such assumptions, such as that of absolutely precise measurements, taken too seriously, lead to ridiculous conclusions. The effect of some of these assumptions on the analysis of the detection task is not completely understood. It is a major area of limitation on the use of the theory.

The second problem is to establish a value to place on the number β. Although the applicable equations are known for many situations, the task of substituting numbers for symbols is not always possible. Frequently, efforts are made to maximize the expected value of the outcome even though the conditions required for an expected-value criterion are rarely satisfied. Here again is a limitation on the use of the theory.

The theory of signal detectability has proven useful in many fields, and promises to be more so in the future. It has been applied to sonar (*q.v.*), radar (*q.v.*), and to the development of psychophysical theory. In some cases, it furnishes only a reference for thinking; in others it leads to quantitative measures.

The theory in its general form constitutes a framework for handling a number of specific problems. It has been extended to include problems of recognition and discrimination. However, each of these applications requires the introduction of additional assumptions. As with most mathematical theories, the assumptions are precise mathematical statements; whereas statements describing physical conditions have no such precision. Hence the success of the application often depends on the resourcefulness of the applier.

The theory is still in its formative stages

with reference to the development of techniques of applications.

WILSON P. TANNER, JR.

Cross-references: *Decision and Game Theory, Noise (Statistical Theory), Probability, Sampling Theory, Signal Fluctuation and Noise, Statistical Communication Theory*

SIGNAL-FLOW GRAPH

A *signal-flow graph* is a representation of a system of linear algebraic equations as a directed linear graph. Two such representations are known. The original graph was described by S. J. Mason (Proc. IRE 41: 1144, 1953 and 44: 920, 1956), and is the one discussed here. The other is due to C. L. Coates (IRE Trans. on Circuit Theory, June 1959).

Let

$$\sum_{j=1}^{n} a_{ij}x_j = y_i \qquad i = 1, 2, \cdots, n$$

be a given set of n linear equations in n unknowns. In physical applications the y_i's are usually multiples of a single source: $y_i = b_i y_0$. The equations are now rewritten as:

$$x_i = c_{i0}y_0 + \sum_{j=1}^{n} c_{ij}x_j \qquad i = 1, 2, \cdots, n$$

by transposing $b_i y_0$ and adding x_i to both sides of the ith equation. To construct the signal flow graph, $(n + 1)$ nodes are drawn and labelled $y_0, x_1, x_2, \cdots, x_n$. When c_{i0} is nonzero, a directed line segment is drawn from node y_0 to node x_i and is labelled c_{i0}. Similarly for each nonzero c_{ij}, a directed line segment is drawn from node x_j to node x_i and is labelled c_{ij}. The line segments are called *edges* and their labels *transmissions*. When the solution for a single unknown x_k is desired, which is a common situation in applications, the graph can be easily manipulated to yield the solution. The manipulation involved is the elimination of all nodes except the source node y_0 and the desired variable node x_k, by the repeated application of the following two rules. (A *self-loop* is an edge of the signal flow graph with coincident end-points, which occurs whenever $c_{ii} \neq 0$.)

Rule 1: To eliminate a self-loop c_{ii} at node i the transmissions of all the incoming edges at node i (that is edges from other nodes x_j to the node x_i) are divided by $1 - c_{ii}$ (assumed nonzero) and then the self-loop is removed from the graph.

Rule 2: To eliminate a node x_i at which no self-loop is present, all transmissions through node x_i are replaced by direct transmissions as follows. For *each* incoming edge c_{ij} and *each* outgoing edge c_{ki} at node i, add the product $c_{ki}c_{ij}$ to the direct transmission c_{kj} from x_j to x_k. (If $c_{kj} = 0$, a new edge is added.) After all transmissions through x_i are so replaced, remove node x_i and all edges connected to x_i.

When all nodes (except y_0, x_k) and any remaining self-loop are removed, the graph reduces to a single edge of transmission g from y_0 to x_k. Thus $x_k = gy_0$ is the solution. The transmission g is the *graph gain*. These two rules are equivalent to successive elimination of variables. (For detailed justifications see S. Seshu and M. B. Reed, *Linear Graphs and Electrical Networks*, Addison-Wesley Publishing Co, 1961). Mason has also given formulas for writing g by inspection from the original graph.

Signal flow graph is a useful learning aid in the theory of feedback. The graph is drawn in such a way that the active parameter (say α) appears only once, and alone, as a transmission, as in Fig. 1a. The basic feedback-theoretic concepts of return

ratio and return difference may now be explained (as an example) as follows. Let all the independent sources be set equal to zero. Move the tail of the edge α away from the node x_i (to which it was originally connected) to produce a new source node x_i' as shown in Fig. 1b. Insert a unit signal at x_i'. (That is, set $x_i' = 1$.) The signal $-x_i$, which is the negative of the signal *returned* by the network to the active element, is the *return ratio* T. The negative sign is a matter of convention. The difference between the forward signal 1 and the returned signal x_i is the return difference $F(= 1 + T)$. Many of the standard theorems of feedback theory have similar simple interpretations in terms of the signal flow graph. (For example, see J. G. Truxal, *Control System Synthesis*, McGraw-Hill, 1955.)

S. Seshu

Cross-references: *Network Theory, Sequential Circuits, System Identification, Systems*

SIGNAL FLUCTUATION AND NOISE

Communication channels, especially radio, often possess time-varying properties. The character of resulting signal fluctuations depends upon both the propagation medium and signal parameters. Phenomenologically, the time-varying media appear to be describable in generality as comprising a multiplicity, perhaps a continuum, of simultaneous transmission paths with possibly additional nonselective *fading* on each path.

Propagation-induced variations often show separate long-term and short-term statistical structures. Long-term variations in transmission are attributed to gross parameters of the medium, e.g., weather or climate in tropospheric propagation, sun-spot cycle or solar storm activity in ionospheric propagation. Such long-term fluctuations require sufficient margin allocation in design to allow satisfactory operation during the worst expected ambient conditions. Short-term fluctuations appear to be an independent phenomenon, attributed to varying constructive or destructive interferences among a multi-

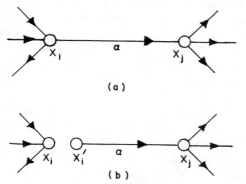

(a)

(b)

Fig. 1. Return ratio.

plicity of paths over which the signal is arriving. The time scale of these fluctuations is commonly in the range 0.01 to 10 sec, consistent with dynamical changes in the detailed (irregular) structure of the propagation medium. Often the short-term variations in received envelope for a steady transmitted signal are distributed according to the Rayleigh law. Such fading is usually interpreted as arising from an interference among many components with randomly changing amplitude and/or radio frequency phase. Quadrature components of bandpass signals would tend towards gaussian distributions (the central limit theorem) in such a model, and Rayleigh envelope distributions follow.

Since Rayleigh fading, for example, has a 13.5-db interdecile ratio, short-term fading presents a formidable design problem in any associated radio system. An economic alternative to designing with sufficient margin for satisfactory operation in the depths of severe fading is to modify the effective fading distribution by employing various redundant signaling schemes, categorized as diversity. The underlying concept is that medium-induced fluctuations should be statistically independent on signals sent via sufficiently different paths. It should then be possible to obtain a composite signal with drastically lower probability of deep fades (all diversity paths simultaneously undergoing a deep fade). The specific diversity arrangement tends to depend on the particular propagation mode. One common method employs spaced receiving antennas within the coverage of a single transmitting beam, but sufficiently spaced so that the transmission paths traversed to the individual receiving antennas involve disjoint segments of the medium. In microwave scatter propagation, for example, 25 wavelengths appears to be a sufficient spacing laterally to the path to effect sufficient independence. Moreover, since the deep fades are relatively rare events, signal fluctuations on the several diversity branches may be moderately correlated without deep fades occurring simultaneously on all branches with too great a probability. Correlations as high as 0.6 to 0.8 can be allowed. Thus, space diversity can still be used at lower frequencies without unreasonable physical distances between antennas. It is very commonly preferred for any situation in which standby antenna and receiving equipment, and perhaps also transmitting equipment, is required anyway for total reliability (concept of the "operating standby"). Other diversity forms include frequency diversity, wherein signals are transmitted at two or more frequencies spaced to provide relatively independent fading on the individual signals; height diversity, often used in microwave line-of-sight systems to account for refractive-index changes which vary the effect of interference from ground reflections; angle (of arrival) diversity employing squinted beans, particularly considered in tropospheric scatter propagation, where all parts of the transmitting beam appear to contribute via "scatter" to the signal level at the receiving site, and antenna economy is available by the use of multiple feeds on a single large reflector; and time diversity, for digital applications, where information symbols are repeated at sufficient intervals so that samples from which the symbol is finally reconstructed occur under a variety of fade conditions. A variant on the latter, the RAKE system, counters multipath on the channel by isolating the path contributions and adding them in a diversity-like combiner. A wideband noise-like signal is transmitted; appropriately delayed replicas of the noise-like signal, used as references in correlation reception, allow resolution of the individual paths (to within the correlation width), and the path contributions can be "lined up" with relative corresponding delays, and combined.

Often, one observes both a Rayleigh-law fluctuating component and a steady signal component, i.e., one whose rf phase does not vary and whose signal level remains constant. At hf, for example, a strong steady component arrives via the major reflection point, with additional fluctuations due to multipaths. The statistics for the envelope of a fluctuating signal which contains both a steady and Rayleigh component are identical with the statistics for the envelope of a combination of a sine wave and noise.

Along with signal amplitude fluctuations, the most significant characteristic of a varying medium is its "bandwidth," i.e., the bandwidth that may be used for signal transmission without significant propagation-induced distortion. The phenomenon of neighboring spectral components fluctuating in a partially decorrelated manner is known as *selective fading*, and is usually attributed to the presence of a multipath structure. For particular multipath delays, constructive interference occurs at some frequencies and destructive interference at others (the variations in path delays causing changes in interference, and hence, the signal fluctuations). Fading then tends to become decorrelated at frequency spacings corresponding roughly to the reciprocal of the range of path-length differences among the multiple paths, and significant distortions of intelligence occur if such wide modulated bandwidths are used. Typical bandwidth limitations due to selective fading are of the order of 1 kc at hf, and 1 Mc for microwave tropospheric scatter propagation. It appears doubtful that diversity operation can improve this characteristic of the propagation-induced fluctuations over sufficient percentages of the total time to allow wider signaling bandwidths.

By applying statistical decision theory, the structures of optimum time-varying maximum likelihood detectors have been elucidated, with diversity operation as special cases. However, performance characterizations for such general optimum structures are generally lacking. For diversity combining, the original (and simplest) sub-optimum procedure is to select at each epoch of the fading that signal with the largest amplitude. A theoretically optimum form of linear combining, termed maximal-ratio combining, weights each signal in proportion to

signal level and inversely proportional to the associated rms noise voltage; the resulting signal-to-noise ratio is the *sum* of the signal-to-noise ratios in the several branches. A simple alternative, almost as efficient when all branches have equal noise levels, is to add all branches unweighted (equal-gain combining).

Current research on advanced techniques for coping with signal fluctuations in digital data applications include the use of long codes for correcting errors; error-detection systems employing coding or null-zone detection with feedback links for appropriately requesting message repeats; and adapting systems in which transmission parameters are adjusted to the variations of the medium, so as to preserve constant quality in the signals received.

SEYMOUR STEIN

Cross-references: *Antennas, Noise, Propagation, Signal Detection, Transmission Reliability*

SINGLE-SIDEBAND MODULATION: see MODULATION AND DEMODULATION

SINGLE-WIRE TRANSMISSION: see DIELECTRIC RODS AND SINGLE-WIRE TRANSMISSION

SKIN EFFECT

An electromagnetic wave impinging on a metallic surface causes currents in the metal that concentrate near the surface. This concentration of current near the surface is known as the *skin effect* and the depth of penetration is termed the *skin depth*.

For a perfect conductor (zero resistivity) this skin depth is identically zero and perfect reflection takes place. For a finite resistivity, some of the electromagnetic wave penetrates the surface and is dissipated by joule heating.

The quantity of interest in describing the absorption of an electromagnetic wave by conduction electrons in a metal is its surface impedance

$$Z = (E/H)$$

where E and H are the electric and magnetic fields at the surface of the metal. This may be written as $Z = R + jX$, where R is the surface resistance and X the surface reactance. The absorption constant

$$A = \frac{cR}{\pi}$$

is the ratio of the power absorbed to the incident power and is the quantity usually measured experimentally. To compute the surface resistance R, knowledge of certain parameters of the metal must be used to find a relation between the current and electric field to be used in solving Maxwell's equations.

To discuss the various regions of interest in computing R, consider a plane wave incident on a plane metal surface. One of the simplest models one can use to describe the motion of conduction electrons is the drift velocity equation

$$m^* \left(\frac{dv_d}{dt} + \frac{v_d}{\tau} \right) = eE$$

where m^* is the effective mass, v_d the drift velocity, and τ the relaxation time. From this, the current in an electric field of frequency ω is computed to be

$$J = nev_d = \frac{\sigma}{1 + j\omega\tau} E$$

where n is the concentration of conduction electrons and

$$\sigma = \frac{ne^2\tau}{m^*}$$

is the dc conductivity. With this current-field relation, Maxwell's equations can now be solved. For a normal metal at room temperature there are three frequency regions to be considered.

The first is the case of low to microwave frequencies, where the displacement current can be neglected and $\omega\tau \ll 1$. Then

$$X = R = \left(\frac{\pi f \mu}{\sigma} \right)^{1/2} = \frac{1}{\sigma\delta}$$

where f is the frequency, μ is the permeability, and the electric field falls off exponentially with a *skin depth*

$$\delta = (\pi f \mu \sigma)^{-1/2}$$

In this region, the current is essentially in phase with the electric field.

In the optical region where $\omega\tau \gg 1$ and the displacement current may still be neglected, one obtains

$$R = \left(\frac{\mu}{2\sigma\tau} \right)^{1/2}$$

$$X = 2\pi\tau R$$

and the current is essentially $90°$ out of phase with the electric field.

When the displacement current may no longer be neglected, one obtains a maximum in absorption at the so-called plasma frequency

$$\omega_p = (\sigma/2\tau)^{1/2}$$

and at higher frequencies the metal is transparent.

The above expressions were derived under the assumption that the mean free path of the conduction electrons is small compared to the skin depth. In pure metals at microwave frequencies and low temperatures this condition is not necessarily met and the above expressions no longer hold. This is the region of the so-called anomalous skin effect.

G. E. SMITH

Cross-references: *Characteristic Frequencies, Conduction, Electromagnetic Theory*

SMITH CHART

A circular impedance chart designed to provide a rapid graphical solution to engineering problems associated with radio-frequency transmission lines and antennas was devised and used by the writer at Bell Telephone Laboratories in 1936. A description of this chart was published by him for the first time in *Electronics* (January, 1939). An improved form was described in the same magazine in January, 1944. Subsequently, the "Smith chart" gained wide-

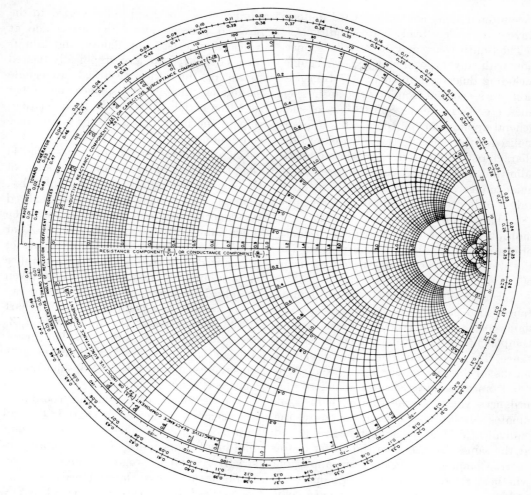

Fig. 1. The Smith chart.

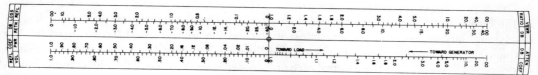

Fig. 2. Radial scales.

spread use for analysis and solution of problems involving uniconductor waveguides and waveguide components, and to provide a coordinate background on which to record performance of such components. That a simple functional name has not been found to identify this chart is possibly due to the fact that it accomplishes such a wide variety of purposes.

The Smith chart (Fig. 1) may be concisely described as a unique impedance coordinate system consisting of two families of orthogonally intersecting circles bounded by an outer circle. The chart coordinates display the complete range of possible values of normalized resistive and reactive components of impedance and/or conductive and susceptive components of admittance encountered along any mismatched uniform waveguide under steady-state conditions.

The Smith chart may be used in connection with any type of uniform waveguide, including dual or multiconductor transmission lines, coaxial conductor transmission lines, etc. To make the Smith chart of such general application the coordinates are normalized with respect to (i.e., divided by) the characteristic impedance or characteristic admittance of the particular uniform waveguide under consideration. The normalized values of impedance or admittance given on the chart coordinates must, therefore, be multiplied by the characteristic impedance or characteristic admittance, respectively, of the waveguide when converting back from chart values to true values.

Normalization of impedances and admittances also permits the display on a common coordinate background of the individual components of either impedance or admittance. This feature of the chart provides a means for directly converting impedances to admittances as desired. A normalized impedances value on the Smith chart coordinates always lies directly opposite the equivalent normalized admittance value and at the same distance from the center of the chart. Common scale values are applicable whether reference is to normalized-impedance or to normalized-admittance components.

The impedance or admittance background of the Smith chart is particularly useful for displaying loci of constant magnitudes of various electrical parameters of waveguide components in relation to their impedance or admittance characteristics. Such parameters include voltage, current, power, and frequency. When used to display power or frequency characteristics of nonlinear devices such as vacuum tubes or transistors the over-all chart is sometimes called a "Rieke diagram," after F. F. Rieke, who is credited with having first used the Smith chart in this application.

The coordinates of the Smith chart are arranged so that normalized impedances (or admittances) are graphically related to the physical position along the waveguide at which they exist. Impedances and admittances displayed are also graphically related to all of the other electrical waveguide parameters that are displayed on either radial or peripheral scales in fixed relationship to the basic impedance or admittance coordinate system.

One of the two families of circles (Fig. 1) comprising the basic coordinate system of the Smith chart, labeled R/Z_0 or G/Y_0, represents all possible values of normalized resistance or conductance, respectively. The other family of circles, labeled $\pm jX/Z_0$ or $\pm jB/Y_0$, represents all possible values of normalized inductive or capacitive reactance or susceptance, respectively. Any given complex impedance or admittance value can be represented as a point on the Smith chart at the intersection of the appropriate R/Z_0 or $\pm jX/Z_0$ (or G/Y_0 and $\pm jB/Y_0$) curves. A locus of impedances (or admittances) is thus represented by a continuous line on the chart coordinates.

A consequence of the unique coordinate arrangement of the Smith chart is that all impedance or admittance loci that represent the input impedance or admittance, respectively, as one progresses along a waveguide with a fixed mismatched load are represented by circles, or arcs of circles concentric with the center of the chart. However, this statement is strictly true only when the waveguide has negligible attenuation in the length represented by the locus of impedance or admittance values under consideration. With attenuation present the individual circles become spirals converging towards the center of the chart as one moves from any point on a waveguide "toward the generator." Conversely, they become spirals expanding outward toward the perimeter of the chart coordinates as one moves from any point on the waveguide "toward the load." A radial attenuation scale calibrated in decibels establishes the rate at which these spiral loci converge or expand.

All peripheral scales of the Smith chart are angularly linear. The two "length" scales, reading in opposite directions, measure the relative angular position on the chart coordinates, from center, of any two impedance or admittance points corresponding to any two physical positions along a mismatched waveguide. These scales are divided in wavelengths to generalize the chart's application. The total length of these peripheral scales (one complete circle at the rim of the chart) corresponds to an electrical length of one-half wavelength of waveguide since all input impedance or admittance values along a lossless uniform waveguide repeat, cyclically, at half-wavelength intervals. The two peripheral length scales shown, one progressing clockwise and the other counterclockwise, permit graphical evaluations to be made in either direction along the waveguide from any desired reference point on the chart coordinates. The rotational direction to move on the chart depends upon whether a chart evaluation is desired of the effect of a physical motion along the waveguide in a direction "toward the generator" (clockwise) or "toward the load" (counterclockwise), respectively, from the initial starting point on the chart coordinates. For convenience, the zero reference point selected for these scales is located at the angular position on the chart coordinates of minimum impedance (maximum admittance) at which position all voltages, standing as waves along any uniform waveguide, are at a minimum.

A third peripheral scale shown in Fig. 1 is the phase angle of the voltage-reflection coefficient. This scale is fixed in relation to the normalized impedance coordinates, as is also the electrical relationship of these two variables. The voltage-reflection coefficient phase angle scale starts at zero degrees at the position on the chart coordinates of maximum impedance, where the standing-voltage wave is maximum, and progresses clockwise in the capacitive reactance region of the chart from $0°$ to $-180°$. It also progresses counterclockwise in the inductive reactance region from $0°$ to $+180°$. The two halves of this scale meet at a point on the rim of the chart corresponding to a $180°$ phase angle for the voltage reflection coefficient. This point is at the angular position on the chart coordinates of minimum normalized impedance (and admittance), at which point all steady-state voltages along the line, standing as waves, are minimum.

The radial scales of the Smith chart include the magnitude of the standing-wave ratio and the attenuation, in decibel steps, from which the attenuation between any two impedance points on the chart coordinates at different distances from the chart center may be determined.

The radial reflection coefficient magnitude scale progresses uniformly from zero at the chart center to unity at the rim. This scale, in combination with the peripheral scale of voltage-reflection-coefficient phase angle, effectively comprises a superimposed reflection coefficient polar grid in the normalized impedance coordinates of the Smith chart. This polar grid is sometimes called a "reflection chart."

A set of radial scales which fit the chart of Fig. 1 is shown on Fig. 2. These scales include, in addition to the scales mentioned above, scales of return loss, reflection loss, power-reflection-coefficient magnitude, and transmission-loss coefficient. The last scale gives the increase in dissipative loss in the waveguide, when it is bearing standing waves, as compared to the dissipative loss in the same waveguide without standing waves, expressed as a coefficient. All of the radial scales display waveguide parameters which, for a given load impedance, have constant magnitude at all positions along a lossless uniform waveguide.

PHILLIP H. SMITH

Cross-references: *Coaxial Lines, Microwave Measurements, Rieke Diagram, Standing-Wave Ratio, Waveguides and Waveguide Components*

SOLAR BATTERY: see ENERGY CONVERSION

SOLDERS AND BRAZING COMPOUNDS

The joining of metallic areas by soldering involves a molten-metal solvent action that takes place at the surface of certain metals. A solder is a readily meltable metal or alloy that produces the bond at the junction. Certain atoms of the solder "wet" the base metal surfaces, an intermetallic reaction taking place at the interface when the solder is at a liquid state. Soldering refers to an operation in which the bonding material has a melting point below 800°F, substantially below the softening point of the base metals being joined. Brazing refers to joining metals using fusible metals that flow at temperatures above 800°F. Brazing materials may consist of metals such as silver, brass, gold, or of eutectic alloys compounded to utilize lower melting temperatures. The basic principles in soldering and brazing are the same, although the details for making reliable bonds between metal parts vary greatly according to the materials and techniques used in either category.

A reliable soldering operation requires:

(1) the shaping of or the mechanical holding of the parts to be joined so that they fit together without strain on the bonding material;

(2) cleaning the joining surfaces of all foreign material before assembly;

(3) application of oxide-removing fluxes;

(4) application of heat and solder;

(5) removal of surplus solder and cooling; and

(6) removal of surplus flux residue.

The name "soft solder" is typically an alloy of tin and lead, possibly with one or more other metallic elements, such as silver, added in small amounts. Tin melting at 450°F and lead at 620°F combine to produce an alloy that melts at 450°F for a 50–50 combination or even lower, 361°F with the eutectic combination of 63% tin and 37% lead. Such alloys form one of the most prominent types of commercial solder for "easily solderable surfaces." The ease with which surfaces are wettable ranges from the simple-to-wet surfaces of copper, silver and gold, through more difficult materials such as nichrome, aluminum, and stainless steel, up to others such as titanium, chromium, and beryllium which are so difficult to handle that brazing temperatures must be used.

Successful soldering or brazing requires that the surfaces should be free of foreign matter and of the natural oxides that may form at the elevated temperatures before complete wetting of the surfaces takes place. Mechanical cleaning, as by abrasion, will serve if the surfaces can be joined before these oxides reappear, as in reducing atmospheres. The difficulties of working in nonoxidizing atmospheres makes it desirable to use a *flux*, which acts as a reducing agent at the temperatures reached during the operation. A flux removes and inhibits the reforming of surface oxides, and also may increase the surface tension of the molten solder to increase its penetration into crevices.

Among the commonly used fluxes, three basic types are found: the *acid* types, usually one or more metallic chlorides (such as zinc chloride), either used as a liquid or mixed with petroleum grease to form a "soldering paste"; the *intermediate* types, which are much less corrosive, consisting of compounds containing amines, hydrohalides, or organic acids; and *noncorrosive* types, of which the best is pure rosin. For electrical equipment the matter of corrosion is of utmost importance and the use of noncorrosive fluxes is required. Sometimes thousands of electrical connections are needed in a single installation and highest reliability requires each connection to be perfect at the start and remain so during years of use.

Reliable connections require the combination of correct materials, adequate heat, and skill on the part of the operator in handling them. Seemingly inevitable nonadherence to all details at all times has caused much research into the improvement of fluxes, and there are many proprietary flux compounds based on additives to pure rosin that are claimed to be noncorrosive and to produce a more effective reducing action. Statistically improved results may thus be found through somewhat wider tolerances in operating techniques. Rosin fluxes with additives are called activated fluxes, and may contain small amounts of material mentioned above as intermediate fluxes. Their use is quite widespread except in the most critical applications involving fine wires.

Aluminum and other alloys of certain types have a highly refractory surface film that is unaffected by the usual fluxes described above. This film quickly re-forms after removal by mechanical abrasion and special techniques or fluxes must be used. One technique is to remove the film by ultrasonic (*q.v.*) vibration of the soldering tool when the surface is below the layer of melted solder which keeps it away from the air. The difference between the softening point of aluminum or its alloys and of the solder types used for aluminum is much lower than, for instance, copper and tin-lead solder. The temperature during soldering and brazing thus must be critically regulated. In addition, the thermal expansion of aluminum is somewhat higher and strains on the bonding metal are greater during the cooling interval. Aluminum solders usually contain zinc instead of lead. Pure zinc or zinc with 5% aluminum added makes an excellent solder. Zinc with various amounts of tin and or cadmium is also used.

Improved solderability of aluminum would enhance its use, so that much research is being applied to this problem. Many special fluxes have been developed that remove the oxide film that is usually present. They may be of the chemical type of an organic fluoboride, or the reaction type, containing zinc (and/or tin) chloride, in combination with certain halides and other additives. One such chemical flux consists of 83% triethanolamide, 10% fluoroboric acid, and 7% $Cd(BF_4)_2$.

In some applications metal joining by other means than soldering or brazing is being considered, including wire-wrap with tensioned wires, spot welding, pressure bonding (cold welding), ultrasonic welding, and conductive cements, to avoid need for application of heat or to improve the reliability. In brazing techniques the greater use of controlled nonoxidizing atmospheres, the use of high-frequency heating techniques, and the use of unusual eutectic alloys are getting increased attention.

Many new and ingenious techniques are also being applied in soldering operations. Mass soldering of electrical connections by the dipping of printed wiring boards containing many separate components is now a common procedure. Special formulations of the solder to prevent accumulation of dross and the precise control of temperature are necessary. Prevention of surface contamination prior to soldering is a requisite as individual handling of various surfaces is impractical. Frequently all surfaces are gold plated after the board is first assembled to provide a surface that resists contamination. A rather thin film of gold (a few microinches) is hardly more expensive than the somewhat thicker silver plate it replaces. Plating of ceramic surfaces to provide a solderable surface permits new forms of assemblies of interest to the electronic field when constructions that withstand higher temperatures are specified, or in the case of evacuated items.

RALPH R. BATCHER

Cross-references: *Materials Used in Tube Technology, Printed Circuits, Semiconductor Manufacture, Wire (Multiconductor)*

SOLID CIRCUITS: see INTEGRATED CIRCUITS

SOLID-STATE DISPLAYS

The purpose of solid-state displays is to provide, by electronic means, a visual presentation corresponding to input information. Although (depending on the display) the input signal energy can have different forms, it usually consists of an electrical signal or a pattern of radiation. As distinguished from vacuum-type displays such as cathode-ray tubes (*q.v.*), solid-state displays do not involve the electron bombardment of, or electron emission from, materials in a vacuum but depend wholly on the electronic processes occurring within certain materials.

Where the input consists of a radiation pattern, solid-state displays can convert the input to a visible image of different spectral distribution, intensify the image (i.e., produce an output of the same spectral distribution as the input but of higher energy), or perform both functions. Simple types of such displays are fluoroscope phosphor powder screens that convert energy of the incident X-ray pattern to a visible image; and phosphor screens that convert energy of ultraviolet or visible images to longer-wavelength visible images. With other phosphor powder screens previously excited with either ultraviolet or blue light, it is also possible to convert infrared to visible images. With special Mn activated, ZnS phosphor films, an ultraviolet image can be converted to a visible image whose radiant output is about $\frac{1}{10}$ the input power. However, the application of a dc field of 10^5 v/cm can increase the output so that it is about 5–7 times greater than the radiant input power. With present layers the response time for changes in input radiation is of the order of seconds.

Image conversion and intensification are also possible with double-layer screens, consisting of photoconductive and electroluminescent phosphor layers in series, across which ac voltage is applied. When local areas of the photoconductor are excited by the input radiation, the resistance is lowered, causing more voltage to be applied across the corresponding phosphor areas, which emit light. Within limits, the spectral response and emission of such screens can be determined by a choice of the photoconductor and phosphor. With CdS powder photoconductor and yellow-emitting phosphor powder such screens are sensitive to X-rays, capable of producing an output image more than 100 times brighter than a conventional fluoroscope screen. When excited with yellow light of the same spectral

distribution as the output the same screens produce an output image whose radiant power is as much as 400 times greater than the input radiation. With sufficient optical feedback, bistability can be obtained so that a transient input image can be used to trigger on an output image whose individual picture elements remain on or off without decay. Owing to limitations in present photoconductive powders the decay time of double-layer screens without feedback is of the order of seconds.

Where the input is an electrical signal intended to show only the presence or absence of a fixed visual pattern, an electroluminescent layer can be used with electrodes that apply voltage across the layer to predetermine areas. If a variety of alternate symbols is to be displayed, one surface of the phosphor can be provided with a number of separate conducting areas, electrically isolated. By applying voltage between the backing electrode and suitable combinations of these electrodes, corresponding phosphor segments can be switched on to form different symbols (alphanumeric display). If a nonlinear resistance is connected in series with each electrode segment, individual groups of electrodes can be permanently connected together. By switching voltage to the corresponding input lead connected to each group of segments, a symbol can be excited, but owing to the nonlinear resistances the excitation of undesired segments is suppressed. Another method for switching voltage to different combinations of phosphor segments is to use an array of photoconductive elements connected to the phosphor segments. A given symbol can then be generated by the illumination of a selected group of photoconductive elements that act as individual switches. For illumination of each photoconductive group, it is convenient to use an auxiliary electroluminescent strip placed adjacent to the photoconductive array but separated from it by an appropriate aperture mask. The photoconductive elements can be in series with the output phosphor segments so that when illuminated they allow voltage to be applied to the phosphor segments; or by shunting the segments, they may remove voltage normally present, the latter method requiring fewer photoconductive switches. The use of such logic circuits composed of auxiliary phosphor and photoconductive elements also allows other types of code translation, e.g., from binary input signals to digital display. For storage purposes, ferroresonant switching can be used by which a stable high or low ac current level is possible through each phosphor segment as a result of series resonating it with a nonlinear inductor, character generation requiring a suitable logic circuit to trigger on groups of segments.

For displays involving large amounts of information (e.g., where complex moving images are involved) a large number of electroluminescent phosphor elements, individually selected and controlled, must be used. One method of selecting an output element of a large array is to provide mutually perpendicular sets of parallel conducting strips on opposite surfaces of an electroluminescent layer. The application of voltage between a pair of strips of opposite surfaces causes the phosphor area at the intersection to light up. Although it is characteristic of such arrays that between $\frac{1}{3}$ and $\frac{1}{2}$ of the applied voltage also appears across unselected elements owing to internal crosscoupling, because of the nonlinear output of the phosphor with voltage the ratio between the light from a selected and unselected element lies between 10 and 10^3 (being highest at low input voltages). By the use of a nonlinear resistive element in series with each phosphor element, selection ratios of over 10^5 have been obtained even at high output levels. In the latter case, with arrays of about 600 elements, high-contrast oscilloscope-type traces have been generated with random-access selection, with the input successively applied only to the elements forming the trace. Alternatively all elements of the array can be scanned sequentially and

in turn modulated by the video signal. In both methods of switching, since the light from a selected element is emitted a much smaller fraction of the time than the light from the unselected elements, the contrast ratio in dynamic operation is much lower than for a steadily excited single spot. Also, the average light from selected phosphor elements is reduced to a small fraction of the peak light (which, for practical purposes, does not at present exceed several hundred foot-lamberts).

A means for increasing the average light from sequentially excited phosphor elements is to provide storage at each element. One method is to use a ferrite transfluxor element in combination with each phosphor element, the function of the transfluxor being to control by means of its magnetic blocking action the power which is transferred to the corresponding phosphor element from a pulsed voltage source. Because of its sharp threshold the degree of blocking of each transfluxor can be made to respond only to the coincidence of current flow through two auxiliary windings. After setting the magnetic state of the transfluxor, the phosphor output level remains fixed until the transfluxor is set to a new level. For selection and modulation purposes, the auxiliary windings of the transfluxor array are connected together in rows and columns to separate input leads. With such 1200-element transfluxor-controlled arrays, half-tone images with an average brightness of about 4 ft-lamberts have been obtained using sequential scanning. An alternative promising method for obtaining storage is to use a ferroelectric element at each phosphor element, the function of the ferroelectric element being analogous to the transfluxor, providing a variable degree of blocking action which is controlled by the state of electric polarization in which it is left. Suitable circuit arrangements for selecting and modulating the individual ferroelectric elements are also required here. Although considerable progress has been made in the generation of images with scanned electroluminescent arrays, serious problems remain to be solved if resolution and switching speeds comparable to commercial television are to be achieved.

B. KAZAN

Cross-references: *Computer Printout and Reading, Electroluminescence Fluorescence, Image Intensifiers, Semiconductors*

SONAR

National defense preparations for undersea warfare, especially where submerged submarines are concerned, rely heavily upon techniques derived from the study of underwater acoustics. Systems in which underwater acoustic energy is used for observation or for communication are known as "sonar" systems. The word sonar is also used to designate the principles and practices employed in the design and operation of these systems. The word itself, coined as a companion to "radar," seems to have been derived from the phrase "SOund, NAvigation, and Ranging."

These equipments embody applications of underwater sound for (a) observation and detection of other craft on or under the sea; (b) location of such craft in range and bearing; and (c) underwater communication between vessels for purposes of command or control.

Sonar systems are widely used by the U.S. Navy and other navies, appropriately designed equipments being installed in destroyers, escort vessels, submarines, cruisers, and fast merchant vessels. Sonar systems have been designed for operation from helicopters, seaplanes, and lighter-than-air craft, and even for use by amphibious forces and by "frogmen." Hydrofoil boats are currently receiving attention as potential carriers of sonar.

Active sonar is equipment in which bursts of sound are generated and transmitted in the hope of receiving an answering echo; *passive* devices are essentially sensitive receivers for whatever sounds may be present.

Thus, a destroyer uses active sonar to echo range on a possible submarine contact, whereas the submarine uses an array of hydrophones to listen to the destroyer's propeller sounds.

Active sonar is easily applied to give both range and bearing of targets within range. Passive sonar, sensitive to much longer ranges, normally provides information on bearing and bearing rate. It can, however, distinguish between many targets when there are several vessels in the area at the same time. Passive devices also have the sometimes critically important characteristic that they obtain information without making telltale sounds or giving away the presence of the receiving vessel. The most widely used submarine sonars are passive systems, although active techniques may also be employed in the late stages of an attack.

Passive sonar arrays for submarines (hydrophones) were used by the U.S. Navy in the 1920's. U.S. submarines were equipped with "blisters" containing groups of carbon button hydrophones. Incoming pulses were fed through delay lines to a compensator, giving target bearings accurate to a few degrees. The Germans had something similar, which developed by World War II into the so-called GHG equipment (group listening sonar), the hydrophones for which were arranged in the shape of a horseshoe about 5 ft across, and enclosed in a blister transparent to sound.

The Japanese copied the German concepts closely in their submarine sonars. The U.S. Navy did not pursue this type of device further at that time because the state of the art did not then permit construction of sensitive hydrophones with sufficient uniformity to provide good beam patterns.

During World War II the U.S. Navy developed the Type JP sonar for listening purposes, a mechanically trained line hydrophone and a selective amplifier leading to the operator's headphones. Since World War II, development of submarine sonar equipment has proceeded along the lines of physically larger arrays, better matching of hydrophones to improve the beam patterns, and more sophisticated information processing in the receivers. The human ear as the final sound receiver and interpreter is difficult to improve upon and remains of first importance in all sonar applications.

Echo ranging sonar of "searchlight" type was developed a decade or more before World War II, and all U.S. anti-submarine vessels were equipped with such sonar at the time of the U.S. entry into the war. By referring to the "search-light" characteristic, attention is called to the fact that this type of sonar projects intense pulses of sound along a relatively narrow beam (e.g., 15–20°). If the beam encounters the target, an echo returns to the projector and gives an audible "beep" or a visual indication of its presence. The distance of the target from the searching vessel can be determined from the time required for the pulse to go out and the echo to return. The limitation of this arrangement is the considerable time required to cover the bearings of interest by successively training the projector, sending out a "ping," and listening for an echo.

An important improvement was made at the close of the war, by the development of scanning sonar. In this system, the sound pulse is sent out in all directions while the receiving beam is rapidly rotated to give a spiral scan presentation. Returning echoes are displayed on the screen of a PPI (Plan Position Indicator) scope, and give a picture of underwater targets closely analogous to that given on the radar screen.

An important difference between radar and scanning sonar is that the velocity of sound, about 5,000 ft/sec in water, is a small fraction of the velocity of electromagnetic waves. In sea water sound waves transmit very well, but electromagnetic waves transmit so poorly that they cannot be used to locate submerged submarines. There are other differences between radar and sonar, most of them deriving from the differences in the physical characteristics of the media and in the types of wave motion.

Scanning sonar has a great advantage over "searchlight" sonar in that all targets in the field are disclosed by each "ping," and no blind spots are left in the forward sectors. One's own propellers may produce sufficient noise to blank out the scope on stern bearings. Various combinations of scanning and searchlight principles have been devised, and modern sonars also take advantage of advanced signal processing to acquire greatly enhanced capabilities in comparison with the simpler early versions.

Many of the difficulties with sonar arise because of the fact that the sea, particularly near the surface, is a nonhomogeneous medium, full of bubbles, disturbances, and thermal gradients caused by sun and wind. These facts bring the science of oceanography into importance in connection with further advances in sonar effectiveness.

JOHN M. IDE

Cross-references: *Acoustics, Electroacoustics, Navigation and Navigational Systems, Radar, Radar Displays, Underwater Sound*

SOUND RECORDING

Sound recording is the process of physical impression of the human voice, instrumental music, and incidental noises on moving stable media for indefinite preservation and reproduction.

The sound recording processes in all their variations require three basic steps: the reception and conversion of sound waves to electrical signals by a microphone; the amplification of these electrical signals with or without modifications in their frequency spectrum; the re-conversion of the amplified signals into mechanical, electronic, magnetic, or luminosity variations depending on the medium used.

Mechanical motions are used to inscribe, with a stylus, (1) laterally modulated or (2) variable-depth grooves on rotating wax, vinylite, or cellulose nitrate surfaces. Modern stereophonic recording requires both forms of modulation simultaneously. The styli are given their motion by cutting heads, which can be magnetic or piezoelectric transducers converting electrical signals into mechanical vibrations. Wax disks are electroplated and masters are made from the electroplated wax impressions by other electrolytic processes for mass production of records by a pressing method. Early pressings of recordings were made from shellac. Most present-day recordings are made from Vinylite.

Disk records rotate at 78, 45, and $33\frac{1}{3}$ rpm and a few at $16\frac{2}{3}$, and vary in diameter from 7 in. for the $16\frac{2}{3}$ and 45 rpm records to 16 in. for professional transcriptions used in the broadcasting and movie film industries. Records vary in the number of grooves they carry: 78-rpm records have from 96 to 120 grooves per inch; $33\frac{1}{3}$ microgroove records carry 224 to 300 grooves per inch. The maximum number of grooves on 45 rpm records is 275 per inch. Playing time of records varies from $2\frac{3}{4}$ min for 10-in. 78 rpm records to 25 min for $33\frac{1}{3}$ rpm 12-in. records. Stereophonic records carry a variable number of grooves per inch to accommodate the variable-width grooves resulting from the dual modes of modulation.

Disk recording reproduction requires a stylus that transfers the modulations of the grooves to a transducer, which in turn transforms the vibrations to electrical signals. The electrical signals are amplified and reproduced by loudspeakers. Originally the recording and reproduction were carried out entirely mechanically with vibrating diaphragms, but these instruments are now largely of historical interest.

The transducer used for reproduction may be piezoelectric, as Rochelle salts or barium titanate, magnetic with moving armature or magnetic with moving coil, or variable reluctance with moving vane. Ceramic pickups predominate.

Fidelity of disk recording and reproduction is generally limited to a range of 50 to 12,000 cps. Mechanical recording of the same type using either disks or cylinders now usually of vinylite, are used in dictating machines.

Stereo reproduction requires two transducers at right angles to each other both connected to the stylus to reproduce both modes of modulation), which are apportioned by the cutting equipment with appropriate portions of the recorded sounds so that reproduction redivides the recorded sound between the two amplifier systems in accordance with the original reception by the microphones.

Another form of mechanical reproduction is the embossing of modulated tracks on acetate film or specially prepared film by a stylus. Continuous loops of film are used varying in length to provide from 2 min to 2 hr playing time. On 16-mm film as many as 40 tracks can be inscribed; 35-mm film carries 100 tracks.

Electronic recording is carried out by means of a direct-writing electron beam in a vacuum on specially prepared three-layer film. The thermoplastic center layer of this film is softened by a heater just prior to being scanned by the electron beam. Variable depth recordings are then created by the electrostatic action of the electron beam. Such film can carry video information as well as sound and reproduction takes place optically with specially directed light beams and photocells.

Magnetic recording requires the reorientation of metallic oxide particles deposited in a layer on a paper or plastic tape, disk, or cylinder, or the reorientation of magnetic domains in stainless-steel wire 0.0036 in. in diameter. Recording and reproduction take place by means of a magnetic head which is essentially a core carrying one or more coils. The core has an airgap of 0.0005 in. or less which is passed by the oxide coating. The width of the gap and the quality of the oxide determine the product of the bandwidth and the tape (or disk) speed, or the resolution of the recording. Common tape speeds are $\frac{15}{16}$, $1\frac{7}{8}$, $3\frac{3}{4}$, $7\frac{1}{2}$ and 15 in./sec. Wire speed is 30 in./sec.

Magnetic recording requires a dc or ac bias to linearize the magnetization curve of the recording medium. The ac bias frequency varies from 30 to 100 kc. Erasure of the recording can be achieved with dc or the ac bias oscillator, the former by saturation and the latter by randomization of magnetic particle orientation.

Optical recording uses brightness variation to achieve variable density records photographically on movie film. Similarly, variable width recordings on film are made by passing light through a variable aperture, Kerr cell, or reflecting light from a mirror galvanometer. Reproduction of optical recordings is achieved by means of photoelectric cells.

Historically mechanical recording can be traced to the Scott phonautograph (1855) in which sound vibrations were recorded on a cylinder with lamp-black.

In 1877 T. A. Edison (*q.v.*) invented the acoustical phonograph. In 1885 A. G. Pell invented the forerunner of the present dictaphone. Credit for invention of disk recording goes to Emil Berliner (1897) with many improvements in his machine attributed to Eldredge Johnson. Sir Charles Parson invented many improvements to the gramophone, and the air-driven auxetophone which used air pressure as a means of amplification and a valve moved by the stylus as a modulator. Magnetic recording was invented in 1898 by Valdemar Poulsen (*q.v.*), Danish engineer. Sound on film was introduced by the Bell Telephone Laboratories in 1926, although as early as 1894 Edison attempted to synchronize phonograph disks with film in his Kinetophone.

Warner Brothers introduced the first sound film. Magnetic sound on film was introduced by Marvin Camras, 1946. In 1907 Poulsen patented dc biasing and in 1927 Carpenter and Carlson took out a patent on ac biasing of magnetic recording media. Pfleumer in Germany invented the oxide-coated paper tape and introduced a machine using this tape in 1935. The year before this de Lorentz and Marconi-Stille had used a steel tape for recording. Sound embossing on film was introduced in the mid-1940's by Western Electric. Stereophonic records were first demonstrated at the 1957 Audio Engineering Society convention in New York by the Western Electric Company and by London Records. The London Records dual-modulation system has been generally adopted. Present stereophonic recording uses as many as four tracks on tape for realistic reproduction.

THOMAS JASKI

Cross-references: *Electroacoustics, Loudspeakers and Microphones, Magnetic Tape, Stereophonics, Video Recording*

SPACE-CHARGE INSTABILITIES

The space charge of an electron stream flowing in the vicinity of a system of electrodes depresses the potential of the interelectrode space, thus slowing the stream in the region of the depression. For low charge densities or with electrodes close to the stream, the primary effect of such depression is an increase in the electron transit time. For higher charge densities or with electrodes removed from the vicinity of the stream, there can be a sufficient potential depression for the stream to become unstable and seek a new spatial configuration.

As a simple example, consider an infinitely broad stream, flowing normal to two infinite, planar, electron-permeable electrodes, separated by a distance a and held at a potential V_0. Electrons are constrained to move in the z-direction by a large z-directed static magnetic field. For small stream currents the potential in the interelectrode space is stable; velocity and potential are related by $v = (-2eV/m)^{1/2}$ and the potential can then be found by repeated integrations of Poisson's equation. The space-charge depression deepens as the current density is increased (curves A and B in Fig. 1) until the value

$$i_{max} = 8(2.33 \times 10^{-6}) \frac{V_0^{3/2}}{a^2} \text{ amp/m}^2 \qquad (1)$$

is reached (curve C), at which current the minimum potential is $V_0/4$. Further increase in current results in a rapid decrease in potential (curve D), with some electrons being reflected toward the plane of injection. The potential minimum also moves away from the center, toward the injection plane. As

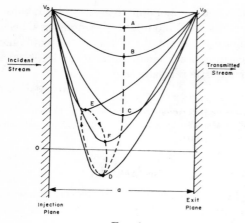

FIG. 1

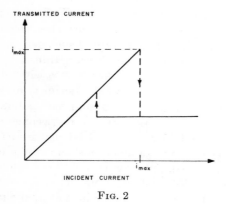

FIG. 2

electrons leave the interelectrode space in both directions, the potential minimum recovers and moves back toward the center (curve E) and the oncoming electrons are again transmitted through the region. The space charge then builds up again, the potential depresses and moves toward the center (curve F), electrons are returned, and so on. (The path of the potential minimum is shown dotted in Fig. 1.) The resulting oscillation is not sinusoidal with time and can have quite large amplitude, with the potential minimum varying by as much as $V_0/2$; the period of oscillation depends directly on the transit time across the interelectrode space and also on the stream-current density. The transmitted stream is both current and velocity modulated; its time-averaged current is always less than that

given by (1), and does not increase as the current of the incident stream is increased.

If the current in the incident stream is reduced sufficiently, a stable potential distribution is recovered at about one-half the maximum current given by (1), thus giving hysteresis in the time-averaged transmitted vs injected current characteristic shown in Fig. 2.

Mathematical solution to Poisson's equation that predict purely dc states for currents greater than that given by (1) can be found by allowing the minimum potential to be zero; these solutions appear in the older literature. Such solutions prove to be unstable when time-variation is allowed, however. The time-varying solutions for space-charge-limited currents cannot be obtained by simple integration of Poisson's equation since velocity and potential are no longer simply related; they have been obtained by numerical computation and are not easily given in compact form.

Similar phenomena occur in a stream flowing between, and parallel to, the two infinite, planar electrodes. The potential depression is now transverse to the direction of motion of the stream, with the minimum potential occurring midway between the two electrodes. As before, there is a current at which the stream becomes unstable. [For a stream filling the region this current density is given by (1), and the minimum potential is again $V_0/4$]. With the exception of the enforced dc solutions analogous to those proving unstable in the stream-normal configuration, the behavior at larger currents is not known. The symmetry of the configuration requires that the potential minimum change only in amplitude, not in position. Only those electrons near the center of the stream are returned, and those near the electrodes always transmitted, so that the time-averaged current transmitted does increase with increasing incident stream current after the initial decrease at the point of instability. The current given by (1) is the maximum *stable* current, but not the maximum current that can be transmitted.

A stream in a cylindrical drift tube exhibits the same physical behavior as the parallel-stream configuration. Instability occurs at a current density

$$i_{max} = 4.4(2.33 \times 10^{-6}) \frac{V_0^{3/2}}{b^2} \text{ amp/m}^2 \quad (2)$$

when the stream fills the drift tube of radius b.

It is possible to have space-charge instability in an electron stream with a neutralizing background of positive ions. For stream-normal configuration with infinitely massive ions, the instability occurs at a current

$$i_{max} = 44(2.33 \times 10^{-6}) \frac{V_0^{3/2}}{a^2} \text{ amp/m}^2 \quad (3)$$

The stream behavior at greater currents is not known.

Applications. Space-charge instability has long been known as the cause of discontinuities in the knee region of ordinary beam-tetrode V-I characteristics. More recently the oscillating potential minimum occurring with currents greater than the limiting value has been proposed as the mechanism of nonconservative transmission of stream fluctuation noise through the cathode-anode region of certain unusually low-noise electron guns. Use of an additional space-charge-limited region further down stream in the gun to give additional noise reduction has also been proposed.

The amount of useful microwave power produced by these space-charge oscillations is limited at present by methods of coupling to the stream; the oscillation is strongest when the electrodes are short circuited. The simple scheme of connecting a resistive load between the electrodes gives a maximum efficiency of only 5 per cent.

The rapid change of transmitted current at the point of instability may be useful as a fast switch in logic devices for microwave computing systems. Arrays of electron streams arranged spatially so that the state of one stream is controlled by the current in other streams could be used to perform the usual logical operations, although the oscillation in the current-limited state may present some difficulty in this application.

WILLIAM B. BRIDGES

Cross-references: *Electron Guns, Space-Charge Waves, Velocity Modulation*

SPACE-CHARGE WAVES

Small, spatially localized, time-sinusoidal disturbances of one or more of the physical parameter which describe an electron beam are transmitted along the beam in the form of waves. Since space-charge forces are responsible for these waves, they are called space-charge waves.

If the electric field caused by local differences in space-charge density does not couple strongly with the environment of the beam as is, for instance, the case in drift regions of klystrons, one speaks of free space-charge waves. In case of strong coupling forced space-charge waves are said to exist. Strong coupling prevails, for instance, in traveling-wave tubes where the environment of the beam is capable of supporting electromagnetic waves that have propagation constants nearly equal to those of the space-charge waves.

The physical picture of free space-charge waves will be briefly described for a particular electron stream consisting of a uniform electron flow of infinite lateral extent. In the absence of any disturbance let the electron velocity be z-directed and equal to u_0, and the current density equal to j_0. For a small disturbance of the velocity at $z = 0$ which is given by $v_i \exp(j\omega t)$ with $v_i \ll u_0$, a small-signal theory yields the following solution:

$$V = [V_i \cos \beta_p z] \exp j(\omega t - \beta z)$$
$$= \tfrac{1}{2} V_i \{\exp j[\omega t - (\beta - \beta_p)z]$$
$$+ \exp j[\omega t - (\beta + \beta_p)z]\}$$
$$I = [jV_i \omega S \epsilon_0 \beta_p \sin \beta_p z] \exp j(\omega t - \beta z)$$
$$= \tfrac{1}{2} V_i \omega S \epsilon_0 \beta_p \{\exp j[\omega t - (\beta - \beta_p)z]$$
$$- \exp j[\omega t - (\beta + \beta_p)z]\}$$

Here V is the kinetic potential related to the velocity modulation v by $V = -(m/e)u_0 v$ and similarly $V_i = -(m/e)u_0 v_i$. The propagation constants are $\beta = \omega/u_0$, $\beta_p = \omega_p/u_0$, where ω_p is the radian plasma frequency given by

$$\omega_p = \left(\frac{e}{m} \frac{j_0}{\epsilon_0 u_0}\right)^{1/2}$$

The current density in the beam cross section S is denoted I. Charge and mass of the electron are e and m, respectively, and ϵ_0 is the permittivity of vacuum.

The second form of the expressions for V and I shows that there are two waves whose phase velocities are $v_{pf} = u_0/[1 - (\omega_p/\omega)]$ and $v_{ps} = u_0/[1 + (\omega_p/\omega)]$ corresponding to the fast and slow space charge wave, respectively. Since $\omega_p \ll \omega$ in most physical situations v_{pf} is a little larger and v_{ps} is a little smaller than u_0. Both waves have the same group velocity which is equal to u_0.

The equations for V and I also describe the behavior of a transmission line which moves physically with a velocity u_0 and which has a series inductance per unit length of $L = 1/S\epsilon_0$ and a shunt capacitance per unit length of $C = S\epsilon_0\beta_p{}^2$. Because of the analogy the real power carried by the beam and the stored energy in the beam may be computed by using the expressions $P = -\frac{1}{2} \operatorname{Re}(IV^*)$ and $W = \frac{1}{2}II^*L + \frac{1}{2}VV^*C$, respectively. Using the expressions for V and I it is seen that $P = 0$ everywhere along the beam and that the two terms in W alternately change from zero to a maximum value in intervals given by

$$l = \frac{1}{4}\lambda_p = \frac{1}{4}\frac{2\pi u_0}{\omega_p}$$

When $\frac{1}{2}VV^*C$ is a maximum the other term $\frac{1}{2}II^*L$ is zero, which means that kinetic stored energy (or velocity modulation) is converted into potential energy (or current density modulation) and back to kinetic energy.

An initial current modulation also produces two space charge waves and the results regarding P and W must be modified appropriately for the case of the simultaneous presence of initial current and velocity modulations with arbitrary phase relation.

For other types of electron beams the physical picture is the same, only the plasma frequency ω_p must be replaced by an effective plasma frequency $\omega_q = k\omega_p$ where k is a correction factor that depends on the nature of the beam and its environment.

R. G. E. HUTTER

Cross-references: *Backward-Wave Tubes, Characteristic Frequencies, Double-Stream Amplification, Klystrons, Traveling-Wave Tubes, Velocity Modulation*

SPECTROSCOPY (LIGHT AND INFRARED)

In its broadest sense, spectroscopy is concerned with the measurement and analysis of both emitted and absorbed radiant energy. Appropriate identifications of the composition or the constituents of organic and inorganic matter can be made using alpha, beta, and gamma particles; X-rays; ultraviolet, visible, and infrared light waves; and microwaves.

Arranged in the order of increasing wavelength, where one angstrom unit (1 Å) of length is equal to 10^{-8} centimeters and one micron (1 μ) is 10,000 Å, the principal fields of spectroscopy may be identified as follows: atomic, <0.125 Å; X-ray, 0.125–120 Å; ultraviolet, 120–4000 Å; visible, 4000 Å to 0.75 μ; infrared, 0.75–1000 μ; microwave, 1000 μ to 1 M; radio, >1 M.

The term *optical* spectroscopy is usually reserved for the fields of ultraviolet, visible, and infrared *emission* spectroscopy, as distinct from absorption spectroscopy (see below). Limited attention may be also given in this context to fluorescent and phosphorescent spectroscopy. Whether for industrial or commercial analytical control purposes or for research and development applications, optical spectroscopy is a powerful qualitative and quantitative tool for the study of atomic and molecular structure. In addition, it provides our primary knowledge of the composition of distant stellar and planetary bodies and their environments.

Spectroscopy had its origin with Sir Isaac Newton (1642–1727) when in 1664, using a glass prism, he separated the white light from the sun into the spectral colors of the rainbow. Later, between 1800 and 1900, Herschel, von Fraunhofer, Kirchoff, Bunsen, Roentgen and others performed basic experiments leading to the association of radiated spectral information with the composition of materials being excited in the sun or in flames, arcs, sparks, etc. Ultimately, the interpretation and evaluation of these ultraviolet, visible, and infrared emission spectra led to the positional assignment of electrons in theoretical models of atomic and molecular structures.

Emission spectra, the product of emission spectroscopy, arise when atoms or molecules, or combinations of them, have been appropriately excited and processed by spectrographic systems or instruments. Excited molecules, in general, yield spectra consisting of bands of lines, referred to as "band" spectra; excited atoms yield discrete "line" spectra. The number and the intensity of the discrete spectral lines depend upon the number and the position of the electrons in the atoms excited, and upon the degree of atomic excitation.

Material to be analyzed, depending upon the analytical requirements, may be excited to emit light in a dc arc, a flame, an ac arc, in a high-voltage discharge spark, or combinations of these. Generally these sources are adequate for the excitation of chemical elements.

The emitted radiation may be analyzed by using nondispersive systems, such as selectively transmitting, reflecting, or absorbing filters; or by using the dispersive characteristics of prism or diffraction-grating spectrographs. Numerous optical arrangements of the elements of spectrographs are available commercially. Photographic spectral-data storage is used extensively, as it was in the past; however, direct-reading equipments employing photomultiplier detection, electrical amplification and storage, and a variety of data readout systems are becoming commonplace.

With photographic techniques, the identification of constituent elements is accomplished by observing the position of the spectral lines on photographic films or plates. The positional pattern formed by atoms serve to "fingerprint" and establish their individual identity. The positions of spectral lines of a specific element relative to themselves or to primary or secondary standards such as cadmium or iron are well documented. Furthermore, the detectability of many chemical trace elements in solid samples can be effective to less than 0.1 or 0.01 parts per million of the amount of sample present.

Quantitative information, derived from a determination of the intensity or density of specific spectral lines, may be estimated visually or measured accurately using electrical-optical densitometric comparators. Very recently, with the quantitative measurement of the relative intensities of the shifted isotope components of a single spectrum line (i.e., U_{238}, U_{235}, U_{236}), emission spectroscopy is probably approaching its theoretical limit of precision, since all isotope components are homologous and have identical self-reversal or absorption properties.

Automatic equipment is fixed or programmed to look at specific spectral lines and to provide data typical of the chemical matrix being analyzed. Data presentations are available on clock or meter faces, in alphanumeric electrooptical presentations, punch card or tape systems, or in typewritten forms as well as cathode-ray-tube presentations. A typical automated routine can be completed in a matter of minutes.

The analysis of materials by emission spectroscopy is generally limited to metallic elements. However, nonmetallic elements, such as sulphur, phosphorus, and carbon do emit spectra when suitable activating sources are utilized. In addition, since their spectral content usually is more readily interpreted in the ultraviolet region of the spectrum, vacuum or inert gas-filled sources and spectrographs often are employed. These instruments are relatively void of the absorbing and interfering gases of normal air.

Years ago, line intensities and densities were used quantitatively only for trace elements in a sample. Today, the percentages of even the principal constituents are measured. The reproducibility and the analytical precision of spectrographic techniques are usually equal to or, in the case of trace constituents, may be better than, those attainable by other methods.

Many samples, if irradiated by discrete or broadband ultraviolet light, absorb it and reradiate longer-wavelength energy. If the reradiation persists only during activation, the effect is called fluorescence (*q. v.*); if the reradiation continues after the activation is interrupted, the effect is called phosphorescence. In either case, the nature of the radiating energy and the spectral intensity distribution together with the time of persistence, quantum yield, etc. can be used effectively for qualitative and quantitative identification. The latter field is called fluorescent or phosphorescent spectroscopy.

Infrared Spectroscopy

Infrared spectroscopy had its origin about 1800 when Sir William Herschel (1738–1822), using a thermometer, detected thermal radiation beyond the visible red of the sun's spectrum. For some time, however, little use was made of these observations due to a lack of suitable sources and detectors.

The present activity in infrared (IR) is concerned with the interaction of the states of matter with the emission, reflection, and absorption of radiant electromagnetic energy between the wavelength of visible light waves and radio waves, (i.e., 0.75 to 1000 μ). In this region, infrared light exhibits some of the properties of visible light waves and in others, it more closely resembles radar or radio waves. Like visible light, it can be reflected and refracted by and through mirrors and lenses, yet it can be transmitted through materials (like silicon and germanium) that are opaque to visible light.

Infrared radiation is generated by molecular thermal action within an object. Thus, every object whose temperature is above absolute zero ($-273°C$), ranging from stellar bodies to jet engines to human beings, is a natural infrared source.

The standard reference source for infrared radiation is a "black body." Such a body radiates the maximum energy possible for any given temperature, which is greater than any other object ("gray body") at the *same* temperature. As the temperature of an object increases, its infrared peak radiation shifts toward shorter wavelengths (Wien's Displacement law) and the total radiated energy increases as the fourth power of the object's absolute temperature (Stefan-Boltzmann law).

Infrared spectroscopy is primarily concerned with the absorption properties of materials particularly because all states of matter—gases, liquids, and solids—absorb energy in this region. The "band" spectra or molecular spectra, of concern in absorption spectroscopy, differ from the "line or discrete" spectra of emission spectroscopy, which reflect the state of the outer electron structure of matter. Molecular spectra result from the vibration of component atoms relative to each other and from the rotation of the molecules as a whole.

Infrared absorption spectroscopy, which has received more attention than infrared emission spectroscopy, takes advantage of the fact that molecules of substances vibrate at various frequencies that depend on their atomic masses, types of chemical bonds, and the configurations of their molecules. Therefore, if infrared radiation energy is directed toward a substance for analysis, portions of the energy are reflected or absorbed by it or transmitted through it. Each of these energy portions may reveal specific molecular characteristics of the substance. These portions, properly analyzed with nondispersive or dispersive types of instrumentation, yield spectrograms, such as infrared absorption curves. The spectrograms, which are specific for the material analyzed, afford a significant tool for quantitative and qualitative analysis.

Many organic compounds that are transparent in the ultraviolet or visible light regions are invariably rich in detailed "band" spectra and these are commonly stored on charts, punch cards, etc., to provide a means of structural diagnosis. Typically, the absorption bands due to O-H and N-H stretching occur in the 2.75- to 3.23-μ region; the aliphatic C-H stretching gives rise to multiple absorption bands in the 3.37- to 3.52-μ region; the C-O group of aldehydes, ketones, acids, esters, etc. gives rise to intense bands in the 5.5- to 6.1-μ region. In addition to these standard correlated data, which are used routinely in industry, applications of specific data has made possible the identification of properties of short-lived molecules, free radicals (e.g., C_2, CH, and NH), the identification of isotopes (e.g., presence of Cl^{37} in Cl^{35}), and studies of the atmospheres or envelopes of stars (e.g., the presence of ammonia and methane in the atmosphere of Jupiter).

The use of infrared spectrophotometry for quantitative analysis is founded upon the Beer-Lambert law, which relates the amount of radiation absorbed at a given wavelength by a material to the concentration and length of the absorbing path. Owing to the adequacy of the quantitative data that can be acquired, these techniques have received almost universal acceptance.

Generally, the source of radiation in IR instrumentation is a silicon-carbide rod (Globar) or a Nerst glower. The source radiation, or a selected bandwidth of the radiation, is usually directed by mirrors or refracting optics through the gaseous, liquid, or solid sample to be analyzed into the instrument's dispersing elements consisting of a prism or prisms, and in some cases, gratings. Since ordinary glasses do not transmit IR adequately, materials such as various synthetic crystals (NaCl, CaF_2, KBr, CsBr) are used for prisms and refracting optics. Similarly, the use of front-surfaced mirrors is prevalent to conserve energy. The dispersed radiation

is then detected by a thermocouple or bolometer and the resulting signals are recorded as a function of wavelength.

IR spectrophotometers are quite sophisticated (effective up to 40 to 50 μ), but further improvements in instrumentation can still be anticipated. For instance, spectral data as presently collected are grossly redundant. Consequently, when means are recognized to remove the effects that are saturating the present information channels, improvements in data handling will be forthcoming. Similarly, source and detector improvements coupled with new and more efficient dispersing and refracting materials will provide continued stimulation for this promising field of analytical instrumentation.

WALTER G. DRISCOLL

Cross-references: *Infrared, Mass Spectrometry, Microwave Spectroscopy, Optics, Statistical Mechanics, Thermodynamics*

SPECTROMETRY: see MASS SPECTROMETRY

STANDARDS

The terms volt, ohm, ampere, coulomb, farad, joule, weber, and gauss were initially defined in cgs nonpractical units. It is obvious that these theoretical definitions were never acceptable to the engineer. In the year 1861 the British Association appointed a committee to study the subject of electrical units and standards. This committee existed until 1912, developing by argument, experiments, and international cooperation a practical system of electrical measurements. In 1893, an international electrical congress was held in Chicago. The complexities of the subject postponed agreements until 1908, when "practical" definitions were adopted for the international ohm, volt, ampere, etc.

The ohm was to be represented as the resistance offered to an unvarying electric current by a column of mercury at the temperature of melting ice 14.4521 g in mass, of a constant cross section and of a length of 106.30 cm.

The ampere was to be that unvarying direct current which, when passed through a solution of nitrate of silver in water, deposits silver at the rate of 0.00111800 g/sec.

The volt was to be the electromotive force that steadily applied to a conductor whose resistance is one international ohm produces a current of one ampere.

The voltage of a Weston normal saturated mercury cadmium cell at 20°C, prepared according to strict specifications, was to be taken as 1.0184 v.

In 1910 calibrations were made at the U.S. National Bureau of Standards in terms of the international units on resistors and cells brought by committees from Germany, France, and Great Britain. Using these results, each laboratory worked further on their problems, and, as measuring techniques improved, discrepancies became apparent. The international definitions were not in sufficient accord with the absolute units on the cgs electromagnetic system.

In 1927, another international committee recommended that an absolute system derived from the cgs system should replace the international system. The national laboratories individually worked out their own conversion factors.

After World War II, cooperation between the great national laboratories was resumed, and on January 1, 1948, values derived from the absolute system of electrical units replaced the international values.

The following relations are now accepted, subject to future changes which will probably amount to only a few parts per million.
1 international

ohm	= 1.000495	absolute	ohms
volt	= 1.000330	"	volts
ampere	= 0.999835	"	amperes
coulomb	= 0.999835	"	coulombs
henry	= 1.000495	"	henry
farad	= 0.999505	"	farad
watt	= 1.000165	"	watt
joule	= 1.000165	"	joule

Material Standards. For practical considerations, the electrical units are represented by material standards for the ohm and the volt to which are assigned appropriate values expressed in absolute units. The standards for the ohm now take the form of resistance coils, and those for the volt the form of voltaic cells—Weston cadmium cells, for example.

The mercury ohm cannot be constructed, maintained, and used with sufficient accuracy in any of the major national laboratories. Accordingly, 1-ohm resistors of manganin resistance wire replace the mercury ohm.*

Similarly, use of the "silver ampere" standard is impractical and has been replaced by the Weston normal cell used in conjunction with the reference standard of resistance. Current is calculated by Ohm's law.

At the National Bureau of Standards, a group of ten selected four-terminal 1-ohm resistors is carefully maintained. They are single-layer helixes of manganin wire. After being wound on a metal form, each is annealed at 550°C in an inert atmosphere. When cool, the helix is "slipped" from the form with minimum deformation and similarly transferred to the final insulated form and sealed within a container to prevent atmosphere corrosion. Some of these 1-ohm standards have not changed by as much as one part in a million over a period of many years.

Major instrument manufacturers furnish four-terminal precision resistance standards in the range of 0.1–1.0 megohm for dc use, with accuracies and allowable wattage dissipation as high as one is willing to pay for. In general, resistors cover the range of 10 K to 1 megohm with limits of error of 0.01 to 0.05 per cent, the latter figure applying when the

---

* Manganin is an alloy of 84% copper, 12% manganese, and 4% nickel. Of all conductors it has the best characteristics for use as a precision resistor. It has high specific resistance, the lowest temperature coefficient of resistance, and almost zero thermoelectric power against copper.

resistors are left in circuit with maximum allowable wattage dissipation.

When used for the measurement of high currents up to thousands of amperes, the resistors are usually termed "shunts."

When the greatest precision is required, it may be more economical to purchase a standard resistance with a limit of error of approximately 0.04 per cent and obtain a National Bureau of Standards certificate expressed to the accuracy required for the specified conditions under which the resistor or shunt is to be used.

The use of ac with standard resistors imposes limitations on the accuracy of these standard resistors. Resistors of low ohmic value made from sheet manganin are used for heavy ac currents, which are generally not available at high frequencies. At the commercial frequencies of 60 to 1000 cps, compensation for the residual inductance or distributed capacity can be affected by special tubular construction and placement of the millivolt drop leads. For higher ohmic values, with the use (preferably) of manganin wire for standards, there are many forms of bifilar windings. In the simplest form, the length of wire is doubled back upon itself, the beginning and end are adjacent, the intermediate length being wound as a helix on a coil form. The magnetic fields of any two adjacent turns cancel, with the residual inductance approaching zero. However, the distributed capacity is high and the insulation between the wires at the terminal end is subjected to the full voltage of the circuit. The inductive reactance and the capacitative reactance tend to cancel. Accordingly, many ingenious forms of winding have been devised to balance out the inductive and capacitative residuals and lessen the voltage strain on the insulation. The balance can be made complete at any particular frequency in the audio range.

At radio frequencies, wire-wound resistors cannot be used as standards. Even if available they would be of doubtful value since stray series inductances and parallel capacities exist in electronic circuits with relatively unknown magnitudes.

Standard Cells. Cells are material standards, as distinguished from the theoretical standard volt defined by the cgs system of electromagnetic units. They are available "to have and to hold." Calibration is in terms of absolute volts. Standard cells are equally well known by the name "Weston" standard cell. They are mercury cadmium cells described in 1891 by Edward Weston, founder of the Weston Electrical Instrument Company. A similar cell is made by the Eppley Laboratories of Newport, R. I. The use of a previous standard cell, the Clark, has been discontinued because of its relatively short life and larger temperature coefficient of electromotive force.

The Weston normal cell is of glass tubing in the form of a letter "H," approximately 2 in. wide and 3 in. high. One vertical limb contains a mercury pool with a platinum wire connection sealed through the glass. Above it and below the cross tubing is a paste of mercurous and cadmium sulphate. The other vertical limb has an amalgam of mercury and cadmium with a platinum wire connection sealed through the glass. Two-thirds filling the remaining space and completely filling the cross section is a saturated solution of cadmium sulphate.

The electromotive force of the normal cell, that is the saturated form, is decreased by approximately 0.0004 v/°C rise in temperature. At the National Bureau of Standards, groups of normal cells are maintained at 28°C to 0.01°C within an oil bath; the emf is given as 1.018250 v at 28°C.

The two limbs of the cell must be at the same temperature; a difference of 2.7°C between them results in a change of 0.1 per cent in emf. No steady current may be drawn from the cell; it must be used in a potentiometric circuit where correct operation of the galvanometer keys, etc., limit the galvanometer unbalance current to short impulses of very few microamperes until true zero is obtained.

The type of standard cell used outside the

national laboratories is the unsaturated form, in which the cadmium sulphate is unsaturated above 4°C. Limits of operation are 4–40°C. The emf of new cells vary in the range of 1.0186 to 1.0193 v and is little affected by temperature. This independence of temperature, along with rugged construction, allows the cell to be used, with reasonable care in transportation, for portable instrument work. Without frequent calibrations, its accuracy cannot be relied upon to closer than 0.02 per cent of error, with frequency of calibration according to severity of transportation.

The writer has a group of twenty Weston unsaturated cells, with ages 1–53 yr. Measurements show that the emf of cells up to 3–4 yr old decreases by about 45 $\mu v/yr$. Four cells 53, 52, 46, and 40 yr old have averaged their yearly microvolt drop as 130, 110, 30, and 120, respectively.

In the last few years a standard voltage unit, has been developed, an adaptation of a circuit embracing a zener diode and requiring a nominal 120-v, 60-yr supply and a warm-up period of 2 hr for it to fit its calibration certificate. Its emf is 1.0185 v and is adjusted to within 0.01 per cent of this nominal value. The temperature error is very small, its life is 30,000 hr, it is very rugged, and costs more than twice as much as a Weston standard cell. In many cases it can be used as a substitute for the voltaic cell, but for accuracy and long life, it may not compete with the Weston standard cell, particularly the Weston normal saturated cell.

N. M. ALBERT

Cross-references: *Errors in Measurements, Impedance Measurements, Resistors, Unit Systems*

STABILITY CRITERIA: see SYSTEMS (LINEAR)

STANDING-WAVE RATIO

The standing-wave ratio is an important quantity in impedance measurements (*q.v.*), and particularly in microwave measurements

(*q.v.*). At ultra-high frequencies and above, the moving-probe slotted line is the most commonly used method of impedance measurement. Unless the impedance of a circuit is exactly equal to that of the transmission line to which it is connected, the transmitted wave is partially reflected through the transmission line to the generator. An interference pattern is created as a result of the periodic addition and cancellation of the incident and reflected waves. This is called a standing wave because it is a spatially fixed variation of amplitude along the line. An electrical standing wave is similar to standing waves of sound in a closed chamber. The ratio of the voltage peaks to the voltage valleys is called Voltage Standing Wave Ratio (VSWR).

The ratio Γ of the reflected wave to the incident wave voltage is related to the load impedance and to the VSWR r:

$$\frac{Z_l}{Z_0} = \frac{1-\Gamma}{1+\Gamma}; \quad r = \frac{1+\Gamma}{1-\Gamma}; \quad \frac{Z_l}{Z_0} = \frac{1}{r}$$

Slotted-line impedance meters are usually constructed with a section of transmission line of the desired type of line (two-wire, coaxial, strip line, waveguide) and desired Z_0, a coupling means to the E field along the direction of propagation, a movable probe to sample the E field at any point in the line, and a scale to ascertain the position of the probe. The probe is set to a point of maximum E, and then to a point of minimum E. The ratio of E_{max} to E_{min} is r, the VSWR. The position of E_{min} is measured. As seen from the relationship between Z_l and r, Z_l is readily obtained. A Smith Chart (*q.v.*) is frequently used to facilitate the determination of Z_l from a VSWR measurement.

The wave pattern in the slotted section will depend on the load. If the load is a short circuit, the standing wave patterns are as in Fig. 1a: the voltage is zero at the load and a maximum at a position $\lambda/4$ away. The minimum voltage points repeat every $\lambda/2$ along the slotted section. Similarly, the maxima repeat at $\lambda/2$ intervals, occurring at

$\lambda/4$, $3\lambda/4$, $5\lambda/4$ along the line starting from the load. It follows that the voltage and impedance minima as well as their maxima are coincidental.

The standing-wave pattern of Fig. 1b is obtained with an open circuit at the load end. This condition is exactly opposite to the short-circuit case of Fig. 1a. It is apparent from these two examples that placing different load impedances at the end of the transmission line produces different standing-wave patterns, with the voltage at the load varying anywhere between zero and maximum. The dashed lines Z_1-Z_1, Z_2-Z_2 and Z_3-Z_3 in Fig. 1c represent three different conditions of load impedance and the corresponding voltage values at the load. It is not necessary (nor desirable) to measure these terminal voltages. From the wavelength, it is quite easy to determine the position of any of these lines in terms of wavelength by measuring the distance from the load to the nearest minimum on the standing-wave pattern.

Impedance Measurement with a Reflectometer

A reflectometer measures VSWR without providing information to determine the phase of the load impedance. Frequently in measurements phase is unimportant, as many devices are specified to have a maximum VSWR with no limitation on phase. A reflectometer consists of two directional couplers (q.v.), one sampling the incident wave, the other sampling the reflected wave. The two outputs are detected and the ratio determined, either by measurement and computation, or directly by a ratio meter calibrated in Γ or in VSWR.

Although the reflectometer method is simple, there are several important sources of error. First, the directional couplers must have a great discrimination between incident and reflected waves (called directivity). In waveguide, directional couplers commonly have 40 db directivity, corresponding to an error of ± 0.01 in reflection coefficient. Coaxial line directional couplers rarely have directivity greater than 30 or 35 db, which correspond to errors of ± 0.03 and ± 0.02 in Γ, respectively.

Second, the relative coupling of the incident and reverse wave couplers must be known accurately. Errors in relative coupling of 0.2 db result in an error in Γ of 2.3 per cent.

STUART CASPER

Cross-references: *Couplers, Impedance Measurements, Microwave Measurements, Refractometer, Resonators and Wavemeters, Smith Chart, Waveguides and Waveguide Components*

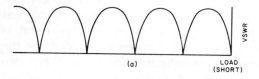

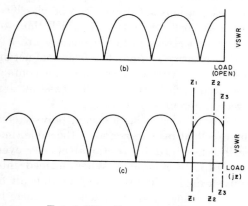

Fig. 1. Standing-wave ratio.

STARK EFFECT

The Stark effect is the splitting of a spectral line from a radiating atom into several components, when the atom is placed in an electric field. The components are spaced unsymmetrically in energy about the zero-field spectrum line, and are linearly polarized when observed in a direction perpendicular to the electric field; some components are missing, and the others are unpolarized when observed parallel to the field. All early observations (1913) were of hydrogen lines, which exhibit a *first-order* or *linear* Stark effect in weak fields, and a *second-order* or *quadratic* Stark effect in large fields. For atoms other than hydrogen, the second-order effect generally predominates, where the splitting is proportional to the square of the electric field strength.

These line splittings arise from a splitting of the energy levels of the atom, and from transitions (ordinarily forbidden) which are induced by the electric field. The atom becomes electrically polarized in the field and then exhibits an electric dipole moment, giving the atom an additional energy dependent upon the orientation of its total angular momentum with respect to the field.

S. P. DAVIS

Cross-references: *Radiation, Zeeman Effect*

STATIC: see INTERFERENCE; RADIATION (TERRESTRIAL)

STATIC (TRIBO-) ELECTRICITY

This term usually implies manifestations of electric charge accumulations resulting in interesting, useful, or undesirable phenomena; as distinguished from *electrostatics*, which treats with quantitative and analytic relationships between charges and static electric fields.

Charge accumulations often produce annoying or dangerous effects. Attraction of dust, lint, and light particles to surfaces, such as phonograph records, photographic films and high-precision apparatus can impair performance; charge collection sufficient to cause electric sparks may result in physical discomfort or trigger combustion in explosive atmospheres.

On a large scale, charge concentrations in parts of thunderclouds can produce potential differences of millions of volts; breakdowns occurring between charge centers in clouds or between clouds and earth are familiar lightning discharges, often of tens of thousands of amperes. Electromagnetic radiation from such discharges propagates over long distances. Radio receivers tuned

to frequencies up to about 30 Mc may have their sensitivity or quality of reception limited by this interference, often called *static*. Static disturbances in the output of receivers result from the summation of atmospheric discharge signals from large areas, being generally worse at locations and times of the year when thunderstorm conditions are most prevalent.

Static-electricity effects depend on excess of charge of one sign existing, on a macroscopic basis, in one or more locations with respect to charge groups of opposite sign. To establish such a condition from an original neutral state requires that energy must be put into the system. This energy is considered to be stored in the electric fields in the space between charge groups.

There are several means for producing charge separation. Insulated conducting bodies may be charged by connection to power supply mains or to batteries. Relatively large amounts of charge and energy may be stored in capacitors. When such charge is not changing with time, the electricity therein is static, but the action of capacitors is generally treated as part of circuit or field phenomena.

Static-electricity effects as generally understood usually result from mechanical rubbing or impact processes. The result is sometimes called *frictional* electricity or the result of *triboelectric* phenomena. When two dissimilar substances are rubbed together they become electrified with opposite polarities. Various substances can be classified into a triboelectric series, in which those of higher dielectric constant generally are left with a positive charge. The frictional action probably serves to accentuate the contact potential difference normally existing between different substances.

Many modern plastics, e.g., polystyrene, are excellent insulators and at the same time easily electrified by frictional effects, even by ordinary handling. When formed into thin sheets or films they may be difficult to handle, owing to their tendency to adhere to other surfaces. Charges developed on these materials may require considerable time to leak off. Discharging trapped charges may be speeded up by keeping the atmospheric humidity high to increase the surface leakage conductivity, by special conductive coatings, or by maintaining a condition of increased ionization rate in the air near the insulator surface. Ions of sign opposite to that of the surface charge are attracted to this charge and act to neutralize it. Radioactive sources or ultraviolet light are sometimes used for this purpose.

Well-insulated metal bodies can be charged when brought into contact with and then separated from insulating materials. Aircraft flying through air containing particles of water, snow, or ice become negatively charged at a rate depending on precipitation nature and airspeed. The potential reached may be as high as 1,000,000 v and is limited when corona discharges occur from points of high electrical stress, such as wing and stabilizer tips. Impulsive corona currents couple energy into the aircraft radio antennas, causing radio noise called *precipitation static*. This noise may be reduced by attaching devices carrying fine points electrically connected to the aircraft through high resistance and, for best results, arranged to discharge in a manner orthogonal to the antenna field patterns.

Static electricity is the basis of several useful processes. Smoke and dust may be removed from air by passing it through *precipitation* cleaning devices, in which particles are charged by corona discharge points or wires and are then attracted to collecting surfaces of opposite polarity. In the Van de Graaff generator, for particle-accelerator applications, charge is applied at low potential to an insulating belt and physically transferred to a large collecting electrode, often at a potential of several million volts.

W. G. Hoover

Cross-references: *Contact Potential, Electrostatic Precipitation, Radiation (Terrestrial), Van de Graaff Accelerator*

STATISTICAL COMMUNICATION THEORY

Post-World War II electronic technology has increasingly recognized that the ultimate limitation on the performance capabilities of electronic equipment is that caused by random disturbances, such as thermal noise, vacuum-tube shot noise, etc. These disturbances differ in essence from deterministic disturbances (e.g., those caused by undesired nonlinearities) in that their effects on signals can neither be exactly predicted nor corrected, *even in theory*. In essence, Statistical Communication (and Control) Theory therefore seeks methods for describing and combating random disturbances on a *statistical* basis, rather than precisely. The over-all theory may be divided roughly into three fields: noise theory, detection and estimation theories, and information theory.

Noise theory, or the study of stochastic (random) processes, is concerned with the mathematical description of random disturbances. These descriptions are necessarily probabilistic in nature: they cannot give the exact functional form to be expected of a random waveform $x(t)$, but only the *probability* that it will lie in some arbitrary range $(x_1, x_1 + dx)$ at time t_1, in some range $(x_2, x_2 + dx)$ at time t_2, etc. A complete description of a random process would give this probability for all possible combinations of values $x(t)$ may take on at all possible combinations of times $t_1, t_2, \ldots$ A more abbreviated, albeit incomplete, description usually suffices, however.

A second concern of noise theory is the analysis of the effect of a physical device on a noise process. A typical problem in this area would be phrased as follows: given a probabilistic description of a noise process at the input of a device, and given the transfer characteristics of the device, derive a probabilistic description of the output of the device. Only a limited number of problems of this sort have been solved, notably when the input noise is Gaussian, as are thermal and shot noises.

Unlike noise theory, which is analytic in nature, detection and estimation theories have to do with the *synthesis* of systems for combating the deleterious effects of random disturbances. Both, in common, seek to devise ways of efficiently determining the true cause of a noisy observation. The former, however, is generally concerned with discrete sets of causes (or "events"), which are not necessarily numerical (e.g., the "dot" and the "dash" in Morse telegraphy). The latter concerns itself generally with continua of numerical causes (e.g., the range of an aircraft being observed by a radar system).

Detection theory has its origins in the hypothesis-testing theory of classical statistics. A representative problem in this theory might be formulated as follows: given a noisy observation A, which may have arisen from any one of n known causes H_1, H_2, $\cdots$, H_n, and given the "costs" C_{ij} of attributing A to H_j when it actually originated from H_i ($C_{ij} - C_{ii} > 0$, all $j \neq i$), find a scheme for inferring from A, with minimum average cost, which cause is the true one. Within this framework lie the problems, for example, of radar detection ($n = 2$, H_1 = no target present, H_2 = target present) and digital communications (e.g., teletype, $H_i = i^{\text{th}}$ letter of the alphabet).

Estimation theory also derives from classical statistics. In the present context there are two types of estimation of importance: parameter estimation and waveform estimation (or extraction). In the first, the noisy observation is a function of one or more unknown continuous parameters to be estimated; for example, the observation may be the noisy return waveform from a radar target, and from this an estimate of the range and relative radial velocity of the target may be required. In waveform-estimation problems, the observation may be a randomly perturbed version of some desired signal waveform, which is to be extracted as well as possible from the observation; the Wiener-Kolmogorov linear filtering theory forms a part of this discipline.

Whereas detection and estimation theories are concerned primarily with the design of the *receiver* of a communication system, i.e., with the inference of a probable cause of a received observation, information theory is concerned essentially with the transmitter. (The term "information theory" is sometimes used to refer to what is here called statistical communication theory; in the present discussion, the term is used in a narrower sense.) This theory first establishes probabilistic definitions of the concepts "amount of information in a message" and "information rate of a message source." Proceeding from these, the theory then shows that through any communication channel, even though randomly perturbed, it is possible to transmit information with *arbitrarily small* probability of error in reception, provided only that the rate of information flow through the channel is less than a certain value, called the channel capacity. However, this is only an existence theorem, which merely promises that a technique exists for achieving essentially error-free communication. Coding theory starts at this point, and attempts to find such a technique. Problems in coding theory may be envisaged as problems in transmitter design: the objective is to translate the output data of an information source, by means of an appropriate "code," into signals that are "matched" to the statistical characteristics of the channel. The characteristics of the receiver also affect the choice of a code.

All of the disciplines described above go into the over-all design of a communication system. A final step in any design is the evaluation of the performance capabilities of the system, *i.e.*, its transmission reliability (*q.v.*).

G. L. Turin

Cross-references: *Coding, Decision and Game Theory, Information Theory, Probability, Noise, Transmission Reliability*

STATISTICAL MECHANICS

Statistical Mechanics has as its object the explanation of observed macroscopic properties of systems in terms of the statistically likely behavior of the microscopic components making up the system. The basic postulate is that the observed equilibrium state of the system will be essentially identical with that state which is most probable. The problem then is to find the appropriate manner for computing this so-called *thermodynamic probability* W for any given state. This is defined as being the number of microscopically described states, or *microstates*, which are consistent with any given macroscopic state, or *macrostate*, of the system. Naturally the specification of the microstates must be such that each has equal *a priori* likelihood of occurrence if this definition is to be valid.

A simple and important example is that of a gas of identical, noninteracting particles. In that case, the microstate of the system is specified by giving the position and momentum of each particle. Actually, the quantum-mechanical Heisenberg uncertainty principle limits the precision of this specification and introduces a natural unit cell in this *phase space* (a space with both position and momentum coordinates). This cell size is such that $\Delta x \Delta p_x = h$, and similarly for y and z, so the cell volume is h^3. The microstate is specified by telling in which cell each particle is located. The macrostate is specified by giving the distribution of particles on a much grosser scale, of the sort that would be measured in macroscopic experiments.

To proceed further we must distinguish between two types of particles that might compose the gas. Experimental evidence has shown that particles with half integral intrinsic spin (such as electrons, protons, and neutrons) obey *Fermi-Dirac* statistics, whereas those with integral spin (such as helium atoms, α-particles, or photons) obey *Bose-Einstein* statistics. Such particles are called *fermions* and *bosons*, respectively. In both cases, the indistinguishability of identical particles means that a microstate is completely defined by giving only the number of particles N_i in each (ith) cell of phase space—one cannot specify which particular ones are in each cell. The two cases are distinguished in that fermions obey the Pauli

exclusion principle, limiting the occupation of a cell to 0 or 1, whereas any number of bosons can occupy a cell.

Using either of these cases, one can set up expressions for W as a function of a set of $\bar{N}_i$, which are average occupation numbers over a macroscopic amount of phase space. By simple differentiation, one then finds the set of $\bar{N}_i$ that give the maximum W, and hence the most probable state of the system. In carrying out the maximization of W, one naturally constrains the total number of particles to be constant (unless one is dealing with a photon gas!) and one also constrains the total energy of the system to be constant. The resulting distribution of particles in phase space is given by

$$\bar{N}_i = \frac{1}{e^{(E_i - \mu)/kT} \pm 1} \tag{1}$$

where the $+$ sign applies to fermions and the $-$ sign to bosons. The quantity E_i is the energy in the ith cell and μ is a constant energy called the chemical potential (or Fermi energy for the fermion case), chosen so that the total number of particles in the distribution has the correct value. The fact that the term kT is actually the usual Boltzmann constant times the absolute temperature is established by relating calculated results to ordinary thermodynamic results. One can also show that the entropy S is given by

$$S = k \ln W, \tag{2}$$

so that we have found the state of maximum entropy, which is the stable thermodynamic state.

Note that according to (1) in the fermion case $\bar{N}_i$ ranges from 1 for $E_i \ll \mu$ to 0 for $E_i \gg \mu$, the change over occurring in an energy range of order kT. The Fermi energy μ is given by

$$\mu = \frac{h^2}{2m} \left(\frac{3n}{4\pi}\right)^{2/3} \tag{3}$$

where n is the number of particles of mass m per unit volume of the gas. For conduction electrons in a typical metal, this energy amounts to approximately 5 ev. Thus even at absolute zero, there are electrons moving with velocities of order 10^6 m/sec because the Pauli exclusion principle keeps them from dropping down into already occupied states with lower energy.

For bosons, the situation is quite different, the negative sign in (1) encouraging "condensation" into the very lowest state. It is believed that this *Bose condensation* is essential in explaining the extraordinary properties of superfluid liquid helium below $T_\lambda = 2.2°$K.

Finally, we note that if $\bar{N}_i \ll 1$, then the exponential in the denominator of (1) must be so large that the ± 1 is negligible. In this low-density limit, the quantum cell size effects are unimportant, and we obtain the *Maxwell-Boltzmann* classical statistics where

$$\bar{N}_i = e^{-(E_i - \mu)/kT} \qquad (4)$$

In this case, the probability of occupancy of any cell is simply proportional to exp $-(E_i/kT)$. This formula is adequate for ordinary gases at ordinary temperatures and pressures, and leads to the familiar Maxwellian distribution of velocities:

$$\frac{dn}{n} = \sqrt{\frac{2}{\pi}} \left(\frac{m}{kT}\right)^{3/2} \exp(-\tfrac{1}{2}mv^2/kT)v^2 \, dv \quad (5)$$

where dn/n is the fraction of particles having speeds in the interval dv about v. In the Maxwell-Boltzmann statistics, typical particles have energies of the order of the thermal energy kT, which approaches zero at the absolute zero of temperature. This fact is useful for giving a microscopic interpretation of the concept of temperature.

MICHAEL TINKHAM

Cross-references: *Distribution Functions, Phase-Space Representation, Probability, Thermal Radiation, Thermodynamics, Thermoelectricity*

STEINMETZ, CHARLES PROTEUS (1865–1923)

Carl August Rudolph Steinmetz was born in Breslau on April 9, 1865, and completed his secondary education there. He had a happy childhood despite the fact that his mother died when he was one year old and that he was a hunchback. He was brought up in his father's house by his grandmother and aunt who encouraged his penchant for mechanical toys, as did his father, an employee of the Silesian State Railways.

In 1882 he entered the University of Breslau, where he studied the sciences and especially mathematics. While at the university he joined a Social Democrat student group and became the *de facto* editor of its paper, an activity that ultimately forced him to leave Breslau for Zurich, after he had submitted his dissertation but before he had received his degree. He came to America the following year, where he became a draftsman in Rudolf Eickemeyer's manufacturing establishment in Yonkers, N.Y. His interests soon changed from mathematics to electrical engineering. During this time he also Americanized his name to Charles Proteus Steinmetz, his middle name harking back to a nickname bestowed on him by his fellow students in Breslau.

In 1891 Steinmetz established the basic law of hysteresis in magnetism (*q.v.*), that the hysteresis loss is proportional to the 1.6th power of the magnetization, which earned him his reputation. In 1893 he formulated his greatest contribution to electrical theory, the use of complex notation (*q.v.*) in solving ac problems. Engineers were slow to grasp the advantages of the new method and it was not until he published a number of textbooks employing complex notation that the subject entered the curricula of engineering schools the world over.

In 1892 the General Electric Co. was formed by a merger of the Edison General Electric Co. of New York and the Thomson-Houston Electric Co. of Lynn, Mass.; the new company grew by the absorption of smaller establishments, of which Eickemeyer's was one, and in 1893 Steinmetz moved to Lynn. He made a number of further important contributions, notably in the fields of electric machine design and lightning protection, as well as the theory of electrical transients. In 1894 Steinmetz was transferred to Schenectady, N.Y. (where he remained until his death), and became an American citizen.

During 1901–02, Steinmetz served as the president of the American Institute of Electrical Engineers, and in the following years received an honorary M.A. from Harvard and a Ph.D. from Union College, where he also served as professor of electrical engineering for 10 years beginning in 1902. During the remainder of his life he acted as a chief consulting engineer to General Electric Co., a man to whom all the company's engineers with difficult problems came for advice. He also devised much apparatus in the fields of street lighting and electric traction. He died in Schenectady on October 26, 1923. His career was a significant demonstration of the importance of advanced mathematics to electrical engineering.

CHARLES SUSSKIND

Cross-references: *Historical Background of Electronics*

STEREOPHONICS

A stereophonic sound reproducing system comprises two or more microphones, transmission channels, and loudspeakers arranged to produce a spatial distribution of the sound sources. Since our ears can detect small differences in the amplitude of the sound emanating from the spaced loudspeakers an illusion of breadth and depth of sound is created. Stereophonic sound systems for motion pictures have used as many as seven channels, but only two channels generally are used for home reproduction from tape and long-playing stereo records. Some systems mix the left and right channels to feed a third center loudspeaker to increase the breadth of the sound sources.

Early two channel stereophonic systems employed headphones and were termed *binaural* systems. This term is still applicable to two-channel headphone reproduction,

especially when the isolation between sound sources is great.

Ambiophonic sound-reproducing systems are modifications of the stereophonic system which employ a number of loudspeakers placed around the perimeter of the room to reproduce the output of a distant microphone, thereby simulating the reverberant qualities of the space where the program was originated. In this manner, a realistic recreation of a performance in a large cathedral can be enjoyed in a small room.

Stereophonic recordings are usually made on three-channel magnetic-tape recorders at a speed of 15 in./sec. The magnetic recording and reproducing head gaps for the three channels or sound tracks are vertically aligned to within a few microinches to maintain the time delay between the tracks within the critical tolerances. The upper track of the recording usually carries the sound originating on the left, the lower track the sound that originated at the right, and the center track the soloist or spatial effects such as the reverberant quality at a distant microphone. The outputs of the three channels are later combined to create a two-track stereophonic submaster tape or an equivalent single-track or monophonic submaster tape. Reverberation, special equalization, a different vocalist or even another instrument can be added to the submaster recording in order to enhance the quality or to update an old recording.

Early releases of stereophonic tape recordings were made with staggered heads; the upper and lower track heads were mounted in separate assemblies. In recent years, staggered heads have been obsoleted by in-line heads contained in one assembly.

Most stereophonic tapes available at present are four-track $7\frac{1}{2}$ ips recordings on a reversible $\frac{1}{4}$-in.-wide tape providing two stereophonic tracks in each direction. Similar recordings have been offered in $3\frac{3}{4}$ ips reversible cartridges and there is currently much interest in $1\frac{7}{8}$ ips tape cartridges.

The frequency response and signal-to-noise ratios of four-track $7\frac{1}{2}$ ips tape recordings are presently superior to those of the slower speed recordings and disks. Typical response is ± 1 db from 100 cps to 10 kc, ± 2 db from 50 cps to 15 kc, and 55 db signal-to-noise ratio.

Stereophonic long-playing records are recorded at $33\frac{1}{3}$ rpm. The right- and left-hand audio signals are engraved on the two sides of a 90° wide groove. Two sets of coils acting in a permanent magnet field drive the recording stylus to modulate the sides of the groove selectively. If a signal drives only the left-hand coil, the stylus records on only one side of the groove; if the signal drives only the right-hand coil, the stylus records on the opposite side of the groove. Since the groove is modulated both in depth and width, it should be reproduced only by cartridges having small stylus pressure and a high degree of vertical compliance lest the vertical component of the recording be damaged. Stereophonic cartridges may be used to reproduce monophonic recordings but some monophonic cartridges are unsuitable for reproducing stereophonic disk recordings. The compatible stereophonic disks which have the lateral modulation controlled by $L + R$ signals and the vertical modulation controlled by $L - R$ signals are less subject to damage when they are reproduced by a stiff monophonic stylus.

Prior to the adoption of stereophonic transmission standards for FM broadcasting by the Federal Communications Commission in June of 1961, stereophonic broadcasting was accomplished by transmitting the L and R channels by separate stations. Two separate receivers were required to receive these programs and the system was wasteful of radio spectrum space.

The compatible stereophonic FM system adopted in the United States of America requires only one FM channel and only one receiver with an appropriate two-channel audio system is needed by the listener. The main carrier of the FM station is modulated by the $L + R$ signal by simply connecting the left and right channels together at the modulator. Monophonic FM receivers can

thereby receive the "compatible" monophonic rendition of the complete stereo program. The same FM station also transmitts a low-level 19-kc pilot carrier and a 38-kc suppressed carrier multiplex FM channel which is amplitude-modulated by the $L - R$ difference signal.

In the stereophonic receiver, the 19 kc pilot carrier is doubled in frequency and is combined with the modulation side bands of multiplex carrier before detection. The $L + R$ and $L - R$ signals are combined through a matrix to obtain L and R signals which feed two stereophonic audio amplifiers and loud speakers.

R. A. Isberg

Cross-references: *Electroacoustics, Loudspeakers and Microphones, Magnetic Tape, Multiplexing, Sound Recording*

STORAGE

General Considerations

In the language of computers, there is a vague distinction between "memory" and "storage." "Memory" has the anthropomorphic implication of dynamics and internal interactions, as in the mind, whereas "storage" implies information that is dead and inactive unless called upon.

Turing showed, and practice proved, that memory is essential to any computation by machine, even though it be very small (one bit) in size, and evanescent. The simplest example is arithmetical addition. The carry, if present, must be stored in memory for control of the addition of the higher-order digits. This memory in machines exists as various kinds of circuits which, although not usually regarded as memory, is such in the Turing sense.

At a more complex level in the computation process, memory is required for the storage of intermediate values, which influence the course of arithmetic events. These values may be stored in registers, "high-speed" memory, or relatively low-speed memory. The power of a machine depends largely on the relative amounts of these memory devices. In practice, power is limited by cost, because of the increase of cost with speed.

High-speed storage in registers can be achieved with various solid-state devices. Rapid-access memories have most commonly taken the form of arrays of magnetic cores (q.v.), although delay lines (q.v.) and cathode-ray tubes (q.v.) have also been used and magnetic thin films and units employing cryotronics (q.v.) are being proposed. Memory with longer access times is predominantly provided by the magnetic surface on tapes or disks. Memory with even longer access times is provided by punched cards, especially of business records that must be kept for a period of time (e.g., to the next pay day). Cards have the peculiar property of meeting the function of a "unit record," and afford a means of selection from and shifting in memory with very high reliability. There is no chance of changing the punching during the mechanical motion.

It is instructive to note that the media mentioned above fall into two classes, erasable and read-only, which correspond to blackboards and scratch pads used to record intermediate and evanescent steps in manual data processing, to assist the human memory.

In solving any problem by computer, the nature of the processing is described in one form or another by a "program," that is, a series of instructions telling the machine what to do next. This sequence of information for the system must be stored rather than memorized. Part is stored in electro-mechanical devices or electronic circuits (e.g., the carry). The bulk of the program is stored on cards, magnetic tape, and some of it in the high-speed memory. Punched paper tape is also a useful storage medium, especially when there is no requirement for unit records.

In the course of computing, other kinds of information are also involved, such as raw input data, numerical constants, the calendar date, lists of names and characteristics, etc., in addition to the program. This kind of information is, for all practical purposes, permanent. Since as a rule it is used more than once, it needs to be stored somewhere in the system (in contrast with being placed in the working memory), and yet be quickly available when desired.

Many media are conceivable for this function. It is current practice to use erasable storage, such as magnetic tapes, drums, or disks. Actually the magnetic nature of these media is useful only because it facilitates loading the store with the information. Other types of media are perfectly suitable. In particular, storage need be "read only," i.e., the feature of quick writing is not essential. The relaxation of the need for extremely rapid writing permits faster access to storage. Some advantage can be gained along these lines by operating magnetic-core memories in a read-only mode. More important still is the introduction of new technologies. Photographic recording is a recent development that permits the fastest access for a given capacity. (The Bell Telephone Laboratories and AN/GSQ-16 photostores are operating examples.)

The storage of permanent or semipermanent data in read-only memories also has its counterpart in human data processing, namely the printed books in a library. It is interesting to note that books, with pages, were found to be more convenient than the earlier scrolls, and that this same development has recently been introduced in computing systems. Disks are replacing tapes.

In the way computing machines and systems are used today there is little regard for the difference between memory and storage indicated above, and the programmer uses all the devices available to maximum advantage without making the philosophic distinction. The difference is of some concern, however, with respect to machine organization theory and the demands on technology. From the point of view of performance, memory and storage devices seem to form a continuous spectrum.

There are two basic characteristics, capacity and time for random access, and one cannot be achieved without sacrifice of the other. Memory devices range in capacity from one to a million bits, with access times from a few nanoseconds to microseconds. Storage devices nowadays have significance only in the range of a million to a billion bits. Access is in fractions of seconds.

The table shows typical numerical values. The rate of access varies from the figures given depending on the system organization and functions (e.g., removal of blocks, and later search for the particular item in a high-speed memory).

Type of Device	Capacity (bits)	Access Time (sec)
1 nanosecond flip-flop	1	10^{-9}
32K 32-bit word memory	10^6	10^{-6}
Photostore	10^8	10^{-2}
Tape	10^9	10

A secondary characteristic is the rate of delivery of data. Delivery can occur as bits in parallel (up to 72 in a microsecond or so) or in series (3×10^6 bits/sec).

GILBERT W. KING

Magnetic Storage

"Memory" is a term commonly used to describe storage as applied to computers. Magnetic materials that produce rectangular hysteresis loops have found wide acceptance in computer "memories" or, more precisely, for magnetic storage of information. Data stored in magnetic elements remains permanently held in a magnetic field and thus requires no additional power to hold it in storage.

The materials that produce these rectangular hysteresis loops possess two readily distinguishable remanent magnetic states. Information, to be stored, is placed into a one-to-one correspondence with these magnetic states—for example, a binary 1 with the positive, and a binary 0 with the negative, state.

When storing information, the state of a magnetic material is changed by the creation of a magnetic field. It is the sense of this field that produces the desired final state of the magnetic material. The data thus stored are retrieved by sensing the state of the material—whether positive or negative. If the material is in the positive state, it tends to switch and thereby produce a voltage in a conductor by magnetic inductance, which is sensed as a 1. If, however, the material is in a negative state, it does not switch and does not induce a voltage. The absence of this voltage is sensed as a 0. (In other schemes, switching from the 0 state does occur, but the obtained output signal is of opposite polarity.)

Conventional magnetic storage systems work generally on the principles just discussed. Storage systems vary, however, in geometry and in sensing schemes. For example, some materials produce a magnetic field that can be sensed without a contact with the material (e.g., drums, disks, and tapes), whereas others must be constructed with separate materials actively in contact (cores, rods, thin films, and twistors).

Magnetic storage systems are, therefore, classified as to whether they are cyclic (disks, drums, and tapes) or parallel random access (ferrite cores, multiaperture cores or plates, twistors, plated rods, or planar thin films).

Cyclic Memories. Tapes, drums, and disks operate in similar fashion; they move mechanically past a fixed reading or writing device. Information is stored on multiple tracks by multiple read or write heads. Iron oxide-coated mylar tapes can store 10^7 characters on a reel. Tape recorders are especially designed to read or write on preselected sections of a tape, with emphasis on fast start and stop operations.

Drums and disks are plated with a magnetic coating that has a high coercive force to prevent accidental loss of stored data owing to stray magnetic fields. The heads are cores with an air gap, and flux leaking from the gap magnetizes the material.

Two recording schemes, the return-to-zero (RZ) and the non-return-to-zero (NRZ) are used. In the RZ system, magnetization is from zero to positive or negative saturation and returned to zero. In the NRZ system, a change in magnetization occurs only when the digit to be stored is changing. Because the NRZ has half as many transitions as the RZ, twice as many bits can be stored in the first system than in the latter, but a timing track, or signal, is required. With good recording techniques, pulse-packing densities of a few thousand per inch are possible.

Parallel Random-Access Memories. All bits of a particular word are either stored or retrieved in parallel, and the storage medium has individually wired elements. These memories have fast operating speeds and access times independent of the storage location. The majority of the memories operating in medium- and large-scale computers are of the random-access type.

Random-access memories are organized into functional sections—control, address, buffer, and storage. The control section generates all signals necessary to keep the memory in step with the computer. The address section locates the particular storage elements into which new data are to be inserted or from which stored data are to be retrieved. The buffer section provides temporary storage of data to be inserted into the selected elements and of the data (later to be transferred to the computer) just received from selected elements. The storage section stores the words in binary form for future reference.

The storage elements are normally arrayed into planes with rows and columns. Interrogation of a selected word can be either by coincidence of two currents (coincident current) or by a single current (linear select).

In the coincident-current system, the storage element is used as a threshold device. A single current generates a sufficient magnetic force to magnetize the element to the knee of the rectangular hysteresis curve, but is unable to change its magnetic state. A second current of the same polarity is needed to remagnetize or switch the element. Storage of a bit in this system is by two currents if a 1 is to be stored; or by three currents, one opposing the other two, if a 0 is to be stored.

In linear selection systems, interrogation of a bit is by a single current, sufficiently large to remagnetize the element. Storage of a 1 in a bit can occur by a single current or by two currents added to each other. A 0 is stored by two currents, one opposing the other, to prevent remagnetization.

Destructive and Nondestructive Operation. When the state of a magnetic element is sensed, it is normally being saturated to the negative state, which destroys the stored data. The data must be reinserted, which is accomplished in the same manner as the insertion of new data into the element. In some systems this method is not desirable. Means have been found that can sense the state of the magnetic element without destroying the stored information, by storage of data in more than one magnetic field (multiaperture cores, biax), by magnetic drive fields that do not allow a switching process to take place (fluxlok), or by taking advantage of the internal structure of the material (anisotropy in thin films).

ERIC E. BITTMANN

Cross-references: *Analog Computers, Coding and Coding Circuits, Computer Printout and Reading, Computer Programming, Digital Computers, Magnetic Cores, Magnetism*

STORAGE TUBES

A storage tube is an electron tube into which information can be introduced and read out at a later time. The output may be an electrical signal and/or a visible image corresponding to the stored information.

The five essential storage-tube operations are: selection, writing, storage, reading, and erasing. The many combinations of the various means of accomplishing these operations have led to a large variety of distinguishable storage tubes. The usual configuration, however, is a cathode-ray tube with a storage target in place of (or in addition to) the customary phosphor target. The electron beam is deflected to *select* the desired storage element. Information is *stored* on the insulating layer as a two-dimensional charge pattern. *Writing* is the process by which information is entered for storage. The stored information is *read out* at a later time. *Erasing* is the deliberate removal of information from storage. In some cases erasing occurs simultaneously with reading.

The storage target is usually a thin insulating or semiconducting layer placed upon a metal plate or fine mesh screen. The conductivity of the storage layer must be low enough to prevent spreading or dissipation of the charge pattern during the desired retention time between writing and reading. The storage-layer material must also possess an electronic property—secondary emission, bombardment-induced conductivity, photoconductivity, or photoemission—which can be used to write in the charge pattern with an electron beam or optical image. The charge pattern in turn must be able to control an electron beam in some way to permit information to be read out. The charge pattern may control the transmission of a reading beam through a storage mesh, or the reading current required to discharge the pattern may be measured.

Storage tubes may be classified according

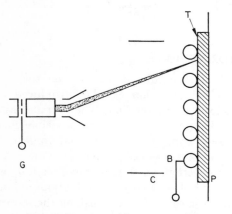

FIG. 1. Barrier-grid storage tube.

to the nature of the input and output signals. There are electrical-to-electrical (electrical signal), electrical-to-visual (display), and visual-to-electrical (camera) storage tubes. All modern television camera tubes are true storage tubes, but special target materials are sometimes used in conventional camera tubes to provide extended retention times, as in the storage orthicon and the Permachon (storage vidicon).

Electrical-Signal Storage Tubes

An electrical-to-electrical storage tube can be used for various kinds of data processing, such as simple signal delay, integration of radar returns, multiple scanning of a single picture, or conversion from PPI to television scanning. (The subclass of computer-storage tubes is discussed separately below.) Three varieties of electrical-signal tubes have been extensively developed—the barrier-grid tube, the scan-conversion tube, and the "recording" storage tube.

Barrier Grid Tube. In the barrier-grid tube (Radechon), Fig. 1, the storage target *T*, usually mica, is sandwiched between a metal plate *P* and a fine-mesh "barrier grid" *B*. The same gun is used sequentially for writing and reading. If the electron beam bombards any element of the storage surface, the element is carried toward a potential approximately equal to that of *B*. The target element is charged by secondary-electron emission or primary-electron collection depending upon whether the target is negative or positive, respectively, compared to *B*. Through capacitive coupling the potential of the target surface *T* can also be varied by changing the potential of *P*. A charge pattern can be written by applying a time-varying input signal to *P* while scanning *T* with a constant-current beam of sufficient intensity. The stored charge pattern can be read out by holding *P* at a constant potential, while rescanning the target with a beam of constant current to re-establish a uniform surface potential on *T*. The output signal can be observed as a current flowing in the *P* lead or alternatively as modulation of the current returned to C from the bombarded target.

In an alternative writing mode, the target surface is first charged uniformly to the potential of B while P is held constant. Then P is shifted to a new value and the input signal is applied to G to vary the beam current as the beam is scanned over the target at a constant speed. In this mode the beam current is never allowed to become large enough to carry T to the potential of B.

Only one faithful reproduction of the stored signal can be read, since either reading or writing erases a previously stored pattern. The barrier-grid tube is particularly well suited for radar moving-target indication (MTI). In addition, as many as 30 amplitude levels (halftones) can be stored with a limiting resolution of about 400 lines, permitting faithful storage of television pictures.

Scan Conversion Tube. In the scan-conversion storage tube (Graphechon), Fig. 2, the target T is a thin dielectric layer evaporated upon a very thin metal film P, supported in turn by a fine-mesh screen S. Writing and reading guns bombard opposite sides of the target. P is held at a constant potential, say 0 v. The reading gun scans the storage surface T with a constant-current beam to maintain it, by secondary emission, at a fixed positive potential approximately equal to the potential of the collector C. The writing beam scans the other side of the target, bombarding it with electrons sufficiently energetic to pass through P and to penetrate into the storage target, where they induce a volume conductivity in the dielectric. This process is called bombardment-induced conductivity. It serves to discharge partially the uniform gradient previously established across the dielectric. The potential shift at T is proportional to the charge delivered by the writing gun. If the beam current of the scanning writing gun is modulated by an input signal at G, a charge pattern is deposited on T. The charging current required from the reading gun to re-establish T to the collector potential can be observed as an output current in the P lead or alternatively as a modulation of the current returned to C from the bombarded target.

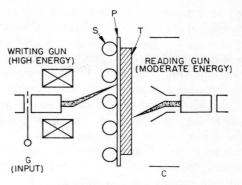

FIG. 2. Scan-conversion storage tube.

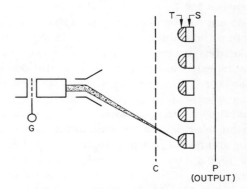

FIG. 3. Recording storage tube.

As in the barrier-grid tube, only one readout can be obtained with a maximum number of output levels (halftones), since the reading beam erases the stored pattern. However, many readouts with fewer output levels can be obtained, particularly with certain target materials. This tube was specifically developed to have simultaneous writing and reading for scan-conversion applications (radar PPI to television raster, television frame-frequency conversion, etc.).

Recording Storage Tube. In the "recording" storage tube (Fig. 3), the storage surface is an insulating film T evaporated onto one side of a fine mesh screen S, behind which is located a metal plate P. One gun is used in turn for writing, reading, and erasing.

A charge pattern is written onto T by secondary-emission charging when the target is scanned by a moderately energetic writing beam, with beam current modulated by the input signal. Collector C is held sufficiently positive to collect the secondary electrons. For reading, the charge pattern controls by grid action the transmission to P of a low-energy beam from the same gun (operating with different electrode potentials). For erasure, a uniform charge pattern can be re-established by writing the entire surface to the collector potential or to the cathode potential of the gun.

With the proper choice of positive potentials for C, S, and P, the entire charge pattern can be negative with respect to the gun cathode during the read cycle so that no electrons can reach T. The reading cycle can be repeated many times without disturbing the stored charge pattern. Thus the recording storage tube is particularly useful for multiple readout of stored radar or narrowband television pictures. Simultaneous writing and reading are not possible in the design of Fig. 3, but the same target is used in a two-gun configuration similar to that shown in Fig. 2, for scan-conversion applications.

Display Storage Tubes

An electrical-to-visual storage tube is called a display or direct-view storage tube. It can display electrical transients and radar or narrowband television pictures for extended intervals or with controlled fade-rate, and with higher light output than available from long persistence phosphors.

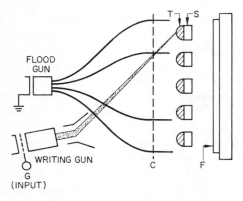

FIG. 4. Display storage tube.

Nearly all display storage tubes can be represented by the schematic of Fig. 4. A flood gun is added to the basic elements of the recording storage tube of Fig. 3. In addition, the metal plate P is replaced by an aluminized phosphor viewing screen F on the faceplate of the tube. The operation is quite similar to that of the recording storage tube. By secondary-emission charging, a moderately energetic writing gun deposits a positive charge pattern on the insulating target T. The secondary electrons are collected at C. The charge pattern controls the transmission of a broad well-collimated beam of electrons which floods the target. Where the charge pattern is positive, the low-energy flood electrons pass through the holes in the screen and are accelerated to F, which is operated at high potential to provide a bright display.

Three types of display tubes—halftone, bistable, and selective erasure—are described below. All of these tubes operate as explained above, but they vary in detail. (Still another type of display storage tube is the dark-trace cathode-ray tube, $q.v.$).

Halftone Tube. In the halftone display storage tube (Iatron, Storatron, Tonotron), the storage surface T is a thin dielectric film evaporated onto a fine mesh screen S (Fig. 4). During viewing, the entire surface T is negative with respect to the flood-gun cathode so that no flood electrons can strike the stored charge pattern. A number of amplitude levels (halftones) can be stored and viewed for times limited only by ion currents due to residual gas in the tube. For erasure, the potential of S is momentarily raised by a few volts, which carries the insulating surface T a few volts positive by capacitive coupling so that flood electrons can strike it and charge it negatively. If the single erasing pulse is replaced by a train of much shorter pulses, the stored pattern fades gradually.

The halftone tube is used for bright, non-flickering display of radar and narrow-band television pictures. Sufficient brightness is available in some halftone tubes to permit projection display. A multicolor halftone storage tube has been built by combining the elements of Fig. 4 with those of a shadow-mask color picture tube.

Bistable Tube. The bistable display storage tube (Memotron, Typotron) incorporates a granular dielectric target T (Fig. 4). Operation is similar to that of the halftone tube, but there are two stable values of target potential, black and white, at the potentials of the flood-gun cathode and collector C, respectively. If a "black" target element drifts a few volts positive, flood electrons can strike it and drive it back to the potential of the flood-gun cathode. Similarly, if a "white" element drifts negative with respect to the positive collector C, secondary-emission charging will return the element to collector potential. The target must be granular to prevent motion of the boundaries between black and white stored areas. To erase, the potential of C is dropped to a value sufficiently low that the secondary-emission ratio falls below unity, thus interrupting the regeneration at collector potential.

The bistable tube has no halftone range. The indefinite retention time is particularly useful for transient oscillography. In the Typotron tube the writing gun incorporates a stencil to permit the beam cross section to be shaped for character writing (as in the Charactron, *q.v.*).

Selective-Erasure Tube. The most promising version of selective-erasure tube is a halftone display storage tube, which operates as described above. However, a special target material is used that can also be charged by *bombardment-induced conductivity* (BIC) if scanned by a sufficiently energetic beam. Thus both positive and negative writing can be obtained, by moderate- and high-energy beams, with charging by secondary-electron emission and BIC, respectively. To make the polarity of the BIC writing be negative, S is operated negative with respect to T. Two writing guns can be used to permit simultaneous white and black writing, or the cathode potential of one gun can be shifted between modes.

For most applications, the erase-before-write feature is preferable to instantaneous or fading erasure, if the additional complexity can be afforded. For example, in a radar display the new information can replace the old, line by line as it is received, in a picture of constant average brightness.

Computer Storage Tubes

Electrical signal storage tubes capable of high-speed random access can serve as memories for high-speed digital computers. A relatively conventional cathode-ray tube can be used (see below). The barrier-grid tube has been employed as a digital random-access memory for telephone switching. Several storage tubes have been designed specifically for computers. The Selectron has an array of 16×16 individual bistable elements, with sets of orthogonal selection bars. The Whirlwind storage tube is a bistable cathode-ray tube similar to the bistable display tube but with electrical output. Storage tubes have been largely displaced by magnetic-core memories in most data-processing computers.

GEORGE F. SMITH

Williams' Tube

This storage system uses a standard type cathode-ray tube fitted with an external signal plate (Fig. 5).

The storage function relies on the observed fact that it is possible to leave, at a particular spot on the phosphor screen, one of two alternative charge distributions. These distributions, representing the digits '0' or '1', depend on the electron bombardment procedure near the spot. Subsequent bombardment of that spot yields either a negative or positive signal at the pickup plate depending on the stored digit. This 'reading out' returns the spot to the "0" charge distribution, so that if a '0' is read out (negative signal) no further action is needed. However, if a '1' is read out (positive signal) a further bombardment procedure is necessary in order to reinstate the '1' charge configura-

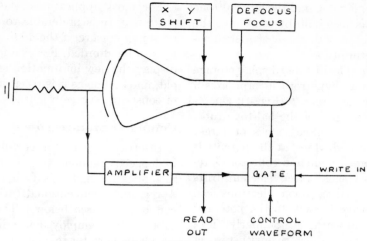

FIG. 5. Williams' tube.

tion. This is arranged by causing a positive signal to actuate the gate circuit so as to switch on the crt beam during the "write 1" procedure. The "write 1" procedure follows each 'read' operation automatically but is rendered ineffective by the gate circuit, which switches off the electron beam if an '0' signal appears at the signal plate.

Various "write 1" procedures have been used of which the "defocus/focus" is perhaps the best. In this arrangement '0' is stored by bombarding the spot for 1 μsec with a spot defocused to twice its normal diameter. During this period a 'read out' signal is obtained and the 'gate' is either actuated or not actuated according as to whether '1' or '0' is read. After the 1-μsec interval the spot is swept smoothly into focus over a period of 4 μsec, during which the beam is 'on' if the gate is open and 'off' if it is not.

Quantized deflections in the X and Y directions can be used to define a large number of separate storage locations, these locations being defined by the deflection potentials, and not by any surface discontinuity in the screen.

Leakage and other effects cause the stored digits to 'fade' and it is essential that they be 'regenerated' in sequence at frequent intervals by the normal 'read' and 'rewrite' procedure.

Depending on the service required, between 1000 and 2000 digits can be stored on a standard 6-in. diameter tube and up to 10,000 on special tubes.

F. C. WILLIAMS

Cross-references: *Cathode-Ray Tubes (Display), Computer Printout and Reading, Dark-Trace Tubes, Image Orthicon, Radar Displays, Solid-State Displays, Storage, Television (Color)*

STRESS TENSOR

The Maxwell stress tensor is defined as the tensor

$$(T_{ji}) = E_j D_i - \tfrac{1}{2}\delta_{ji}E_k D_k + H_j B_i - \tfrac{1}{2}\delta_{ji}H_j D_i$$

$$= \epsilon'\epsilon_0 \begin{pmatrix} \tfrac{1}{2}(E_x{}^2 - E_y{}^2 - E_z{}^2) & E_x E_y & E_x E_z \\ E_x E_y & \tfrac{1}{2}(E_y{}^2 - E_z{}^2 - E_x{}^2) & E_y E_z \\ E_x E_z & E_y E_z & \tfrac{1}{2}(E_z{}^2 - E_x{}^2 - E_y{}^2) \end{pmatrix}$$

$$+ \mu'\mu_0 \begin{pmatrix} \tfrac{1}{2}(H_x{}^2 - H_y{}^2 - H_z{}^2) & H_x H_y & H_x H_z \\ H_x H_y & \tfrac{1}{2}(H_y{}^2 - H_z{}^2 - H_x{}^2) & H_y H_z \\ H_x H_z & H_y H_z & \tfrac{1}{2}(H_z{}^2 - H_x{}^2 - H_y{}^2) \end{pmatrix}$$

This tensor was introduced by Maxwell in an attempt to make the analogy between elastic media and electric and magnetic fields more concrete. Faraday suggested that the lines of force of the electric and magnetic fields were responsible for the continuous transmission of tension and compression forces from one body to another in much the same way that elastic bands transmit mechanical force continuously from one point to another.

In elastic media, the surface force, which is represented by the stress vector $\mathbf{T}$, is related to the stress tensor (τ_{ji}) by

$$\mathbf{T} = (T_1, T_2, T_3) = (\tau_{j1}\nu_j, \tau_{j2}\nu_j, \tau_{j3}\nu_j)$$

where ν_1, ν_2, and ν_3 are the direction cosines of the normal to the surface element (at a given point) to which $\mathbf{T}$ is referred. If $\mathbf{F} = (F_1, F_2, F_3)$ is the body force per unit volume and $\mathbf{T}$ is the stress vector, then for equilibrium we have from the theory of elasticity:

$$\mathrm{div}\ (\tau_{ji}) + F_i = 0$$

where

$$\mathrm{div}\ (\tau_{ji}) = \left(\frac{\partial\tau_{11}}{\partial x} + \frac{\partial\tau_{21}}{\partial y} + \frac{\partial\tau_{31}}{\partial z},\ \frac{\partial\tau_{12}}{\partial x} + \frac{\partial\tau_{22}}{\partial y} + \frac{\partial\tau_{32}}{\partial z},\right.$$
$$\left.\frac{\partial\tau_{31}}{\partial x} + \frac{\partial\tau_{32}}{\partial y} + \frac{\partial\tau_{33}}{\partial z}\right)$$

This equation states that, in the case of equilibrium, the body force is derivable from the stress tensor which is specified only on the surface.

In the case of the Maxwell stress tensor we have a similar relation for quasi-stationary fields.

The tensor divergence of the Maxwell stress tensor is:

$$\mathrm{div}\ (T_{ji}) = \left(\frac{\partial T_{xx}}{\partial x} + \frac{\partial T_{yx}}{\partial y} + \frac{\partial T_{zx}}{\partial z},\right.$$
$$\frac{\partial T_{xy}}{\partial x} + \frac{\partial T_{yy}}{\partial y} + \frac{\partial T_{zy}}{\partial z},$$
$$\left.\frac{\partial T_{xz}}{\partial x} + \frac{\partial T_{yz}}{\partial y} + \frac{\partial T_{zz}}{\partial z}\right)$$

$$= \mathbf{E}\nabla\cdot(\epsilon'\epsilon_0\mathbf{E}) - \frac{\epsilon_0}{2}\,(\mathbf{E}\cdot\mathbf{E})\,\nabla\epsilon' + (\nabla\times\mathbf{E})\times(\epsilon_0\epsilon'\mathbf{E})$$

$$+ \mathbf{H}\nabla\cdot(\mu'\mu_0\mathbf{H}) - \frac{\mu_0}{2}\,(\mathbf{H}\cdot\mathbf{H})\,\nabla\mu'$$

$$+ (\nabla\times\mathbf{H})\times(\mu_0\mu'\mathbf{H})$$

which follows by direct computation. By Maxwell's equations we have:

$$\nabla\cdot(\epsilon'\epsilon_0\mathbf{E}) = \nabla\cdot\mathbf{D} = \rho_r$$
$$\nabla\cdot(\mu'\mu_0\mathbf{H}) = \nabla\cdot\mathbf{B} = 0$$
$$\nabla\times\mathbf{E} = -\frac{\partial\mathbf{B}}{\partial t}$$
$$\nabla\times\mathbf{H} = \mathbf{j}_r + \frac{\partial\mathbf{D}}{\partial t}$$

and therefore:

$$\mathrm{div}\ (T_{ji}) = \mathbf{E}\rho_r - \frac{\epsilon_0}{2}\,E^2\nabla\epsilon' - \frac{\partial\mathbf{B}}{\partial t}\times\mathbf{D} - \frac{\mu_0}{2}\,H^2\nabla\mu'$$

$$+ \mathbf{j}_r\times\mathbf{B} + \frac{\partial\mathbf{D}}{\partial t}\times\mathbf{B}$$

$$= \mathbf{f}_{el} + \mathbf{f}_{mag} + \mathbf{f}_N$$

where

$$\mathbf{f}_{el} = \mathbf{E}\rho_r - \frac{\epsilon_0}{2}\,E^2\nabla\epsilon'$$

$$\mathbf{f}_{mag} = \mathbf{j}_r\times\mathbf{B} - \frac{\mu_0}{2}\,H^2\nabla\epsilon'$$

$$\mathbf{f}_N = \frac{\partial}{\partial t}\,(\mathbf{D}\times\mathbf{B}) = \mu\epsilon\frac{\partial}{\partial t}\,(\mathbf{E}\times\mathbf{H})$$

$$= \epsilon'\epsilon_0\mu'\mu_0\frac{\partial}{\partial t}\,(\mathbf{E}\times\mathbf{H}) = \frac{\epsilon'\mu'}{c^2}\frac{\partial}{\partial t}\,\mathbf{N}$$

$$\mathbf{N} = \mathbf{E}\times\mathbf{H} = \text{Poynting vector}$$

$$\epsilon_0\mu_0 = \frac{1}{c^2}$$

(1) $\mathbf{f}_{el}$ is made up of the volume force on real charges and on inhomogeneous dielectrics in an electric field. The latter term appears, for example, at the interface between an insulator and free space, the gradient being normal to the surface of constant ϵ'; $\epsilon'(x, y, z)$-constant means that this force is normal to the surface of the dielectric.

In the case of electrostriction the term $\frac{1}{2}\delta_{ji}\epsilon_0 g E_k E_k\,(d\epsilon'/dg)$, where g is the mass density, is added to the Maxwell stress tensor.

(2) $\mathbf{f}_{mag}$ is made up of the volume force on real currents and on inhomogeneous permeable matter in a magnetic field.

(3) $\mathbf{f}_N$ does not appear in a quasi-stationary electromagnetic field. However, for a nonstationary electromagnetic field, this term appears, even in a vacuum. In a vacuum $\epsilon' = \mu' = 1$ and in keeping with the special theory of relativity, we consider $\mathbf{N}/c^2$ as a momentum density. Thus, if we assume that mechanical force arises from material charges and currents only, we have for the mechanical momentum $\mathbf{p}$

$$\frac{d\mathbf{p}}{dt} = \int [\mathbf{f}_{el} + \mathbf{f}_{mag}] \, dv$$

and

$$\frac{d}{dt}\left[\mathbf{p} + \frac{1}{c^2}\int \mathbf{N} \, dv \right] = \int \text{div } (T_{ji}) \, dv$$

$$= \int \mathbf{T}\cdot \mathbf{ds} \text{ (by Gauss's}$$

theorem for tensors)

where $\mathbf{T}$ is the stress vector. This equation states that the time rate of change of the mechanical momentum plus the volume integral of $\mathbf{N}/c^2$ is equal to the surface integral of the Maxwell stress transmitted through the surface surrounding the volume.

If we consider only an electric field, then the stress vector $\mathbf{T}$ has the following meaning:

$$|\mathbf{T}| = \frac{\epsilon'\epsilon_0}{2} E^2 = \frac{\mathbf{E}\cdot \mathbf{D}}{2}$$

and the direction of $\mathbf{T}$ is determined by the fact that the direction of $\mathbf{E}$ bisects the angle between the normal to the surface element to which $\mathbf{T}$ is referred and $\mathbf{T}$.

When there are only magnetic fields, a similar interpretation holds with

$$|\mathbf{T}| = \frac{\mu'\mu_0}{2} H^2$$

In the special theory of relativity the Maxwell stress tensor is replaced by the energy momentum tensor in four-dimensional space.

$$(T^{ji}) = \begin{pmatrix} -T_{xx} & -T_{xy} & -T_{xz} & N_x/c \\ -T_{xy} & -T_{yy} & -T_{yz} & N_y/c \\ -T_{zy} & -T_{zy} & -T_{zz} & N_z/c \\ N_x/c & N_y/c & N_z/c & \frac{1}{2}(\epsilon_0 E^2 + \mu_0 H^2) \end{pmatrix}$$

From this relation it is seen that

$$\left(\frac{\partial}{\partial x}, \frac{\partial}{\partial y}, \frac{\partial}{\partial z}, \frac{\partial}{c\partial t} \right) (T^{ji})$$

yields the two quantities

$$-\text{div } (T_{ji}) + \frac{1}{c^2}\frac{\partial \mathbf{N}}{\partial t}$$

and

$$\frac{1}{c}\nabla\cdot \mathbf{N} + \frac{1}{c}\frac{\partial}{\partial t}\left[\frac{\epsilon_0 E^2}{2} + \frac{\mu_0 H^2}{2} \right]$$

where the first quantity is equal to $-\mathbf{f}_{el} - \mathbf{f}_{mag}$ and the second quantity is equal $-(\mathbf{E}\cdot \mathbf{j})/c$. This last fact comes from taking the scalar product of $\mathbf{H}$ and $\mathbf{E}$ with $\nabla \times \mathbf{E} = -\partial \mathbf{B}/\partial t$ and $\nabla \times \mathbf{H} = \mathbf{j}_r + \partial \mathbf{D}/\partial t$, respectively, and subtracting.

J. M. SLOSS

Cross-references: *Electromagnetic Theory, Matrix Algebra, Vector Algebra*

STRIP LINE

The term "strip line" describes a kind of waveguide which is similar in many respects to coaxial transmission line. It may, in fact, be regarded as a simple variation of the coaxial line, although it has a great many practical advantages over the latter. The basic guide is uniform in cross section and consists of a thin center conductor of rectangular cross section situated midway between two parallel metal plates with the long dimension of the central strip conductor parallel to the outer plates. The outer plates are somewhat greater in width than the central strip. The strip may be held in place by solid dielectric filling the guide or, as is more common, on a thin dielectric sheet held in position by posts at the edge of the parallel plates.

As with the coaxial line, the dominant mode and the one that is generally used is the TEM mode with the field existing between the strip and the outer plates (which are at the same dc potential). The field is largely confined to the region between the strip and the parallel plates with the field intensity decreasing rapidly away from the strip. Thus, if the distance from the edge of the strip to the edge of the parallel-plate region is as much as twice the spacing between the plates, the field at the edge is negligible. For the TEM mode the characteristic impedance of the line is simply given by the inverse product of the capacitance per unit length and the speed of light in the dielectric filling the guide. An exact formula for the capacitance per unit length is rather complicated. However, since it is essentially a parallel-plate capacitor, it is clear that the impedance is made lower by increasing the strip width or decreasing the spacing. There is a limit on how wide the strip may be made. In order that higher-order modes may not propagate, the strip width must be less than approximately one-half wavelength. For the same reason, the plate spacing must be less than one-half wavelength. Practical characteristic impedances range between 20 and 100 ohms.

The useful frequency range of strip line extends to 10 kMc and the attenuation is small, typically 0.02 db per wavelength at 3 kMc. Also, the power-handling capacity of the line is very high. Of course, standard rectangular waveguide propagating the TE_{10} mode is somewhat superior in both respects.

All of the standard microwave circuits can be constructed in strip line, including, for example, filters, hybrid Tee's and mixers, directional couplers, attenuators, and slot radiators. The great advantage of the strip line is the ease, precision, and compactness with which these components can be designed and constructed as compared with corresponding structures in either coaxial line or conventional rectangular waveguide. Transmission-line junctions are constructed by simply joining the strips together between the same parallel plates. Because the field is confined to the region of the strips, little interaction between the lines occurs. At the same time, coupled transmission lines may be obtained by placing strips parallel and very close to one another.

For experimental work, one may quickly and easily construct a circuit by, for example, cutting the strip out of copper foil with scissors and sandwiching it between two dielectric slabs that are put between two metal plates. For precision applications, the strip circuit may be photoengraved on a thin dielectric sheet and mounted between the two plates as described above. With this technique it is possible to produce a device as complicated as a bandpass filter that will work without further experimental adjustment. This ease of construction is seldom possible with the comparable device in either coaxial line or standard rectangular waveguide.

Because of the ease of construction, compactness, and precision obtainable with the strip line, it is now in very wide use. This is particularly true in airborne installations where size and weight are important considerations.

The symposium on microwave strip lines held in 1954 is an excellent source of additional information on strip lines (*IRE Trans.* **MTT-3,** No. 2, March 1955).

W. J. WELCH

Cross-references: *Antennas, Attenuators and Isolators, Circulators, Coaxial Lines, Delay Lines, Resonators, Waveguide and Waveguide Components*

STROBES

Xenon-filled quartz or glass discharge tubes are useful for producing short flashes of visible, infrared, or ultraviolet radiation of high intensity when excited by electrical energy stored in capacitors. The spectral output of the normal xenon flashlamp is continuum radiation extending from 0.3 to 2.0 μ, with superimposed xenon spectral lines. A broad peak occurs at 0.45 μ and one

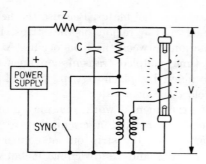

FIG. 1. Basic flashtube circuit.

or more peaks occur at 1.0 μ. Of the many gases used in flashtubes, xenon seems to be the most efficient converter of electrical energy to radiant energy. Widely used as a flashlight source for photography, the output of a xenon flashtube approximates a blackbody source at 6900 K, and gives good color rendition on daylight color film with little or no filtering.

A basic flashlamp circuit is shown in Fig. 1. The power supply charges an energy storage capacitor C to a voltage V through the charging impedance Z, which limits current flow from the power supply so that the flashtube can deionize and extinguish after each flash. Energy stored in the capacitor, equal to $\frac{1}{2} CV^2$ joules, is discharged in the flashtube when a high-voltage trigger pulse is applied to the flashtube from the trigger transformer T.

A high-voltage trigger pulse impressed on metal wire or band wrapped around the flashtube ionizes the xenon gas sufficiently to cause breakdown at the applied voltage V.

A flashtube is operable over a voltage range of about 5 to 1. The upper limit is the self-flash voltage and the lower limit is the minimum starting voltage below which the lamp does not trigger reliably. Tubes are given a voltage rating between these two limits. Rated voltages range from 300 to 4,000 v and depend mainly on the fill pressure and arc length.

Flash duration is defined as the time between the $\frac{1}{3}$ peak light points on the rising and falling portions of the light–time curve. Flash duration depends chiefly on the effec-

tive resistance of the flashtube and size of the storage capacitor discharging into the lamp. An approximate relation for flash duration of flashtubes loaded higher than 10 w-sec/cm³ has been found to be:

$$\text{Flash Duration} = \frac{RC}{2}$$

where R is the effective flashtube resistance equal to operating voltage V divided by peak current and C is the value of the energy storage capacitor. Light flashes as short as a few microseconds can be achieved with short gap length tubes and small values of C. At high-loading flash duration can be as long as 5.0 msec. The effective flashlamp resistance is given approximately by $R = \eta L/A$, where L = tube arc length (cm), A = cross section area (cm²), and η = 0.0165 ohm-cm (resistivity of xenon plasma).

Efficiency is expressed in lumens per watt and is found by dividing the measured total light output expressed in lumen-seconds by the energy stored in the capacitor expressed in watt-seconds (joules). At large loadings (higher than 100 w-sec/cm³) a flashtube's efficiency is as great as 50 l/w. At small loadings (less than 1.0 w-sec/cm³), particularly for short-gap tubes, efficiency can be a low as 5 l/w.

Two methods of coupling the trigger pulse to the gas are (1) internal, in which an electrode is brought through the tube envelope, and (2) external, in which a metallic band, stripe, or helix wrapped around the outside of the envelope couples capacitively to the gas. External triggering is used most frequently and requires peak trigger voltage of 4,000 to 20,000 v, depending on rated voltage and arc length. Internal triggering, used in short-gap tubes (up to $\frac{1}{2}$ in. arc length), requires a 2,000- to 8,000-v peak trigger of 5-μsec duration.

As life is accumulated on a flashtube, its efficiency drops slowly as evaporated electrode material darkens the tube walls. As an example the FX-1, a quartz tube with an arc length of 6 in. and an ID of 4 mm shows a decrease of about 15 per cent in efficiency after 100,000 flashes at the rated input of 200 w-sec. The tube continues to operate normally, however, and may be used if lower efficiencies can be tolerated.

Evaporated electrode material usually causes minimum starting voltage to increase and self-flashing voltage to decrease, thus reducing the operating range of the flashtube. Life is limited in low-voltage tubes (300 v) which become "hard starters" as well as in high-voltage tubes (4,000 v) which become "self-starters," because of this narrowing of the operating range as life is accumulated.

A light flashing in synchronism with a rotating or oscillating object freezes the motion for human observation or recording on film. This is the *stroboscopic* effect.

Maximum permissible flashing rate is governed by the flashtube's ability to dissipate input power and the tube's ability to deionize. Control circuits have been used to force operation at very high frequencies. Phenomena at very high speeds can be observed by (1) operating a flashtube at high repetition rate for a short time or (2) flashing two or more short-duration flashtubes at a fixed time interval between flashes. The FX-2 quartz lamp is rated at 6,000 flashes/ sec for 0.8 sec operating time at 0.3 w-sec input per flash. This lamp has been operated for 20 flashes at 10-μsec intervals with 0.3 w-sec per flash.

Two areas in which flashtubes have found extensive use are photographic light sources for color and black and white film, and stroboscopic instrumentation. A unique property of flashtubes is their long life, making them useful as standards of light. Rated life times of 10^{10} flashes are available at low loadings. The ultraviolet output of flashtubes is used to produce direct printout with photochromic materials deposited on paper. Very high peak radiation flux and short duration make flashtubes superior to other optical pumping methods requiring high peak power such as required for optical masers or lasers (*q.v.*). There is about as much energy in the infrared portion of the spectrum as there is in the visible portion but few applications have been made.

HAROLD E. EDGERTON
JOHN H. GONCZ

Cross-references: *Electric Discharge, Glow Tubes, Photocell, Thyratrons*

STRONG FOCUSING: see ALTERNATING-GRADIENT FOCUSING

SUPERCONDUCTIVITY

Superconductivity is that property of metals by virtue of which they lose all electrical resistance and become perfectly diamagnetic below characteristic transition temperatures. It is a property observed only at low temperatures, the highest transition temperature (T_c) now known being that for Nb_3Sn near 18°K.

Superconductivity was discovered by H. Kammerlingh-Onnes (1853–1926) in 1913 during measurements of the electrical resistance of mercury in the liquid helium range; 22 other elements have since been added to mercury as superconductors. A few elements which are not superconducting become so in certain compounds. Superconductivity is not a rare property of metals, although it is probably not a general one. None of the monovalent elements and none of the ferromagnetic elements are superconductors. There is no assurance, however, that these elements and others do not become superconducting at sufficiently low temperatures.

The most successful correlations of the occurrence of superconductivity are with electrical resistivity or atomic volume. The superconductors are characterized by relatively high resistivity at room temperature. Fröhlich and Bardeen have each pointed out rules for the occurrence of superconductivity, each rule stating roughly that a metal is a superconductor if $n\rho > 10^6$, where n is the number of valence electrons per cm³ and

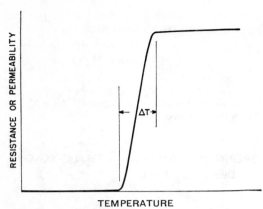

FIG. 1. The superconducting transition.

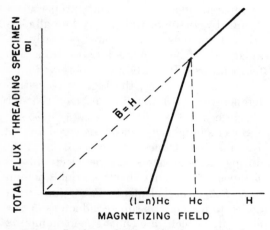

FIG. 2. Isothermal magnetization curve of superconducting ellipsoid in uniform field.

ρ is the room temperature resistivity in esu. Matthias has devised an empirical formula showing the dependence of the transition temperature on the valence N, the atomic volume V, and the atomic mass M, having the form $T_c = f(N)V^\alpha M^\beta$; $f(N)$ is a function having a sharp minimum at $N = 6$ and maxima at $N = 5$ and 7. The constant α lies between 5 and 10, and β ranges from 0.5 to 0.8.

The resistance of a "good" superconductor decreases to zero, as shown in Figure 1, in a temperature interval ΔT as small as $0.003°K$. Experiments at Leiden have shown the resistance decrease to be by a factor of at least 10^{15}. The magnetic permeability has a simi-

lar temperature dependence in the absence of a magnetic field. The perfect diamagnetism of superconductors is called the "Meissner effect" after its 1933 discoverer.

A sufficiently strong magnetic field destroys superconductivity. The threshold field strength (H_c) required to do this varies roughly parabolically with temperature for a number of superconductors. H_c is that magnetic field parallel to the surface of the superconductor just sufficient to start flux penetration. Further penetration with increasing magnetic field depends on the configuration of the superconductor, owing to the field distortion caused by the Meissner effect. Thus H_c is reached at a lower magnetizing field H for some points on the surface than for other points. Figure 2 shows the total flux B threading an ellipsoid of revolution in a magnetic field parallel to the major axis, as a function of H; n is the demagnetizing factor of the ellipsoid, being unity for a flat disk and zero for a cylinder. Flux does not penetrate uniformly over the cross section of the specimen, but rather threads through normal local regions spread more or less uniformly throughout the volume, whereas the remainder of the specimen is superconducting. The shapes of these regions vary with the shape and physical state of the sample, and are thought of as filamentary for spheres and probably plate-like for cylinders and flat sheets normal to the field. A superconductor through which flux threads is said to be in the "intermediate state," a mixture of the normal and superconductive states.

Flux expulsion is complete and the B-H curve is reversible only for "good" superconductors. In most alloys and in Ta and Nb, considerable hysteresis occurs and an appreciable fraction of the critical field flux may remain "frozen in" on demagnetizing.

The existence of a maximum magnetic field in which a metal can be superconducting sets an upper limit to the current that can be carried in a superconducting wire, namely, that current which just creates H_c at the surface of the wire.

The heat capacity of a metal increases discontinuously upon becoming superconducting, with a latent heat of transition in a magnetic field. The transition is thermodynamically reversible to a good approximation. Since the difference in the Gibbs free energy densities between normal and superconductive states is just the threshold field energy density $H_c^2/8\pi$, it follows that the entropy difference per unit volume between the two states is

$$S_n - S_s = -(dH_c/dT)H_c/4\pi$$

The change in heat capacity at the transition calculated from this basis is in excellent agreement with experimentally determined values.

The macroscopic electrodynamic phenomenology of superconductivity may be described using the London equations, $-\nabla \times [(4\pi\lambda^2/c)\mathbf{J}_s] = \mathbf{H}$ and $\partial[(4\pi\lambda^2/c^2)\mathbf{J}_s]/\partial t = \mathbf{E}$, where $\mathbf{J}_s$ is the density of the supercurrent component of the total current density $J = J_{super} + J_{normal}$, H and E are the magnetic and electric field strengths, c is the velocity of light, and λ is a constant called the penetration depth. The London equations supplemented by Maxwell's equations show that J_s decreases exponentially into a conductor falling to $1/e$ of its surface value in a distance $\lambda \approx 2 \times 10^{-6}$ cm. Thus a supercurrent is essentially a surface current.

Prior to 1957 there was no satisfactory fundamental theory of superconductivity. The discovery in 1950 that the transition temperatures of the isotopes of a superconducting element vary inversely with the square root of the isotopic mass suggested that superconductivity arises from interactions between conduction electrons and vibrations of the crystalline lattice. This discovery inspired work leading to the theory published in 1957 by J. Bardeen, L. N. Cooper, and J. R. Schrieffer. According to this theory conduction electrons in a superconductor tend to interact in pairs in being scattered by lattice vibrations, with the result that there is an over-all lowering of electron energies near the Fermi energy.

The resultant gap of forbidden energies is responsible for the principal phenomena of superconductivity.

The Bardeen-Cooper-Schrieffer theory and its further refinements have successfully interpreted virtually all the significant features of superconductivity. Recent experimental observations which this theory has explained include: the exponential temperature dependence of the electronic specific heat; microwave, infrared, and ultrasonic absorption; and phenomena associated with electron tunneling between superconductors separated by a thin insulating layer. It may be said that superconductivity is now better understood than normal conductivity.

MILAN D. FISKE

Cross-references: *Cryogenics, Cryotronics, Skin Effect*

SUPERHETERODYNE: see MODULATION AND DEMODULATION

SUPPRESSED CARRIER: see MODULATION AND DEMODULATION

SWITCHES

A class of controlling device capable of being altered by manual, mechanical, electrical, or electronic means, from a state of very high impedance to a state of very low impedance (from "off" to "on"). In general, it serves to permit or inhibit flow of electric current, or to apply or remove sources of electric potential to equipment via appropriate circuitry.

Precision Snap-Acting Switches

A class of switch mechanism in which a spring system is employed to maintain contact pressures while operating energy is being applied to its actuating member. Upon attaining a proper energy-storage condition, the spring mechanism transfers, causing switching action, and energy stored in the spring system maintains contact pressures in the transferred state until release of applied force from the actuating member permits the stored energy to be released and the mechanism and contacts to regain their original or inoperated state.

These devices are generally characterized by all or many of the following features:

(a) Small motion or differential travel between operating and release positions or actuator device (from as low as 0.0002 in. to perhaps as much as 0.0050 in.)

(b) Low differential force requirements between operated and released positions (from 3 to 5 oz characteristically).

(c) High ac interrupting capacity. Values of up to 20 amp at 440 v are possible.

(d) High contact pressures that minimize response to external forces tending to separate contacts.

(e) Small size; units with 20 amp, 440 v, 60 cps capacity requiring approximately $\frac{1}{2}$ in.³; units capable of handling 5 amp at 250 v being as small as 0.05 in.³.

(f) Unaffected by position.

(g) Unaffected by normal barometric pressures up to 20,000 ft above sea level. When sealed in a dry gas, such as nitrogen, these switches perform suitably in almost any environment not deleterious to the enclosure.

(h) Rate of actuation may safely range to as high as 400 cpm under moderate load, or perhaps to 600 cpm where only an establishment of potential is essential.

(i) Very long mechanical operating life, ranging as high as 150×10^6 operations for certain types.

Mercury Switches

This class of switch is characterized by a pool of refined mercury enclosed in an hermetically sealed chamber, and caused to bridge two or more electrodes sealed through the enclosure (or one electrode may be the chamber wall if conducting) and connected externally to leads by which the current flow is conducted to the switch. In general, mercury-switch devices are actuated by tilting the enclosure to the angle necessary to

cause the mercury pool to engulf or part from the contacts, inserts, or electrodes. By use of platinum or molybdenum electrodes, very superior "wetting" of contacts is possible, and very clean contact action occurs.

Mercury switches in general may be said to possess the following characteristics:

(a) Very low and very stable circuit resistance.

(b) Very high "make" and "break" capacities for dc and ac loads.

(c) Very low torque requirements for operation, and capable of operation with tilt angles of very small size (such as from an angle of 12.0° maximum to an angle of 0.15° minimum).

(d) Inherent hermetic sealing.

(e) Capable of enclosure in containers rugged enough to prevent damage to the sealing envelope.

(f) A minimum of irregularities as compared to mechanical contacts that exhibit "bouncing" at closure.

The device in diverse forms is versatile enough to serve as sensor for aircraft gyroscope-controlled systems; and rugged, electrically stable, and inexpensive enough to be useful in major home appliances.

Proximity Switches

By definition, a proximity switch is any device with an ultimate switch function, capable of actuation by presence or absence, or by notable change in strength, of an external field to which the actuating controls of the switches have been adjusted.

This sensitive response to changes in field conditions is by one of two types: (1) detection of the presence of a field by a sensor or transducer; or (2) unbalance of a field established around the sensor to which the switch system is sensitive.

In general, proximity switches require sensors, amplifiers, power supplies, and adjusting means; and transform weak signals into levels capable of driving relays, electronic switches, or signal devices. There are simpler mechanical proximity switches sensing ferrous material by permanent magnets and operating contacts through linkages.

In those systems in which the sensing is by unbalance of an established field projected from the sensor, it is generally necessary to provide the field energy through magnetic coils, or by projectors radiating a field charge. Thus, the sensing action is one of lowering the reluctance of a magnetic field, disturbing the tuning of an oscillator, or changing capacitance of a system.

The industrial proximity switch possesses all or most of the following characteristics:

(a) Capability to sense without physical contact; hence, ability to sense devices of low mass or size.

(b) Capacity to control large loads through built-in amplifiers and relaying equipment.

(c) Capability for operation at great repetition rates.

(d) Ability to withstand very severe environments, such as dirt, abrasive materials, liquids, etc.

(e) Easy integration into logic elements for simplification by control at low energy levels.

(f) Almost infinite operating life as far as sensors and exposed parts are concerned, and to very extended operation in respect to the life of the amplifier device.

JERRE V. MANNING

Cross-references: *Circuit Breakers, Relays, Sequential Circuits, Switching Circuits*

SWITCHING CIRCUITS

A switching circuit is one that ideally has at its input and at its output terminals signals that may each have one of just two possible values. These constitute an important class of circuits, which are especially useful in processing information in which the details must be preserved exactly, since the perturbing effect of noise on binary signals is relatively easy to recognize and to compensate for. It is natural that switching circuits find application in modern computers, industrial control equipment, telephone systems, and in all applications where precision is paramount.

Switching circuits may be broadly classified into two types: combinational and sequential. In the former the combination of input signals uniquely determines the output signals at any given time. In the latter the output signals may depend upon earlier input signals as well. When some of the output signals of a combinational circuit are reintroduced after some delay as input signals of that same circuit the possibility is created that the resulting sequential circuit may have a memory. A measure of the complexity of this memory is the number of output signals which are fed back as input signals, which number in turn determines how many different circuit states are possible.

In order to describe the terminal action of a sequential circuit it is necessary to show how its internal memory state and its output depend upon the circuit input and the previous memory state. The synthesis procedure for a sequential circuit consists of going from a description of this dependence back to an explicit description of the terminal action for an appropriate corresponding combinational circuit.

Since the values of the output signals of a combinational circuit depend only upon the values of the input signals, the terminal action of a combinational circuit can be described by listing in a table (known as a table of combinations, or "truth" table) the entire set of possible input signal combinations and the output signals associated with each of them. For a circuit having N binary inputs there are 2^N different input combinations. Since each of these may in general produce either of the two possible output signals at a given output terminal, there are 2^{2^N} different functions of N variables.

The tabular description of a switching function is somewhat cumbersome and is equivalent to one in the Boolean algebra (*q.v.*). In this algebra each variable may have one or the other of the complementary values, 0 or 1. When a variable X has the value 0 the variable $\bar{X}$ has the value 1, and vice versa. The two operations used in the algebra are usually denoted $\cdot$ and $+$. These operations are defined so that the expression $X \cdot Y$ has the value 1 only when both X *and* Y have the value 1 and so that the expression $X + Y$ has the value 1 when either X *or* Y *or both* have the value 1. In the algebra the function $F = XY + \bar{X}Z$ then has the value 1 when X and Y have the value 1, or when X has the value 0 and Z has the value 1.

The classical "minimization" problem for combinational switching circuits is that of proceeding from the tabular description of a given switching function to an equivalent representation in Boolean algebra and finally to the "simplest" algebraic description. Although there is no single universally accepted notion of "simplest" there are identities in the algebra, the use of which certainly yields a local minimization of algebraic complexity. Some useful identities are:

$$X + X = X \qquad X + \bar{X} = 1 \qquad X + 1 = 1$$

$$X + XY = X \qquad X + \bar{X}Y = X + Y$$

$$XY + \bar{X}Z + YZ = XY + \bar{X}Z$$

The utility of the algebraic minimization depends in part upon the elements to be used in the switching circuit. If these elements are relay contacts the correspondence with the algebra is close. For instance, our earlier example of the function $F = XY + \bar{X}Z$ describes the parallel combination of (i) a normally open contact on a relay X in series with a normally open contact on a relay Y, and (ii) a normally closed contact on X in series with a normally open contact on Z.

The Boolean algebra as a descriptive means applies to all combinational switching circuits whether they are comprised of, for instance, contacts (*q.v.*), diodes, transistors, cryotrons (*q.v.*), magnetic cores, parametrons (*q.v.*), or threshold elements. In spite of this universality of the algebra as a form

in which the terminal action of circuits may be described, the techniques for achieving simple circuit representations of switching functions depend to a large extent on which elements are to be used. In a typical threshold element, for example, a weighted sum of the values of the various inputs to the element are compared with an element threshold value. The output will be 1 or 0 according to whether this weighted sum of the input values exceeds or fails to exceed the threshold. The conventional algebraic procedures are not as useful for these elements as for contact networks.

It is not even certain that it is always advisable to search for a switching circuit of minimum complexity. For instance, the contact network described by $F = XY + \bar{X}Z$ has the property that when the contacts on relays Y and Z are closed the network effectively consists of the normally open and the normally closed contacts on relay X in parallel with each other. Ideally, when one of these two contacts is open the other is closed, and vice versa, and thus there is always a path through the network. However, when the state of operation of the relay X is changing it is physically possible to have these contacts (X and $\bar{X}$) both open simultaneously for a transient interval of time. This nonideal behavior constitutes what is known as a "hazard." The contact network described by the equivalent, but more complex, expression $F' = XY + \bar{X}Z + YZ$ has no such hazard. By the "reverse" use of the last simplification theorem quoted earlier, hazards can always be completely eliminated.

Another reason why the minimization problem may in the future come to be of less practical import is that the switching elements themselves may be quite inexpensive to produce in large quantities. In this case it may be worthwhile to build switching networks in redundant form so that the permanent indisposition of one or more elements does not change the desired circuit action. For instance, the terminal action of a series-parallel network of four normally open contacts from the same relay will be unaffected if any one of these four contacts is permanently opened or closed.

The currently indicated direction for growth of the theory of combinational switching circuits seems to lie in two areas. First, in the investigation of presently unexploited physical phenomena leading to novel bistable elements and the specialized synthesis problems associated with them. And second, in the investigation of formal analysis and synthesis procedures valid for very large numbers of switching elements and the utilization of these additional numbers of elements in achieving reliability through redundancy.

The subject of sequential circuits, of which combinational circuits constitute the essential part, is treated elsewhere in this volume.

D. A. HUFFMAN

Cross-references: *Boolean Algebra and Symbolic Logic, Coding and Coding Circuits, Logic Circuits, Sequential Circuits*

SWITCHING TUBES: see BEAM-SWITCHING TUBES

SYMBOLIC LOGIC: see BOOLEAN ALGEBRA AND SYMBOLIC LOGIC

SYMBOLS

Graphical symbols for electronics components and circuit diagrams vary somewhat from country to country, although the basic symbols are largely the same throughout the world. The standards generally accepted in the U.S. are contained in the publications of Committees 20 (Standards) and 21 (Symbols) of the Institute of Radio Engineers, which appear from time to time in its *Proceedings* (see, for instance, June 1954 and February 1961). These standards can be obtained for a moderate charge from the IRE, 1 East 79 Street, New York 21, N.Y., and

also form part of a dictionary of terms and symbols published by the IRE.

CHARLES SUSSKIND

Cross-references: *Abbreviations*

SYNCHROTRON AND BEVATRON

A *synchrotron* is an accelerator for charged particles using the principle of magnetic resonance of the cyclotron

$$f_a = f_0 = \frac{eB_z}{2\pi m} \tag{1}$$

where

e = charge
m = relativistic mass
B_z = magnetic field, vertical component
f_a = frequency of accelerating field
f_0 = rotational frequency

and exploiting the characteristics that these orbits are stable in phase for small deviations from the proper resonance energy to permit a variation of the magnetic field or both the magnetic field and the accelerating frequency during the acceleration. These variations circumvent the energy limitation of the cyclotron caused by the failure to satisfy Eq. (1) as the relativistic mass increases with energy. The variation of magnetic field also makes it possible to hold the orbit radius essentially constant so that the magnetic field occupies an annular space rather than a disk-shaped space as in a cyclotron (*q.v.*). This reduction in volume of magnetic field makes it possible to reach energies with synchrotrons that would be economically impossible with cyclotrons.

The inherent phase stability of cyclotron orbits can be readily seen if the relativistic mass in Eq. (1) is converted to total energy. Then, since the rotational frequency is a function of energy, if the particles have an energy that is not correct for resonance, the phase relation with respect to the accelerating field changes. This change results in an increasing energy gain during half the rf cycle and a decreasing energy gain during the other half. Stable acceleration occurs during the portion of the cycle when for an initial energy deficiency the change in phase results in an energy gain.

In the application of these principles to the acceleration of electrons, the magnetic field is varied, and the accelerating frequency is either constant or varies only over a small range, because at even a few Mev electrons have essentially attained the constant velocity of light. The electrons may either be accelerated in another device (e.g., linear accelerator, *q.v.*), to a few Mev and injected into the synchrotron orbit; or they may be injected at a lower energy and accelerated by a betatron action before the accelerating field is turned on. *Electron synchrotrons* are sometimes called simply synchrotrons.

The *proton synchrotron* employs both a varying magnetic field and a varying accelerating frequency. The latter is required because proton velocity is changing significantly up to an energy of several Bev, and easily realizable injection energies are in the range of a few tens of Mev.

Both types of synchrotron achieve radial and vertical stability of the orbits by providing a gradient in the magnetic field. The gradient index number n is defined by

$$n = - \frac{\rho}{B} \frac{\partial B}{\partial \rho} \qquad (2)$$

where

ρ = radius
B = magnetic field

In the older or conventional synchrotron n is a constant. The vertical force is supplied by the radial component of the magnetic field. The radial focusing force is a balance between the radial force due to the vertical component of the field, $B_z ev$, and the centrifugal force mv^2/ρ. Vertical focusing requires that $n > 0$. Radial focusing requires that $n < 1$. These focusing forces will cause particles that deviate from the correct direction to execute oscillations about the equilibrium orbit with frequencies:

$$f_z = f_0 \sqrt{n}$$

$$f_\rho = f_0 \sqrt{1 - n}$$

The oscillations are called betatron oscillations because the theory was first worked out in connection with betatrons. A further restriction is placed on the value of the gradient index by the necessity of avoiding coupling between the vertical and radial oscillations so that n is usually limited to values of about 0.6. The wavelength of the oscillations is then somewhat greater than the circumference of the orbit. Electron or proton synchrotrons using this type of focusing are described as *weak-focusing* or *constant-gradient focusing*.

A much more powerful system of focusing may be devised if the gradient is allowed to have values greater than 1 and the magnet is divided into segments with the sign of the gradient alternately $+$ and $-$. In a given segment there are then strong vertical focusing and radial defocusing forces. In the next segment there are vertical defocusing and radial focusing forces. It can be shown that the effect of a succession of such alternations is a strong net focusing force in both directions. One can see intuitively that such a system can be focusing by the following argument. Consider a particle traveling through successive focusing and defocusing regions with the forces increasing with the transverse distance from the axis. Passing through a defocusing region the particle is deflected outward so that in the following focusing region it encounters a stronger focusing force. Passing through a focusing region the particle is turned towards the axis so that in the following region it encounters a weaker defocusing force. Synchrotrons using this type of focusing are described as *strong focusing* (*q.v.*) or *alternate-gradient focusing*. Very high values of n ($\sim$100) may be used, resulting in betatron oscillations whose wavelength is small compared to the circumference of the orbit and confining the particles very closely to the equilibrium orbit, so that a further reduction in the volume of the magnetic field compared with weak-focusing synchrotrons is obtained, making it possible to reach still higher energies at a reasonable cost.

The most important difference between

electron synchrotrons and proton synchrotrons is that the radiative loss due to acceleration of charged particles in circular obits (bremsstrahlung, *q.v.*) is important only in the former case. It results in the requirement of a comparatively high energy gain per turn and in a practical limit to the energy of electron synchrotrons of about 10 Bev, whereas in the case of proton accelerators, the effect is unimportant even at hundreds of Bev.

Both kinds of synchrotrons require a laminated magnet and a vacuum chamber and other parts constructed so as to minimize the effects of eddy currents because of the pulsed magnetic field. Some of the details of an accelerator of each class are given in Table I.

A number of weak-focusing electron synchrotrons have been built with energies ranging from tens of Mev to 1.2 Bev. Weak-focusing proton synchrotrons have been built with energies of 1, 3, 6, and 10 Bev. Strong-focusing electron synchrotrons of about 1 Bev are in operation and others up to 6 Bev are under construction. Two strong-focusing proton synchrotrons of about 30 Bev have recently come into operation.

A few of the larger accelerators have acquired proper names. The Bevatron is a 6.2-Bev weak-focusing proton synchrotron at Berkeley. The Cosmotron and Saturne are 3-Bev weak-focusing proton synchrotrons at Brookhaven and Saclay, France, respectively. Nimrod is a 7-Bev weak-focusing

TABLE I

	Location			
	National Institute of Nuclear Physics, Rome, Italy	University of California Lawrence Radiation Laboratory, Berkeley, California (*Bevatron*)	*Cambridge Electron Accelerator Cambridge, Mass.	European Center for Nuclear Studies Geneva, Switzerland
Focusing	Weak	Weak	Strong	Strong
Particle	Electron	Proton	Electron	Proton
Energy-bev	1	6.2	6	28
Intensity-particles/pulse	5×11^9	3×10^{11}	10^{11}	3×10^{11}
Pulse rate	20 pps	10 ppm	20 pps	20 ppm
Orbit radius (ft)	11.8	50	86	230
Gradient index	0.61	0.63	91	288
Magnet weight (tons)	100	9500	250	3530
No. magnet sectors	4	4	48	100
Magnet power supply	Generator with choke and capacitor bank	Flywheel motor-generator set with ignitrons	Generator with choke and capacitor bank	Flywheel motor-generator set with ignitrons
Magnet power (average KVA)	510	9200	650	2600
Aperture of vacuum tank-(in.)	3×8	10×47	$1\frac{1}{2} \times 5\frac{1}{4}$	$2\frac{3}{4} \times 5\frac{1}{2}$
Accelerating system	2 cavities	1 drift tube saturable-reactor tuned	16 cavities	16 ferrite-loaded cavities
Accelerating frequency (Mc)	42.8–43.7	0.8–2.4	476	3–10
Accelerating harmonic-(rf cycles/turn)	4	1	360	20
Energy gain (kev/turn)	>25	1.5	860	54
Injector	Cockcroft-Walton	Linear accelerator	Linear accelerator	Linear accelerator
Injector energy (Mev)	2.5	10	20	50

* Scheduled to go into operation in 1962.

proton synchrotron under construction at Harwell, England.

Future developments in synchrotrons appear to be going along two lines. One is a study of the possibilities of extending the design of strong focusing proton synchrotrons to energies of hundreds of Bev. Another is to achieve the effect of strong focusing by an azimuthally varying constant magnetic field resulting in the higher intensity obtainable from a dc (as compared to a pulsed) device.

E. J. LOFGREN

Cross-references: *Accelerators, Alternating-Gradient Focusing, Characteristic Frequencies, Cosmotron*

SYSTEM IDENTIFICATION

A system is an aggregation of individual components combined so as to perform a specific function. When incorporated into a system, individual components tend to lose their detailed identity and their characteristics are projected onto the system in such a way that the individual details not directly significant to the system operation are lost. For example, the gain, bandwidth, and noise figure of an individual amplifier in a communication link probably are parameters significant to the system performance, whereas power-supply voltages and physical size may not be. The system objective or function to be performed is the characteristic that ties together all the system components and determines which parameters of each component are vital. Several separate types of individual or component functions exist and components can be classed according to the type of component function they perform. Over-all system description and design is involved with showing how individual components combine to provide the system characteristics. The system structure characterizes the interrelationship between the components. Thus the three key aspects of system identification are (1) function to be performed, (2) component opera-

tions, and (3) over-all system structure. The aspects will be considered individually.

Functions to Be Performed. *Physical control systems* were perhaps the earliest types of systems of moderate complexity that operated automatically. Such systems receive physical signals and provide physical responses that actuate the systems which they control. Simple regulators, such as the speed governor on a steam engine or a room thermostat, are typical of the elementary controllers. The next more sophisticated type of physical controller is a follow-up device such as an automatic gun director or an automatic contouring lathe. The class of physical controllers can be enlarged to include such devices as automatic pilots and even remote-controlled navigation systems by incorporation of more sophisticated commands and a larger set of inputs.

Simulation and *data processing* represent a second type of system function to be performed. The systems of this type include the range of simulators from automatic equation solvers and differential analyzers to simulators of such complicated operations as the air defense system. General-purpose digital computers are not characterized so much by the kinds of equations they solve (they generally do several kinds of numerical analysis problems automatically) as by the way they carry out the operations. Often computing systems are used to simulate physical systems. In this case they allow fairly extensive experimentation without actual building of physical hardware. The mechanization of logical operations by switching circuits provide an important class of data-processing systems.

A third type of function to be performed is that of *operational control*. The allocation of effort is one very important class of operational control. Load dispatching in a power system or assignment of interceptors in a defense system are examples of such allocation problems. Inventory control, which mechanizes a re-order pattern in accordance with estimated demands and delays in delivery, is a second sort of operational control. A third type of operational control is the scheduling of component operation in a large system of operations such as a manufacturing process. Initially these various operational functions have been performed by human controllers. Such man-machine systems are still in the class of operational controllers. With the advent of automatic computers and data-transmission equipment, those operational control systems which can be described exactly in advance can be mechanized.

Probably the most sophisticated type of function to be performed by a system is *performance control*. Generally, there is a hierarchy in control systems. Often the lowest-order system processes physical signals directly. The performance of the lowest-order system is often controlled by a higher-order system whose input signals are the parameters describing input and desired output quantities (and possibly environmental conditions) and whose output is the desired performance characteristic of the low-order system. With the availability of sophisticated data-processing equipment an automatic system can be given the commands very indirectly and it can perform even complicated computations and make fairly sophisticated choices as component operations in the carrying out of its function. Such adaptive systems as pattern recognizers or system self-optimizers are at present about the most sophisticated to be encountered.

Component Operations. The second aspect of system identification is by the type of component operation involved in the system. There are three basic types of component operations: sensing, actuating, and data processing. Any automatic system must sense its environment parameters as well as the quantities which it is controlling. Sensors for systems can vary from simple counters and thermometers to radar sets and star trackers.

Most physical systems involve the control of physical quantities and accordingly require actuators that provide power to change the output quantity. Such actuators might be loudspeakers in some systems, electric motors in others, or rocket motors in still others.

Data processors provide component operations in some systems. In this component role, they have the same characteristics as they do in computing or simulation systems, where data processing is the primary function instead of being a component function.

Over-all System Structure. Being an aggregate of components, any system usually is characterized by a set of simultaneous equations of some sort. The use of signal flow graphs to represent the interrelationships of component operations in a system is often convenient. The configuration of the flow graph usually points out the form of the control. Open-loop controllers have component operations in cascade from the initial to final operation with little interaction between individual operations but with over-all system characteristics being very sensitive to the component characteristics. The closed-loop configuration implies a feedback from the output to the input with its attendant interaction between component operations brought in. The primary objective of a closed-loop configuration is to decrease the sensitivity of the system performance to variations in component operations. The examples of closed-loop control vary from conventional servomechanisms, in which a powerful but inaccurate drive is monitored by an accurate feedback channel, to iterative types of equation solvers, in which the simple but crude guesses of the solution are corrected by a careful evaluation of the residuals.

A given system could have a set of units operating in an over-all openloop configuration but with the individual operations employing feedback to insure the fidelity of the individual operation.

Once a system has been identified as to type, the problem remains of determining its actual perameters. This problem is the problem of modelmaking and represents nothing new beyond the problem of physical measurement which has been studied by physical scientists and statisticians for many years. Because a system has many features specified in it by the designer, it may well be that the problem of design and model making may have strong interactions.

W. K. LINVILL

Cross-references: *Automation, Cybernetics, Data Processing, Signal-Flow Graphs*

SYSTEMS (LINEAR)

A system is said to be linear if it can be described by linear differential equations. In this section, further restrictions are placed on the systems by requiring that the coefficients of the differential equations be time invariant and also that the derivatives be ordinary rather than partial. The first assumption implies that the parameters R, L, J, etc., in equations like

$$v_R(t) = R i_R(t),$$
$$v_L(t) = L \frac{d i_L(t)}{dt},$$
$$f_J(t) = J \frac{d\omega(t)}{dt}, \text{ etc.}$$

(1)

which relate variables for the elements of the system, must be constants. The second assumption implies that the system may be considered lumped rather than spatially distributed.

The limitations of linear-system analysis are evident from these assumptions since actual devices are nonlinear and distributed, and often time varying. The use of linear theory is justified when the system is linear over an important range of operation with an acceptable degree of accuracy, the system dimensions are small, and the time variations of parameters of the system are slow. There is also the fact that linear equations are much more easily solved than nonlinear equations and that approximate answers are better than no answers at all.

In formulating the equilibrium equations for a system, the equations must be written in such a way that they form an independent set, so that for the case of electrical networks

$$l = e - N + s$$ (2)

equations must be written on the loop basis, and

$$n = N - s$$ (3)

on the node basis, where e is the number of elements, N the number of nodes, s the number of separate parts, l the number of independent loops, and n the number of independent node pairs. In complicated systems, *Kirchhoff's rules* should be used in selecting the actual l loop-current variables or n node-pair voltage variables. In simple systems or systems made from isolated subsystems, the appropriate variables will be evident by inspection.

The independent equilibrium equations may be written in the following general form (using the loop-basis equations for illustration)

$$\sum_{k=1}^{l} a_{jk} i_k = v_j \qquad j = 1, 2, \cdots, l$$ (4)

where a_{jk} involves the linear operations of multiplication, differentiation, and integration. The solution of these equations for i_k is

$$i_k = \sum_{j=1}^{l} \frac{\Delta_{jk}}{\Delta} v_j$$ (5)

where $\Delta = |a_{jk}|$ is the loop-basis system determinant and Δ_{jk} are cofactors of Δ. From Eq. (5), we may deduce the important *superposition property* of linear systems. It states than i_k may be found as a summation of components i_{kx} each due to a particular v_j or component of v_j, with i_{kx} computed with all v_j except the appropriate one set to zero. Thus if v_1 causes i_1 and v_2 causes i_2, then $v = a_1 v_1 + a_2 v_2$ causes the current $i = a_1 i_1 + a_2 i_2$. This property may be used as an alternate definition of a linear system: a linear system is one for which the *superposition* property applies.

The system determinant Δ has the form of a quotient of polynomials in the operator $p = d/dt$ identified as $\Delta = n(p)/d(p)$. Thus Eq. (5) may be written

$$n(p) i_k = d(p) \sum_{j=1}^{l} \Delta_{jk} v_j$$ (6)

The solution of this differential equation may be found by the employment of standard techniques. The complementary function part of the solution, the solution of the homogeneous equation $n(p) \, i_k = 0$, is, for nonrepeated zeros of $n(p)$,

$$i_{kC} = \sum_{j=1}^{v} K_j e^{s_j t} \qquad (7)$$

where v is the degree of the polynomial $n(p)$. Here s_j are the *natural frequencies* of the system. Components of the particular integral part of the solution, i_{kP}, having the same form as Eq. (7), have s_j values identified as the *forced frequencies*.

A useful artifice in the analysis of linear systems is the *transfer function*. In the system described by Eq. (6), $v_1(t)$ is designated as the input and $i_1(t)$ is the output, with all other $v(t)$ set equal to zero. The transfer function is defined for the input signal

$$v_1(t) = V_1 e^{st} \text{ for all } t \qquad (8)$$

This signal is known as the *characteristic signal* for linear systems. The output is found to be

$$i_1(t) = I_1 e^{st} = V_1 G(s) e^{st} \qquad (9)$$

The function $i(t)/v(t)$ with $v(t) = V e^{st}$ is defined as the transfer function and is $G(s)$, a quotient of polynomials in s. An alternate approach to the study of transfer functions begins by determining the Laplace transforms of $i_1(t)$ and $v_1(t)$ assuming zero initial conditions. These transforms are arranged as the quotient of output to input, $I_1(s)/V_1(s)$. The transfer function found in this way using Laplace transforms is identical with that found using characteristic input signals.

M. E. VAN VALKENBURG

Stability Criteria

The central element in an intuitive definition of system stability is the idea that the response to any perturbation of finite amplitude and duration must eventually die out. If the system is linear it is possible to state

a simple definition of stability which meets this requirement and leads to convenient mathematical properties.

Definition: *A linear system is stable if and only if its response to every bounded input is bounded.*

It is clear that this definition is not suitable for nonlinear systems, because saturation effects would cause the response to remain bounded in most cases falling intuitively into the unstable category.

A linear system can be characterized by its weighting function $w(t)$, defined as the response of the system to a unit impulse. Alternatively one often uses the transfer function

$$G(s) = \int_0^\infty w(t) \, e^{-st} \, dt$$

the Laplace transform of the weighting function. With $s = j\omega$ the transfer function becomes $G(j\omega)$, the frequency response function of the system.

Stability conditions in the time domain:

Theorem: *A linear system is stable if and only if*

$$\int_0^\infty |w(t)| \, dt < \infty$$

If the system has a bounded input $x(t)$ of magnitude no larger than M, its output $y(t)$ is given by

$$y(t) = \int_0^\infty w(\tau) x(t - \tau) \, d\tau$$

hence

$$|y(t)| < M \int_0^\infty |w(\tau)| \, d\tau < \infty$$

if

$$\int_0^\infty |w(\tau)| \, d\tau < \infty$$

On the other hand, if

$$\int_0^\infty |w(\tau)| \, d\tau$$

diverges, one can always choose x such that $x(t - \tau) = 1$ where $w(\tau) > 0$, and $x(t - \tau) =$

−1 where $w(\tau) < 0$. Thus one obtains a divergent $y(t)$.

In physical terms the theorem requires primarily that $w(t)$ must approach zero more rapidly than $1/t$ as $t \to \infty$.

Stability conditions in the complex frequency domain:

Theorem: *A sufficient condition for the stability of a linear system is analyticity of the transfer function $G(s)$ on the imaginary axis and in the right half plane.*

If $G(s)$ is rational, $w(t)$ is composed of a sum of terms of the form $t^n e^{\alpha_i t}$, the α_i being the poles of $G(s)$. Thus the condition "real part of all α_i negative" is clearly necessary and sufficient for stability. If $G(s)$ is not rational the theorem is more difficult to prove, but it remains valid and is, for most purposes, necessary as well as sufficient.

In practice one finds that no significant restriction is made by assuming that transfer functions of linear systems are analytic outside of the left half plane except for possible poles. Practical stability tests therefore tend to concern themselves exclusively with the identification of poles of $G(s)$ outside of the left half plane. Aside from formal solution of the characteristic equation, which is very tedious in all but the simplest cases, stability tests fall into two broad classes: Algebraic procedures and graphical procedures.

A typical algebraic technique is the *Hurwitz criterion*. It assumes that the characteristic equation of the system (obtained by setting equal to zero the denominator of the transfer function from input to output) is of the form:

$$a_n s^n + a_{n-1} s^{n-1} + \cdots + a_1 s + a_0 = 0, \quad a_n > 0$$

All roots of this equation are located in the left half plane, and hence the system is stable, if and only if the following conditions are satisfied:

(1) $a_i > 0$ for all i in $0 \le i \le n$.

(2) The determinants $D_1, D_2, \cdots, D_{n-1}$ are all positive. D_k is the determinant of the matrix consisting of the first k rows and columns of the array of coefficients

$$
\begin{array}{llllll}
a_1 & a_0 & 0 & 0 & 0 & \cdots \\
a_3 & a_2 & a_1 & a_0 & 0 & \cdots \\
a_5 & a_4 & a_3 & a_2 & a_1 & \cdots \\
a_7 & a_6 & a_5 & a_4 & a_3 & \cdots \\
\cdot & \cdot & \cdot & \cdot & \cdot & \cdots
\end{array}
$$

Coefficients of order higher than n appearing in the determinants are replaced by zeros.

The Hurwitz criterion is convenient for determining quickly whether a system with given parameters is stable and if not, what adjustments of one or more parameters would stabilize it. The criterion does not provide a great deal of insight into the nature of the transient response, nor does it furnish much information concerning general procedures for equalizer design. The requirement of an algebraic characteristic equation limits its application almost entirely to lumped parameter systems.

A fundamental technique of the graphical type is the *Nyquist diagram*. It is based on the following theorem of complex variable theory.

If $f(s)$ is analytic inside a closed contour C except for an at most finite number of poles, and if it is analytic and different from zero on C, then

$$\frac{1}{2\pi j} \int_C \frac{f'(s)}{f(s)} \, ds = N - P$$

where

$$j = \sqrt{-1}, \, f'(s) = \frac{d}{ds} f(s)$$

and N and P are respectively the numbers of zeros and poles of $f(s)$ inside C (a pole or zero of order n is counted as n poles or zeros). Since

$$\frac{f'(s)}{f(s)} \, ds = d[\ln f(s)]$$

and the net change of $\ln |f(s)|$ as s traverses a closed contour is zero, the theorem leads to the following conclusion: *The net change in the argument of $f(s)$ as s traverses the closed contour C is $2\pi(N - P)$.* Consider now a negative-feedback system with transfer

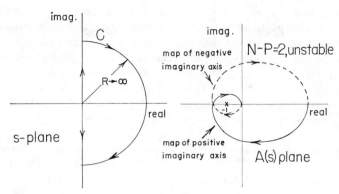

imag.

FIG. 1

functions $G(s)$ and $H(s)$ in the forward path and feedback path respectively. The closed loop transfer function $G(s)/[1 + G(s)H(s)]$ has poles at the zeros of $1 + G(s) H(s)$. These are the only poles of the closed-loop transfer function unless $H(s)$ has a zero coincident with one of the poles of $G(s)$. A stability test must determine whether $1 + G(s) H(s)$ has zeros outside the left half of the s plane. The contour C of the theorem is therefore chosen as the imaginary axis and a semicircle of radius $R \to \infty$ centered at the origin and enclosing the right half plane (Fig. 1). A plot of $1 + G(s)H(s)$ for this succession of values of s gives, by its encirclements of the origin, the difference between the number of zeros and poles of $1 + G(s) H(s)$ in the right half plane. In practice it is usually more convenient to plot $G(s) H(s) = A(s)$, the negative of the loop gain, and observe encirclements of the point $-1 + j0$ rather than the origin. The stability test may be summarized as follows:

(1) Plot $A(s)$ for values of s ascending along the imaginary axis. The infinite semicircle in the s plane usually maps into the origin of the $A(s)$ plane, hence rarely requires detailed consideration. The plot for negative imaginary s is the reflection about the real axis of the plot for positive imaginary s.

(2) Observe the net number and direction of encirclements of the point $-1 + j0$.

(3) Note the number of poles of $A(s)$ in the right half plane. In a single-loop system this can usually be done by inspection of the loop gain equation. In a multiple-loop system it may require construction of the Nyquist diagram for minor loops.

The system is stable if and only if the number of counterclockwise encirclements observed in (2) is equal to the number of right half plane poles of $A(s)$ identified in (3). If the system is open-loop stable, closed-loop stability is therefore indicated by a Nyquist diagram which fails to encircle the critical point $(-1 + j0)$.

When the loop gain function has poles on the imaginary axis it is customary to modify the s plane contour by small semicircular indentations into the right half plane, thus excluding the poles from the interior of the contour. The interpretation of the Nyquist diagram remains unchanged.

P. M. SCHULTHEISS

Cross-references: *Feedback Systems, Laplace and Fourier Transforms, Randomly Varying Systems, Sampled-Data Systems, Signal-Flow Graph, System Identification, Systems (Nonlinear), Systems (Time-Varying)*

SYSTEMS (NONLINEAR)

Adaptive Systems

The term *adaptive* is borrowed from the biological sciences where it refers to the ability of an organism to change itself to meet changing conditions of environment. An adaptive system, the physical counterpart of an adaptive organism, is capable of automatic change to meet changing inputs or changing characteristics of the device or process being controlled. An adaptive system is sometimes referred to as self-adjusting or self-optimizing, or, redundantly, as self-adaptive.

An adaptive system is characterized by three properties:

(1) It must have means for determining the state of the device or process being controlled. This is designated *identification*.

(2) It must have means for comparing this state with a desired condition to form a basis for change to improve performance. This is designated *decision*.

(3) It must have means for changing the system in closed-loop fashion in accordance with the decision.

Not all systems that are changed in accordance with changing operating conditions can be considered adaptive. For example, programmed changes in control parameters, as in an automatic pilot (*q.v.*) that changes parameters as predetermined functions of altitude and speed, are performed in open-loop fashion. Such a system could not be considered adaptive.

The need for an adaptive system arises in situations where characteristis of the device or process to be controlled are not well known, or where operating conditions may vary widely and unpredictably. Under these circumstances a requirement may exist for a system including all three of the enumerated properties, that is, for an adaptive system.

The many ways in which the necessary properties can be implemented fall into broad categories, which are described below.

Identification. The identification of the state of the system can be performed by deliberately introducing a test signal or by observing the system under normal operating conditions.

Test signals may consist of impulses, steps, or random signals, for example. These signals have the disadvantage of creating un-

desirable disturbances, but may be necessary if adequate measurements under normal operating conditions are impossible. The latter situation might arise if an error signal in part of a system designed to drive error to zero were to be observed.

The results of the application of a test signal might yield, for example, impulse response. Another result might be the nature of the deviation of the output of a system from a steady-state operating point.

Observations of input and output of a system under normal operating conditions could yield a system transfer function. Another type of observation of this type would detect the presence and characteristics of a limit cycle of a nonlinear system, or frequency of oscillation of a linear one.

Whatever the characteristics of the observed quantity, it must bear a relation to the state of the system.

Decision. The decision to change the system is based on the identification measurement just defined. This operation implies the existence of a standard for comparison. The *model* is a common source of this standard.

A model is a physical device capable of simulating the behavior of an ideal system. The input to the model is the same as the test signal or normal operating signal described above. The output of the model is compared with the corresponding quantity in the device or process being controlled. The difference is the basis for system change to reduce the difference to zero.

Fixed models having desired characteristics can be used. A more sophisticated model might be programmed to change in accordance with measured environmental characteristics. Proceeding still further, the model might be changed to reflect an optimum for the input being applied to the system.

Another type of basis for decision is the requirement for operation of a system in the steady state in such a way that some state variable is maximized or minimized. The system operation state relative to an extremum could be observed, for example, by noting changes in output due to changes in otherwise steady input quantities. (Systems with decisions based on extremum operation are sometimes called *optimalizing* systems.)

A third type of decision basis can be the observation of some characteristic of normal operating behavior. Examples include presence or absence of a limit cycle and frequency of a limit cycle or other oscillation. These measures are indirect in that they do not yield system characteristics explicitly. They may be useful, however, as the basis for a decision leading to desired performance.

Modification. Having provided for identifying the state of the system and for making a decision to take corrective action, it remains to close the adaptive loop with means for the correction itself. This action may involve changing of the parameters of the controller which provides an input for the device or process being controlled; the changing of the function of the controller; or the modification of system inputs to produce desired results.

Parameter changes can be effected by changing gains and time constants of an analog controller or by changing coefficients of a digital one. Changing the function of the controller can be accomplished by switching in or out parts of an analog controller or reprogramming a digital one. Preparation of input signals to implement the decision may be a complicated operation requiring a digital computer. The addition of the adaptive loop may bring with it stability problems and equipment complexity which must be counterbalanced by improved performance.

J. A. ASELTINE

Maximum-Effort Systems

Maximum effort or "bang-bang" control techniques are applicable to systems containing a linear plant preceded by a saturating component. The control of relay servomechanisms, attitude control of space vehicles, and trajectory control of rockets fall into this category. To define the problem,

consider a linear, time-invariant plant, whose output is the controlled variable; given that the input to the plant is provided by a saturating element, the problem of controlling the output of the plant to execute some predescribed task is of major importance in the theory of control systems. If a deterministic input is applied to the system and the imposed requirement is to generate an output signal such that the error and its time derivatives are reduced to zero simultaneously and in minimum time, then the theory dealing with minimal-time problems (*q.v.*) indicates that the saturating element must always be in the saturating mode, providing either maximum positive force or minimum negative force to the controlled plant. Thus, the input to the plant is piecewise constant and may change its polarity at a finite number of times, called the switching times.

Analysis. The techniques employed in the analysis of a maximum-effort, minimum-time system may be roughly divided into two categories. The first technique is based on the computation of the switching times as a function of the initial error variables and the dynamics of the controlled plant. Hence, the compensating device in the loop must determine the times at which the output of the saturating element must change from one saturation level to the other. The dynamic system with the adjoint differential equation of the controlled plant may be used for this purpose, since the output of the adjoint system has the property that if the correct initial conditions are given, its output (as a function of time) has its zeroes at the switching times.

The second method of analysis is a geometrical one. Time is eliminated from the equation of the error and its time derivatives and the response of the system is considered from the point of view of trajectories in n-dimensional phase space, where n is the order of the system. The coordinates in the phase-space representation (*q.v.*) may be the error and $n - 1$ of its time derivatives or some linear combination thereof. It is very convenient to expand the error and its time derivatives along the principal axes of the differential equation. Between switchings the constant input applied to the plant defines a trajectory in phase space. If the error and its derivatives are to be reduced to zero simultaneously, then the state point must follow a series of trajectories which terminate at the origin of the phase space. One may thus isolate particular families of trajectories in phase space that will provide the desired path to the origin. These families of trajectories define a sequence of switching sets, which may be curves, surfaces, or hypersurfaces, such that a switching policy is associated with each switching set. Whenever the system trajectory intersects a switching set, the output of the saturating element must change, say, from positive level to negative level, or vice versa.

The equations and the total number of the switching sets depend on the transfer function of the plant. If the plant has only real, nonpositive poles, then at most $n-1$ switchings are required which define the number of switching sets to be $n-2$. If the plant has, in addition to the real poles, some complex pole pairs, it is not possible to place an upper bound on the number of switchings required. Rather, the number of switchings is a function of the initial conditions and, in general, initial state points far from the origin of the phase space require a greater number of switchings than points close to the origin. In sampled-data systems (*q.v.*), where the sampling instants are not coincident with the switching times, no upper bound exists in the total number of switchings required. As was the case with the complex pole system the total number of switchings depends on the initial conditions. However, in each of the above cases one may define a switching hypersurface which separates the space into two distinct parts and associates with each point in space the correct output of the saturating element.

Synthesis. The only decision that must be made by the compensating device is whether to apply full positive force to the

plant or full negative force. However, this simple decision involves the solution of either n or $n-1$ nonlinear algebraic equations. If the adjoint system is used in the loop, the compensator must provide the correct initial conditions for it. The compensator may also be designed to construct a distance function from each state point to the switching hypersurface or the switching sets. The polarity of the distance function may be used to provide the correct input to the plant. In general, the compensator must solve, by iteration techniques, the equations of the switching sets or use a fast-time analog in order to determine whether an assumed switching policy is optimal.

Conclusions. The advantages of maximum-effort control systems lie in their fast response time and in the simplicity of the power-saturating elements that may be utilized, such as relays, magnetic amplifiers, switching transistors, on-off valves, etc. The disadvantages are that a complex system of equations must be solved for high-order systems, accurate measurements of the derivatives are required, and any noise in the variables result in imperfect switching and hence in longer response times.

M. ATHANASSIADES AND H. K. KNUDSEN

Relay Systems

Duty Cycle. In order for a unit relay to deliver a constant average output which lies anywhere between -1 and $+1$, it is necessary for the relay to oscillate with an unsymmetrical square wave. The duty cycle d of a two-position relay is the ratio of the time during which the output is positive to the total time in one cycle. The average output is $2d-1$. When the duty cycle is $\frac{1}{2}$, the average output is zero. Theoretically, a saturating amplifier could deliver an average output without oscillations, but when it is connected in a feedback system it usually oscillates in the same manner as a bistable relay. With three-position relays, twice the duty cycle is defined as the average output plus 1.

When relay systems are operating near

half duty cycle, the relay output is a symmetrical square wave of the maximum possible frequency. As the duty cycle approaches either zero or 1, the frequency diminishes approximately as a function of $d(1 - d)$, when $G(s)$ is a first-order linear system, and the frequency diminishes approximately as $\sqrt{d(1 - d)}$ when $G(s)$ is a second-order linear system. It is usually desirable to attenuate the relay frequency in the dynamics of the linear element $G(s)$ and therefore the relay frequency should be kept high.

Nonlinear Gain. A waveshape for the steady-state oscillatory frequency at the input to the relay is assumed, and with the desired duty cycle, the gain of the relay for fundamental frequency as a function of the amplitude of the input is calculated. This nonlinear gain is called $N(a,d)$ because it is a function of the peak-to-peak oscillation amplitude $2a$ at the input to the unit relay as well as a function of the duty cycle d. The condition for steady-state oscillations is:

$$N(a,d) \cdot kKG(s) = -1 \quad \text{or}$$
$$kKG(s) = -1/N(a,d) \tag{1}$$

where $2/k$ is the dead zone or hysteresis band of the relay, and K is the magnitude of the relay output. This condition for oscillation can be found in a graphical manner by the intersection of two plots on coordinates of log gain vs phase. The coordinate system to be used is nepers of gain vs radians of phase lag. This system is the same as a graph paper on which 40° of phase lag is the same distance as 6 decibels of gain. On this coordinate system plot the gain versus the phase of the linear part of the closed loop system, log $kKG(j\omega)$, and also plot the gain vs phase of the negative reciprocal of the nonlinear gain of the unit relay, $-1/N$. A scale of frequency can be placed along the first curve. A scale of amplitude can be placed along the second curve. Where the two curves intersect, (1) is satisfied. Curve $G(j\omega)$ is a conformal transformation of the $j\omega$ axis of the Laplace s plane. The nonlinear gain curve is a conformal transformation of

the root locus in the Laplace s plane. The intersection is where the root locus crosses from the left half s plane into the right half s plane or vice versa. The intersection represents sustained steady state oscillations, if, looking in the direction of increasing frequency, the nonlinear gain curve crosses from right to left in the direction of increasing amplitude. At the intersection the frequency and amplitude can be read from the scales.

High-Frequency Minor-Loop Feedback Around Relay. Significant improvements can be made in the performance of relay systems by the inclusion of a feedback loop around the relay, which passes only the high frequencies in the band surrounding the desired steady-state oscillation frequency. This minor loop converts the relay into an oscillator, irrespective of the characteristics of the system G. The high oscillating frequency is so attenuated in the transference $G(s)$ that the feedback from the system output is essentially a dc signal whose only function is to change the phase and duty cycle of the high-frequency oscillation. If the characteristics of this minor loop are $H(s)$, then the condition for steady-state oscillation is given by:

$$kK(H + G) = -1/N(a,d)$$

The gain-phase plot of the negative reciprocal of the nonlinear gain for the unit relay is unaltered. The linear transference is replaced by the sum of the minor loop transference and the major system transference.

The steady-state error is greatly reduced in the system with a minor loop because the average error is approximately proportional to the amplitude of high frequency oscillation a and a decreases as f increases.

Input Dither. The benefits of high-frequency relay operation can be achieved by adding to the input of the relay a fixed high-frequency dither signal. The dither frequency should be chosen to be the maximum consistent with relay life and with undesired system resonances. The magnitude of the input dither should be sufficient to exceed the hysteresis band of the relay. In this case minor-loop feedback is not needed.

Lock-Up Oscillations. A conditionally stable linear system can be controlled by a relay. As long as the attenuation of the linear system is high, the feedback loop oscillates at a high frequency, low amplitude. But if the high frequency is stopped by a transient, and the relay becomes motionless, then the attenuation of the linear system drops to a very low value represented by the low-frequency components passing through it.

There is a second steady-state solution of $G = -1/N$ which occurs for this low-frequency, high-amplitude condition. The frequency of oscillation is the lowest frequency for which the phase shift in the linear system is 180°. These high-amplitude, low-frequency oscillations are called lock-up oscillations because they will not stop of their own accord. They may destroy any mechanical components of the feedback system. Care must be taken to prevent lock-up oscillations in all conditionally stable feedback systems. One safeguard is to limit the magnitude of the steps, ramps, and accelerations in the input signal to the system. Another way of preventing these oscillations is to introduce a nonlinear phase lead which is a function of signal amplitude, which produces phase leads of the $N(a,d)$ characteristics such that there is one and only one intersection of the two curves, G and $-1/N$.

Nonpolarized Relay. The relay must be polarized for a feedback control system to operate satisfactorily. If a negative input can produce a positive output, then the polarity of the feedback has been reversed and the system locks into an unusable condition. Rectifying the signal presented to a nonpolarized relay can convert it into a polarized relay.

Relay Transients. Accurate analysis of the transient response of a relay feedback system to a large input step function can be obtained from plots in the log gain vs phase plane. The transient decrement rate is

proportional to the distance between the $-1/N$ and $G(s)$ curves. The decrement rate of the pole in the s plane representing the transient oscillation is given by the stability angle in the s plane, $\psi = j\beta/\gamma$, where the attenuation rate at this point on the G curve is

$$\gamma = \frac{d \ln G(s)}{d \ln s}$$

and β is the distance of minimum approach between the two curves measured in nepers. The envelope of the transient oscillation is $e^{-\omega t \sin \psi}$. The time constant of the transient envelope is $\tau = 1/\omega \sin \psi$. It can be seen that the new amplitude a_1 at the time t_1 is given by

$$a_1 = ae^{-\omega t_1 \sin \psi}$$

Corresponding to this new amplitude, there is a new closed-loop pole location on the N curve in the gain-phase plane and new values of minimum approach β, frequency ω, vector attenuation γ, and stability angle ψ.

Otto J. M. Smith

Undesirable Nonlinearities

An undesirable nonlinearity, as the name implies, is a nonlinearity which the system designer would have left out of the system if he had a choice in the matter. The source of undesirable nonlinearities is nature. Virtually every component selected to perform a necessary system function brings with it a list of limitations and peculiarities that affect the system's behavior in an undesirable manner. For example, consider a typical servomechanism. The gear train introduced to match the speed and torque requirements of the load shaft to those available from a control motor typically brings with it backlash and nonlinear friction of an undesirable sort. The wirewound potentiometer selected to measure shaft position has finite resolution because of the discrete jumps in voltage from one wire turn to the next. The electronic amplifier selected to drive the motor provides power gain up to a certain level and then saturates, and the motor has a nonlinear relation between torque, speed, and applied voltage as shown on its characteristic curves.

The effect of undesirable nonlinearities on system performance varies widely, as might be expected. The range of possible effects begins with a more or less slight variation in transient and frequency response with amplitude, includes a limitation on the speed of response for large inputs, and ends with instability. In the first class, generally speaking, are such phenomena as the nonlinear characteristics of servo-motor and hydraulic valves. The characteristic curves of these devices show curvature and nonuniform separation of the curves and the effect is to cause the system response to change by perhaps 20 per cent in equivalent damping factor over the range of expected inputs. This first category of effects can usually be taken care of by designing the system on a "worst case" basis so that the least desirable transient or frequency response meets the system specification and the best performance is better than required.

A saturation-type nonlinearity that limits the force which may be applied to a mechanically controlled member limits the time required to bring the member to a new position. In general, a limit on the forcing function that may be applied to a plant under control places limits on the speed of response obtainable from the system. This important problem has been treated at great length in the control literature and is discussed above in the subsection on **Minimal-Time Problems.**

In many cases, as pointed out in that subsection, it is possible to determine the minimum bound placed on response time by the saturation and to design nonlinear controllers deliberately to achieve optimum (least time) response.

The final effect to be considered is that of instability. It is possible for the undesirable nonlinearities to lead to instability, which ruins the system's usefulness. The analysis and design tool that is probably the most valuable in this situation is the de-

scribing function in one or another of its forms. The describing function is a technique of equivalent linearization which applies the linear methods of frequency response or root locus plots to a nonlinear problem.

In terms of frequency response, one defines the describing function of a nonlinear element in terms of the *fundamental* component of its response to a sinusoid input. Specifically, if the input to a nonlinear element N is given by

$$x(t) = \mathrm{Re}\{Xe^{j\omega t}\}$$

then except for the possibility of subharmonics, which is ignored in the present analysis, the output is periodic with the same period as the input and for any given amplitude X can be expanded in a complex Fourier series as

$$y(t) = \mathrm{Re}\left\{\sum_{k=0}^{\infty} Y_k(jk\omega, X)\, e^{jk\omega t}\right\}$$

The describing function of N is then defined as the equivalent gain

$$K(j\omega, x) = \frac{Y_1(j\omega, x)}{X}$$

Stability analysis based on the describing function requires that one investigate the stability of the system in question for *each amplitude X* of inputs, treating $K(j\omega, x)$ as a linear transfer function in the process. The analysis can usually be done on one plot, with either polar or logarithm coordinates (Nyquist or Nichols) by including all amplitudes of X at once. The hypothesis is that the system is capable of sustained oscillations at those amplitudes and frequencies (there may be more than one such set, of course) at which the stability test predicts constant amplitude oscillations. That is, possible oscillations correspond to the points in amplitude and frequency where the plot passes directly through the critical point.*

* The points found by the above conditions represent possible oscillations but some of them may be unstable *as oscillations.* That is, a slight perturbation of the amplitude of the oscillations may

Design by means of the describing function requires that one must determine appropriate compensation such as error networks, feedback arrangements, or other changes so that the plots indicate sufficient stability margin for *all amplitudes* of the input. In some cases it is not practical to remove the oscillations entirely and the system is operated with low amplitude oscillations present.

If the nonlinearity being considered is nondynamic or zero memory, the describing function is independent of frequency. If, further, the nonlinearity is single valued, the describing function *is real*. In these cases, the analysis can be performed on a root locus plot. The root locus is plotted with respect to a variable gain that replaces the nonlinearity and the hypothesis is that the system can sustain oscillations at those frequencies where the root locus crosses the imaginary axis and that the amplitude of oscillation will be such that the value of the describing function equals the root locus gain at this point.

The success of the describing-function method of analysis depends upon the assumption that the fundamental component of the output of the nonlinear element is a sufficient approximation to the true output in determining the signals in the rest of the system. Generally speaking, this leads to the assumption that the nonlinear element is followed by a linear dynamic system which is a low-pass structure having very reduced transmission at frequencies corresponding to harmonics of every possible oscillation frequency. The method is not expected to give good results when the oscillations are such that the input to the nonlinear element is far removed from sinusoidal. The conditions under which the method or some modification of it gives the exactly correct

answer to the question of stability are difficult if not impossible to state. About the best that it seems possible to say is that the method is the best available to give a quick indication of the possible effects of undesirable nonlinearities and that it works adequately well in a large number of cases of practical interest.

The describing function for a nonlinear element may be obtained experimentally or from a mathematical model. The choice obviously depends upon whether an adequate model is possible or not and whether the element is available to experimentation at the time the analysis is needed, or not. Describing functions for a number of widely used elements have been obtained and are plotted in the control systems literature, notably in O. J. M. Smith's *Feedback Control Systems* (McGraw-Hill, New York, 1958).

G. F. FRANKLIN

Cross-references: *Feedback Systems, Minimal-Time Problems, Network Theory, Nonlinear Circuits, Randomly Varying Systems, Relays, Sampled-Data Systems, Systems (Linear), Systems (Time-Varying)*

SYSTEMS (TIME-VARYING)

Physical systems are called time-varying or time-variant if one or more of its components change with time. The component change may be unavoidable and inherent in the system or it may be intentional. A missile in flight using liquid fuel has a total mass which decreases with time. This is an example of an inherently time-varying system. On the other hand, a carbon microphone whose resistance varies with the sound pressure is intentionally time-varying. Regardless of whether the time variation is intentional or unavoidable, the mathematical description of the system is the same.

Variable Electrical Networks. The defining differential equations for linear time-varying resistance, inductance, and capacitance are

---

drive the system *away* from the critical point. The system can physically oscillate only at those amplitudes and frequencies at which a slight perturbation in amplitude acts so as to return the amplitude back to the critical point.

$$v_R(t) = R(t)i_R(t)$$

$$v_L(t) = \frac{d}{dt}[L(t)i_L(t)] \tag{1}$$

$$= L(t)\frac{d}{dt}i_L(t) + i_L(t)\frac{d}{dt}L(t) \tag{2}$$

$$i_C(t) = \frac{d}{dt}[C(t)v_C(t)]$$

$$= C(t)\frac{d}{dt}v_C(t) + v_C(t)\frac{d}{dt}C(t) \tag{3}$$

If R, L, and C are not time-varying, i.e., $dR/dt = 0$, $dL/dt = 0$, and $dC/dt = 0$, then the equations reduce to those for fixed linear elements.

For a network consisting of linear time-varying elements, the loop or node equations are a set of integro-differential equations in the unknown currents or voltages. It is always possible, although usually laborious, to eliminate all but one of the unknowns by algebraic manipulation of the equations to yield a single differential equation in one unknown. In general, the form of the equation is

$$a_n(t)\frac{d^n}{dt^n}y(t) + a_{n-1}(t)\frac{d^{n-1}}{dt^{n-1}}y(t) + \cdots$$

$$+ a_0(t)y(t) = b_m(t)\frac{d^m}{dt^m}x(t) + \cdots + b_0(t)x(y) \tag{4}$$

where $y(t)$ is the unknown voltage or current, and $x(t)$ is the input current or voltage.

The above equation is an nth-order ordinary linear differential equation with variable coefficients. Except for some special first-order and second-order equations, the solution is not obtainable in closed form. That is, the solution $y(t)$ is usually only obtainable as a power series in t. The method is to let

$$y(t) = \sum_{k=0}^{\infty} C_k t^k \tag{5}$$

and substitute in (4). Also, the various coefficients are expressed in power series. Forcing the various power terms on both sides of the resulting equation to be equal yields recur-

sion formulas for the unknown C_k coefficients.

Impulse Response. A method of analysis that is familiar to electrical engineers is the application of the principle of superposition to linear systems and the use of an impulse or Dirac *delta function*. That is, a unit impulse is applied to the system and its response is measured or determined. Based on this response, the response to any input is expressible as a convolution of the input and the impulse-response function. For example, let $h(t,\tau)$ be the response, measured at time t, to an input of unit impulse applied at time τ, i.e., $\delta(t - \tau)$. Then for any general input, since

$$x(t) = \int_{-\infty}^{\infty} \delta(t - \tau)x(\tau)\,d\tau \tag{6}$$

the principle of superposition yields.

$$y(t) = \int_{-\infty}^{\infty} h(t, \tau)x(\tau)\,d\tau \tag{7}$$

as the output due to $x(t)$. Equation (7) is a general convolution integral for time-varying linear systems. Once $h(t,\tau)$ is determined, $y(t)$ is obtained from (7) for any given $x(t)$. This technique is advantageous if it is desired to analyze a specific system for a class of inputs. Then, instead of solving several different differential equations, we may just solve for the impulse response $h(t,\tau)$ and then use (7) for the various input functions specified.

Frequency Response. Another technique that is familar to the electrical engineer is the frequency response method. We define impedance as

$$\left.\frac{v(t)}{i(t)}\right|_{i=e^{i\omega t}} = Z(j\omega, t) \tag{8}$$

where $Z(j\omega,t)$ may be driving-point or transfer impedance depending on whether v and i are at the same terminal pair or not. For fixed linear networks, Z does not depend on time t. Similarly, admittance is defined as

$$\left.\frac{i(t)}{v(t)}\right|_{v=e^{i\omega t}} = Y(j\omega, t) \tag{9}$$

Unlike the time-invariant case, $Z(j\omega,t)$ and $Y(j\omega,t)$ are not reciprocals of each other. That is, if $i = e^{j\omega t}$ and we solve for $v(t)$, the ratio v/i is not the reciprocal of i/v if $v = e^{j\omega t}$ and we solve for i for the same network. For the general case, if $y(t)$ is the output and $x(t)$ the input, then the system transfer function is defined as

$$H(j\omega, t) = \frac{y(t)}{x(t)}\bigg|_{x=e^{j\omega t}} \qquad (10)$$

With these definitions, it turns out that just as in fixed networks, if two-terminal networks are in series, their impedances add, i.e.,

$$Z(j\omega, t) = \sum_{i=1}^{N} Z_i(j\omega, t) \qquad (11)$$

Similarly, for two-terminal networks in parallel

$$Y(j\omega, t) = \sum_{i=1}^{N} Y_i(j\omega, t) \qquad (12)$$

Most important of all, if $X(j\omega)$ is the Fourier transform of $x(t)$ then, $y(t)$ is

$$y(t) = \int_{-\infty}^{\infty} \frac{1}{2\pi} X(j\omega)H(j\omega, t) e^{j\omega t} d\omega \qquad (13)$$

which is the inverse Fourier transform of $X(j\omega)H(j\omega,t)$. The actual determination of $y(t)$ does not have to make use of (13) at all if a table of Fourier transforms is available. All that is necessary is to expand $X(j\omega) \cdot H(j\omega,t)$ in partial fractions, treating t as a constant, and then looking up the inverse transforms of the individual terms from a table. The remaining problem is how to obtain $H(j\omega,t)$. One way is to substitute $x(t) = e^{j\omega t}$ and $y(t) = H(j\omega,t)e^{j\omega t}$ in (4), thus obtaining a differential equation which specifies $H(j\omega,t)$. Unfortunately, the resulting differential equation is essentially of the same complexity as the original. The frequency-response method is advantageous if a network or system is to be analyzed for many inputs. In general, expanding in partial

fractions and using a table is usually easier than using (7) for the impulse-response method.

An interesting property of system functions defined in (10) is that singularities, which are usually poles in the $j\omega$ plane, are all fixed. This statement seems to violate physical intuition at first. For example, if we have an LC parallel network, and we vary C, we expect the resonant frequency to "shift" as we shift C. That is, we expect the poles of $Z(j\omega,t)$ to "shift." However, a rigorous analysis shows that $Z(j\omega,t)$ usually has an infinite number of poles that do not move. The shift in the resonance curve is caused by time-varying zeros or time-varying residues. Thus at a particular time, the effect of most of the poles may be negligible compared to a dominant pole or pair of poles. At some other time, the residues may change and in effect another pair of poles may be dominant. For slowly varying systems, this transfer of dominance from pole to pole may be approximately represented as an actual "movement" of poles. It should be remembered that this is only an approximation.

Compatible Systems. In addition to the use of the unit impulse $\delta(t - \tau)$ and the unit rotating phasor $e^{j\omega t}$ as basic input signals, more elaborate choices may be made. Subsequent simplification of analysis is the underlying motivation. We may modify the definition of system function in (10) to

$$\frac{y(t)}{x(t)}\bigg|_{x=k(t,\lambda)} = H(\lambda, t) \qquad (14)$$

If $x(t) = k(t,\lambda)$ is such that $y/x = H(\lambda,t)$ is really independent of time, we say that the particular $k(t,\lambda)$ is a characteristic input for the system in question. For fixed linear systems, e^{st} is a characteristic input. It is not easy to determine the characteristic input of a general linear time-varying system. However, once it is found, the rest of the analysis is very simple. For example, if two systems have the same characteristic input, then the overall system function is the product of the individual system functions. These systems are said to be compatible. The analysis of interconnected compatible systems is identical to that for fixed linear systems. An equation similar to (13) is used in converting from the λ domain to time domain.

Sampled-Data Systems. Linear systems where discrete data or signals are involved are usually described by difference equations. For time-varying sampled-data systems, the coefficients in the difference equations relating input and output are variables depending on the sampling instants. The general solution is usually obtainable only in open series form. Instead of the general convolution integral in (7), we have the general convolution sum

$$y(nT) = \sum_{k=-\infty}^{\infty} h(nT, kT)x(kT),$$

$$\text{for } n = 0, 1, 2, \cdots$$

where T is the uniform sampling period and $h(nT, kT)$ is a discrete version of the impulse response, i.e., output at the nth sampling instant when a unit impulse is applied at kth sampling instant. Since physical systems do not respond before the excitation is applied, $h(nT, kT)$ is zero for $k > n$. If $x(kT)$ is defined only for non-negative time, then (15) reduces to a finite sum and it may be written in matrix form as

$$\begin{bmatrix} y(0) \\ y(T) \\ y(2T) \\ \cdot \\ \cdot \\ \cdot \end{bmatrix} =$$

$$\begin{bmatrix} h(0,0) & & & 0 \cdots \\ h(T,0) & & h(T,T) & 0 \cdots \\ h(2T,0) & h(2T,T) & h(2T,2T) & 0 \cdots \\ \cdot & & & \\ \cdot & & & \\ \cdot & & & \end{bmatrix} \begin{bmatrix} x(0) \\ x(T) \\ x(2T) \\ \cdot \\ \cdot \\ \cdot \end{bmatrix} \quad (16)$$

One advantage of the representation in (16) is that for systems in cascade, the overall h matrix is the product of the individual h matrices. Sampled-data feedback systems may be analyzed using the matrix approach above. The h matrix is commonly called the transmission matrix.

Feedback systems in which the process to be controlled has dynamic characteristics that vary with time usually require time-varying controllers. If the system is sampled, then the transmission matrix representation is useful in the design of the digital or discrete compensators.

J. B. CRUZ, JR.

Cross-references: *Laplace and Fourier Transforms, Feedback Systems, Minimal-Time Problems, Randomly Varying Systems, Sampled-Data Systems, Systems*

T

TACAN: see NAVIGATION

TAPE RECORDING: see SOUND RECORDING;
VIDEO RECORDING

TELEGRAPHY: see RADIOTELEGRAPHY

TELEMETRY

Telemetry is the process by which experimental data are communicated directly from an instrument at one point to an observer at a remote point. The data may be conveyed by wire lines, as in remote-process control systems, or by radio waves, as with guided missiles and space probes.

The types of sensors that may supply data to a telemetry system are varied; however, two classes stand out. Frequently sensors measure such parameters as voltage, temperature, pressure, or magnetic field, and the information that is desired at the receiving end of the telemetry link is the value of the parameter as a function of time. Such sensors are called *analog* sensors. Alternatively, certain experiments produce outputs that have abrupt changes at certain instants of time and it is either the time of occurrence, or certain statistical properties relating to multiple occurrences, such as the number of events per unit time, that are desired. Cosmic-ray counters and micro-meteorite detectors are examples of sensors of this class, and are called *digital* sensors.

Usually data from more than one source are transmitted by a telemetry system; therefore, multiplexing is one of the principal aspects of a telemetry system. Multiplexing falls into two broad classes, time-division multiplexing and frequency-division multiplexing. In a frequency-multiplexed system, data from various sources are isolated from each other by confining them to nonoverlapping portions of the frequency spectrum.

Bandpass filters are used in the terminal equipment to separate the various data. In a time-multiplexed system, isolation is accomplished by confining data from the different sources to nonoverlapping segments of time. A time multiplexing system utilizes a commutator to sample each sensor in sequence. A similar commutator running synchronously is used by the terminal equipment to separate the samples into their appropriate channels again. The commutators at each end of the link may be mechanical or electronic depending upon the system requirements.

The only method of frequency multiplexing that has received notice, and indeed has been a standard telemetry method in recent years, is frequency modulation of a number of distinct subcarriers. The Inter-Range Instrumentation Group (IRIG) has established standards for this system which provide for a ± 7.5-percent deviation of each subcarrier with optional ± 15-percent deviation for certain of the high-frequency subcarriers. Subcarriers start with nominal values of 400, 560, and 730 cps and occur regularly in approximately 35-percent increments up to 70 kc. The value of the frequency of each particular subcarrier within its ± 7.5-percent deviation represents the information being communicated. The collection of subcarriers that have been added is used to modulate an FM, AM, or PM transmitter. These methods give rise, respectively, to the nomenclature describing the systems as FM-FM, FM-AM, or FM-PM.

Time-division multiplexing systems have been mechanized in a variety of ways. The simplest method of time multiplexing is pulse amplitude modulation (PAM) in which the amplitude of the signal during the appropriate time segment represents the information being conveyed. The multiplexed signal can be used to amplitude-modulate a carrier, giving rise to PAM-AM, or to frequency-modulate a carrier giving rise to PAM-FM. Because of signal-to-noise ratio problems and in order to standardize receivers, only the latter method has received emphasis.

Slightly more complex, but having compensating advantages, are pulse-duration modulation (PDM) and pulse-position modulation (PPM). In a PDM system information is conveyed by varying the duration of a pulse in accord with the incoming signal between some minimum value and a maximum equal to the duration of the allotted time segment. PPM utilizes a constant-width pulse but varies its position also within the same limits to convey information. Both PDM and PPM systems can be transmitted using AM or FM, giving rise to PDM-AM, PDM-FM, PPM-AM, and PPM-FM systems.

Pulse-code modulation (PCM) systems are only recently beginning to receive wide application because of the substantially greater complexity. In a PCM system the value of the parameter to be conveyed is converted to a binary number and this binary number is encoded as a sequence of binary pulses occurring within the appropriate time segment. Carrier amplitude modulation, frequency-shift keying, or phase-shift keying can be employed to convey PCM signals, giving rise to PCM-AM, PCM-FS, and PCM-PS systems. PCM systems are attractive because calibration inaccuracies are restricted to the analog-to-digital converter and any multiplexing equipment which precedes it, both of which can be made quite accurate through careful design.

In comparing the advantages of the various multiplexing and modulating methods, a variety of factors, including the desired data rate, must be considered. First, emphasis is usually given to the average transmitter power required to ensure a sufficient accuracy of received data. In the light of this consideration, PPM-AM and PCM-PS systems are most favorable. Peak transmitter power is also usually of importance

and for satisfying this consideration systems that use equal peak and average powers such as FM, PM, and PS are most favorable. Bandwidth or channel utilization is sometimes an important consideration and when such is the case the AM systems generally are more favorable. Accuracy, of course, is always important and most of the previously mentioned systems can easily provide medium accuracies (2 to 5 percent). Extremely high accuracies (0.1 percent) usually require the use of a PCM system. Last and usually a binding consideration is receiving-equipment compatibility. For missile and space applications, standard receiving equipments are provided at launch sites and tracking stations, and it is important that a telemetry designer should consider the current standards for such equipment. To date, IRIG has established telemetry standards for FM-FM, FM-PM, PDM-FM, PDM-PM, PCM-FM, and PCM-PM systems.

JOHN E. TABER

Cross-references: *Modulation and Demodulation*

TELEPHONY: see RADIOTELEPHONY

TELETYPE

The word *Teletype* is a registered trademark owned by Teletype Corp. of Chicago, Ill., applying to its manufactured line of printing telegraph equipment. It is widely used to describe a system that may be more generally designated as a *teleprinter*.

The teleprinter is an electromechanical device that transmits and receives messages or data over a two-wire line, using a certain signaling code, to be described below. Outwardly the machine resembles an electric typewriter in that it has a platen carriage for holding a continuous strip of paper upon which the *receiving printer* imprints, and a three-row 32-key *sending keyboard* for transmitting therefrom. Generally speaking, anyone who can use a typewriter can operate a teleprinter, taking note of several special keys required for carriage return, platen line feed, figure and letter shifts, etc.

Teleprinters also are designed to imprint upon gummed paper tape for later affixing to telegram blanks, etc.; to cut perforated tape—a memory scheme in which data may be stored and used at a later time; and in some applications such as remote control devices to accomplish desired message routings, machine controls, or similar functions as signalled by appropriate key impressions.

There is no mechanical connection between the keyboard unit and the printer unit, aside from a common motor power drive. An electrical connection exists between these two units, which are in series and are connected to the energized incoming-outgoing two-wire line. Much as a simple telegraph

system, the keyboard has a set of contacts for interrupting the line current in a definite code pattern for each key-character, and the printer employs an electromagnet to receive these impulses to translate into the recognized character to imprint onto paper or tape. Additional teleprinters in this line also receive and send, and hence form a complete two (or more) station communication link. Stations may be separated by few feet or thousands of miles.

The teleprinter signalling system is based on a 5-unit permutation code as devised (circa 1875) by Emile Baudot, a French telegraph engineer. It is an equal-length code, each combination or character consisting of five signalling impulses of equal length. By forming combinations of *Marks* (line-current pulses) and *Spaces* (no-line-current pulses) five at a time, a total of $2^5 = 32$ different combinations can be set up. This is the maximum capacity of this 5-unit two-element code—Mark and Space being the two elements thus defined. To take care of numbers, special symbols, or extra control functions, a scheme akin to upper-case—lower-case typing in a typewriter is employed, along with FIGS (figures) and LTRS (letters) keys for signaling the machines to shift as required. Most of the keys have two characters available for each code combination, and are thus illustrated in the Baudot code chart of Fig. 1. (This chart also shows a perforated tape sample; the vertical row of smaller holes are for engaging into feed pins in a tape reader, to step the tape along.)

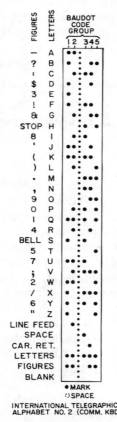

Fig. 1. The teleprinter code.

The five impulses in each code group are transmitted over the "loop" or two-wire line by sequential scanning of the five impulses using a distributor as set up and triggered by the keyboard for each character. The receiving printer has a similar distributor, properly synchronized, to sort out the five sequential impulses for translation into the required typewritten impression. The keyboard sets up a parallel presentation of each code group, which is then converted

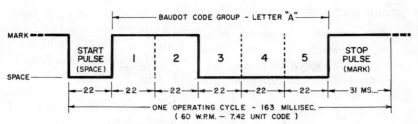

FIG. 2. The teleprinter signal-waveform.

into a time-sequential form for transmission over a line. At the other end, the signal is converted back to a parallel presentation, which is compared with the printer's code memory, resulting in an imprint.

Synchronization is the crux of the signaling method. With a separate synchronizing procedure, the five-unit code group alone is sufficient, as in multiplex printing telegraph systems. However owing to inherent operational characteristics, such as random typing speeds, line switchings to different stations, etc., the teleprinter must be self-synchronizing. Hence two extra signaling impulses, termed *Start* and *Stop*, are added at the beginning and end of each Baudot code group, as shown in Fig. 2. This figure also shows the complete specifications for the widely used teleprinter signal standard.

The teleprinter is at rest on a steady Mark (*Stop*) when line current is flowing without any signal interruption. Keyboard actuation at any point on the line results in transmission of one complete set of interruptions; the first interruption being the *Start* impulse. This signals the receiving printer's distributor start scanning, and during its cycle, the next five Mark and Space impulses of the code group are received and stored into the printer's memory system for its subsequent printing cycle. The last impulse, after the group, is the *Stop*, which is employed to signal the printer to translate the previous code group into an impression, and also to ready the machine for the next cycle.

It follows that both sending and receiving distributors must be so designed that slight variations in the speed of either one do not affect synchronization. This goal is accom-

plished by having the receiving distributor run somewhat faster than the sending one. Both units, driven by slipping clutches, are held at rest by latches, the triggering one on the keyboard and a similar one mounted on the armature of the printer magnet. During operation, both distributors are triggered; first the sending one, which by means of the Start impulse triggers the receiving unit, resulting in one complete cycle during which the faster moving latter unit becomes latched just before the keyboard's unit is latched. Teleprinters as designed are capable of satisfactory printing despite of as much as 10-percent variation in relative speed and hence they tolerate to a similar degree distortions in the signal waveform as received.

Approximately 90 per cent of all telegraphic work the world over is done using this Start-Stop printing telegraph system; the rest use multiplex. The binary-code impulses are easily handled by wirelines, by radio using FSK (frequency shift keying), by carrier techniques using audio FSK, or in special cases by interruptions in a tone-carrier (make-break). Several teleprinter speed ratings are in use (60, 75, and 100 words/min) and any teleprinter can intercommunicate with any other within its speed rating.

Teleprinters are manufactured by Teletype Corp., Creed Ltd., Siemens and Halske, Kleinschmidt Labs., and others.

ROBERT H. WEITBRECHT

Cross-references: *Computer Printout and Reading, Electrostatic Printing, Modulation and Demodulation, Radiotelegraphy*

TELEVISION (BLACK AND WHITE)

Television systems represent a means of transmitting picture information from its source to a remote point where it is reproduced. One illustrative, although impractical, television system is known as a parallel television system. The pickup device in this case is a mosaic of photoelectric devices each generating an electrical signal proportional to the light intensity impinging on it. Each one of the cells is connected via a separate communications link, be it wire or radio, to a corresponding controlled light source, each generating an amount of light proportional to the intensity at the corresponding point in the scene. The total bandwidth required by this system is the number of channels or picture elements multiplied by the bandwidth required for each channel. The bandwidth per channel depends directly on the motion capabilities desired or inversely as the time required for a change. Thus the total bandwidth required is proportional to the number of picture elements divided by the time allotted for motion. This will be true in general for analog types of television systems.

The parallel arrangement described is obviously impractical because of the huge number of transducers and communications channels required. In order to reduce this number, the property of the eye known as "persistence of vision" is exploited. This property allows a picture element to be periodically excited for a short time duration with a resultant illusion of a continuous light source. Persistence thus allows for the mechanism of "scanning" wherein a single light source is rapidly swept over every element of the picture. This light source is modulated to correspond to the correct value as it occupies the position of each picture element. Correspondingly, the pickup device consists of a single photoelectric device which is scanned so as to determine the intensity of every point in the scene and communicate it to the scanned light source. For reasonably slow scanning, mechanical devices can be employed, although for high-speed systems (such as those employed in home entertainment systems) electron-beam scanning must be employed. Where electron beam scanning is used, the camera pickup device employs a continuous film of photo-sensitive material, whereas the reproducer employs a continuous structure of phosphorescent material. Both are synchronously swept by their electron beams, with the camera tube reading the amount of light intensity at each point and the display tube having its electron beam intensity modulated so as to reproduce the required light intensity.

In general three pieces of information are required in order to reproduce a two-dimensional monochrome image: the intensity, abscissa, and ordinate of each picture element as it is scanned. In order to restrict the required information needed at any time, a system of synchronization is used. Positioning or synchronizing information is transmitted in the form of pulses at specific times to tell the reproducer how to position its scanning beam. Between these synchronization pulses both camera and display beams are scanned in some predetermined manner until the next synchronization pulse comes along. In the case of commercial television this prescribed manner involves a sawtooth pattern in which the beam is swept from left to right and then rapidly retraced. At the same time the beam is scanned with a much slower sawtooth pattern from top to bottom and rapidly retraced at what is known as field intervals. The resultant pattern, known as a *raster*, consists of a close-spaced array of horizontal lines. The positioning or synchronizating pulse causes each line and field scan to retrace and begin the next line synchronously with the camera at the left side and at the top, respectively. Other television systems use methods of scan other than sawtooth waveforms, such as spiral or triangular waveforms. The sawtooth pattern has the desirable characteristic of being less susceptible to relative nonlinearities of scanning at either the transmitter or receiver. Nonlinearities in sawtooth scan cause stretching or compression of the resultant display, but nonlinearities in other scan systems cause parts of the resultant picture to separate and be entirely incoherent. Sawtooth scan has certain undesirable aspects, however, such as the time lost in the retrace intervals during which no picture information is presented.

The number of lines generated per field in a raster is determined by the ratio of the time of field scan to the time of line scan. The desired number of lines is determined by consideration of the acuity of the eye, and the normal viewing distance from the screen. The eye's acuity is generally accepted to be an angle of approximately 1′ of arc. This acuity corresponds to a 500-line image when observed at a distance of five to ten times the height of the television screen. Commercial television systems have used between 405 and 819 lines, with the United States using 525. These numbers represent total number of lines rather than active lines, since 5 to 10 per cent is used for the retrace interval.

It would be desirable to have approximately the same number of picture elements in the horizontal direction to allow for roughly equal resolution in both directions. The resolution in the horizontal direction is determined by the maximum rate at which the video signal can vary as the spot is scanned across the screen. Thus the horizontal resolution is determined by the product of the time of a line and the video bandwidth. The time of the line is determined by the time per picture divided by the number of lines.

The time required to transmit each repetitive picture is an interesting consideration. One criterion is based on persistence of vision or flicker consideration. At somewhere between 45 to 60 pictures or frames per second, depending on the light intensity, the eye ceases to see flickering pictures and perceives a continuous image. However, this flicker requirement is approximately twice as great as that necessary for the eye to perceive continuous motion. If 20 to 30 new frames per second are presented to the eye,

the motion appears continuous although the entire scene is flickering. Motion-picture and television engineers have used ingenious means of resolving the disparity between these two requirements. In motion pictures, 24 frames per second are viewed. However, while each frame is in position, a light-chopping wheel with alternate opaque and open regions interrupts the light twice for each frame, or 48 times per second. Thus both the motion and flicker requirements are met. In television, a system known as "interlace" is employed. Two successive fields are used to supply each frame, with each field providing half of the total number of lines. Thus, on alternate fields the odd and even lines are presented, each interlacing within the other. For flicker considerations, an entire field of information is presented 60 times per second, although each picture element is scanned on alternate fields or only 30 times per second. Since only half the number of lines (half the information) is presented during each field time, the bandwidth requirements are cut in half. The only price paid for this 2:1 increase in spectrum utilization is that of resolution of objects in motion. An object in rapid motion does not stay in one place long enough to be scanned by both odd and even fields, and thus has only half the normal resolution. However, the eye's ability to recognize resolution of rapidly moving objects is correspondingly poor. The numbers used in this discussion, 60 fields per second and 30 frames per second, represent the United States Standards. The international standards use 50 fields and 25 frames per second. The prime incentive in each of these cases is to be synchronous with the power-line frequency, be it 50 or 60 cps. Synchronism has the distinct advantage of rendering stationary all power-line components that inadvertently appear in the picture in either the positioning or intensity circuits. These components would otherwise cause annoying, moving patterns at the difference frequency between the field and power-line frequncies.

The interlace patterns are generated by simply making the total number of lines an odd number, with each field having an integer plus one half in scanning lines. This relationship insures that on alternate scans the lines will appear between the previously scanned set since they begin one half line later.

The camera tubes used in commercial television systems include image orthicons, iconoscopes, and vidicons, each of which are described in detail elsewhere. The principal difference between the camera tubes is the manner in which the electron beam reads the charge image formed on a photosensitive screen. In the case of the iconoscope the charge is read using a high-velocity beam resulting in secondary emission, which causes each point to charge to the collector potential. In the vidicon and image orthicon, each picture element is discharged by means of low-velocity electron beam causing each point to reach cathode potential. The vidicon and image orthicon differ principally in their utilization of photoconductive and photoemissive screens, respectively. In any of these camera tubes an electrical signal is developed that is proportional to the light intensity as the beam is scanned. During the retrace intervals, the beam is turned off and develops a voltage corresponding to black or zero light. The resulting video signal consists of a repetitive blanking signal occurring during the retrace intervals, with the picture information occurring between these blanking intervals. In closed-circuit television systems this signal is amplified and applied directly to a display device. In broadcast television this signal is used to amplitude-modulate a high-frequency carrier, and then propagated.

In conventional AM systems, the total ratio frequency bandwidth is twice that of the modulating signal, or 8 Mc for a 4-Mc video bandwidth. As with any amplitude modulation system, this bandwidth can be reduced by the use of single-sideband techniques. Since single-sideband techniques involve difficult filtering problems and give substantial envelope distortion, a vestigial sideband system is used. The transmitted signal is double sideband for the first 0.75

Mc, providing a total of 4.75 Mc. The total bandwidth of a television channel is 6 Mc, with the remaining 1.25 Mc of spectrum taken up with the sound signal and guard bands. Thus, the vestigial-sideband techniques substantially reduce the required bandwidth and allow for more channels within a given spectrum. The normal envelope distortion associated with single-sideband transmission is minimized since the high-amplitude sideband components occur mostly in the 0.75-Mc double-sideband region. The television channel allocations are divided into vhf and uhf regions, with the vhf occupying 50–200 Mc and the uhf occupying 500–1000 Mc.

The receivers for this system are basically conventional superheterodyne type structures; most utilize an intermediate frequency of about 40 Mc. In the IF amplifier the required selectivity takes place to reject adjacent channels and to provide the correct bandpass characteristic to compensate for the vestigial-sideband transmission. Following detection the video signal is amplified and used to modulate the beam current of a cathode-ray kinescope as it is scanned over the phosphorescent material. To time the deflection circuits with those of the transmitter camera properly, the synchronizing pulses must be separated from the composite video signal and used to synchronize the horizontal and vertical deflection oscillators. This operation is particularly difficult since noise impulses have similar characteristics to synchronization pulses. To allow for adequate timing under noisy conditions, various controlled limiting circuits are used in addition to a system of automatic frequency control (AFC) of the horizontal oscillator. As in most such AFC systems, a number of horizontal synchronization pulses are compared in a phase detector with the horizontal oscillator signal, and then integrated to form a control voltage. Thus, random-noise pulses are prevented from triggering the horizontal oscillator. Although a similar system could be used to stabilize the synchronization of the vertical oscillator, the integration of a number of 60-cps synchronization pulses takes an appreciable length of time. The "pull-in time" of the vertical oscillator would take an amount of time that would interfere with the switching between television channels. As such, in modern television receivers, the vertical synchronization is the weakest link and is the first to fail under severe impulse noise conditions.

ALBERT MACOVSKI

Cross-references: *Cathode-Ray Tubes (Display), Flying-Spot Scanning, Iconoscope, Image Orthicon, Modulation and Demodulation, Television (Color), Video Recording*

TELEVISION (COLOR)

The color television signal broadcast in the U.S.A. consists of:

(1) a high-definition *luminance* signal, similar to that used for monochrome TV, which carries as much of the luminance information as practicable, plus

(2) a "coloring" or *chrominance* signal, carrying only as much color information as the eye can use, and contained within the luminance passband.

The scanning standards, the 6-Mc channel, the location within the channel of the picture and sound carriers, and the methods of picture and sound modulation are the same for color and monochrome transmission.

The color signal is therefore compatible, so that color programs are reproduced in black and white by unmodified monochrome receivers; conversely, monochrome programs are received in black and white by color receivers.

Monochrome receivers use only the luminance signal so that the added chrominance signal must not affect the monochrome picture adversely. Color receivers add the chrominance to the luminance to produce color pictures. Any monochrome transmission channel can be converted to color.

Monochrome pictures are produced by varying only the *luminance* of the scanning spot as it generates the complete picture.

Color television makes the additional requirements that the scanning spot must vary also in *hue* and *saturation*. For this reason, early color television operated by transmitting red, green, and blue pictures with 4-Mc bandwidth for each color, requiring a total of 12 Mc.

It is only when the signal was designed to carry *no more color information than the eye can use* that it became possible to reduce materially the total requirement for bandwidth. In addition the rediscovery that television pictures produce a signal having a line spectrum, and not a continuous spectrum, allowed the added color information to be frequency interleaved within these spectrum lines and completely contained within the 4-Mc monochrome video passband.

The color television signal can produce pictures having almost the same resolution as monochrome pictures and all the color detail that the eye can usefully distinguish.

Acuity of the Eye. In the normal viewing of a TV picture, the eye can distinguish detail in luminance corresponding to approximately 4.0 Mc. Its acuity to detail in chromaticity, when the luminance is held constant, is limited to about 1.3 Mc along the orange-cyan chromaticity axis and about 0.5 Mc along the green-magenta axis, as they appear in the CIE diagram.

The eye is also less sensitive to flicker in chromaticity than in luminance.

Television Spectrum. Television pictures are scanned periodically at line rate. This technique results in a line spectrum corresponding to a Fourier series whose components are located essentially at harmonics of line frequency (f_H), as shown in Fig. 1. Information introduced in the vacant space between these harmonics (at odd harmonics of half-line frequency) produce effects *having very low visibility in the picture*, as explained below.

Chrominance Signal. The chrominance information, reduced to optimum bandwidth, is transmitted by a carrier called the "color subcarrier."

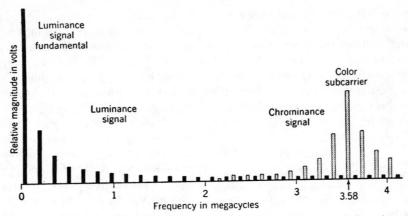

FIG. 1. Color-television video spectrum showing interleaved luminance and chrominance frequency components separated from each other by line frequency f_H (not to scale).

The subcarrier is located within the luminance band and interleaved between the 227th and 228th harmonic of line frequency, making it equal to $455f_H/2 = 3.58$ Mc (approx.). The sidebands are displaced from the subcarrier and from each other by f_H so that all are automatically interleaved (Fig. 1).

Low Visibility of Frequency-Interleaved Subcarrier Sidebands. With reference to Fig. 1, the luminance signal occurs at frequencies equal to mf_H (where m is the order of each harmonic of line frequency f_H). A sine wave interleaved between these harmonics has a frequency $f_s = (2m + 1)f_H/2$, which is usually expressed as an "*odd* harmonic of $f_H/2$" to differentiate it from the normal spectrum which consists of "*even* harmonics of $f_H/2$" (Fig. 2).

The scanning spot increases and decreases in brightness f_s times per second and, in the time $(1/f_H)$ required to scan one line, produces $f_s/f_H = (2m + 1)f_H/2f_H = m + \frac{1}{2}$ cycles. The half-cycle left over at the end of each line displaces the alternating brightness pattern by 180° on successive lines in time, so that a complete field has the appearance of Fig. 3A. The pattern of Fig. 3A is less visible than that of Fig. 2A, produced by a signal consisting of whole numbers of cycles in each line, because its distribution makes it fade into a uniform gray at a shorter distance.

The same reasoning can be extended to show that the interleaved and noninterleaved signals result in the patterns of Figs. 3B and 2B, respectively, after fields 1 and 2. The blanks of Fig. 3B fill in during fields 3 and 4, during which the pattern of Fig. 2B is reinforced. Interleaving, therefore, results in patterns of low visibility for each field which, in addition, average to a uniform gray in four fields.

As shown later the color subcarrier is modulated in phase and in amplitude. The phase modulation carries the *hue* information. The amplitude is approximately proportional to *luminance* multiplied by *saturation*. This relationship has the advantage that the chrominance signal vanishes on achromatic and dark picture elements because the saturation or the luminance are zero.

The visibility of the chrominance signal in a monochrome receiver is further reduced because its high frequencies produce only fine grain patterns; and, in addition, it is largely attenuated by the limited passband of most monochrome receivers.

Constant-Luminance Principle. The luminance signal is proportioned to produce as much, and the chrominance signal as little, of the luminance variation of successive picture elements as possible. The operation of the chrominance channel at nearly constant luminance makes it less vulnerable to

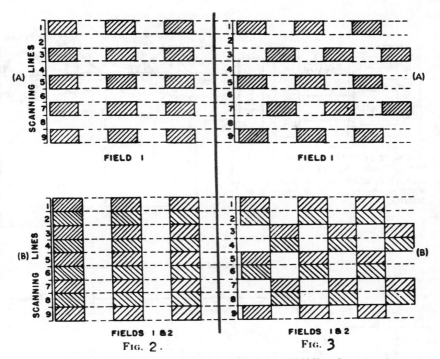

FIG. 2. Pattern created by even harmonics of half line frequency.
FIG. 3. Pattern created by odd harmonics of half line frequency.

noise which appears as rapid (30 per second) variations of chromaticity to which the eye is less sensitive than it is to corresponding variations of luminance. In practice, *constant-luminance* operation is only approximated because the luminance signal does not carry all the luminance and because the picture tube is not linear.

Limitations of Cameras and Picture Tubes. At the present time, practical cameras and picture tubes can pick up and display only luminance information. For this reason, the camera resolves the scene to be televised into red, green, and blue color separation images by optical filters. The three images are focused on three camera tubes to produce voltages (E_R, E_G, E_B) respectively proportional to the intensities of the three primaries on each picture element. The studio equipment encodes E_R, E_G, E_B into the luminance and chrominance signal for transmission. The receiver decodes the signal and applies voltages, derived from E_R, E_G, E_B, to the picture tube to produce three primary

lights proportional to their intensities in the original scene. The encoding process will be clarified by reference to Figs. 4 and 5.

Encoder. The triple output of the camera and the over-all system gains are standardized so that $E_G = E_R = E_B$ on gray. These voltages are then "gamma-corrected" ($\gamma \simeq 2.2$) to $E_R' = E_R^{1/\gamma}$, etc., so that the light intensity $L = KE^\gamma$ (produced by a voltage E applied to the receiving picture tube) is made proportional to E_R, etc., as follows: $L_R = K(E_R^{1/\gamma})^\gamma = KE_R$, etc.

The three reproducing primaries of the picture tube (standardized by the National Television System Committee, and shown in Fig. 6) contribute differently to luminance. Thus, on gray when $E_G = E_R = E_B$, the relative contributions are 59 per cent from E_G; 30 per cent from E_R; and 11 per cent from E_B. The luminance signal should then be proportioned according to $E_Y = 0.59 E_G + 0.30E_R + 0.11E_B$ and gamma-corrected to $E_Y^{1/\gamma} = (0.59E_G + 0.30E_R + 0.11E_B)^{1/\gamma}$. However, the extraction of

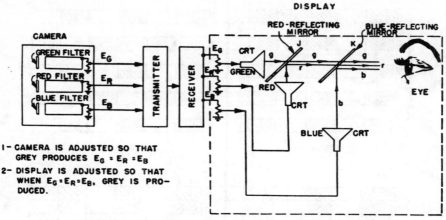

FIG. 4. Simultaneous system with dichroic-mirror display.

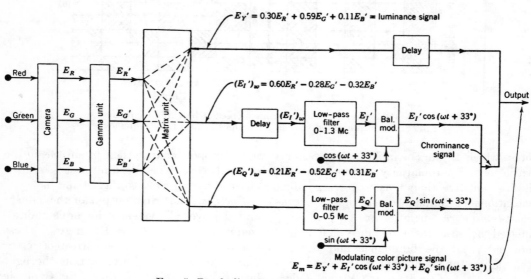

FIG. 5. Block diagram of typical encoder.

$E_G^{1/\gamma}$, $E_R^{1/\gamma}$, $E_B^{1/\gamma}$ from $E_Y^{1/\gamma}$ at the receiver would require complicated and costly non-linear operations. For this reason the "gamma-corrected" luminance signal is compromised to $E_Y' = 0.59E_G' + 0.30 E_R' + 0.11E_B'$. Note, from this equation, that on gray where $E_G' = E_R' = E_B'$, one also has $E_Y' = E_G' = E_R' = E_B'$. (Primes indicate gamma-corrected voltages.)

E_R', E_B', and E_Y' are combined to form signals voltages E_I' and E_Q' corresponding to the orange-cyan (I) and green-magenta (Q) chromaticity axes (dotted lines in Fig. 6) as follows:

$$E_I' = -0.27(E_B' - E_Y') + 0.74(E_R' - E_Y')$$

limited to 1.3 Mc

$$= 0.60E_R' - 0.28E_G' - 0.32E_B'$$

$$E_Q' = 0.41(E_B' - E_Y') + 0.48(E_R' - E_Y')$$

limited to 0.5 Mc

$$= 0.21E_R' - 0.52E_Q' + 0.31E_B'$$

Note that $E_Q' = E_I' = 0$ on gray.

Although E_G' is not explicitly expressed in the signals, it is present in E_Y'. E_Y' and E_I' are differently delayed to coincide in time with E_Q' which is most delayed by the drastic limitation of its bandwidth.

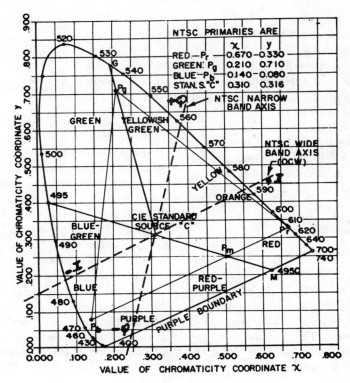

FIG. 6. CIE chromaticity diagram.

E_Q' and E_I', respectively, modulate two components of the subcarrier on quadrature: $E_Q' \sin(\omega t + 33°)$ and $E_I' \cos(\omega t + 33°)$. The reason for the 33° phase shift is explained below. Balanced modulators are used to suppress the subcarrier and leave only the sidebands in the output. The outputs of the two modulators are added to form the chrominance signal:

$$E_c' = E_Q' \sin(\omega t + 33°) + E_I' \cos(\omega t + 33°)$$

whose amplitude is $|E_c'| = \sqrt{(E_Q')^2 + (E_I')^2}$

$$= |E_c'| \left[\frac{E_Q'}{|E_c'|} \sin(\omega t + 33°) \right.$$

$$\left. + \frac{E_I'}{|E_c'|} \cos(\omega t + 33°) \right] \qquad \text{(see Fig. 7)}$$

Let

$$\frac{E_Q'}{|E_c'|} = \cos(\theta - 33°); \text{ then } \frac{E_I'}{|E_c'|} = \sin(\theta - 33°),$$

$$\text{and } \tan(\theta - 33°) = \frac{E_I'}{E_Q'}$$

$$E_c' = |E_c'| [\cos(\theta - 33°) \sin(\omega t + 33°)$$

$$+ \sin(\theta - 33°) \cos(\omega t + 33°)]$$

$$= |E_c'| \sin(\omega t + \theta) = E_{Y'} \frac{|E_c'|}{E_{Y'}} \sin(\omega t + \theta)$$

Note that E_c', as stated earlier, is modulated (1) in phase by the angle $\theta = 33° +$

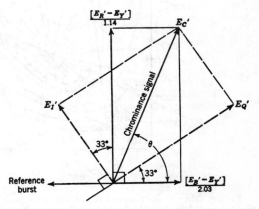

FIG. 7. Phase relations of reference burst and two sets of axes for chrominance signals. [Fig. 4(c) of Appendix III of FCC Standards.]

$\tan^{-1}(E_I{'}/E_Q{'})$ which depends on the ratio $E_I{'}/E_Q{'}$ of the two components of chrominance and therefore is closely related to *hue*; and (2) in amplitude by the *product* of luminance $E_Y{'}$ and the chrominance per unit of luminance $|E_c{'}|/E_Y{'}$, which is an approximation to *saturation*.

Examination of the equations for $E_c{'}$, $E_Q{'}$, and $E_I{'}$ reveals, with the assistance of Fig. 7, that for modulation frequencies below 0.5 Mc, the chrominance subcarrier can also be expressed as:

$$E_c{'} = \frac{1}{1.14}\left[\frac{1}{1.78}(E_B{'} - E_Y{'})\sin\omega t\right.$$

$$\left. + (E_R{'} - E_Y{'})\cos\omega t\right]$$

The signal $(E_B{'} - E_Y{'})\sin\omega t$ is easily generated and is used for phase reference. This is the reason for the 33° phase shift mentioned above. The luminance and chrominance signals are added to form the composite color TV signal

$$E_m = E_Y{'} + E_Q{'}\sin(\omega t + 33°) + E_I{'}\cos(\omega t + 33°)$$

$$= E_Y{'} + \frac{1}{1.14}\left[\frac{1}{1.78}(E_B{'} - E_Y{'})\sin\omega t\right.$$

$$\left. + (E_R{'} - E_Y{'})\cos\omega t\right]$$

for modulation frequencies below 0.5 Mc.

The composite signal is bandwidth limited to about 4.3 Mc to prevent interference to the sound signal. It is then applied to the picture transmitter for radiation.

Figure 8 is a map, assuming the system to be linear, on the CIE diagram, of the phase θ. The amplitude-to-luminance ratio $E_c{'}/E_Y{'}$ of the chrominance signal is shown by the curved contours.

Figure 9 shows the relative amplitude for one scanning line of the luminance and chrominance signals for black, white, and saturated color bars. It also shows the location of the phase-reference signal $-(E_B{'} - E_Y{'})\sin\omega t$ which is transmitted as a burst of about 8 cycles on the "back porch" of

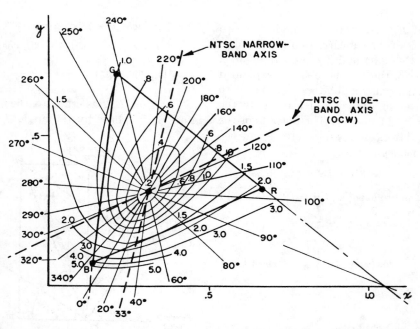

Fig. 8. Map of normalized NTSC chrominance signal for linear case. [From F. J. Bingley's colorimetry paper D/794, NTSC Panel 12. (Courtesy Philco Corp.)]

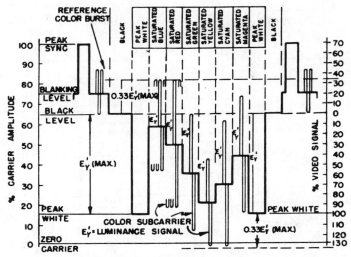

FIG. 9. Complete color signal for one line of color bars.

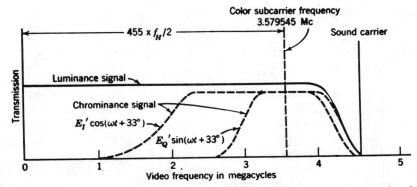

FIG. 10. Video bands occupied by components of complete color picture signal.

horizontal sync. The slight excursion below zero carrier amplitude is of no consequence.

Figure 10 shows the location of the picture carrier, chrominance subcarrier, E_I' and E_Q' sidebands, and sound carrier within the channel.

Figure 11 is a block diagram of a typical color receiver. The composite video signal is reproduced at the output of the second detector. It is then used as a luminance signal after passing through a filter which removes the subcarrier and its near sidebands. Part of the second-detector output is passed through a filter having the passband shown to separate the chrominance from the low-frequency luminance components and to compensate for the asymmetrical E_I' sidebands. The output of the filter is impressed on two synchronous demodulators to recover E_I' and E_Q'.

The reference burst is gated from the signal to generate two cw reference signals in quadrature, $\sin(\omega t + 33°)$ and $\cos(\omega t + 33°)$, which are respectively applied to the E_Q' and E_I' synchronous demodulators. The output of the E_Q' demodulator is

$$E_c' \sin(\omega t + 33°) = E_Q' \sin(\omega t + 33°) \sin(\omega t + 33°)$$
$$+ E_I' \cos(\omega t + 33°) \sin(\omega t + 33°)$$
$$= \tfrac{1}{2}E_Q' - \tfrac{1}{2}E_Q' \cos 2(\omega t + 33°)$$
$$+ \tfrac{1}{2} E_I' \sin 2(\omega t + 33°)$$

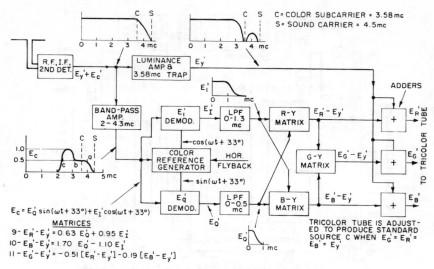

FIG. 11. Block diagram of color receiver.

The output of the E_I' demodulator is similarly derived

$$E_c' \cos(\omega t + 33°) = \tfrac{1}{2}E_Q' \sin 2(\omega t + 33°)$$
$$+ \tfrac{1}{2}E_I' + \tfrac{1}{2}E_I' \cos 2(\omega t + 33°)$$

The LPF in the output of each demodulator removes the terms in $2(\omega t + 33°)$ leaving $\tfrac{1}{2}E_Q'$ and $\tfrac{1}{2}E_I'$ separated at the outputs of their respective demodulators. The 0.5-Mc cutoff of the LPF in the output of the E_Q' demodulator removes the cross-modulation from E_I', which occurs only for modulation frequencies of E_I' above 0.5 Mc because the lower sideband of the E_I' signal is not balanced by an upper sideband. E_Q' does not cross-modulate on the E_I' because its sidebands are symmetrical. E_I' and E_Q' are then combined to produce:

(1) $E_B' - E_Y' = 1.70\,E_Q' - 1.10\,E_I'$
(2) $E_R' - E_Y' = 0.63\,E_Q' + 0.95\,E_I'$

These equations are in turn combined to produce:

(3) $E_G' - E_Y' = -0.41\,(E_R' - E_Y') - 0.19\,(E_B' - E_Y')$

$E_G' - E_Y'$ could also have been obtained from a third synchronous detector with the phase $\sin(\omega t + 235.5°)$.

E_Y' is then added to each of these voltages to produce E_B', E_R', E_G' which are respectively impressed on the three guns of a shadowmask picture tube to produce red, green, and blue light as follows:

$$L_r = (KE_r^{1/\gamma})^\gamma = KE_r \quad \text{etc.}$$

In the three-gun shadowmask tube, the red, green, and blue phosphor dots are arranged in small triads which blend at a very short viewing distance to produce the same additive effect as if they were coincident.

Each picture element is reproduced with its primaries having the same relative intensity as in the scene before the camera.

The *simultaneous presence of the three primary voltages* makes it possible to adapt the signal to other forms of picture tubes such as those of the line screen or beam-switching types. The image has almost the same luminance detail as the best available from a black and white picture transmitted through the same channel plus all the detail in hue and saturation that the eye can distinguish. Yet the complete color signal occupies the same channel as the signal intended only for black and white pictures.

The color-television signal carries simultaneously all the information required for three-color reproduction. It can, therefore, be used by receivers designed to reproduce the full three colors, or by lower-performance receivers designed for two colors, or only one color (black and white).

Colorimetry

Colorimetry deals with the measurement of colored light as it appears to the eye. The measurement is usually made by optically matching an unknown color to one of known specifications. Two colors that match visually are colorimetrically identical even though their spectral distributions differ. They are called metameric pairs.

The eye recognizes three independent characteristics of light: (1) *Brightness* is the intensity of the light; (2) *hue* is the quality of redness, yellowness, etc; and (3) *purity*, or psychophysical saturation, is the proportion of the intensity of the color of the single wavelength (100-percent pure) having the same hue as the color to be specified in a mixture with white (0-percent pure). The combination of *hue* and *purity* is called chromaticity, which is what is usually meant when speaking of "color."

Brightness depends on adaptation and is difficult to measure. For this reason, it is usually replaced by *luminance*, the "luminous flux per unit area," which is more conveniently measured. The luminous flux is calculated from the function $\bar{y}(\lambda)$, the relative eye-sensitivity of the Standard Observer for different wavelengths (λ) of light (Fig. 12). The luminance Y of a source having a spectral distribution $S(\lambda)$ is given by

$$Y = \int_{400}^{700} S(\lambda)\bar{y}(\lambda)\,d\lambda$$

Lights of any color can be matched exactly by a proper mixture of three lights of different colors, called primaries. The matching is done by a colorimeter (Fig. 13). The color C to be compared is projected on one half of a screen. Red (R), green (G), and blue (B) primaries are projected on the other half and their intensities (r, g, b) adjusted until the two halves of the screen match exactly in appearance. The match is

expressed by:

$$C_1 = r_1(R) + g_1(G) + b_1(B)$$

A match cannot be achieved for some colors unless one primary is transferred to the unknown. This case is illustrated in Fig. 13b, for which the color equation is: $C_2 + r_2(R) = g_2(G) + b_2(B)$; or $C_2 = g_2(G) + b_2(B) - r_2(R)$. Any color can be matched by any set of three primaries provided that (1) no primary can be matched by a mixture of the other two, and (2) *the concept of negative color just described is included*. The amount of each primary required for a color match is called its tristimulus value.

Figure 14 shows the tristimulus values of red at 700 mμ, green at 546.1 mμ, and blue at 435.6 mμ which match the color of each

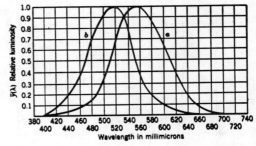

FIG. 12. Luminosity functions of the Standard Observer for (a) photopic vision at normal light levels, and (b) scotopic vision at very low light levels. For absolute values multiply curve a by 680 l/w and curve b by 1750 l/w.

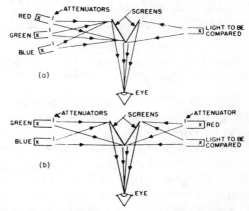

FIG. 13. Colorimeter arranged for (a) all primaries combined, and (b) red added to unknown light.

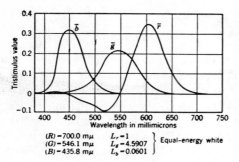

FIG. 14. Tristimulus values for equal-energy spectrum.

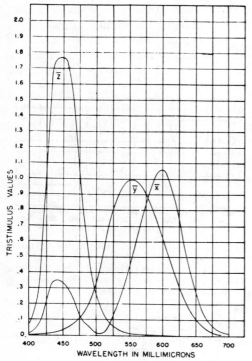

FIG. 15. Tristimulus values for the XYZ primaries and equal-energy stimulus.

wavelength of light when the intensities of the three primaries are said to be equal when matching equal energy white.

The CIE (Comité International de l'Eclairage) has standardized three primaries (X, Y, Z) for convenient computation. The most important objectives sought to specify X, Y, Z were: (1) X, Y, Z should lie outside the realm of real colors, so that all real colors are matched by positive values of X, Y, Z.

(2) The specification of luminance should require only one primary (Y). For this reason, the quantity ($\bar{y}$) of Y required to match each wavelength of light, was made equal to the eye-sensitivity $\bar{y}(\lambda)$ of the Standard Observer. (3) Equal energy white should be matched by X = Y = Z. (4) A match of reds and yellows should require substantially only two primaries (X and Y) with a minimum of the third (Z).

These considerations, along with others, resulted in the curves of Fig. 15, which give the tristimulus values $\bar{x}$, $\bar{y}$, $\bar{z}$ of the CIE primaries required to match each wavelength of light. (Warning: $\bar{x}$, $\bar{y}$, $\bar{z}$ are *not* the spectral distribution of the energies of X, Y, Z.)

The tristimulus values of a color having a spectral distribution $S(\lambda)$ are:

$$X = \int_{400}^{700} S(\lambda)\bar{x}\, d\lambda; \quad Y = \int_{400}^{700} S(\lambda)\bar{y}\, d\lambda;$$

$$Z = \int_{400}^{700} S(\lambda)\bar{z}\, d\lambda$$

Y is equal to the luminance.

There is an infinite number of distributions $S(\lambda)$ which have the same tristimulus values, but they all match visually. Colors are usually specified in terms of luminance Y, and rationalized chromaticity coordinates defined by:

$$x = X/(X + Y + Z); \quad y = Y/(X + Y + Z);$$

$$z = Z/(X + Y + Z)$$

z is redundant and may be omitted from the specification because $z = 1 - x - y$.

The tristimulus values of a combination of colored lights is equal to the sum of their tristimulus values. Thus a mixture (c) of lights (a) and (b) results in the following: $X_c = X_a + X_b$; $Y_c = Y_a + Y_b$; $Z_c = Z_a + Z_b$. The light (c) can then be specified by its luminance Y_c and its chromaticity coordinates $x_c = X_c/(X_c + Y_c + Z_c)$ and $y_c = Y_c/(X_c + Y_c + Z_c)$.

These equations are used to calculate the result of mixtures of colored lights and to transfer from one system of primaries, such as the red, green, and blue of the colorimeter or color television, to another such as X, Y, Z.

Figure 6 shows the chromaticity diagram standardized by the CIE. The chromaticity of the spectral colors is given by the horseshoe curve. It is calculated from the data of Fig. 15 by means of the equations given above. Figure 6 also shows the primaries and the reference chromaticity (Standard Source C) for color television. The chromaticity of a mixture of two colored lights lies on the line joining them in the CIE diagram, the distance from each color being inversely proportional to its relative intensity. All chromaticities lying within the polygon formed by a set of primaries on the CIE dia-

gram can be obtained by a combination of the primaries. Chromaticities outside the polygon cannot be produced by mixing of lights.

The chromaticity of a color specimen can be specified by x and y or by the *dominant wavelength* and *saturation* with respect to a specified reference, usually Standard Source C. A straight line drawn from the reference through the color specimen intersects the spectral locus at the dominant wavelength. The saturation is equal to the distance from the reference to the specimen divided by the distance from the reference to the spectral locus. Thus, the color television green primary P_g (0.210–0.710) has a dominant wave-

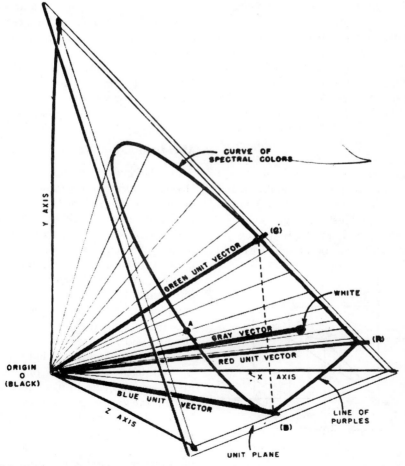

FIG. 16. Color space model with unit plane determined by unit vectors representing spectral primary colors.

length of 534 mμ and a saturation $CP_g/CG = 0.84$ referred to Standard Source C. Because magentas do not occur as single spectral lines, they are specified in terms of the dominant wavelength of their complementary color. Thus, P_m has a dominant wavelength expressed as 495c and a saturation equal to $CP_m/CM = 0.60$ referred to Standard Source C.

Since the specification of color requires three dimensions, the locus of all colors occurs in a color solid. Figure 16 is a representation of the color solid with X, Y, Z as orthogonal coordinates. The CIE chromaticity diagram of Fig. 6 is the projection of the unit plane ($X + Y + Z = 1$) on the XY plane of Fig. 16.

Color television has added the concept of chrominance to colorimetry. *Chrominance* is the colorimetric difference between any color and a reference color of equal luminance, the reference color having a specified chromaticity. With reference to Fig. 17, color OA has tristimulus values X_A, Y_A, Z_A. The reference color W has tristimulus values X_w, $Y_w = Y_A$, Z_w. The chrominance is given by the vector WA whose components are $X_A - X_w$ and $Z_A - Z_w$ and whose magnitude is proportional to Y_A.

With reference to the CIE diagram, it is seen that the greatest inscribed triangle, resulting in the greatest color gamut, is obtained by *adding* red, green, and blue primary lights. White can be matched by add-

ing these in suitable proportion, say, $W = R + G + B$. This is not contrary to the experience of those who work with subtractive methods such as color photographers and painters. The subtractive primaries are obtained by filters which subtract red, green, and blue respectively from white light, leaving

$$W - R = G + B \quad \text{called cyan}$$
$$W - G = R + B \quad \text{called magenta}$$
$$W - B = R + G \quad \text{called yellow}$$

These are sometimes loosely referred to as blue, red, and yellow.

A combination of magenta and yellow filters remove green and blue from white, leaving red light. Yellow and cyan filters remove blue and red leaving green. Magenta and cyan filters remove green and red leaving blue.

The above discussion is based on measurements and does not depend on any mechanism of color vision.

CHARLES J. HIRSCH

Abridged Color Reproduction

For Maxwell's original color photographs (1861), separate monochrome transparencies taken through red, green, and blue filters were projected in register, using corresponding filters. Hauron (1895), making paper prints with red, yellow, and blue pigments, noticed that prints bearing only red and blue impressions looked nearly fully colored in dim light. Two-color photography later became popular in motion pictures. Red and blue-green primaries were common but in the Fox and Hickey system (1914), the positive photographed by red light was projected by red light while that photographed by green was projected by white light. The resulting image was remarkably colorful. Troland (1926) correctly attributed this to the psychological effects of contrast, adaptation, and memory. Judd (1940) published a study of colors perceived with chromatic illumination, including formulas which predict the

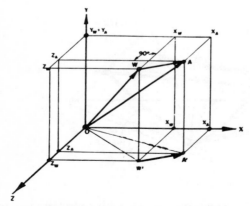

FIG. 17. Chrominance in the color solid.

colors perceived in "red-and-white" displays. Land (1959) elaborated on the Fox-Hickey experiments and proposed a graphical method of mapping colors perceived, but it lacked the generality of Judd's formulation.

The color of practically any spot of light in a dark surround can be matched by a mixture of three suitably chosen colored lights. Three such *primaries* are necessary and sufficient for most purposes. The required amounts of the primaries constitute a measure of the matched color for these conditions of viewing. This is the basis of colorimetry. However, when areas of different colors are seen together or in rapid succession, the color perception of one area affects that of another. If, in addition, these areas comprise a real or depicted scene, the interpretive portion of the visual system can strongly affect color perception. Thus in complex scenes, colors perceived are often not those that simple colorimetry might imply and would be seen if the parts were viewed separately in a dark surround.

If one stares at a bright red spot on gray paper and then looks at white paper, he perceives a bluish-green *after-image*. Every hue has an *after-image complementary* and for red, it is bluish-green. The eye scans involuntarily and the after-image of one area "thrown on" another causes interaction between the color perceptions. When red is seen beside green or immediately after it, both colors look more vivid. If spots of red, green, and blue light are partly superimposed, one can see the three primaries, the mixture of red and green giving yellow, green and blue giving cyan, blue and red giving magenta, and all three giving white. If the green spot is replaced by dim white light, it still looks green and this *induced* green appears to mix with red and blue to give yellow and cyan. Removing the blue leaves red, induced green, and the yellow mixture. If the spots are separated, they look red and white, showing the importance of *proximity* to have induction. If, when the spots are adjacent, the white light is made *brighter* than the red light, the green color is

not induced. Thus a "red-and-white" television system does not produce a satisfactory color in the sky if that is the brightest area in the scene. McCamy (1958) demonstrated that in a dim projected picture of familiar objects, many observers saw chromatic colors though the image was black-and-white. This demonstrated the effect of *memory*.

The visual system *adapts* to the quality of illumination, to a large extent almost immediately after a change and to a greater extent after 15 min. Though the illumination changes, the perceived colors of objects tend to remain constant. Objects seen in "red-and-white" displays appear to reflect light as though illuminated by pink light and the process of adaptation restores, as well as it can, the daylight colors. Of the many possible "chromatic-primary-and-white" systems, "red-and-white" gives the best effects.

It is sometimes argued that the ratio of two primaries should specify any wavelength in the spectrum, thus any color. This argument neglects the fact that purple is not a *spectral color*, having the hue of some single wavelength, but has the hue of a mixture of wavelengths at the ends of the spectrum. Every two-primary system renders alike some colors differentiated by the normal eye. The "red-and-white" system is *color blind* with respect to certain purples and greens. Selected scenes can be satisfactorily reproduced with abridged color television systems but, for general use, three primaries are needed.

C. S. McCamy

Shadowmask Tube

The shadowmask color picture tube is a directly viewed display device, capable of reproducing either full-color or black-and-white pictures. The viewing screen is composed of an orderly array of phosphor dots arranged in triangular fashion, such that each triangle consists of a red-emitting, a green-emitting, and a blue-emitting dot. Each triangle is aligned with a hole in the

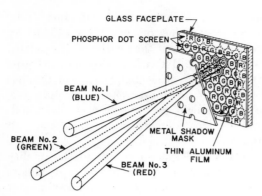

Fig. 18. Enlarged view of shadowmask tube screen assembly.

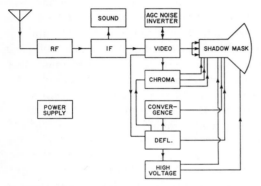

Fig. 19. Block diagram of shadowmask type of color receiver.

shadowmask located approximately 0.5 in. behind the phosphor screen.

Each electron beam, intensity-modulated by the picture signal corresponding to a particular primary color, approaches the aperture mask from such a direction that it can strike only the phosphor dot of its particular color (Fig. 18). The relative beam intensities are controlled in proportion to the relative brightness of the primary colors in the scene being reproduced. Figure 19 shows a block diagram of a typical shadowmask type color receiver.

The shadowmask is a thin metal dome with an array of round holes that increase gradually in diameter from the outer edge of the mask inward to the center. Each aperture is tapered to a sharp edge to minimize scattering of electrons from the wall of the hole. The mask array in the RCA-21FJP22

consists of holes 0.010 to 0.012 in. in diameter spaced 0.028 in. on centers.

The shadowmask tube utilizes three electrostatic-focus guns spaced 120° apart around the neck axis, with axes tilted toward the tube axis to facilitate convergence of the three beams at the shadowmask. Individual radial convergence control of each beam is achieved by excitation of internal radial-converging magnetic poles; supplemental control of the three beams horizontally is achieved by the internal lateral-converging magnetic poles (Fig. 20). The three beams are deflected simultaneously by a magnetic yoke, common to the three beams, while the radial-convergence waveforms are varied at scanning rate to maintain accurate convergence over the entire screen area. Other features of the electron gun are similar to those of a black-and-white picture tube.

The basic design dimensions are determined by ordinary geometry. Assume for simplicity that Fig. 21 represents a small planar segment of the screen assembly located on the axis of the tube. The mask and phosphor surfaces are shown parallel to each

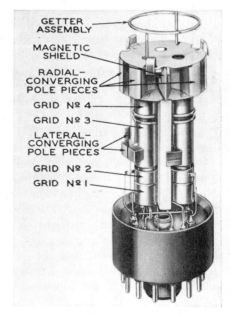

Fig. 20. Three-gun assembly utilized in RCA 21FJP22 shadowmask color picture tube.

other, spaced at distances p and L, respectively, from the source O, which is a distance S from the axis. The center-to-center spacing of the apertures in the mask is a and the center-to-center spacing of the phosphor dots is D. It can be seen that the phosphor array is a projection of the mask array having D/a times the corresponding mask dimensions. This ratio D/a which is equal to L/p, is termed the magnification λ. For a parallel-plane structure the magnification is constant regardless of the angle at which the rays strike the mask.

In a practical curved-screen structure, it is desirable that constant magnification, or uniform trio spacing, be maintained over the entire screen area to allow uniform coverage of the screen surface with tangent phosphor dots. This condition is met if the radius of curvature of the mask is equal to $1/\lambda$ times the radius of curvature of the phosphor screen. The efficiency of the system, in terms of mask transmission, T, is given by the relation

$$T = k[\sqrt{3} - (M/S)]^2$$

where k is a constant, M is the diameter of the electron beam in the deflection plane, and S is the spacing of the beam axis to the tube axis.

In the manufacture of the shadowmask kinescope, the phosphor-dot array is printed on the bulb faceplate by means of photographic deposition techniques. The phosphor is suspended in a photo-resist and is applied to the inside of the face panel. With the shadowmask in place, a light source is positioned at the center of deflection; an optical system is used to simulate movement of the electron beam in the deflection center corresponding to its motion under conditions of dynamic convergence and deflection. The array is exposed through the aperture mask and developed until only the phosphor dots of the color corresponding to that deflection center remain. The process is then repeated for each of the three colors; red, blue, and green. The screen is then coated with a conducting aluminum film, sealed to the lower-

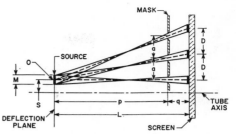

Fig. 21. Shadowmask color-tube design configuration.

funnel gun-neck assembly, and baked and evacuated as in normal cathode-ray-tube processing.

D. D. VanOrmer

Chromatron

The Chromatron ("Lawrence" color cathode-ray tube) was designed to generate color pictures especially for color television. The practical form of the tube is characterized by the following qualities:

(1) A single electron gun is used.

(2) Color selection is achieved by a bipotential deflection grid or wire grill near the phosphor screen.

(3) The phosphor screen consists of a line pattern of different color-emitting phosphor strips, essentially parallel to the strands of the selection grid.

(4) The electron beam is accelerated after passage through the selection grid.

The basic tube structure (Fig. 22) is notable for its similarity in form and construction to ordinary monochrome display cathode-ray tubes. A conventional electron gun, beam focusing unit, and deflection system are used in the typical structure. The basic design is exceptional in that satisfactory tubes with electrostatic focus, electrostatic deflection, and electrostatic selection have been manufactured.

As in monochrome television practice, the electron beam scans a field in the vicinity of the phosphor screen by means of the deflection system. Typically, a rectangular raster is generated. The beam approaches the color selector grid, which usually consists of a

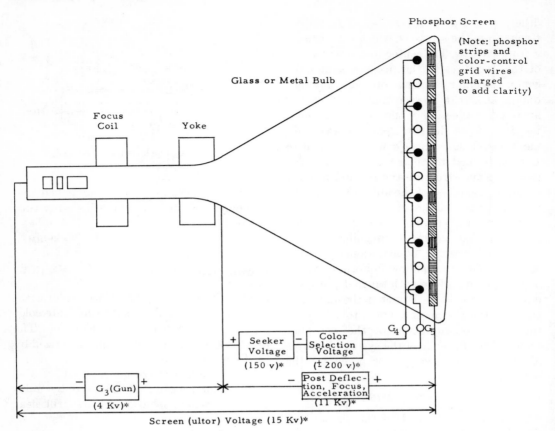

Fig. 22. Chromatron (Lawrence) color tube.

planar structure of wires in the parallel pattern with alternate wires connected to a common terminal or "bus." The trajectory of an electron beam upon passage through the grid zone may be influenced by the potentials applied to the alternate strands of the grid. The beam tends to bend in the direction of the grid wire with the most nearly positive potential, and away from the grid wire with the most negative potential. This arrangement permits the landing zone of the beam on the phosphor pattern to be determined by the voltage applied to the grid system.

In addition to the feature of color selection-deflection in a typical tube, the electron beam is accelerated after passage through the color selector grid. The screen is usually connected to a considerably higher voltage than

any other electrode in the tube. The resultant acceleration produces a constricting or focusing action so that the physical dimensions of the electron beam may be smaller than the separation of the wires of the grid. In the limit the beam may be reduced to one-third or one-fourth of the grid passage size.

When three color phosphor strips (for color television: red, blue, and green) are used, one of the series of color strips occurs in the pattern at twice the frequency of the other two colors. This comes about because two adjacent beam impingements coincide (as shown in Fig. 23) at the extreme deflected positions.

The potential arrangement cited ("post-deflection acceleration") has a tendency to increase the raster deflection sensitivity of the device, to improve the beam landing tolerances permitted for color selection, and to enhance the selector grid deflection sensitivity. The arrangement, however, brings about a difficulty in that secondary electrons originating from the selector grid wires impinge upon the screen in a random pattern and tend to limit the maximum obtainable contrast ratio. This effect may be minimized by low-secondary-emission coatings on the grid structure and relatively thick "metallized" coatings on the phosphor screen.

A number of variations of the basic tube have been described, including a form with a plurality of guns and another type using two, orthogonally disposed, selective grids. The latter tube was called a "Quadratron." In the "Quadratron" the color phosphor pattern was essentially a checkerboard array that more or less matched the openings of the crossed grills. The deflection is composite and a four-color phosphor array is possible.

In the practical form of tube with a single gun, the selection grid usually has an effective transmission (to electron beams) of about 80 to 85 per cent. When the tube is used for very fast switching (for instance, the 3.579545 Mc of NTSC type color TV) a resonant circuit for deflection is usually made up with an auxiliary inductor and the capacitance represented by the grid pairs. In this mode of operation the deflection is essentially sinusoidal with a maximum transit velocity occurring as the beam is passing the middle phosphor strip. A color switching voltage of plus or minus several hundred volts is typical of operating requirements.

The early forms of the tube employed photographic patterns to obtain the proper match to the electron beam landing, color selecting grid, and phosphor screen. In recent work, the electron beam has been used in demountable vacuum systems to obtain the exact required pattern in the phosphor array directly. The latter technique permits a departure from flat or near flat face plate structures.

The basic tube retrofits relatively easily

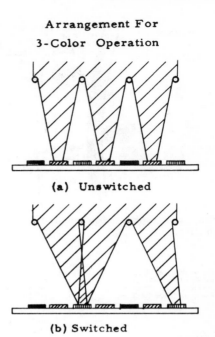

Arrangement For 3-Color Operation

(a) Unswitched

(b) Switched

Fig. 23. Switching in the Chromatron color tube.

into some existing monochrome systems because of the similarity with the monochrome cathode-ray tube both in circuit and component requirements and because of the feature that the specific color may be determined by a signal on the color selection grid.

N. F. Fyler

Apple Tube

Index-control color-television displays (Apple) are characterized by the use of triplets of color phosphors arranged on the cathode-ray-tube face in fine vertical stripes, a single electron beam, and an index mechanism, integral with the phosphor screen, to indicate instantaneous postion of the electron beam (Fig. 24). Selective excitation of the color phosphors is achieved by modulating the amplitude of the beam as it traverses the phosphor stripes in accordance with the positional information derived from the index mechanism. No aperture masks or color switching wire grids are employed.

On 21-in. tubes for the display of com-

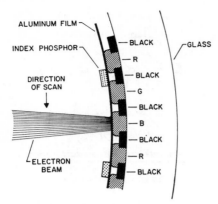

FIG. 24. Phosphor screen in an index-controlled color tube.

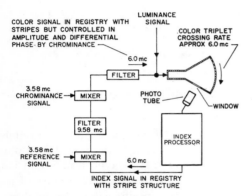

FIG. 25. Heterodyne color processing in index-control display.

mercial television, the phosphor triplets consist of alternate red, green and blue stripes each 0.010 in. wide and separated from each neighbor by a 0.010-in.-wide black guard band. At least one triplet exists for every horizontal picture element. The three phosphors are balanced to produce white light (typically 6500° K) under equal electron excitation.

The index is typically provided by stripes of a secondary emitter (such as magnesium oxide) or a photo-emitter (such as P-16) deposited in registry with the color stripes on the back side of the phosphor screen.

In reproduction of monochrome images, the tube is used exactly as a monochrome tube with luminance information directly modulating the CRT beam. In the reproduc-

tion of color images, the beam is further amplitude modulated with a high-frequency sinusoid to excite selectively the desired color phosphors; i.e., to produce red light output the beam is turned on as it crosses the red stripe, off as it crosses green and blue. The sinusoid is maintained in basic registry with the color-stripe structure by the index signal. The differential phase (with respect to the screen structure) and the amplitude of the sinusoid are controlled by the chrominance information.

The index signal resulting from the electron beam striking the index stripes is collected, amplified and processed by appropriate means to provide a signal in registry with the color-line structure on the tube face. The signal at the output of the index-signal processor, if applied to the gun of the CRT, would generate a uniform color over the tube screen. Figure 25 shows a heterodyne color-processing technique for modulating the beam as it passes over individual color stripes to produce color in accordance with transmitter instructions (chrominance information).

The index processing system must provide a means of eliminating apparent shifts in the location of individual index pulses owing to modulation of the beam by chrominance information. Two alternative techniques have been employed. The first involves the use of a second low-current electron beam, closely tracking the main beam and modulated with a high-frequency carrier. The beat product between the index structure and the high-frequency carrier is collected as the index signal.

The second method involves the use of a nonintegral number of index stripes per color triplet to average out apparent shifts in index-pulse location.

The electron-optic structure in index-controlled color displays, although simple, is unusually refined. Spot sizes one-third that of comparable monochrome tubes in horizontal dimension (necessary to resolve individual color stripes) are obtained through the use of elliptic grid apertures (typically 0.015 × 0.064 in.).

A 21-in., 74-deg-deflection-angle tube, operating at 27 kv and 300–400 μa of average beam current, produces 50 ft-lamberts average highlight brightness. Typical receivers use a circuit arrangement modified with respect to Fig. 25 to compensate for network time delay and hence permit variation in horizontal sweep linearity up to ±5%.

STEPHEN W. MOULTON

Kaiser-Aiken Thin Tube

This tube, invented by W. R. Aiken, has certain advantages in displaying color images, although most of its applications to date have exploited its principal feature, the small depth, for purposes for which black-and-white images were sufficient.

The tube's configuration differs from that of conventional cathode-ray tubes in that the basic elements that comprise a display tube (electron gun, accelerating and deflecting structures, and display screen) are arrayed in a novel way (Fig. 26). The electron beam is injected along the bottom edge of the display screen and travels in a field-free region past a set of horizontal deflection plates. If they are all at the same (anode) potential the beam continues all the way to

the right. When the voltage on one of the deflection plates is lowered, the beam is deflected upward. The position at which this deflection occurs can thus be moved in a continuous manner from right to left (or left to right) by a sequential lowering of the voltage on adjacent plates in the appropriate direction.

The upward-deflected beam enters another field-free region, bounded on one side by the display surface and on the other by the vertical deflection plates, each of which extends all the way across the tube. If the vertical deflection plates are all at the same potential, the beam continues all the way to the top. When the voltage on one of the deflection plates is lowered, the beam is deflected into the phosphor. Again, the position at which the deflection occurs can be varied continuously by sequential variation of the voltage on adjacent deflection plates. The tube can thus sweep out a raster if an appropriate sequence for each of the two sets of deflection plates is chosen. It is not necessary to have as many deflection plates as the number of horizontal or vertical elements to be resolved, since the application of time-varying (and overlapping) voltage waveforms to the deflection plates makes a smooth deflection possible.

When an electron beam of finite thickness is deflected by a uniform electrostatic field,

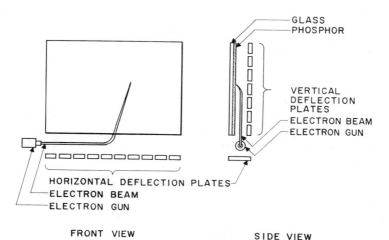

FIG. 26. Kaiser-Aiken thin cathode-ray tube.

the beam is also focused. In conventional CRT's, a phenomenon known as "deflection defocusing" occurs if the beam comes to a crossover as a result of this action and then diverges before arriving at the display screen. In the Kaiser-Aiken thin CRT, on the other hand, deflection focusing is actually turned to advantage and produces a powerful focusing action. As a result, it is possible to utilize larger beam currents for a given spot size, or to obtain a smaller spot size with the same current, than in conventional CRT's, with attendant improvements in brightness or resolution (or both).

If transparent phosphor is used and the vertical deflection plates are made of strips of transparent conductive coating on glass, the entire display becomes transparent, a feature that has resulted in the use of the Kaiser-Aiken thin CRT in the cockpit of manned aircraft, as the final display stage for the contact-analog display in integrated instrumentation (*q.v.*). In contact flight, the pilot can switch off the display and look through the tube.

A two-color display can be formed quite readily by using two beams and two sets of vertical deflection plates on opposite sides of a glass insert plate. For a three-color display several configurations have been proposed, one of which would employ a solid color on one side of the glass plate, and alternating thin phosphor strips of the other two colors on the other, with switching between the two sets of phosphor strips accomplished by one of the means described in the preceding articles. Experimental models of both the two- and three-color versions have shown very promising results, especially with regard to ease in obtaining linearity and raster registration. High levels of brightness are obtained, since the beam is subjected to the powerful focusing action described above and is not intercepted by a mask; in addition, brightness is enhanced by the circumstance that a portion of the display is viewed from the side on which the beam impinges.

CHARLES SUSSKIND

Cross-references: *Cathode-Ray Tubes (Display), Image Orthicon, Radar Displays, Solid-State Displays, Storage Tubes, Television (Black and White)*

TELEVISION [SUBSCRIPTION (PAY) TV]

Pay TV may be considered a distributing means of mass entertainment primarily in the fields of theatre, motion pictures, sports, etc. by the use of a television transmission system. In order that fees may be charged as a condition for viewing a television performance, the method of transmission of the TV signal, consisting of video and audio, must be secure. Second, some device must be used at the receiver that requires payment from the subscriber for the privilege of viewing the program.

Security. The transmission of the TV signal may be rendered secure by either transmission by coaxial cable or broadcasting over allocated TV channels. Transmission by coaxial cable is automatically secure because only those individuals subscribing to the service are provided with a cable connection. This method requires the use of a band of frequencies not normally received by domestic television receivers. Broadcasting over allocated TV channels requires some form of picture and sound scrambling which should be effective enough so that a program viewed and heard without unscrambling is substantially unintelligible.

The security of the system depends on the display device used at the receiving location. In order that the system may be economically feasible it is desirable to make use of conventional television receivers owned by the subscribers.

Transmission by Coaxial Cable. Three bands of frequencies may be used to transmit the program video and audio. The transmission may consist of:

(1) Essentially unmodified baseband video frequencies (0–4.5 Mc). This method is the simplest that may be devised; however, unfortunately, the method also has a number of inherent defects. The frequency

range involved is very wide—some 17 octaves from one extreme to the other. Because of the nature of the losses in coaxial cable, equalization must be introduced to make the attenuation in the video frequency range essentially constant.

(2) A standard vestigial sideband TV signal heterodyned down to the frequency range of 1–7.0 Mc.

(3) A standard vestigial sideband TV signal at frequencies far above baseband video frequencies.

Any one of these three bands of frequencies may be chosen to be outside the normal broadcast television channels. Thus some device must be used at the receiving site so that conventional television receivers may be used to display the program.

Broadcasting over Allocated TV Channels. This method makes use of the standard broadcast TV channels to transmit a program that has been scrambled. The use of an unscrambling device to clear up the scrambled program should be economically practical only for those viewers who have an authorized decoder and who have received the necessary decoding information in consideration of payment or their agreement to pay for the program viewed.

Encoding. The scrambling process adopted for one form of pay TV cuts the picture horizontally into segments of 7 scanning lines each and displaces alternate segments in a horizontal direction. In addition, the division between segments randomly shift their position relative to the start of the scanning field. Black-to-white inversion may be used for additional scrambling.

The displacement of video-line segments in a given field is accomplished by shifting the phase of such lines with respect to the horizontal synchronizing pulses that remain regularly spaced. The phase adjustment is accomplished by an electronic switch in combination with a video delay line having approximately 1.7 μsec of delay. The electronic switch that inserts or removes the delay is controlled by a square wave with

period of 14 lines and a starting phase relative to the vertical synchronizing pulses that is changed from field to field in accordance with the proper application of random air-code pulses transmitted during the vertical blanking interval of the composite TV signal. There are 14 possible starting phase positions of the segments formed by the delay line switch. These starting phase positions are called modes.

Transitions from mode to mode are made during the vertical synchronizing interval just mentioned under control of the air-code information. The viewer looking at a TV receiver sees in rapid succession fields in several of the 14 possible modes. Because of the persistence of vision, this gives rise to confusion and unintelligibility adequate to require the use of an unscrambling device to be able to enjoy the program.

Sound accompanying the picture is scrambled by shifting all audio components upward with respect to frequency in equal amounts. The effect of this shifting is to confuse the ear such that all intelligence is removed from the audio program.

Decoding. Fundamentally, decoding is the same process as employed in encoding but practiced in a complementary sense; i.e. when the decoder inserts delay in the video path, the decoder does not, and vice versa.

Transitions from mode to mode are made during the air-code interval just as in the encoding process. Proper application of the transmitted random air-code pulses to a mode-determining circuit supply a square wave identical to that used in the encoding process for controlling the electronic switch that inserts or removes the video delay line.

The air-code pulses consist of a random series of 6 specified video frequency bursts which, at the decoder, are separated from one another by tuned circuits and are demodulated with an envelope detector. These 6 detected frequencies are routed in thousands of different ways to 5 actuating terminals of the mode-determining circuit, thus forming the square wave for controlling the electronic switch.

Sound decoding is basically the converse of the operation employed in sound encoding; i.e., decoding is accomplished by the downward shifting in frequency of all audio components by an amount equal to the upward shifting in frequency employed in encoding.

Program Identification. A program-identification number given to the subscriber, for which a fee is charged, determines the proper setting of one or more code-setting knobs which, when accomplished correctly, effects the proper interpretation of the transmitted random air-code pulses.

Payment of Fee. The fee that is charged as a condition for viewing a television performance may be in the form of coins or tokens inserted in a coin-box decoder or it may be in the form of credit requiring periodic billing reflecting the programs viewed. An alternative method is to charge a flat monthly fee regardless of the number of programs viewed. The specific method that is employed depends greatly on whether the transmission of the TV signal is accomplished by coaxial cable or by broadcasting over allocated TV channels.

CARL G. EILERS

Cross-references: *Television (Black and White)*

TEMPERATURE SCALES

Definitions. Temperature scales have been devised to make possible the precise quantitative measurement of temperature as contrasted with its qualitative and subjective characterization. The more commonly used scales are known by the following names and abbreviations: Celsius or centigrade (°C), Fahrenheit (°F), Réaumur (°R), and centigrade absolute or Kelvin (°K). The last is essentially the thermodynamic scale of temperature. Each of these scales is based in general on a principal fixed point which determines its relative position and a secondary fixed point which

determines the size of the unit or degree, measurements being made with standard thermometric substances. Actually, the establishment of these scales has been characterized by varying degrees of precision and rigor; of current importance is the fact that today these scales are based essentially on the same primary reference point, the so-called "ice-point"—the temperature at which pure, macroscopic ice-crystals are in equilibrium with pure liquid water of normal isotopic content, saturated with and under the pressure of one standard atmosphere (1,013,250 dynes/cm² = 1.01325 bar) of air. This primary point is designated in the different scales, respectively, as 0°C, 32°F, 0°R, and 273.15°K. The designation of the ice-point for the first three scales is completely arbitrary. The value of 273.15°K is based on the acceptance of the value of 273.16°K for the ice-water-vapor triple point, which is believed to bring the Kelvin scale as close to the ideal thermodynamic scale as is possible with the present available precision of measurement.

The secondary fixed point which sets the size of the degree is the temperature at which liquid water is in equilibrium with water vapor at one atmosphere pressure. The temperature interval between the primary and the secondary points is divided respectively into 100°C, 180°F, 80°R, and 100°K.

Conversion Formulas. As a result of these definitions, relations are established between the different scales which may be expressed by the following conversion formulas:

$$n°C = [(9/5)n + 32]°F$$

$$n°C = [(4/5)n]°R$$

$$n°C = (n + 273.15)°K$$

$$n°F = (5/9)(n - 32)°C$$

$$n°F = (4/9)(n - 32)°R$$

$$n°F = [(5/9)(n - 32) + 273.15]°K$$

$$n°R = (5/4)n°C$$

$$n°R = [(9/4)n + 32]°F$$

$$n°R = [(4/5)n + 273.15]°K$$

$$n°K = (n - 273.15)°C$$

$$n°K = (4/5)(n - 273.15)°R$$

$$n°K = [(9/5)(n - 273.15) + 32]°F$$

The following examples are given to illustrate the use of these formulas:

$$100°C = 212°F = 80°R = 373.15°K$$

$$100°F = 37.78°C = 30.22°R = 310.93°K$$

$$100°R = 257°F = 125°C = 398.15°K$$

$$100°K = -279.67°F = 138.52°R = -173.15°C$$

Uses of the Temperature Scales. (1) The centigrade scale is in world-wide use for measurements in every field of pure science, and for engineering and practical measurements in countries which have adopted the metric system of units. It was invented in 1742 by Anders Celsius, a Swedish astronomer; originally, the boiling point of water was designated as 0° and the freezing point as 100°, giving an inverted scale. In 1887 the International Committee on Weights and Measures took the first steps to make this a truly international scale. It is now called the International Celsius Scale and is defined by a series of fixed points in terms of standard thermometers of various types.

(2) The Fahrenheit scale is in use principally in the British Commonwealth and the United States for everyday reference and in engineering and medical practice. It was first proposed by Gabriel Daniel Fahrenheit, who invented the alcohol thermometer in 1709 and the mercury thermometer in 1714. The zero point originally corresponded to the temperature of a mixture of equal parts of salt and snow.

(3) The Réaumur scale is still in limited use in France, Germany, and Russia. It was invented by René Antoine Ferchault de Réaumur about 1730.

(4) The Kelvin scale was proposed by Lord Kelvin in 1848, who pointed out that the second law of thermodynamics leads to a fundamental temperature scale, which is logically expressed by putting the zero point at the temperature at which all the thermal motion of atoms stops. This is the lowest conceivable temperature, the so-called "absolute zero." By selecting a value for one fixed point at some higher temperature, the whole scale is defined. In 1954 the Comité Consultativ of the International Committee of Weights and Measures recommended the value 273.16°K for the triple point, ice-water-vapor, which makes the value of the ice point at 0°C equal to 273.15°K.

DONALD H. ANDREWS

Cross-references: *Thermodynamics*

TENSORS: see MATRIX ALGEBRA; VECTOR ANALYSIS

TESLA, NIKOLA (1856–1943)

Nikola Tesla was born on July 9, 1856, in Smiljan in Serbia and after study in local schools entered the Institute of Technology at Graz in Austria, graduating in 1877. He next studied at the University of Prague and then joined a newly formed telephone company in Budapest, where he made his first invention (a telephone repeater) in 1881 and conceived the idea of a rotating magnetic field that later resulted in his development of a system of generating, distributing, and utilizing ac power. He came to the U.S. in 1884 and gradually made his mark through this all-important contribution to electrical engineering and through several allied inventions, including the utilization of oil to prevent sparking in high-voltage transformers. He received many patents on dynamos, glow tubes, rectifiers, measuring instruments, and ac technology generally.

He participated in the early development of radio transmission, notably through the development of an rf generator and of the air-core transformer known as the *Tesla coil;* he also devised a method of radio transmission and was among the first to recognize the importance of tuned circuits to long-distance communications. Around the turn of the century he became interested in a problem that preoccupied him until his death, the radio transmission of electric power. Toward the end of his life, he became something of a man of mystery, only partially revealing some of his ideas; as a result, not a few of his admirers have proposed that he came close to anticipating many inventions generally credited to others, including radar.

He received many honors during his long life, including the Edison Medal of the AIEE and several honorary degrees; nevertheless his final years were spent in relative obscurity in New York, where he died on January 7, 1943.

CHARLES SUSSKIND

Cross-references: *Historical Background of Electronics*

TETRODES: see ELECTRON TUBES (CONVENTIONAL); TRANSISTORS

THERMAL DETECTORS

In thermal detectors the incident radiation is absorbed and transformed into heat in the detector. The resulting temperature rise causes a change in some property; measurement of this change is used to indicate the influx of radiation. Examples are bolometers, thermopiles, and pneumatic detectors.

The spectral response of thermal detectors depends on the absorption characteristics of the energy receiver and on the transmission of windows between receiver and source. In general, response is independent of wavelength between ultraviolet and wavelengths approaching the receiver dimensions.

One widely used thermal detector, the *thermopile,* consists of several thermocouples series-connected, with one set of junctions against a "black" radiation receiver and the other set against a heat sink.

When radiation of a particular intensity and spectral distribution is incident on the receiver, part of the energy is absorbed, which causes the temperature of the receiver to increase until the rate of energy absorption equals the rate of energy loss by the receiver. Losses occur by convection and gaseous conduction through the surrounding atmosphere, by solid conduction through the wires of the thermopile and any other receiver supports, and by radiation from the receiver. If the thermopile enclosure is evacuated to 10^{-4} mm of Hg or less the gaseous-conduction losses are negligible. The solid-conduction losses depend on the thermal conductivity, cross-sectional area, and length of the wires supporting the receiver. With proper design such losses can be made small. The temperature rise of the receiver is small and loss by re-radiation is usually very small.

The sensitivity is dependent on the change in receiver temperature produced by a change in source intensity, the thermoelectric power of each junction, and the number of junctions in the thermopile.

The speed of response is determined by the time required for the receiver to reach equilibrium. The smaller the receiver's heat capacity the faster the response. If the conduction heat losses from the receiver were removed, its temperature would rise until its rate of re-radiation equalled the rate of absorption. There would be a great increase in sensitivity but it would be accompanied by a similar increase in time required to reach equilibrium. To increase the speed of response without increasing the sensitivity, the heat capacity of the receiver must be reduced. If the sensitivity is increased by reducing heat losses it must be done by sacrificing speed of response.

When the thermopile is exposed to high intensity radiation the temperature of the reference junctions may change. This change usually can be compensated by resistances having proper temperature coefficients. However, other factors also contribute in a lesser degree and these must be compensated.

Johnson noise is the principal noise source, although a very small noise contribution can arise from fluctuations in radiation received by the detector from, and emitted to, its environment.

Many commercial thermopiles are available. Response times vary from 2 sec for 90 per cent of maximum emf on large 12-junction thermopiles, to 0.01 sec for single-junction vacuum thermocouples. Sensitive thermopiles produce 1×10^{-6} v with 14×10^{-8} w/mm^2 incident on the receiver.

The *pneumatic detector* was developed by Marcel Golay in 1947. The Golay cell consists of a small cylindrical gas cell closed at one end with a distensible diaphragm and the other with an infrared transmitting window. Radiation passing through the window falls on an absorbing film, which transfers heat to the surrounding gas. The resulting increase in pressure causes the diaphragm to bulge. The external surface of the diaphragm is a mirror. Light from a secondary source passes through a grid, falls on the mirror, and is reflected back through a second grid to a phototube. The grids are arranged so that no light reflected from the mirror falls onto the phototube when the diaphragm is in its neutral position. A slight distension of the mirror causes light to fall on the photocathode. The amplitude of the signal produced is a function of the intensity of radiation incident on the cell.

These cells usually have time constants from 0.015 to 0.30 sec. Their sensitivity is comparable to a good vacuum thermocouple or bolometer. They can be made much faster at a sacrifice in sensitivity and are especially suited for chopped-beam detectors. Their sensitivity-time response relation is governed by considerations similar to those of thermopiles.

W. J. FREDERICKS

Cross-references: *Bolometers, Energy Conversion, Noise, Thermistors, Thermocouples, Thermoelectricity*

THERMAL RADIATION

All material objects emit electromagnetic radiation because of the thermal agitation of the electrons and nuclei of which they are composed. The amount of radiation emitted increases with increasing temperature and with increasing "blackness" of the surface. In engineering terms, blackness is a measure of the impedance match between the object and the space into which it radiates. The *emissivity e* of a surface is the ratio of the power actually emitted to that which would be emitted by an ideally black surface at the same temperature. By consideration of dynamic equilibrium between an object and a field of thermal radiation, one can see that e is also equal to the absorptivity of the surface. For common materials and wavelengths, e ranges from a few per cent to essentially unity.

A useful idealized concept is *blackbody radiation*. This is radiation of the sort emitted by an ideally black body at a given temperature T. More realistically, it is the radiation that exists inside an enclosure held at uniform temperature T, regardless of the emissivity of the walls. A small hole in such a cavity emits and absorbs radiation like an ideal black body. This cavity radiation is independent of e because if e is small, the reflectivity $(1 - e)$ is large in such a way as to exactly compensate. Because of its universality, blackbody radiation has been studied for many years—empirically, thermodynamically, and by statistical mechanics. We now cite some of the results.

Blackbody radiation is emitted in a continuous spectrum, with the power per unit bandwidth having a maximum at a frequency that is directly proportional to the absolute temperature. This is the *Wien displacement law*. If we let λ_m be the wavelength of the maximum in the energy distribution curve, we have

$$\lambda_m T = 2.898 \times 10^{-3} \text{ m-deg} \qquad (1)$$

The total radiation emitted is given by Stefan's law

$$w = \sigma T^4$$

where $\sigma = 5.67 \times 10^{-8}$ w/m^2-deg^4. The forms of both (1) and (2) may be derived by considering the radiation as a gas carried through a thermodynamic cycle. The numerical constants may be obtained empirically or from statistical mechanics.

The detailed form of the spectral distribution of blackbody radiation was first derived by Planck by introducing the concept that radiation of frequency f can only be emitted in quantum units of magnitude hf, where $h = 6.62 \times 10^{-34}$ joule-sec is Planck's constant. Combining this concept with the methods of statistical mechanics, he found the *Planck radiation law*

$$w_f = \frac{2\pi hf^3/c^2}{e^{hf/kT} - 1} \qquad (3)$$

where w_f is the power radiated per unit area per cycle of bandwidth at f, c is the speed of light (3×10^8 m/sec), and k is the Boltzmann constant 1.38×10^{-23} joule/deg. For $hf \ll kT$, this power rises as f^2; but for $hf \gg kT$, it falls exponentially as $\exp(-hf/kT)$. The maximum occurs when

$$hf_m = 2.82\, kT \qquad (4)$$

which is another form of the Wien displacement law. [The frequency f_m in (4) does not correspond to exactly the wavelength λ_m in (1) because f_m is the frequency at which there is maximum thermal radiation per unit frequency interval, whereas λ_m gives the maximum per unit wavelength interval.]

If the same statistical approach is applied to thermal radiation into a transmission line from a two-terminal network one obtains the *Nyquist* or *Johnson noise* results, so long as $hf \ll kT$. That is, for frequencies up to microwave frequencies even at temperatures as low as 1°K, we have simply

$$w_f = kT \qquad (4)$$

Introducing impedance match considerations, one can show that this requires a resistance R to generate an rms thermal noise voltage in bandwidth $\Delta f = B$ which is given by

$$V_{rms} = \sqrt{4R\, kT\, B} \qquad (6)$$

This noise level sets the ultimate limitation on the sensitivity of electronic equipment. It can be minimized by operation at low temperatures (as in masers, *q.v.*), or by use of reactive amplification (as in parametric amplifiers, *q.v.*).

MICHAEL TINKHAM

Cross-references: *Noise, Statistical Mechanics, Thermodynamics, Thermoelectricity*

THERMIONIC EMISSION

Thermionic emission is a physical phenomenon involving the liberation of electrons or ions from heated solids or liquids. The emission of electrons and ions are basically quite different. In this discussion, only electron emission from heated solids will be considered. In 1883, Edison (*q.v.*) observed the escape of negative electricity from a hot solid in his experiments with the evacuated carbon-filament lamp. W. Preece and Fleming (*q.v.*) applied Edison's discovery to the making of thermionic "valves" and the basic phenomenon was investigated more comprehensively by J. J. Thomson (*q.v.*). Thomson identified the charge carriers emitted from a negatively charged hot cathode as electrons. O. W. Richardson in 1912 was the first to derive a thermionic emission equation giving a relationship between the temperature of the cathode and the rate of emission of electrons. This equation was based on the classical electronic theory of metallic conduction. In 1922, S. Dushman applied the quantum theory to this same problem and derived the following expression:

$$I = AT^2\, e^{-\varphi/kT} \quad \text{or} \quad I = AT^2\, e^{-11600\varphi/T} \qquad (1)$$

where I is the thermionic emission current density (amp/cm^2), T is the absolute temperature (deg Kelvin), k is Boltzmann's constant, A is a semi-empirical constant, and φ is an empirical constant of the emitting surface called its work function, measured in electron volts. The quantity A as originally derived by Dushman was a universal constant equal to 60.2. Subsequent observations on atomic spectra showed that the electron has two directions of spin, and that its statistical weight should be 2, thus making A equal to 120.4. Experimentally determined values of A for pure metal surfaces fall in the range of 10 to 100.

The work function φ is a measure of the energy required for an electron to escape from the interior of a metal cathode to the field-free space outside. Its value is usually between 1 and 6 ev. The major part of the work involved in an electron escaping from the cathode surface is in overcoming the electrostatic image force. This force extends over a large distance compared with the interatomic spacing, thus making it possible to counteract it by applying a strong external accelerating electric field. The application of a field of E v/cm to a homogeneous cathode surface reduces the work function by $3.78 \times 10^{-4} E^{1/2}$ ev. This field effect is taken into account by modifying Eq. (1) to read:

$$I = AT^2 e^{-(11600\varphi - 4.38E^{1/2})/T} \qquad (2)$$

The increase in thermionic emission obtained from a constant temperature cathode by increasing the accelerating field is called the "Schottky effect."

With a fixed accelerating field applied to the cathode, the emission current does not increase indefinitely as the temperature is increased. When the number of electrons traveling in the space between the cathode and anode becomes equal to the total charge maintained on the anode surface by an externally applied voltage V, the electric field at the surface of the cathode is reduced to zero. Further increase in cathode temperature results in very little increase in anode current because of the development of a retarding field at the surface of the cathode produced by space charge. The space-charge-limited emission current I may be expressed by the following relation due to C. D. Child (1911) and Langmuir (1913, q.v.):

$$I = SV^{3/2} \qquad (3)$$

S is a constant for any given geometrical arrangement of electrodes. (For parallel planes, $S = 2.33 \times 10^{-6}/d^2$, if d is the

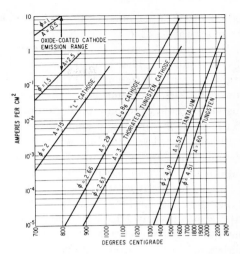

FIG. 1. The thermionic emission of several cathodes and their emission constants. ϕ is in electron volts and A is in amp/cm² deg K².

distance between the electrodes in cm, I is in amp/cm², and V is in volts.)

The engineering applications of thermionic emission occur chiefly in vacuum and gas discharge tubes where a heated cathode is used to supply free electrons. Tungsten and tantalum have found the widest use for pure metal cathodes because of their low evaporation rate when heated to elevated temperatures. Their emission constants are given in the figure. These values are for polycrystalline materials and consequentially describe the average electron emission obtained from an assembly of clean heterogeneous surfaces. The refractory-metal cathodes are quite stable and not easily subjected to emission poisoning by surface contamination, but their emission efficiencies are very low. At 1800°C, tungsten has an emission current density of 0.3 amp/cm² with an emission efficiency of only 5 ma/w of heater power.

More efficient thermionic emitters may be produced by depositing electro-positive metals such as Cs, Ba, La, or Th on a refractory base metal such as tungsten in the form of films about 0.7 of a monolayer thick. These adsorbed atoms become polarized, producing a dipole moment which reduces the work function below the value characteristic of the adsorbed metal in bulk. The evaporation rate of the atoms from the fractional monolayer is much less than for the bulk metal. The thermionic emission obtained from these surfaces may be expressed by the Dushman equation, but the constants A and φ become purely empirical. Useful cathodes are made from these composite surfaces by providing a mechanism for replacing those atoms which are lost by evaporation. Several mechanisms are used: by an independent source that continually evaporates the active material onto the cathode surface (Hull dispenser cathode); by continuous decomposition of a compound (matrix or impregnated cathodes); and by diffusion of the active material through a porous base (Lemmens "L" cathode). The thoriated tungsten cathode has a composite surface of thorium on tungsten. The thorium diffuses over the tungsten surface from grain boundaries where occluded thoria is reduced by special heat treatment. The lanthanum hexaboride cathode consists of a monolayer of lanthanum on an inert metallic refractory compound of LaB_6. The surface is maintained active by diffusion of lanthanum through the compound.

By far the most important thermionic emitter is the oxide cathode discovered by A. Wehnelt in 1903. This cathode consists of a layer of alkaline earth oxide crystals on a nickel base. The coating is a porous structure of small crystallites consisting of a solid solution of Ba, Sr, and frequently Ca oxides. High thermionic activity in this n-type semiconductor coating would appear to depend on donor centers produced by an excess of Ba. Reducing agents are added to the nickel to maintain a Ba excess during the life of the cathode. The oxide cathode has the highest thermionic emission efficiency. At 800°C the efficiency is 50 ma/w.

J. M. LAFFERTY

Cross-references: *Field Emission, Photoelectric Emission, Secondary Emission, Work Function*

THERMISTORS

A thermistor is a thermally sensitive resistor whose primary function is to exhibit a change in electrical resistance with a change in body temperature. Of greatest interest are thermistors that are hard, ceramic-like, electronic semiconductors which exhibit a relatively large negative temperature coefficient of resistance. This discussion is limited to such thermistors.

Types of Thermistors. The types of thermistors that are generally available are shown in Table I. A much greater variety of geometrical shapes, sizes, resistance values and temperature coefficient values are available, on special request, from most manufacturers.

Since most thermistors are made of a combination of metallic oxides, their stability, to a large extent, depends on the stability of the oxide system used. For this reason, hermetically sealed thermistors exhibit greater stability than those which are not sealed.

Hermetically sealed bead-type thermistors have a maximum temperature rating of

TABLE I

Thermistor Type	Size (in.)	R_t @ 25°C (ohms)	Temperature coefficient $(-\%/°C)$
Glass-coated bead	0.01–0.088 dia.	5–17.5 Meg	2.0–5.5
Bead in glass probe or rod	0.04 dia. × ⅛ long	5–12 Meg	2.0–5.5
	0.1 dia. × 2 long		
Bead in glass bulb	0.09–0.5 dia.	500–5.4 Meg	2.5–4.6
Disk	0.05–1.0 dia.	4–521 K	1.35–5.25
Wafer	0.1 × 0.1–0.41 × 0.41	10–1 Meg	3.9–6.8
Rod	0.05–0.625 dia.	4.5–1 Meg	1.35–6.5
Washer	0.2–0.8 dia.	5–1.5 K	1.35–5.25

300°C although they may be used at temperatures as high as 500°C for some applications. Disk, wafer, rod, and washer type thermistors without leads are generally rated at 200°C. When leads are attached, this maximum temperature rating is reduced to 150°C, although some special types may be used successfully at temperatures as high as 600°F.

Almost all thermistors are available with a variety of standard and special mountings.

Thermal Characteristics. If power is applied to a thermistor, the differential heat-transfer equation that describes the situation is

$$P = dH/dt = \delta(T - T_a) + C\,dT/dt \quad (1)$$

where $P = dH/dt$ is the rate of energy applied to the thermistor, δ is the dissipation constant of the thermistor, C is the heat capacity of the thermistor, and T and T_a are the thermistor and ambient temperatures, respectively.

The solution of Eq. (1) is

$$T = T_a + (P/\delta)(1 - e^{-\delta t/c}) \quad (2)$$

which, for the case of thermal equilibrium, reduces to

$$T_E = T_a + P/\delta \quad (3)$$

If the power dissipated in the thermistor is negligibly small so that the equilibrium temperature of the thermistor does not differ significantly from its surrounding ambient temperature (i.e., $P/\delta \ll |T_a|$), Eq. (1) may be restated as

$$dT/dt = -(\delta/C)(T - T_a) \quad (4)$$

Equation (4) is a mathematical statement of Newton's law of cooling, which has the well-known solution,

$$T = T_a + (T_i - T_a)e^{-t/\tau} \quad (5)$$

where T_i is the initial temperature and $\tau = C/\delta$ is the time constant of the thermistor.

It is clear from Eqs. (1) and (3) that the *dissipation constant* δ may be defined as a constant of proportionality between the power dissipated and the resultant temperature rise in a thermistor. The dissipation constant of a thermistor generally increases slightly with increasing temperature.

The *thermal time constant* τ obtained from Eq. (5) may be defined as the time required for a thermistor to change 63 per cent of the difference between its initial temperature value and that of its surroundings when negligible power is being dissipated in it.

Since both of these constants depend on the rate of heat transfer between the thermistor and its surroundings, they are considerably affected by the method of mounting the thermistor as well as the medium or environment in which it is located.

For a simple thermistor structure and mounting, such as a bead, disk, wafer, or rod supported by its leads, the product of the dissipation and time constants is approximately equal to a constant ($\tau\delta = C$). For more complex thermal structures, such as a bead sealed in a solid glass probe, this relationship is not valid.

Electrical Characteristics. Three fundamental electrical characteristics form the basis of all circuit analysis and applications involving the use of thermistors.

(a) *Resistance-Temperature Characteristic.* The resistance-temperature characteristics of two of the most commonly used thermistor materials are shown in Fig. 1 in terms of their specific resistance and inverse absolute temperature. The curves shown are nearly linear, which is characteristic of semicon-

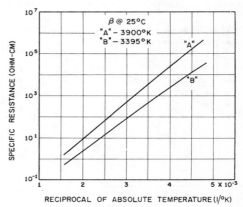

FIG. 1

ductors whose temperature-dependence of resistivity can be assumed to arise from the thermal excitation of carriers over a single energy gap. Hence, the relationship between resistance and temperature of a thermistor may be expressed mathematically as

$$\ln R = a + \beta/T; \qquad T_1 \leq T \leq T_2 \quad (6)$$

where β is the slope of the curve assumed to be constant in the range $T_1 \leq T \leq T_2$ and T is the absolute temperature (°C + 273.15) of the thermistor. Over any limited temperature range, $T_1 \leq T \leq T_2$, for which β may be considered constant, the following relationships may be used:

$$R(T) = R(T_0)e^{\beta(1/T - 1/T_0)}; \quad T_1 \leq T, T_0 \leq T_2 \quad (7)$$

$$\alpha(T) \equiv [1/R(T)][dR(T)/dT] \cong -\beta/T^2 \quad (8)$$

where α is the temperature coefficient of resistance expressed, generally in ohms/ohm/°C or %/°C.

More accurate equations which, to some extent, take into account the temperature dependence of β, are

$$R(T) = AT^{-c} e^{D/T} \quad (9)$$

$$\ln R(T) = a + b/(T + \theta) \quad (10)$$

$$\ln R(T) = a + [b/(T + \theta)] + cT \quad (11)$$

(b) *Voltage-Current Characteristic.* Current passing through a thermistor causes a self-heating effect given by

$$T - T_a = P/\delta \quad (12)$$

where P is the power dissipated in the ther-

mistor and T, T_a, and δ are as previously defined. This effect is readily shown on a static voltage-current curve. A typical curve, for a bead type thermistor mounted in an evacuated glass bulb, is shown in Fig. 2. At low currents, for which the power dissipated is small compared with the dissipation constant, the effective change in temperature is small and Ohm's law is obeyed. Hence, at low power levels, voltage is proportional to current and the characteristic is a straight line. With increasing current the effects of self-heating become evident and the temperature of the thermistor rises with a resultant decrease in its resistance. The corresponding steady state voltage deviates increasingly from a straight line. At some particular current the voltage attains a maximum value and actually decreases with a further increase in current. The absolute temperature at which this peak in voltage occurs is given by

$$T_p = (\beta/2) - \sqrt{(\beta/2)^2 - \beta T_a} \quad (13)$$

At this temperature, the peak voltage is given by

$$E_p = \sqrt{R_p \delta (T_p - T_a)} \quad (14)$$

where R_p is the resistance corresponding to T_p obtained from the resistance-temperature characteristic.

The voltage-current characteristic is of basic importance for the analysis of circuits in which self-heated thermistors are used. Such circuits are generally analyzed graphically. The equilibrium operating condition of the thermistor is obtained from the intersection of the voltage-current characteristic (plotted on linear coordinates) and a load line given by

$$E = E_{Thév} - IR_{Thév} \quad (15)$$

where $E_{Thév}$ and $R_{Thév}$ are obtained from the Thévenin equivalent circuit for the thermistor. A necessary constraint is that the operating point correspond to a power level which is below the maximum allowable rated power of the thermistor. If $R_{Thév}$ is too low, the thermistor may be heated to

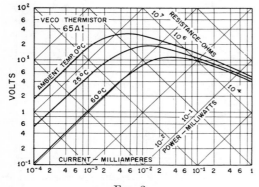

FIG. 2

destruction before a steady-state condition is reached.

From the voltage-current characteristic, it is apparent that the thermistor exhibits a negative-resistance characteristic when it is operated beyond the peak of the curve. In designing thermistor circuits, consideration of this fact is of prime importance if circuit stability is to be achieved.

Given the dissipation constant δ and the resistance-temperature characteristic of a thermistor, its voltage-current characteristic may be obtained graphically on log-log coordinates as follows:

(a) Obtain E_p from Eqs. (13) and (14).

(b) Assume lines of constant power.

(c) Determine the temperature corresponding to each power from Eq. (12).

(d) Obtain the resistance corresponding to each of these temperatures.

(d) Plot points at the intersections of the constant resistance and assumed constant power lines.

(c) *Current-Time Characteristic.* The decrease in resistance, which results from a current sufficient to self-heat a thermistor, cannot occur instantaneously. When a thermistor is excited from an equivalent Thévenin source, a time delay must occur before the equilibrium operating condition is reached. The initial current is determined by the source voltage, source impedance, and cold resistance of the thermistor. In general, the initial rate of current increase is small. As the thermistor becomes hot, the rate of current increase is more rapid at first and then decreases to zero as the equilibrium condition is approached asymptotically. Hence, the current-time characteristic takes the form of an S-shaped curve. The curvature is dependent upon the circuit design parameters as well as the dissipation constant and thermal capacity of the thermistor. By proper choice of thermistor and circuit design, it is possible to vary the time delay from a few milliseconds to several minutes.

Thermistor Applications. Thermistor applications are based on the three fundamental electrical characteristics described.

Those which depend upon the resistance-temperature characteristic are temperature measurement, control, and compensation. Included also are applications in which temperature is used as a dependent variable. For example, in an *hypsometer*, the temperature of a boiling fluid is used to determine the vapor pressure to which the fluid is exposed.

Applications that make use of the voltage-current characteristic of a thermistor may be subdivided into two classes: those for which the dissipation constant is varied due to changes in the environment or heat-transfer medium to which the thermistor is exposed and those for which the dissipation constant is fixed and either the equivalent source voltage, source impedance, or power level of the thermistor is varied. Applications which are based on a variation in the dissipation constant include vacuum, liquid-level, and fluid-flow measurement and control as well as thermal-conductivity gas analysis. Included in applications that make use of a fixed dissipation constant are voltage and current regulation, volume limiting, audio-frequency signal compression or expansion, power-level measurement and bolometry, automatic volume level or gain regulation, and switching circuits (*q.v.*). Analysis of thermistor bolometers is somewhat different than other applications which make use of the voltage-current characteristic. In this application the measuring thermistor is connected in a balanced, self-heated dc bridge. This thermistor is then heated further by rf power. The change in the dc bridge required to re-establish balance is generally used as a measure of the rf power.

Applications that depend on the current-time characteristic of a thermistor include time delay, surge suppression, and overload protection.

Indirectly heated thermistors, in which an electrically isolated heater winding is used in close thermal coupling with the thermistor, may be employed for most applications in which self-heated thermistors are used. When such thermistors are used, the voltage-current or current-time characteristic is replaced by the resistance-temperature characteristic of the thermistors. Indirectly heated thermistors are most commonly used for ac-to-dc transfer devices, automatic gain control, and fluid-flow measurement.

MEYER SAPOFF

Cross-references: *Bolometers, Thermal Detectors, Thermocouples*

THERMOCOUPLES

A thermocouple is a temperature sensing device consisting of two wires, bare or insulated, of different metals or alloys and twisted, welded or soldered at one end to form a junction. The device is based on the discovery of the *thermoelectric effect* by Seebeck in 1821. The thermoelectric effect is the generation of a current in a closed circuit containing two thermocouple junctions at different temperatures. The electric current is the result of two other effects, the *Peltier effect* and the *Thomson effect*.

The Peltier effect (discovered in 1834) is the liberation or absorption of heat at the junction of two different conductors when an electric current passes through the junction. The sign of the heat transfer depends on the direction of the current. The quantity of heat depends on the density of the current and a constant related to the absolute temperature of the junction and the nature of the conductors.

The Thomson effect is the liberation or absorption of heat when a current passes through a region of a homogenous conductor in which a temperature gradient exists. The sign of the heat transfer depends on the direction of current flow and the nature of the conductor. The quantity of heat depends on the current density, the temperature gradient in the region considered, and a constant relating to the absolute temperature of the region and the nature of the conductor.

Both Peltier effect and Thomson effect are independent of the Joule heating of the wires.

Thermocouple behavior accordingly can be expressed in three empirically derived laws:

(1) *The law of homogenous conductors*, which states that heat alone cannot generate an electric current in a conductor irrespective of its shape.

(2) *The law of intermediate metals*, which states that in a junction of different conductors with a uniform temperature the thermoelectromotive force generated in the junction is independent of the conductors in the junction except the terminal conductors, and is the same as if these terminal conductors were in direct contact.

(3) *The law of intermediate temperatures*, which states that the thermoelectromotive force developed by thermocouples of homogenous different metals with a temperature differential at the junctions is the algebraic sum of the emf's developed by the same couples at any intermediate temperature differences (making the developed emf's independent of the temperature gradient in the wires).

Thermocouples are selected on the basis of their sensitivity, temperature range and their ability to withstand corrosive, (oxidizing and reducing) environments at elevated temperatures. In practice they are frequently sheathed in ceramic or metallic protective covering. The most sensitive thermocouple junctions are made from Constantan and Chromel wire (approximately 80 μv/°C, -100 to $+1000$°C). Highest-temperature-range thermocouples are made from platinum wire and a wire made from 90 per cent platinum and 10 per cent rhodium (discovered by H. L. le Châtelier) (approximately 8 μv/°C, 0 to 1450°C). Most resistant to reducing and oxidizing atmospheres is a thermocouple made from copper and Constantan wires (approx. 60 μv/°C, -200 to $+350$°C).

THOMAS JASKI

Cross-references: *Bolometers, Thermal Detectors, Thermistor, Thermoelectricity*

THERMODYNAMICS

Thermodynamics treats systems whose states are determined by thermal parameters, such as temperature, in addition to mechanical and electromagnetic parameters. By *system* we mean a geometric section of the universe whose boundaries may be fixed or varied, and which may contain matter or energy or both. The *state* of a system is a reproducible condition, defined by assigning fixed numerical values to the measurable attributes of the system. These attributes may be wholly reproduced as soon as a fraction of them have been reproduced. In this case the fractional number of attributes determines the state, and is referred to as the *number of variables of state* or the *number of degrees of freedom* of the system.

The concept of *temperatures* can be evolved as soon as a means is available for determining when a body is "hotter" or "colder." Such means might involve the measurement of a physical parameter such as the volume of a given mass of the body. When a "hotter" body A is placed in contact with a "colder" body B, it is observed that A becomes "colder" and B "hotter". When no further changes occur, and the joint system involving the two bodies has come to equilibrium, the two bodies are said to have the same temperature. It is a fact of experience that two bodies that have been shown to be individually in equilibrium with a third, will be in equilibrium when placed in contact with each other, i.e., will have the same temperature. This statement is sometimes called the *zeroth law* of thermodynamics. The physical parameter used to specify the "hotness" of the third body might be adopted as a quantitative measure of temperature, in which case, that body becomes the thermometer.

From what has been said above it is apparent that temperature can only be measured at equilibrium. Therefore thermodynamics is a science of equilibrium, and a thermodynamic state is necessarily an equilibrium state. Furthermore, it is a macroscopic discipline, dealing only with the properties of matter and energy in bulk, and does not recognize atomic and molecular structure. Although severely limited in this respect, it has the advantage of being completely insensitive to any change in our ideas concerning molecular phenomena, so that its laws have broad and permanent generality. Its chief service is to provide mathematical relations between the measurable parameters of a system in equilibrium so that, for example, a variable like the pressure may be computed when the temperature is known, and *vice versa*.

It provides these relations with the aid of three postulates or *laws* (in addition to the zeroth law) which we shall now proceed to explain.

The *first law* of thermodynamics may be expressed in the following form,

$$dE = Dq - Dw \qquad (1)$$

where dE represents a differential change in the *internal energy* of a system during some change defined by the passage of the system from one thermodynamic state to another. Dq and Dw are, respectively, the *heat* absorbed by the system and the *work* done by the system on its environment during the differential change. The small d preceding E in (1) implies that dE is an exact differential, or that E depends only on the state of the system, and is independent of the path of the change. The large D in Dq and Dw implies that in general this is not true for the *heat* and *work*.

To understand clearly what is meant by *heat* and *work* and to gain further insight into the meaning of (1), consider a system set up in such a manner that it can exchange energy only with its surroundings in the form of well-defined mechanical or electrical work. Such an arrangement might involve surrounding the system by an *adiabatic* wall. Then it is observed that the system always undergoes the same change when a given amount of work is given to it or extracted from it. This observation prompts us to define a quantity, E, the internal energy, to be associated with each state of the system, whose change (and therefore whose value to within a constant) can be measured by the amount of work passing between system and environment when the change of state is performed under adiabatic conditions.

If, now, the same change of state (defined by the thermodynamic states between which the system passes) is conducted under non-adiabatic conditions, it is found that the work involved does not equal the previously measured change in E. Conservation of energy then demands that an exchange take place between the system and its environment that is not recognizable as work. This quantity of energy is defined as *heat*, and is nothing more than a discrepancy term designed to transform (1) into the equality which it is. Heat, therefore, has no measurable existence of its own. It is incorrect to say that a body contains a particular amount of heat, even though the quantity of heat passing in or out of a system is measurable because the work done by the system and its internal energy can both be measured.

The *second law* of thermodynamics may be expressed as follows,

$$T \, dS - Dq \geq 0 \qquad (2)$$

Here T stands for the temperature and S denotes the *entropy* of the system. Dq has the same meaning as in (1). To understand fully the entropy as well as the inequality in (2) is necessary to understand *reversible* and *irreversible* processes. A *reversible* process is one in which an infinitesimal change in driving force of the process completely reverses the process in all of its detailed aspects. For example, consider a gas enclosed in a cylinder by a weighted frictionless piston. Let the pressure exerted by the weighted piston be just insufficient (by an infinitesimal amount) to contain the gas in equilibrium. A slow expansion occurs that can be completely reversed by an infinitesimal change in driving force, i.e., by an

infinitesimal increase in the weight of the piston.

Another example of a reversible process, more chemical in nature, is the slow discharge of an electrochemical cell, maintained slow by the action of an impressed electromotive force. A slight increase in this electromotive force not only reverses the flow of current, but also the chemical reaction of discharge, and causes a slow electrolysis to occur.

A distinguishing feature of a reversible process is its physical impossibility. It occurs infinitely slowly and may be aptly described as a sequence of equilibrium states. Nevertheless, calculations of phenomena as they would occur, were reversibility truly possible, are feasible (for example, it is possible to calculate the volume work performed by a gas as it passes through a sequence of equilibrium states or the electrical work performed by a cell as it discharges through a sequence of equilibrium states), and it is this aspect that lends importance to the concept of reversibility.

By contrast, an *irreversible* process is any real process, occurring at a finite rate, and with any degree of violence. In (2) the inequality refers to an irreversible, and the equality to a reversible change of state. As indicated by the use of d in front of S, the differential of S is exact, so that S is a function only of the thermodynamic state of the system. This is part of the postulate. Equation (2) also specifies how S is to be measured, for if the change of state is conducted reversibly,

$$dS = \frac{Dq}{T} \qquad (3)$$

Measurement of the heat absorbed by a system in a change conducted reversibly then yields dS directly by division by T.

An immediate consequence of (2) is that in a system isolated from its surroundings, so that Dq is zero, any irreversible change is necessarily accompanied by an increase in entropy, whereas for a reversible change no variation in entropy occurs. Since irreversible changes are to be associated with real changes this is tantamount to the assertion that the entropy of an isolated system increases for real spontaneous changes so that it is maximized when the system achieves equilibrium, i.e., when no further real spontaneous change is possible. In line with this assertion, (2) shows that $dS = 0$, for a reversible change, i.e., one involving a system in equilibrium.

The quantity S seems somewhat more abstract than E. Logically, however, the two are on the same basis. E is generally more familiar than S since the latter is a thermal quantity, associated specifically with thermodynamics. A nonthermodynamic, molecular interpretation of S can be given. This interpretation asserts that S measures the logarithm of the relative probability of a given state. It is not surprising, then, that S increases in a spontaneous process.

In its early development thermodynamics was an engineering subject. A good deal of its inquiries were directed toward the efficiency of machines. The inequality (2) tells immediately how to get the most work out of a system. Thus by substituting the value of Dq, obtained through solution of (1), the following result is obtained,

$$DW \leq T\, dS - dE \qquad (4)$$

the inequality still referring to an irreversible process. Since the right member contains exact differentials only, its value is determined by the states between which the change occurs rather than by the path of the change. Therefore it is apparent that the left side (the work performed by the system) is maximized when the equality holds, i.e., when the system operates reversibly or when the change is conducted over such a path that it occurs reversibly.

A machine that converts heat into work generally operates in cycles, abstracting an amount of heat Q_2 from a reservoir at a higher temperature T_2, performing a certain amount of work W, and returning an amount of heat $-Q_1$ to a reservoir at the tempera-

ture T_1. The efficiency η of the machine is defined as the fraction of the amount of heat absorbed at the higher temperature that is converted into work during one cycle. Thus

$$\eta = W/Q_2 \qquad (5)$$

After one cycle the machine returns to its original state and, therefore, the total changes in its internal energy E and entropy S are zero. From what has been said above, the maximum efficiency is achieved when the machine operates reversibly. But, then, since dS is zero and the total change of entropy is Q_2/T_2 plus Q_1/T_1, we have

$$\frac{Q_2}{T_2} + \frac{Q_1}{T_1} = 0 \qquad (6)$$

Furthermore, since dE is also zero, Eq. (1) demands that

$$Q_1 + Q_2 = W \qquad (7)$$

The simultaneous solution of (6) and (7) yields

$$\eta = \frac{W}{Q_2} = \frac{T_2 - T_1}{T_2} \qquad (8)$$

This shows that no machine operating in cycles can be 100-percent efficient, i.e., that it is impossible to convert heat entirely into work without effecting permanent changes. The latter statement is often taken as an alternative form of the second law.

The universal efficiency η, depending only, as it does, on the temperatures of the two reservoirs, can be used to define the thermodynamic scale of temperature. Thus two reservoirs have the ratio of thermodynamic temperatures

$$\frac{K_2}{K_1} = \frac{1}{1 - \eta} \qquad (9)$$

where η is the efficiency of a machine (any machine) operating reversibly between them. If to (9) we add the requirement

$$K_2 - K_1 = 100 \qquad (10)$$

when the high-temperature reservoir is boiling water, and the low temperature is a mixture of ice and water, then K proves to be identical with T, the Kelvin temperature. The thermodynamic temperature has the advantage of being independent of the properties of any special substance.

The *third law* of thermodynamics asserts that *the entropy of a system at the absolute zero of temperature (T or $K = 0$) is zero, provided that the system is in its lowest energy state.* In reality this cannot be said to be strictly a law of thermodynamics, since it presumes an acquaintance with the detailed structure of the system, especially in regard to its spectrum of energy states. Despite these nonthermodynamic overtones, the third law is extremely useful in many applications. For example, if a system is observed to undergo a change at absolute zero involving a loss of entropy, one may conclude that originally it was not in its lowest energy state. Another application involves the calculation of the equilibrium constant of a chemical system from purely thermal measurements.

Some of the most important applications of thermodynamics are achieved by substituting Dq from (1) into (2), i.e., by combination of the first and second laws. The result is

$$D\varphi = dE + DW - T\,dS \leq 0 \qquad (11)$$

where the inequality still stands for an irreversible spontaneous process. $D\varphi$ is used as a shorthand for the three terms on its right. $D\varphi$ assumes a special form depending upon the work that the system is capable of doing. For example, if the system can only do volume work,

$$DW = p\,dV \qquad (12)$$

where p is the pressure and V the volume of the system. Then

$$D\varphi = dE + p\,dV - T\,dS \leq 0 \qquad (13)$$

It is convenient to find some function ψ, dependent only on the thermodynamic state of the system, which imitates $D\varphi$ when certain restricted changes of state are carried out. For example, let $\psi = E$; E imi-

tates $D\varphi$ for changes of state in which V and S are maintained constant, since then dV and dS are zero. Suppose the initial state of the system is one of equilibrium. Then no spontaneous change can occur and all possible changes are the reverse of spontaneous ones. Then

$$D\varphi = (dE)_{S,V} > 0 \qquad (14)$$

for all possible changes, where the subscripts S and V indicate the maintained constancy of those variables. Equation (14) implies that if the initial state is one of equilibrium E is a minimum for all displacements along paths of constant entropy and volume.

The displacement involved is *not* one leading *out of equilibrium*, for then functions like S could not be given experimental meaning along its path. Rather, additional forces are added to the system against which the system can perform other than volume work, so that a new state of equilibrium is reached subject to these new forces. This statement will be elaborated below.

Another choice of ψ might be

$$\psi = F = E + pV - TS \qquad (15)$$

the so called Gibbs' free energy. This function imitates $D\varphi$ along paths of constant temperature and pressure, and can be shown (in the same manner employed in the case of E) to be minimized along these paths in a state of equilibrium. This minimization may be expressed by

$$(dF)_{T,p} = 0 \qquad (16)$$

Here again a displacement from equilibrium is not implied. Rather an additional force is added, leading to a new equilibrium. For example, suppose the system represents a solution involving a chemical reaction. If the reaction is set up in a chemical cell, no electromotive force persists when chemical equilibrium has been achieved. The state of the system is determined by variables of state including temperature, pressure, and composition. If, now, a new force is added in the form of an impressed electromotive force, electrolysis occurs and a new state of equilibrium is achieved subject to the magnitude of the impressed electromotive force. The variables of state are greater by one (the E.M.F.) than in the original equilibrium state. It is to this kind of displacement that (16) refers.

It can be shown that the change ΔF in F can be measured by the electrical work performed in the displacement. Equation (16) can be used as a differential equation connecting the variables of state in the initial equilibrium state. So can (14), for that matter, by writing dF more explicitly in terms of the variations of variables of state.

In this manner it can be shown that when a solute is distributed between two phases 1 and 2, at equilibrium, and F_1 and F_2 are the free energies of the two phases, then

$$\left(\frac{\partial F_1}{\partial n_1^{1}}\right)_{T,p,n^1} = \left(\frac{\partial F_2}{\partial n_1^{2}}\right)_{T,p,n^2} \qquad (17)$$

where n_1^{1} and n_1^{2} are the numbers of moles of the solute in phases 1 and 2, respectively, and n^1 and n^2 represent the mole numbers of other components. For many solutes it is observed that

$$\left(\frac{\partial F}{\partial n}\right)_{T,p} = K + RT \ln c \qquad (18)$$

where K and R are constants at any one temperature and pressure and c is the concentration of the solute. Substitution of (18) into (17) with appropriate attachment of subscripts yields

$$\frac{c_1^{2}}{c_1^{1}} = \exp\left[-\left(\frac{K_2 - K_1}{RT}\right)\right] = K \qquad (19)$$

and defines the partition coefficient k.

Since F is minimized at constant temperature and pressure in the equilibrium state, any reaction system that is in a state in which F is not minimized at the temperature and pressure in question drifts toward the state in which it is. A knowledge of F as a function of composition thus permits the prediction of the direction in which a particular reaction will proceed.

Many other applications are possible, for example other thermodynamic potentials like F and E can be invented, with consequent utility.

HOWARD REISS

Cross-references: *Statistical Mechanics, Temperature Scales, Thermal Radiation, Thermoelectricity*

THERMOELECTRICITY

Thermoelectric effects may be separated into two classes, reversible and irreversible. The dominant *irreversible* process is the generation of Joule heat by an electric current in a resistive medium. The heat produced per unit time is given by

$$w_J = i^2 R \qquad (1)$$

where i is the current and R is the resistance. Clearly this heating effect is always positive regardless of the direction of current flow. The *reversible* thermoelectric effects, however, produce heating *or* cooling, depending on the direction of current flow. Conversely, an electromotive force (emf) is produced when temperature differences exist, and this emf changes sign when the temperature difference is reversed. This reversible thermoelectric effect was discovered by Seebeck in 1826. Further investigation showed it to consist of two parts, the Peltier and Thomson effects. The Peltier effect is a surface effect at the junction between two metals. The *Peltier coefficient* π (units: volts), which depends on temperature T, gives the quantity of heat produced (or absorbed) at a junction per unit charge transferred across the junction. It represents the emf that resides in the junction. The Thomson effect refers to a reversible heating (or cooling) effect produced when an electric current flows through a material in which there is also a temperature gradient and associated heat current. The *Thomson coefficient* σ of a metal (units: volts/degree) characterizes this effect. Combining them, we have the total emf in a thermocouple circuit of two metals (a, b) with junctions at temperatures T_0 and T being given by

$$e = \pi - \pi_0 + \int_{T_0}^{T} \sigma_b \, dT - \int_{T_0}^{T} \sigma_a \, dT \qquad (2)$$

This is the thermal emf measured with a potentiometer under zero-current conditions, so that there is no Joule heating. The *thermoelectric power* of the two metals is defined as $P = de/dT$, with the temperature of the junction at T_0 being held constant. Hence,

$$P = de/dT = d\pi/dT + (\sigma_b - \sigma_a) \qquad (3)$$

By application of thermodynamics, these two reversible effects can be separately determined from the measured temperature-dependent emf. We consider an element of charge q to move around the circuit, and ignore the irreversible Joule heating. (More rigorous treatments handle the reversible and irreversible effects together, but lead to the same result.) Applying the second law of thermodynamics to this reversible cycle, we add up the entropy changes around the cycle, and set the sum equal to zero:

$$q\left\{\frac{\pi}{T} - \frac{\pi_0}{T_0} + \int_{T_0}^{T} \frac{\sigma_b\, dT}{T} - \int_{T_0}^{T} \frac{\sigma_a\, dT}{T}\right\} = 0 \qquad (4)$$

Holding T_0 fixed, and differentiating with respect to T, we obtain

$$\sigma_b - \sigma_a = -T \frac{d}{dT}\left(\frac{\pi}{T}\right) \qquad (5)$$

Inserting this in (3), we find

$$\pi = TP = T\, de/dT \qquad (6)$$

and putting this into (5), we find

$$\sigma_b - \sigma_a = -T \frac{d^2e}{dT^2} = -T \frac{dP}{dT} \qquad (7)$$

For most pairs of metals, $e(T)$ is roughly parabolic in form. Hence $(\sigma_b - \sigma_a)/T$ is roughly constant. Lead is conventionally chosen as the reference metal for tables of thermoelectric coefficients because its Thomson coefficient is supposed to be nearly zero. A more rigorous zero reference is provided by a superconducting metal, because there is no entropy associated with the flow of a supercurrent, and hence no Thomson heat.

Although we have separated the reversible effects from the irreversible ones for our discussion, they are in reality inextricably linked. This fact limits the practical applica-

tion of thermoelectric devices as sources of electrical energy or as refrigerators. The thermodynamic relations derived above are rigorously correct, however.

MICHAEL TINKHAM

Cross-references: *Energy Conversion, Statistical Mechanics, Superconductivity, Thermal Radiation, Thermodynamics*

THERMOPLASTIC RECORDING: see VIDEO RECORDING

THOMSON, SIR JOSEPH JOHN (1856–1940)

Born at Chetham Hill in England in 1856, Joseph John Thomson entered Cambridge when he was 20 years old and remained associated with that university for the rest of his life. During the early years of his studies Thomson was interested in the mechanics of vortex rings, but he soon shifted to the study of electrical phenomena. It was in that field that Thomson, leader of the Cavendish group of physicists, made his greatest contributions. During an intensive study of cathode rays he found that the rays could be deflected by either an electric or a magnetic field and that they were made up of minute particles. Thomson then proceeded to measure the ratio of mass over charge of these particles and found that it was very small, as compared with a deter-

Sir J. J. Thomson

mination of this ratio for electrolytes, even though the latter carried the same charge. He therefore concluded that they were charged particles one to two thousand times lighter than the hydrogen atom, which was then considered to be the lightest particle.

This discovery of the electron was announced at the Royal Institution in 1897. Its implications were far-reaching, and led to the theory of the electrical nature of the atom, later expanded by Rutherford's and Bohr's brilliant contributions. Thomson's investigations, in association with Aston, of the nature of positive rays, led to the discovery of a new method for the separation of atoms that could not be recognized or separated readily by ordinary chemical techniques. This resulted in the discovery of a large number of isotopes and was the beginning of mass spectroscopy, a technique that gained great importance in both the laboratory and industry.

Thomson was a Fellow of the Royal Society, a Member of the Order of Merit and the recipient of the Nobel prize for physics in 1906 "in recognition of the great services rendered by him in his theoretical and experimental investigations into the transmission of electricity through gases." He was knighted in 1908.

BERNARD JAFFE

Cross-references: *Historical Background of Electronics*

THYRATRONS

Thyratrons are a class of grid-controlled, gas-filled hot-cathode tubes characterized by having two stable states. In the quiescent or unfired state, the tube acts as a switch in the open position; in the second or fired state, the tube approximates a short circuit. Transition from the unfired to fired state is accomplished by application of a low-energy triggering signal to the thyratron grid electrode. The transition to the "open-circuit" state may be accomplished only by interruption of the anode current for a duration of time sufficient for the plasma

(i.e., the positive-ion and electron) density to de-ionize to a sufficiently low value for the tube to regain anode holdoff ability.

The time necessary for the anode to recover its holdoff ability may be reduced by application of negative bias. The effect of negative bias is to prevent electrons in the residual ionization from flowing to the anode. With negative bias applied, appreciable ion currents flow to the grid so that the grid circuit impedance is important in determining the actual bias level and thus the recovery time.

Three general circuit methods exist for the interruption of anode current:

(1) The use of a mechanical switch or a relay (*q.v.*) in the anode circuit to remove anode voltage for a suitable period of time.

(2) The use of ac potentials on the anode, as in service with rectifier tubes (*q.v.*), where the reversal of anode potential causes the current to interrupt for the duration of the negative half cycle.

(3) The use of a condenser in the anode circuit, which causes the anode current to interrupt after the condenser has delivered its charge to the anode circuit. The condenser is then recharged at a suitably slow rate by means of a large charging resistor or inductor to allow the tube to recover. This method is typically used in pulse generation (*q.v.*).

High-voltage holdoff in the unfired state is obtained by designing the anode space and adjusting the gas pressure such that the electron mean free path in the anode space is sufficiently large compared to the anode space dimension to make cumulative ionization improbable. In this mode of operation anode-voltage holdoff ability increases as either the pressure or anode space dimensions are reduced.

Figure 1 shows the essential elements of a thyratron. The close-fitting box structure around the anode is sometimes omitted in low-pressure tubes. A system of baffles or grids are interspersed between anode and cathode in order to confine the dimensions in the direction of the anode field to small

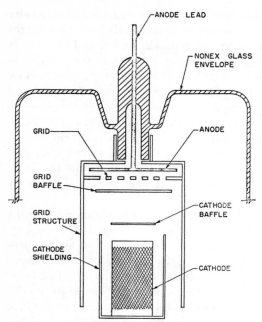

FIG. 1. Structure of a thyratron.

values. The cathodes generally contain heat shields to conserve heater power.

Triggering is accomplished either by suddenly reducing the negative bias on the grid so that the anode field penetrates into the grid cathode space, allowing electron current to flow to the anode, which causes cumulative ionization (negative-control thyratrons); or, in the case of baffled grids used in the hydrogen thyratron, as shown in Fig. 1, by raising the grid potential sufficiently to generate an ionized discharge in the grid cathode space which discharge then commutes to the anode.

The switching power gain (ratio between switching power and triggering power) exceeds 10^7 for negative-control tubes and approaches 10^5 in tubes requiring ionization by the trigger pulse.

An oxide cathode supplies the discharge current thermionically. The gaseous discharge plasma formed supplies a means of neutralizing the electron space charge, which allows the passage of very high currents with low tube drop. This operation results in the discharge current being determined by the external circuit parameters.

For moderate current levels, of the order of several amperes, the tube drop is determined by the gas fill used and is in the order of 10 v for mercury or xenon fillings and about 40 v for hydrogen fillings. At high peak currents, as in hydrogen thyratrons operated in pulse generating circuits, the tube drop increases owing to cathode resistivity and may be of the order of 100 v.

The gas fillings commonly used are mercury vapor, xenon, or hydrogen. Mercury is added in bulk quantities (seen as droplets) and supplies a pressure of mercury as determined by the vapor pressure of mercury at the "cool spot" temperature of the tube. Because of the strong dependence of pressure on temperature, the ratings of mercury tubes depend on temperature. At operating temperatures the vapor pressure is on the order of 20 microns. Mercury-filled tubes are characterized as having low tube drop in the fired state because of the low ionization potential of mercury; they are also free from gas clean-up effects because of the reservoir of bulk mercury. De-ionization times are long because of the slow diffusion of mercury ions and the presence of long-lived metastable states.

Xenon-filled tubes have discharge properties similar to mercury but they do not suffer from the extreme temperature dependence of mercury. Because xenon tubes have no gas reservoir, operation at high-frequency conditions that result in gas clean-up must be avoided. The xenon gas pressures used are in the range of 100 microns.

Hydrogen-filled tubes have the advantage of high anode holdoff voltage, fast switching and recovery times, and the ability to pass high peak currents. The major disadvantages are high tube drop because of the high ionization potential of hydrogen and about 25 per cent more heater power for a given cathode area.

They were developed during World War II to supply the need for a switching tube capable of switching high current pulses to radar oscillator tubes at rates often exceeding several kilocycles per second. The short de-ionization time of hydrogen (it may approach 10 μsec) permits rapid recovery of anode holdoff ability and thus allows operation at high repetition rates. The grids of hydrogen thyratrons are normally highly baffled to facilitate high anode holdoff voltage and short recovery times, and to alleviate grid-emission problems. These tubes thus require generation of trigger plasma in the grid cathode space to cause anode firing. Hydrogen, though susceptible to some degreee of gas clean-up, does not suffer to the same extent as the rare gases under high-repetition-rate conditions. Furthermore, it has been possible to construct hydrogen reservoirs in the form of titanium or zirconium-hydrogen mixtures which when heated yield the desired pressure.

Xenon and mercury tubes are generally used in low-frequency or semi-dc application. Their low tube drop results in minimum dissipation and the long de-ionization time and clean-up problem of xenon does not become a serious disadvantage.

Typical ratings range from 650 v and 100 ma in a negative-control xenon-filled 7-pin miniature tube size to 25 kv and 5 amp in a mercury-filled tube 20 in. long and 7 in. in diameter.

Hydrogen thyratrons for pulse generator service range from the 7-pin miniature size rated at 1000 v and 20 amp peak current to tubes 7 in. in diameter and 20 in. long rated at 30 kV anode voltage and 2000 amp peak current.

Recent development of ceramic-envelope hydrogen thyratrons has permitted a considerable degree of size reduction. For example, tubes 3 in. in diamter and 6 in. long are capable of handling 25,000 v and 1500 amp of peak current.

For low-voltage applications in the range up to 500 v thyratrons are receiving severe competition from solid-state switching devices. It is quite probable that at operating voltages below a few kilovolts solid-state devices will completely replace thyratrons in the coming years.

Seymour Goldberg

Cross-references: *Gases, Ignitron, Pulse Generation, Switches, TR and ATR Tubes*

TOPOLOGICAL ANALYSIS: see NETWORK THEORY

TR AND ATR TUBES

In radar systems that use one antenna for both reception and transmission, some form of switch must be provided that will (a) connect the antenna to the transmitter during the transmission interval and at the same time disconnect the receiver from the antenna, and (b) connect the antenna to the receiver during the reception interval and at the same time disconnect the transmitter from the antenna.

Transmit Receive (TR) and Anti-Transmit Receive (ATR) tubes are important parts of the assembly that provide these switching actions.

The antenna switching system employed is called a *duplexer*. It includes gas-filled switching tubes mounted within waveguide sections. The simplest form of duplexer is a branched duplexer shown in Fig. 1. The ATR tube is basically a $\lambda_g/4$ section of waveguide filled with a low-pressure gas that ionizes when subjected to high microwave power. The end of the ATR tube nearest the duplexer is sealed by a glass-to-metal window that is transparent to microwave energy. The TR tube depending upon the bandwidth required can either be a low-Q or high-Q bandpass filter. It is also filled with a

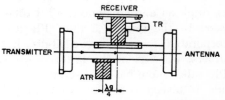

Fig. 1. Branched duplexer with ATR and TR tube.

low-pressure gas and enclosed at each end by resonant window structures. In the circuit shown, the ATR and TR tubes are both in series with the duplexer circuit; hence, the terminal windows are spaced by $\lambda_g/4$. Shunt or series-shunt combinations may be used and may require different spacings. Broadband operation of the duplexer can be achieved by using multiple ATR tubes suitably spaced.

On transmission of the high rf power, the gas in both the ATR and TR tubes ionizes presenting very low impedances at the terminal windows. Hence, the transmitted energy is passed directly to the antenna with only small amounts of energy dissipated in the ATR and TR circuits. The low impedance of the discharge in the TR tube greatly attenuates the energy reaching the receiver arm. The receiver is sufficiently isolated from the transmitter so that damage of the sensitive detector elements in the receiver is avoided. After the transmission interval the discharge within the ATR and TR tubes is rapidly neutralized so that the receiver is rapidly connected to the antenna. If targets close to the radar are to be seen, the action of the switch must be extremely fast. During reception the received signal passes directly from the antenna to the receiver through the unfired TR tube. The high impedance presented by the unfired ATR tube prevents receiver energy from being absorbed in the transmitter and hence provides a low loss transmission path from the antenna to the receiver.

In general, TR and ATR tubes can be combined in a number of different duplexer configurations. For broadband and high-power operation, the tubes can be coupled into duplexers such as a balanced dual TR tube duplexer and a balanced ATR tube duplexer. In the former, a dual TR tube is incorporated between two 3-db hybrid couplers, whereas in the latter, a series of ATR tubes mounted in a section of waveguide is placed between two 3-db hybrid couplers in order to provide the proper switching action.

TR tubes are fabricated from one or more resonant structures spaced $\lambda_g/4$ apart and enclosed in a vacuum-tight envelope which contains a low pressure gas (usually argon or argon and water vapor). There are two general types of tubes. The high-Q, narrow-passband type is, generally, mechanically tunable by either an integral or separate cavity envelope. The low-Q, broadband TR type consists of a number of resonant elements and has a passband of approximately 10 per cent or more. A cut-away view of a typical four-element broadband tube is shown in Fig. 2. It consists of resonant input and output windows and two resonant filter sections. The resonant filter section consists of truncated cones as the capacitive element and baffles or posts as the inductive element. The prime function of the filter section is to produce a relatively higher value of electric field in the gap spacing between the truncated cones in order to enhance the rapid ionization of the gas in the gap spacing upon application of the transmitter pulse. An ignitor electrode or keep-alive structure is placed within one truncated cone. A dc discharge is operated to insure the existence of a residual electron density in the gap. This is necessary for proper initiation of the discharge and reduction of TR tube leakage energy. The input window of the tube controls the efficiency of switching the transmitter pulse. In general, the values of leakage energy and switching efficiency are optimized by incorporating as high a value Q for the elements as consistent with the rf bandpass.

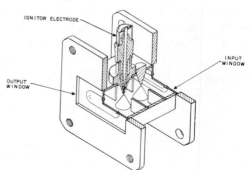

FIG. 2. Broadband TR tube.

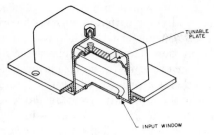

Fig. 3. ATR tube.

The construction of a typical ATR tube is shown in Fig. 3. The ATR tube basically contains a rectangular cavity whose resonant frequency is governed by the distance from the face of the tube to the tunable back plate. The window has an opening that resonates as a dielectric window at the desired frequency. A diaphragm across the back of the tube permits movement of a tuning plate so that the resonant frequency can be adjusted. The entire tube is sealed and contains a low-pressure gas.

Under received conditions, the broadband duplexer tube merely attenuates signal frequencies outside the passband; if a very high-level signal is received within its passband, it fires, thus affording receiver protection. The ATR tube basically presents an open circuit to the line; its loaded Q is determined by the window Q and the efficiency of the open circuit is determined by the losses in the window structure.

When a high-power microwave pulse is applied, a gas discharge breakdown occurs between the truncated cones. The rapidly increasing electron density in the filter section results in a very rapid increase in attenuation of the power transmitted through the filter section. The attenuation is due to both the reflective and absorbed properties of a filter containing an ionized medium. Some 10^{-7}–10^{-8} sec after the breakdown of the filter gap, the gas in the vicinity of the input window breaks down and a high-density plasma (q.v.) is created behind the input window, producing an effective short circuit. The plasma at the window approaches a quasi-steady state condition providing an additional attenuation to the

incident power. The leakage energy through the discharge is also attenuated by the plasma in the filter section. The combined attenuation provided by the discharges at the window and the filter section can be of the order of 60 to 80 db.

The leakage energy transmitted through the TR tube to the receiver during the firing time of the filter structure is commonly known as the "spike" leakage energy. The leakage energy transmitted through the tube to the receiver from the time the filter sections are fired until the end of the pulse is referred to as the "flat" leakage energy. The spike leakage energy is controlled to a first order by the filter characteristics and configuration and by the nature of the gas fill and gas pressure. The flat leakage energy depends upon the combined attenuation produced by the discharge at the window and at the filter section. If the power leakage through the window discharge is sufficiently high to maintain the discharge at the filter section, the leakage energy through the filter section is independent of the characteristics of the window discharge.

The arc loss (fraction of the incident power absorbed within the window) is a measure of the switching efficiency of the tube. It depends upon the characteristics of the input window and the gas discharge at the window, since practically all of the incident microwave power is controlled and reflected by the discharge at the input window. These losses are important since the heat dissipation within the window can become a limiting factor on both life and high-power operation.

The time required for deionization to occur during the off period of the transmitter is designated as the "recovery time." It is controlled predominantly by the gas characteristics and physical conditions in the vicinity of the input window since the electron density at the window is much higher than the electron density at the filter section.

At low and moderate power levels TR and ATR tubes generally rely on water vapor to speed recovery by the process of electron attachment. Because water vapor can react chemically with the walls of the tube during the high-power interval, some cleanup of the water vapor occurs during the life of the tubes and, hence, recovery time increases with tube life. For high power operation, in general, water vapor is not used and other techniques in conjunction with gases such as argon and krypton are employed which basically increase the electron diffusion rate. These techniques are found to be more stable during tube life at high powers.

TR and ATR tubes have been used in many applications varying from frequencies as low as 400 Mc up to frequencies of the order of 70 kMc. The tubes can be designed into many types of duplexer circuits depending upon the bandwidth and power requirements. By proper design, operation can be achieved over a wide range of environmental conditions and power levels and life times from 500 to over 5000 hr can be realized.

LAWRENCE GOULD

Cross-references: *Electric Discharge, Radar, Resonators and Wavemeters, Switches, Waveguides and Waveguide Components*

TRAFFIC CONTROL: see AUTOMOBILE TRAFFIC CONTROL; NAVIGATION

TRANSDUCERS

A transducer is a device designed to transform a physical stimulus into a change in an electrical circuit parameter, usually to provide remote readout, print-out, or data input for subsequent computer processing either as information or for a control function.

The general definition above has, through current usage, been confined largely to classes of instruments that are small in size and closely related to the aircraft, missile, and space fields. Other applications exist in industrial process controls and experimental work of many kinds.

Transducers may logically be grouped by the stimulus to which they are subjected and further subdivided with reference to the principle used to transfer that stimulus into useful information. The essential characteristics of such instruments are (1) performance, which is the measure of the transducer's ability to supply faithfully accurate data, and (2) the effect of the environments in which they will have to function on such performance. Other considerations, usually less significant, are size, weight, and configuration.

The stimuli to be measured occur as a result of basic physical phenomena such as *displacement*, which may be linear or angular. The time derivatives of displacement in increasing order are also of interest: *velocity*, *acceleration* and, less frequently, *jerk*. These again may be either linear or angular. Other stimuli are *pressure* and *temperature*. Although time derivatives of these last are not specifically defined, time dependence, as in transient or dynamic situations, strongly influences the design of transducers intended to measure it.

The field may be greatly broadened if all phenomena were to be included but in the context of the term 'transducer,' as it is now most generally understood, the above description covers the majority of situations.

The transduction principles or means of transforming a change in physical stimulus into a change in an electric circuit are as varied as the many physical relationships known to modern science. However, current technology has limited the use of these methods to a relative few. They are essentially those which involve variations in resistance, inductance, and reluctance. Useful data are obtained by supplying such transducers with an input voltage and developing an output voltage as a function of the changes in one of the parameters mentioned. This change in turn is produced through the application of the physical stimulus to be measured.

In addition to the three methods mentioned above, many instruments are also manufactured using piezo-electric, vibrating-wire, photoelectric, capacitive, electrokinetic, ionization, magnetostrictive, ohm-strictive, and other special phenomena, although to a lesser extent. Depending on the method used the *transfer function* of the transducer may be as high as 1.0 or as low as 0.002. The transfer function is defined as the ratio of the full-scale output voltage (maximum voltage due to the application of the highest value of the stimulus to be measured) to the input or supply voltage.

As an example, one of the most common transducer principles utilizing change in resistance is the potentiometric type, which uses the voltage across a fixed resistance element as a potential source, and a contact movable in electrical continuity with that resistance, giving a voltage drop between itself and one end of the element. In this specific case the contact is moved by the input stimulus. The transfer function is 1.0 because maximum voltage output is equal to the voltage input. In absolute terms, depending on the current-carrying capacity of the element, the output voltage may be 5 v or more, thus providing a substantial potential with which to supply control information, telemetry data, etc.

A different variable-resistance technique is that which uses strain-sensitive material as a means of providing changes in electrical output with input stimulus. In this instance, wire or semiconductor materials may be used that provide a change in resistance with change in strain. These strain-sensitive elements are connected to form a Wheatstone bridge with a constant voltage applied across the bridge as the material is strained. An electrical unbalance occurs and a voltage appears across the output terminals of the bridge. In this case the output voltage is small relative to the input voltage and the transfer function is correspondingly approximately 0.002, with an absolute value of the voltage output of approximately 0.020 v.

The above comparison is interesting in other respects in that each of these transducer types have other advantages and disadvantages that closely relate their usage to the specific function they are called upon to serve.

The potentiometric type has resulted in instruments using displacements of the moving contact from 0.100 in. to several feet. The strain-gage transducer, however, because of its necessary dependency on the strain limits of materials used, permits displacement from 0.0003 to 0.002 in. only.

The potentiometer type most frequently uses a wirewound element consisting of a fine 0.001-in.-diameter (or thinner) wire wound closely spaced on an insulating mandrel. The moving contact, usually of precious metal, moves across the turns in contact with two or more turns at any one time. In this type of instrument, friction between the two moving parts is of major concern, as is the number of turns of the element, which becomes a measure of the instrument's ability to sense small changes. This *resolution* is considered equal to the spacing from one wire to the next.

Conductive materials have been developed that may be substituted for the wirewound element in many applications. Such materials, because of their homogeneous construction, do not exhibit finite resolution in the same sense as the wirewound element. Instruments utilize such components where continuous resolution is necessary as part of the final circuitry.

In the variable-inductance transducer an electromagnetic field generated by the current flowing through a primary coil is usually coupled to a secondary coil by a magnetically permeable material, which may be moved relative to the fixed coils. A stimulus may actuate this moving part and alter the voltage developed in the secondary coil by changing the amount of inductive coupling. This principle is used largely in linear-motion devices consisting of cylindrically wound primary and secondary coils coupled through their center by a movable core.

The same principle is used in rotating devices, where the coils are wound on a stator and the rotor consists of a magnetically permeable material.

This variable inductance principle produces a usable output over a relatively wide range of displacements from a few thousandths of an inch to several inches in the linear type and from a few degrees to over 90° in the rotary type.

A related transducer type utilizing the principle of variable reluctance produces an output change in a secondary coil as a function of change in the reluctance of a magnetic circuit. This relation is usually accomplished by providing a portion of the magnetic circuit as a movable section or armature in such a way that a change in air gap substantially alters its reluctance. The applied stimulus then moves this armature. Large changes in the circuit reluctance occur with small displacements in the armature, which usually do not exceed a few thousandths of an inch.

Of the remaining transduction principles, two, the piezo-electric and vibrating-wire types, are used most frequently. The piezoelectric differs from the examples just described in that it utilizes a crystalline material which, under dynamic strain, produces an output voltage proportional to that strain. Because the output is only generated under dynamic conditions, this type of device cannot be used for static or steady-state measurements. It is normally manufactured as a miniature instrument intended to measure vibration or dynamic pressures.

The vibrating-wire transducer comprises a fine wire supported in such a way that its tension is varied by the applied stimulus. When this wire lies between the poles of a permanent magnet it vibrates at its natural frequency when an oscillating voltage of that frequency is applied to it. The output of this transducer, then, consists of an oscillating voltage which changes in frequency with the resonant frequency of the wire as it in turn varies in tension with the applied stimulus. This principle is frequently used as an accelerometer with a small mass attached to the wire at its mid-point.

Each transducer principle, it will be noted, requires a displacement before an output

from the instrument can be obtained. This displacement, as has been mentioned, can vary from a fraction of a thousandth of an inch to as much as several feet. Because of the differences of displacements required, certain transduction principles lend themselves to the measurement of certain physical stimuli. Linear motions, for example, may be sensed by many of the principles discussed depending on the limits of travel. For that reason very small displacements are frequently measured with strain-gage instruments; very large displacements are measured with linear potentiometers or linear differential transformers. The choice between these latter two types of instrumentation then depends on the rest of the system and its properties as effected by the performance characteristics of the transducer.

Acceleration may be measured by a wide number of transduction principles but the choice of principle now becomes dependent on another property, the natural frequency. An *accelerometer* consists of a mass-spring system whose natural frequency is a function of the ratio of spring constant to the mass. Depending on the range of acceleration to be measured and these two parameters, the mass displacement can vary over a considerable range. Thus, depending on the natural frequency desired in such an instrument, a number of choices are available. When accelerations due to vibration are important, the instrument must reproduce that vibration to as high a frequency as possible. This condition is satisfied with transducer types that have the very smallest displacement for full-scale output. Hence, piezoelectric and strain-gage accelerometers are used largely in this application. If longer-term or steady-state accelerations are to be investigated and the short-term, higher-frequency vibration effects to be ignored, the accelerometers using a larger displacement such as the potentiometric types become very effective. All the accelerometers, in order to avoid large errors near their natural or resonant frequency, require damping. This damping may be achieved through several means and is usually accomplished by viscous effects of oil or gas or through energy losses in magnetic materials.

At the present time the gas-damped and oil-damped techniques are most prevalent, with a number of means now being used to make viscous effects independent of temperature. Another important performance characteristic of an accelerometer is its ability to withstand significant acceleration at right angles to its sensitive axis, without inducing appreciable outputs in the sensitive direction. This requirement imposes certain design restrictions and most accelerometers of the types mentioned have errors less than 0.01 G per G of cross axis acceleration.

Pressure measurements are achieved by summing this stimulus over a flexible material which in turn is permitted limited travel. The flexible member may be a diaphragm, capsule, bellows, or several variations of bourdon tubes. All of these under the influence of pressure produce a limited displacement. Again, displacements and transduction principle are matched so that those sensors which under pressure have very short travel (such as flat, small-diameter diaphragms) are, in turn, coupled by those devices that best utilize small displacements (such as strain-gage or variable-reluctance transducers). The bellows sensing devices have relatively long travel and are, hence, compatible with variable-inductance or the potentiometric type of transducer.

Absolute pressures are measured by sealing either the capsule or bellows assembly, or the instrument chamber, at a reference pressure usually cose to zero. Gage pressure is measured by giving the reference side of the instrument access to the ambient conditions. Differential pressure may be measured by permitting the two pressures in question access to opposite sides of the sensing member. In those situations where the fluids are corrosive, the sensing member must be of corrosion-resistant material and the internal portion of the instrument must be, in turn, isolated through another flexible member from the fluid.

Temperature may be measured by several techniques: (1) the expansion or contraction of fluids with temperature which, in turn, produce changes in pressure; (2) expansion and contraction of materials which, in turn, produce displacements; and (3) changes in electrical property of materials directly with change in temperature. The first two are simple extensions of the transducers already discussed and any principle that utilizes pressure changes may be accommodated by the first method; any transduction principle utilizing the appropriate displacements may accommodate the second method. The third technique is related in a sense to the strain-gage type except that the change in electrical resistance of the wire used is produced by changes in temperature either to the wire itself or the members to which they are attached. Such devices must, of course, be isolated from strains or such strains must be cancelled by the mechanical arrangement in order to avoid errors induced from this source.

The performance parameters of transducers in general reflect the capability of such instruments of faithful electrical reproduction of the stimuli they are expected to measure. Since instrument output is usually expected to be proportional to input, this proportionality is expected, in turn, to remain constant. Variations in this constant are usually expressed as nonlinearities. The degree of nonlinearity may be a percentage of full-scale reading or of each reading depending on the accuracy requirements of the user. Other performance characteristics are hysteresis, repeatability, friction, and resolution, which are defined as follows.

Hysteresis is the maximum difference in output of a transducer at a given stimulus point when that point is approached with increasing stimulus followed by decreasing stimulus.

Repeatability is expressed as half the total spread of outputs at a given stimulus point under repeated calibration under identical conditions.

Friction is the effect caused by contact

between two or more moving parts within the instrument and is usually determined by taking the difference between readings under static conditions and readings following light tapping or vibration intended to remove such sources of friction.

Resolution is usually considered as the smallest change in stimulus that will produce a measurable change in instrument output.

A technique now receiving general approval throughout the transducer field is the total-error-band concept, which simply includes all the above effects within a single error envelope. In special cases both an error band and specific limits on parameters may be required simultaneously.

GEORGE J. BROWN

Cross-references: *Computer Printout and Reading, Missile Guidance, Piezoelectricity, Potentiometers, Telemetry, Thermal Detectors*

TRANSFORMERS

A transformer comprises two or more coils coupled by a magnetic field that is common to all. The purpose of so arranging coils is generally to transform the magnitude of an electrical voltage or current to a more desirable or useful magnitude. The original electrical quantity is then the *primary* current or voltage and the resultant electrical quantity or quantities the *secondary*, *tertiary*, etc., voltage or current.

Transformers may be classified by the range of frequencies at which they can be efficiently applied as audio, intermediate-frequency, and radio-frequency transformers. Audio-frequency transformers are subclassified according to their principal function such as power transformers, interstage transformers, output transformers, driver transformer, modulation transformer, and so on.

Audio-frequency transformers contain a ferric core in a closed magnetic-circuit configuration. The shape of the magnetic circuit is determined by the requirements of the primary voltage or current. In most electronic circuits this is a single-phase current, except in large power transformers, where three-phase current may be used, with corresponding complication of core structure. Materials used for efficient transformer cores are specially alloyed steels containing silicon. Cores are built up from many electrically isolated thin sheets of steel to reduce eddy-current losses in the cores.

Special forms of transformer cores, designed to minimize losses through leakage fields, are the spirally wound cores and torroidal cores.

Important design parameters of transformers are the ampere-turns required to obtain a desirable flux density in the core, the turns ratio of primaries and secondaries, the inductances of the windings and their distributed capacitances, and the primary and secondary impedances. Efficiently designed transformers for use at a single frequency in the audio range have efficiencies of 90 per cent or more.

Losses in audio-frequency transformers include the joule heating of the windings, leakage of flux, and hysteresis and eddy-current losses in the cores. Very large power transformers are liquid cooled, but the majority of transformers used in electronic circuits are air cooled without special design to facilitate cooling.

Regulation of the transformer expresses its ability to maintain secondary voltage under load variations and is a function of resistive losses in the windings in properly designed transformers. Transformers are specified in terms of capacity at a particular temperature rise, quality of insulation, regulation, turns ratios, impedances of the windings, and protective enclosures. Quality of insulation is specified in terms of resistance to moisture, high temperatures, and high potentials.

High-frequency transformers are air-cored or have cores of special ferrite materials. High-frequency transformers generally consist of two or more windings on a common coil form. For moderately high frequencies the coils are wound duolaterally. For high frequencies single-layer solenoids are common. Transformers are rarely used above 60

Mc, where other methods of transformation must be used. Special forms of high-frequency transformers consist of etched laminate spirals on two sides of a low-loss dielectric support. High-frequency transformers are virtually always shielded.

Losses in high-frequency transformers are the same as for single coils used at the same frequencies. High-frequency transformers are generally used at a relatively narrow range of frequencies and are tuned by means of capacitance for the center frequency of this range.

Although Faraday conceived the basic concepts of transformers, Nikola Tesla (*q.v.*) was the first to experiment extensively with high-frequency transformers as well as high-voltage transformers beyond the primitive "inductorium" of the mid-Nineteenth century. Power transformers were not applied to any extent until the advent of distribution of ac power later in the century demanded transmission at high voltages for economic reasons. At present such transformers are used for voltages up to 360,000 v and with capacities exceeding 100,000 kw.

THOMAS JASKI

Cross-references: *Autotransformers (Variable), Coils, Magnetism, Pulse Generation*

TRANSIENTS: see NETWORK THEORY

TRANSISTORS

Junction Transistors

The junction transistor is a solid-state component consisting basically of three layers of alternating conductivity type in a body of semiconductor material. The overwhelming majority of all transistors are of the junction type. The great importance of this device arises from its ability to supply useful power gain in a wide variety of applications. Probably more than any other single invention, the junction transistor is responsible for the recent rapid growth of the electronics industry. This is particularly

true in the computer field, for without this component the large-scale computers of today could not function.

The junction transistor was invented in 1948 by Shockley from a theoretical consideration of the electronic processes taking place at a PN junction in semiconductors. Since the basic three-layer structure necessary to obtain transistor action can be achieved by a wide variety of processes in several different materials, rapid evolution has occurred since the original invention.

The first junction transistors were made from germanium, since the technology for preparing and processing other semiconductors of adequate quality was not yet developed. Today germanium and silicon are the principal semiconductor materials, although laboratory devices have been prepared in gallium arsenide. Although other materials will become important in special applications, it appears that silicon and germanium may remain the most important. Germanium transistor usage has been dominant from the beginning. It seems likely, however, that silicon will replace it as the most common semiconductor material during the 1960's.

The two boundaries between the three layers of a junction transistor are PN junctions, which individually exhibit rectifier characteristics like a conventional semiconductor diode. The operation of a transistor is different from that of two diodes connected together because there is an interaction between the two junctions resulting from the finite rate of recombination of holes and electrons in the center region.

When the junction between the emitter and base regions is forward biased so that current flows across this junction, the current is carried principally by the flow of carriers from the emitter into the base; i.e., by holes in the case of a PNP transistor and by electrons for an NPN. Since these injected minority carriers have a finite lifetime in the base region, they flow through the base by diffusion because of concentration gradient or by drift because of an electric field. If the collector junction is biased in the reverse direction, then those minority carriers reaching the high electric field in this junction are rapidly swept into the collector and appear as collector current. Those minority carriers recombining in the base require a flow of base current to maintain the bias on the junctions. In rough analogy to a vacuum triode, the emitter, base, and collector are comparable to cathode, grid, and plate, respectively.

The common-base current gain h_{FB}, defined as the fraction of the emitter current that appears at the collector, can be considered to be a product of two terms: (1) the injection efficiency, which is the fraction of the total current flowing across the emitter-base junction by minority-carrier injection into the base and (2) the transport factor, which is the fraction of carriers injected into the base that arrive at the collector junction. The first term is determined primarily by the relative majority carrier concentrations on each side of the junction. The second term depends upon the ratio of minority-carrier lifetime in the base to the transit time through the base. The common-emitter current gain h_{FE}, defined as the ratio of collector current to base current, is related to h_{FB} by $h_{FE} = h_{FE}/(1 - h_{FB})$.

When compared with a vacuum tube, the transistor offers several advantages of importance in various applications. Probably the most important is reliability. In operation all the parts of a junction transistor are at such moderate temperatures that the structure is essentially stable. With a few exceptions, the structure of transistors contains no mechanism by which the units can "wear out" in any reasonable time. Thus for practical purposes, the useful life of the device is infinite, with operating failures occurring only on those devices which exhibit some accidental defect in their structure. Failure rates as low as 10^{-4} per 1000 hr of operation have been achieved. Such reliability is imperative in the operation of systems containing thousands of components.

A second major advantage of transistors is their ability to operate at low power levels. Systems with power dissipation of a few milliwatts per transistor are commonplace; for special applications operation at the microwatt level and below can be achieved. The first practical application of transistors was in hearing aids (q.v.), taking advantage of this property. It is important wherever power availability or power dissipation is limited.

The third major advantage in the application of transistors results from their near-ideal switching characteristics. For example, a typical silicon transistor can be switched from an impedance of the order of 10^9 ohms at 100 volts to a dynamic impedance of the order of ohms with a total voltage drop across the transistor of a few tenths of a volt.

The frequency response of a transistor is limited by the transit time of carriers through the base region and by the various resistances and capacitances associated with the contacts, thin layers, junctions, and the package. Which effects are limiting in a given case depends upon the detailed structure. In drift transistors and other diffused-base transistors the transit time is decreased by a built-in electric field across the base layer resulting from the gradient of chemical-impurity concentration. In addition, this gradient aids in achieving relatively low base resistance and low collector junction capacitance. Since diffusion also results in the narrowest practical base layers, the highest frequency transistors are made by the diffusion process.

The maximum operating voltages of a transistor are always limited by the avalanche breakdown of the junctions. In some types of transistors below their avalanche voltage, the space-charge region associated with the collector junction extends through the base to the emitter junction, a phenomenon called *punch-through*. The transistor behaves essentially as an emitter-collector short above this voltage. Depending upon the specific circuit configuration, limitations other than avalanche or punch-through can occur.

For high-current application, it is necessary to have the collector and emitter resistances low. In this case, the alloy structure has the advantage of metal contacts very close to the junctions. The introduction of the epitaxial process to the diffused structures, in which high-conductivity semiconductor is brought close to the collector junction, results in resistances comparable to the alloy structures with the high-frequency performance of the diffused structures.

The maximum temperature of operation is related to the magnitude of the energy gap between the valence and conduction bands of the particular material. Hence, the saturation current (I_{c0}) in junctions in germanium become excessive at about 100°C; the greater gap in silicon allows operation up to about 220°C. Other materials such as gallium arsenide and silicon carbide offer the possibility of extending the range to higher temperatures.

GORDON E. MOORE

Point-Contact Transistors

The point contact, the first type of transistor (announced in 1948) was invented by Bardeen and Brattain during an investigation of modulation of conductivity by surface charges. The point-contact transistor consists of two spring-loaded point-contact rectifying electrodes, and a third larger-area low-resistance, ohmic, nonrectifying contact. The point contacts are usually 0.001–0.005-in. phosphor bronze wires, which are spaced from 0.001 to 0.005 in. apart on a small block of n-type germanium. In operation, one point contact, the emitter, is forward biased; the other, the collector, is reverse biased. A signal between the emitter and base connections appears between the collector and base in amplified form. In manufacture, the collector is electrically "formed," usually by passage through it of a suitably large pulse discharged from an RC network; this pulse causes small diffusions of donor and acceptor ions and gives the point contact effectively a PNPN structure between emitter and collector. Point-contact transistors also have

been fabricated out of p-type germanium, both p- and n-type silicon, 5-percent silicon-germanium, and some III-V intermetallic materials. Certain variations of the point-contact transistor are worthy of mention. These are the coaxial transistor (Bell Telephone Laboratories), the spacistor (Raytheon Manufacturing Co.), and the multiple-point transistor (Air Force Cambridge Research Laboratories). Values of current gain

$$\alpha = \frac{\partial I_C}{\partial I_E}\bigg|_{V_C}$$

where I_C is the collector current, I_E is the emitter current, and V_C is the collector voltage, are greater than one in the point-contact transistor, a condition which is conducive to electrical instability, but may be utilized in oscillator and switching applicators.

The point contact transistor is characterized in grounded-base operation by relatively low input impedance ($\sim$200 K), relatively high output impedance ($\sim$20 K), and a large mutual resistance ($\sim$35 K). It is a low-power device with a power output of about 20 mw. Typically, its currents range from 0.5 ma for the emitter to 2 ma for the collector; its voltages range from less than 1 v on the emitter to 80 v on the collector. As a class A amplifier in grounded-base operation, with matched generator and input impedances and matched load and output impedances, operating power gains of 20 db are typical. Other modes of operation are the grounded emitter and grounded collector, the latter equivalent to a cathode follower. Alpha frequency cutoffs of 10 Mc are obtained. Noise figures, for narrow bands centered on 1000 cps, range to 50 db.

The point-contact transistor, of historical and scientific importance, has been almost entirely replaced by transistors fabricated by other techniques such as alloying and diffusion.

The major limitations of the point-contact transistor are reproducibility, power dissipation, operational frequency and, for some time, reliability. Poor yields in manufacture owing to basic difficulties in reproducibly pointing and placing the contacts, and in forming the collector, prevented achievement of predicted low prices. Power limitations were inherent in the small point contacts and formed areas. The mechanical limitations in the juxtaposition of the emitter and collector contacts prevented extension of the frequency range. Semiconductor surface changes led to lack of stability and reliability in the device characteristics.

J. J. Bowe

Unipolar Field-Effect Transistors

The unipolar field-effect transistor was first described by Shockley in 1952. The name unipolar refers to the fact that current is transported by carriers of one polarity (majority carriers) only, whereas in the conventional (bipolar) transistor carriers of both polarities (majority and minority) are involved.

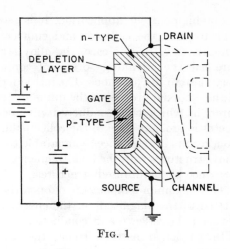

Fig. 1

In its most elementary version it consists of a piece of high-resistivity semiconductor constituting a channel for majority carrier flow (Fig. 1), two ohmic contacts called "source" and "drain" (of majority carriers),

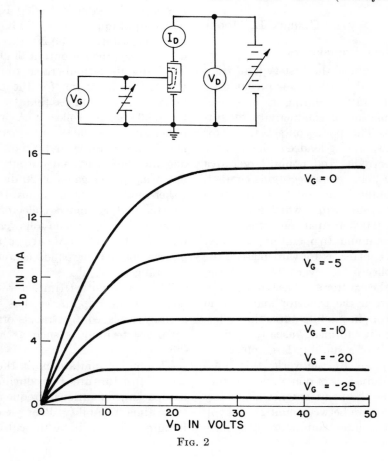

Fig. 2

and one (or two) region of opposite conductivity type and high doping called a "gate."

When the gate is reverse-biased relative to the channel, and the bias voltage is low, the junction depletion layer is relatively thin and a large current can flow through the channel from source to drain. However, when the reverse bias is increased the depletion layer grows until finally the entire channel is pinched off and no current can flow.

When the drain voltage is increased the current increases but at the same time the depletion layer between the drain and gate grows, constricting the drain end of the channel. Further increase of drain voltage results in less and less current increase until a current saturation value is reached when the sum of gate and drain voltage is equal to the pinch-off voltage (Fig. 2). At higher drain voltages the current remains nearly constant. As an amplifier the unipolar transistor is characterized by very high input impedance (1–100 megohms) and relatively low output impedance (1–100 kohms) somewhat similar to an electron tube.

The transconductance is largest at near zero gate voltage and directly proportional to the dimension perpendicular to the plane of Fig. 1. The maximum transconductance is the inverse of the source-drain resistance. Typical values are 100–10,000 μmhos.

The high-frequency response is limited by the RC time-constant of the channel (approximately gate capacitance and source-drain resistance). The cut-off frequency f for not too large power is

$$f = \frac{5.7 \cdot 10^5}{d} \text{ cps}$$

where d is the length of the channel in the direction of the current flow in cm.

                                        J. T. WALLMARK

Cross-references: *Diodes (Semiconductor), Four-Layer Semiconductor Devices, Semiconductor Manufacture, Tunnel Diode*

TRANSLATION BY MACHINE

Although the mechanical or automatic translation of natural languages has been a subject of interest for the past several decades, it was not until the advent of large-scale digital computers (*q.v.*) in the early 1950's that the problem came into its own as deserving a major research effort. The bulk of research in mechanical translation has been devoted to the Russian and English languages; other efforts have investigated French, German, Italian, and Chinese. Of urgent interest to military intelligence, the problem is emphasized by the increase in communication speed relating one language to another. An obvious means of satisfying this need is in the application of digital and logical equipment as represented by modern digital computers.

The mechanical translation problem can be stated as the requirement that a high-speed means should be developed to provide accurate and intelligible translation from one natural language to another, clearly expressing the original thoughts of the author in the form of the target language. This process must take place by means of a combination of an extensive dictionary and processing capability. The translation problem can be grossly bifurcated into (1) that area related to the function of the translation process system, and (2) that area related to the system itself, considered as a combination of components.

Memory. An obvious necessity for translation is the presence of a dictionary, bilingual between the languages being considered. Certain information related to the grammatical characteristics and meaning function of the dictionary entries must be available as a part of the dictionary itself. As in bilingual dictionaries for human use, it may often be necessary to include several target equivalents for a single source dictionary entry. The scope of the bilingual dictionary required varies between languages, within the style requirements and subject of the text. A dictionary to be used exclusively for technical or scientific translations within a specific field will be different and more restricted than one for more general translation. Current estimates of dictionary size are between 100,000 to

300,000 canonical forms for the source entries.

Logical Processing. A simple dictionary look-up process will deliver a "word-for-word" translation of the source text. This translation appears in a structural form ordered exactly as the source, with such multiple target equivalents as may appear in the dictionary. Inflections of the source language may result in ambiguities in the "word-for-word" translation that reduce or obscure the intended meaning.

Dictionary output processing is primarily linguistic in basis, having two broad functions. The dictionary output must be organized in structure to resemble the target language usage, with deletions and insertions provided for intelligibility and ease of reading; selection must be made between the multiple equivalents appearing in the dictionary. Such processing must be accomplished on the basis of grammar and context and be primarily logical or probabilistic in nature.

Conventional rules of grammar and structure only partially define a natural language. Although there is much that has been considered intuitive in the use of such languages, when an electronic device must be instructed and trained in the nuances of translation, intuition must be omitted and context must be formally considered.

Translation System. The majority of past research related to mechanical translation has been within the framework of large-scale digital computers. Indeed, many scientists working with translation feel that general-purpose devices may ultimately be the most economical and expedient operating solution for production translation. It is possible, however, that an entire special-purpose computer system may better serve the translation requirements. The memory requirements of the bilingual dictionary are such that some form of permanent memory would be adequate.

As the requirements of the output processing section of the system are largely logical, the principal numerical functions of general purpose computers are not used. Reading from memory, buffering for system component inputs and outputs could often be accomplished more efficiently by a special-purpose computer. The logic requirements of the system are extensive but standard. It is obvious that until the specifics of the processing section are completely and adequately defined, the use of general-purpose computers is justifiable.

Before mechanical translation can be economically competitive with human translation, an automatic form of system input from the printed page is required. Devices are currently available that electronically or optically scan a printed page and code text information directly into the computer. Further development will yield more versatility and reliability of recognition. Research is currently active in investigation of satisfactory means of encoding spoken text. The output of the translation process is a function not particularly critical. Standard printers are of sufficient speed that they can provide output in acceptable formats at a speed consistent with the translation process. Ultimate forms of translation output may incorporate speech synthesis into the system.

Current Status. This discussion has been concerned with the relationship between digital computers and mechanical translation systems. Few specifics have been provided concerning the processing details with which the computers deal because this is an extremely complex linguistic problem. It should be emphasized that the area of mechanical translation of natural language is, and for the next decade will be, flexible and changing. Current mechanical translations provide results which are usually intelligible, often easily read, generally limited to narrow fields of scientific or technical literature. Only further research and development will yield improved quality and extended limits of translation.

DAVID L. JOHNSON

Cross-references: *Computer Applications, Information Theory, Phonetic Typewriting, Vocoder*

TRANSMISSION LINES: see COAXIAL LINES;
DELAY LINES; STRIP LINES; WAVEGUIDES

TRANSMISSION RELIABILITY

The term "transmission reliability" refers to the extent to which the actual output of a system approaches the desired output. Many measures of reliability exist, the one used in any particular case depending primarily on the type of system under consideration and on the mathematical ease with which the measure can be used. Mean-square, probabilistic, and entropic measures are the most common.

Mean-square measures of reliability are the simplest to apply, and are almost universally used in evaluating the performance of parameter- and waveform-estimating systems, as in statistical communication theory (q.v.). In a parameter-estimating system, for example, the estimate made by the system of the true value of a parameter (e.g., the range of a radar target) almost never equals the true value, because of the random noise disturbances in the system. The statistical average of the squared deviation of the estimate from the true value of the parameter (i.e., the mean-square deviation) is therefore often used to indicate the accuracy, on the average, with which the parameter is estimated. In waveform-estimating systems, the mean-square deviation of the estimate of the desired waveform from the desired waveform itself is often a function of time; generally, the time average of this mean-square deviation is then used to measure system performance. Another mean-square performance measure is signal-to-noise ratio, which compares the mean-square deviation from the desired signal with the desired signal itself. One definition of signal-to-noise ratio is the ratio of the average system output power in the absence of noise to the average power in the deviation, in the presence of noise, of the actual output from the noiseless output.

More detailed measures of reliability involve probabilistic statements. In param-eter estimation, for example, reliability might be expressed in terms of a confidence interval, i.e., an interval, centered on the estimated value of the parameter, which may be asserted to contain the true value in, say, P per cent of the cases in which the parameter is estimated. Again, in systems designed to make decisions among multiple discrete hypotheses, the reliability may be given in terms of the joint probabilities, P_{ij}, of falsely deciding the jth hypothesis is true when in fact the ith is true $(j \neq i)$. For example, the sum of all the P_{ij} (the average probability of error) may suffice. Alternatively, if the costs of making these various errors are given, as well as the (negative) costs of making correct decisions, the average cost of a decision may serve as a performance measure.

Another measure of reliability, used especially in information-theoretic problems, is informational entropy. If a system is called upon to select one of a set of hypotheses as being true, it is most uncertain in the case in which all hypotheses are equally probable; it is least uncertain when one hypothesis has unit probability, and all the others have zero probability. Between these extremes are varying degrees of uncertainty, which may be measured in terms of a mathematical entity called informational entropy. In this context, of two systems which receive a perturbed transmission, the more reliable is the one which, according to the entropic expression, is the less uncertain about the nature of the true transmission. The entropic "uncertainty" of a system after reception is called the equivocation; in discrete systems, the equivocation is zero when the average probability of error is zero.

G. L. TURIN

Cross-references: *Information Theory, Noise, Probability, Statistical Communication Theory*

TRAVELING-WAVE MAGNETRON

A class of tube combining the controllability of the traveling-wave tube with the power-handling capacity of the magnetron.

It differs from the ordinary traveling-wave tube by:

(1) the flat rectangular rather than cylindrical cross section of beam and propagating structure;

(2) the orientation of the magnetic field, which is across the beam (across the narrow side of the rectangle, along the broad side), rather than along the beam; and

(3) the orientation of the dc electric field which, instead of being restricted to the gun region, acts across the broad side of the beam (and not along the beam) for the entire beam length.

It differs from the magnetron by:

(1) its asymmetry with regard to the rf power flow, which has a beginning and an end instead of circulating continuously;

(2) its ability to act as an amplifier as well as an oscillator, being used mainly as an amplifier (it is a backward-wave oscillator otherwise);

(3) its geometrical adaptability, over-all and in circuit construction; it is usually straightened out, like a magnetron of very many segments unwrapped;

(4) the localization of its cathode (usually) at one end—although continuous cathodes are employed in many versions, for instance the amplitron (*q.v.*).

For a circuit one can employ the slotted line (as in a conventional magnetron), an interdigital line, a flattened helix, and other slow-wave structures.

For a localized cathode one employs a "crossed-field gun" at the entrance to the circuit. The magnetic field is continued into this region; the cathode surface, instead of lying across the beam as in the ordinary traveling-wave tube, is a surface parallel to the broad side of the beam.

The electrons are extracted by an anode more or less parallel to the cathode and emerge at right angles to their eventual direction of travel in the beam. They are turned into this direction by the magnetic field before reaching the anode. Shaping the anode and adding "Pierce wings" to the

ends of the cathode can insure a dense beam that enters the circuit with none of its initial transverse electron motion left. (The "French gun" was developed empirically, the "Kino gun" was calculated.)

In the circuit region the dc electric field is maintained by means of a plate under the beam, parallel to its broad side, held at a high negative potential relative to the circuit structure. This plate is called the "sole." It is almost a "dead" continuation of the cathode but held at a somewhat lower potential (10–100 v). The circuit, similarly, may be a continuation of the anode or differ from it by up to several kilovolts.

The beam is maintained in equilibrium drift motion of velocity E/B by the magnetic field. If the beam enters the space between sole and circuit with residual transverse motion, or with a longitudinal velocity differing from the equilibrium value, it describes cycloids about the mean straight path. Gun design aims at avoiding cycloids.

Space-charge pressure amounts to the lowering of the dc electric field on the side facing the "sole" and an increase on the opposite side, facing the structure. The equilibrium velocity E/B changes across the beam, and if the beam is introduced with such a sheared velocity it remains in equilibrium in spite of large space-charge forces.

Extremely dense beams can therefore be accommodated by the traveling-wave magnetron, which makes for its high power yield. Perveance is not quite the relevant measure of beam intensity for this tube; as a measure of gun and injection efficiency one should compare the plasma frequency in the observed beam with the electron cyclotron frequency. Ideally they should be equal and the former frequency has, in practice, been brought up to 90 per cent of the latter.

The interaction between beam and circuit, and the amplification of rf by the beam, are similar to those in an ordinary traveling-wave tube and synchronism between the beam and the circuit wave is a fairly good criterion for efficient operation. However, the velocity shear across dense beams brings in new considerations and modes of operation resembling those of magnetrons.

Indeed, when the cathode extends into the circuit space and takes the place of the "sole," a full range of velocities (in the direction of the wave) occurs, from zero to a maximum, and the wave is synchronous with a stream somewhat below the fastest.

Historically, suggestions to straighten out the magnetron and to use it as a device with rf input as well as output date back to the World War II successes of the magnetron. The electronic theory of such a system was available. However, the first successful tubes of this kind were made by the French after experience had been gained with ordinary traveling-wave tubes, in the late 1940's. Since then, some of the developments have gone back very close to the original magnetron in that the electrons are guided around a curved cylindrical sole or cathode, the electron stream is made to close on itself, and only the path of the rf is interrupted, entering at one segment of a multivane magnetron and leaving after it has gone nearly 360° around, with an rf septum to separate the exit from the entrance.

O. BUNEMAN

Cross-references: *Amplitron,   Backward-Wave Tubes, Crossed-Field Interaction, Electron Guns, Magnetron, Traveling-Wave Tubes*

TRAVELING-WAVE TUBES

A traveling-wave tube may be defined as an electron tube in which electrons of a stream move in the field of a traveling electromagnetic wave in such a manner that a fraction of the energy of the stream is converted into field energy. Compliance with a more restrictive definition requires the addition of two more conditions: 1. The electrons in the beam are moving in a region free of dc electric fields (the presence of a beam confining longitudinal dc magnetic field generated by a solenoid S shown in Fig. 1 may be a practical requirement in an actual tube). 2. The electromagnetic field is that of a so-called forward wave.

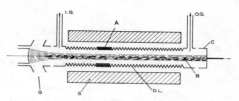

FIG. 1. Schematic diagram of a traveling-wave tube amplifier.

A traveling-wave tube amplifier includes the following essential components shown in the schematic diagram of Fig. 1. An electron gun G generates an electron beam B which passes in succession through an input region, a slow-wave guide, also called delay line $D.L.$, and an output region before the beam is collected by an electrode C.

At the input region an electromagnetic signal coming from a source along an input guide $I.G.$ is transferred to the slow-wave guide. At the output region the amplified signal is removed from the slow-wave guide and carried away to a load by the output guide $O.G.$ In order to maximize the transfer of power, the guides which join in these regions must be well matched. Practically speaking, however, reflections owing to unavoidable mismatches may cause feedback and hence oscillations. This danger may be reduced by means of a localized attenuator A which is placed in the slow-wave guide to absorb electromagnetic power. Its function can be better understood after the description of the operation of the tube.

The energy of the electron stream in the region of the slow-wave guide is in the form of kinetic energy. To reduce this energy the electromagnetic wave on the guide must slow down the electrons, at least on an average. A first requirement for the electric field of an electromagnetic wave to have an effect on the velocity of the electrons is the existence of a component of this field in the direction of the axis of the electron beam. The most important condition, however, is that of equality or near equality of the phase velocity of the traveling electromagnetic field wave and the velocity of the electrons, a condition called synchronism. Electrons

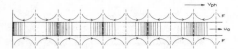

FIG. 2. Density modulation in a beam produced by a traveling field wave.

traveling in this manner in the field of an electromagnetic wave are exposed all along their path to a nearly time-constant force which, although small, can be effective. The instantaneous force field F and the resulting density modulation of the electron beam are shown in Fig. 2. Electrons which entered the slow-wave guide at a time when the field changed from accelerating to decelerating become centers of bunches if phase and beam velocities are equal ($v_p = u_0$). If the electron velocity is made slightly higher than the phase velocity, these bunches move through decelerating and accelerating regions of the force field. Since they stay in decelerating regions longer than in accelerating regions, the slowing-down process has more effect than the speeding-up process; and hence on the average the beam loses kinetic energy. Since energy is conserved, the lost kinetic energy must reappear and in a lossless guide it can only reappear in the form of electromagnetic energy. The conversion of energy is effected by the appearance of an electromagnetic field owing to induced charges and currents in the walls of the guide by the moving electron bunches. The induced wave modifies the original wave since the beam bunches are traveling at a slightly higher velocity than the original electromagnetic wave. The modification actually results in the appearance of several waves in place of the one free circuit wave which may exist in the absence of the beam.

Another way of describing the interaction between a beam and an electromagnetic wave is suggested by the analogy of a beam exhibiting space-charge waves to a transmission line; namely, as a coupling phenomenon between two transmission lines. One line is represented by the beam carrying a mode P_b, the other by the slow-wave guide carrying a mode P_c. The coupled mode equations are:

$$\frac{dP_b}{dz} = -j(\beta_e + \beta_p)P_b + KP_c$$

$$\frac{dP_c}{dz} = -j\beta_c P_c + KP_b$$

where $\beta_c = \omega/v_p$ is the propagation constant of the free circuit wave and

$$\beta_e + \beta_p = (\omega/u_0) + (\omega_p/u_0)$$

is the propagation constant of the slow space-charge wave,

ω_p is the radian plasma frequency,

K is the coupling coefficient between the two modes

The new modes resulting from the coupling have propagation constants given by

$$\beta_{1,2} = \tfrac{1}{2}[(\beta_e + \beta_p) + \beta_c]$$
$$\pm \sqrt{\tfrac{1}{4}[(\beta_e + \beta_p) - \beta_c]^2 - K^2}$$

If $\beta_c = \beta_e + \beta_p$ or $u_0 = [1 + (\omega_p/\omega)]v_p$ i.e., u_0 slightly greater than v_p, one has $-j\beta_{1,2} = \pm k - j\beta_c$ which means that exponentially growing and decaying waves exist. This means that after an initial loss in signal strength (because two waves are set up at the input) an exponential increase in amplitude takes place along the interaction region.

Upon reaching the localized attenuator, the amplitude of the field wave is attenuated usually by an amount somewhat greater than the gain of the tube, the space-charge waves are essentially unaffected and again set up field waves on the second region of the slow-wave guide. This is not the case for a reflected wave traveling against the electron stream, since no interaction with the beam occurs.

The two requirements for coupling of beam and wave stated above are satisfied to varying degrees in a number of structures shown schematically in Figs. 3a, b, c, d, e, and f.

The common feature of these guides is the periodic nature of their structure. A general analysis leads to a Brillouin diagram or ω, β diagram for waves on such guides, which is shown in Fig. 4. A number of characteristics of the periodic guides may be recognized.

(1) The guide exhibits stop and pass bands similar to the behavior of filter networks.

(2) For a given frequency within a pass-band there are partial waves called forward and backward space harmonics. At a fixed frequency these space harmonics, sometimes called Hartree harmonics, have different phase velocities v_p, but all have the same group velocity v_g. Phase and group velocities are in the same direction for forward waves and are in opposite directions for backward waves.

(3) If phase and group velocities are equal or very nearly equal over a wide range of frequencies within a band, the structure is called nondispersive.

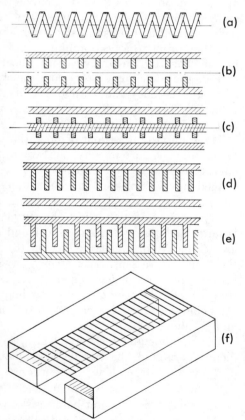

FIG. 3. Delay lines for traveling-wave tubes.
(a) Helix
(b) Disk-loaded wave guide
(c) Disk-loaded coaxial line
(d) Finned wave guide
(e) Interdigital line
(f) Ladder line

Traveling-wave-tube operation is based on interaction between a beam and a forward wave. Wideband traveling-wave amplification has been possible over a range of an octave with some structures, notably the helix.

A figure of merit for a slow-wave guide in connection with traveling-wave tube operation is the so-called beam coupling impedance defined as

$$Z = E_z E_z{}^*/\beta^2 P$$

where E_z is the z component of the electric field of a particular space harmonic with which interaction is considered, P is the total power transmitted along the guide, and β is the propagation constant of the space harmonic. The asterisk indicates the conjugate complex of a quantity. It is apparent that for strong coupling Z should be as large as possible.

The shape of the Brillouin diagram and the beam coupling impedance may be altered by modification of the coupling between the sections of the periodic structure. This has been done extensively with the disk-loaded guide of Fig. 3b where additional coupling apertures of various shapes and location have been introduced into the disks giving descriptive names to the resulting structures such as clover-leaf structure or centipede structure.

In addition to the basic type of traveling-wave tube which has been discussed so far, there are many derivatives and related traveling-wave amplifiers. One of them is known as the electron-wave tube or double-stream amplifier in which the role of the slow-wave guide is assumed by a second electron beam. The electrons in the two intermingled beams travel at slightly different dc velocities. The electrons in one beam are exposed to the electric field caused by the bunches of electrons in the other beam. Another form of traveling-wave interaction may be obtained by exposing periodically in space the electrons of a beam to the traveling wave in an unloaded guide. If the periodicity of exposure and the propagation constant of the fast wave are chosen

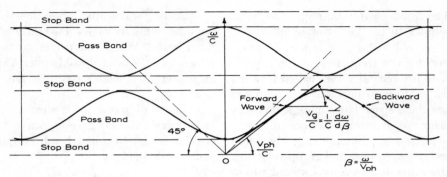

Fig. 4. Brillouin diagram.

properly, the electrons are deceived into experiencing a "slow" wave. Still other methods of traveling-wave amplification are based on periodic changes of the impedance of space-charge waves by means of dc velocity changes or changes in beam or wall diameter. The resistive wall amplifier is based on a damping action of the two space-charge waves caused by the losses of induced currents in the resistive walls surrounding the electron beam. This causes the amplitude of the slow space-charge wave to increase and the amplitude of the fast wave to decrease exponentially.

R. G. E. Hutter

Cross-references: *Backward-Wave Tubes, Bunching, Coupled-Mode Theory, Double-Stream Amplification, Helitron, Space-Charge Waves, Velocity Modulation*

TRIBOELECTRICITY: see STATIC (TRIBO-) ELECTRICITY

TROPOSPHERE: see PROPAGATION

TRIODES: see ELECTRON TUBES (CONVENTIONAL); TRANSISTORS

TUNNEL DIODE

The tunnel diode is an abrupt-junction diode made with degenerate semiconductor so as to exhibit a voltage-controlled negative resistance over a region of small forward bias. At low dc bias, the current is carried by tunneling of majority carriers through the barrier layer of the junction. As described by Esaki, the relative displacement of the energy bands on opposite sides of the junction gives the I-V characteristic an N shape under forward bias. The tunneling current first rises to a sharp maximum and then drops to a deep minimum. At still higher bias, the minority-carrier injection exceeds the tunneling current, and the characteristic assumes the normal exponential behavior. The tunneling current increases monotonically for all reverse bias.

Three important regions of operation are (1) around the current maximum where the curvature is large and negative; (2) at intermediate bias where the conductance is large and negative; (3) for bias giving minority-carrier injection where the curvature is large and positive. Regions (1) and (2) are temperature insensitive; region (3) has the temperature sensitivity of any forward biased junction diode. For a germanium tunnel diode the regions are approximately (1) below 50 mv; (2) from 50 to 300 mv; and (3) above 300 mv.

The simple equivalent circuit of a tunnel diode consists of the parallel combination of the voltage-dependent junction resistance $R(v)$ and voltage-sensitive capacitance $C(V)$ in series with the constant base resistance r. At high frequency the case inductance appears in series with the diode, and the whole is shunted by the case capacitance. Except near frequency cutoff, r is negligible.

The diode is specified in various ways. One

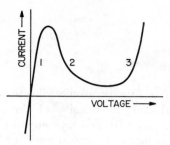

Fɪɢ. 1. Tunnel-diode static characteristic.

pair of parameters is the current at the peak, I_p, and the ratio I_p/C_v; C_v is the capacitance in the valley. These parameters indicate the impedance and frequency response of the diode. Typical values for a 50-ohm germanium diode for use below 1 kMc are 2 ma and 0.2 ma/pf.

A related parameter is $1/2\pi RC$, where R and C are the magnitudes of resistance and capacitance at the steepest point in region (2). This is the peak value for the voltage gain-bandwidth product of a single tuned amplifier as well as the reciprocal of the diode switching time. The diode cutoff frequency is $f_0 = [(R/r) - 1]^{1/2}/2\pi RC$.

The diode is a good low-level detector in region (1), since its curvature is higher than for conventional diodes. The conversion loss is around 3 db. Biased to the current maximum, the diode can give a large conversion gain with an optimum noise around 3 db. For such operations the important parameters are C_v and f_0.

The diode becomes a negative-resistance oscillator or amplifier when biased into region 2 by a low-impedance source. It is a very good oscillator for power of a milliwatt up to 10 kMc, delivering 15 per cent of the dc input to the fundamental. Modulating the bias gives an FM signal.

Negative resistance amplifiers with large (100-Mc) bandwidth are readily made. Like all negative-resistance amplifiers, they require isolation between stages. The noise figure is limited by the shot noise of the bias current. In germanium, the noise temperature is about 300°K. For linear circuits the diode is specified by I_p, $1/2\pi RC$, and f_0.

Biased from a high impedance source, the diode is bistable with operating point in either region (1) or (3). A trigger can switch it to the other point. This operation permits high-speed logic, switching, and memory with switching speeds under 1 ns. Circuit tolerances limit the fanout ratio to four in the simplest circuits. The important diode parameters are I_pV_p (dissipation) and $1/2\pi RC$ (speed).

H. S. Sommers, Jr.

Cross-references: *Diode (Semiconductor), Four-Layer Semiconductor Devices, Transistors*

U

ULTRASONICS

Ultrasonics is the generation and detection of ultrasonic vibrations in materials having elastic properties. The frequency range is above the top limit of the audible range and extends from approximately 18,000 cps to above 200 Mc. Ultrasonic vibrations are easily propagated in most liquids, metals, and many other materials such as glass, ceramics, plastics, and concrete, but are highly attenuated in air and gases.

Principles of Operation

The most important and widely used mode is the compressional or longitudinal wave with particle vibration in the direction of propagation. Other modes of vibration are transverse or shear waves with particle motion in a direction at right angles to the direction of propagation; surface or Rayleigh waves propagated on the surface with an elliptical particle motion resembling waves traveling over the surface of water; and plate or Lamb waves usually propagated in thin metal sheets or plate and having an infinite number of modes in two types, either symmetrical or asymmetrical. It should be noted that the velocities of the various modes of vibration are different and the ratio of velocities is not the same for different materials. For example, the velocity in 1080 steel may be 2.33×105 in./sec for (bulk) compressional mode; 1.25 for shear mode; and 1.10 for surface mode.

The specific acoustic impedance of materials governs the reflection of ultrasonic vibrations at the boundary between two different materials (steel-air; water-air; steel-water or vice versa) and the ratio between the reflected energy and the incident energy at a boundary. This specific acoustic impedance of a material is the product of the velocity of the ultrasonic vibration in that material and the density of the material.

Propagation is accomplished by driving electromechanical transducers of various types with a high-frequency oscillating voltage that the transducer converts into mechanical vibrations that are introduced into the material by providing intimate surface contact. The nature of the associated electronic circuits is governed by the nature of the application. Power generators for ultrasonic cleaning and material processing are usually of the electronic oscillator-amplifier type providing cw transmission. In the low-frequency range (18–20 kc) special high-speed motor-generators and sirens have been successfully applied. Other applications, such as ultrasonic testing, require pulsed oscillators and circuits that generate short pulses of vibrations with repetition rates in the range of 60 to 1500 pps and receiving circuits with high-gain amplifiers and many methods of displaying measures of the reflected or received energy. Display methods include the conventional oscilloscope with "A," "B," and "C" type scans, as well as meters and various types of recorders.

The electro-mechanical transducers may be magnetostrictive or piezoelectric materials. Some of the piezoelectric materials that are suitable are quartz, tourmaline, rochelle salt, ammonium dihydrogen phosphate, lithium sulphate, and polarized ceramics such as barium titanate and lead zirconium titanate. The magnetostrictive and polarized ceramics are widely used for high-energy ultrasonic applications such as cleaning, chemical and materials processing, sonar, and other applications in which cavitation in a liquid or realignment of particles in a material require the application of relatively large amounts of ultrasonic power. Quartz, lithium sulphate, and the polarized ceramics are used for nondestructive testing and measurement of physical properties of materials where a relatively low level of ultrasonic energy is adequate.

The properties of ultrasonic vibrations that make them especially useful for many applications are as follows:

(1) Cavitation induced in liquids by a strong ultrasonic field at the lower energy levels degasses and at the higher energy levels generates gas bubbles that implode, releasing small shock waves at high pressure levels. (Contributes to cleaning, dispersion, emulsification, homogenization, depolymerization, extraction, and other materials processing.)

(2) Well-defined beaming and focusing of ultrasonic energy with reflectors or concave or convex lenses, in a manner similar to the handling of light beams, provides control for many applications (sonar, materials testing, surgery, etc.)

(3) Particle motion induced in one liquid or material may be transferred to another when there is intimate contact or coupling between the materials (surface wetting as well as a union such as in welds). Poor coupling or lack of bond reduces transmission proportionally. (Provides a test for lack of bond in adhesive, brazed, and welded joints and in bearing pressures.) A spot concentration of ultrasonic power can induce particle joining of materials, providing a strong joint or weld between metal foils and thin sheets; or between plastic film and sheeting.

(4) Tuning the driving oscillator to provide a transmitted ultrasonic frequency that induces resonance in the material at the natural frequency or harmonic frequencies. (Provides a basis for determining thickness of materials and coupling mechanisms for drilling, grinding, joining, etc.)

(5) Travel long distances through liquids and materials. Actually many miles through water for sounding and over 200 ft through steel for nondestructive testing. (Provides sounding and testing through almost unlimited distances.)

(6) The velocity of ultrasonic vibrations in materials depends on the material density and dynamic elastic properties and is a function of the elastic moduli of the materials. (Provides a basis for locating nonhomogeneous areas and determining differences in structure and physical properties of materials, especially metals.)

(7) Reflection of ultrasonic vibrations at interfaces of materials and refraction when passing between materials of different acoustic velocity similar to the action of light beams passing from one medium to another. Associated with the reflection or refraction is a change of mode of vibration, which occurs at certain favorable angles that vary with differences in the specific acoustic impedance of the materials. (Provides basis for testing materials for internal discontinuities, measuring thickness, and techniques for generating modes of vibration other than the compressional mode.)

(8) Attenuation, scattering, and absorption of the ultrasonic vibrations occurs in all materials but varies widely owing to the wide variation in structure of materials and material mixtures to which ultrasonics may be applied. Metal structures vary widely from extremely coarse grained cast structures to very fine grained heat treated and worked (forged, rolled, etc.) metals. Low-frequency vibrations penetrate more readily than high-frequency vibrations, which are attenuated, scattered, or absorbed to a greater extent owing to the shorter wavelength.

Industrial Applications

The range of applications to which ultrasonics has already been applied extends into most industries, medicine, navigation, biology, and agriculture. Some typical applications are:

Metal Industries

Basic Metal Production—All Metals.
    Quality Control—testing for defects in ingots, blooms, billets and plate.
    Ingots and Castings—agitation of molten metal during casting to improve grain structure.

Metal Processing—All metalworking.

Quality Control—testing for defects and homogeneity in forgings; extrusions; rolled sheet, plate and shapes; and sintered metals.

Thickness testing from one side.

Metal Fabrication—All metal machining and forming.

Quality Control—testing for defects in stampings and drawn parts; weldments, brazed and cemented parts; lack of bond in sandwich and honeycomb panels.

Cleaning of parts—faster and cleaner.

Electroplating—higher current density with improved quality.

Heat treating—improvement of grain dispersion.

Drilling and impact grinding—especially of the harder materials such as carbides.

Welding—cold joining of foils and thin sheets.

Welding, brazing and soldering—An assist in hot joining with improved structure and without use of fluxes because of dispersion of oxidation.

Thickness testing from one side of pressure and storage vessels, propellers and other critical assemblies.

Measurement of physical properties of metals and other materials.

Miscellaneous Materials—Fabrication and Processing

Concrete—determination of deterioration by measurement of ultrasonic velocity changes, location and measurement of cracks in dams and other large structures.

Textiles—assist to penetration and dispersion of dyes and bleaching chemicals. Cleaning of textiles and fibers.

Plastics—location of laminations and lack of homogeneity.

Food

Milk—homogenizes.

Meat—measures thickness of fat on live pigs and cattle to determine fat-lean

ratio. Also, power application can break down tough fibers of meat to tenderize.

Wines, liquors, and alcohols—assists in aging.

Chemical Industry

Processing—accelerates chemical reactions and degasses.

Polymerization and depolymerization—promotes molecular rearrangement.

Mixtures of solids and gases, solids and liquids—promotes particle separation, breaks up large particles, and causes agglomeration. Precipitates solid particles from smoke and disperses as well as generates fog.

Medical

Therapy—some value owing to generation of heat but control must be exercised to prevent breakdown of blood cells.

Diagnostic—provides (as in metal testing) a tool for locating benign and malignant tumors and kidney stones.

Surgical—with focused transducers has been applied to removal of brain tumors and other growths.

Dental—using slurry of cutting particles provides painless drilling and grinding of teeth.

Surgical Instruments—supercleans instruments removing particles not always removed by scrubbing.

Marine

Echo Sounding—provides means of locating ships and submarines (sonar) by beam pulsing and reflection timing. Also measuring distance to bottom and location of schools of fish (fathometer).

Biological

Bacteria—application of ultrasonics to various bacteria and microorganisms has resulted in the immediate rupture of and killing of some but not all.

Seeds—high-power ultrasonics applied to various seeds has resulted in mutations

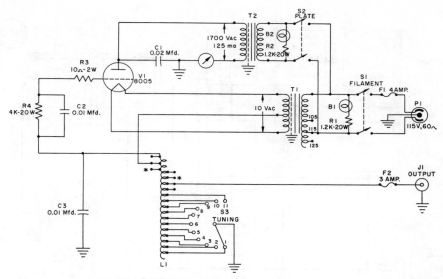

FIG. 1. Ultrasonic generator schematic.

and other effects depending on the exposure.

Ultrasonic Instrumentation

Power Generator. A typical 500-w ultrasonic-power generator is diagrammed in Fig. 1. This particular rf generator is designed to drive an array of barium titanate transducers at 40 to 45 kc. It consists of an oscillator, tuned rf transformer, and power supply. Many variations of this circuit are used, including solid-state generators. Power range is from 50 w to 10 kw and higher. Transducers may be of the magnetostrictive or piezoelectric types and usually range in frequency from 18 kc to 1 Mc.

Similar generators are used for ultrasonic cleaning, materials, processing, drilling, and other applications requiring relatively high energy levels.

Materials Tester. The circuits of a typical "pulse-echo" type of ultrasonic testing instrument are block diagrammed in Fig. 2. The nine sections of this instrument and the functions they perform are as follows:

Power Supply (not included in diagram) provides the necessary operating voltages to all other circuit sections.

Clock. Originates all timing signals which synchronize all circuit functions. Consists of twin-triode tube and circuit components operating as a free-running (astable) multivibrator with symmetrical outputs.

Pulse Generator. Provides properly timed, high-voltage pulses to the transducer. These adjustable pulses are short trains of oscillating radio frequency voltages of 1 to 12 μsec that are repeated at either fixed or adjustable repetition rates of 60 to 1500 pps.

Crystal Transducer. This test instrument can use one transducer for both transmitting and receiving ultrasonic signals or separate transducers for transmitting and receiving. In both cases the crystal transducer converts oscillating electrical pulses from the pulse generator into pulses of ultrasonic vibrations and reconverts the ultrasonic echo pulses received from the material under test into oscillating electrical voltages that are amplified and detected in the receiver.

Receiver. Provides readable signals of a desired amplitude by amplification through three tuned rf stages and detection by the diode. A selector switch provides selection of a test frequency of 0.5, 1, 2.25, 5, or 10 Mc. A potentiometer controls the ratio of input signal to output signal by adjusting the grid voltage level of the TRF amplifier

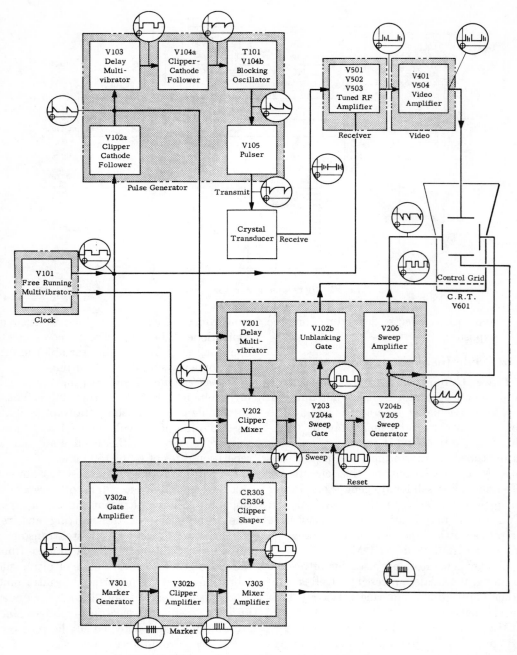

Fig. 2. Ultrasonic materials tester block diagram.

tube. A reject control cuts off signals or noise below a selected level.

Video. Amplifies the video (detected) signal through two stages. Waveform is also shaped to a sharp pulse and negative feed back increases the linearity and dynamic range of the video circuit. The video signal goes to the vertical deflection plates of the CRT.

Marker. Provides adjustable markers on

the sweep line to give depth measurements which, must be calibrated for each material under test.

Sweep. Two distinct sweeps result from two separate trigger pulses of the clipper-mixer tube. First in time of these two is the video sweep, followed by the marker sweep.

Cathode-Ray Tube. The CRT presents the ultrasonic-inspection results in visual form.

JOHN C. SMACK

Cross-references: *Magnetostriction, Medical Electronics, Piezoelectricity, Sonar, Transducers*

UNDERWATER SOUND

Underwater sound is used today primarily for the detection of ships, submarines, and mines, and to a lesser extent for navigational aids, for fish finding, and communication in water.

The first recorded observations of sound in open water occurred in 1827 when Colladon and Sturms measured the speed of sound in Lake Geneva using a bell as a sound source. Some early applications of underwater sound in navigation were the measurements of ocean depth by explosive sources and the use of submerged bells on light ships, which in bad weather signaled approaching ships equipped with stethoscopes or hull-mounted microphones.

The advance of electroacoustics made possible more sophisticated uses of sound energy in water, such as the moving-coil transducer, developed by R. A. Fessenden (1866–1932) in 1914 for the detection of icebergs by echo ranging.

The advent of the submarine as a weapon of importance in World War I gave the science of sound in the sea more than an academic priority, and large-scale development of sound generating and receiving equipment for submarine detection was begun. Piezoelectric materials made practical the development of ultrasonic transducers that produce beams of sound which can be trained like a searchlight for echo ranging. The French physicist P. Langevin (1872–

1946) used a quartz resonator in the first sonar detection of a submarine in 1918.

Today, electroacoustic transducers used in water range in size from a small fraction of a centimeter to several meters, from a fraction of a gram to hundreds of kilograms. The frequency spectrum ranges from a fraction of a cycle per second to several megacycles. These instruments serve a variety of purposes. Standard broadband hydrophones (underwater microphones) and standard broadband projectors (underwater sound sources) serve to measure the performance of many passive listening devices and active echo-ranging devices; special hydrophones are designed to measure ships' noises; large high-power scanning transducers are used to echo range from ships and submarines. Weapons such as homing torpedoes use highly specialized transducers with variable radiation patterns. Whereas most air acoustic problems are concerned with the audio-frequency range and hearing, underwater sound devices are usually not concerned with the hearing process and the range and type of equipment is very broad.

The design formulas for transducers for use in water are fundamentally the same as those for the air electroacoustic equipment. The obvious difference, of course, is the need for waterproofing and protection against hydrostatic pressure.

The basic difference in design of underwater transducers results from the high acoustic impedance of water, the high sound speed, and the energy distribution.

The average energy density of a plane acoustic wave in a fluid can be represented as $D = p^2/\rho c^2$ where p is the rms acoustic pressure, ρ the density of the medium, and c is the speed of sound in the medium. Since ρc^2 for air is much less than it is for water, the pressure in water is much greater for equal energy density. For this reason underwater-sound devices are usually pressure-sensing devices, and are more dense and stiff than air equipment.

The wavelength in water is between four and five times that in air. This means that the linear dimensions of an underwater sound radiator must be greater in that ratio to achieve the same directional characteristics as a radiator in air.

Since the specific acoustic impedance of water does not differ greatly from that of the metals used in diaphragms and housings, vibrations caused by flexural resonances of these metals radiate into the water very well. Large radiators for water are usually made in arrays of relatively small elements to avoid problems inherent in large pistons and diaphragms. Because of the high acoustic impedance of water, horns offer little advantage and are seldom used except at very low frequencies.

Most scanning sonar transducers use magnetostrictive, piezoelectric, or ferroelectric-ceramic elements. These transducers operate at mechanical resonance and are electrically tuned for optimum efficiency. The dimensions of the transducer, and electrical delay lines, control the directivity. Sonar transducers usually consist of a cylindrical array with the beam rotated electrically, a method of scanning now being adapted to large radar antennas. The trend to low frequencies has made variable-reluctance, electrodynamic, mechanical, and hydraulic projectors more useful than formerly. Explosive sound sources and electric spark sources can be used when extremely long ranges are necessary.

A fundamental limitation on the power output of a transducer is imposed by cavitation of the water. If the sound energy is of sufficient intensity to produce peak pressure amplitudes greater than the hydrostatic pressure, the water ruptures and gas bubbles are released. Some factors influencing the maximum acoustic pressure that can be tolerated are the depth and the presence of impurities. A nominal value of maximum attainable intensity at the surface is $\frac{1}{3}$ w/cm^2 steady state.

Some projectors made as sound sources for measurements in the audio range are similar to air loudspeakers, and are high-fidelity broadband instruments. These projectors have also been used commercially to reproduce music in swimming pools for water ballet and entertainment.

The passive listening devices, hydrophones, serve to detect ships and submarines and also to measure the characteristics of projectors. Most of the standard hydrophones in use are piezoelectric or ferroelectric. The size, shape, sensitivity, and electrical impedance depend on the purpose the hydrophone has to serve. In most cases, these instruments are made to operate at frequencies below resonance where the pressure response as a function of frequency is constant. For hydrophones designed primarily to measure ambient noise, a design criterion for the signal-to-noise ratio is the ability to measure the ocean noise at zero sea state.

The advent of the nuclear-powered missile-carrying submarine has increased the need for larger and more complex transducer systems. At this time sound energy is the only means by which intelligence can be transmitted for an appreciable distance underwater.

CLAUDE C. SIMS

Cross-references: *Electroacoustics, Ferroelectrics, Magnetostriction, Piezoelectricity, Propagation, Sonar, Transducers, Ultrasonics*

UNDULATOR

From Latin "unda" wave, "wave maker," a name coined by H. Motz for a device for the generation of submillimeter waves. This device was also, independently, proposed by P. D. Coleman. An electron beam with an energy of several megavolts is passed through an assembly of magnets arranged along a main axis so that their fields are perpendicular to the axis and alternate periodically with axial distance (Fig. 1). When suitably injected the electrons describe a periodic orbit. The electrons radiate electromagnetic waves with wavelengths depending on the direction of propagation. In the axial direction the wavelength is short compared to the magnet spacing l_0. From the point of view of special relativity one may say that an observer attached to an electron would see the magnet system Lorentz-contracted. Moreover, the oscillating electron is moving towards an observer in the laboratory system who therefore sees a Doppler-shortened wavelength. The radiation process is illustrated from the viewpoint of wave kinematics by Fig. 2. The electron is moving from O to P with velocity v in a time l_0/v. The direction of propagation of the electromagnetic wave radiated makes an angle θ with the undulator axis z. The surface PQ represents a surface of constant phase of the radiation. This can be the case if the phases at Q and P differ by one period λ/c. The radiation takes a time $(l_0/c) \cos \theta$ to get from O to P. Hence

$$\lambda/c = l_0/v - (l_0/c) \cos \theta$$

and

$$\lambda = (l_0 c/v)[1 - (v/c) \cos \theta]$$

In the direction $\theta = 0$

$$\lambda = (l_0 c/2v)[1 - (v^2/c^2)]$$

in agreement with the foregoing relativistic argument. In practice the electron movement takes place in a waveguide placed along the axis between the magnet poles.

One can show that the radiated spectrum in the guide is a line spectrum with frequencies given by

$$\omega_{m,n} = \gamma^2 \omega_0 p \pm \gamma^2 v[(\omega_0 p^2/c^2) - (\alpha^2_{m,n}/\gamma^2)]^{\frac{1}{2}}$$

where $1 - v^2/c^2 = 1/\gamma^2$, $2\pi v/l_0 = \omega_0$, and,

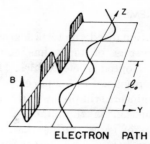

FIG 1. Magnetic flux curve and electron path of a magnetic undulator. (*Previously published in Jour. Appl. Phys.*)

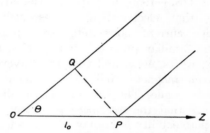

FIG. 2. Illustration of wave-kinematics.

for a rectangular guide with sides a, b,

$$\alpha^2_{m,n} = (m^2\pi^2/a^2) + (n^2\pi^2/b^2)$$

m,n,p, integers

The radiation output by an undulator is much enhanced if the electrons are bunched, i.e., if they arrive in packets with a longitudinal extension which is short compared to the wavelength to be radiated. Enhancement factors of 10^6 and more can be achieved by such close bunching.

Radiation with wavelengths down to a fraction of a millimeter have been generated by means of electron beams of 2 Mev passing through an undulator. With a 100-Mev electron beam visible light was generated. Powers of the order of 1 w have been obtained in the millimeter range and can probably be produced down to a wavelength of 0.5 mm.

HANS MOTZ

Cross-references: *Linear Accelerators, Milli-meter-Wave Generation*

UNIT SYSTEMS

The rationalized meter-kilogram-second (MKS) system of units has come to be generally adopted in electronics. (There are some exceptions: for instance, many electronics engineers still prefer to think of magnetic induction in the practical cgs (and emu) units of gauss, rather than the MKS unit, weber per square meter; fortunately, the conversion unit is a simple one—1 weber/m² = 10^4 gauss.) The rationalized MKS system, first proposed by Giovanni Giorgi (1871–1950) in 1904, has the advantages that electrical quantities such as voltage, current, power, etc., are expressed in the familiar practical units (volts, amperes, watts, etc.), and that no conversion between magnetic and electric quantities need be made. The system has the disadvantage that the free-space permittivity ϵ_0 and permeability μ_0 are not unity, as in the classical esu and emu unit systems; but these are almost the only constants whose values need be memorized, and moreover they have definite physical significance. In the rationalized MKS system, free-space permittivity $\epsilon_0 = 1/(36\pi \times 10^9) = 8.85 \times 10^{-12}$ farad/m is the capacitance of a parallel-plate condenser with plates each 1 m² in area and 1 m apart; free-space permeability $\mu_0 = 4\pi \times 10^{-7}$ henry/m is the self-inductance per unit (meter) length of a transmission line comprising two parallel-plate conductors 1 m wide and 1 m apart. (Edge effects are neglected in these definitions.)

A convenient method of conversion from emu and esu units into MKS units is given in Table 1.

Still another advantage of the rationalized MKS system is that dimensional analysis is simplified by the fact that with charge q chosen as the fourth physical dimension (in addition to the usual length L, mass M, and time T), no fractional exponents result, as can be seen from Table 2.

CHARLES SUSSKIND

Cross-references: *Abbreviations, Dielectric Theory, Electromagnetic Theory, Magnetism*

TABLE 1. CONVERSION FROM esu AND emu UNITS TO RATIONALIZED MKS UNITS

To convert a quantity from esu or emu into rationalized MKS units, note that the number in the appropriate column shows the equivalent esu or emu quantity. Examples: capacitance C in MKS units (farads) is equivalent to $9 \times 10^{11}\, C'$, where C' is expressed in esu; magnetic induction B in MKS units (webers/m²) is equivalent to $10^4 B'$, where B' is expressed in emu.

Quantity (MKS unit)	esu	emu
Capacitance (farad)	9×10^{11}	10^{-9}
Charge (coulomb)	3×10^9	10^{-1}
Conductivity (mho)	9×10^{11}	10^{-9}
Conductivity, surface (mho)	9×10^{11}	10^{-9}
Conductivity, volume (mho/m)	9×10^9	10^{-11}
Current (amp)	3×10^9	10^{-1}
Current density, surface (amp/m)	3×10^7	10^{-3}
Current density, volume (amp/m²)	3×10^5	10^{-5}
Displacement, electric (D, coulomb/m²)	$12\pi \times 10^5$	$4\pi \times 10^{-5}$
Electromotive force (v)	300^{-1}	10^8
Field intensity, electric (E, v/m)	$3^{-1} \times 10^{-4}$	10^6
Field intensity, magnetic (H, amp-turn/m)	$12\pi \times 10^7$	$4\pi \times 10^{-3}$
Flux, magnetic (weber)	300^{-1}	10^8
Impedance (ohm)	$9^{-1} \times 10^{-11}$	10^9
Inductance (henry)	$9^{-1} \times 10^{-11}$	10^9
Induction, magnetic (B, weber/m²)	$3^{-1} \times 10^{-6}$	10^4
Magnetomotive force (amp-turn)	$12\pi \times 10^9$	$4\pi \times 10^{-1}$
Permeability (henry/m)	$(36\pi)^{-1} \times 10^{-13}$	$(4\pi)^{-1} \times 10^7$
Permittivity (farad/m)	$36\pi \times 10^9$	$4\pi \times 10^{-11}$
Potential, electric scalar (v)	300^{-1}	10^8
Potential, magnetic vector (weber/m)	$3^{-1} \times 10^{-4}$	10^6
Reactance (ohm)	$9^{-1} \times 10^{-11}$	10^9
Reluctance (amp-turn/weber)	$36\pi \times 10^{11}$	$4\pi \times 10^{-9}$
Resistance (ohm)	$9^{-1} \times 10^{-11}$	10^9
Resistivity, surface (ohm)	$9^{-1} \times 10^{-11}$	10^9
Resistivity, volume (ohm-m)	$9^{-1} \times 10^{-9}$	10^{11}

TABLE 2. DIMENSIONS OF UNITS IN esu, emu, AND MKS SYSTEMS

Quantity	esu ($\epsilon = 1$)	emu ($\mu = 1$)	MKS
Capacitance	ϵL	$\mu^{-1}L^{-1}T^2$	$M^{-1}L^{-2}T^2q^2$
Charge	$\epsilon^{1/2}M^{1/2}L^{3/2}T^{-1}$	$\mu^{-1/2}M^{1/2}L^{1/2}$	q
Conductance	ϵLT^{-1}	$\mu^{-1}L^{-1}T$	$M^{-1}L^{-2}Tq^2$
Conductivity, surface	ϵLT^{-1}	$\mu^{-1}L^{-1}T$	$M^{-1}L^{-2}Tq^2$
Conductivity, volume	ϵT^{-1}	$\mu^{-1}L^{-2}T$	$M^{-1}L^{-3}Tq^2$
Current	$\epsilon^{1/2}M^{1/2}L^{3/2}T^{-2}$	$\mu^{-1/2}M^{1/2}L^{1/2}T^{-1}$	$T^{-1}q$
Current density, surface	$\epsilon^{1/2}M^{1/2}L^{1/2}T^{-2}$	$\mu^{-1/2}M^{1/2}L^{-1/2}T^{-1}$	$L^{-1}T^{-1}q$
Current density, volume	$\epsilon^{1/2}M^{1/2}L^{-1/2}T^{-2}$	$\mu^{-1/2}M^{1/2}L^{-3/2}T^{-1}$	$L^{-2}T^{-1}q$
Displacement, electric (D)	$\epsilon^{1/2}M^{1/2}L^{-1/2}T^{-1}$	$\mu^{-1/2}M^{1/2}L^{-3/2}$	$L^{-2}q$
Electromotive force	$\epsilon^{-1/2}M^{1/2}L^{1/2}T^{-1}$	$\mu^{1/2}M^{1/2}L^{3/2}T^{-2}$	$ML^2T^{-2}q^{-1}$
Field intensity, electric (E)	$\epsilon^{-1/2}M^{1/2}L^{-1/2}T^{-1}$	$\mu^{1/2}M^{1/2}L^{1/2}T^{-2}$	$MLT^{-2}q^{-1}$
Field intensity, magnetic (H)	$\epsilon^{1/2}M^{1/2}L^{1/2}T^{-2}$	$\mu^{-1/2}M^{1/2}L^{-1/2}T^{-1}$	$L^{-1}T^{-1}q$
Flux, magnetic	$\epsilon^{-1/2}M^{1/2}L^{1/2}$	$\mu^{1/2}M^{1/2}L^{3/2}T^{-1}$	$ML^2T^{-1}q^{-1}$
Impedance	$\epsilon^{-1}L^{-1}T$	μLT^{-1}	$ML^2T^{-1}q^{-2}$
Inductance	$\epsilon^{-1}L^{-1}T^2$	μL	ML^2q^{-2}
Induction, magnetic (B)	$\epsilon^{-1/2}M^{1/2}L^{-3/2}$	$\mu^{1/2}M^{1/2}L^{-1/2}T^{-1}$	$MT^{-1}q^{-1}$
Magnetomotive force	$\epsilon^{1/2}M^{1/2}L^{3/2}T^{-2}$	$\mu^{-1/2}M^{1/2}L^{1/2}T^{-1}$	$T^{-1}q$
Permeability	$\epsilon^{-1}L^{-2}T^2$	μ	MLq^{-2}
Permittivity	ϵ	$\mu^{-1}L^{-2}T^2$	$M^{-1}L^{-3}T^2q^2$
Potential, electric scalar	$\epsilon^{-1/2}M^{1/2}L^{1/2}T^{-1}$	$\mu^{1/2}M^{1/2}L^{3/2}T^{-2}$	$ML^2T^{-2}q^{-1}$
Potential, magnetic vector	$\epsilon^{-1/2}M^{1/2}L^{-1/2}$	$\mu^{1/2}M^{1/2}L^{1/2}T^{-1}$	$MLT^{-1}q^{-1}$
Reactance	$\epsilon^{-1}L^{-1}T$	μLT^{-1}	$ML^2T^{-1}q^{-2}$
Reluctance	ϵLT^{-2}	$\mu^{-1}L^{-1}$	$M^{-1}L^{-2}q^2$
Resistance	$\epsilon^{-1}L^{-1}T$	μLT^{-1}	$ML^2T^{-1}q^{-2}$
Resistivity, surface	$\epsilon^{-1}L^{-1}T$	μLT^{-1}	$ML^2T^{-1}q^{-2}$
Resistivity, volume	$\epsilon^{-1}T$	μL^2T^{-1}	ML^3Tq^{-2}

V

VACUUM GAGES

A convenient way of classifying gages is according to the effect or physical property used in their operation. Gages depending on the actual hydrostatic force exerted by the gas are known as hydrostatic-pressure gages. The viscosity of a rarified gas varies with pressure, and this fact is made use of in viscosity gages. Thermal-conductivity gages operate on the principle that the thermal conductivity of a rarified gas depends on its pressure. The radiometer effect is utilized in radiometer gages. Ionization gages depend on measuring an artificially produced ion current in the rarified gas. Finally, an electrical discharge may be produced in a tube connected to the vacuum chamber and its characteristics examined, as is done in discharge gages.

Hydrostatic-Pressure Gages. The most important among them is the McLeod gage. Its principle consists in compressing a given volume V of the gas whose pressure is to be measured to a much smaller volume v and observing the resultant pressure p. Then, according to Boyle's law,

$$p = PV/v$$

The McLeod gage is an absolute manometer which is reproducible, accurate, and reliable. Hence it is used as a primary laboratory standard for checking and calibrating other types of vacuum gages. It operates in the pressure range 1 to 10^{-4} mm of Hg.

Viscosity Gages. There are two principal varieties of viscosity gages. In one variety the time taken for vibrations set up in a quartz fiber or strip to drop to one-half amplitude is determined; this time is then used as a measure of the pressure. In the other variety, a rotating disk is made to turn a suspended disk through the viscous action of the rarified gas in between. The torque on the suspended disk is balanced by the torsion in the fiber suspension. The angle of twist obviously depends on the gas pressure. The latter principle is used in the Langmuir molecular gage, which is useful in the range 10^{-3} to beyond 10^{-6} mm of Hg.

Thermal-Conductivity Gages. Examples of this type are the thermocouple gage and the Pirani gage. The former uses a thermocouple (*q.v.*) fixed to a heated wire exposed to the vacuum. The heat loss by molecular transfer diminishes as the pressure goes down. Hence, for a constant heater current, the thermocouple junction temperature goes up as the pressure falls. A meter in the thermocouple circuit indicates the pressure. The thermocouple gage is simple in construction and operation but has a highly nonlinear scale.

The Pirani gage also uses a heated wire in which the current is maintained constant. The change in resistance of the wire, resulting from its temperature change, is then observed as a function of the pressure. A Wheatstone bridge arrangement is generally used for measuring the resistance.

These gages read down to 10^{-4} mm of Hg and have several advantages: they read continuously and remotely, need not be fragile or bulky, are rugged, and may be used in automatic-control systems.

Radiometer Type of Gages. The Knudsen gage, which is best known in this group, consists of two sets of vanes parallel to, and facing, each other. One set is kept fixed and is heated separately. The other set is suspended and is free to rotate. Radiometric action introduces a torque on the movable vane and the torsion in the suspension is used to measure the pressure. A necessary condition for gage operation is that the separation between the repelling surfaces must be small compared to the molecular mean free path. Pressures down to 10^{-6} mm of Hg can be measured with this instrument.

Ionization Gages. All ionization gages measure an ionization current produced in the gage chamber. There are three main types of ionization gages, as indicated below.

In thermionic ionization gages, a hot cathode emits electrons which are accelerated by a potential of 100 to 300 v. A negative electrode serves as the collector of the ion current. An electronic power supply and metering system are generally used for operating the triode ionization gage. In the Philips gage, a rectangular loop forming an anode is placed in between two parallel cathode plates. A magnetic field is applied by an external magnet. On applying about 2000 v the ionizing electrons traverse a helical path of such length as to ionize gas molecules even though the electron mean free path is many times the interelectrode spacing. In the third type of ionization gage, radium is mounted inside the gage so that its alpha activity provides a source of ions. No power supply is required.

The ionization gage covers a wide range of pressures, 10^{-2} to 10^{-8} mm of Hg. However, it requires considerable auxiliary equipment, its sensitivity varies for different gases and vapors, and its filament is susceptible to poisoning and burn-out. Furthermore, the electrodes must be outgassed very thoroughly before the gage can be used to give reliable readings.

T. K. LAKSHMANAN

Cross-references: *Vacuum Techniques*

VACUUM TECHNIQUES

The evacuation of gases and vapors from a volume for the attainment of subatmospheric pressures can be accomplished in several ways. By far the most widely used method is the employment of mechanical vacuum pumps, either alone or in series with diffusion pumps, depending on the ultimate pressure to be obtained. Since such a pumping system must not only remove atmospheric air and permanent gases, but also

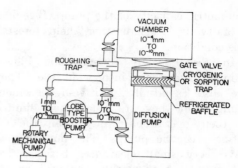

FIG. 1. Typical vacuum system.

reduce the pressure of the condensable vapors to an acceptable value, appropriate associated equipment must occasionally be employed.

Figure 1 is a schematic representation of the assembly of elements constituting a typical diffusion-pumped vacuum system. The ranges of usual pressures obtained at various locations in the system are also indicated. A discussion of the individual elements follows.

Mechanical Pumps

Mechanical positive-displacement pumps are essential in the usual vacuum system. No matter what pumping means is used for obtaining high vacuums, a positive-displacement pump is required for the initial pumping, "roughing down," of the vacuum system as well as for the subsequent backing of the diffusion pump. Positive-displacement pumps utilizing a vane or rotating-eccentric-pumping principle are available in a wide variety of capacities from a fraction of a cubic foot per minute to over 700 ft³/min. Their usual operating pressures cover the range of vacuum system total pressure from 760 to 0.001 mm of Hg.

The pumps all utilize a dual-function lubricating and sealing oil. The vapor pressure of this oil is one of the determining factors of the base pressure of the pump. The oil may deteriorate after prolonged operation, usually because of contamination from pumped water vapor or other condensables. This contamination increases the attainable base pressure and decreases the volumetric capacity of the pump. Bleeding-in of dry air, "gas ballasting," helps forestall this condition.

In recent years rotating-lobe blower pumps have come into wide use. They are also essentially positive-displacement pumps, but they are much more limited in their operational range than the rotating eccentric pumps. The pumps must have very small clearances between the rotating lobes themselves, as well as between the lobes and the housing, in order to yield low base pressures. At high pressures, the heat of compression of the pumped gas can cause sufficient heating and expansion of the rotating parts to cause them to seize. Hence the usual upper limit of operating pressure is about 15 mm of Hg, although certain specially built pumps can operate up to 50 mm of Hg. Total pressure gages indicate base pressures for typical lobe pumps of 10^{-3} to 10^{-4} mm of Hg.

A lobe-type booster pump in series with a standard mechanical pump is often an advantageous combination that can provide the same pump-down time as a much larger single mechanical pump, maintain a much lower backing pressure for the diffusion pump, and eliminate the sensitivity of the pumping system to oil deterioration in the mechanical pump. Booster pumps are often represented as being oil free. This is not the actual case, and they should be baffled if installed directly to a system in which hydrocarbons are to be kept to a minimum.

Another type of mechanical pump, the molecular pump, consists of one or more rotor disks that rotate at very high speeds (4,000–15,000 rpm) between very closely spaced plates in a stator housing. The pumping is accomplished by the tendency of gaseous molecules which impinge on the rotor to be re-emitted in the direction of motion of the rotor surface. Molecular pumps are oil free and capable of producing pressures down to 10^{-8} mm of Hg in properly conditioned systems. They must be backed by an ordinary mechanical pump.

Diffusion Pumps

Diffusion pumps are available in a wide variety of sizes and types ranging in size from a fraction of an inch in diameter by 6 in. long to 4 ft in diameter by 8 ft long. They vary in capacity from less than a liter per second to 50,000 l/sec. The lowest pressure that a diffusion pump can attain is determined by a combination of the characteristics of the system being pumped as well as the characteristics of the pump itself. The ultimate pressure for a given pump depends on the stability of the pumping fluid and on the vapor pressure characteristics of the fluid. Thus, in selecting a pump and pumping fluid, consideration of the application of the complete vacuum system is important.

It is not unusual for diffusion pumps to reach pressures of 10^{-10} mm of Hg or less on thoroughly clean ultra-high-vacuum systems. Oil of very low vapor pressure is required for this application. At the other end of the operating range, diffusion pumps are sometimes used to handle huge volumetric gas loads at 10^{-3} mm of Hg. The pump fluid for this application should be a very stable chemical compound, and the vapor-pressure characteristics would be of secondary importance.

It is occasionally a requirement of the end use of a vacuum system that no hydrocarbons can be tolerated in the pumped volume. For this type of application, pumps using mercury as a pumping fluid are often employed.

One of the prime considerations in using any diffusion pump, regardless of the type of pump fluid, is the prevention of the migration of the pumping fluid into the chamber proper. Since the complete elimination of backstreaming by the inherent design of the pump has not yet been accomplished, various auxiliary equipment must be employed, including:

(1) cold caps or barrier rings over the top nozzle;

(2) water-cooled or refrigerated baffles;

(3) liquid-nitrogen baffles with "no creep" walls;

(4) thermoelectric-cooled baffles; and

(5) sorption traps and baffles of various kinds.

In addition to these accessories to minimize backstreaming, proper operation of the diffusion pump is essential. Adequate fore-pump capacity should be provided to maintain the fore pressure at a minimum. The portion of the pump-down cycle during which the diffusion pump exhausts the tank to the operational pressure should start at the lowest pressure consistent with the time available and the characteristics of the roughing pump. Diffusion pumps do not operate ideally above 1 μ and considerable backstreaming occurs in this pumping range.

A typical vacuum system as shown in Fig. 1 can be built up from components available as standard items from a number of manufacturers. The criteria for the selection of these components again must be established from the nature of the application of the vacuum system. In general, off-the-shelf vacuum hardware is suitable for application down to the 10^{-6} mm of Hg range. The attainment of lower pressures requires considerable care in properly specifying the material characteristics of components. Of particular concern are the gasketing systems for joining together the various elements of the vacuum system. Table I summarizes the types of materials, gasketing, and system processing required for several ranges of pressures. It is seen that ultra-high vacuum systems require rather severe restrictions in material selection. The attainment of pressures below 10^{-7} mm of Hg is directly related to the amount of gas adsorbed on the vacuum chamber surfaces. "Baking out" of the vacuum system drives off these adsorbed layers. The ultimate pressure attained is directly related to the bake-out temperature, other things being equal.

Cold traps and baffles are often used to assist in the pumping by acting as condensation surfaces for gases and vapors as

TABLE 1

PRESSURE RANGES			
	10^{-3}-10^{-6}mm	10^{-6}-10^{-8}mm	10^{-8}-10^{-10}mm
GASKETING	COMMERCIAL SYNTHETIC RUBBER	VITON TEFLON OR METALS	DEGASSED VITON OR METALS
COMPONENT MATERIAL	BRASS ALUMINUM STEEL	ST. STEEL ALUMINUM GLASS	ST. STEEL GLASS
SYSTEM PROCESSING	CAREFUL CLEANING	SCRUPULOUS CLEANING MILD BAKE	SCRUPULOUS CLEANING 400°C BAKE

well as helping control the migration of the pumping fluids. Temperatures employed cover a wide range from that of liquid helium at 4° K up to those obtainable with standard commercial refrigeration equipment.

Highly sensitive mass-spectrometry (q.v.) types of leak detectors are available that permit rendering any vacuum system essentially leak free. Therefore no provision for leakage need be considered here and vacuum-system performance can be quite accurately predicted from the considerations outlined above.

HUGH R. SMITH, JR.

Getter-Ion Pumps

Getter-ion vacuum pumps differ from mechanical and diffusion pumps in that gases are removed through chemical combination and by physical entrapment within the pump rather than by ejection into the external atmosphere. This difference leads to features which are attractive in many applications. Because pump fluids (such as oil or mercury) are not employed, refrigerated traps and baffles are not required. Since gases are pumped internally, getter-ion pumps can be used in systems that are completely closed following the initial rough pumping. Retention of pumped gases does not require continuous application of the electrical power employed for the pumping process. These features contribute to reduced contamination of the system by the pump, convenient operation, portability, and comparative immunity to damage by power failure.

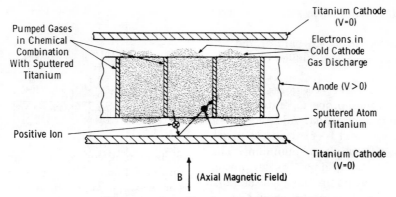

FIG. 2. Cross-section side view of a VacIon® pump.

For many years gettering and electrical cleanup of gases have been utilized to maintain adequate vacua in sealed-off electron tubes. The amounts of gas pumped in these cases are small in comparison with quantities removed by other means during processing. Only recently have getter-ion pumps evolved to the point where they can perform major pumping operations of the sort normally assigned to diffusion pumps. It has developed that one of the most effective getter materials is titanium, and that pumping is often greatly enhanced by the presence of an ionizing gas discharge.

The first successful demonstration of the feasibility of pumping large quantities of gas by getter-ion means was provided by the Evapor-ion pump, in which titanium is evaporated by being fed in wire form onto a post heated by electron bombardment, and in which a limited amount of ionization is produced. Several other pumps employing alternative means of titanium evaporation have been developed subsequently. In general, however, the low rate of evaporation of titanium even at its melting point has given rise to serious difficulties and limitations in pumps which employ thermal evaporation.

Another variety of getter-ion pump is one in which a cold-cathode gas discharge is utilized in a dual role. First, *sputtering* of titanium produced by positive ions of the discharge is used instead of *thermal evaporation*, and second, the discharge produces the ionization, etc., necessary for effective pumping. The first sputtering type of getter-ion pump to achieve widespread practical applicability was the VacIon® pump (Fig. 2). Recognition of its utility has led to the development of several pumps in this category under a variety of trade names. Because of their relative simplicity and effectiveness, getter-ion pumps of the sputtering type are more useful for most applications than those employing thermal evaporation. A further description of their operation is therefore appropriate.

A cold-cathode gas discharge is established through proper combinations of electrode configuration, voltage, and magnetic field, as shown for example in the figure. Operating voltages are typically in the range 3 to 10 kv, and magnetic fields are usually in the range 1 to 2 kilogauss. Such discharges can exist over the pressure range from above 10^{-2} to below 10^{-10} mm of Hg. Over a large portion of this range, current flow and the rates of positive-ion production and sputtering are proportional to pressure. The pump therefore acts as its own pressure gauge. For constant pumping speed the rate at which titanium is required is also proportional to pressure. Sputtering thus automatically dispenses titanium as needed, leading to its efficient utilization and to long pump life. Pump life varies inversely with pressure. Lives in excess of 20,000–50,000 hr at a pressure of 10^{-6} mm of Hg are typical.

Several pumping mechanisms are operative. Most of the pumped nitrogen and oxygen reside at the anode in chemical combination with sputtered titanium. Hydrogen and helium, which cause comparatively little sputtering, are pumped primarily by diffusion into the cathodes. Argon and other heavy noble gases are pumped chiefly in regions where both ion bombardment and net buildup of sputtered titanium take place. Dissociation and cracking contribute to the pumping of complex molecules.

R. L. Jepsen

Cross-references: *Electron-Tube Manufacture, Vacuum Gages*

VACUUM-TUBE VOLTMETER (VTVM): see INDICATING INSTRUMENTS

VACUUM TUBES: see ELECTRON TUBES (CONVENTIONAL)

VAN DE GRAAFF ACCELERATOR

The Van de Graaff electrostatic accelerator is essentially a belt conveyor of electric charge designed for the attainment of high constant potentials together with a suitably evacuated tube for the acceleration of charged particles. Robert J. Van de Graaff (b. 1901) invented the principle of the belt-type generator, and, by the addition of an accelerator tube, developed the means of producing millions of electron volts of high-energy radiation needed by the physicist to investigate the atom. The word "generator" is used for the voltage source and "accelerator" for the complete particle or radiation source. The accelerated particles can be electrons, protons, or ions such as deuterons, alpha particles, and heavier ions. By bombarding light-metal targets, such as beryllium, with positive ions, the Van de Graaff is capable of providing intense neutron fluxes. Using a heavy-metal target, such as gold or tungsten, with electron bombardment, produces X-rays.

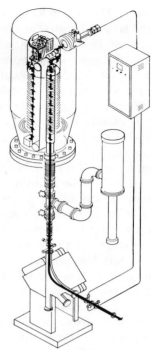

Fig. 1. Schematic of Van de Graaff accelerator.

The Van de Graaff electrostatic generator is a simple device consisting of an insulating support structure, a belt-charging system, a high voltage terminal, and, in the case of pressurized generators, an insulating gas enclosure (Fig. 1). Unlike other electrostatic generators, the Van de Graaff utilizes a rotating belt to transfer the charge deposited onto the belt *below* the ground plane and removed from the belt *inside* the isolated sphere. The Van de Graaff accelerator is a source of high energy particles like the cyclotron, betatron, and synchrotron, but differs from these machines in that it directly generates the total potential instead of accelerating the ions many times by the same voltage increment. Acceleration within a Van de Graaff takes place on a straight path.

A Van de Graaff generator is limited in the current-carrying capacity of its belt. Currents of up to 5 ma have been carried on belts of practical width. The present, practical upper limit of maximum voltage would appear to be 12 Mv, the limitation here being the physical size and cost. The compactness of the Van de Graaff generator is made possible by the use of high-pressure gas insulation for the terminal potential. Inert gas atmospheres between 100 and 375 psig are used for the insulation, which permits operating gradients on the high-potential terminal of six times the 76-kv/in. breakdown gradient for atmospheric air. The *insulating gas* used most generally is a mixture of 80% nitrogen and 20% carbon dioxide. The support column for the high-voltage terminal consists, usually, of a series of metal plates separated by glass or porcelain insulators. Uniform reduction of the voltage potential between the terminal and ground is maintained on most generators by the use of column resistors. The *charging system* for the Van de Graaff consists of a flat neoprene-fabric belt, a drive motor and terminal pulley, a belt-charge power supply, and the charging and collecting devices. Filament-type cathodes are used as the electron source for the accelerator tubes. The rf type ion source is generally used for the positive-ion accelerators. Accelerators may be converted from positive to negative operation by the substitution of an electron tube and cathode for a positive-ion tube and source, and

reversal of the polarity of the terminal. The *accelerator tubes* are constructed of alternating metal electrodes and short porcelain or glass insulating rings. A mercury diffusion pumping system, suitably trapped, is customarily used to attain a vacuum of 10^{-5} to 10^{-6} mm of Hg.

Commercially available Van de Graaffs include instruments ranging from a 400-kv accelerator used as a neutron source for reactor research and engineering training, to the 12-Mev accelerator used for physics research programs. A recent Van de Graaff accelerator design, employing the tandem or charge exchange principle, consists of two conventional 6-Mev accelerators placed end-to-end and sharing a common high-voltage terminal (Fig. 2). Negative ions are produced at ground, and then accelerated to a high-voltage positive terminal. Within the terminal, the swiftly moving negative ions are stripped of electrons, thus becoming positive ions. They then receive a second acceleration stage from the terminal to ground. Thus, by charge exchange, negative to positive, the voltage of the accelerator is used twice. Extensions of this tandem principle to allow three or more accelerations by the same voltage using Van de Graaff accelerators show promise of attaining higher

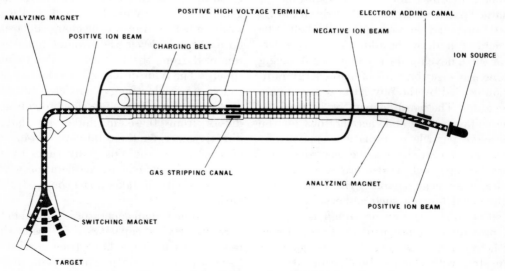

FIG. 2. Operating principle of the tandem Van de Graaff accelerator.

proton-beam energies in the 20- to 30-Mev range.

DENIS M. ROBINSON

Cross-references: *Accelerators*, *Cockcroft-Walton Accelerator*, *Static (Tribo-) Electricity*

VARACTOR: see PARAMETRIC AMPLIFIERS

VARISTOR

The term *varistor* has been used to denote the entire class of variable or nonlinear resistors composed of semiconducting materials. This class includes all semiconductor rectifiers such as point-contact and junction diodes made from germanium and silicon as well as those in which copper oxide or selenium are employed. It also includes devices made from silicon-carbide that do not exhibit rectification.

The silicon carbide (SiC) varistor is a symmetrical nonlinear resistor having a voltage-current characteristic which may, over a relatively wide range, be represented by the equation $I = KE^n$, where I is the direct or instantaneous current, E is the dc or instantaneous voltage, K is a constant, and n is the "exponent" having values between 1 and about 6. Both K and n depend on the material, geometry and processing of the varistor.

Another equation frequently used is $E = CI^{(1-a)}$ where $C = (1/K)^{1/n}$ and $a = 1 - (1/n)$.

The temperature coefficient of the voltage at constant current of the silicon carbide varistor is approximately $-0.1\%/°C$. The temperature coefficient of the current at constant voltage is $+0.1\%/°C$ to $0.6\%/°C$ depending on the value of the exponent. To some extent, the temperature coefficient depends on the material and processing of the varistor as well as its operating condition.

The effect of humidity on SiC varistors is minimized by the use of a silicone impregnating fluid. The effectiveness of the impregnant as well as long term stability re-quirements limits the operating temperature of such varistors to 110°C for continuous use and 150°C for intermittent use.

Power ratings depend upon the mounting used and heat dissipation qualities of a specific unit. A continuous rating of 0.25 w/in.² of varistor surface is adequate for individual units mounted vertically in still air at 25°C. This rating may be increased by other means of cooling such as forced air, oil immersion, or the use of radiating fins.

Silicon carbide varistors may be used as circuit protectors, as shunts across contacts to prevent sparking, or placed in parallel with the field windings or series reactors to prevent over-voltages with current surges. They may be used for control devices in combination with other resistors, to regulate voltage or current. They may also be used as balancing resistors for control of current wave shapes in impulse generators, for reduction of variations in load voltage, and for stabilization of variable loads.

MEYER SAPOFF

Cross-references: *Diodes (Semiconductor)*, *Resistors*, *Thermistors*

VECTOR ALGEBRA

Many familiar quantities such as mass, temperature, charge, pole strength, etc., are completely specified when a single number representing their magnitude is given. These quantities are known as *scalars*. Other quantities, such as velocities, forces, currents, electric and magnetic field strength, etc., require for their specification not only a magnitude but a direction in space. These quantities are known as *vectors*. A vector may be represented geometrically by an arrow; the length of the arrow on some arbitrary scale represents the magnitude of the vector, and the direction associated with the vector is that in which the arrow points. It is thus evident that rectilinear displacements of a point and all physical quantities that can be represented by such displacements are vectors. It is customary to repre-

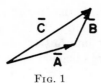

FIG. 1

sent vectors by letters in boldface type and scalars in lightface italics.

Addition and Subtraction of Vectors; Multiplication of a Vector by a Scalar.

A vector having been defined as an entity that behaves in the same manner as the rectilinear displacement of a point, vector addition is reduced to a composition of linear displacements.

Consider two vectors $\mathbf{A}$ and $\mathbf{B}$ as shown in Fig. 1. The vector $\mathbf{C}$ which is obtained by moving a point along $\mathbf{A}$ and then along $\mathbf{B}$, is called the resultant or sum, of the vectors $\mathbf{A}$ and $\mathbf{B}$ and we write,

$$\mathbf{C} = \mathbf{A} + \mathbf{B}$$

From the nature of the definition of vector addition it is apparent that

$$\mathbf{A} + \mathbf{B} = \mathbf{B} + \mathbf{A}$$

and therefore vector addition is commutative. The sum of several vectors such as $\mathbf{A} + \mathbf{B} + \mathbf{C}$ is obtained by adding $\mathbf{C}$ to the vector $(\mathbf{A} + \mathbf{B})$.

If we are given a vector $\mathbf{B}$, the negative of this vector $-\mathbf{B}$ is obtained by reversing the direction of the arrow that represents $\mathbf{B}$. If it is now desired to subtract the vector $\mathbf{B}$ from the vector $\mathbf{A}$ it is only necessary to add the vector $-\mathbf{B}$ to the vector $\mathbf{A}$ and thus obtain the vector

$$\mathbf{D} = (\mathbf{A} - \mathbf{B})$$

Two vectors are said to be equal when they have the same magnitude and the same direction. If $\mathbf{A} = \mathbf{B}$ the difference $\mathbf{D}$ is zero.

Multiplication of a Vector by a Scalar. Let $\mathbf{a}$ be a given vector whose magnitude is a; then by the product of the vector $\mathbf{a}$ by the scalar n is meant a vector that has the same direction as $\mathbf{a}$ but whose magnitude is na. We therefore write

$$\mathbf{A} = n\mathbf{a}$$

to denote this new vector.

Unit Vectors. A vector having unit magnitude or length is called a *unit vector*. The most commonly used unit vectors are those which have the direction of a right-handed Cartesian coordinate system as shown in Fig. 2. Let $\mathbf{i}, \mathbf{j}$, and $\mathbf{k}$ be unit vectors in the directions of the axes OX, OY, and OZ as shown. The vector $\mathbf{R}$ with initial point 0 and terminal point (x, y, z) may be expressed in terms of its components R_x, R_y, and R_z in terms of the unit vectors $\mathbf{i}, \mathbf{j}, \mathbf{k}$ in the form,

$$\mathbf{R} = \mathbf{i}R_x + \mathbf{j}R_y + \mathbf{k}R_z$$

If two vectors $\mathbf{A}$ and $\mathbf{B}$ are expressed in terms of their components, so that

$$\mathbf{A} = \mathbf{i}A_x + \mathbf{j}A_y + \mathbf{k}A_z$$

$$\mathbf{B} = \mathbf{i}B_x + \mathbf{j}B_y + \mathbf{k}B_z$$

then the sum $(\mathbf{A} + \mathbf{B})$ is given in terms of components by the equation,

$$(\mathbf{A} + \mathbf{B}) =$$

$$\mathbf{i}(A_x + B_x) + \mathbf{j}(A_y + B_y) + \mathbf{k}(A_z + B_z)$$

Multiplication of Vectors.

The multiplication of a vector by a scalar has already been discussed. Besides multiplication by scalars there are two other types of multiplication defined in vector algebra, the scalar product and the vector product.

The Scalar Product. The scalar product of two vectors is sometimes called the inner

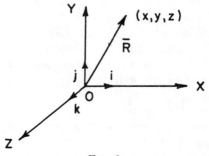

FIG. 2

or dot product. It is defined by the equation

$$\mathbf{A} \cdot \mathbf{B} = AB \cos \theta$$

In this equation A and B are the lengths or magnitudes of the two vectors and θ is the angle between their directions as shown in Fig. 3. It can be shown that the following relations exist:

$$\mathbf{A} \cdot \mathbf{B} = \mathbf{B} \cdot \mathbf{A}$$

$$\mathbf{A} \cdot (\mathbf{B} + \mathbf{C}) = \mathbf{A} \cdot \mathbf{B} + \mathbf{A} \cdot \mathbf{C}$$

$$\mathbf{A} \cdot \mathbf{A} = A^2$$

$$\mathbf{i} \cdot \mathbf{i} = \mathbf{j} \cdot \mathbf{j} = \mathbf{k} \cdot \mathbf{k} = 1$$

$$\mathbf{i} \cdot \mathbf{j} = \mathbf{j} \cdot \mathbf{k} = \mathbf{k} \cdot \mathbf{i} = 0$$

From the definition of the scalar product it can be seen that if $\mathbf{A} \cdot \mathbf{B} = 0$, then either $\mathbf{A} = 0$, $\mathbf{B} = 0$, or the two vectors are orthogonal to each other. In terms of components, if $\mathbf{A}$ and $\mathbf{B}$ are given by their rectangular components, we have

$$\mathbf{A} \cdot \mathbf{B} = A_x B_x + A_y B_y + A_z B_z$$

The Vector Product. The vector product of two vectors is sometimes also called the cross product. This product is written in the form,

$$\mathbf{A} \times \mathbf{B} = \mathbf{C}$$

where $\mathbf{C}$ is defined to be a vector that is perpendicular to the plane of $\mathbf{A}$ and $\mathbf{B}$ and with a magnitude of $AB \sin \theta$. The sense in which $\mathbf{C}$ is taken is made clear by Fig. 4. The direction of $\mathbf{C}$ is fixed in the sense of the motion of a right-handed screw turned from the position of the vector $\mathbf{A}$ to that of $\mathbf{B}$. It may be noted that the magnitude of the vector product $\mathbf{A} \times \mathbf{B}$ is equal to the area of the parallelogram of Fig. 4. From the definition of the vector product it may be shown that the following relations are

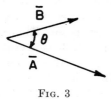

FIG. 3

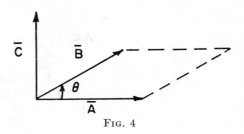

FIG. 4

valid:

$$\mathbf{A} \times \mathbf{B} = -\mathbf{B} \times \mathbf{A}$$

$$\mathbf{A} \times (\mathbf{B} + \mathbf{C}) = \mathbf{B} \times \mathbf{A} + \mathbf{C} \times \mathbf{A}$$

$$(\mathbf{B} + \mathbf{C}) \times \mathbf{A} = \mathbf{B} \times \mathbf{A} + \mathbf{C} \times \mathbf{A}$$

$$\mathbf{i} \times \mathbf{i} = \mathbf{j} \times \mathbf{j} = \mathbf{k} \times \mathbf{k} = 0$$

$$\mathbf{i} \times \mathbf{j} = \mathbf{k} = -\mathbf{j} \times \mathbf{i}$$

$$\mathbf{j} \times \mathbf{k} = \mathbf{i} = -\mathbf{k} \times \mathbf{j}$$

$$\mathbf{k} \times \mathbf{i} = \mathbf{j} = -\mathbf{i} \times \mathbf{k}$$

It is apparent that if $\mathbf{A} \times \mathbf{B} = 0$, then either $\mathbf{A} = 0$, $\mathbf{B} = 0$ or the vectors $\mathbf{A}$ and $\mathbf{B}$ are parallel. If the vectors $\mathbf{A}$ and $\mathbf{B}$ are written in component form, the vector product in component form can be shown to be given by the following determinant:

$$\mathbf{A} \times \mathbf{B} = \begin{vmatrix} \mathbf{i} & \mathbf{j} & \mathbf{k} \\ A_x & A_y & A_z \\ B_x & B_y & B_z \end{vmatrix}$$

The following two identities are very useful:

$$(\mathbf{A} \times \mathbf{B}) \times \mathbf{C}$$
$$= (\mathbf{A} \cdot \mathbf{C})\mathbf{B} - (\mathbf{B} \cdot \mathbf{C})\mathbf{A} = -\mathbf{C} \times (\mathbf{A} \times \mathbf{B})$$

$$(\mathbf{A} \times \mathbf{B}) \cdot (\mathbf{C} \times \mathbf{D})$$
$$= (\mathbf{A} \cdot \mathbf{C})(\mathbf{B} \cdot \mathbf{D}) - (\mathbf{A} \cdot \mathbf{D})(\mathbf{B} \cdot \mathbf{C})$$

Differentiation and Integration of Vectors. *Differentiation.* A vector function of one or more scalar variables is called a variable vector or a vector field. Let it be supposed that all the components of a vector $\mathbf{V}$ are functions of the scalar variable t so that we may write symbolically

$$\mathbf{V} = \mathbf{V}(t)$$

By definition, the derivative of the vector $\mathbf{V}(t)$ with respect to the scalar variable t

is given by

$$\frac{d\mathbf{V}}{dt} = \lim_{\Delta t \to 0} \frac{\mathbf{V}(t + \Delta t) - \mathbf{V}(t)}{\Delta t} = \lim_{\Delta t \to 0} \frac{\Delta \mathbf{V}}{\Delta t}$$

If the *magnitude* of the vector **V** remains unaltered, then we have $\mathbf{V} \cdot \Delta \mathbf{V} = 0$. If the *direction* of **V** is not altered, then $\mathbf{V} \times \Delta \mathbf{V} = 0$. From the definition of the derivative of a vector field, we have

$$d(\mathbf{A} + \mathbf{B}) = d\mathbf{A} + d\mathbf{B}$$

$$d(\mathbf{A} \cdot \mathbf{B}) = \mathbf{A} \cdot d\mathbf{B} + \mathbf{B} \cdot d\mathbf{A}$$

$$d(\mathbf{A} \times \mathbf{B}) = d\mathbf{A} \times \mathbf{B} + \mathbf{A} \times d\mathbf{B}$$

The Basic Differential Operators. In the vector analysis of fields, the following vector operator plays a very prominent role:

$$\nabla = \text{del} = \mathbf{i}D_x + \mathbf{j}D_y + \mathbf{k}D_z$$

where **i**, **j**, and **k** are the unit vectors associated with the Cartesian coordinate system of Fig. 2, and D_x, D_y, D_z are the partial derivative operators with respect to the variables x, y, and z. This operator is called the operator "del." If the vector operator del is multiplied by itself in a scalar manner, we obtain,

$$\nabla \cdot \nabla = \nabla^2 = D_x{}^2 + D_y{}^2 + D_z{}^2$$

$$= \text{the Laplacian operator}$$

The Gradient of a Scalar. If $V(x,y,z)$ is a scalar function of the space coordinates x, y, z, then

$$\nabla V = \mathbf{i}D_x V + \mathbf{j}D_y V + \mathbf{k}D_z V = \text{grad } V$$

The result of operating on the scalar function with del is to obtain the vector function called the gradient of V.

The Divergence of a Vector Field. If **A** is a vector field so that the components of **A** are functions of the space variables x, y, z, then the scalar product of del and **A** produces a scalar function, called the divergence of **A** defined by

$$\nabla \cdot \mathbf{A} = D_x A_x + D_y A_y + D_z A_z = \text{div } \mathbf{A}$$

The Curl of a Vector Field. If **A** is a vector field, then the vector product of del and **A** produces a vector function which is called the curl of **A**. This function is defined by

$$\nabla \times \mathbf{A} = \text{curl } \mathbf{A} = \begin{vmatrix} \mathbf{i} & \mathbf{j} & \mathbf{k} \\ D_x & D_y & D_z \\ A_x & A_y & A_z \end{vmatrix}$$

This determinant gives the components of the curl in Cartesian coordinates if it is expanded in terms of the first row.

Useful Differentiation Formulas. There are several basic identities involving the differentiation of vector fields that can be established by expanding in Cartesian coordinates. A few of these identities will be given here for reference. In the following equations let u and v be scalar functions and **A** and **B** be vector fields. We then have

$$\nabla \cdot (u\mathbf{A}) = u(\nabla \cdot \mathbf{A}) + \mathbf{A} \cdot (\nabla u)$$

$$\nabla \times (u\mathbf{A}) = u(\nabla \times \mathbf{A}) + (\nabla u) \times \mathbf{A}$$

$$\nabla \cdot (\mathbf{A} \times \mathbf{B}) = \mathbf{B} \cdot (\nabla \times \mathbf{A}) - \mathbf{A} \cdot (\nabla \times \mathbf{B})$$

$$\nabla \times (\nabla \times \mathbf{A}) = \nabla(\nabla \cdot \mathbf{A}) - \nabla^2 \mathbf{A}$$

$$\nabla \times (\nabla u) = 0$$

$$\nabla \cdot (\nabla \times \mathbf{A}) = 0$$

Many more identities of this type exist and will be found in the references at the end of this article.

The Line Integral of a Vector Field. The line integral of a vector field **F** along a curve C from the point A to the point B is denoted by I, where

$$\int_A^B \mathbf{F} \cdot d\mathbf{R} = I$$

This integral is taken in the sense shown in Fig. 5; $d\mathbf{R}$ is a vector tangential to the curve C at every point. The line integral is a scalar quantity. If **F** is a vector force field, then the line integral I is the work done by the force **F** in acting along the curve C from the point A to the point B. It can be shown

F ɪ ɢ. 5

that if the line integral around a closed path is zero, so that

$$I = \oint_A^B \mathbf{F} \cdot d\mathbf{R} = 0 = \oint \mathbf{F} \cdot d\mathbf{R}$$

then the curl of the vector field $\mathbf{F}$ vanishes so that

$$\nabla \times \mathbf{F} = 0$$

and in this case the vector field $\mathbf{F}$ is the gradient of a scalar function $U(x,y,z)$ called the potential function, so that

$$\mathbf{F} = \text{grad } U = \nabla U$$

The Surface Integral of a Vector Field. In vector analysis it is customary to represent the element of area of a surface by the differential $d\mathbf{S}$. The differential vector $d\mathbf{S}$ has the direction of the normal to the surface dS and has a magnitude equal to the element of surface area. If the surface is a closed one, $d\mathbf{S}$ has the direction of the outward drawn normal as shown in Fig. 6. The surface integral of a vector field $\mathbf{F}$ over a given surface is denoted by

$$\emptyset = \iint_S \mathbf{F} \cdot d\mathbf{S}$$

This integral represents the flux of the vector field crossing the surface S. If $\mathbf{F}$ represents the velocity of an incompressible fluid, the above integral represents the total mass of fluid crossing the surface S in unit time. If the surface S is a closed one, then the integral represents the total flux emerging from the closed surface S.

The Basic Integral Theorems of Vector Analysis. *The Divergence or Gauss' Theorem.* If a vector field $\mathbf{F}$ and its first derivatives are continuous at all points in a region of volume V bounded by a closed surface $\mathbf{S}$, then it may be shown that

$$\iint_S \mathbf{F} \cdot d\mathbf{S} = \iiint_V \nabla \cdot \mathbf{F} \, dV$$

This theorem transforms a surface integral into a volume integral.

The Theorem of Stokes. If a vector field $\mathbf{F}$ and its first derivatives are continuous at all

Fig. 6

points in a region of area S bounded by a closed curve, then it may be shown that

$$\iint_S (\nabla \times \mathbf{F}) \cdot d\mathbf{S} = \oint \mathbf{F} \cdot d\mathbf{R}$$

This theorem transforms a surface integral into a line integral.

These two theorems are fundamental in the study of vector fields and are the basis for showing that the curl and the divergence of a vector field are invariants of the field and do not depend on the coordinate system in which they are expressed.

L. A. PIPES

REFERENCES

H. B. PHILLIPS, Vector Analysis, Wiley, New York, 1933.

L. A. PIPES, Applied Mathematics for Engineers and Physicists, McGraw-Hill, New York, 1958; Chap. 15.

Cross-references: *Electromagnetic Theory, Matrix Algebra, Stress Tensor*

VEHICULAR COMMUNICATIONS: see MOBILE (VEHICULAR) COMMUNICATIONS

VELOCITY MODULATION

Grid-controlled electron amplifying tubes using density control of the electron current are limited at very high frequencies by the inertia of the electrons resulting in finite transit times. This finite transit time, which limits density modulation, is the essential element in velocity modulation. In velocity-modulated tubes the transit time usually amounts up to several high-frequency cycles.

A stream of electrons of constant density is controlled in its velocity by a high-frequency field. On account of their variable transit time, the electrons group themselves into bunches, transforming the initially constant current into a pulsating current. This process is called velocity modulation.

Since electrons move with full velocity, when they are being controlled the dimensions of the control electrodes are relatively big. Velocity-modulation tubes are long in contrast to density-modulation tubes. For this reason the frequency range of tubes using the velocity-modulation principle extends about two orders of magnitude towards higher frequencies. All very-high-frequency tubes use the velocity modulation principle: klystrons, reflex klystrons, traveling-waves tubes, backward-wave oscillators, and magnetrons. In addition, the principle is used in high-energy particle accelerators for electrons as well as for ions.

The formation of bunches from velocity-modulated electrons can take place in two different ways, as we see in comparing the electron mechanism of a linear klystron with that of a reflex klystron. The electron with the longest transit time in the linear klystron is the slowest electron; in the reflex klystron it is the fastest electron because it is forced to travel the longest path before returning. In the second case velocity modulation results in path-length modulation, which predominates.

Velocity modulation can be applied to a beam once, as in the two-cavity and reflex klystrons, or multiple times, as in the multicavity klystron, or continuously as in the traveling-wave tube.

The following will more precisely define the concept of velocity modulation or phase focusing. An electron stream moving in the direction of a homogeneous high-frequency field experiences a periodic increase and decrease of electron velocity, but this variation is the same for all electrons and no electron comes phase-wise closer to the other. This is not understood to be velocity modulation, even though the velocity of all electrons is modulated; it does not lead to any phase focusing. The term velocity modulation might be more precisely called differential velocity modulation. It also requires, besides time variation,

inhomogeneity of the electric field. The *amount of velocity modulation or phase focusing taking place in each volume element at any time is proportional to the product of inhomogeneity and time variation of the electric field*. The phase-focusing effect for a group of electrons is obtained by integrating this product for these electrons over time and space.

Another conclusion can be drawn. No longitudinal phase focusing is possible without some lateral effect on the electrons, because any field inhomogeneity is necessarily connected with lateral field components. It can easily be shown that electrons being phase focused get radially defocused and radially focused electrons get phase defocused. These focusing effects are always opposite in sign and equal in value. As a result the volume density of electrons stays constant in the first approximation. *Phase focused electrons behave like an incompressible liquid*, if only phase-focusing fields are considered and space-charge fields are neglected. They differ, however, from the liquid in so far as volume elements can be overimaged. Electron currents penetrate one another, leading to causticas, which vary in space as a function of time. Only by this overimaging is a real density increase within the electron bunches possible. All velocity-modulation tubes work with this overimagining. A pure compression of the electron gas does not exist in velocity-modulation tubes.

OSKAR HEIL

Cross-references: *Accelerators, Applegate Diagram, Backward-Wave Tubes, Bunching, Klystron, Magnetrons, Traveling-Wave Tubes*

VIDEO RECORDING

There are three methods of television recording: (a) optical, (b) magnetic or signal-waveform, and (c) thermoplastic recording.

Optical

Basically, optical recording is the production of a motion picture record of the television image displayed on a high-quality picture monitor. The process is known as kinerecording, telerecording or film recording. For reproduction of these films through a television system separate equipments, namely telecine or film camera machines, are necessary. Either 16- or 35-mm film is used for the recordings; the former is preferred where economy is a consideration despite its lower resolution and poorer picture quality.

An advantage of optical recording is that the recorded film may be reproduced on a television system of different line-standards from that on which it was recorded; the film may also be shown through a standard projector. Copies of the film are easily made by normal motion-picture printing techniques.

Disadvantages include the need for, and the time involved in, processing of the film and the fact that the over-all transfer characteristic is not unity. The latter feature gives rise to an effect known as gamma (γ) distortion (γ = ratio log output/log input).

Major factors contributing to γ distortion are: (a) the transfer characteristic of the crt used for the image display; (b) the basic characteristics of the original (negative) and printing (positive) film stock; and (c) the development process of the films. The processing of the film stock must be very carefully controlled to produce recordings of consistent γ. Uncorrected γ distortion causes tonal degradation in the reproduced picture. This effect may largely be overcome by control of the amplitude-vs-linearity characteristics of the video amplifiers in the recording monitor and in the telecine apparatus.

Picture Display. The recording monitor crt displays a positive picture and from this a negative film record is made; this negative is then used to print a positive film for reproduction. However, for economy of film material reversal film may be employed. Other alternatives are (a) the reproduction of the original negative in the telecine apparatus (the video signal polarity must be reversed in the reproducing amplifiers) and

(b) the display of a negative picture on the crt, resulting in the production of a direct positive recording with negative stock in the recording camera. The latter two methods are normally used where film cost considerations and speed of production of recordings are important; γ distortion is less effectively corrected.

Camera Considerations. Various methods of advancing the film in the recording camera are used. The choice in many cases depends upon the field repetition frequency of the television system, since a specific timing relationship between the film frame rate and the television field rate must be maintained. Two basic television field rates are in general use: 50 cps (on the 405-, 625- and 819-line systems) and 60 cps (on the 525-line system). The standard film projection rate is 24 frames/sec, but by increasing it to 25 frames/sec synchronism with 50-cps television field rates is easily achieved.

The type of film advancement may be either by intermittent or continuous motion.

Intermittent Motion Cameras. Intermittent motion cameras require a period during which the film is stationary and in which the actual exposure is made. The film is then transported in preparation for the next exposure. The interval while the film is moving must be as short as possible, compatible with accurate registration as the film is arrested. These two requirements are mutually conflicting.

Ideally the transportation (pull-down) time must be accomplished within the field blanking time of the television waveform (1.2 to 1.9 msec on the 625-line system, 0.8–1.3 msec on the 525-line system, and 1.1–1.6 msec on the 405-line system). This procedure allows the full picture information to be recorded but necessitates elaborate mechanical design. The problem is less acute when 16-mm film is used as the frame size is smaller than that of 35-mm film, and a lower mass of material has to be accelerated and decelerated.

The best fast pull-down recording equipment at present in use has a pull-down time of 1.9 msec. Two television fields are recorded on one film frame on 50-cps systems and the film is pulled down during each alternate vertical blanking period. A fully interlaced picture is thus recorded. On 60-cps systems the pull-down occurs alternately after two fields and then after three fields. Exposure of alternate frames is equalized by a specially shaped shutter.

On 60-cps standards the following sequence is commonly used: two television fields ($\frac{1}{30}$ sec) are recorded on one film frame; a shutter is closed for the first half of the next field ($\frac{1}{120}$ sec), during which time the film is transported one frame; the shutter remains open for the rest of this field, the complete following field and for the first half of the succeeding field; the shutter is closed for the remaining part of this latter field, while the film is once more advanced one frame. This five-field cycle is repetitive. Two complete fields are recorded on each film frame; alternate frames incorporate a picture "join." Accurate electrical and/or mechanical shutter adjustment reduces picture impairment from this cause.

Another type of camera employs a shutter with alternate closed periods of two fields and then one. Each open time is for one field period. The film is pulled down at the standard rate during every shutter closure. Although the shutter is open only for one field at a time, the actual recorded picture includes information from the previous field owing to persistence storage on the crt.

The simplest method (50-cps suppressed-field recording) incorporates a shutter open for one complete field and closed for the next. The film is pulled down during this latter period. Alternate fields only reach the film resulting in loss of interlace as only half the total number of lines are recorded.

This effect is largely overcome in other equipment by crt persistence storage. The brightness of the images of the fields coincident with the pull down is raised. The crt phosphor partially retains the images of these fields through the succeeding (exposure) fields. An almost complete interlaced picture is thus recorded.

Continuous Motion Cameras. The film is transported smoothly at 24 or 25 frames/sec. The images of the television picture are projected on to the film through moving optical components, either glass prisms or mirrors (Mechau machine), which serve to compensate for the movement of the film. The projected image is moved so that there is no relative film/image displacement during each frame. No additional shutter is needed. Complete interlaced pictures are recorded.

In the double optical system two identical images of the picture with twice the normal aspect ratio are projected onto the film, spaced vertically by one-half of a film frame pitch. Separate optical systems are used and a shutter obscures each image alternately. The continuously moving film restores the aspect ratio and an interlaced picture is recorded by superimposition of the two images.

Reproduction of Optical Recordings. In the *iconoscope* film camera (60-cps systems), a television film projector throws 60 short-duration (0.8- to 1.05-msec) images per second on to the photocathode of the camera tube. The storage ability of the tube holds the image flashes for complete field scanning periods. Standard rate intermittent film transport is used. The flashes are synchronously interleaved with the pull down giving an alternating 2–3–2–3 image projection from each frame. Correction waveforms must be applied for keystone scanning distortion and image shading. The latter is due to secondary-emission effects, and is a function of the light distribution on the tube face. The black level must be independently established. Resolutions between 560 and 600 lines are obtained.

Nonsynchronous operation of the film projectors is possible with a *Vidicon* (photoconductive) type of pick-up tube. The light application time is between approximately 11 and 14 msec with a normal intermittent film projection rate. Very good reproduction of film is obtained with this type of equipment; output signals have high resolution (600–800 lines) and signal-to-noise ratios of up to 48 db. No spurious signals are generated. Absolute black level is inherent in the Vidicon tube.

In the flying-spot telecine (50-cps systems) two images of an unmodulated raster are projected through the film onto a photomultiplier tube. The film moves continuously and the images are shuttered to allow each to fall alternately on the phototube. An aspect ratio of 8:3 is used for the raster; the film motion effectively provides the extra requisite vertical scan. The principle is similar to that used in the continuous-motion double-optical-system recording camera.

A single raster image of normal aspect ratio may also be used; a moving optical system maintains the image stationary on the moving film, as in the Mechau projector.

Flying-spot equipment has no inherent storage capability; its use is restricted to continuous motion or fast pull-down projectors. The scanned raster must have high brightness, good geometry, small spot size and short persistence characteristics. Typical picture resolution may be up to 800 lines with 46-db signal-to-noise ratio

Magnetic

Magnetic or signal-waveform recorders utilize magnetic-tape apparatus and are known as television tape recorders. Recorded tapes are reproduced on the same type of equipment; no special reproducer is required.

The recording of a television waveform on magnetic tape possesses the advantages of immediate reproduction of a recording without processing, fidelity of picture reproduction, erasability, and re-usability of the recording medium.

The range of frequencies for television recording is approximately from 5 Mc down to dc, about 18 octaves.

A conventional magnetic recording system is limited in bandwidth to about 10 octaves, with a practical signal-to-noise ratio. This limitation is imposed at high frequencies by the impossibility of satisfactorily reproducing recorded wavelengths shorter than the head-gap width. Lower frequencies on reproduction suffer a 6-db loss in signal level per octave, owing to the reduced rate of change of flux across the gap. The signal level 10 octaves below a given reference frequency thus has a 60-db lower signal-to-noise ratio.

A very high head-to-tape speed is necessary to record longitudinally the short wavelengths corresponding to the high frequencies. Using a head-gap of 0.0001 in. a head-to-tape speed of 500 in./sec would be necessary to record frequencies of 5 Mc satisfactorily.

A high writing speed is obtained by *transverse* recording of the video information, and the number of octaves to be recorded is reduced by modulating the signal on to a rf carrier.

Two-in. wide, 0.001 in. thick, plastic-based tape is used traveling at a speed of 15 in./sec. Four recording heads equiangularly mounted on the periphery of a 2-in. diameter drum are rotated across the tape, at 14,400 rpm, by a 3-phase, synchronous motor that provides a head-to-tape speed of approximately 1500 in./sec. In order to maintain the desired contour, the tape is cupped around the head drum by a hollow concave guide from which air is exhausted.

The inductance of each video recording head is approximately 30 μh; the heads are fed in parallel from individual, constant-current, plate-loaded pentode amplifiers through slip-rings on the head drum assembly. An overlap of information is recorded because during certain periods of the rotation of the drum two adjacent heads are simultaneously in contact with the tape.

The tracks laid down across the tape are 0.010 in. wide; they are spaced 0.005 in. apart due to the longitudinal tape motion. An average of 16.4 lines of video signal is recorded (excluding redundant overlap information) along each transverse track.

To insure optimum head-to-tape contact, the tips of the recording heads are made to protrude into the tape, temporarily deforming it to a depth of between 0.003 to 0.001 in.

Modulation. By utilizing the lower sidebands of an FM system the video spectrum is contained within a range of 3 octaves, consistent with a high degree of signal transfer linearity. The undeviated carrier frequency is typically between 5 and 5.5 Mc, corresponding to the blanking level of the waveform. A peak white signal deviates the carrier to approximately 7 Mc and at the synchronizing pulse tips to 4.3 Mc. Picture resolution is in the range 350–450 lines, and signal-to-noise ratios of 42–48 db are obtained.

The FM signals are generated by either multivibrator or heterodyne circuits. The former method uses a pair of power pentode tubes in an astable multivibrator circuit operating normally at the carrier frequency. The control grids are directly coupled to the output of a cathode follower, to the input of which is applied the clamped modulating video signal. The output of the modulator is taken from a balanced transformer coupled between the plates of the multivibrator tubes. This method removes the modulating-frequency components, and effectively prevents the addition of the sidebands and modulating frequencies.

With the heterodyne method of producing the FM signal, the output of a 50-Mc fixed oscillator is mixed with the output of a modulated oscillator operating in its undeviated state at 45 Mc. The frequency of this modulating oscillator is varied in accordance with the amplitude of the video signal by a reactance tube.

Pre-emphasis networks are incorporated with either method of modulation, in order to improve signal-to-noise ratio.

Reproduction. During the reproduction process the FM signals picked-up from the tape are preamplified, sequentially switched, limited and then passed to a demodulator. The switching between one head and the next is automatically arranged to fall either immediately before or immediately after the horizontal synchronizing signal. Switching discontinuities in the picture area are thus avoided.

Various methods of demodulation are used, for example an FM-to-AM delay-line converter, a delay-line phase-comparator, or a heterodyne system.

In the former case the signal is fed simultaneously, through a delay line, and also directly to one input of an adding circuit. The second input of the adder is the output of the delay line. The delay line produces a 90° lag at the undeviated carrier frequency. Thus the vector output of the adding circuit varies as a function of the input frequency. This output is an amplitude modulated waveform, corresponding to the input FM signal. The AM output is then demodulated with a full-wave detector circuit.

A phase-comparator tube is used in the second method of demodulation. Pulses are produced the widths of which are related to the phase-difference between direct and delayed modulated signal. These pulses are integrated by a low-pass filter, providing the video output signal.

In the heterodyne system the signal after switching is heterodyned to the region of 50–60 Mc, amplified and then demodulated by a conventional FM discriminator.

The video signal after demodulation is passed to a signal processing unit for the regeneration of synchronizing signals, re-blanking, and the control of the relative levels of video and synchronizing information.

Time-Base Stability. A high degree of mechanical accuracy is required of the head drum angular position. An error of 1° represents a timing error of about 12 μsec (approximately $\frac{1}{5}$ of a television line). A servo-mechanism in the equipment samples the timing error between the horizontal-rate pulses of the reproduced and reference synchronizing signals, in order to sense dynamic-head positional errors. The phase of the drive signal to the drum motor is continuously modified to correct this error. Positional accuracy of the head drum corresponding to a timing error of less than 0.1 μsec is obtained.

In the reproduction mode the driving capstan controling the longitudinal motion of the tape must be exactly controlled in speed and phase in order that each video head may accurately track the recorded video information. A 240-cps signal is generated on the video head drum (by optical or magnetic means) the phase of which indicates the exact angular position of the drum. During the recording process this signal is laid down along one edge of the tape by a control-track-head mounted close to the video head. This signal is re-generated from the tape during reproduction by the control-track-head and is compared in phase with the direct 240-cps signal from the video head drum. Any phase error is detected and the capstan motor driving signal adjusted to ensure that the video head drum is precisely tracking the recorded video tracks.

Further automatic compensation is applied to correct for geometric errors in the displayed picture due to video head drum tolerances.

AUBREY HARRIS

Thermoplastic

In this system the recording is made in the form of small ripples on the surface of a plastic film. The ripples are formed by means of an electron beam, which scans the surface of the film. The recorder has an electrical input similar to a magnetic tape recorder and an image output that is similar to photographic film. The image output can be changed to an electrical output signal by standard techniques.

Figure 1 shows the recording process and one type of thermoplastic film. The film has a base that is similar to the standard moving-picture film base. On top of it is a transparent conducting coating, and on top of the transparent coating there is a thin coating of thermoplastic material. This material

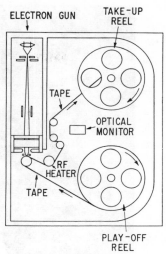

FIG. 2

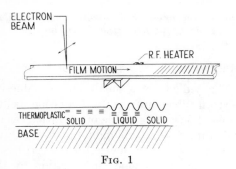

FIG. 1

melts if it is raised to a fairly high temperature.

The surface of the thermoplastic is charged with an electron beam in a pattern that corresponds to the pattern of ripples that is to form the image. As the film moves on, it is heated so that the thermoplastic coating melts. The charges are attracted to the transparent conducting coating and depress the surface of the thermoplastic. After the surface has been deformed by the charges, the film is allowed to cool, which freezes the ripple pattern in place.

To erase the information, the thermoplastic is simply heated again to a higher temperature, so that the charges leak away and surface tension smooths the surface back out to its original state. The film is then reusable.

Figure 2 is a diagram of a recording machine that records on thermoplastic film in this way. The film, of course, must be handled in a vacuum, since the electron gun has to work in a vacuum. It takes about one minute to pump the machine down from atmospheric pressure to a vacuum low enough for effective operation.

The signal input, in this particular recorder, is the IF signal from a monochrome TV set, at about a 1-v level. If the images are to be recorded in color, another signal

FIG. 3

has to be added to another electrode, also at about a 1-v level.

In projecting black and white, the optical system used is a modification of a Schlieren optical system; in color, it is necessary to use a special optical system.

For black-and-white projection a series of line light sources are imaged on a set of bars in front of the projection lens. If there are ripples on the surface of the film at any particular point, they scatter light through the bar system. Whenever light passes through the projection lens, it images the ripple on the screen as a white spot.

This system can be modified so that it can be used to produce color pictures. Each picture element has in it a set of ripples that form a small diffraction grating. The light that is diffracted by this grating forms a spectrum on each side of the central beam. The slots are made small enough so that only one color from the spectrum gets through to the projection lens. Since the projection lens can receive only one color of the spectrum, the spot that appears on the screen appears in a single color, which depends on the grating spacing. A color that

is formed by a superposition of two or more colors may be produced by the superposition of two or more gratings.

The film used at our present stage of development is the size of standard 16-mm film. Large-size recordings use half the width of the film—the images are actually 5 mm wide—and the film runs at 10 in./sec. Recording with full resolution at half this picture size is also possible, so that the width of the track on the film is 0.1 in. wide, with the film running 5 in./sec.

A photograph of a 0.1-in.-wide recording compared to an ordinary straight pin is shown in Fig. 3.

W. E. GLENN

Cross-references: *Electrostatic Printing, Magnetic Tape, Sound Recording, Television*

VIDICON

The vidicon is a small photoconductive electron tube employed for television pickup applications and capable of operation over a wide range of scene illumination levels. Fundamentally, it is a device for converting an optical image to video information by the mechanism of an electron beam scanning a light-irradiated photoconductive element. By this means a video component is generated, which is further amplified to reproduce the original image at some remote point, either by television broadcast or by means of a closed-circuit television system. Because of its small size and simplicity the vidicon is widely used in television broadcast and industrial applications where portability and simplicity of the television camera chain equipment is important. By means of a relatively inexpensive lens useful pictures can be obtained from scenes having a highlight brightness of less than 4 ft-lamberts.

Basically, the vidicon consists of a highly evacuated envelope of glass or ceramic containing an electron gun at one end and a transparent optical flat at the other. An extremely thin electrically conductive film which is also light transparent is deposited on the inner surface of this optical flat and acts as the video output or signal plate. Upon this layer is deposited a photoconductive film on which the image to be televised is focused by means of an external optical lens. A well-defined low-velocity electron beam scans the vacuum side of the photoconductive layer, which consists of a thin film of selenium, antimony tri-sulphide, lead sulphide, or other photoconductor. The photoconductor used depends upon the spectral response desired; selenium is employed for the ultraviolet and blue, antimony tri-sulphide for the visible spectrum, and lead sulphide for the near infrared. These materials exhibit the property of being electrical insulators in the dark. When light from a subject is focused upon the photoconductor it becomes conductive to a degree related to the relative brightness of each corresponding portion of the image. Individual photoconductive areas behave similarly to a charged capacitor with leaky insulation with one plate at a fixed potential and the other plate floating. This action causes the photoconductor surface potential to rise toward the signal plate potential to a degree related to the individual illumination of each picture

element. While scanning, the electron beam deposits electrons on the photoconductive layer in sufficient quantities to return each surface element to cathode potential. This process creates a current flow in the signal plate proportional to the rate of scan and the surface potential on the photoconductor. This video signal current is then used to develop a signal output voltage across a load resistor, which is further amplified to reproduce the original image on a large visual display.

Another version of the vidicon employs electrostatic focus and deflection and therefore eliminates the necessity for the bulky external focusing and deflecting coils. The deflection and focusing elements are small electrodes within the tube that are voltage actuated by relatively high-impedance transistor circuits and therefore eliminate the need for power sources capable of the higher currents employed to focus and deflect the magnetic version. This improvement further simplifies and reduces the television camera size and weight. However, the electrostatic vidicon lacks the resolution capability of the magnetic version and is used where high resolution is not required but where weight and size considerations are critical. Its resolution capabilities are of the order of 450–500 lines as compared to 600–1200 lines for the magnetic type.

In addition to the vidicon being used in closed-circuit and television broadcast it is finding numerous uses in other areas of science and industry. Sattelite-borne vidicons 0.5 in. in diameter are currently being used for outer-space observations and meteorological forecasting by means of telecast pictures of cloud formations over vast areas of the earth.

Other uses include ultraviolet microscopy studies where the vidicon is sensitive to short wavelength ultraviolet (2300 Å) and is used in conjunction with an ultraviolet microscope for the study of cancer organisms. Unlike the normal cell the cancer organism selectively absorbs the short-wavelength ultraviolet radiation. Because of this phenomenon a high degree of contrast is obtained, which obviates the use of chemical dyes and other agents normally employed to achieve this effect with optical microscopes. Because of the high sensitivity of the ultraviolet vidicon very-low-intensity ultraviolet can be employed which further enhances the contrast level and diminishes the chances of cell destruction during observation. This general technique is also finding use in the study of the penetration of chemical dyes in cloth and synthetic fibers.

Today the vidicon in conjunction with closed-circuit systems is used extensively in many quality-control and inspection applications. A system of great utility is used in medicine, where the vidicon is employed to pick up an X-ray image of a patient. This image is sent to a remote area by means of a closed-circuit system to a large display for easy diagnosis.

Special vidicons are now being used for atomic reactor inspection. These tubes are made with ceramic envelopes (high alumina) and with the internal structures of materials with small neutron cross sections such as titanium, aluminum, and the like. The vidicon window and other optical portions in such a camera are made with high-purity transparent quartz or sapphire. These materials, unlike the conventional glass employed for standard vidicons, do not exhibit the degree of solarization or darkening under severe neutron bombardment. The use of these tubes greatly facilitates the inspection of nuclear reactor components, which is displayed by means of closed-circuit television at some remote location.

Extensive work is being performed on various photoconductors to extend the use of the vidicon into the infrared region. The sensitivity and long-wavelength response of the vidicon are sufficient so that it can be used for the study of thermal distribution of devices operated at elevated temperatures such as nuclear reactor cores, electrical equipment, boilers, etc. Another interesting application is in the examination and selection of various semiconducting material

with infrared transmissive properties. Germanium, as an example, becomes transparent at approximately 1.8 μ and vidicons with appropriate optics can be employed to study strain patterns and other characteristics of the material. The range of this type of tube can be further extended into the infrared region by cooling the photoconductor to liquid-nitrogen or liquid-helium temperatures for studies in spectroscopy beyond the wavelength that can be covered by means of an image converter or photographic techniques.

VICTOR E. DeLucia

Cross-references: *Cathode-Ray Tubes (Display), Flying-Spot Scanning, Iconoscope, Image Orthicon, Photoconductivity*

VISIBLE SPEECH

The information in speech is represented by a distribution of energy in frequency and time. Sound spectrograms, such as are illustrated in Fig. 1, portray this distribution. In these patterns frequency is spread vertically, time horizontally, and momentary energy level is indicated qualitatively by darkness of the recording. Some of the details in the words pictured are indicated by marginal notation.

The Sound Spectrograph. Sound spectrograms are recorded with an instrument called the "sound spectrograph." One version of this instrument is pictured schematically in Fig. 2. A short sequence of the sound to be analyzed is recorded on a loop of magnetic tape. The recording is then reproduced repeatedly at a higher speed (to reduce analyzing time). With each repetition a band of different frequency is selected and changes in energy within the band are traced by a stylus on electrically sensitive recording paper that is wrapped around a revolving cylinder. Each frequency interval produces a separate line trace and the completed grid of about 200 lines forms the final picture.

Many experimental variations of the sound spectrograph have been developed,

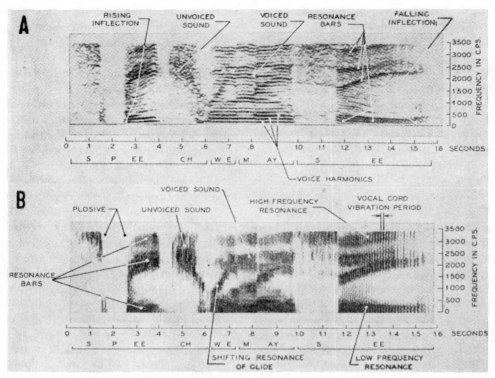

FIG. 1. A, narrow-band spectrogram and B, broad-band spectrogram of words, "Speech we may see."

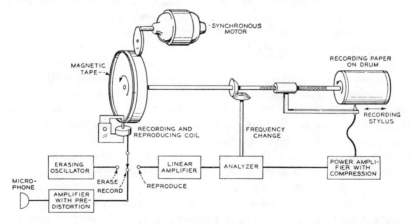

FIG. 2. Schematic representation of the basic method of the sound spectrograph. The sound is recorded on the loop of magnetic tape, and analyzed while repeatedly reproduced. The fluctuating analyzer output builds up a pattern of light and dark areas on the electrically sensitive paper.

including types suitable for analyzing long sound samples, types that record on photographic paper by optical methods, and an instrument that records the energy levels in color-steps (color-contour map). Commercially available instruments produce spec-trograms of the kind shown in Fig. 1. The recording paper is made conductive by embedded carbon and one surface is covered with a very thin coating of white pigment. The stylus current literally burns a record into this coating.

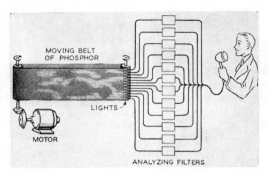

FIG. 3. Principle of the visible speech translator.

Narrow and Wide-Band Patterns. A basic variable in sound spectrograph design is bandwidth of the "analyzer" in Fig. 2. Largely through experimental experience, two bandwidths are rather widely used for speech analysis. A bandwidth of about 50 cps produces the so-called "narrow-band spectrogram" of A in Fig. 1; a 300-cps bandwidth is responsible for the "wide-band spectrogram" of B. When the concern is with structural detail the narrow-band type is desirable. This type displays some of the "quality" features of interest in speech education and voice identification. In particular it shows the harmonics, inflections, evidence of vibrato and other effects that are lost in the broadband patterns. When the emphasis is upon phonetic content, detail of the kind pictured by the narrow-band analysis may only contribute confusion. Then the wide-band spectrograms are generally preferred.

Nonspeech Uses. The sound spectrograph has been employed for recording many complex waves other than those of speech. A few examples are: the singing voice, musical instrument sounds, animal sounds, bird songs, frog calls, insect signals, underwater sound (*q.v.*), heart rhythms, brain waves, radio "whistlers," machinery noise.

Complex waveforms outside the audible range may be recorded on conventional sound spectrograph equipment by supplementary speed-up, or slow-down recording techniques. One example is the subaudible heart potential variation traced by the familiar electrocardiograph. When these potential variations are recorded on very slow-moving magnetic tape and speeded up a few hundred times for reproduction, the result is an audible note that may be fed into the conventional sound spectrograph and analyzed in the usual way.

Visible Speech Translator. For continuous conversion of speech sounds into patterns, instruments called "visible speech translators" have been developed. The principle is suggested by Fig. 3. Speech is impressed upon a bank of analyzing filters. The filters select successive frequency intervals in the speech spectrum. Their outputs go to individual recording elements, shown as "lights" in the illustration. These recording elements trace the separate energy variations in a transient pattern upon a moving belt with a phosphorescent surface. When the speaker talks, his speech patterns appear as a parade of voice symbols drifting across the screen.

Such visible speech translators are normally designed to produce broad-band patterns. An experimental type, much superior to the phosphorescent belt arrangement of Fig. 3, uses a special cathode ray tube that rotates around a vertical axis. Its screen is in the shape of a broad belt encircling the barrel-shaped glass envelope. The beam, bent from the vertical by a fixed magnetic field, is held in one circumferential position as the speech patterns are laid down by commutation between the analyzing filter outputs.

Deaf Interests. Visible speech translators have received considerable attention in relation to problems of the deaf. Obstacles to more than limited use in this field have been cost, size, and complication of equipment capable of producing suitable patterns. Experimental training and visual intelligibility tests have shown that the broad-band patterns may be learned at about the same rate as an unfamiliar language and the intelligence content is far above that available in lip movements. But a major problem of the congenitally deaf concerns pattern quality rather than readability. Without hearing, speech training is difficult so the speech is usually unnatural. This limits social contact. Translators for speech education must show narrow-band detail, a requirement that adds considerably to design dimensions.

Play-Back Experiments. The sound-to-sight translation process pictured in Fig. 3 is reversed in an instrument that plays back visible speech patterns. Play-back is of interest to students of speech and language because it provides a reverse check on the aural-visual relationship. The experimenter may synthesize speech patterns and make progressive changes in them to correlate with the audible result.

RALPH K. POTTER

Cross-references: *Electroacoustics, Hearing Aids, Larynx (Electronic), Phonetic Typewriting, Vocoder*

VOCODER

The word vocoder is an acronym for *voice coder.* Speech signals transmitted over telephone lines require a transmission bandwidth of about 3000 cps. Transmission of speech in digital form (PCM) requires a

channel with a capacity of about 50,000 bits/sec. The purpose of vocoders is to encode speech signals for more efficient electrical transmission. Since its invention (by H. W. Dudley at Bell Telephone Laboratories) several decades ago, vocoders have been built that require a bandwidth or channel capacity of only a fraction of that of uncoded speech.

The classical vocoder is the *spectrum-channel* vocoder (Fig. 1). It consists of an analyzer that produces electrical signals proportional to the short-time amplitude spectrum and the fundamental frequency of the speech input, and of a synthesizer that reconstructs intelligible speech on the basis of the electrical signals appearing at the analyzer output by means of electrical filters and modulators.

The analyzer consists of a bank of contiguous bandpass filters each followed by a rectifier and a low-pass filter with a cutoff frequency of about 20 cps. Typically, a vocoder analyzer has 16 bandpass filters covering the frequency range from 200 to 3200 cps. In addition to the "channel signals" the vo-

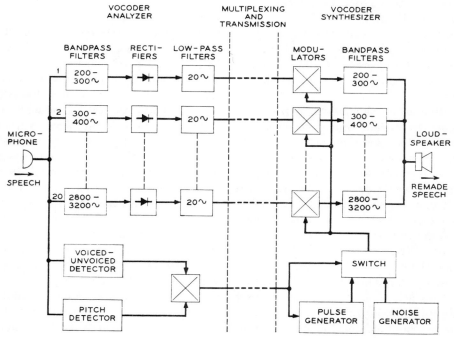

FIG. 1. Spectrum-channel vocoder.

coder analyzer develops a "pitch signal" proportional to the fundamental voice frequency for voiced sounds and zero in the case of unvoiced sounds. This signal is also filtered by a 20-cps low-pass filter. Thus the total bandwidths of all 17 vocoder signals is 340 cps or approximately $\frac{1}{10}$ of the original bandwidth. For transmission over long distances the 17 vocoder signals are combined into a single signal by frequency or time multiplexing. In the multiplexing process some additional bandwidth is required for "guard spaces" between the individual channel signals, thus lowering the practically realizable bandwidth compression to about 5 to 1.

For digital transmission, an additional saving is afforded by the fact that the spectrum channel signals can be encoded by as few as 3 bits per sample. For 17 signals, each 20 cps wide, the information rate is thus only 2040 bits/sec or less than $\frac{1}{20}$ of that required for the uncoded speech.

Even more impressive are the compression ratios of so-called "formant" or resonance vocoders that analyze speech in terms of its formants, i.e., the resonances of the vocal tract, and synthesize it by means of an electrical analog network of the vocal tract. Transmission requirements for this type of vocoder are of the order of 100-cps bandwidths or less than 1000 bits/sec for digital transmission.

The ultimate in compression is promised by phonemic vocoders, which encode speech in terms of successive phonemes. For 32 different phonemes and a rate of 10 phonemes/sec the required channel capacity is but 50 bits/sec. However, phonemic vocoders demonstrated to date are rather imperfect owing largely to the lack of good phonemic recognizers.

The reconstructed speech from a good spectrum channel vocoder is usually very intelligible but lacks in quality and "naturalness." This lack of naturalness can in part be traced to an improper analysis and reproduction of the fundamental frequency of voiced speech sounds. To avoid this so-called

"pitch problem" a new kind of vocoder has recently been suggested and demonstrated that avoids the pitch problem in the following manner. The low-frequency portion of the speech signal (up to 1000 cps) is sent to the synthesizer without encoding. At the synthesizer this so-called "baseband" is nonlinearly distorted in order to generate harmonic frequency components of approximately equal amplitudes up to the highest speech frequency to be reconstructed by the synthesizer. The excitation signal derived in this manner is then modulated by the channel signals much as in a conventional vocoder. Since the excitation signal is derived directly from (a portion of) the voice signal, vocoders employing this principle are called "voice-excited" vocoders. Their naturalness (as measured, for instance, by talker identification) exceeds that of conventional vocoders considerably. Because of the uncoded baseband (about 700 cps) required at the synthesizer, the bandwidth compression is limited to about 3 to 1. However, even a bandwidth compression of only 2 to 1 is still substantial from a commercial viewpoint when applied to expensive telephone circuits such as transatlantic cables.

Still another degradation of vocoder speech is due to the band-pass filters in the analyzer and, particularly, in the synthesizer. This degradation is primarily a consequence of the fact that the band-pass filters do not analyze and synthesize individual harmonics of voiced speech but are fixed in frequency. Also, they usually have considerable phase distortion, particularly at the crossover frequencies. A possible remedy would be the use of harmonic tracking band-pass filters.

Another approach to speech analysis, which avoids band-pass filters altogether, is auto- or cross-correlation analysis. Figure 2 shows the block diagram of an autocorrelation vocoder. After a variable equalizer, which essentially takes the square root of its short-time amplitude spectrum, the speech is applied to a multitap delay line. The undelayed speech is multiplied by the differently delayed speech signals and the products

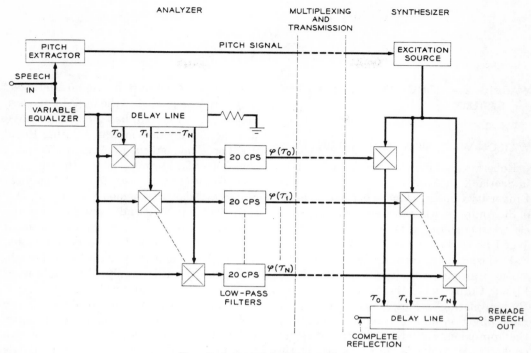

Fig. 2. Autocorrelation vocoder.

are averaged by low-pass filters. The output of the auto-correlation analyzer is a set of "delay channel" signals, representing Nyquist samples of the short-time auto-correlation function of the equalized speech signal, and the fundamental frequency. At the synthesizer these signals are converted into a time signal with the same period lengths as the original speech signal. Each period consists of the transmitted auto-correlation function made symmetrical by the reflecting delay line shown at the lower right of Fig. 2. The spectral envelope of the remade speech is the *square* of that of the equalized speech signal and, consequently, an approximation to that of the input speech signal. The same is true for unvoiced sounds except that the spectral fine structure is not discrete.

In a cross-correlation vocoder, the undelayed speech signal is multiplied by delayed versions of a speech-derived signal whose spectrum has been flattened by nonlinear distortion techniques similar to those required for voice-excited vocoders. Thus, there is no need for an equalizer to take the square root of the spectrum. Otherwise, cross-correlation vocoders are similar in design to autocorrelation vocoders.

M. R. Schroeder

Cross-references: *Bandwidth Reduction, Electroacoustics, Larynx (Electronic), Phonetic Typewriting, Pulse Code Modulation (PCM)*

VOLTAGE MULTIPLIERS: see COCKCROFT-WALTON ACCELERATOR

VOLTMETERS: see INDICATING INSTRUMENTS

VOR: see NAVIGATION

WAITING: see CONGESTION AND WAITING SYSTEMS

WATSON-WATT, SIR ROBERT (b. 1892)

Robert Alexander Watson-Watt was born in Scotland on April 13, 1892, and attended University College, Dundee in the University of St. Andrews, where he received a degree in electrical engineering in 1914. During World War I he worked in the British Meteorological Office on the problem of giving thunderstorm warnings to aircraft of the Royal Flying Corps (later the Royal Air Force). By correlating atmospherics observed by radio direction finders at different locations, the approximate location of a thunderstorm could be determined. He continued in this work under the auspices of the Radio Research Board of the Department of Scientific and Industrial Research, greatly advancing the usefulness of his apparatus when he developed a method of displaying the direction of arrival of individual atmospherics on a cathode-ray tube. His "Instantaneous Visual Radio Direction Finder," adapted to high frequencies, was described by the historian of the U. S. Navy in World War II as probably more important to victory in the Battle of the Atlantic than was radar itself.

His laboratory became part of the National Physical Laboratory in 1933, and early in 1935 he was asked by the British Air Ministry to consider the feasibility of a "death ray" by means of which electromagnetic energy could be directed at an attacking aircraft in sufficient amounts to interfere with its operation. His recommendations were negative, but he suggested that attention should be turned "to the still difficult, but less unpromising problem of radio-detection," and was encouraged to go on with the alternate problem. In February 1935 he submitted a secret memorandum on the "Detection of Aircraft by Radio Methods" that may be regarded as the basis for modern radar (q.v.). A system based on his proposal was successfully demonstrated during Royal Air Force maneuvers in April 1937 and a chain of radar stations on the British coast was installed; in August 1937 the first fully airborne radar was demonstrated and IFF (identification of friend from foe) was described in a secret patent application dated 15 September 1936. It was demonstrated late in 1938, and from it, almost immediately, the versatile family of radar beacons or "racons" was also developed.

As a result, the British armed forces were well equipped to meet enemy onslaughts; radar is widely credited for tipping the balance in Britain's favor during the air Battle of Britain of 1940 (a victory that in turn forestalled German invasion of the British Isles), as well as in various naval battles; and in the anti-U boat war radar was indis-

Sir Robert Watson-Watt

pensable to the strategic bombing of Germany and to the invasion of Europe in 1944.

The usefulness of radar was greatly enhanced by the employment of short pulses at centimetric wavelengths, a feature made possible by the development of a high-power magnetron (q.v.) by J. T. Randall and H. A. H. Boot at Birmingham University in 1940. Another important component was the klystron (q.v.), invented by R. H. and S. F. Varian with the help of W. W. Hansen, which saw radar service as a local oscillator in superheterodyne operation.

The inception of systematic Operational Research by Watson-Watt and Rowe in 1937, and its introduction in the defense services of the United States (on his recommendation of January 1942 to the Secretaries of War and the Navy) led to the widespread adoption of operations research (q.v.) and operations analysis in fields far beyond those of defense and of governmental activity. Before and during World War I Watson-Watt also made important contributions to electronic countermeasures (q.v.).

Throughout the wartime emergency he was guided by his oft-quoted motto, "Give them the third best to go on with, the second best comes too late, the best never comes." He was knighted in 1942 and received many other honors, including the Hughes Medal of the Royal Society. After World War II, Watson-Watt entered private industry in the United Kingdom, the United States, and Canada.

CHARLES SUSSKIND

Cross-references: *Historical Background of Electronics*

WATTMETERS: see INDICATING INSTRUMENTS

WAVEGUIDES AND WAVEGUIDE COMPONENTS

Waveguides

A waveguide is a hollow pipe used as a transmission line. Its cross section is usually rectangular, square, or round, but irregular shapes are sometimes used for special applications. The electromagnetic wave in the waveguide can have an infinite variety of patterns, called modes, and, in general, these modes are of two kinds. In one set of modes, the electric vector is always transverse to the direction of propagation; in the other set the magnetic vector is always transverse to this direction. The former are called TE or *transverse electric* modes, the latter are TM or *transverse magnetic*. Two subscripts are used to designate a particular mode. The first subscript (in either kind of mode) designates the number of half-wave variations of the electric field across the wide dimension of the waveguide, and the second designates the number of half-wave variations of the electric field across the narrower dimension. Thus, a $TE_{2,1}$ mode would designate a field pattern in which the electric field is always transverse to the propagation direction and in which the electric field has two half-wave variations across the wide dimension and one across the narrow.

For each mode of operation there is a cut-off wavelength, determined by the size and shape of the waveguide. For the $TE_{1,0}$ mode in rectangular waveguide, the cut-off wavelength is twice the wide dimension. This means that when the signal wavelength is less than cut-off, the energy will propagate in the waveguide; but, when it is greater, the energy is attenuated exponentially. In the latter case, the frequency is too low to propagate through the waveguide and is said to be "below cut-off." Cut-off for other modes in rectangular guide is higher than for the $TE_{1,0}$. Consequently, for any frequency it is possible to choose dimensions so that only the $TE_{1,0}$ mode is above cut-off, and all other modes will be rapidly attenuated. The $TE_{1,0}$ mode is called the *dominant mode* and is the one most commonly used.

The attenuation through a waveguide is a function of the material of which it is fabricated. With suitable materials the waveguide will have less attenuation at a particular frequency than a coaxial line of the same size. The losses in the waveguide are copper losses in the walls, and consequently the walls should be made of a highly conducting material. At microwave frequencies, the skin depth is only a few thousandths of an inch. Therefore, it is common practice to make the waveguide out of an inexpensive material, such as brass, or a lightweight material, such as aluminum, and then to plate it with silver or copper for good conductivity. For prevention of oxidation, the conducting layer may be plated with a thin coating of rhodium. However, since rhodium has a higher resistivity than silver, this coating must be thinner than the skin depth of rhodium so that the current flows mainly in the silver layer.

Brass is the most common metal for waveguides because it is easily machined and easily soldered. For airborne applications where weight is a consideration, aluminum or magnesium is preferred. At very high frequencies, above 40 kMc, silver is frequently used, since the amount of metal used is small and costs less than the cost of brass guide, silver plated.

Besides the simpler construction and lower loss, waveguides have higher power carrying capacity than coaxial cables. The waveguide is a completely shielded transmission line and may be bent and twisted with no radiation loss. However, whenever the waveguide is made to change direction, care must be taken to keep the cross section uniform or there will be a reflection from the discontinuity.

All discontinuities in waveguides are equivalent to lumped-circuit elements in conventional transmission lines. A screw inserted in the broad wall or a dent in this wall is a shunt capacity. A post across the waveguide is a shunt inductance. An iris across the waveguide with its edges parallel to the voltage vector is a shunt inductance. If its edges are parallel to the magnetic vector, the iris is a shunt capacity. A change in dimensions of the waveguide is a change in characteristic impedance, and a quarter-wave length of guide with new dimension is thus a quarter-wave transformer. All of these elements are used to match out the effects of more complicated mismatches.

In matching impedances or making quarter-wave transformers the wavelength used is not the wavelength in free space, for the wave travels in the waveguide at a velocity apparently greater than that of light. Actually, this is the *phase velocity* of the wave and is the apparent speed of an unmodulated wave. The signal or modulation on the wave travels at a speed less than that of light, called the *group velocity*. The product of the group velocity and the phase velocity is equal to the square of the speed of light. The phase velocity divided by the frequency is equal to a quantity called the *guide wavelength*, which is used for all matching calculations.

Waveguide Components

Two pieces of waveguide or two waveguide components may be joined together by means of flanges soldered on the ends of the guides. Flanges are of two types: (1) *cover* flanges, which are flat plane surfaces, and (2) *choke* flanges, which have a quarter-wave deep groove cut in them. This groove is also a quarter-wave from the waveguide wall. The choke presents a short-circuit impedance between the two pieces of guide even if they are separated slightly or misaligned. It is thus possible to have a microwave coupling which is a short at rf and an open circuit at dc. By using a quarter-wave transformer, the reverse is also possible.

A choke joint is also used in a rotary or motional joint, where it is desired to move one waveguide with respect to another and at the same time to maintain electrical continuity. This goal is accomplished by physically separating the two pieces and using the choke to present an electrical short circuit at the microwave frequency.

In the rotary joint and in other microwave circuits it is necessary to change from one form of waveguide to another or from waveguide to coaxial line. The problem in designing such adapters is basically one of matching impedances over a required frequency range. Coaxial line-to-waveguide adapters have been built with a voltage standing-wave ratio (VSWR) of 1.10 or better over a 30-percent frequency band. Adapters from the dominant mode ($TE_{1,0}$) in rectangular guide to the dominant mode ($TE_{1,1}$) in round guide have been built with a VSWR of 1.05 over the same frequency range. In both cases the rectangular guide may be either perpendicular to or in line with the other transmission line.

The VSWR is measured by means of a *slotted line*. This is a section of waveguide, identical to that being tested, with a thin slot in the center of one broad wall, parallel to the direction of propagation. A probe is lightly coupled through the slot, and, as it is moved along the slot, voltage maxima and minima may be determined. This information can be used to calculate the impedance of the piece being tested.

In making the impedance measurements (*q.v.*), the piece being tested must be properly terminated. That is, in order to measure only the discontinuity at the face of the slotted line, there must be no other discontinuities reflecting energy back to this point. The termination or *matched load* is usually a piece of waveguide containing an absorbent material which has been tapered to a point in the direction from which the energy is coming. Absorbent materials frequently used are resistance cards, carbon, plastics loaded with metal particles, sand, and wood. For very accurate measurements the load material may be slid along the guide to determine whether it is properly matched. If a load is perfect, there will be no voltage variations observed at the slotted line probe as the load is moved in the guide.

A tee is a component consisting of a straight piece of waveguide with another piece fastened to it at right angles. The junction is open so that energy fed into any arm sees two possible paths at the junction. When the auxiliary arm is fastened to the broad wall of the main waveguide, the voltage or

E vector in the side arm is perpendicular to the E vector in the main guide. Such a tee is called an *E-plane tee*. When properly matched, energy fed into the E-arm will divide equally in the other two arms but 180° out of phase. This tee is also called a *series junction tee*. When the auxiliary arm is fastened to the narrow wall of the main waveguide, the magnetic or H vector in the side arm is perpendicular to the H vector in the main guide. This is an *H-plane tee* or *shunt junction tee*. When properly matched, energy fed into the H-arm will divide equally and in phase in the other two arms.

When the component has both an E-arm and an H-arm at the same point in the main line, it is called a *hybrid tee*. (The two main line terminals are now called side arms.) When properly matched, the tee has special properties and is called a *magic tee*. In this tee, energy fed into the E-arm or the H-arm divides equally in the other two arms and there is no coupling between the E and H arms. Energy fed into one side arm divides equally between the E and H arms, and there is no coupling to the other side arm.

When energy is fed into both side arms, the algebraic sum of the signal intensities appears at the H-arm, and the difference appears at the E-arm.

When two waveguides are joined together by two or more coupling paths, it is possible to choose dimensions such that energy in the first guide will be coupled a predetermined amount to the second and will travel in only one direction in the second guide. Then the output at one terminal in the second guide will be a measure of the power flowing in one direction only in the first guide. This component is called a *directional coupler*.

A piece of waveguide with two large discontinuities will have strong reflections between them. If the two discontinuities are spaced a multiple of half wavelengths apart, the reflections will reinforce each other and the section will be *resonant*. A resonant section or cavity is analogous to a fixed tuned circuit at lower frequencies. If the spacing of the discontinuities is adjustable, it is a variable tuned circuit. Since the frequency of resonance depends on the spacing, resonant cavities are used as wavemeters. The Q of the cavity depends upon the conductivity of the walls, the shape, the magnitude of the discontinuities, and the lightness of coupling. With silver plated walls and short-circuits, Q's above 5000 have been obtained.

Attenuators and phase shifters are made by moving a piece of material into the waveguide so that it couples with the electric field. The motion can be calibrated and related to the amount of attenuation or phase shift. If the material is lossy, the component is an attenuator. If the material has low loss, but a dielectric constant more than unity, the velocity of propagation through it will be different from that in the empty guide, and phase shift results.

GERSHON J. WHEELER

Cross-references: *Attenuators and Isolators, Circulators, Dielectric Rods, Microwave Measurements, Resonators and Wavemeters, Smith Chart, Standing-Wave Ratio*

WAVEMETERS: see RESONATORS AND WAVE-METERS

WELDING (ELECTRONIC)

Process. Fusion welding by electron bombardment is a relatively new process using long-established vacuum-tube principles. Electrons from a filament cathode are accelerated and focused electrostatically and/or electromechanically to form a dense electron spot. As the spot strikes the part(s) to be welded (the work) the abrupt energy transformation causes the work to fuse. The entire process is performed in vacuum.

This form is known as a "self-accelerated" system as contrasted to the "work-accelerated" form in which the work itself serves as the anode. Since the latter has had negative response from users because of poor over-all beam control, no further reference to this system will be made. In order to implement the process outlined physically, several subsystems are necessary. The first is a vacuum chamber whose shape and dimensions must be adequate to accommodate the work, its motion, and the tooling and accessories, such as automatic filler wire feed, mechanical manipulators, etc. A sufficient number of ports are provided for viewing and mounting accessories. Typical chambers are made in AISI Type 304 stainless steel, using high-vacuum-quality welded joints. The evacuation of the chamber is accomplished with a pumping system usually consisting of a mechanical roughing pump, a diffusion type of finishing pump, and a small mechanical holding pump, along with appropriate valves and controls which must provide fail-safe interlocks. The emission, acceleration, and focusing are normally carried out in a single assembly; the anode, usually shaped to provide some focusing, the magnet(s), and cooling devices, if used.

The electron gun (*q,v.*) requires three power supplies for operation. The emission supply heats the filament, the high-voltage supply accelerates the electrons, and the focus supply energizes the magnet coils for beam focusing. Voltages are normally controllable over a substantial range. The final major subsystem comprises the tooling and controls. Basic tooling involves rotary and one or more planes of linear motion; the mechanisms are usually driven by controllable electric motors. Since the welding process is performed in vacuum, tooling motion must be remotely controllable.

Key Characteristics. The vacuum system provides pressures in the range of 10^{-4} to 10^{-6} mm of Hg. In rating the pump capacity, it should be emphasized that not only must the primary air volume be evacuated, but the surfaces of the work and the tooling must be degassed before suitable welding range pressures are reached. Ability to hold pressures of 10^{-4} mm of Hg during welding is important from the standpoints of better beam quality, longer filament life, and less contamination of sensitive materials, e.g., beryllium.

The mechanical design of the gun must permit rapid and repeatable accurate installation of filaments, since the electron optics (q.v.) is highly susceptible to small dimensional differences in the cathode-anode configuration. In a multiple-purpose installation, the gun should be small so that it can be at least manually mobile. If mounted on one end of a shaft which is admitted into the tank through a ball socket seal, the gun can be prepositioned by manual movement of the shaft's external extension, which makes for more flexibility as to size and shape of work and to the internal tooling. Small gun size and the need for accurate heat control at the weld makes it desirable to cool the gun with water and/or radiant heat shields. Otherwise, under conditions of high heat and long usage, the gun temperature rises, the beam optics changes because of the temperature sensitivity of the magnets, and the magnet wire insulation may outgas and degrade.

The two most important—and most elusive—features that determine dependability and reliability are (1) a fully tuned high-voltage supply gun combination, and (2) attenuation of beam-power transients. Electron bombardment welding by its very nature outgasses the fusion zone of residual gasses and of some vapor from the metallic constituents. The presence of this matter in widely varying amounts causes changes to the impedance presented to the beam, and moreover normally causes a certain amount of arcing or beam shorting, which in turn can result in rf feedbacks damaging to the high-voltage supply components. Consequently, electron emission must be properly controlled with respect to acceleration power changes so as to (1) produce uniform and repeatable welds, (2) avoid scrappage of the work in which labor and material investment may be high, and (3) maximize filament life for better equipment utility. Protection of the work is important since on many joints it is distressingly difficult to resume a weld once it has been so interrupted. These problems can be solved to a satisfactory degree by the proper use of magnetic-amplifier and shunt-reactor techniques.

Applications. Among applications of electron-bombardment welding are the following:

(1) High-quality joints, like to like and like to unlike, in uncommon metals and their alloys, such as columbium, tantalum, molybdenum, tungsten, titanium, beryllium, etc.

(2) High-quality joints in the highly ferrous or nickel alloys, OFHC copper, and aluminum alloys, where severe requirements obtain in such properties as fatigue life, weld efficiency, weld workability, and infinitesimally small leakage rates.

(3) Dissimilar materials joints such as metals to ceramics and ceramic to ceramic.

(4) Material removal, particularly with the very-high-voltage machines, by cutting, drilling, and milling.

(5) Highly localized vacuum brazing where the entire work cannot be exposed to brazing temperature, usually because of sensitive contained components.

(6) Outgassing or cleansing of small vacuum component parts, using the defocused beam for heating.

(7) Metal cladding by means of an automatic filler-wire feed mechanism.

These applications appear mainly in high-performance propulsion systems, in nuclear and chemical processing, and in electronic usage. The process is relatively expensive compared to atmospheric tungsten arc welding (TIG), but costs less than TIG in a high-vacuum-purged, inert-gas-filled chamber (drybox). The metallurgical quality of the joint is almost without exception superior to other known joining processes.

WILLARD SWEETMAN, JR.

Cross-references: *Machining (Electronic), Refining (Electronic), Vacuum Techniques, Zone Melting (Electronic)*

WHISTLERS: see RADIATION (TERRESTRIAL)

WILLIAMS' TUBE: see STORAGE TUBES

WIRE (MULTICONDUCTOR)

Multiconductor cables can be defined as having a multiple number of parallel, insulated conductors with all conductors lying in a single plane. The variables utilized are the dimensions of the conductor, the type and thickness of insulation, and the distance between conductors.

Extruded Multiconductor Cable. The extruded type of cable consists of conventional insulated round wire in which the insulation covering one conductor is bonded or fused to the insulation of adjacent conductors at the line of tangential contact.

The insulating materials most often used are vinyl or fluorocarbon plastics. The conducting material is usually soft copper and may be either stranded or solid wire, circular in cross section. The type of conductors in a cable may differ from one another, if desired, so that it is possible to incorporate standard conductors, twisted pairs, or shielded conductors in one cable. The spacing between conductors may also vary, making it possible to alter the electrical properties, particularly the capacitance, as measured from one conductor to adjacent conductors. A fairly wide range of conductors are available with stock items ranging from 10 to 30 AWG wire sizes. The diameter of individual conductors, which controls cable thickness, is identical to that available in individual insulated wires of corresponding current ratings. The width dimension of a cable is determined by the conductor diameter, the spacing between conductors, and

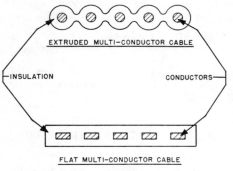

FLAT MULTI-CONDUCTOR CABLE

Fig. 1

the total number of conductors (Fig. 1). Termination devices employed are identical to those used for individual round wires. Preparation for connections is accomplished by separating the insulated conductors from each other and then removing the insulation using standard wire stripping techniques (mechanical, thermal, or abrasion).

The advantages of this construction are reduced assembly costs, largely as a result of lower cable-harness costs; change of the harness configuration from a round to a flat form; and control of certain electrical properties through controlled conductor spacing.

Flat-Sandwich Multiconductor Cables. The second type of flat cable departs substantially in design from that which is considered conventional. Solid conductors, which are usually of soft copper and rectangular in cross section, are sandwiched between two films of a suitable plastic. The laminate resulting has each copper strip insulated from ground as well as from adjacent strips. A typical cable uses copper conductors that are 0.002 in. thick by 0.062 in. wide. The space between conductors is 0.040 in. The number of conductors can vary from one to over one hundred depending on the application. The over-all cable thickness is usually about 0.010 in. (Fig. 1).

This type of "polystrip" or "ribbon" cable is much thinner than conventional types. The manufacturing process is sufficiently flexible to permit a wide variety of insulations, conductor sizes, and different spacings, to be incorporated into one cable. The maximum thickness of conductor used seldom exceeds 0.010 in. The width, however, can be varied greatly making it possible to produce multiconductor cables having the equivalent of a complete range of AWG sizes. The insulating films employed encompass all of the conventional thermoplastic materials (vinyls, polyolefins, fluorocarbons, etc.). In addition, film materials such as polyesters, which are not normally associated with primary wire insulation, may be used. Combinations of two or more insulating materials including reinforced thermosetting plastics have also been used for special purposes and permit thinner polymer films to be used, thereby substantially reducing the cable weight and volume, without affecting the insulating properties of the cable. An example would be a cable having 0.002 in. of Mylar® insulation on each side of the conductor. Such a cable does not fail until a potential of approximately 6000 v is applied between a conductor and ground. This value is about four times greater than could be expected from a vinyl insulation four times as thick.

Electrical shielding is accomplished by bonding solid or perforated copper foils, or aluminum foils, to one or both surfaces of the cable. Woven metal screens or grids may also be used. Nearly perfect shields are obtained when foils are placed on both surfaces and the conductors on each side of the signal carrying conductor are grounded. Additional layers of insulation may be bonded to the outermost surfaces of the shielding. Other cable configurations give the equivalents of coaxial cables and twisted wire pairs.

Connectors are in some cases based on modifications of existing designs. Recently, however, new connector designs have evolved based either on pressure contacts or insulation piercing contacts. Preparation for connection, when required, is accomplished by removal of the insulation from one or both surfaces by thermal, mechanical, or abrasion methods.

The advantages of this construction are reduced cable harness assembly costs; change of cable form from round to flat; and controlled electrical properties stemming from adjustable conductor spacing. In addition, greater heat dissipation from the conductors occurs because of the large radiating surface area of a rectangular compared with a round cross section, so that smaller conductor sizes may be used where temperature rise in a cable is a determining design factor. Lastly, the weight and volume of this cable form is substantially less than comparable round types as a result of using thin insulating films that exhibit high performance qualities.

SIDNEY J. STEIN AND DAVID MCELROY

Cross-references: *Coaxial Lines, Connectors, Strip Lines*

WORK FUNCTION

The electronic work function ϕ may be defined as the energy required for a free electron to escape from the interior of a material (at the Fermi energy level) to a field-free point in vacuum outside the surface of the material. This definition applies to metals, semiconductors, and insulators.

The value of ϕ may be determined experimentally by four methods: thermionic emission, field emission, photoelectric threshold, and contact potential difference. These techniques will be described here and some representative values given for materials used in electronics.

Any measurement of the work function is affected radically by the purity and surface condition of the specimen. The value of ϕ for metals, for example, is highly sensitive to surface oxides and to occluded gases and vapors. In the presence of surface oxygen, ϕ for tungsten may rise from 4.52 ev (the normal value for clean, polycrystalline tungsten) to about 9 ev; for molybdenum, it jumps from 4.20 ev also to about 9 ev. Smaller effects, of the order of several tenths of an electron-volt, may be due to the temperature coefficient of ϕ, to allotropy, and (in the case of single crystals) to anisotropy. In polycrystalline materials a "patch effect" of ϕ variation over the surface area is due to heterogeneity of the surface. There is also a small dependence of the apparent work function ϕ^* on applied electric field.

The *thermionic method* usually involves measurements on a test diode in which the test specimen is the cathode. The Richardson-Dushman equation gives the thermionic current density:

$$j = AT^2 \exp(-\phi/kT)$$

where A is a constant depending on the material and k is Boltzmann's constant. The work function is determined by obtaining emission current data for a range of applied fields at a fixed temperature. The resulting curve is then extrapolated to zero field and the process is repeated for several temperatures. The zero-field current densities are then divided by T^2 and plotted vs $1/T$. The slope of the plot is the apparent work function ϕ^*. The relation to the true work function ϕ is as follows:

$$\phi^* = \phi - T \frac{d\phi}{dT} - \frac{kT^2}{e}(1 - r)\frac{dr}{dT}$$

in which k is Boltzmann's constant and r is a reflection coefficient for electrons crossing the potential barrier at the metal surface when the external field is zero. The work function determined from the slope is thus equal to the true work function ϕ only when ϕ and r are independent of temperature. For a critical analysis of thermionic emission, see C. Herring and M. H. Nichols, *Rev. Mod. Physics* **21**: 185, 1949.

Another convenient way of measuring the apparent work function ϕ^*, particularly for metals, is to determine the *photoelectric threshold* $h\nu_0$, in which h is Planck's constant and ν is the threshold frequency of incident light. In this method, a photocell is constructed in which the specimen becomes the cathode and is exposed to incident light. The collector electrode (anode) is kept at a positive potential and the cathode at a negative potential. The threshold of photoelectric current is indicated by a microammeter. For determining the absolute value of ϕ, the photoelectric emission data near threshold are fitted to the Fowler-Dubridge theory. (For a critical review, see the chapter by G. L. Weissler in the *Handbuch der Physik* XXI, Springer-Verlag, 1956, page 304.)

The method of *contact difference of potential* originally proposed by Kelvin is a useful and accurate method of determining ϕ.

When the work function of a reference material a is precisely known, the absolute value ϕ for a specimen b can be obtained by measuring the potential difference V_{ab}, from which $\phi_b = V_{ab} - \phi_a$, neglecting small Peltier potentials when current flows in the circuit. The electrodes a and b, mounted in a tube envelope, are made to vibrate with respect to each other, as shown in Fig. 1. An ac signal will then appear across resistor R_L because the potential difference V_{ab} causes a fluctuating current to flow in the external circuit of capacitor ab. Retarding potential V_R is then adjusted to give a null point in the amplifier output. Then $V_{ab} = V_R$. The accuracy of this technique for determining ϕ_b is about 10^{-4} ev. The pre-

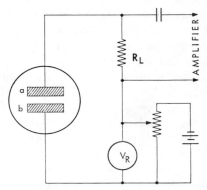

FIG. 1. Kelvin contact-potential method of measuring work function.

TABLE I. WORK FUNCTION, IN ev

Element	Thermionic	Photoelectric	Contact Potential
Aluminum	—	4.08	3.38
Barium	2.11	2.49	2.39
Copper	4.38	4.86	4.46
Iron	4.23	4.72	4.40
Carbon	4.39	4.81	—
Molybdenum	4.20	4.15	4.08
Gold	4.32	4.92	4.46
Nickel	4.61	5.05	4.98
Silver	4.08	4.74	4.79
Tantalum	4.19	4.16	4.25
Thorium	3.35	3.47	3.46
Tungsten	4.52	4.50	4.38
Caesium	1.81	1.9	—
Germanium	—	4.7	4.50
Silicon	3.59	4.37	4.2

cision depends partly on the reliability of the ϕ value for the reference specimen a. The method is especially useful for semiconductors and insulators.

Field-emission measurements, in which electrons penetrate the surface energy barrier of the specimen by means of the "tunnel effect," can also be used to determine ϕ^*. With this method, surface field strengths of the order of 10^8 v/m produce electron emission at room temperature. In order to obtain such strong electric fields, a specimen with a fine point—smaller than 1 μ—is generally used. From data for the current density j and surface field F_0, a plot is constructed of $jF_0{}^2$ as a function of $1/F_0$.

The slope of this plot, which is approximately a straight line, then gives the work function. This method neglects a small error which is due to the dependence of ϕ^* on the applied electric field.

In Table I are representative published values of the work function for several materials used in electronics. The variations in ϕ are mostly due to minor differences in the surface condition of the particular specimens used.

HERBERT B. MICHAELSON

Cross-references: *Contact Potential, Field Emission, Photoelectric Emission, Secondary Emission, Thermionic Emission*

X

X-RAYS

Production of X-rays

When electrons with energies in the order of 10,000 ev or more impinge upon an anode, for some cases made of a heavy material (e.g., tungsten), X-rays are produced. This phenomenon was discovered by Roentgen in 1895. The radiation wavelength λ is determined by the electron energy and equals $12,400/V$ (Å), where V is the accelerating voltage. In most X-ray tubes, the electron source is a tungsten spiral powered by a variable supply so that the emission may be temperature limited, independently of anode voltage, according to Richardson's equation. The current is such devices is limited to about 1 amp. Other electron sources have been used, especially where large X-ray intensities are required for relatively short times. These other sources include the metallic-discharge type in which, owing to field emission (q.v.) resulting from a pulse across a gap in the cathode structure, a metallic arc results that is capable of emitting extreme electron current densities for short periods of time ($\sim 10^3$ amp). In another type of tube, field emission from extremely small points, exposed to the anode, results again in similar currents for short time intervals ($< 10^{-6}$ sec). A further approach is to use an oxide-coated cathode, which is capable of relatively high current densities but is subject to cathode damage from positive-ion bombardment. Recent developments have verified that this approach is practical with the use of ion traps.

It is highly desirable for the electron beam to be focused so as to represent the smallest spot possible on the tube anode, usually by electrostatic configurations in the cathode region. Since X-rays, for diagnostic purposes, result in a shadowgraph of the subject, the beam is focused so as to form a line source on the anode which is set at a slight angle; when viewed from a position at right angles to the beam, the "effective" spot is relatively small. Depending on the application, this effective spot size will vary between 0.3 and 3.0 mm. The tubes are normally operated so as to give the minimum beam loading on the target. For this reason, rotating anodes have been developed such that the line energy source, which appears as a radius on the anode, is distributed over the entire disk area. These rotating anodes frequently operate at temperatures of 1,000°C.

The range of energies used in X-ray sources vary from approximately 10 kv to at least 35 million volts. The kilovoltage used usually depends on the material being diagnosed. In the medical field 50 to 150 kv is appropriate since this energy range provides sufficient penetration so that the various substances are readily distinguishable. On the other hand, in the examination of very heavy industrial castings X-rays are frequently used to locate flaws, and in this case radiation in the million-volt range is frequently required.

X-ray Energy Intensity Distribution for a Fixed Anode Potential

If electrons accelerated to a constant potential V bombard a target, a black-body type of distribution results. Electrons accelerated continuously at the potential V yield essentially no energy at the wavelength corresponding to V. A plot of intensity vs wavelength indicates that the maximum intensity occurs at a wavelength given approximately by $\lambda = 1.5\lambda_0$ where λ_0 represents the shortest wavelength in the spectrum as represented by a beam of voltage V. Beyond this region the intensity decreases more gradually.

Geometrical Distribution of Radiation

If an infinitesimally small target is bombarded with electrons of various energies, intensity patterns result that vary quite drastically, depending on the energy of the incident electrons. For example, a 50-kv beam provides a cardioid shape pattern such that the apex is directly beyond the target relative to the incident beam. The maximum radiation occurs on a cone with a half angle of 60° relative to this apex. Radiation in the backward direction is in the order of 30 per cent of this maximum. If the kilovoltage is increased, this apex slowly inverts so that at 20 million volts the radiation is confined to an extremely small angle (about 4°), with the radiation almost completely in the direction of the original beam. In such cases transmission targets are essential.

Absorption of X-rays

In general the transmission of X-rays through materials follows the usual exponential equation

$$I_x = I_0 e^{-\mu x}$$

where I_x is the intensity after penetrating a thickness of material x, I_0 is the initial intensity, and μ the absorption coefficient. For simplification, most tables give values of μ/ρ (ρ = material density) and the above equation should be modified accordingly. With careful measurements it is possible to detect a density variation in material of the order of 5 per cent.

L. C. FOSTER

X-ray Microscopy

The refractive index of matter for X-rays is so close to unity that no lens materials can be used for practicable focusing of the radiation. Kirkpatrick constructed in 1947 the reflection type of X-ray microscope utilizing the total reflection at grazing incidence (1 or 2°) on concave glass surfaces. Two mirrors in planes at right angles gave a point focus and a resolution of 1 μ. This is the true X-ray microscope. Pattee and others calculated optimum resolution of 500 and 200 Å in compound mirror systems over fields of 200 and 40 μ, respectively. Technical difficulties in preparing mathematically perfect reflecting surfaces have not been overcome. Crystal defects and chromatic aberration also prevented the proposed use of Bragg reflection to form X-ray images.

The present microscopy with X-rays consists of projection of microscopic details by means of practically monochromatic X-rays originating from a microscopic focal spot, where an electron beam hits a target foil. We distinguish between the contact method and point projection according to the specimen-to-detector distance. When the specimen is moved to a distance from the detector, there is a direct magnification by X-ray projection, but also a magnification of the projection errors. Soft X-rays (1 Å $\leq$ λ $\leq$ 12 Å) and ultrasoft X-rays (12 Å $\leq$ λ $\leq$ 100 Å) are mainly used in microscopy. The image contrasts are produced in the soft region exclusively by absorption. Errors due to scattering and fluorescent radiation are negligible. Mass absorption coefficient μ of a chemical compound is equal to the sum of the corresponding atomic coefficients. Determination of the dry mass as function of the incident intensity I_0 and transmitted intensity I [$I = I_0 \exp(-\mu m)$] then becomes possible and a comparison of absorption values on either side of the critical absorption edges of certain elements allows a chemical mapping of the sample. Another microanalytical X-ray microscopic method is the scanning of the fluorescent radiation from the irradiated surfaces.

The great penetration of X-rays simplifies the examination of the specimens, which are opaque to light and difficult to be prepared as electron microscopic specimens. The low absorption in air and the intensity of the present microfocus systems facilitate the study of the specimen under atmospheric conditions. The penetration is disadvantageously high in organic materials consisting mainly of light atoms. The contrast, as necessary for accurate photometric measurements in absorptiometry, is enhanced by proper selection of the X-ray spectrum or by staining with heavy atoms.

Technical details rather than the wavelength determine the ultimate resolution. The spatial resolution is a combined effect of the projection geometry and diffraction resolution. The penumbral width p is proportional to the size of the source s and the object-to-detector distance b, being inversely proportional to the source-to-object distance a. Requirements concerning intensity and the recording speed prohibit the maximizing of b and the minimizing of s. The width of the first Fresnel fringe depends linearly on the detector-to-source distance $(a + b)$, being 500 Å at 5 mm according to Nixon. An optimum resolution is attained, if the geometric and diffraction resolving distances are equal. Since b and the specimen thickness are small in the contact method, only a moderately small source (about 10 μ) is required.

Fine grain photographic films, special fluorescent screens, xerography and a variety of materials sensitive to X-rays as well as scanning have been employed as detectors. A practical resolution limit of 2,000 Å is caused by the fluctuation of the distribution of grain in photographic emulsions and independently by the resolving power of the optical systems employed for enlargement of the X-ray record. These limitations are eliminated in the point projection, which gives a direct magnification. The drawbacks of a reduced source-size (about 1 μ or less), a low intensity, complicated focusing and requirements for insuring the stability then exceed the importance of the recording system.

Combination of the X-ray recording on structureless materials and a subsequent electron microscopic enlargement of the thin recording film (suitable for electron microscopy by transmission) gave a resolution better than 600 Å according to Asunmaa

in the contact method. Silver-activated nitrocellulose as a recording material contained a radiation trap and was characterized by the decreased range of photoelectrons in the recorder. The work was based on previous experimental evidence that the electron microscope can be used for semiquantitative investigations under constant instrumental conditions in the region of magnification, where the scattering-absorption dominates in the formation of image contrasts. For instrumentation see V. E. Cosslett et al., "X-ray Microscopy," New York, Academic Press, 1957, and "X-ray microscopy and microanalysis," Proceedings of Stockholm Conference 1959 (Engstrom, Cosslett, and Pattee, eds.), Elsevier, Amsterdam, 1961.

Saara Asunmaa

Spectrometry

On November 8, 1895, W. C. Röntgen, Professor of Physics of the University of Würzburg in Germany, discovered X-rays or roentgen rays while experimenting with a cathode-ray tube. Invisible radiation from the tube covered with black paper fell on a fluorescent screen, which became luminescent. Before the discovery was announced after Christmas, Röntgen conducted a searching investigation to elucidate the nature of the radiation, and was unable to demonstrate reflection, refraction, diffraction, and polarization, four characteristic optical properties of light, but proved that the rays are produced by the sudden stoppage of a stream of electrons (cathode or β-rays) accelerated by high voltage at an anode target. Hence, the designation x for unknown was given by Röntgen. Also demonstrated were the nonelectrical nature of the radiation, and the penetrating power and differential absorption in passing through matter of varying density, giving rise at once to the development of diagnostic medical radiography. Certain chemical and biological effects of the rays were also observed early in 1896, leading to X-ray therapy, or treatment of cancer, and to radiogenetics, or the production of mutations in species by affecting the reproductive material in cell nuclei.

In 1905 Barkla was able to demonstrate polarization of X-rays, and found indications of a wavelength measured in a few Ångstrom units (10^{-10} m). In 1912 Laue diffracted X-rays with a crystal, acting as a three-dimensional grating; in 1913, W. H. (Sir William) and W. L. (Sir Laurence) Bragg derived the famous Bragg law: $n\lambda = 2d \sin \theta$, in which n is an integer, λ is the wavelength, d is the spacing of the crystal "grating" or the distance between parallel planes (also of the order of a few Ångstrom units), and θ is the angle of incidence of the x-ray beam upon this set of planes. In 1921 Professor Arthur Compton, of Washington University in St. Louis, found the necessary conditions for reflecting X-rays from mirrors, diffracting from ruled optical gratings, and refracting in prisms. Thus X-rays are like light in being transverse electromagnetic vibrations, and occupy a range in the electromagnetic spectrum from 1000 to 0.00001 Å or shorter, along with secondary cosmic rays, γ rays, ultraviolet rays, visible light, infrared rays, and Hertzian or radio waves. In some phenomena, like light, X-rays behave as corpuscles (quanta or photons).

Since 1895, there has been a spectacular development in X-ray tubes and the power plants for generating high potentials, from Röntgen's simple, pear-shaped, cathode-ray tube and a Ruhmkorff induction coil, to present-day tubes operating at millions of volts generated in resonance transformers, van de Graaff electrostatic generators, betatrons, synchotrons, and linear accelerators. "Pocket-sized" X-ray generators utilize radioisotopes which emit high energy β-rays which impinge on metal foil targets. The law of Duane and Hunt shows that the maximum frequency ν_0, or a minimum wavelength λ_0, in an X-ray beam depends upon the voltage applied by the equation $Ve = h\nu_0 = hc/\lambda_0$, where e is the charge on the electron, h the Planck action constant and c the velocity of light. The *intensity* of the X-ray beam depends on the electron current through the tube. The engineering developments to meet the insulation requirements for ever higher voltages, and the target-cooling requirements of ever higher currents, have led to continually improving equipment.

There are several branches of X-ray science today, each depending upon a particular property of the radiation. Some of those already mentioned are medical diagnostic radiography, medical therapy, industrial and art radiography, microradiography, and radiochemical and radiobiological effects. The absorption of X-rays by solids, liquids and solutions, and gases may be used, with proper calibration, as a method of analysis and of control of gage, particularly since the advent of multiplier phototubes (*q.v.*) and electronic amplification.

Radiation with wavelengths characteristic of each chemical element is emitted above critical voltage excitation in sharp-line series designated K, L, M, N, O, P, respectively, from the shortest wavelength and highest energy to the longest. There is a continuous progression in characteristic wavelengths in passing from one element to another instead of a periodic function as is true for light spectra, as found by Moseley in 1913 to give significance to atomic number. A crystal is used as the analyzer for the beam by the Bragg law $n\lambda = 2d \sin \theta$, where λ is unknown, d is a known crystal grating constant, and 2θ is the experimental angular measurement. The same spectra are obtained whether the unknown sample is made the target and bombarded by electrons, or is irradiated with primary X-rays to excite secondary fluorescent characteristic spectra. The latter method is now almost universally used with the advent of such sensitive detectors as Geiger counters. The K spectrum is distinguished by great simplicity for principal lines, in contrast with the complexities of optical spectra.

The measurement of λ then makes qualitative analysis possible, and by use of intensities properly calibrated against standards, quantitative analysis of elementary compositions as well. Fluorescence spectrometry has been the most rapidly progressing instrumental method, because of relative simplicity of apparatus and technique and nondestructive excitation of the specimen. Under ordinary conditions elements with as low atomic numbers as potassium (19) and calcium (20) have K-series wavelengths short enough to operate the spectrometer with air paths; but for lower atomic numbers, helium "tunnels" or vacuum transmit the fluorescent rays incident upon and diffracted by the crystal. By application of the Moseley law, which indicates an essentially linear relationship between atomic number and the frequency, wave number, or wavelength of a given spectral line, characteristic wavelengths may be predicted by interpolation. This technique has led to the positive proof of the discovery of new chemical elements, especially since that of relatively abundant hafnium. Even the new transuranium elements to 103 have in most cases been so identified.

There are also associated characteristic absorption spectra which may be utilized for identification and analysis, there being 1 K absorption discontinuity associated with K emission lines, 3L edges with 3 groups of L lines, 5M, 7N, 5O, and 3P. Aside from the analytical importance of x-ray spectra, they have made probable the greatest contribution to the present theory of atomic structure and to the quantum-mechanical, vector model of the atom replacing the Bohr model. (See **Atoms**.) Characteristic X-rays are associated with processes in the electron shells or orbitals, or energy levels, nearest the atomic nucleus. Thus K-rays are emitted when electrons are removed from the innermost level (quantum number 1) by impact of electrons or photons (the so-called K-state or K-ionized atom); the K-level is then replenished by electrons from the L or higher levels. Even the details of fine structure have made important contributions. As a result the 92 electrons in uranium can all be

assigned the characteristic quantum numbers that identify energy level, spin, interaction, etc. The characteristic absorption wavelengths prove that there is 1K level, 3L, 5M, 7N, 5O, and 3P levels, proceeding outward from the nucleus of the atoms. Sometimes, an atom may emit X-rays after its nucleus captures one of its own K-electrons, as, for example, Fe^{55} + K-electron capture $\rightarrow Mn^{55}$ which emits characteristic K-rays of Mn.

Diffraction Analysis

Since all crystals act as three-dimensional gratings for X-rays, the pattern of diffracted rays from the various sets of parallel planes that constitute the crystal lattice is characteristic for each crystalline material. Here the Bragg law applies: $n\lambda = 2d \sin \theta$, where n is an integer, λ is the wavelength (generally known), d is the unknown spacing for each set of planes, and 2θ is the experimentally measured diffraction angle. Hence, the interpretation of each pattern leads to the analysis of the crystal structure and thereby to the identification of the solid exactly as it is. It is a straightforward process to determine the dimensions of the fundamental unit cell (the smallest parallelopiped building unit) containing an integral number of atoms and molecules that has the properties of the macrocrystal itself. Ordinarily, these dimensions are the distances between planes in three sets which enclose the unit cell.

Optical and X-ray data lead to the assignment to one of seven crystal systems (triclinic, monoclinic, orthorhombic, tetragonal, cubic, hexagonal and rhombohedral, or trigonal) which are distinguished by unit distances along X, Y, and Z axes and by the angles between these axes. Data on macrosymmetry of outer form (rotation axes, mirror planes, rotation-inversion axes) leads to classification into 32 crystallographic classes or point groups. When these symmetry elements around a single point are repeated on 14 lattices, additional microsymmetry operations are introduced (screw axes and glide planes) detectable only by x-ray patterns, with the result that there are 230 space groups, or ways of arranging atoms and molecules in space. In addition, then, to unit-cell dimensions, the X-ray patterns provide the necessary information, from extinctions or *missing* diffraction interferences, to permit the assignment of the crystal to one of these space groups that uniquely describes the structure of the crystal. These criteria are listed in the International Tables for X-Ray Crystallography.

The final and most difficult procedure is the evaluation from intensity data of the actual positions of atoms within molecules that may be acting as crystal units, which is derived from electron density contour maps either in three dimensions or projected upon a plane in the unit cell. The calculations involve the use of Fourier equations. This is the step in which bond lengths, bond angles, and all the details of molecular configuration are ascertained. This information, derived from diffraction patterns almost entirely for single crystals, has been of immeasurable value to theoretical and structural chemistry, even of such complex compounds as penicillin, strychnine, proteins, hormones, and many other natural products. There are several powerful techniques of single-crystal analysis, some involving moving films, which provide a maximum amount of data.

From a practical point of view, the most important diffraction analysis is that of crystalline powders. In these patterns of rings or lines on photographic films or peaks on a Geiger counter diffractometer chart, diffracted beams from all the important sets of planes in the crystal are registered simultaneously as a highly characteristic "fingerprint" of the crystalline material or a mixture. It is sufficient to match the powder lines against standard patterns of known pure materials in order to identify the sample in its solid form. Of great usefulness for analysis is the ASTM card index of several thousand crystalline elements and compounds. Again, quantitative analysis is possible from observation of intensities of characteristic interferences as a function of percentage composition of a given crystalline phase. In X-ray laboratories all over the world, powder diffraction analysis is being applied to every imaginable type of material, chemical, metallurgical, and mineralogical, and to ceramics, soils, pharmaceuticals, textiles, and other manufactured products. From the broadening of powder diffraction lines as particle size decreases, measurements of particle size and shape in the colloidal range may be made, as well as the effects of strain (especially significant in metallurgical structures), and the effects of stretching or cold work (such as rolling sheets or drawing wires) in introducing fibering or a preferred orientation of powder grains. Significant information is derived even from the scattering of X-rays by noncrystalline glasses, liquids, solutions, and gases.

GEORGE L. CLARK

Cross-references: *Radiation (Ionizing)*

Z

ZEEMAN EFFECT

The *Zeeman effect* is the splitting of a spectral line from a radiating atom into two or more components, when the atom is placed in a weak magnetic field. Early experiments and theory led to the observation (1896) of three components, called the *normal* Zeeman effect. The central component is undisplaced from the zero-field position of the line, whereas the other two components are spaced equally in energy on each side of the central line. The components are linearly polarized when observed in a direction perpendicular to the magnetic field; the central component is missing and the outer two are circularly polarized when observed parallel to the magnetic field.

Most spectral lines are split into more than three components and exhibit the *anomalous* Zeeman effect, with lines from complex atoms often having fifty or more components.

These line splittings arise from a splitting of the energy levels of the atom, or a dependence of the energy on the orientation of the atom in the magnetic field. The number of Zeeman levels into which a single zero-field level is split depends upon the total angular momentum of the atom. The magnitude of the splitting generally depends directly upon the magnitude of the field and the Landé g-factor, the ratio of the magnetic moment of the atom to its total angular momentum.

When the magnetic field begins seriously to disturb the motions of the atomic electrons, the field is no longer considered weak, and the Zeeman effect changes to the *Paschen-Back effect*.

S. P. DAVIS

Cross-references: *Hall Effect, Radiation, Stark Effect*

ZONE MELTING

Zone melting is the modern application of the principle of fractional crystallization to a range of techniques for purifying or controlling the impurity content of a material. It has been applied to many substances, but its main use is in the processing of semiconductor materials, and the production of high purity metals, both usually in single-crystal form.

In all these techniques one or more narrow molten zones are traversed, unidirectionally, and at a controlled rate, along an ingot of the material. Segregation of an impurity occurs when its solubility in the liquid phase is different from its solubility in the solid phase. The efficiency with which an impurity segregates is determined by its segregation coefficient K, defined as the equilibrium ratio of the impurity concentration in the solid phase to its concentration in the liquid phase. A value for K can be calculated from the phase diagram of the system. The greater the deviation of K from unity the more efficient the segregation. For $K < 1$ the impurity lowers the melting point of the solvent, and there is a net transport of impurity in the direction of zone travel. For $K > 1$ the inverse is true, although at a slower rate. The theoretical distribution of an impurity after any number of passes can be calculated from a knowledge of K and the ratio of zone length to ingot length R. After an infinite number of passes an equilibrium distribution is obtained which represents a greater transport of impurity the smaller the value of R. However, the smaller the R the greater the number of passes needed to establish the equilibrium distribution. This theoretical segregation coefficient only applies where the zone traverse speed is slow enough to insure an equilibrium distribution of impurities in the liquid zone at all times. For faster traverse speeds a gradient in impurity distribution in the liquid zone occurs and segregation is less efficient. The actual speed at which this effect becomes noticeable depends on the amount of stirring that can be introduced to the liquid zone either by directly coupled induction heating or other means.

In the group of techniques closely allied to zone refining, and known as zone leveling, segregation is arranged to be only partial, or to be completely eliminated by careful control of the freezing conditions. By these techniques it is possible to produce an ingot with a known concentration of a known impurity distributed over the major portion of an ingot with a uniformity not possible by any other freezing process.

Given suitable conditions, a zone-melting process usually results in single-crystal formation. This is an advantage for semiconductors and saves further processing.

For simplicity it is preferable to zone-refine horizontally in a boat-shaped crucible, but where a material is reactive with, or has too high a melting point for, known boat materials, the floating-zone method can be used. In this method, the ingot is held at both ends and in a vertical position. The molten zone is held stable by surface tension. Crucible contamination is thus avoided. The maximum diameter of ingot that can be zoned by this method is a function of surface tension, density of material, and length of zone.

Floating-zone melting can be combined with electron-bombardment heating for the zone refining of refractory metals and materials in high vacuum. The heat input is highly concentrated and radiation losses are small. Purification in this case is by zone refining, outgassing, and evaporation of volatile impurities. The method is not suitable for materials of high melting point vapor pressure because of loss by evaporation.

Germanium, the most widely used device material, is zone-refined easily by the horizontal method. Its usual impurities have segregation coefficients favorable to zone refining and it is not reactive with boat materials. The degree of purity obtained is higher than by any chemical purification method. A total impurity content of less than 1 in 10^{10} atoms has been reached.

Silicon presents certain difficulties. It is highly reactive with known boat materials, and its usual impurities include boron with a segregation coefficient of 0.8. It is usually floating-zone refined, and ingots up to 1.5 in. in diameter have been obtained by this method.

Zone melting has also been applied to binary compounds.

Compounds with one component volatile at the melting point can be zone-refined in a sealed system, in an atmosphere of the volatile component at a pressure equivalent to the dissociation pressure of the compound at its melting point.

F. E. BIRBECK

Cross-references: *Refining (Electronic), Semiconductor Manufacture, Welding (Electronic)*

ZWORYKIN, VLADIMIR KOSMA (b. 1889)

V. K. Zworykin was born in Mourom in Russia on July 30, 1889, and received his undergraduate training at the Petrograd Institute of Technology, graduating in 1912. He next entered the College of France in Paris, where he engaged in X-ray researches that were interrupted by World War I, when he returned to Russia to serve as an officer in the Signal Corps of the Russian Army. At the close of the war, he emigrated to the United States and became a citizen in 1924. In 1926 he received the Ph.D. degree from the University of Pittsburgh.

Soon after his arrival in the United States Zworykin joined the research staff of Westinghouse Electric and Manufacturing Co., where he engaged in investigations in the fields of photoelectric emission and television. These studies led to his conception of the basic principles of the iconoscope (*q.v.*) a new type of television pick-up tube, which he developed into a form suitable for prac-

V. K. Zworykin

tical picture transmission. Zworykin's second major step toward all-electronic television was the development of the kinescope or television picture tube. In 1930, Zworykin became associated with the Radio Corporation of America and in 1947 he became a vice-president of RCA Laboratories; he retired in 1954, but continued his association with RCA as a technical consultant. In the same year he became director of a Medical Electronics Center at the Rockefeller Institute in New York, concerning himself particularly with the extension of the use of electronics in medicine and in the life sciences.

His research activities were not confined to television, but included many phases of electronics and electron optics. As a result of this work, important devices such as various forms of secondary-emission multipliers and image tubes were developed and perfected. The "snooperscope" and "sniperscope," important military developments used in World War II, were practical applications of his research on infrared tubes. Another vital contribution to the war effort was his formulation of plans for an airborne television system to serve in guiding radio-controlled flying torpedoes, an early form of missile guidance (*q.v.*).

His intensive study of electron optics directed his interest to electron microscopes (*q.v.*). As a result of concentrated efforts, a group under his direction perfected the electron microscope into a versatile research tool that now serves in many laboratories and institutions throughout the world.

In recognition of his important contributions, Zworykin has been the recipient of many honors, including the IRE Morris Liebmann Memorial Prize (1934) and Medal of Honor (1951), the Rumford Medal (1941), the Presidential Certificate of Merit (1948), the Chevalier Cross of the French Legion of Honor (1948), and the Lammé Award of the AIEE (1948). He has been awarded over 100 U.S. patents. The achievement of practical all-electronic television stems to a large extent from his pioneering work on the iconoscope and the kinescope, which form the basis for all important later advances in the field of picture transmission.

CHARLES SUSSKIND

Cross-references: *Historical Background of Electronics*

INDEX